Introduction to Econometrics: ECON 1620

Brown University

David R. Anderson | Dennis J. Sweeney
Thomas A. Williams | Jeffrey M. Wooldridge

CENGAGE Learning®

Australia • Brazil • Japan • Korea • Mexico • Singapore • Spain • United Kingdom • United States

CENGAGE Learning

Introduction to Econometrics: ECON 1620: Brown University

David R. Anderson | Dennis J. Sweeney
Thomas A. Williams | Jeffrey M. Wooldridge

Senior Project Development Manager:
Linda deStefano

Market Development Manager:
Heather Kramer

Senior Production/Manufacturing Manager:
Donna M. Brown

Production Editorial Manager:
Kim Fry

Sr. Rights Acquisition Account Manager:
Todd Osborne

Printed in the United States of America

ISBN-13: 978-1-285-55963-6

ISBN-10: 1-285-55963-0

Cengage Learning
5191 Natorp Boulevard
Mason, Ohio 45040
USA

Cengage Learning is a leading provider of customized learning solutions with office locations around the globe, including Singapore, the United Kingdom, Australia, Mexico, Brazil, and Japan. Locate your local office at:
international.cengage.com/region.
Cengage Learning products are represented in Canada by Nelson Education, Ltd.
For your lifelong learning solutions, visit **www.cengage.com/custom.**
Visit our corporate website at **www.cengage.com.**

Brief Contents

Excerpted from:
Statistics for Business and Economics, Revised
11th Edition
Anderson | Sweeney | Williams

--COLOR DIVIDER--

Excerpted from:
Introductory Econometrics: A Modern Approach
5th Edition
Wooldridge

Preface

This text is the revised 11th edition of *STATISTICS FOR BUSINESS AND ECONOMICS.* The revised edition updates the material in *STATISTICS FOR BUSINESS ECONOMICS* 11e for use with Microsoft Excel 2010 and Minitab 16. Current users of the 11th edition will find changes to the chapter-ending appendices, which now describe Excel 2010 and Minitab 16 procedures. In addition to the updated the chapter-ending appendixes, we have added an appendix to the book entitled Microsoft Excel 2010 and Tools for Statistical Analysis. This appendix provides an introduction to Excel 2010 and its tools for statistical analysis. Several of Excel's statistical functions have been upgraded and improved.

The remainder of this preface describes the author's objectives in writing *STATISTICS FOR BUSINESS AND ECONOMICS* and the major changes that were made in developing the 11th edition. The purpose of the text is to give students, primarily those in the fields of business administration and economics, a conceptual introduction to the field of statistics and its many applications. The text is applications oriented and written with the needs of the nonmathematician in mind; the mathematical prerequisite is knowledge of algebra.

Applications of data analysis and statistical methodology are an integral part of the organization and presentation of the text material. The discussion and development of each technique is presented in an application setting, with the statistical results providing insights to decisions and solutions to problems.

Although the book is applications oriented, we have taken care to provide sound methodological development and to use notation that is generally accepted for the topic being covered. Hence, students will find that this text provides good preparation for the study of more advanced statistical material. A bibliography to guide further study is included as an appendix.

The text introduces the student to the software packages of Minitab 16 and Microsoft® Office Excel 2010 and emphasizes the role of computer software in the application of statistical analysis. Minitab is illustrated as it is one of the leading statistical software packages for both education and statistical practice. Excel is not a statistical software package, but the wide availability and use of Excel make it important for students to understand the statistical capabilities of this package. Minitab and Excel procedures are provided in appendixes so that instructors have the flexibility of using as much computer emphasis as desired for the course.

Changes in the Eleventh Edition

We appreciate the acceptance and positive response to the previous editions of *STATISTICS FOR BUSINESS AND ECONOMICS*. Accordingly, in making modifications for this new edition, we have maintained the presentation style and readability of those editions. The significant changes in the new edition are summarized here.

Content Revisions

- **Revised Chapter 18 — "Time Series Analysis and Forecasting."** The chapter has been completely rewritten to focus more on using the pattern in a time series plot to select an appropriate forecasting method. We begin with a new Section 18.1 on time series patterns, followed by a new Section 18.2 on methods for measuring forecast accuracy. Section 18.3 discusses moving averages and exponential smoothing. Section 18.4 introduces methods appropriate for a time series that exhibits a trend. Here we illustrate how regression analysis and Holt's linear exponential smoothing can be used for linear trend projection, and then discuss how regression analysis can be used to model nonlinear relationships involving a quadratic trend and an exponential growth. Section 18.5 then shows how dummy variables can be used to model seasonality in a forecasting equation. Section 18.6 discusses classical time series decomposition, including the concept of deseasonalizing a time series. There is a new appendix on forecasting using the Excel add-in StatTools and most exercises are new or updated.

- **Revised Chapter 19 — "Nonparametric Methods."** The treatment of nonparametric methods has been revised and updated. We contrast each nonparametric method with its parametric counterpart and describe how fewer assumptions are required for the nonparametric procedure. The sign test emphasizes the test for a population median, which is important in skewed populations where the median is often the preferred measure of central location. The Wilcoxon Rank-Sum test is used for both matched samples tests and tests about a median of a symmetric population. A new small-sample application of the Mann-Whitney-Wilcoxon test shows the exact sampling distribution of the test statistic and is used to explain why the sum of the signed ranks can be used to test the hypothesis that the two populations are identical. The chapter concludes with the Kruskal-Wallis test and rank correlation. New chapter ending appendixes describe how Minitab, Excel, and StatTools can be used to implement nonparametric methods. Twenty-seven data sets are now available to facilitate computer solution of the exercises.
- **StatTools Add-In for Excel.** Excel 2010 does not contain statistical functions or data analysis tools to perform all the statistical procedures discussed in the text. StatTools is a commercial Excel 2010 add-in, developed by Palisade Corporation, that extends the range of statistical options for Excel users. In an appendix to Chapter 1 we show how to download and install StatTools, and most chapters include a chapter appendix that shows the steps required to accomplish a statistical procedure using StatTools.

  We have been very careful to make the use of StatTools completely optional so that instructors who want to teach using the standard tools available in Excel 2010 can continue to do so. But users who want additional statistical capabilities not available in standard Excel 2010 now have access to an industry standard statistics add-in that students will be able to continue to use in the workplace.
- **Change in Terminology for Data.** In the previous edition, nominal and ordinal data were classified as qualitative; interval and ratio data were classified as quantitative. In this edition, nominal and ordinal data are referred to as categorical data. Nominal and ordinal data use labels or names to identify categories of like items. Thus, we believe that the term categorical is more descriptive of this type of data.
- **Introducing Data Mining.** A new section in Chapter 1 introduces the relatively new field of data mining. We provide a brief overview of data mining and the concept of a data warehouse. We also describe how the fields of statistics and computer science join to make data mining operational and valuable.
- **Ethical Issues in Statistics.** Another new section in Chapter 1 provides a discussion of ethical issues when presenting and interpreting statistical information.
- **Updated Excel Appendix for Tabular and Graphical Descriptive Statistics.** The chapter-ending Excel appendix for Chapter 2 shows how the Chart Tools, PivotTable Report, and PivotChart Report can be used to enhance the capabilities for displaying tabular and graphical descriptive statistics.
- **Comparative Analysis with Box Plots.** The treatment of box plots in Chapter 3 has been expanded to include relatively quick and easy comparisons of two or more data

sets. Typical starting salary data for accounting, finance, management, and marketing majors are used to illustrate box plot multigroup comparisons.

- **Revised Sampling Material.** The introduction of Chapter 7 has been revised and now includes the concepts of a sampled population and a frame. The distinction between sampling from a finite population and an infinite population has been clarified, with sampling from a process used to illustrate the selection of a random sample from an infinite population. A practical advice section stresses the importance of obtaining close correspondence between the sampled population and the target population.
- **Revised Introduction to Hypothesis Testing.** Section 9.1, Developing Null and Alternative Hypotheses, has been revised. A better set of guidelines has been developed for identifying the null and alternative hypotheses. The context of the situation and the purpose for taking the sample are key. In situations in which the focus is on finding evidence to support a research finding, the research hypothesis is the alternative hypothesis. In situations where the focus is on challenging an assumption, the assumption is the null hypothesis.
- **New PrecisionTree Software for Decision Analysis.** PrecisionTree is another Excel add-in developed by Palisade Corporation that is very helpful in decision analysis. Chapter 21 has a new appendix which shows how to use the PrecisionTree add-in.
- **New Case Problems.** We have added 5 new case problems to this edition, bringing the total number of case problems to 31. A new case problem on descriptive statistics appears in Chapter 3 and a new case problem on hypothesis testing appears in Chapter 9. Three new case problems have been added to regression in Chapters 14, 15, and 16. These case problems provide students with the opportunity to analyze larger data sets and prepare managerial reports based on the results of the analysis.
- **New Statistics in Practice Applications.** Each chapter begins with a Statistics in Practice vignette that describes an application of the statistical methodology to be covered in the chapter. New to this edition are Statistics in Practice articles for Oceanwide Seafood in Chapter 4 and the London-based marketing services company dunnhumby in Chapter 15.
- **New Examples and Exercises Based on Real Data.** We continue to make a significant effort to update our text examples and exercises with the most current real data and referenced sources of statistical information. In this edition, we have added approximately 150 new examples and exercises based on real data and referenced sources. Using data from sources also used by *The Wall Street Journal*, *USA Today*, *Barron's*, and others, we have drawn from actual studies to develop explanations and to create exercises that demonstrate the many uses of statistics in business and economics. We believe that the use of real data helps generate more student interest in the material and enables the student to learn about both the statistical methodology and its application. The eleventh edition of the text contains over 350 examples and exercises based on real data.

Features and Pedagogy

Authors Anderson, Sweeney, and Williams have continued many of the features that appeared in previous editions. Important ones for students are noted here.

Methods Exercises and Applications Exercises

The end-of-section exercises are split into two parts, Methods and Applications. The Methods exercises require students to use the formulas and make the necessary computations. The Applications exercises require students to use the chapter material in real-world situations. Thus, students first focus on the computational "nuts and bolts" and then move on to the subtleties of statistical application and interpretation.

Self-Test Exercises

Certain exercises are identified as "Self-Test Exercises." Completely worked-out solutions for these exercises are provided in Appendix D at the back of the book. Students can attempt the Self-Test Exercises and immediately check the solution to evaluate their understanding of the concepts presented in the chapter.

Margin Annotations and Notes and Comments

Margin annotations that highlight key points and provide additional insights for the student are a key feature of this text. These annotations, which appear in the margins, are designed to provide emphasis and enhance understanding of the terms and concepts being presented in the text.

At the end of many sections, we provide Notes and Comments designed to give the student additional insights about the statistical methodology and its application. Notes and Comments include warnings about or limitations of the methodology, recommendations for application, brief descriptions of additional technical considerations, and other matters.

Data Files Accompany the Text

Over 200 data files are available on the website that accompanies the text. The data sets are available in both Minitab and Excel formats. Webfile logos are used in the text to identify the data sets that are available on the website. Data sets for all case problems as well as data sets for larger exercises are included.

Acknowledgments

A special thank you goes to Jeffrey D. Camm, University of Cincinnati, and James J. Cochran, Louisiana Tech University, for their contributions to this eleventh edition of *Statistics for Business and Economics*. Professors Camm and Cochran provided extensive input for the new chapters on forecasting and nonparametric methods. In addition, they provided helpful input and suggestions for new case problems, exercises, and Statistics in Practice articles. We would also like to thank our associates from business and industry who supplied the Statistics in Practice features. We recognize them individually by a credit line in each of the articles. Finally, we are also indebted to our senior acquisitions editor Charles McCormick, Jr.; our developmental editor Maggie Kubale; our content project manager, Jacquelyn K Featherly; our Project Manager at MPS Content Services, Lynn Lustberg; our marketing manager, Adam Marsh; our media editor, Chris Valentine; and others at Cengage South-Western for their editorial counsel and support during the preparation of this text.

David R. Anderson
Dennis J. Sweeney
Thomas A. Williams

About the Authors

David R. Anderson. David R. Anderson is Professor of Quantitative Analysis in the College of Business Administration at the University of Cincinnati. Born in Grand Forks, North Dakota, he earned his B.S., M.S., and Ph.D. degrees from Purdue University. Professor Anderson has served as Head of the Department of Quantitative Analysis and Operations Management and as Associate Dean of the College of Business Administration at the University of Cincinnati. In addition, he was the coordinator of the College's first Executive Program.

At the University of Cincinnati, Professor Anderson has taught introductory statistics for business students as well as graduate-level courses in regression analysis, multivariate analysis, and management science. He has also taught statistical courses at the Department of Labor in Washington, D.C. He has been honored with nominations and awards for excellence in teaching and excellence in service to student organizations.

Professor Anderson has coauthored 10 textbooks in the areas of statistics, management science, linear programming, and production and operations management. He is an active consultant in the field of sampling and statistical methods.

Dennis J. Sweeney. Dennis J. Sweeney is Professor of Quantitative Analysis and Founder of the Center for Productivity Improvement at the University of Cincinnati. Born in Des Moines, Iowa, he earned a B.S.B.A. degree from Drake University and his M.B.A. and D.B.A. degrees from Indiana University, where he was an NDEA Fellow. Professor Sweeney has worked in the management science group at Procter & Gamble and spent a year as a visiting professor at Duke University. Professor Sweeney served as Head of the Department of Quantitative Analysis and as Associate Dean of the College of Business Administration at the University of Cincinnati.

Professor Sweeney has published more than 30 articles and monographs in the area of management science and statistics. The National Science Foundation, IBM, Procter & Gamble, Federated Department Stores, Kroger, and Cincinnati Gas & Electric have funded his research, which has been published in *Management Science, Operations Research, Mathematical Programming, Decision Sciences,* and other journals.

Professor Sweeney has coauthored 10 textbooks in the areas of statistics, management science, linear programming, and production and operations management.

Thomas A. Williams. Thomas A. Williams is Professor of Management Science in the College of Business at Rochester Institute of Technology. Born in Elmira, New York, he earned his B.S. degree at Clarkson University. He did his graduate work at Rensselaer Polytechnic Institute, where he received his M.S. and Ph.D. degrees.

Before joining the College of Business at RIT, Professor Williams served for seven years as a faculty member in the College of Business Administration at the University of Cincinnati, where he developed the undergraduate program in Information Systems and then served as its coordinator. At RIT he was the first chairman of the Decision Sciences Department. He teaches courses in management science and statistics, as well as graduate courses in regression and decision analysis.

Professor Williams is the coauthor of 11 textbooks in the areas of management science, statistics, production and operations management, and mathematics. He has been a consultant for numerous *Fortune* 500 companies and has worked on projects ranging from the use of data analysis to the development of large-scale regression models.

STATISTICS FOR BUSINESS AND ECONOMICS 11e REVISED

CHAPTER 1

Data and Statistics

CONTENTS

STATISTICS *in* PRACTICE

*BUSINESSWEEK**
NEW YORK, NEW YORK

With a global circulation of more than 1 million, *BusinessWeek* is the most widely read business magazine in the world. More than 200 dedicated reporters and editors in 26 bureaus worldwide deliver a variety of articles of interest to the business and economic community. Along with feature articles on current topics, the magazine contains regular sections on International Business, Economic Analysis, Information Processing, and Science & Technology. Information in the feature articles and the regular sections helps readers stay abreast of current developments and assess the impact of those developments on business and economic conditions.

Most issues of *BusinessWeek* provide an in-depth report on a topic of current interest. Often, the in-depth reports contain statistical facts and summaries that help the reader understand the business and economic information. For example, the February 23, 2009 issue contained a feature article about the home foreclosure crisis, the March 17, 2009 issue included a discussion of when the stock market would begin to recover, and the May 4, 2009 issue had a special report on how to make pay cuts less painful. In addition, the weekly *BusinessWeek Investor* provides statistics about the state of the economy, including production indexes, stock prices, mutual funds, and interest rates.

BusinessWeek also uses statistics and statistical information in managing its own business. For example, an annual survey of subscribers helps the company learn about subscriber demographics, reading habits, likely purchases, lifestyles, and so on. *BusinessWeek* managers use statistical summaries from the survey to provide better services to subscribers and advertisers. One recent North American subscriber survey indicated that 90% of *BusinessWeek* subscribers use a personal computer at home and that 64% of *BusinessWeek* subscribers are involved with computer purchases at work. Such statistics alert *BusinessWeek* managers to subscriber interest in articles about new developments in computers. The results of the survey are also made available to potential advertisers. The high percentage of subscribers using personal computers at home and the high percentage of subscribers involved with computer purchases at work would be an incentive for a computer manufacturer to consider advertising in *BusinessWeek*.

In this chapter, we discuss the types of data available for statistical analysis and describe how the data are obtained. We introduce descriptive statistics and statistical inference as ways of converting data into meaningful and easily interpreted statistical information.

BusinessWeek uses statistical facts and summaries in many of its articles. © Terri Miller/E-Visual Communications, Inc.

*The authors are indebted to Charlene Trentham, Research Manager at *BusinessWeek*, for providing this Statistics in Practice.

Frequently, we see the following types of statements in newspapers and magazines:

- The National Association of Realtors reported that the median price paid by first-time home buyers is $165,000 (*The Wall Street Journal,* February 11, 2009).
- NCAA president Myles Brand reported that college athletes are earning degrees at record rates. Latest figures show that 79% of all men and women student-athletes graduate (Associated Press, October 15, 2008).
- The average one-way travel time to work is 25.3 minutes (U.S. Census Bureau, March 2009).

- A record high 11% of U.S. homes are vacant, a glut created by the housing boom and subsequent collapse (*USA Today,* February 13, 2009).
- The national average price for regular gasoline reached $4.00 per gallon for the first time in history (Cable News Network website, June 8, 2008).
- The New York Yankees have the highest salaries in major league baseball. The total payroll is $201,449,289 with a median salary of $5,000,000 (*USA Today Salary Data Base,* April 2009).
- The Dow Jones Industrial Average closed at 8721 (*The Wall Street Journal,* June 2, 2009).

The numerical facts in the preceding statements ($165,000, 79%, 25.3, 11%, $4.00, $201,449,289, $5,000,000 and 8721) are called statistics. In this usage, the term *statistics* refers to numerical facts such as averages, medians, percents, and index numbers that help us understand a variety of business and economic situations. However, as you will see, the field, or subject, of statistics involves much more than numerical facts. In a broader sense, **statistics** is defined as the art and science of collecting, analyzing, presenting, and interpreting data. Particularly in business and economics, the information provided by collecting, analyzing, presenting, and interpreting data gives managers and decision makers a better understanding of the business and economic environment and thus enables them to make more informed and better decisions. In this text, we emphasize the use of statistics for business and economic decision making.

Chapter 1 begins with some illustrations of the applications of statistics in business and economics. In Section 1.2 we define the term *data* and introduce the concept of a data set. This section also introduces key terms such as *variables* and *observations,* discusses the difference between quantitative and categorical data, and illustrates the uses of cross-sectional and time series data. Section 1.3 discusses how data can be obtained from existing sources or through survey and experimental studies designed to obtain new data. The important role that the Internet now plays in obtaining data is also highlighted. The uses of data in developing descriptive statistics and in making statistical inferences are described in Sections 1.4 and 1.5. The last three sections of Chapter 1 provide the role of the computer in statistical analysis, an introduction to data mining, and a discussion of ethical guidelines for statistical practice. A chapter-ending appendix includes an introduction to the add-in StatTools which can be used to extend the statistical options for users of Microsoft Excel.

1.1 Applications in Business and Economics

In today's global business and economic environment, anyone can access vast amounts of statistical information. The most successful managers and decision makers understand the information and know how to use it effectively. In this section, we provide examples that illustrate some of the uses of statistics in business and economics.

Accounting

Public accounting firms use statistical sampling procedures when conducting audits for their clients. For instance, suppose an accounting firm wants to determine whether the amount of accounts receivable shown on a client's balance sheet fairly represents the actual amount of accounts receivable. Usually the large number of individual accounts receivable makes reviewing and validating every account too time-consuming and expensive. As common practice in such situations, the audit staff selects a subset of the accounts called a sample. After reviewing the accuracy of the sampled accounts, the auditors draw a conclusion as to whether the accounts receivable amount shown on the client's balance sheet is acceptable.

Finance

Financial analysts use a variety of statistical information to guide their investment recommendations. In the case of stocks, the analysts review a variety of financial data including price/earnings ratios and dividend yields. By comparing the information for an individual stock with information about the stock market averages, a financial analyst can begin to draw a conclusion as to whether an individual stock is over- or underpriced. For example, *Barron's* (February 18, 2008) reported that the average dividend yield for the 30 stocks in the Dow Jones Industrial Average was 2.45%. Altria Group showed a dividend yield of 3.05%. In this case, the statistical information on dividend yield indicates a higher dividend yield for Altria Group than the average for the Dow Jones stocks. Therefore, a financial analyst might conclude that Altria Group was underpriced. This and other information about Altria Group would help the analyst make a buy, sell, or hold recommendation for the stock.

Marketing

Electronic scanners at retail checkout counters collect data for a variety of marketing research applications. For example, data suppliers such as ACNielsen and Information Resources, Inc., purchase point-of-sale scanner data from grocery stores, process the data, and then sell statistical summaries of the data to manufacturers. Manufacturers spend hundreds of thousands of dollars per product category to obtain this type of scanner data. Manufacturers also purchase data and statistical summaries on promotional activities such as special pricing and the use of in-store displays. Brand managers can review the scanner statistics and the promotional activity statistics to gain a better understanding of the relationship between promotional activities and sales. Such analyses often prove helpful in establishing future marketing strategies for the various products.

Production

Today's emphasis on quality makes quality control an important application of statistics in production. A variety of statistical quality control charts are used to monitor the output of a production process. In particular, an x-bar chart can be used to monitor the average output. Suppose, for example, that a machine fills containers with 12 ounces of a soft drink. Periodically, a production worker selects a sample of containers and computes the average number of ounces in the sample. This average, or x-bar value, is plotted on an x-bar chart. A plotted value above the chart's upper control limit indicates overfilling, and a plotted value below the chart's lower control limit indicates underfilling. The process is termed "in control" and allowed to continue as long as the plotted x-bar values fall between the chart's upper and lower control limits. Properly interpreted, an x-bar chart can help determine when adjustments are necessary to correct a production process.

Economics

Economists frequently provide forecasts about the future of the economy or some aspect of it. They use a variety of statistical information in making such forecasts. For instance, in forecasting inflation rates, economists use statistical information on such indicators as the Producer Price Index, the unemployment rate, and manufacturing capacity utilization. Often these statistical indicators are entered into computerized forecasting models that predict inflation rates.

Applications of statistics such as those described in this section are an integral part of this text. Such examples provide an overview of the breadth of statistical applications. To supplement these examples, practitioners in the fields of business and economics provided chapter-opening Statistics in Practice articles that introduce the material covered in each chapter. The Statistics in Practice applications show the importance of statistics in a wide variety of business and economic situations.

1.2 Data

Data are the facts and figures collected, analyzed, and summarized for presentation and interpretation. All the data collected in a particular study are referred to as the **data set** for the study. Table 1.1 shows a data set containing information for 25 mutual funds that are part of the *Morningstar Funds500* for 2008. Morningstar is a company that tracks over 7000 mutual funds and prepares in-depth analyses of 2000 of these. Their recommendations are followed closely by financial analysts and individual investors.

Elements, Variables, and Observations

Elements are the entities on which data are collected. For the data set in Table 1.1 each individual mutual fund is an element: the element names appear in the first column. With 25 mutual funds, the data set contains 25 elements.

A **variable** is a characteristic of interest for the elements. The data set in Table 1.1 includes the following five variables:

- *Fund Type:* The type of mutual fund, labeled DE (Domestic Equity), IE (International Equity), and FI (Fixed Income)
- *Net Asset Value ($):* The closing price per share on December 31, 2007

WEB file
Morningstar

Data sets such as Morningstar are available on the website for this text.

TABLE 1.1 DATA SET FOR 25 MUTUAL FUNDS

Fund Name	Fund Type	Net Asset Value ($)	5-Year Average Return (%)	Expense Ratio (%)	Morningstar Rank
American Century Intl. Disc	IE	14.37	30.53	1.41	3-Star
American Century Tax-Free Bond	FI	10.73	3.34	0.49	4-Star
American Century Ultra	DE	24.94	10.88	0.99	3-Star
Artisan Small Cap	DE	16.92	15.67	1.18	3-Star
Brown Cap Small	DE	35.73	15.85	1.20	4-Star
DFA U.S. Micro Cap	DE	13.47	17.23	0.53	3-Star
Fidelity Contrafund	DE	73.11	17.99	0.89	5-Star
Fidelity Overseas	IE	48.39	23.46	0.90	4-Star
Fidelity Sel Electronics	DE	45.60	13.50	0.89	3-Star
Fidelity Sh-Term Bond	FI	8.60	2.76	0.45	3-Star
Gabelli Asset AAA	DE	49.81	16.70	1.36	4-Star
Kalmar Gr Val Sm Cp	DE	15.30	15.31	1.32	3-Star
Marsico 21st Century	DE	17.44	15.16	1.31	5-Star
Mathews Pacific Tiger	IE	27.86	32.70	1.16	3-Star
Oakmark I	DE	40.37	9.51	1.05	2-Star
PIMCO Emerg Mkts Bd D	FI	10.68	13.57	1.25	3-Star
RS Value A	DE	26.27	23.68	1.36	4-Star
T. Rowe Price Latin Am.	IE	53.89	51.10	1.24	4-Star
T. Rowe Price Mid Val	DE	22.46	16.91	0.80	4-Star
Thornburg Value A	DE	37.53	15.46	1.27	4-Star
USAA Income	FI	12.10	4.31	0.62	3-Star
Vanguard Equity-Inc	DE	24.42	13.41	0.29	4-Star
Vanguard Sht-Tm TE	FI	15.68	2.37	0.16	3-Star
Vanguard Sm Cp Idx	DE	32.58	17.01	0.23	3-Star
Wasatch Sm Cp Growth	DE	35.41	13.98	1.19	4-Star

Source: Morningstar Funds 500 (2008).

- *5-Year Average Return (%):* The average annual return for the fund over the past 5 years
- *Expense Ratio:* The percentage of assets deducted each fiscal year for fund expenses
- *Morningstar Rank:* The overall risk-adjusted star rating for each fund; Morningstar ranks go from a low of 1-Star to a high of 5-Stars

Measurements collected on each variable for every element in a study provide the data. The set of measurements obtained for a particular element is called an **observation**. Referring to Table 1.1 we see that the set of measurements for the first observation (American Century Intl. Disc) is IE, 14.37, 30.53, 1.41, and 3-Star. The set of measurements for the second observation (American Century Tax-Free Bond) is FI, 10.73, 3.34, 0.49, and 4-Star, and so on. A data set with 25 elements contains 25 observations.

Scales of Measurement

Data collection requires one of the following scales of measurement: nominal, ordinal, interval, or ratio. The scale of measurement determines the amount of information contained in the data and indicates the most appropriate data summarization and statistical analyses.

When the data for a variable consist of labels or names used to identify an attribute of the element, the scale of measurement is considered a **nominal scale**. For example, referring to the data in Table 1.1, we see that the scale of measurement for the Fund Type variable is nominal because DE, IE, and FI are labels used to identify the category or type of fund. In cases where the scale of measurement is nominal, a numeric code as well as nonnumeric labels may be used. For example, to facilitate data collection and to prepare the data for entry into a computer database, we might use a numeric code by letting 1 denote Domestic Equity, 2 denote International Equity, and 3 denote Fixed Income. In this case the numeric values 1, 2, and 3 identify the category of fund. The scale of measurement is nominal even though the data appear as numeric values.

The scale of measurement for a variable is called an **ordinal scale** if the data exhibit the properties of nominal data and the order or rank of the data is meaningful. For example, Eastside Automotive sends customers a questionnaire designed to obtain data on the quality of its automotive repair service. Each customer provides a repair service rating of excellent, good, or poor. Because the data obtained are the labels—excellent, good, or poor—the data have the properties of nominal data. In addition, the data can be ranked, or ordered, with respect to the service quality. Data recorded as excellent indicate the best service, followed by good and then poor. Thus, the scale of measurement is ordinal. As another example, note that the Morningstar Rank for the data in Table 1.1 is ordinal data. It provides a rank from 1 to 5-Stars based on Morningstar's assessment of the fund's risk-adjusted return. Ordinal data can also be provided using a numeric code, for example, your class rank in school.

The scale of measurement for a variable is an **interval scale** if the data have all the properties of ordinal data and the interval between values is expressed in terms of a fixed unit of measure. Interval data are always numeric. College admission SAT scores are an example of interval-scaled data. For example, three students with SAT math scores of 620, 550, and 470 can be ranked or ordered in terms of best performance to poorest performance in math. In addition, the differences between the scores are meaningful. For instance, student 1 scored $620 - 550 = 70$ points more than student 2, while student 2 scored $550 - 470 = 80$ points more than student 3.

The scale of measurement for a variable is a **ratio scale** if the data have all the properties of interval data and the ratio of two values is meaningful. Variables such as distance, height, weight, and time use the ratio scale of measurement. This scale requires that a zero value be included to indicate that nothing exists for the variable at the zero point.

For example, consider the cost of an automobile. A zero value for the cost would indicate that the automobile has no cost and is free. In addition, if we compare the cost of $30,000 for one automobile to the cost of $15,000 for a second automobile, the ratio property shows that the first automobile is $30,000/$15,000 = 2 times, or twice, the cost of the second automobile.

Categorical and Quantitative Data

Data can be classified as either categorical or quantitative. Data that can be grouped by specific categories are referred to as **categorical data**. Categorical data use either the nominal or ordinal scale of measurement. Data that use numeric values to indicate how much or how many are referred to as **quantitative data**. Quantitative data are obtained using either the interval or ratio scale of measurement.

The statistical method appropriate for summarizing data depends upon whether the data are categorical or quantitative.

A **categorical variable** is a variable with categorical data, and a **quantitative variable** is a variable with quantitative data. The statistical analysis appropriate for a particular variable depends upon whether the variable is categorical or quantitative. If the variable is categorical, the statistical analysis is limited. We can summarize categorical data by counting the number of observations in each category or by computing the proportion of the observations in each category. However, even when the categorical data are identified by a numerical code, arithmetic operations such as addition, subtraction, multiplication, and division do not provide meaningful results. Section 2.1 discusses ways for summarizing categorical data.

Arithmetic operations provide meaningful results for quantitative variables. For example, quantitative data may be added and then divided by the number of observations to compute the average value. This average is usually meaningful and easily interpreted. In general, more alternatives for statistical analysis are possible when data are quantitative. Section 2.2 and Chapter 3 provide ways of summarizing quantitative data.

Cross-Sectional and Time Series Data

For purposes of statistical analysis, distinguishing between cross-sectional data and time series data is important. **Cross-sectional data** are data collected at the same or approximately the same point in time. The data in Table 1.1 are cross-sectional because they describe the five variables for the 25 mutual funds at the same point in time. **Time series data** are data collected over several time periods. For example, the time series in Figure 1.1 shows the U.S. average price per gallon of conventional regular gasoline between 2006 and 2009. Note that higher gasoline prices have tended to occur in the summer months, with the all-time-high average of $4.05 per gallon occurring in July 2008. By January 2009, gasoline prices had taken a steep decline to a three-year low of $1.65 per gallon.

Graphs of time series data are frequently found in business and economic publications. Such graphs help analysts understand what happened in the past, identify any trends over time, and project future levels for the time series. The graphs of time series data can take on a variety of forms, as shown in Figure 1.2. With a little study, these graphs are usually easy to understand and interpret.

For example, Panel (A) in Figure 1.2 is a graph that shows the Dow Jones Industrial Average Index from 1997 to 2009. In April 1997, the popular stock market index was near 7000. Over the next 10 years the index rose to over 14,000 in July 2007. However, notice the sharp decline in the time series after the all-time high in 2007. By March 2009, poor economic conditions had caused the Dow Jones Industrial Average Index to return to the 7000 level of 1997. This was a scary and discouraging period for investors. By June 2009, the index was showing a recovery by reaching 8700.

FIGURE 1.1 U.S. AVERAGE PRICE PER GALLON FOR CONVENTIONAL REGULAR GASOLINE

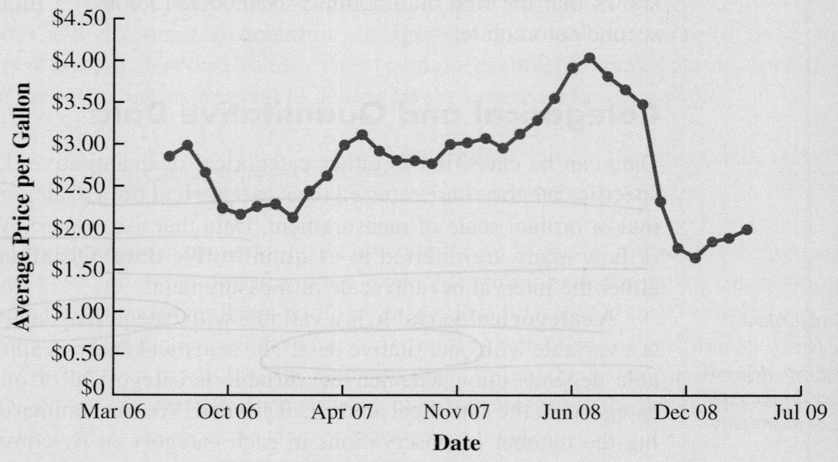

Source: Energy Information Administration, U.S. Department of Energy, May 2009.

The graph in Panel (B) shows the net income of McDonald's Inc. from 2003 to 2009. The declining economic conditions in 2008 and 2009 were actually beneficial to McDonald's as the company's net income rose to an all-time high. The growth in McDonald's net income showed that the company was thriving during the economic downturn as people were cutting back on the more expensive sit-down restaurants and seeking less-expensive alternatives offered by McDonald's.

Panel (C) shows the time series for the occupancy rate of hotels in South Florida over a one-year period. The highest occupancy rates, 95% and 98%, occur during the months of February and March when the climate of South Florida is attractive to tourists. In fact, January to April of each year is typically the high-occupancy season for South Florida hotels. On the other hand, note the low occupancy rates during the months of August to October, with the lowest occupancy rate of 50% occurring in September. High temperatures and the hurricane season are the primary reasons for the drop in hotel occupancy during this period.

NOTES AND COMMENTS

1. An observation is the set of measurements obtained for each element in a data set. Hence, the number of observations is always the same as the number of elements. The number of measurements obtained for each element equals the number of variables. Hence, the total number of data items can be determined by multiplying the number of observations by the number of variables.
2. Quantitative data may be discrete or continuous. Quantitative data that measure how many (e.g., number of calls received in 5 minutes) are discrete. Quantitative data that measure how much (e.g., weight or time) are continuous because no separation occurs between the possible data values.

FIGURE 1.2 A VARIETY OF GRAPHS OF TIME SERIES DATA

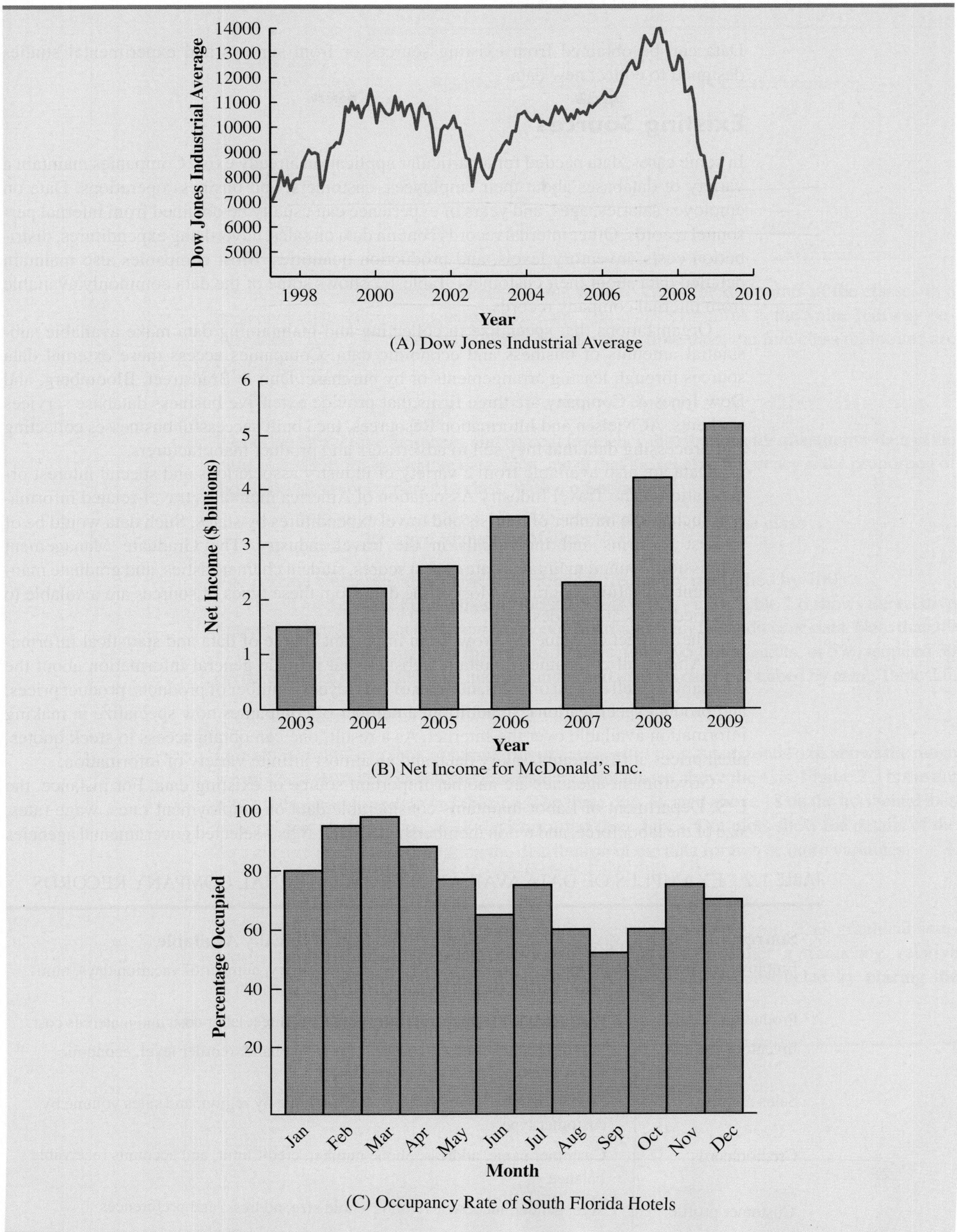

1.3 Data Sources

Data can be obtained from existing sources or from surveys and experimental studies designed to collect new data.

Existing Sources

In some cases, data needed for a particular application already exist. Companies maintain a variety of databases about their employees, customers, and business operations. Data on employee salaries, ages, and years of experience can usually be obtained from internal personnel records. Other internal records contain data on sales, advertising expenditures, distribution costs, inventory levels, and production quantities. Most companies also maintain detailed data about their customers. Table 1.2 shows some of the data commonly available from internal company records.

Organizations that specialize in collecting and maintaining data make available substantial amounts of business and economic data. Companies access these external data sources through leasing arrangements or by purchase. Dun & Bradstreet, Bloomberg, and Dow Jones & Company are three firms that provide extensive business database services to clients. ACNielsen and Information Resources, Inc., built successful businesses collecting and processing data that they sell to advertisers and product manufacturers.

Data are also available from a variety of industry associations and special interest organizations. The Travel Industry Association of America maintains travel-related information such as the number of tourists and travel expenditures by states. Such data would be of interest to firms and individuals in the travel industry. The Graduate Management Admission Council maintains data on test scores, student characteristics, and graduate management education programs. Most of the data from these types of sources are available to qualified users at a modest cost.

The Internet continues to grow as an important source of data and statistical information. Almost all companies maintain websites that provide general information about the company as well as data on sales, number of employees, number of products, product prices, and product specifications. In addition, a number of companies now specialize in making information available over the Internet. As a result, one can obtain access to stock quotes, meal prices at restaurants, salary data, and an almost infinite variety of information.

Government agencies are another important source of existing data. For instance, the U.S. Department of Labor maintains considerable data on employment rates, wage rates, size of the labor force, and union membership. Table 1.3 lists selected governmental agencies

TABLE 1.2 EXAMPLES OF DATA AVAILABLE FROM INTERNAL COMPANY RECORDS

Source	Some of the Data Typically Available
Employee records	Name, address, social security number, salary, number of vacation days, number of sick days, and bonus
Production records	Part or product number, quantity produced, direct labor cost, and materials cost
Inventory records	Part or product number, number of units on hand, reorder level, economic order quantity, and discount schedule
Sales records	Product number, sales volume, sales volume by region, and sales volume by customer type
Credit records	Customer name, address, phone number, credit limit, and accounts receivable balance
Customer profile	Age, gender, income level, household size, address, and preferences

TABLE 1.3 EXAMPLES OF DATA AVAILABLE FROM SELECTED GOVERNMENT AGENCIES

Government Agency	Some of the Data Available
Census Bureau	Population data, number of households, and household income
Federal Reserve Board	Data on the money supply, installment credit, exchange rates, and discount rates
Office of Management and Budget	Data on revenue, expenditures, and debt of the federal government
Department of Commerce	Data on business activity, value of shipments by industry, level of profits by industry, and growing and declining industries
Bureau of Labor Statistics	Consumer spending, hourly earnings, unemployment rate, safety records, and international statistics

and some of the data they provide. Most government agencies that collect and process data also make the results available through a website. Figure 1.3 shows the homepage for the U.S. Census Bureau website.

Statistical Studies

The largest experimental statistical study ever conducted is believed to be the 1954 Public Health Service experiment for the Salk polio vaccine. Nearly 2 million children in grades 1, 2, and 3 were selected from throughout the United States.

Sometimes the data needed for a particular application are not available through existing sources. In such cases, the data can often be obtained by conducting a statistical study. Statistical studies can be classified as either *experimental* or *observational.*

In an experimental study, a variable of interest is first identified. Then one or more other variables are identified and controlled so that data can be obtained about how they influence the variable of interest. For example, a pharmaceutical firm might be interested in conducting an experiment to learn about how a new drug affects blood pressure. Blood pressure is the variable of interest in the study. The dosage level of the new drug is another variable that is hoped to have a causal effect on blood pressure. To obtain data about the effect of the

FIGURE 1.3 U.S. CENSUS BUREAU HOMEPAGE

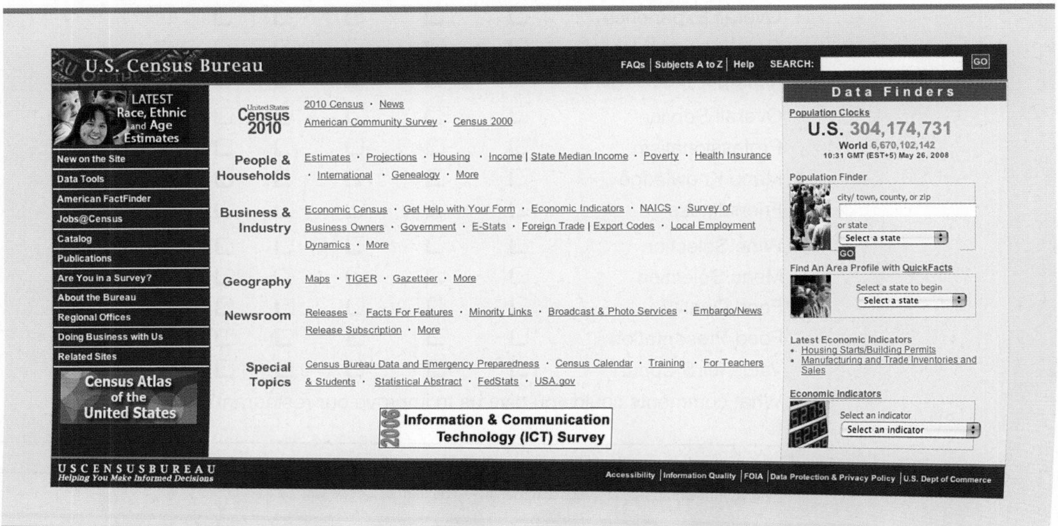

new drug, researchers select a sample of individuals. The dosage level of the new drug is controlled, as different groups of individuals are given different dosage levels. Before and after data on blood pressure are collected for each group. Statistical analysis of the experimental data can help determine how the new drug affects blood pressure.

Nonexperimental, or observational, statistical studies make no attempt to control the variables of interest. A survey is perhaps the most common type of observational study. For instance, in a personal interview survey, research questions are first identified. Then a questionnaire is designed and administered to a sample of individuals. Some restaurants use observational studies to obtain data about customer opinions on the quality of food, quality of service, atmosphere, and so on. A customer opinion questionnaire used by Chops City Grill in Naples, Florida, is shown in Figure 1.4. Note that the customers who fill out the questionnaire are asked to provide ratings for 12 variables, including overall experience, greeting by hostess, manager (table visit), overall service, and so on. The response categories of excellent, good, average, fair, and poor provide categorical data that enable Chops City Grill management to maintain high standards for the restaurant's food and service.

Studies of smokers and nonsmokers are observational studies because researchers do not determine or control who will smoke and who will not smoke.

Anyone wanting to use data and statistical analysis as aids to decision making must be aware of the time and cost required to obtain the data. The use of existing data sources is desirable when data must be obtained in a relatively short period of time. If important data are not readily available from an existing source, the additional time and cost involved in obtaining the data must be taken into account. In all cases, the decision maker should

FIGURE 1.4 CUSTOMER OPINION QUESTIONNAIRE USED BY CHOPS CITY GRILL RESTAURANT IN NAPLES, FLORIDA

Chop's
CITY GRILL

Date: ____________ Server Name: ____________

Our customers are our top priority. Please take a moment to fill out our survey card, so we can better serve your needs. You may return this card to the front desk or return by mail. Thank you!

SERVICE SURVEY	Excellent	Good	Average	Fair	Poor
Overall Experience	□	□	□	□	□
Greeting by Hostess	□	□	□	□	□
Manager (Table Visit)	□	□	□	□	□
Overall Service	□	□	□	□	□
Professionalism	□	□	□	□	□
Menu Knowledge	□	□	□	□	□
Friendliness	□	□	□	□	□
Wine Selection	□	□	□	□	□
Menu Selection	□	□	□	□	□
Food Quality	□	□	□	□	□
Food Presentation	□	□	□	□	□
Value for $ Spent	□	□	□	□	□

What comments could you give us to improve our restaurant?

Thank you, we appreciate your comments. —The staff of Chops City Grill.

consider the contribution of the statistical analysis to the decision-making process. The cost of data acquisition and the subsequent statistical analysis should not exceed the savings generated by using the information to make a better decision.

Data Acquisition Errors

Managers should always be aware of the possibility of data errors in statistical studies. Using erroneous data can be worse than not using any data at all. An error in data acquisition occurs whenever the data value obtained is not equal to the true or actual value that would be obtained with a correct procedure. Such errors can occur in a number of ways. For example, an interviewer might make a recording error, such as a transposition in writing the age of a 24-year-old person as 42, or the person answering an interview question might misinterpret the question and provide an incorrect response.

Experienced data analysts take great care in collecting and recording data to ensure that errors are not made. Special procedures can be used to check for internal consistency of the data. For instance, such procedures would indicate that the analyst should review the accuracy of data for a respondent shown to be 22 years of age but reporting 20 years of work experience. Data analysts also review data with unusually large and small values, called outliers, which are candidates for possible data errors. In Chapter 3 we present some of the methods statisticians use to identify outliers.

Errors often occur during data acquisition. Blindly using any data that happen to be available or using data that were acquired with little care can result in misleading information and bad decisions. Thus, taking steps to acquire accurate data can help ensure reliable and valuable decision-making information.

1.4 Descriptive Statistics

Most of the statistical information in newspapers, magazines, company reports, and other publications consists of data that are summarized and presented in a form that is easy for the reader to understand. Such summaries of data, which may be tabular, graphical, or numerical, are referred to as **descriptive statistics.**

Refer again to the data set in Table 1.1 showing data on 25 mutual funds. Methods of descriptive statistics can be used to provide summaries of the information in this data set. For example, a tabular summary of the data for the categorical variable Fund Type is shown in Table 1.4. A graphical summary of the same data, called a bar chart, is shown in Figure 1.5. These types of tabular and graphical summaries generally make the data easier to interpret. Referring to Table 1.4 and Figure 1.5, we can see easily that the majority of the mutual funds are of the Domestic Equity type. On a percentage basis, 64% are of the Domestic Equity type, 16% are of the International Equity type, and 20% are of the Fixed Income type.

TABLE 1.4 FREQUENCIES AND PERCENT FREQUENCIES FOR MUTUAL FUND TYPE

Mutual Fund Type	Frequency	Percent Frequency
Domestic Equity	16	64
International Equity	4	16
Fixed Income	5	20
Totals	**25**	**100**

FIGURE 1.5 BAR CHART FOR MUTUAL FUND TYPE

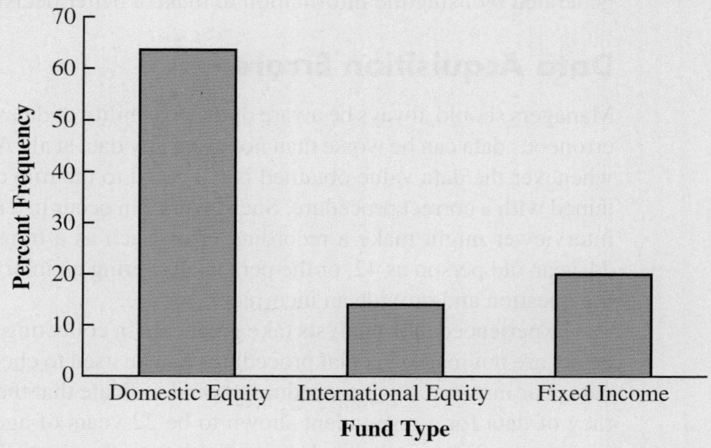

A graphical summary of the data for the quantitative variable Net Asset Value, called a histogram, is provided in Figure 1.6. The histogram makes it easy to see that the net asset values range from \$0 to \$75, with the highest concentration between \$15 and \$30. Only one of the net asset values is greater than \$60.

In addition to tabular and graphical displays, numerical descriptive statistics are used to summarize data. The most common numerical descriptive statistic is the average, or

FIGURE 1.6 HISTOGRAM OF NET ASSET VALUE FOR 25 MUTUAL FUNDS

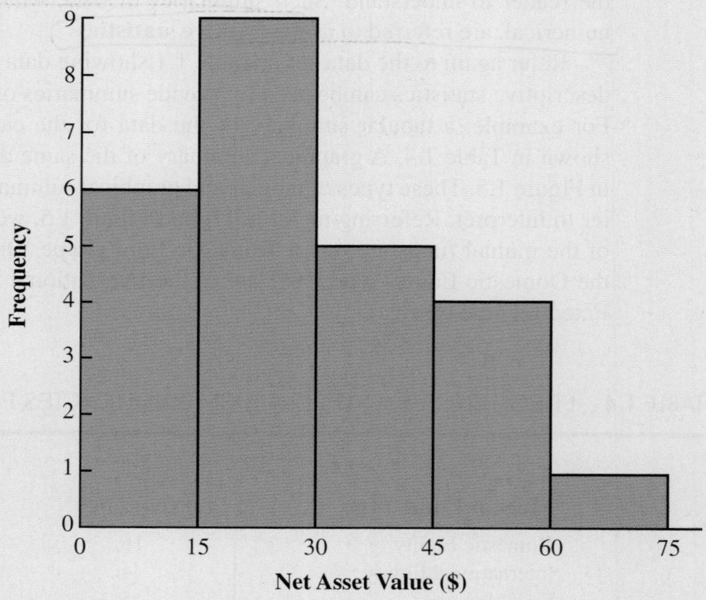

mean. Using the data on 5-Year Average Return for the mutual funds in Table 1.1, we can compute the average by adding the returns for all 25 mutual funds and dividing the sum by 25. Doing so provides a 5-year average return of 16.50%. This average demonstrates a measure of the central tendency, or central location, of the data for that variable.

There is a great deal of interest in effective methods for developing and presenting descriptive statistics. Chapters 2 and 3 devote attention to the tabular, graphical, and numerical methods of descriptive statistics.

1.5 Statistical Inference

Many situations require information about a large group of elements (individuals, companies, voters, households, products, customers, and so on). But, because of time, cost, and other considerations, data can be collected from only a small portion of the group. The larger group of elements in a particular study is called the **population**, and the smaller group is called the **sample**. Formally, we use the following definitions.

> POPULATION
>
> A population is the set of all elements of interest in a particular study.

> SAMPLE
>
> A sample is a subset of the population.

The U.S. government conducts a census every 10 years. Market research firms conduct sample surveys every day.

The process of conducting a survey to collect data for the entire population is called a **census**. The process of conducting a survey to collect data for a sample is called a **sample survey**. As one of its major contributions, statistics uses data from a sample to make estimates and test hypotheses about the characteristics of a population through a process referred to as **statistical inference**.

As an example of statistical inference, let us consider the study conducted by Norris Electronics. Norris manufactures a high-intensity lightbulb used in a variety of electrical products. In an attempt to increase the useful life of the lightbulb, the product design group developed a new lightbulb filament. In this case, the population is defined as all lightbulbs that could be produced with the new filament. To evaluate the advantages of the new filament, 200 bulbs with the new filament were manufactured and tested. Data collected from this sample showed the number of hours each lightbulb operated before filament burnout. See Table 1.5.

Suppose Norris wants to use the sample data to make an inference about the average hours of useful life for the population of all lightbulbs that could be produced with the new filament. Adding the 200 values in Table 1.5 and dividing the total by 200 provides the sample average lifetime for the lightbulbs: 76 hours. We can use this sample result to estimate that the average lifetime for the lightbulbs in the population is 76 hours. Figure 1.7 provides a graphical summary of the statistical inference process for Norris Electronics.

Whenever statisticians use a sample to estimate a population characteristic of interest, they usually provide a statement of the quality, or precision, associated with the estimate.

TABLE 1.5 HOURS UNTIL BURNOUT FOR A SAMPLE OF 200 LIGHTBULBS FOR THE NORRIS ELECTRONICS EXAMPLE

WEB file
Norris

107	73	68	97	76	79	94	59	98	57
54	65	71	70	84	88	62	61	79	98
66	62	79	86	68	74	61	82	65	98
62	116	65	88	64	79	78	79	77	86
74	85	73	80	68	78	89	72	58	69
92	78	88	77	103	88	63	68	88	81
75	90	62	89	71	71	74	70	74	70
65	81	75	62	94	71	85	84	83	63
81	62	79	83	93	61	65	62	92	65
83	70	70	81	77	72	84	67	59	58
78	66	66	94	77	63	66	75	68	76
90	78	71	101	78	43	59	67	61	71
96	75	64	76	72	77	74	65	82	86
66	86	96	89	81	71	85	99	59	92
68	72	77	60	87	84	75	77	51	45
85	67	87	80	84	93	69	76	89	75
83	68	72	67	92	89	82	96	77	102
74	91	76	83	66	68	61	73	72	76
73	77	79	94	63	59	62	71	81	65
73	63	63	89	82	64	85	92	64	73

FIGURE 1.7 THE PROCESS OF STATISTICAL INFERENCE FOR THE NORRIS ELECTRONICS EXAMPLE

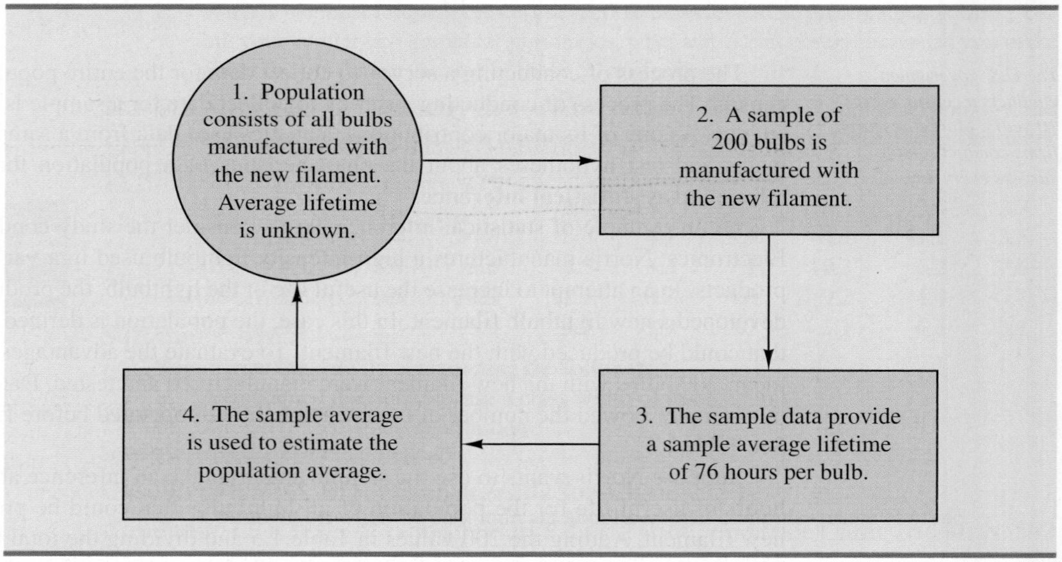

For the Norris example, the statistician might state that the point estimate of the average lifetime for the population of new lightbulbs is 76 hours with a margin of error of ±4 hours. Thus, an interval estimate of the average lifetime for all lightbulbs produced with the new filament is 72 hours to 80 hours. The statistician can also state how confident he or she is that the interval from 72 hours to 80 hours contains the population average.

1.6 Computers and Statistical Analysis

Minitab and Excel data sets and the Excel add-in StatTools are available on the website for this text.

Statisticians frequently use computer software to perform the statistical computations required with large amounts of data. For example, computing the average lifetime for the 200 lightbulbs in the Norris Electronics example (see Table 1.5) would be quite tedious without a computer. To facilitate computer usage, many of the data sets in this book are available on the website that accompanies the text. The data files may be downloaded in either Minitab or Excel formats. In addition, the Excel add-in StatTools can be downloaded from the website. End-of-chapter appendixes cover the step-by-step procedures for using Minitab, Excel, and the Excel add-in StatTools to implement the statistical techniques presented in the chapter.

1.7 Data Mining

With the aid of magnetic card readers, bar code scanners, and point-of-sale terminals, most organizations obtain large amounts of data on a daily basis. And, even for a small local restaurant that uses touch screen monitors to enter orders and handle billing, the amount of data collected can be significant. For large retail companies, the sheer volume of data collected is hard to conceptualize, and figuring out how to effectively use these data to improve profitability is a challenge. For example, mass retailers such as Wal-Mart capture data on 20 to 30 million transactions every day, telecommunication companies such as France Telecom and AT&T generate over 300 million call records per day, and Visa processes 6800 payment transactions per second or approximately 600 million transactions per day. Storing and managing the transaction data is a significant undertaking.

The term *data warehousing* is used to refer to the process of capturing, storing, and maintaining the data. Computing power and data collection tools have reached the point where it is now feasible to store and retrieve extremely large quantities of data in seconds. Analysis of the data in the warehouse may result in decisions that will lead to new strategies and higher profits for the organization.

The subject of **data mining** deals with methods for developing useful decision-making information from large data bases. Using a combination of procedures from statistics, mathematics, and computer science, analysts "mine the data" in the warehouse to convert it into useful information, hence the name *data mining.* Dr. Kurt Thearling, a leading practitioner in the field, defines data mining as "the automated extraction of predictive information from (large) databases." The two key words in Dr. Thearling's definition are "automated" and "predictive." Data mining systems that are the most effective use automated procedures to extract information from the data using only the most general or even vague queries by the user. And data mining software automates the process of uncovering hidden predictive information that in the past required hands-on analysis.

The major applications of data mining have been made by companies with a strong consumer focus, such as retail businesses, financial organizations, and communication companies. Data mining has been successfully used to help retailers such as Amazon and Barnes & Noble determine one or more related products that customers who have already purchased a specific product are also likely to purchase. Then, when a customer logs on to the company's website and purchases a product, the website uses pop-ups to alert the customer about additional products that the customer is likely to purchase. In another application, data mining may be used to identify customers who are likely to spend more than $20 on a particular shopping trip. These customers may then be identified as the ones to receive special e-mail or regular mail discount offers to encourage them to make their next shopping trip before the discount termination date.

Data mining is a technology that relies heavily on statistical methodology such as multiple regression, logistic regression, and correlation. But it takes a creative integration of all

Statistical methods play an important role in data mining, both in terms of discovering relationships in the data and predicting future outcomes. However, a thorough coverage of data mining and the use of statistics in data mining are outside the scope of this text.

these methods and computer science technologies involving artificial intelligence and machine learning to make data mining effective. A significant investment in time and money is required to implement commercial data mining software packages developed by firms such as Oracle, Teradata, and SAS. The statistical concepts introduced in this text will be helpful in understanding the statistical methodology used by data mining software packages and enable you to better understand the statistical information that is developed.

Because statistical models play an important role in developing predictive models in data mining, many of the concerns that statisticians deal with in developing statistical models are also applicable. For instance, a concern in any statistical study involves the issue of model reliability. Finding a statistical model that works well for a particular sample of data does not necessarily mean that it can be reliably applied to other data. One of the common statistical approaches to evaluating model reliability is to divide the sample data set into two parts: a training data set and a test data set. If the model developed using the training data is able to accurately predict values in the test data, we say that the model is reliable. One advantage that data mining has over classical statistics is that the enormous amount of data available allows the data mining software to partition the data set so that a model developed for the training data set may be tested for reliability on other data. In this sense, the partitioning of the data set allows data mining to develop models and relationships and then quickly observe if they are repeatable and valid with new and different data. On the other hand, a warning for data mining applications is that with so much data available, there is a danger of overfitting the model to the point that misleading associations and cause/effect conclusions appear to exist. Careful interpretation of data mining results and additional testing will help avoid this pitfall.

1.8 Ethical Guidelines for Statistical Practice

Ethical behavior is something we should strive for in all that we do. Ethical issues arise in statistics because of the important role statistics plays in the collection, analysis, presentation, and interpretation of data. In a statistical study, unethical behavior can take a variety of forms including improper sampling, inappropriate analysis of the data, development of misleading graphs, use of inappropriate summary statistics, and/or a biased interpretation of the statistical results.

As you begin to do your own statistical work, we encourage you to be fair, thorough, objective, and neutral as you collect data, conduct analyses, make oral presentations, and present written reports containing information developed. As a consumer of statistics, you should also be aware of the possibility of unethical statistical behavior by others. When you see statistics in newspapers, on television, on the Internet, and so on, it is a good idea to view the information with some skepticism, always being aware of the source as well as the purpose and objectivity of the statistics provided.

The American Statistical Association, the nation's leading professional organization for statistics and statisticians, developed the report "Ethical Guidelines for Statistical Practice"[1] to help statistical practitioners make and communicate ethical decisions and assist students in learning how to perform statistical work responsibly. The report contains 67 guidelines organized into eight topic areas: Professionalism; Responsibilities to Funders, Clients, and Employers; Responsibilities in Publications and Testimony; Responsibilities to Research Subjects; Responsibilities to Research Team Colleagues; Responsibilities to Other Statisticians or Statistical Practitioners; Responsibilities Regarding Allegations of Misconduct; and Responsibilities of Employers Including Organizations, Individuals, Attorneys, or Other Clients Employing Statistical Practitioners.

[1]American Statistical Association "Ethical Guidelines for Statistical Practice," 1999.

One of the ethical guidelines in the professionalism area addresses the issue of running multiple tests until a desired result is obtained. Let us consider an example. In Section 1.5 we discussed a statistical study conducted by Norris Electronics involving a sample of 200 high-intensity lightbulbs manufactured with a new filament. The average lifetime for the sample, 76 hours, provided an estimate of the average lifetime for all lightbulbs produced with the new filament. However, consider this. Because Norris selected a sample of bulbs, it is reasonable to assume that another sample would have provided a different average lifetime.

Suppose Norris's management had hoped the sample results would enable them to claim that the average lifetime for the new lightbulbs was 80 hours or more. Suppose further that Norris's management decides to continue the study by manufacturing and testing repeated samples of 200 lightbulbs with the new filament until a sample mean of 80 hours or more is obtained. If the study is repeated enough times, a sample may eventually be obtained—by chance alone—that would provide the desired result and enable Norris to make such a claim. In this case, consumers would be misled into thinking the new product is better than it actually is. Clearly, this type of behavior is unethical and represents a gross misuse of statistics in practice.

Several ethical guidelines in the responsibilities and publications and testimony area deal with issues involving the handling of data. For instance, a statistician must account for all data considered in a study and explain the sample(s) actually used. In the Norris Electronics study the average lifetime for the 200 bulbs in the original sample is 76 hours; this is considerably less than the 80 hours or more that management hoped to obtain. Suppose now that after reviewing the results showing a 76 hour average lifetime, Norris discards all the observations with 70 or fewer hours until burnout, allegedly because these bulbs contain imperfections caused by startup problems in the manufacturing process. After discarding these lightbulbs, the average lifetime for the remaining lightbulbs in the sample turns out to be 82 hours. Would you be suspicious of Norris's claim that the lifetime for their lightbulbs is 82 hours?

If the Norris lightbulbs showing 70 or fewer hours until burnout were discarded to simply provide an average lifetime of 82 hours, there is no question that discarding the lightbulbs with 70 or fewer hours until burnout is unethical. But, even if the discarded lightbulbs contain imperfections due to startup problems in the manufacturing process—and, as a result, should not have been included in the analysis—the statistician who conducted the study must account for all the data that were considered and explain how the sample actually used was obtained. To do otherwise is potentially misleading and would constitute unethical behavior on the part of both the company and the statistician.

A guideline in the shared values section of the American Statistical Association report states that statistical practitioners should avoid any tendency to slant statistical work toward predetermined outcomes. This type of unethical practice is often observed when unrepresentative samples are used to make claims. For instance, in many areas of the country smoking is not permitted in restaurants. Suppose, however, a lobbyist for the tobacco industry interviews people in restaurants where smoking is permitted in order to estimate the percentage of people who are in favor of allowing smoking in restaurants. The sample results show that 90% of the people interviewed are in favor of allowing smoking in restaurants. Based upon these sample results, the lobbyist claims that 90% of all people who eat in restaurants are in favor of permitting smoking in restaurants. In this case we would argue that only sampling persons eating in restaurants that allow smoking has biased the results. If only the final results of such a study are reported, readers unfamiliar with the details of the study (i.e., that the sample was collected only in restaurants allowing smoking) can be misled.

The scope of the American Statistical Association's report is broad and includes ethical guidelines that are appropriate not only for a statistician, but also for consumers of statistical information. We encourage you to read the report to obtain a better perspective of ethical issues as you continue your study of statistics and to gain the background for determining how to ensure that ethical standards are met when you start to use statistics in practice.

Summary

Statistics is the art and science of collecting, analyzing, presenting, and interpreting data. Nearly every college student majoring in business or economics is required to take a course in statistics. We began the chapter by describing typical statistical applications for business and economics.

Data consist of the facts and figures that are collected and analyzed. Four scales of measurement used to obtain data on a particular variable include nominal, ordinal, interval, and ratio. The scale of measurement for a variable is nominal when the data are labels or names used to identify an attribute of an element. The scale is ordinal if the data demonstrate the properties of nominal data and the order or rank of the data is meaningful. The scale is interval if the data demonstrate the properties of ordinal data and the interval between values is expressed in terms of a fixed unit of measure. Finally, the scale of measurement is ratio if the data show all the properties of interval data and the ratio of two values is meaningful.

For purposes of statistical analysis, data can be classified as categorical or quantitative. Categorical data use labels or names to identify an attribute of each element. Categorical data use either the nominal or ordinal scale of measurement and may be nonnumeric or numeric. Quantitative data are numeric values that indicate how much or how many. Quantitative data use either the interval or ratio scale of measurement. Ordinary arithmetic operations are meaningful only if the data are quantitative. Therefore, statistical computations used for quantitative data are not always appropriate for categorical data.

In Sections 1.4 and 1.5 we introduced the topics of descriptive statistics and statistical inference. Descriptive statistics are the tabular, graphical, and numerical methods used to summarize data. The process of statistical inference uses data obtained from a sample to make estimates or test hypotheses about the characteristics of a population. The last three sections of the chapter provide information on the role of computers in statistical analysis, an introduction to the relative new field of data mining, and a summary of ethical guidelines for statistical practice.

Glossary

Statistics The art and science of collecting, analyzing, presenting, and interpreting data.

Data The facts and figures collected, analyzed, and summarized for presentation and interpretation.

Data set All the data collected in a particular study.

Elements The entities on which data are collected.

Variable A characteristic of interest for the elements.

Observation The set of measurements obtained for a particular element.

Nominal scale The scale of measurement for a variable when the data are labels or names used to identify an attribute of an element. Nominal data may be nonnumeric or numeric.

Ordinal scale The scale of measurement for a variable if the data exhibit the properties of nominal data and the order or rank of the data is meaningful. Ordinal data may be nonnumeric or numeric.

Interval scale The scale of measurement for a variable if the data demonstrate the properties of ordinal data and the interval between values is expressed in terms of a fixed unit of measure. Interval data are always numeric.

Ratio scale The scale of measurement for a variable if the data demonstrate all the properties of interval data and the ratio of two values is meaningful. Ratio data are always numeric.

Categorical data Labels or names used to identify an attribute of each element. Categorical data use either the nominal or ordinal scale of measurement and may be nonnumeric or numeric.
Quantitative data Numeric values that indicate how much or how many of something. Quantitative data are obtained using either the interval or ratio scale of measurement.
Categorical variable A variable with categorical data.
Quantitative variable A variable with quantitative data.
Cross-sectional data Data collected at the same or approximately the same point in time.
Time series data Data collected over several time periods.
Descriptive statistics Tabular, graphical, and numerical summaries of data.
Population The set of all elements of interest in a particular study.
Sample A subset of the population.
Census A survey to collect data on the entire population.
Sample survey A survey to collect data on a sample.
Statistical inference The process of using data obtained from a sample to make estimates or test hypotheses about the characteristics of a population.
Data mining The process of using procedures from statistics and computer science to extract useful information from extremely large databases.

Supplementary Exercises

1. Discuss the differences between statistics as numerical facts and statistics as a discipline or field of study.

SELF test

2. The U.S. Department of Energy provides fuel economy information for a variety of motor vehicles. A sample of 10 automobiles is shown in Table 1.6 (Fuel Economy website, February 22, 2008). Data show the size of the automobile (compact, midsize, or large), the number of cylinders in the engine, the city driving miles per gallon, the highway driving miles per gallon, and the recommended fuel (diesel, premium, or regular).
   a. How many elements are in this data set?
   b. How many variables are in this data set?
   c. Which variables are categorical and which variables are quantitative?
   d. What type of measurement scale is used for each of the variables?

SELF test

3. Refer to Table 1.6.
   a. What is the average miles per gallon for city driving?
   b. On average, how much higher is the miles per gallon for highway driving as compared to city driving?

TABLE 1.6 FUEL ECONOMY INFORMATION FOR 10 AUTOMOBILES

Car	Size	Cylinders	City MPG	Highway MPG	Fuel
Audi A8	Large	12	13	19	Premium
BMW 328Xi	Compact	6	17	25	Premium
Cadillac CTS	Midsize	6	16	25	Regular
Chrysler 300	Large	8	13	18	Premium
Ford Focus	Compact	4	24	33	Regular
Hyundai Elantra	Midsize	4	25	33	Regular
Jeep Grand Cherokee	Midsize	6	17	26	Diesel
Pontiac G6	Compact	6	15	22	Regular
Toyota Camry	Midsize	4	21	31	Regular
Volkswagen Jetta	Compact	5	21	29	Regular

TABLE 1.7 DATA FOR SEVEN COLLEGES AND UNIVERSITIES

School	State	Campus Setting	Endowment ($ billions)	% Applicants Admitted	NCAA Division
Amherst College	Massachusetts	Town: Fringe	1.7	18	III
Duke	North Carolina	City: Midsize	5.9	21	I-A
Harvard University	Massachusetts	City: Midsize	34.6	9	I-AA
Swarthmore College	Pennsylvania	Suburb: Large	1.4	18	III
University of Pennsylvania	Pennsylvania	City: Large	6.6	18	I-AA
Williams College	Massachusetts	Town: Fringe	1.9	18	III
Yale University	Connecticut	City: Midsize	22.5	9	I-AA

c. What percentage of the cars have four-cylinder engines?
d. What percentage of the cars use regular fuel?

4. Table 1.7 shows data for seven colleges and universities. The endowment (in billions of dollars) and the percentage of applicants admitted are shown (*USA Today,* February 3, 2008). The state each school is located in, the campus setting, and the NCAA Division for varsity teams were obtained from the National Center of Education Statistics website, February 22, 2008.
   a. How many elements are in the data set?
   b. How many variables are in the data set?
   c. Which of the variables are categorical and which are quantitative?
5. Consider the data set in Table 1.7
   a. Compute the average endowment for the sample.
   b. Compute the average percentage of applicants admitted.
   c. What percentage of the schools have NCAA Division III varsity teams?
   d. What percentage of the schools have a City: Midsize campus setting?
6. *Foreign Affairs* magazine conducted a survey to develop a profile of its subscribers (Foreign Affairs website, February 23, 2008). The following questions were asked.
   a. How many nights have you stayed in a hotel in the past 12 months?
   b. Where do you purchase books? Three options were listed: Bookstore, Internet, and Book Club.
   c. Do you own or lease a luxury vehicle? (Yes or No)
   d. What is your age?
   e. For foreign trips taken in the past three years, what was your destination? Seven international destinations were listed.

   Comment on whether each question provides categorical or quantitative data.
7. The Ritz-Carlton Hotel used a customer opinion questionnaire to obtain performance data about its dining and entertainment services (The Ritz-Carlton Hotel, Naples, Florida, February 2006). Customers were asked to rate six factors: Welcome, Service, Food, Menu Appeal, Atmosphere, and Overall Experience. Data were recorded for each factor with 1 for Fair, 2 for Average, 3 for Good, and 4 for Excellent.
   a. The customer responses provided data for six variables. Are the variables categorical or quantitative?
   b. What measurement scale is used?
8. The *FinancialTimes*/Harris Poll is a monthly online poll of adults from six countries in Europe and the United States. A January poll included 1015 adults in the United States. One of the questions asked was, "How would you rate the Federal Bank in handling the

credit problems in the financial markets?" Possible responses were Excellent, Good, Fair, Bad, and Terrible (Harris Interactive website, January 2008).

a. What was the sample size for this survey?
b. Are the data categorical or quantitative?
c. Would it make more sense to use averages or percentages as a summary of the data for this question?
d. Of the respondents in the United States, 10% said the Federal Bank is doing a good job. How many individuals provided this response?

9. The Commerce Department reported receiving the following applications for the Malcolm Baldrige National Quality Award: 23 from large manufacturing firms, 18 from large service firms, and 30 from small businesses.
a. Is type of business a categorical or quantitative variable?
b. What percentage of the applications came from small businesses?

10. *The Wall Street Journal (WSJ)* subscriber survey (October 13, 2003) asked 46 questions about subscriber characteristics and interests. State whether each of the following questions provided categorical or quantitative data and indicate the measurement scale appropriate for each.
a. What is your age?
b. Are you male or female?
c. When did you first start reading the *WSJ*? High school, college, early career, mid-career, late career, or retirement?
d. How long have you been in your present job or position?
e. What type of vehicle are you considering for your next purchase? Nine response categories include sedan, sports car, SUV, minivan, and so on.

11. State whether each of the following variables is categorical or quantitative and indicate its measurement scale.
a. Annual sales
b. Soft drink size (small, medium, large)
c. Employee classification (GS1 through GS18)
d. Earnings per share
e. Method of payment (cash, check, credit card)

12. The Hawaii Visitors Bureau collects data on visitors to Hawaii. The following questions were among 16 asked in a questionnaire handed out to passengers during incoming airline flights in June 2003.
- This trip to Hawaii is my: 1st, 2nd, 3rd, 4th, etc.
- The primary reason for this trip is: (10 categories including vacation, convention, honeymoon)
- Where I plan to stay: (11 categories including hotel, apartment, relatives, camping)
- Total days in Hawaii

a. What is the population being studied?
b. Is the use of a questionnaire a good way to reach the population of passengers on incoming airline flights?
c. Comment on each of the four questions in terms of whether it will provide categorical or quantitative data.

SELF test

13. Figure 1.8 provides a bar chart showing the amount of federal spending for the years 2002 to 2008 (*USA Today,* February 5, 2008).
a. What is the variable of interest?
b. Are the data categorical or quantitative?
c. Are the data time series or cross-sectional?
d. Comment on the trend in federal spending over time.

FIGURE 1.8 FEDERAL SPENDING

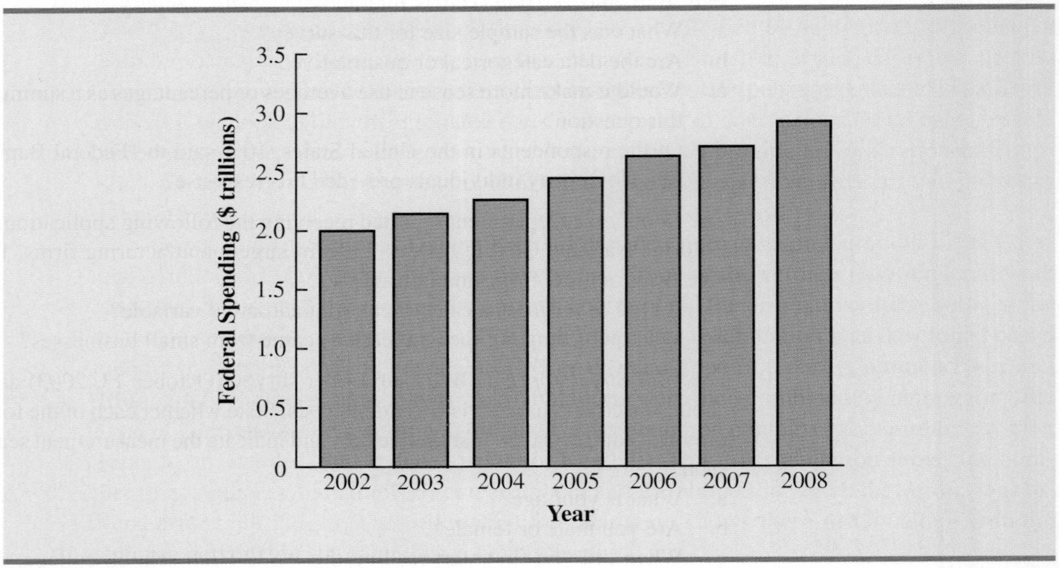

14. CSM Worldwide forecasts global production for all automobile manufacturers. The following CSM data show the forecast of global auto production for General Motors, Ford, DaimlerChrysler, and Toyota for the years 2004 to 2007 (*USA Today,* December 21, 2005). Data are in millions of vehicles.

Manufacturer	2004	2005	2006	2007
General Motors	8.9	9.0	8.9	8.8
Ford	7.8	7.7	7.8	7.9
DaimlerChrysler	4.1	4.2	4.3	4.6
Toyota	7.8	8.3	9.1	9.6

a. Construct a time series graph for the years 2004 to 2007 showing the number of vehicles manufactured by each automotive company. Show the time series for all four manufacturers on the same graph.
b. General Motors has been the undisputed production leader of automobiles since 1931. What does the time series graph show about who is the world's biggest car company? Discuss.
c. Construct a bar graph showing vehicles produced by automobile manufacturer using the 2007 data. Is this graph based on cross-sectional or time series data?

15. The Food and Drug Administration (FDA) reported the number of new drugs approved over an eight-year period (*The Wall Street Journal,* January 12, 2004). Figure 1.9 provides a bar chart summarizing the number of new drugs approved each year.
a. Are the data categorical or quantitative?
b. Are the data time series or cross-sectional?
c. How many new drugs were approved in 2003?
d. In what year were the fewest new drugs approved? How many?
e. Comment on the trend in the number of new drugs approved by the FDA over the eight-year period.

FIGURE 1.9 NUMBER OF NEW DRUGS APPROVED BY THE FOOD AND DRUG ADMINISTRATION

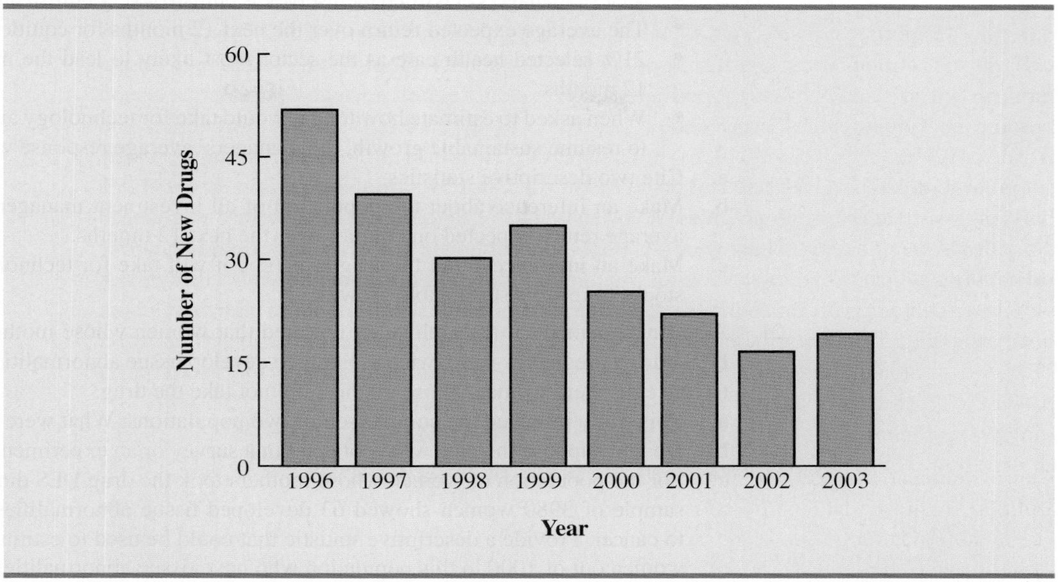

16. The Energy Information Administration of the U.S. Department of Energy provided time series data for the U.S. average price per gallon of conventional regular gasoline between July 2006 and June 2009 (Energy Information Administration website, June 2009). Use the Internet to obtain the average price per gallon of conventional regular gasoline since June 2009.
    a. Extend the graph of the time series shown in Figure 1.1.
    b. What interpretations can you make about the average price per gallon of conventional regular gasoline since June 2009?
    c. Does the time series continue to show a summer increase in the average price per gallon? Explain.
17. A manager of a large corporation recommends a $10,000 raise be given to keep a valued subordinate from moving to another company. What internal and external sources of data might be used to decide whether such a salary increase is appropriate?
18. A survey of 430 business travelers found 155 business travelers used a travel agent to make the travel arrangements (*USA Today,* November 20, 2003).
    a. Develop a descriptive statistic that can be used to estimate the percentage of all business travelers who use a travel agent to make travel arrangements.
    b. The survey reported that the most frequent way business travelers make travel arrangements is by using an online travel site. If 44% of business travelers surveyed made their arrangements this way, how many of the 430 business travelers used an online travel site?
    c. Are the data on how travel arrangements are made categorical or quantitative?
19. A *BusinessWeek* North American subscriber study collected data from a sample of 2861 subscribers. Fifty-nine percent of the respondents indicated an annual income of $75,000 or more, and 50% reported having an American Express credit card.
    a. What is the population of interest in this study?
    b. Is annual income a categorical or quantitative variable?
    c. Is ownership of an American Express card a categorical or quantitative variable?
    d. Does this study involve cross-sectional or time series data?
    e. Describe any statistical inferences *BusinessWeek* might make on the basis of the survey.

20. A survey of 131 investment managers in *Barron's* Big Money poll revealed the following:
    - 43% of managers classified themselves as bullish or very bullish on the stock market.
    - The average expected return over the next 12 months for equities was 11.2%.
    - 21% selected health care as the sector most likely to lead the market in the next 12 months.
    - When asked to estimate how long it would take for technology and telecom stocks to resume sustainable growth, the managers' average response was 2.5 years.

    a. Cite two descriptive statistics.
    b. Make an inference about the population of all investment managers concerning the average return expected on equities over the next 12 months.
    c. Make an inference about the length of time it will take for technology and telecom stocks to resume sustainable growth.

21. A seven-year medical research study reported that women whose mothers took the drug DES during pregnancy were twice as likely to develop tissue abnormalities that might lead to cancer as were women whose mothers did not take the drug.
    a. This study involved the comparison of two populations. What were the populations?
    b. Do you suppose the data were obtained in a survey or an experiment?
    c. For the population of women whose mothers took the drug DES during pregnancy, a sample of 3980 women showed 63 developed tissue abnormalities that might lead to cancer. Provide a descriptive statistic that could be used to estimate the number of women out of 1000 in this population who have tissue abnormalities.
    d. For the population of women whose mothers did not take the drug DES during pregnancy, what is the estimate of the number of women out of 1000 who would be expected to have tissue abnormalities?
    e. Medical studies often use a relatively large sample (in this case, 3980). Why?

22. The Nielsen Company surveyed consumers in 47 markets from Europe, Asia-Pacific, the Americas, and the Middle East to determine which factors are most important in determining where they buy groceries. Using a scale of 1 (low) to 5 (high), the highest rated factor was *good value for money*, with an average point score of 4.32. The second highest rated factor was *better selection of high-quality brands and products,* with an average point score of 3.78, and the lowest rated factor was *uses recyclable bags and packaging*, with an average point score of 2.71 (Nielsen website, February 24, 2008). Suppose that you have been hired by a grocery store chain to conduct a similar study to determine what factors customers at the chain's stores in Charlotte, North Carolina, think are most important in determining where they buy groceries.
    a. What is the population for the survey that you will be conducting?
    b. How would you collect the data for this study?

23. Nielsen Media Research conducts weekly surveys of television viewing throughout the United States, publishing both rating and market share data. The Nielsen rating is the percentage of households with televisions watching a program, while the Nielsen share is the percentage of households watching a program among those households with televisions in use. For example, Nielsen Media Research results for the 2003 Baseball World Series between the New York Yankees and the Florida Marlins showed a rating of 12.8% and a share of 22% (Associated Press, October 27, 2003). Thus, 12.8% of households with televisions were watching the World Series and 22% of households with televisions in use were watching the World Series. Based on the rating and share data for major television programs, Nielsen publishes a weekly ranking of television programs as well as a weekly ranking of the four major networks: ABC, CBS, NBC, and Fox.
    a. What is Nielsen Media Research attempting to measure?
    b. What is the population?
    c. Why would a sample be used in this situation?
    d. What kinds of decisions or actions are based on the Nielsen rankings?

TABLE 1.8 DATA SET FOR 25 SHADOW STOCKS

WEB file
Shadow02

Company	Exchange	Ticker Symbol	Market Cap ($ millions)	Price/ Earnings Ratio	Gross Profit Margin (%)
DeWolfe Companies	AMEX	DWL	36.4	8.4	36.7
North Coast Energy	OTC	NCEB	52.5	6.2	59.3
Hansen Natural Corp.	OTC	HANS	41.1	14.6	44.8
MarineMax, Inc.	NYSE	HZO	111.5	7.2	23.8
Nanometrics Incorporated	OTC	NANO	228.6	38.0	53.3
TeamStaff, Inc.	OTC	TSTF	92.1	33.5	4.1
Environmental Tectonics	AMEX	ETC	51.1	35.8	35.9
Measurement Specialties	AMEX	MSS	101.8	26.8	37.6
SEMCO Energy, Inc.	NYSE	SEN	193.4	18.7	23.6
Party City Corporation	OTC	PCTY	97.2	15.9	36.4
Embrex, Inc.	OTC	EMBX	136.5	18.9	59.5
Tech/Ops Sevcon, Inc.	AMEX	TO	23.2	20.7	35.7
ARCADIS NV	OTC	ARCAF	173.4	8.8	9.6
Qiao Xing Universal Tele.	OTC	XING	64.3	22.1	30.8
Energy West Incorporated	OTC	EWST	29.1	9.7	16.3
Barnwell Industries, Inc.	AMEX	BRN	27.3	7.4	73.4
Innodata Corporation	OTC	INOD	66.1	11.0	29.6
Medical Action Industries	OTC	MDCI	137.1	26.9	30.6
Instrumentarium Corp.	OTC	INMRY	240.9	3.6	52.1
Petroleum Development	OTC	PETD	95.9	6.1	19.4
Drexler Technology Corp.	OTC	DRXR	233.6	45.6	53.6
Gerber Childrenswear Inc.	NYSE	GCW	126.9	7.9	25.8
Gaiam, Inc.	OTC	GAIA	295.5	68.2	60.7
Artesian Resources Corp.	OTC	ARTNA	62.8	20.5	45.5
York Water Company	OTC	YORW	92.2	22.9	74.2

24. A sample of midterm grades for five students showed the following results: 72, 65, 82, 90, 76. Which of the following statements are correct, and which should be challenged as being too generalized?
    a. The average midterm grade for the sample of five students is 77.
    b. The average midterm grade for all students who took the exam is 77.
    c. An estimate of the average midterm grade for all students who took the exam is 77.
    d. More than half of the students who take this exam will score between 70 and 85.
    e. If five other students are included in the sample, their grades will be between 65 and 90.
25. Table 1.8 shows a data set containing information for 25 of the shadow stocks tracked by the American Association of Individual Investors. Shadow stocks are common stocks of smaller companies that are not closely followed by Wall Street analysts. The data set is also on the website that accompanies the text in the file named Shadow02.
    a. How many variables are in the data set?
    b. Which of the variables are categorical and which are quantitative?
    c. For the Exchange variable, show the frequency and the percent frequency for AMEX, NYSE, and OTC. Construct a bar graph similar to Figure 1.5 for the Exchange variable.
    d. Show the frequency distribution for the Gross Profit Margin using the five intervals: 0–14.9, 15–29.9, 30–44.9, 45–59.9, and 60–74.9. Construct a histogram similar to Figure 1.6.
    e. What is the average price/earnings ratio?

Appendix An Introduction to StatTools

StatTools is a professional add-in that expands the statistical capabilities available with Microsoft Excel. StatTools software can be downloaded from the website that accompanies this text.

Excel does not contain statistical functions or data analysis tools to perform all the statistical procedures discussed in the text. StatTools is a Microsoft Excel statistics add-in that extends the range of statistical and graphical options for Excel users. Most chapters include a chapter appendix that shows the steps required to accomplish a statistical procedure using StatTools. For those students who want to make more extensive use of the software, StatTools offers an excellent Help facility. The StatTools Help system includes detailed explanations of the statistical and data analysis options available, as well as descriptions and definitions of the types of output provided.

Getting Started with StatTools

StatTools software may be downloaded and installed on your computer by accessing the website that accompanies this text. After downloading and installing the software, perform the following steps to use StatTools as an Excel add-in.

Step 1. Click the **Start** button on the taskbar and then point to **All Programs**
Step 2. Point to the folder entitled **Palisade Decision Tools**
Step 3. Click **StatTools for Excel**

These steps will open Excel and add the StatTools tab next to the Add-Ins tab on the Excel Ribbon. Alternately, if you are already working in Excel, these steps will make StatTools available.

Using StatTools

Before conducting any statistical analysis, we must create a StatTools data set using the StatTools Data Set Manager. Let us use the Excel worksheet for the mutual funds data set in Table 1.1 to show how this is done. The following steps show how to create a StatTools data set for the mutual funds data.

Step 1. Open the Excel file named Morningstar
Step 2. Select any cell in the data set (for example, cell A1)
Step 3. Click the **StatTools** tab on the Ribbon
Step 4. In the **Data** group, click **Data Set Manager**
Step 5. When StatTools asks if you want to add the range $A$1:$F$26 as a new StatTools data set, click **Yes**
Step 6. When the StatTools—Data Set Manager dialog box appears, click **OK**

Figure 1.10 shows the StatTools—Data Set Manager dialog box that appears in step 6. By default, the name of the new StatTools data set is Data Set #1. You can replace the name Data Set #1 in step 6 with a more descriptive name. And, if you select the Apply Cell Format option, the column labels will be highlighted in blue and the entire data set will have outside and inside borders. You can always select the Data Set Manager at any time in your analysis to make these types of changes.

Recommended Application Settings

StatTools allows the user to specify some of the application settings that control such things as where statistical output is displayed and how calculations are performed. The following steps show how to access the StatTools—Application Settings dialog box.

Step 1. Click the **StatTools** tab on the Ribbon
Step 2. In the **Tools Group**, click **Utilities**
Step 3. Choose **Application Settings** from the list of options

FIGURE 1.10 THE STATTOOLS—DATA SET MANAGER DIALOG BOX

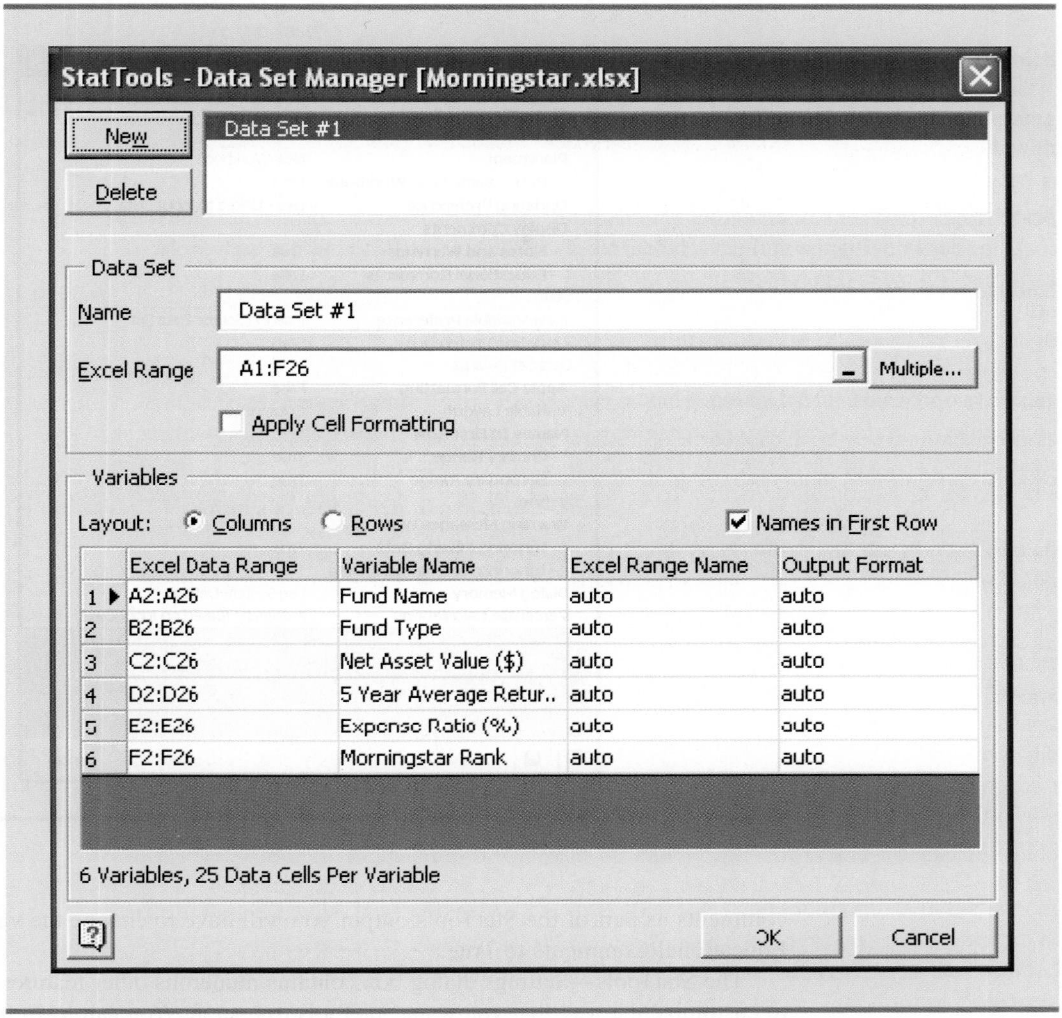

Figure 1.11 shows that the StatTools—Application Settings dialog box has five sections: General Settings; Reports; Utilities; Data Set Defaults; and Analyses. Let us show how to make changes in the Reports section of the dialog box.

Figure 1.11 shows that the Placement option currently selected is **New Workbook**. Using this option, the StatTools output will be placed in a new workbook. But suppose you would like to place the StatTools output in the current (active) workbook. If you click the words **New Workbook**, a downward-pointing arrow will appear to the right. Clicking this arrow will display a list of all the placement options, including **Active Workbook**; we recommend using this option. Figure 1.11 also shows that the Updating Preferences option in the Reports section is currently **Live—Linked to Input Data**. With live updating, anytime one or more data values are changed StatTools will automatically change the output previously produced; we also recommend using this option. Note that there are two options available under Display Comments: **Notes and Warnings** and **Educational Comments**. Because these options provide useful notes and information regarding the output, we recommend using both options. Thus, to include educational

FIGURE 1.11 THE STATTOOLS—APPLICATION SETTINGS DIALOG BOX

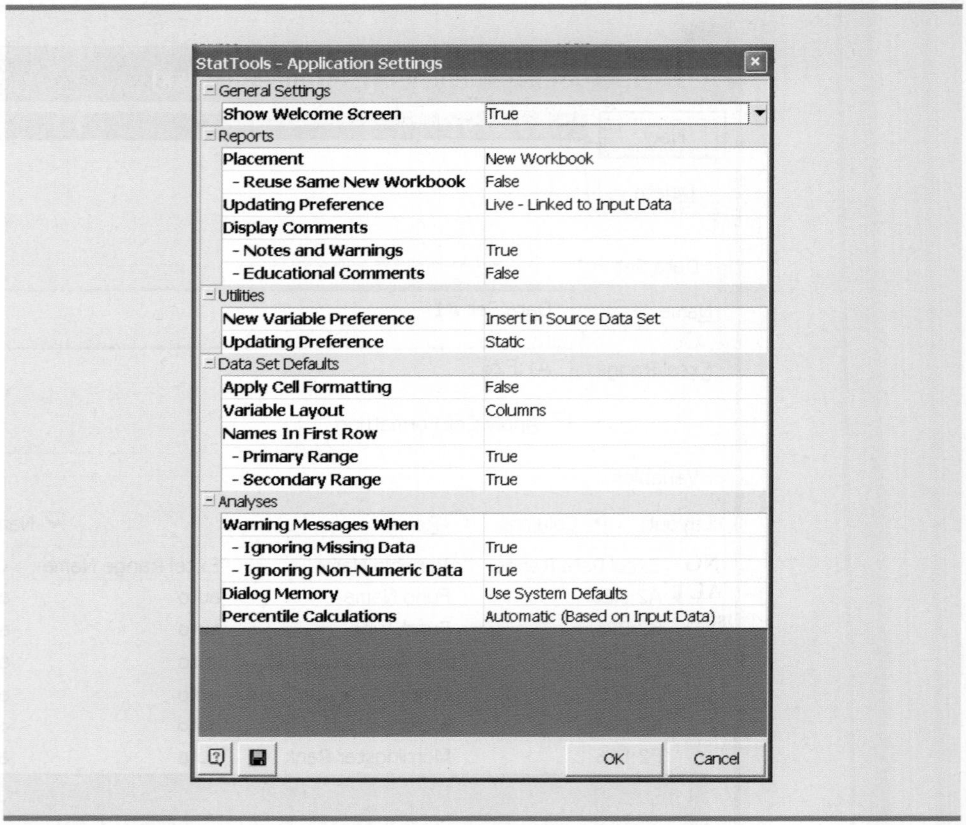

comments as part of the StatTools output you will have to change the value of False for Educational Comments to True.

The StatTools—Settings dialog box contains numerous other features that enable you to customize the way that you want StatTools to operate. You can learn more about these features by selecting the Help option located in the Tools group, or by clicking the Help icon located in the lower left-hand corner of the dialog box. When you have finish making changes in the application settings, click OK at the bottom of the dialog box and then click Yes when StatTools asks you if you want to save the new application settings.

CHAPTER 2

Descriptive Statistics: Tabular and Graphical Presentations

CONTENTS

STATISTICS *in* PRACTICE

COLGATE-PALMOLIVE COMPANY*
NEW YORK, NEW YORK

The Colgate-Palmolive Company started as a small soap and candle shop in New York City in 1806. Today, Colgate-Palmolive employs more than 40,000 people working in more than 200 countries and territories around the world. Although best known for its brand names of Colgate, Palmolive, Ajax, and Fab, the company also markets Mennen, Hill's Science Diet, and Hill's Prescription Diet products.

The Colgate-Palmolive Company uses statistics in its quality assurance program for home laundry detergent products. One concern is customer satisfaction with the quantity of detergent in a carton. Every carton in each size category is filled with the same amount of detergent by weight, but the volume of detergent is affected by the density of the detergent powder. For instance, if the powder density is on the heavy side, a smaller volume of detergent is needed to reach the carton's specified weight. As a result, the carton may appear to be underfilled when opened by the consumer.

To control the problem of heavy detergent powder, limits are placed on the acceptable range of powder density. Statistical samples are taken periodically, and the density of each powder sample is measured. Data summaries are then provided for operating personnel so that corrective action can be taken if necessary to keep the density within the desired quality specifications.

A frequency distribution for the densities of 150 samples taken over a one-week period and a histogram are shown in the accompanying table and figure. Density levels above .40 are unacceptably high. The frequency distribution and histogram show that the operation is meeting its quality guidelines with all of the densities less than or equal to .40. Managers viewing these statistical summaries would be pleased with the quality of the detergent production process.

In this chapter, you will learn about tabular and graphical methods of descriptive statistics such as frequency distributions, bar charts, histograms, stem-and-leaf displays, crosstabulations, and others. The goal of these methods is to summarize data so that the data can be easily understood and interpreted.

*The authors are indebted to William R. Fowle, Manager of Quality Assurance, Colgate-Palmolive Company, for providing this Statistics in Practice.

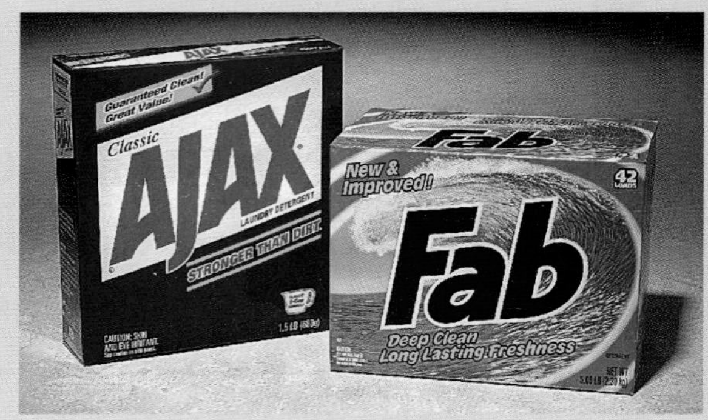

Graphical summaries help track the demand for Colgate-Palmolive products. © Victor Fisher/ Bloomberg News/Landov.

Frequency Distribution of Density Data

Density	Frequency
.29–.30	30
.31–.32	75
.33–.34	32
.35–.36	9
.37–.38	3
.39–.40	1
Total	150

Histogram of Density Data

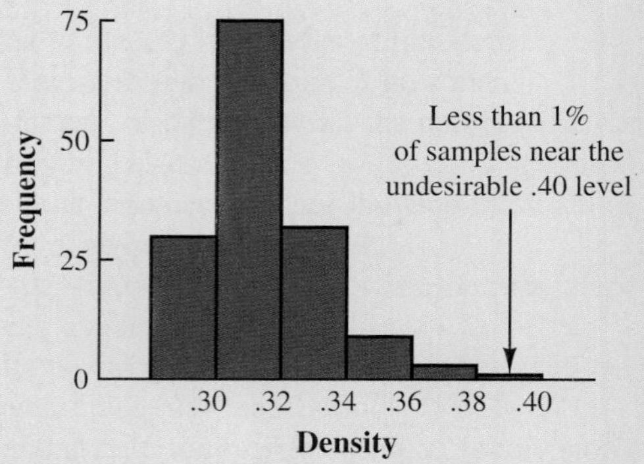

As indicated in Chapter 1, data can be classified as either categorical or quantitative. **Categorical data** use labels or names to identify categories of like items. **Quantitative data** are numerical values that indicate how much or how many.

This chapter introduces tabular and graphical methods commonly used to summarize both categorical and quantitative data. Tabular and graphical summaries of data can be found in annual reports, newspaper articles, and research studies. Everyone is exposed to these types of presentations. Hence, it is important to understand how they are prepared and how they should be interpreted. We begin with tabular and graphical methods for summarizing data concerning a single variable. The last section introduces methods for summarizing data when the relationship between two variables is of interest.

Modern statistical software packages provide extensive capabilities for summarizing data and preparing graphical presentations. Minitab and Excel are two packages that are widely available. In the chapter appendixes, we show some of their capabilities.

2.1 Summarizing Categorical Data

Frequency Distribution

We begin the discussion of how tabular and graphical methods can be used to summarize categorical data with the definition of a **frequency distribution**.

FREQUENCY DISTRIBUTION

A frequency distribution is a tabular summary of data showing the number (frequency) of items in each of several nonoverlapping classes.

Let us use the following example to demonstrate the construction and interpretation of a frequency distribution for categorical data. Coke Classic, Diet Coke, Dr. Pepper, Pepsi, and Sprite are five popular soft drinks. Assume that the data in Table 2.1 show the soft drink selected in a sample of 50 soft drink purchases.

TABLE 2.1 DATA FROM A SAMPLE OF 50 SOFT DRINK PURCHASES

WEB file
SoftDrink

Coke Classic	Sprite	Pepsi
Diet Coke	Coke Classic	Coke Classic
Pepsi	Diet Coke	Coke Classic
Diet Coke	Coke Classic	Coke Classic
Coke Classic	Diet Coke	Pepsi
Coke Classic	Coke Classic	Dr. Pepper
Dr. Pepper	Sprite	Coke Classic
Diet Coke	Pepsi	Diet Coke
Pepsi	Coke Classic	Pepsi
Pepsi	Coke Classic	Pepsi
Coke Classic	Coke Classic	Pepsi
Dr. Pepper	Pepsi	Pepsi
Sprite	Coke Classic	Coke Classic
Coke Classic	Sprite	Dr. Pepper
Diet Coke	Dr. Pepper	Pepsi
Coke Classic	Pepsi	Sprite
Coke Classic	Diet Coke	

TABLE 2.2 FREQUENCY DISTRIBUTION OF SOFT DRINK PURCHASES

Soft Drink	Frequency
Coke Classic	19
Diet Coke	8
Dr. Pepper	5
Pepsi	13
Sprite	5
Total	50

To develop a frequency distribution for these data, we count the number of times each soft drink appears in Table 2.1. Coke Classic appears 19 times, Diet Coke appears 8 times, Dr. Pepper appears 5 times, Pepsi appears 13 times, and Sprite appears 5 times. These counts are summarized in the frequency distribution in Table 2.2.

This frequency distribution provides a summary of how the 50 soft drink purchases are distributed across the five soft drinks. This summary offers more insight than the original data shown in Table 2.1. Viewing the frequency distribution, we see that Coke Classic is the leader, Pepsi is second, Diet Coke is third, and Sprite and Dr. Pepper are tied for fourth. The frequency distribution summarizes information about the popularity of the five soft drinks.

Relative Frequency and Percent Frequency Distributions

A frequency distribution shows the number (frequency) of items in each of several nonoverlapping classes. However, we are often interested in the proportion, or percentage, of items in each class. The *relative frequency* of a class equals the fraction or proportion of items belonging to a class. For a data set with n observations, the relative frequency of each class can be determined as follows:

RELATIVE FREQUENCY

$$\text{Relative frequency of a class} = \frac{\text{Frequency of the class}}{n} \quad \textbf{(2.1)}$$

The *percent frequency* of a class is the relative frequency multiplied by 100.

A **relative frequency distribution** gives a tabular summary of data showing the relative frequency for each class. A **percent frequency distribution** summarizes the percent frequency of the data for each class. Table 2.3 shows a relative frequency distribution and a percent frequency distribution for the soft drink data. In Table 2.3 we see that the relative frequency for Coke Classic is 19/50 = .38, the relative frequency for Diet Coke is 8/50 = .16, and so on. From the percent frequency distribution, we see that 38% of the purchases were Coke Classic, 16% of the purchases were Diet Coke, and so on. We can also note that 38% + 26% + 16% = 80% of the purchases were the top three soft drinks.

Bar Charts and Pie Charts

A **bar chart** is a graphical device for depicting categorical data summarized in a frequency, relative frequency, or percent frequency distribution. On one axis of the graph (usually the horizontal axis), we specify the labels that are used for the classes (categories). A frequency, relative frequency, or percent frequency scale can be used for the other axis of the chart

TABLE 2.3 RELATIVE FREQUENCY AND PERCENT FREQUENCY DISTRIBUTIONS OF SOFT DRINK PURCHASES

Soft Drink	Relative Frequency	Percent Frequency
Coke Classic	.38	38
Diet Coke	.16	16
Dr. Pepper	.10	10
Pepsi	.26	26
Sprite	.10	10
Total	1.00	100

FIGURE 2.1 BAR CHART OF SOFT DRINK PURCHASES

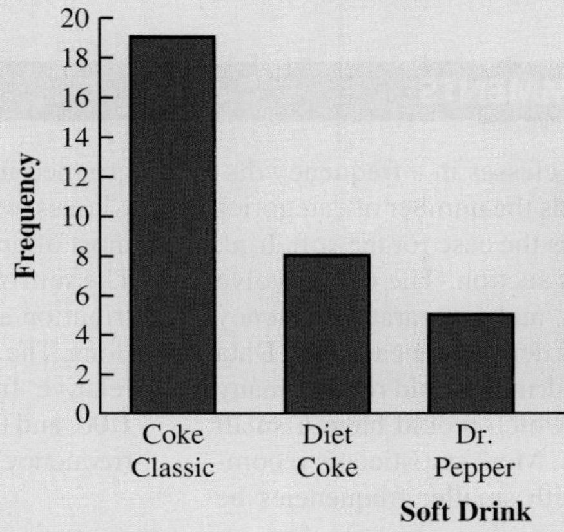

In quality control applications, bar charts are used to identify the most important causes of problems. When the bars are arranged in descending order of height from left to right with the most frequently occurring cause appearing first, the bar chart is called a pareto diagram. *This diagram is named for its founder, Vilfredo Pareto, an Italian economist.*

(usually the vertical axis). Then, using a bar of fixed width drawn above each class label, we extend the length of the bar until we reach the frequency, relative frequency, or percent frequency of the class. For categorical data, the bars should be separated to emphasize the fact that each class is separate. Figure 2.1 shows a bar chart of the frequency distribution for the 50 soft drink purchases. Note how the graphical presentation shows Coke Classic, Pepsi, and Diet Coke to be the most preferred brands.

The **pie chart** provides another graphical device for presenting relative frequency and percent frequency distributions for categorical data. To construct a pie chart, we first draw a circle to represent all the data. Then we use the relative frequencies to subdivide the circle into sectors, or parts, that correspond to the relative frequency for each class. For example, because a circle contains 360 degrees and Coke Classic shows a relative frequency of .38, the sector of the pie chart labeled Coke Classic consists of .38(360) = 136.8 degrees. The sector of the pie chart labeled Diet Coke consists of .16(360) = 57.6 degrees. Similar calculations for the other classes yield the pie chart in Figure 2.2. The

FIGURE 2.2 PIE CHART OF SOFT DRINK PURCHASES

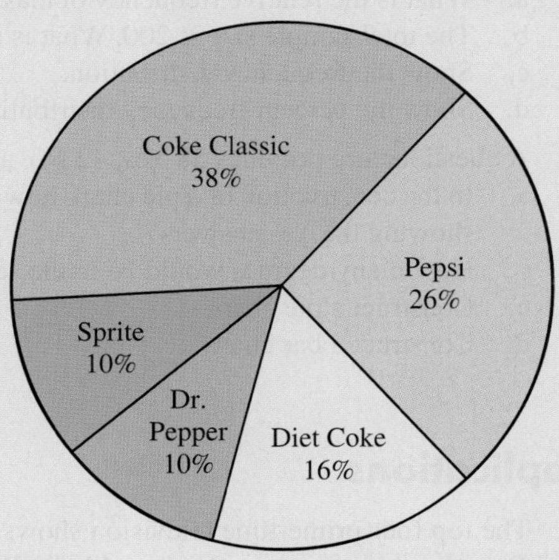

numerical values shown for each sector can be frequencies, relative frequencies, or percent frequencies.

NOTES AND COMMENTS

1. Often the number of classes in a frequency distribution is the same as the number of categories found in the data, as is the case for the soft drink purchase data in this section. The data involve only five soft drinks, and a separate frequency distribution class was defined for each one. Data that included all soft drinks would require many categories, most of which would have a small number of purchases. Most statisticians recommend that classes with smaller frequencies be grouped into an aggregate class called "other." Classes with frequencies of 5% or less would most often be treated in this fashion.
2. The sum of the frequencies in any frequency distribution always equals the number of observations. The sum of the relative frequencies in any relative frequency distribution always equals 1.00, and the sum of the percentages in a percent frequency distribution always equals 100.

Exercises

Methods

1. The response to a question has three alternatives: A, B, and C. A sample of 120 responses provides 60 A, 24 B, and 36 C. Show the frequency and relative frequency distributions.
2. A partial relative frequency distribution is given.

Class	Relative Frequency
A	.22
B	.18
C	.40
D	

   a. What is the relative frequency of class D?
   b. The total sample size is 200. What is the frequency of class D?
   c. Show the frequency distribution.
   d. Show the percent frequency distribution.

SELF test

3. A questionnaire provides 58 Yes, 42 No, and 20 no-opinion answers.
   a. In the construction of a pie chart, how many degrees would be in the section of the pie showing the Yes answers?
   b. How many degrees would be in the section of the pie showing the No answers?
   c. Construct a pie chart.
   d. Construct a bar chart.

Applications

WEB file
BestTV

4. The top four prime-time television shows were *Law & Order, CSI, Without a Trace,* and *Desperate Housewives* (Nielsen Media Research, January 1, 2007). Data indicating the preferred shows for a sample of 50 viewers follow.

DH	CSI	DH	CSI	L&O
Trace	CSI	L&O	Trace	CSI
CSI	DH	Trace	CSI	DH
L&O	L&O	L&O	CSI	DH
CSI	DH	DH	L&O	CSI
DH	Trace	CSI	Trace	DH
DH	CSI	CSI	L&O	CSI
L&O	CSI	Trace	Trace	DH
L&O	CSI	CSI	CSI	DH
CSI	DH	Trace	Trace	L&O

a. Are these data categorical or quantitative?
b. Provide frequency and percent frequency distributions.
c. Construct a bar chart and a pie chart.
d. On the basis of the sample, which television show has the largest viewing audience? Which one is second?

5. In alphabetical order, the six most common last names in the United States are Brown, Davis, Johnson, Jones, Smith, and Williams (*The World Almanac,* 2006). Assume that a sample of 50 individuals with one of these last names provided the following data.

WEB file
Names

Brown	Williams	Williams	Williams	Brown
Smith	Jones	Smith	Johnson	Smith
Davis	Smith	Brown	Williams	Johnson
Johnson	Smith	Smith	Johnson	Brown
Williams	Davis	Johnson	Williams	Johnson
Williams	Johnson	Jones	Smith	Brown
Johnson	Smith	Smith	Brown	Jones
Jones	Jones	Smith	Smith	Davis
Davis	Jones	Williams	Davis	Smith
Jones	Johnson	Brown	Johnson	Davis

Summarize the data by constructing the following:
a. Relative and percent frequency distributions
b. A bar chart
c. A pie chart
d. Based on these data, what are the three most common last names?

6. The Nielsen Media Research television rating measures the percentage of television owners who are watching a particular television program. The highest-rated television program in television history was the *M*A*S*H Last Episode Special* shown on February 28, 1983. A 60.2 rating indicated that 60.2% of all television owners were watching this program. Nielsen Media Research provided the list of the 50 top-rated single shows in television history (*The New York Times Almanac,* 2006). The following data show the television network that produced each of these 50 top-rated shows.

WEB file
Networks

ABC	ABC	ABC	NBC	CBS
ABC	CBS	ABC	ABC	NBC
NBC	NBC	CBS	ABC	NBC
CBS	ABC	CBS	NBC	ABC
CBS	NBC	NBC	CBS	NBC
CBS	CBS	CBS	NBC	NBC
FOX	CBS	CBS	ABC	NBC
ABC	ABC	CBS	NBC	NBC
NBC	CBS	NBC	CBS	CBS
ABC	CBS	ABC	NBC	ABC

a. Construct a frequency distribution, percent frequency distribution, and bar chart for the data.

b. Which network or networks have done the best in terms of presenting top-rated television shows? Compare the performance of ABC, CBS, and NBC.

SELF test

7. Leverock's Waterfront Steakhouse in Maderia Beach, Florida, uses a questionnaire to ask customers how they rate the server, food quality, cocktails, prices, and atmosphere at the restaurant. Each characteristic is rated on a scale of outstanding (O), very good (V), good (G), average (A), and poor (P). Use descriptive statistics to summarize the following data collected on food quality. What is your feeling about the food quality ratings at the restaurant?

G	O	V	G	A	O	V	O	V	G	O	V	A
V	O	P	V	O	G	A	O	O	O	G	O	V
V	A	G	O	V	P	V	O	O	G	O	O	V
O	G	A	O	V	O	O	G	V	A	G		

8. Data for a sample of 55 members of the Baseball Hall of Fame in Cooperstown, New York, are shown here. Each observation indicates the primary position played by the Hall of Famers: pitcher (P), catcher (H), 1st base (1), 2nd base (2), 3rd base (3), shortstop (S), left field (L), center field (C), and right field (R).

L	P	C	H	2	P	R	1	S	S	1	L	P	R	P
P	P	P	R	C	S	L	R	P	C	C	P	P	R	P
2	3	P	H	L	P	1	C	P	P	P	S	1	L	R
R	1	2	H	S	3	H	2	L	P					

a. Use frequency and relative frequency distributions to summarize the data.
b. What position provides the most Hall of Famers?
c. What position provides the fewest Hall of Famers?
d. What outfield position (L, C, or R) provides the most Hall of Famers?
e. Compare infielders (1, 2, 3, and S) to outfielders (L, C, and R).

WEB file
LivingArea

9. The Pew Research Center's Social & Demographic Trends project found that 46% of U.S. adults would rather live in a different type of community than the one where they are living now (Pew Research Center, January 29, 2009). The national survey of 2260 adults asked: "Where do you live now?" and "What do you consider to be the ideal community?" Response options were City (C), Suburb (S), Small Town (T), or Rural (R). A representative portion of this survey for a sample of 100 respondents is as follows.

Where do you live now?

S	T	R	C	R	R	T	C	S	T	C	S	C	S	T
S	S	C	S	S	T	T	C	C	S	T	C	S	T	C
T	R	S	S	T	C	S	C	T	C	T	C	T	C	R
C	C	R	T	C	S	S	T	S	C	C	C	R	S	C
S	S	C	C	S	C	R	T	T	T	C	R	T	C	R
C	T	R	R	C	T	C	C	R	T	T	R	S	R	T
T	S	S	S	S	S	C	C	R	T					

What do you consider to be the ideal community?

S	C	R	R	R	S	T	S	S	T	T	S	C	S	T
C	C	R	T	R	S	T	T	S	S	C	C	T	T	S
S	R	C	S	C	C	S	C	R	C	T	S	R	R	R
C	T	S	T	T	T	R	R	S	C	C	R	R	S	S
S	T	C	T	T	C	R	T	T	T	C	T	T	R	R
C	S	R	T	C	T	C	C	T	T	T	R	C	R	T
T	C	S	S	C	S	T	S	S	R					

a. Provide a percent frequency distribution for each question.
b. Construct a bar chart for each question.
c. Where are most adults living now?
d. Where do most adults consider the ideal community?

e. What changes in living areas would you expect to see if people moved from where they currently live to their ideal community?

WEB file FedBank

10. The *Financial Times*/Harris Poll is a monthly online poll of adults from six countries in Europe and the United States. The poll conducted in January 2008 included 1015 adults. One of the questions asked was, "How would you rate the Federal Bank in handling the credit problems in the financial markets?" Possible responses were Excellent, Good, Fair, Bad, and Terrible (Harris Interactive website, January 2008). The 1015 responses for this question can be found in the data file named FedBank.
    a. Construct a frequency distribution.
    b. Construct a percent frequency distribution.
    c. Construct a bar chart for the percent frequency distribution.
    d. Comment on how adults in the United States think the Federal Bank is handling the credit problems in the financial markets.
    e. In Spain, 1114 adults were asked, "How would you rate the European Central Bank in handling the credit problems in the financial markets?" The percent frequency distribution obtained follows:

Rating	Percent Frequency
Excellent	0
Good	4
Fair	46
Bad	40
Terrible	10

Compare the results obtained in Spain with the results obtained in the United States.

2.2 Summarizing Quantitative Data

Frequency Distribution

TABLE 2.4 YEAR-END AUDIT TIMES (IN DAYS)

12	14	19	18
15	15	18	17
20	27	22	23
22	21	33	28
14	18	16	13

As defined in Section 2.1, a frequency distribution is a tabular summary of data showing the number (frequency) of items in each of several nonoverlapping classes. This definition holds for quantitative as well as categorical data. However, with quantitative data we must be more careful in defining the nonoverlapping classes to be used in the frequency distribution.

For example, consider the quantitative data in Table 2.4. These data show the time in days required to complete year-end audits for a sample of 20 clients of Sanderson and Clifford, a small public accounting firm. The three steps necessary to define the classes for a frequency distribution with quantitative data are:

1. Determine the number of nonoverlapping classes.
2. Determine the width of each class.
3. Determine the class limits.

Let us demonstrate these steps by developing a frequency distribution for the audit time data in Table 2.4.

WEB file Audit

Number of classes Classes are formed by specifying ranges that will be used to group the data. As a general guideline, we recommend using between 5 and 20 classes. For a small number of data items, as few as five or six classes may be used to summarize the data. For a larger number of data items, a larger number of classes is usually required. The goal is to use enough classes to show the variation in the data, but not so many classes that some contain only a few data items. Because the number of data items in Table 2.4 is relatively small ($n = 20$), we chose to develop a frequency distribution with five classes.

Making the classes the same width reduces the chance of inappropriate interpretations by the user.

Width of the classes The second step in constructing a frequency distribution for quantitative data is to choose a width for the classes. As a general guideline, we recommend that the width be the same for each class. Thus the choices of the number of classes and the width of classes are not independent decisions. A larger number of classes means a smaller class width, and vice versa. To determine an approximate class width, we begin by identifying the largest and smallest data values. Then, with the desired number of classes specified, we can use the following expression to determine the approximate class width.

$$\text{Approximate class width} = \frac{\text{Largest data value} - \text{Smallest data value}}{\text{Number of classes}} \tag{2.2}$$

The approximate class width given by equation (2.2) can be rounded to a more convenient value based on the preference of the person developing the frequency distribution. For example, an approximate class width of 9.28 might be rounded to 10 simply because 10 is a more convenient class width to use in presenting a frequency distribution.

For the data involving the year-end audit times, the largest data value is 33 and the smallest data value is 12. Because we decided to summarize the data with five classes, using equation (2.2) provides an approximate class width of $(33 - 12)/5 = 4.2$. We therefore decided to round up and use a class width of five days in the frequency distribution.

No single frequency distribution is best for a data set. Different people may construct different, but equally acceptable, frequency distributions. The goal is to reveal the natural grouping and variation in the data.

In practice, the number of classes and the appropriate class width are determined by trial and error. Once a possible number of classes is chosen, equation (2.2) is used to find the approximate class width. The process can be repeated for a different number of classes. Ultimately, the analyst uses judgment to determine the combination of the number of classes and class width that provides the best frequency distribution for summarizing the data.

For the audit time data in Table 2.4, after deciding to use five classes, each with a width of five days, the next task is to specify the class limits for each of the classes.

Class limits Class limits must be chosen so that each data item belongs to one and only one class. The *lower class limit* identifies the smallest possible data value assigned to the class. The *upper class limit* identifies the largest possible data value assigned to the class. In developing frequency distributions for qualitative data, we did not need to specify class limits because each data item naturally fell into a separate class. But with quantitative data, such as the audit times in Table 2.4, class limits are necessary to determine where each data value belongs.

Using the audit time data in Table 2.4, we selected 10 days as the lower class limit and 14 days as the upper class limit for the first class. This class is denoted 10–14 in Table 2.5. The smallest data value, 12, is included in the 10–14 class. We then selected 15 days as the lower class limit and 19 days as the upper class limit of the next class. We continued defining the lower and upper class limits to obtain a total of five classes: 10–14, 15–19, 20–24, 25–29, and 30–34. The largest data value, 33, is included in the 30–34 class. The difference between the lower class limits of adjacent classes is the class width. Using the first two lower class limits of 10 and 15, we see that the class width is $15 - 10 = 5$.

TABLE 2.5 FREQUENCY DISTRIBUTION FOR THE AUDIT TIME DATA

Audit Time (days)	Frequency
10–14	4
15–19	8
20–24	5
25–29	2
30–34	1
Total	20

With the number of classes, class width, and class limits determined, a frequency distribution can be obtained by counting the number of data values belonging to each class. For example, the data in Table 2.4 show that four values—12, 14, 14, and 13—belong to the 10–14 class. Thus, the frequency for the 10–14 class is 4. Continuing this counting process for the 15–19, 20–24, 25–29, and 30–34 classes provides the frequency distribution in Table 2.5. Using this frequency distribution, we can observe the following:

1. The most frequently occurring audit times are in the class of 15–19 days. Eight of the 20 audit times belong to this class.
2. Only one audit required 30 or more days.

Other conclusions are possible, depending on the interests of the person viewing the frequency distribution. The value of a frequency distribution is that it provides insights about the data that are not easily obtained by viewing the data in their original unorganized form.

TABLE 2.6 RELATIVE FREQUENCY AND PERCENT FREQUENCY DISTRIBUTIONS FOR THE AUDIT TIME DATA

Audit Time (days)	Relative Frequency	Percent Frequency
10–14	.20	20
15–19	.40	40
20–24	.25	25
25–29	.10	10
30–34	.05	5
Total	1.00	100

Class midpoint In some applications, we want to know the midpoints of the classes in a frequency distribution for quantitative data. The **class midpoint** is the value halfway between the lower and upper class limits. For the audit time data, the five class midpoints are 12, 17, 22, 27, and 32.

Relative Frequency and Percent Frequency Distributions

We define the relative frequency and percent frequency distributions for quantitative data in the same manner as for qualitative data. First, recall that the relative frequency is the proportion of the observations belonging to a class. With *n* observations,

$$\text{Relative frequency of class} = \frac{\text{Frequency of the class}}{n}$$

The percent frequency of a class is the relative frequency multiplied by 100.

Based on the class frequencies in Table 2.5 and with $n = 20$, Table 2.6 shows the relative frequency distribution and percent frequency distribution for the audit time data. Note that .40 of the audits, or 40%, required from 15 to 19 days. Only .05 of the audits, or 5%, required 30 or more days. Again, additional interpretations and insights can be obtained by using Table 2.6.

Dot Plot

One of the simplest graphical summaries of data is a **dot plot**. A horizontal axis shows the range for the data. Each data value is represented by a dot placed above the axis. Figure 2.3 is the dot plot for the audit time data in Table 2.4. The three dots located above 18 on the horizontal axis indicate that an audit time of 18 days occurred three times. Dot plots show the details of the data and are useful for comparing the distribution of the data for two or more variables.

Histogram

A common graphical presentation of quantitative data is a **histogram**. This graphical summary can be prepared for data previously summarized in either a frequency, relative frequency, or percent frequency distribution. A histogram is constructed by placing the

FIGURE 2.3 DOT PLOT FOR THE AUDIT TIME DATA

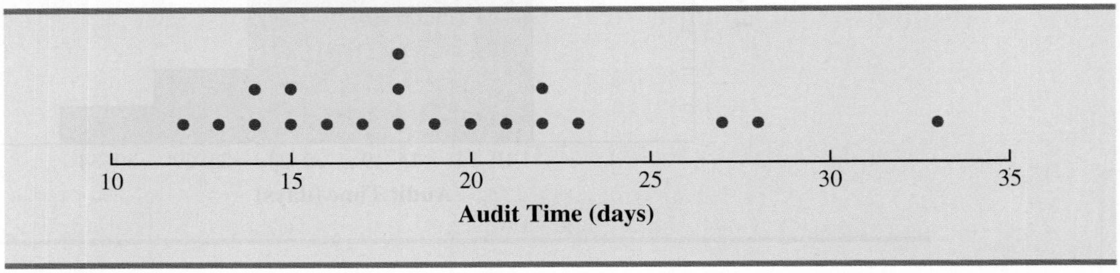

variable of interest on the horizontal axis and the frequency, relative frequency, or percent frequency on the vertical axis. The frequency, relative frequency, or percent frequency of each class is shown by drawing a rectangle whose base is determined by the class limits on the horizontal axis and whose height is the corresponding frequency, relative frequency, or percent frequency.

Figure 2.4 is a histogram for the audit time data. Note that the class with the greatest frequency is shown by the rectangle appearing above the class of 15–19 days. The height of the rectangle shows that the frequency of this class is 8. A histogram for the relative or percent frequency distribution of these data would look the same as the histogram in Figure 2.4 with the exception that the vertical axis would be labeled with relative or percent frequency values.

As Figure 2.4 shows, the adjacent rectangles of a histogram touch one another. Unlike a bar graph, a histogram contains no natural separation between the rectangles of adjacent classes. This format is the usual convention for histograms. Because the classes for the audit time data are stated as 10–14, 15–19, 20–24, 25–29, and 30–34, one-unit spaces of 14 to 15, 19 to 20, 24 to 25, and 29 to 30 would seem to be needed between the classes. These spaces are eliminated when constructing a histogram. Eliminating the spaces between classes in a histogram for the audit time data helps show that all values between the lower limit of the first class and the upper limit of the last class are possible.

One of the most important uses of a histogram is to provide information about the shape, or form, of a distribution. Figure 2.5 contains four histograms constructed from relative frequency distributions. Panel A shows the histogram for a set of data moderately skewed to the left. A histogram is said to be skewed to the left if its tail extends farther to the left. This histogram is typical for exam scores, with no scores above 100%, most of the scores above 70%, and only a few really low scores. Panel B shows the histogram for a set of data moderately skewed to the right. A histogram is said to be skewed to the right if its tail extends farther to the right. An example of this type of histogram would be for data such as housing prices; a few expensive houses create the skewness in the right tail.

Panel C shows a symmetric histogram. In a symmetric histogram, the left tail mirrors the shape of the right tail. Histograms for data found in applications are never perfectly symmetric, but the histogram for many applications may be roughly symmetric. Data for SAT scores, heights and weights of people, and so on lead to histograms that are roughly symmetric. Panel D shows a histogram highly skewed to the right. This histogram was constructed from data on the amount of customer purchases over one day at a women's apparel store. Data from applications in business and economics often lead to histograms that

FIGURE 2.4 HISTOGRAM FOR THE AUDIT TIME DATA

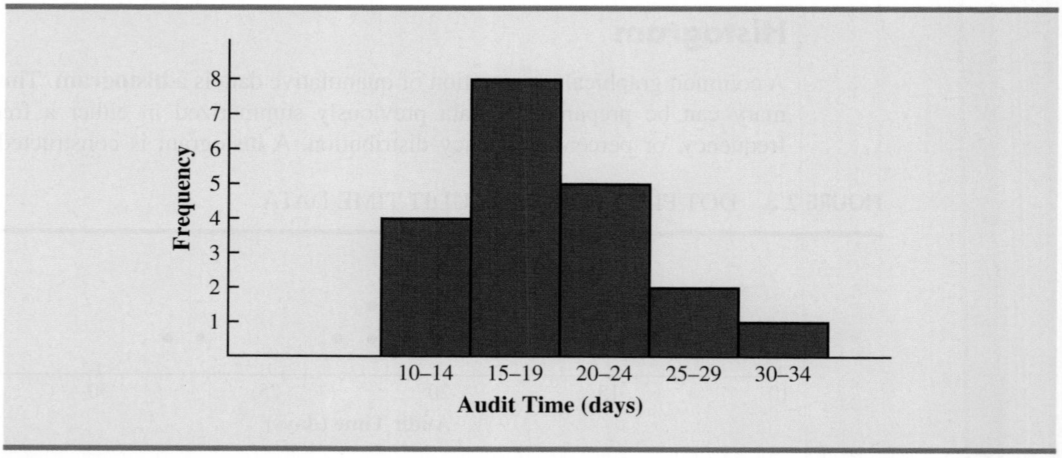

FIGURE 2.5 HISTOGRAMS SHOWING DIFFERING LEVELS OF SKEWNESS

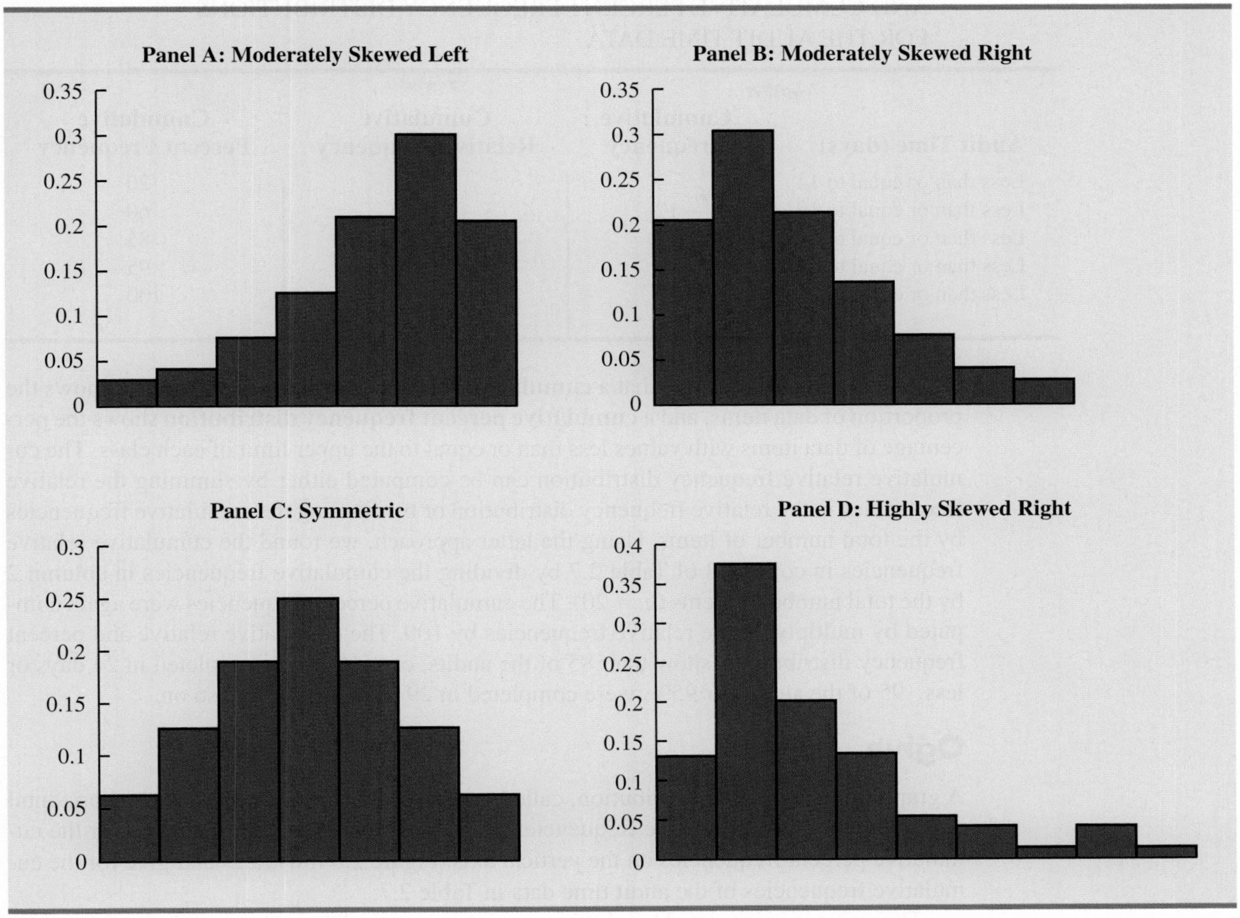

are skewed to the right. For instance, data on housing prices, salaries, purchase amounts, and so on often result in histograms skewed to the right.

Cumulative Distributions

A variation of the frequency distribution that provides another tabular summary of quantitative data is the **cumulative frequency distribution**. The cumulative frequency distribution uses the number of classes, class widths, and class limits developed for the frequency distribution. However, rather than showing the frequency of each class, the cumulative frequency distribution shows the number of data items with values *less than or equal to the upper class limit* of each class. The first two columns of Table 2.7 provide the cumulative frequency distribution for the audit time data.

To understand how the cumulative frequencies are determined, consider the class with the description "less than or equal to 24." The cumulative frequency for this class is simply the sum of the frequencies for all classes with data values less than or equal to 24. For the frequency distribution in Table 2.5, the sum of the frequencies for classes 10–14, 15–19, and 20–24 indicates that $4 + 8 + 5 = 17$ data values are less than or equal to 24. Hence, the cumulative frequency for this class is 17. In addition, the cumulative frequency distribution in Table 2.7 shows that four audits were completed in 14 days or less and 19 audits were completed in 29 days or less.

TABLE 2.7 CUMULATIVE FREQUENCY, CUMULATIVE RELATIVE FREQUENCY, AND CUMULATIVE PERCENT FREQUENCY DISTRIBUTIONS FOR THE AUDIT TIME DATA

Audit Time (days)	Cumulative Frequency	Cumulative Relative Frequency	Cumulative Percent Frequency
Less than or equal to 14	4	.20	20
Less than or equal to 19	12	.60	60
Less than or equal to 24	17	.85	85
Less than or equal to 29	19	.95	95
Less than or equal to 34	20	1.00	100

As a final point, we note that a **cumulative relative frequency distribution** shows the proportion of data items, and a **cumulative percent frequency distribution** shows the percentage of data items with values less than or equal to the upper limit of each class. The cumulative relative frequency distribution can be computed either by summing the relative frequencies in the relative frequency distribution or by dividing the cumulative frequencies by the total number of items. Using the latter approach, we found the cumulative relative frequencies in column 3 of Table 2.7 by dividing the cumulative frequencies in column 2 by the total number of items ($n = 20$). The cumulative percent frequencies were again computed by multiplying the relative frequencies by 100. The cumulative relative and percent frequency distributions show that .85 of the audits, or 85%, were completed in 24 days or less, .95 of the audits, or 95%, were completed in 29 days or less, and so on.

Ogive

A graph of a cumulative distribution, called an **ogive**, shows data values on the horizontal axis and either the cumulative frequencies, the cumulative relative frequencies, or the cumulative percent frequencies on the vertical axis. Figure 2.6 illustrates an ogive for the cumulative frequencies of the audit time data in Table 2.7.

The ogive is constructed by plotting a point corresponding to the cumulative frequency of each class. Because the classes for the audit time data are 10–14, 15–19, 20–24, and so

FIGURE 2.6 OGIVE FOR THE AUDIT TIME DATA

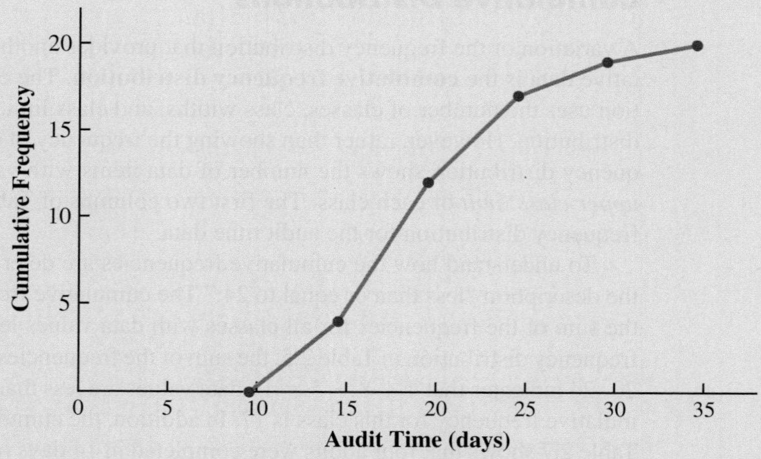

on, one-unit gaps appear from 14 to 15, 19 to 20, and so on. These gaps are eliminated by plotting points halfway between the class limits. Thus, 14.5 is used for the 10–14 class, 19.5 is used for the 15–19 class, and so on. The "less than or equal to 14" class with a cumulative frequency of 4 is shown on the ogive in Figure 2.6 by the point located at 14.5 on the horizontal axis and 4 on the vertical axis. The "less than or equal to 19" class with a cumulative frequency of 12 is shown by the point located at 19.5 on the horizontal axis and 12 on the vertical axis. Note that one additional point is plotted at the left end of the ogive. This point starts the ogive by showing that no data values fall below the 10–14 class. It is plotted at 9.5 on the horizontal axis and 0 on the vertical axis. The plotted points are connected by straight lines to complete the ogive.

NOTES AND COMMENTS

1. A bar chart and a histogram are essentially the same thing; both are graphical presentations of the data in a frequency distribution. A histogram is just a bar chart with no separation between bars. For some discrete quantitative data, a separation between bars is also appropriate. Consider, for example, the number of classes in which a college student is enrolled. The data may only assume integer values. Intermediate values such as 1.5, 2.73, and so on are not possible. With continuous quantitative data, however, such as the audit times in Table 2.4, a separation between bars is not appropriate.
2. The appropriate values for the class limits with quantitative data depend on the level of accuracy of the data. For instance, with the audit time data of Table 2.4 the limits used were integer values. If the data were rounded to the nearest tenth of a day (e.g., 12.3, 14.4, and so on), then the limits would be stated in tenths of days. For instance, the first class would be 10.0–14.9. If the data were recorded to the nearest hundredth of a day (e.g., 12.34, 14.45, and so on), the limits would be stated in hundredths of days. For instance, the first class would be 10.00–14.99.
3. An *open-end* class requires only a lower class limit or an upper class limit. For example, in the audit time data of Table 2.4, suppose two of the audits had taken 58 and 65 days. Rather than continue with the classes of width 5 with classes 35–39, 40–44, 45–49, and so on, we could simplify the frequency distribution to show an open-end class of "35 or more." This class would have a frequency of 2. Most often the open-end class appears at the upper end of the distribution. Sometimes an open-end class appears at the lower end of the distribution, and occasionally such classes appear at both ends.
4. The last entry in a cumulative frequency distribution always equals the total number of observations. The last entry in a cumulative relative frequency distribution always equals 1.00 and the last entry in a cumulative percent frequency distribution always equals 100.

Exercises

Methods

11. Consider the following data.

WEB file
Frequency

14	21	23	21	16
19	22	25	16	16
24	24	25	19	16
19	18	19	21	12
16	17	18	23	25
20	23	16	20	19
24	26	15	22	24
20	22	24	22	20

a. Develop a frequency distribution using classes of 12–14, 15–17, 18–20, 21–23, and 24–26.
b. Develop a relative frequency distribution and a percent frequency distribution using the classes in part (a).

SELF test

12. Consider the following frequency distribution.

Class	Frequency
10–19	10
20–29	14
30–39	17
40–49	7
50–59	2

Construct a cumulative frequency distribution and a cumulative relative frequency distribution.

13. Construct a histogram and an ogive for the data in exercise 12.
14. Consider the following data.

8.9	10.2	11.5	7.8	10.0	12.2	13.5	14.1	10.0	12.2
6.8	9.5	11.5	11.2	14.9	7.5	10.0	6.0	15.8	11.5

a. Construct a dot plot.
b. Construct a frequency distribution.
c. Construct a percent frequency distribution.

Applications

SELF test

15. A doctor's office staff studied the waiting times for patients who arrive at the office with a request for emergency service. The following data with waiting times in minutes were collected over a one-month period.

2 5 10 12 4 4 5 17 11 8 9 8 12 21 6 8 7 13 18 3

Use classes of 0–4, 5–9, and so on in the following:
a. Show the frequency distribution.
b. Show the relative frequency distribution.
c. Show the cumulative frequency distribution.
d. Show the cumulative relative frequency distribution.
e. What proportion of patients needing emergency service wait 9 minutes or less?

16. A shortage of candidates has required school districts to pay higher salaries and offer extras to attract and retain school district superintendents. The following data show the annual base salary ($1000s) for superintendents in 20 districts in the greater Rochester, New York, area (*The Rochester Democrat and Chronicle,* February 10, 2008).

187	184	174	185
175	172	202	197
165	208	215	164
162	172	182	156
172	175	170	183

Use classes of 150–159, 160–169, and so on in the following.
a. Show the frequency distribution.
b. Show the percent frequency distribution.
c. Show the cumulative percent frequency distribution.
d. Develop a histogram for the annual base salary.
e. Do the data appear to be skewed? Explain.
f. What percentage of the superintendents make more than $200,000?

17. The Dow Jones Industrial Average (DJIA) underwent one of its infrequent reshufflings of companies when General Motors and Citigroup were replaced by Cisco Systems and Travelers (*The Wall Street Journal,* June 8, 2009). At the time, the prices per share for the 30 companies in the DJIA were as follows:

WEB file
DJIAPrices

Company	$/Share	Company	$/Share
3M	61	IBM	107
Alcoa	11	Intel	16
American Express	25	J.P. Morgan Chase	35
AT&T	24	Johnson & Johnson	56
Bank of America	12	Kraft Foods	27
Boeing	52	McDonald's	59
Caterpillar	38	Merck	26
Chevron	69	Microsoft	22
Cisco Systems	20	Pfizer	14
Coca-Cola	49	Procter & Gamble	53
DuPont	27	Travelers	43
ExxonMobil	72	United Technologies	56
General Electric	14	Verizon	29
Hewlett-Packard	37	Wal-Mart Stores	51
Home Depot	24	Walt Disney	25

a. What is the highest price per share? What is the lowest price per share?
b. Using a class width of 10, develop a frequency distribution for the data.
c. Prepare a histogram. Interpret the histogram, including a discussion of the general shape of the histogram, the midprice range, and the most frequent price range.
d. Use the *The Wall Street Journal* or another newspaper to find the current price per share for these companies. Prepare a histogram of the data and discuss any changes since June 2009. What company has had the largest increase in the price per share? What company has had the largest decrease in the price per share?

18. NRF/BIG research provided results of a consumer holiday spending survey (*USA Today,* December 20, 2005). The following data provide the dollar amount of holiday spending for a sample of 25 consumers.

WEB file
Holiday

1200	850	740	590	340
450	890	260	610	350
1780	180	850	2050	770
800	1090	510	520	220
1450	280	1120	200	350

a. What is the lowest holiday spending? The highest?
b. Use a class width of $250 to prepare a frequency distribution and a percent frequency distribution for the data.
c. Prepare a histogram and comment on the shape of the distribution.
d. What observations can you make about holiday spending?

19. Sorting through unsolicited e-mail and spam affects the productivity of office workers. An InsightExpress survey monitored office workers to determine the unproductive time per day devoted to unsolicited e-mail and spam (*USA Today,* November 13, 2003). The following data show a sample of time in minutes devoted to this task.

2	4	8	4
8	1	2	32
12	1	5	7
5	5	3	4
24	19	4	14

Summarize the data by constructing the following:
a. A frequency distribution (classes 1–5, 6–10, 11–15, 16–20, and so on)
b. A relative frequency distribution
c. A cumulative frequency distribution
d. A cumulative relative frequency distribution
e. An ogive
f. What percentage of office workers spend 5 minutes or less on unsolicited e-mail and spam? What percentage of office workers spend more than 10 minutes a day on this task?

20. The *Golf Digest 50* lists the 50 professional golfers with the highest total annual income. Total income is the sum of both on-course and off-course earnings. Tiger Woods ranked first with a total annual income of $122 million. However, almost $100 million of this total was from off-course activities such as product endorsements and personal appearances. The 10 professional golfers with the highest *off-course* income are shown in the following table (Golf Digest website, February 2008).

Name	Off-Course Income ($1000s)
Tiger Woods	99,800
Phil Mickelson	40,200
Arnold Palmer	29,500
Vijay Singh	25,250
Ernie Els	24,500
Greg Norman	24,000
Jack Nicklaus	20,750
Sergio Garcia	14,500
Michelle Wie	12,500
Jim Furyk	11,000

The off-course income of all 50 professional golfers in the *Golf Digest 50* can be found on the website that accompanies the text. The income data are in $1000s. Use classes of 0–4999, 5000–9999, 10,000–14,999, and so on to answer the following questions. Include an open-ended class of 50,000 or more as the largest income class.

WEB file OffCourse

a. Construct a frequency distribution and percent frequency distribution of the annual off-course income of the 50 professional golfers.
b. Construct a histogram for these data.
c. Comment on the shape of the distribution of off-course income.
d. What is the most frequent off-course income class for the 50 professional golfers? Using your tabular and graphical summaries, what additional observations can you make about the off-course income of these 50 professional golfers?

21. The *Nielsen Home Technology Report* provided information about home technology and its usage. The following data are the hours of personal computer usage during one week for a sample of 50 persons.

WEB file Computer

4.1	1.5	10.4	5.9	3.4	5.7	1.6	6.1	3.0	3.7
3.1	4.8	2.0	14.8	5.4	4.2	3.9	4.1	11.1	3.5
4.1	4.1	8.8	5.6	4.3	3.3	7.1	10.3	6.2	7.6
10.8	2.8	9.5	12.9	12.1	0.7	4.0	9.2	4.4	5.7
7.2	6.1	5.7	5.9	4.7	3.9	3.7	3.1	6.1	3.1

Summarize the data by constructing the following:
a. A frequency distribution (use a class width of three hours)
b. A relative frequency distribution
c. A histogram
d. An ogive
e. Comment on what the data indicate about personal computer usage at home.

2.3 Exploratory Data Analysis: The Stem-and-Leaf Display

The techniques of **exploratory data analysis** consist of simple arithmetic and easy-to-draw graphs that can be used to summarize data quickly. One technique—referred to as a **stem-and-leaf display**—can be used to show both the rank order and shape of a data set simultaneously.

TABLE 2.8 NUMBER OF QUESTIONS ANSWERED CORRECTLY ON AN APTITUDE TEST

WEB file

ApTest

112	72	69	97	107
73	92	76	86	73
126	128	118	127	124
82	104	132	134	83
92	108	96	100	92
115	76	91	102	81
95	141	81	80	106
84	119	113	98	75
68	98	115	106	95
100	85	94	106	119

To illustrate the use of a stem-and-leaf display, consider the data in Table 2.8. These data result from a 150-question aptitude test given to 50 individuals recently interviewed for a position at Haskens Manufacturing. The data indicate the number of questions answered correctly.

To develop a stem-and-leaf display, we first arrange the leading digits of each data value to the left of a vertical line. To the right of the vertical line, we record the last digit for each data value. Based on the top row of data in Table 2.8 (112, 72, 69, 97, and 107), the first five entries in constructing a stem-and-leaf display would be as follows:

```
 6 | 9
 7 | 2
 8 |
 9 | 7
10 | 7
11 | 2
12 |
13 |
14 |
```

For example, the data value 112 shows the leading digits 11 to the left of the line and the last digit 2 to the right of the line. Similarly, the data value 72 shows the leading digit 7 to the left of the line and last digit 2 to the right of the line. Continuing to place the last digit of each data value on the line corresponding to its leading digit(s) provides the following:

```
 6 | 9 8
 7 | 2 3 6 3 6 5
 8 | 6 2 3 1 1 0 4 5
 9 | 7 2 2 6 2 1 5 8 8 5 4
10 | 7 4 8 0 2 6 6 0 6
11 | 2 8 5 9 3 5 9
12 | 6 8 7 4
13 | 2 4
14 | 1
```

With this organization of the data, sorting the digits on each line into rank order is simple. Doing so provides the stem-and-leaf display shown here.

6	8	9									
7	2	3	3	5	6	6					
8	0	1	1	2	3	4	5	6			
9	1	2	2	2	4	5	5	6	7	8	8
10	0	0	2	4	6	6	6	7	8		
11	2	3	5	5	8	9	9				
12	4	6	7	8							
13	2	4									
14	1										

The numbers to the left of the vertical line (6, 7, 8, 9, 10, 11, 12, 13, and 14) form the *stem,* and each digit to the right of the vertical line is a *leaf.* For example, consider the first row with a stem value of 6 and leaves of 8 and 9.

6 | 8 9

This row indicates that two data values have a first digit of six. The leaves show that the data values are 68 and 69. Similarly, the second row

7 | 2 3 3 5 6 6

indicates that six data values have a first digit of seven. The leaves show that the data values are 72, 73, 73, 75, 76, and 76.

To focus on the shape indicated by the stem-and-leaf display, let us use a rectangle to contain the leaves of each stem. Doing so, we obtain the following:

6	8	9									
7	2	3	3	5	6	6					
8	0	1	1	2	3	4	5	6			
9	1	2	2	2	4	5	5	6	7	8	8
10	0	0	2	4	6	6	6	7	8		
11	2	3	5	5	8	9	9				
12	4	6	7	8							
13	2	4									
14	1										

Rotating this page counterclockwise onto its side provides a picture of the data that is similar to a histogram with classes of 60–69, 70–79, 80–89, and so on.

Although the stem-and-leaf display may appear to offer the same information as a histogram, it has two primary advantages.

1. The stem-and-leaf display is easier to construct by hand.
2. Within a class interval, the stem-and-leaf display provides more information than the histogram because the stem-and-leaf shows the actual data.

Just as a frequency distribution or histogram has no absolute number of classes, neither does a stem-and-leaf display have an absolute number of rows or stems. If we believe that our original stem-and-leaf display condensed the data too much, we can easily stretch the display by using two or more stems for each leading digit. For example, to use two stems for each leading digit,

In a stretched stem-and-leaf display, whenever a stem value is stated twice, the first value corresponds to leaf values of 0–4, and the second value corresponds to leaf values of 5–9.

we would place all data values ending in 0, 1, 2, 3, and 4 in one row and all values ending in 5, 6, 7, 8, and 9 in a second row. The following stretched stem-and-leaf display illustrates this approach.

6	8 9
7	2 3 3
7	5 6 6
8	0 1 1 2 3 4
8	5 6
9	1 2 2 2 4
9	5 5 6 7 8 8
10	0 0 2 4
10	6 6 6 7 8
11	2 3
11	5 5 8 9 9
12	4
12	6 7 8
13	2 4
13	
14	1

Note that values 72, 73, and 73 have leaves in the 0–4 range and are shown with the first stem value of 7. The values 75, 76, and 76 have leaves in the 5–9 range and are shown with the second stem value of 7. This stretched stem-and-leaf display is similar to a frequency distribution with intervals of 65–69, 70–74, 75–79, and so on.

The preceding example showed a stem-and-leaf display for data with as many as three digits. Stem-and-leaf displays for data with more than three digits are possible. For example, consider the following data on the number of hamburgers sold by a fast-food restaurant for each of 15 weeks.

1565	1852	1644	1766	1888	1912	2044	1812
1790	1679	2008	1852	1967	1954	1733	

A stem-and-leaf display of these data follows.

Leaf unit = 10

15	6
16	4 7
17	3 6 9
18	1 5 5 8
19	1 5 6
20	0 4

A single digit is used to define each leaf in a stem-and-leaf display. The leaf unit indicates how to multiply the stem-and-leaf numbers in order to approximate the original data. Leaf units may be 100, 10, 1, 0.1, and so on.

Note that a single digit is used to define each leaf and that only the first three digits of each data value have been used to construct the display. At the top of the display we have specified Leaf unit = 10. To illustrate how to interpret the values in the display, consider the first stem, 15, and its associated leaf, 6. Combining these numbers, we obtain 156. To reconstruct an approximation of the original data value, we must multiply this number by 10, the value of the *leaf unit.* Thus, $156 \times 10 = 1560$ is an approximation of the original data value used to construct the stem-and-leaf display. Although it is not possible to reconstruct the exact data value from this stem-and-leaf display, the convention of using a single digit for each leaf enables stem-and-leaf displays to be constructed for data having a large number of digits. For stem-and-leaf displays where the leaf unit is not shown, the leaf unit is assumed to equal 1.

Exercises

Methods

22. Construct a stem-and-leaf display for the following data.

70	72	75	64	58	83	80	82
76	75	68	65	57	78	85	72

SELF test

23. Construct a stem-and-leaf display for the following data.

11.3	9.6	10.4	7.5	8.3	10.5	10.0
9.3	8.1	7.7	7.5	8.4	6.3	8.8

24. Construct a stem-and-leaf display for the following data. Use a leaf unit of 10.

1161	1206	1478	1300	1604	1725	1361	1422
1221	1378	1623	1426	1557	1730	1706	1689

Applications

SELF test

25. A psychologist developed a new test of adult intelligence. The test was administered to 20 individuals, and the following data were obtained.

114	99	131	124	117	102	106	127	119	115
98	104	144	151	132	106	125	122	118	118

Construct a stem-and-leaf display for the data.

26. The American Association of Individual Investors conducts an annual survey of discount brokers. The following prices charged are from a sample of 24 discount brokers (*AAII Journal,* January 2003). The two types of trades are a broker-assisted trade of 100 shares at $50 per share and an online trade of 500 shares at $50 per share.

WEB file

Broker

Broker	Broker-Assisted 100 Shares at $50/Share	Online 500 Shares at $50/Share	Broker	Broker-Assisted 100 Shares at $50/Share	Online 500 Shares at $50/Share
Accutrade	30.00	29.95	Merrill Lynch Direct	50.00	29.95
Ameritrade	24.99	10.99	Muriel Siebert	45.00	14.95
Banc of America	54.00	24.95	NetVest	24.00	14.00
Brown & Co.	17.00	5.00	Recom Securities	35.00	12.95
Charles Schwab	55.00	29.95	Scottrade	17.00	7.00
CyberTrader	12.95	9.95	Sloan Securities	39.95	19.95
E*TRADE Securities	49.95	14.95	Strong Investments	55.00	24.95
First Discount	35.00	19.75	TD Waterhouse	45.00	17.95
Freedom Investments	25.00	15.00	T. Rowe Price	50.00	19.95
Harrisdirect	40.00	20.00	Vanguard	48.00	20.00
Investors National	39.00	62.50	Wall Street Discount	29.95	19.95
MB Trading	9.95	10.55	York Securities	40.00	36.00

a. Round the trading prices to the nearest dollar and develop a stem-and-leaf display for 100 shares at $50 per share. Comment on what you learned about broker-assisted trading prices.
b. Round the trading prices to the nearest dollar and develop a stretched stem-and-leaf display for 500 shares online at $50 per share. Comment on what you learned about online trading prices.

27. Most major ski resorts offer family programs that provide ski and snowboarding instruction for children. The typical classes provide four to six hours on the snow with a certified instructor. The daily rate for a group lesson at 15 ski resorts follows (*The Wall Street Journal,* January 20, 2006).

Resort	Location	Daily Rate	Resort	Location	Daily Rate
Beaver Creek	Colorado	$137	Okemo	Vermont	$ 86
Deer Valley	Utah	115	Park City	Utah	145
Diamond Peak	California	95	Butternut	Massachusetts	75
Heavenly	California	145	Steamboat	Colorado	98
Hunter	New York	79	Stowe	Vermont	104
Mammoth	California	111	Sugar Bowl	California	100
Mount Sunapee	New Hampshire	96	Whistler-Blackcomb	British Columbia	104
Mount Bachelor	Oregon	83			

a. Develop a stem-and-leaf display for the data.
b. Interpret the stem-and-leaf display in terms of what it tells you about the daily rate for these ski and snowboarding instruction programs.

28. The 2004 Naples, Florida, minimarathon (13.1 miles) had 1228 registrants (*Naples Daily News,* January 17, 2004). Competition was held in six age groups. The following data show the ages for a sample of 40 individuals who participated in the marathon.

WEB file Marathon

49	33	40	37	56
44	46	57	55	32
50	52	43	64	40
46	24	30	37	43
31	43	50	36	61
27	44	35	31	43
52	43	66	31	50
72	26	59	21	47

a. Show a stretched stem-and-leaf display.
b. What age group had the largest number of runners?
c. What age occurred most frequently?
d. A *Naples Daily News* feature article emphasized the number of runners who were "20-something." What percentage of the runners were in the 20-something age group? What do you suppose was the focus of the article?

2.4 Crosstabulations and Scatter Diagrams

Crosstabulations and scatter diagrams are used to summarize data in a way that reveals the relationship between two variables.

Thus far in this chapter, we have focused on tabular and graphical methods used to summarize the data for *one variable at a time.* Often a manager or decision maker requires tabular and graphical methods that will assist in the understanding of the *relationship between two variables.* Crosstabulation and scatter diagrams are two such methods.

Crosstabulation

A **crosstabulation** is a tabular summary of data for two variables. Let us illustrate the use of a crosstabulation by considering the following application based on data from Zagat's Restaurant Review. The quality rating and the meal price data were collected for a sample of 300 restaurants located in the Los Angeles area. Table 2.9 shows the data for the first 10 restaurants. Data on a restaurant's quality rating and typical meal price are reported. Quality rating is a categorical variable with rating categories of good, very good, and excellent. Meal price is a quantitative variable that ranges from $10 to $49.

A crosstabulation of the data for this application is shown in Table 2.10. The left and top margin labels define the classes for the two variables. In the left margin, the row labels (good, very good, and excellent) correspond to the three classes of the quality rating variable. In the top margin, the column labels ($10–19, $20–29, $30–39, and $40–49) correspond to

TABLE 2.9 QUALITY RATING AND MEAL PRICE FOR 300 LOS ANGELES RESTAURANTS

WEB file Restaurant

Restaurant	Quality Rating	Meal Price ($)
1	Good	18
2	Very Good	22
3	Good	28
4	Excellent	38
5	Very Good	33
6	Good	28
7	Very Good	19
8	Very Good	11
9	Very Good	23
10	Good	13
.	.	.
.	.	.
.	.	.

the four classes of the meal price variable. Each restaurant in the sample provides a quality rating and a meal price. Thus, each restaurant in the sample is associated with a cell appearing in one of the rows and one of the columns of the crosstabulation. For example, restaurant 5 is identified as having a very good quality rating and a meal price of $33. This restaurant belongs to the cell in row 2 and column 3 of Table 2.10. In constructing a crosstabulation, we simply count the number of restaurants that belong to each of the cells in the crosstabulation table.

In reviewing Table 2.10, we see that the greatest number of restaurants in the sample (64) have a very good rating and a meal price in the $20–29 range. Only two restaurants have an excellent rating and a meal price in the $10–19 range. Similar interpretations of the other frequencies can be made. In addition, note that the right and bottom margins of the crosstabulation provide the frequency distributions for quality rating and meal price separately. From the frequency distribution in the right margin, we see that data on quality ratings show 84 good restaurants, 150 very good restaurants, and 66 excellent restaurants. Similarly, the bottom margin shows the frequency distribution for the meal price variable.

Dividing the totals in the right margin of the crosstabulation by the total for that column provides a relative and percent frequency distribution for the quality rating variable.

Quality Rating	Relative Frequency	Percent Frequency
Good	.28	28
Very Good	.50	50
Excellent	.22	22
Total	1.00	100

TABLE 2.10 CROSSTABULATION OF QUALITY RATING AND MEAL PRICE FOR 300 LOS ANGELES RESTAURANTS

	Meal Price				
Quality Rating	$10–19	$20–29	$30–39	$40–49	Total
Good	42	40	2	0	84
Very Good	34	64	46	6	150
Excellent	2	14	28	22	66
Total	78	118	76	28	300

From the percent frequency distribution we see that 28% of the restaurants were rated good, 50% were rated very good, and 22% were rated excellent.

Dividing the totals in the bottom row of the crosstabulation by the total for that row provides a relative and percent frequency distribution for the meal price variable.

Meal Price	Relative Frequency	Percent Frequency
$10–19	.26	26
$20–29	.39	39
$30–39	.25	25
$40–49	.09	9
Total	1.00	100

Note that the sum of the values in each column does not add exactly to the column total, because the values being summed are rounded. From the percent frequency distribution we see that 26% of the meal prices are in the lowest price class ($10–19), 39% are in the next higher class, and so on.

The frequency and relative frequency distributions constructed from the margins of a crosstabulation provide information about each of the variables individually, but they do not shed any light on the relationship between the variables. The primary value of a crosstabulation lies in the insight it offers about the relationship between the variables. A review of the crosstabulation in Table 2.10 reveals that higher meal prices are associated with the higher quality restaurants, and the lower meal prices are associated with the lower quality restaurants.

Converting the entries in a crosstabulation into row percentages or column percentages can provide more insight into the relationship between the two variables. For row percentages, the results of dividing each frequency in Table 2.10 by its corresponding row total are shown in Table 2.11. Each row of Table 2.11 is a percent frequency distribution of meal price for one of the quality rating categories. Of the restaurants with the lowest quality rating (good), we see that the greatest percentages are for the less expensive restaurants (50% have $10–19 meal prices and 47.6% have $20–29 meal prices). Of the restaurants with the highest quality rating (excellent), we see that the greatest percentages are for the more expensive restaurants (42.4% have $30–39 meal prices and 33.4% have $40–49 meal prices). Thus, we continue to see that the more expensive meals are associated with the higher quality restaurants.

Crosstabulation is widely used for examining the relationship between two variables. In practice, the final reports for many statistical studies include a large number of crosstabulation tables. In the Los Angeles restaurant survey, the crosstabulation is based on one qualitative variable (quality rating) and one quantitative variable (meal price). Crosstabulations can also be developed when both variables are qualitative and when both variables are quantitative. When quantitative variables are used, however, we must first create classes for the values of the variable. For instance, in the restaurant example we grouped the meal prices into four classes ($10–19, $20–29, $30–39, and $40–49).

TABLE 2.11 ROW PERCENTAGES FOR EACH QUALITY RATING CATEGORY

	Meal Price				
Quality Rating	$10–19	$20–29	$30–39	$40–49	Total
Good	50.0	47.6	2.4	0.0	100
Very Good	22.7	42.7	30.6	4.0	100
Excellent	3.0	21.2	42.4	33.4	100

Simpson's Paradox

The data in two or more crosstabulations are often combined or aggregated to produce a summary crosstabulation showing how two variables are related. In such cases, we must be careful in drawing a conclusion because a conclusion based upon aggregate data can be reversed if we look at the unaggregated data. The reversal of conclusions based on aggregate and unaggregated data is called **Simpson's paradox**. To provide an illustration of Simpson's paradox we consider an example involving the analysis of verdicts for two judges in two different courts.

Judges Ron Luckett and Dennis Kendall presided over cases in Common Pleas Court and Municipal Court during the past three years. Some of the verdicts they rendered were appealed. In most of these cases the appeals court upheld the original verdicts, but in some cases those verdicts were reversed. For each judge a crosstabulation was developed based upon two variables: Verdict (upheld or reversed) and Type of Court (Common Pleas and Municipal). Suppose that the two crosstabulations were then combined by aggregating the type of court data. The resulting aggregated crosstabulation contains two variables: Verdict (upheld or reversed) and Judge (Luckett or Kendall). This crosstabulation shows the number of appeals in which the verdict was upheld and the number in which the verdict was reversed for both judges. The following crosstabulation shows these results along with the column percentages in parentheses next to each value.

	Judge		
Verdict	Luckett	Kendall	Total
Upheld	129 (86%)	110 (88%)	239
Reversed	21 (14%)	15 (12%)	36
Total (%)	150 (100%)	125 (100%)	275

A review of the column percentages shows that 86% of the verdicts were upheld for Judge Luckett, while 88% of the verdicts were upheld for Judge Kendall. From this aggregated crosstabulation, we conclude that Judge Kendall is doing the better job because a greater percentage of Judge Kendall's verdicts are being upheld.

The following unaggregated crosstabulations show the cases tried by Judge Luckett and Judge Kendall in each court; column percentages are shown in parentheses next to each value.

	Judge Luckett		
Verdict	Common Pleas	Municipal Court	Total
Upheld	29 (91%)	100 (85%)	129
Reversed	3 (9%)	18 (15%)	21
Total (%)	32 (100%)	118 (100%)	150

	Judge Kendall		
Verdict	Common Pleas	Municipal Court	Total
Upheld	90 (90%)	20 (80%)	110
Reversed	10 (10%)	5 (20%)	15
Total (%)	100 (100%)	25 (100%)	125

From the crosstabulation and column percentages for Judge Luckett, we see that the verdicts were upheld in 91% of the Common Pleas Court cases and in 85% of the Municipal Court cases. From the crosstabulation and column percentages for Judge Kendall, we see that the verdicts were upheld in 90% of the Common Pleas Court cases and in 80% of the Municipal Court cases. Thus, when we unaggregate the data, we see that Judge Luckett has a better record because a greater percentage of Judge Luckett's verdicts are being upheld in both courts. This result contradicts the conclusion we reached with the aggregated data crosstabulation that showed Judge Kendall had the better record. This reversal of conclusions based on aggregated and unaggregated data illustrates Simpson's paradox.

The original crosstabulation was obtained by aggregating the data in the separate crosstabulations for the two courts. Note that for both judges the percentage of appeals that resulted in reversals was much higher in Municipal Court than in Common Pleas Court. Because Judge Luckett tried a much higher percentage of his cases in Municipal Court, the aggregated data favored Judge Kendall. When we look at the crosstabulations for the two courts separately, however, Judge Luckett shows the better record. Thus, for the original crosstabulation, we see that the *type of court* is a hidden variable that cannot be ignored when evaluating the records of the two judges.

Because of the possibility of Simpson's paradox, realize that the conclusion or interpretation may be reversed depending upon whether you are viewing unaggregated or aggregate crosstabulation data. Before drawing a conclusion, you may want to investigate whether the aggregate or unaggregate form of the crosstabulation provides the better insight and conclusion. Especially when the crosstabulation involves aggreagrated data, you should investigate whether a hidden variable could affect the results such that separate or unaggregated crosstabulations provide a different and possibly better insight and conclusion.

Scatter Diagram and Trendline

A **scatter diagram** is a graphical presentation of the relationship between two quantitative variables, and a **trendline** is a line that provides an approximation of the relationship. As an illustration, consider the advertising/sales relationship for a stereo and sound equipment store in San Francisco. On 10 occasions during the past three months, the store used weekend television commercials to promote sales at its stores. The managers want to investigate whether a relationship exists between the number of commercials shown and sales at the store during the following week. Sample data for the 10 weeks with sales in hundreds of dollars are shown in Table 2.12.

Figure 2.7 shows the scatter diagram and the trendline[1] for the data in Table 2.12. The number of commercials (x) is shown on the horizontal axis and the sales (y) are shown on the vertical axis. For week 1, $x = 2$ and $y = 50$. A point with those coordinates is plotted on the scatter diagram. Similar points are plotted for the other nine weeks. Note that during two of the weeks one commercial was shown, during two of the weeks two commercials were shown, and so on.

The completed scatter diagram in Figure 2.7 indicates a positive relationship between the number of commercials and sales. Higher sales are associated with a higher number of commercials. The relationship is not perfect in that all points are not on a straight line. However, the general pattern of the points and the trendline suggest that the overall relationship is positive.

TABLE 2.12 SAMPLE DATA FOR THE STEREO AND SOUND EQUIPMENT STORE

WEB file

Stereo

Week	Number of Commercials x	Sales ($100s) y
1	2	50
2	5	57
3	1	41
4	3	54
5	4	54
6	1	38
7	5	63
8	3	48
9	4	59
10	2	46

[1]The equation of the trendline is $y = 36.15 + 4.95x$. The slope of the trendline is 4.95 and the y-intercept (the point where the line intersects the y-axis) is 36.15. We will discuss in detail the interpretation of the slope and y-intercept for a linear trendline in Chapter 14 when we study simple linear regression.

FIGURE 2.7 SCATTER DIAGRAM AND TRENDLINE FOR THE STEREO AND SOUND EQUIPMENT STORE

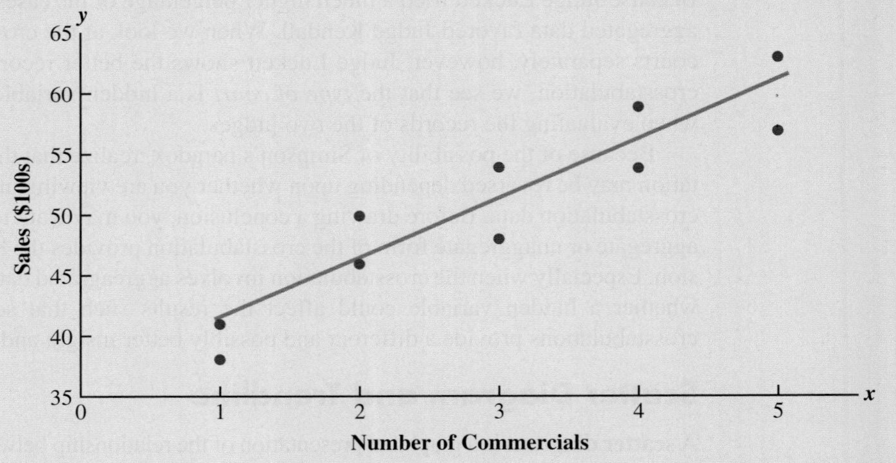

FIGURE 2.8 TYPES OF RELATIONSHIPS DEPICTED BY SCATTER DIAGRAMS

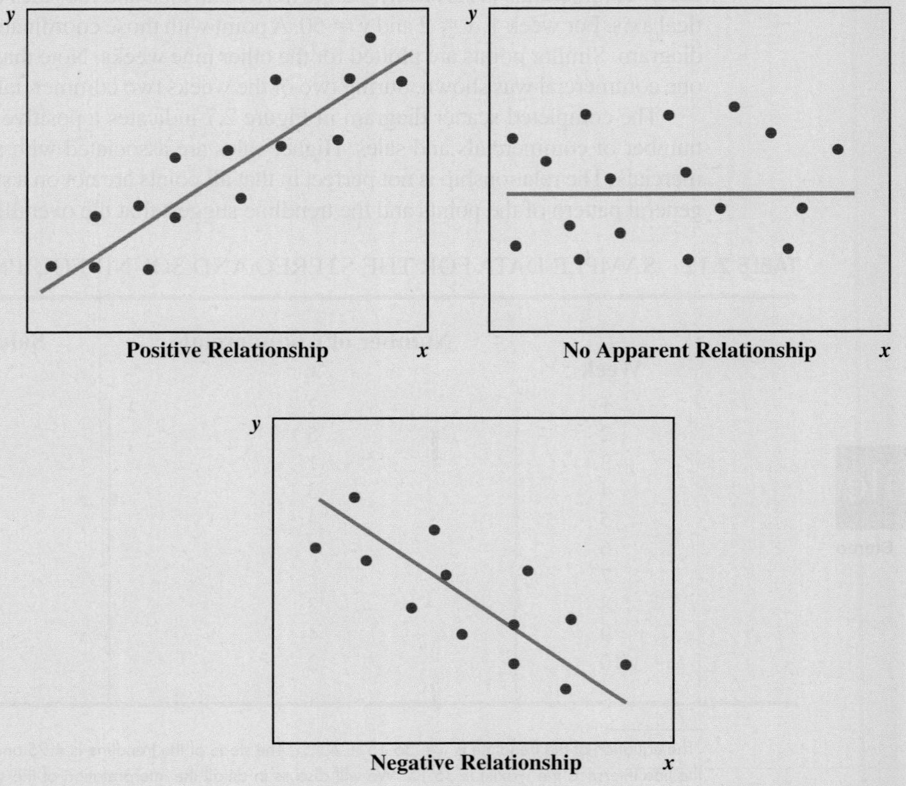

Some general scatter diagram patterns and the types of relationships they suggest are shown in Figure 2.8. The top left panel depicts a positive relationship similar to the one for the number of commercials and sales example. In the top right panel, the scatter diagram shows no apparent relationship between the variables. The bottom panel depicts a negative relationship where *y* tends to decrease as *x* increases.

Exercises

Methods

SELF test

29. The following data are for 30 observations involving two qualitative variables, *x* and *y*. The categories for *x* are A, B, and C; the categories for *y* are 1 and 2.

WEB file
Crosstab

Observation	*x*	*y*	Observation	*x*	*y*
1	A	1	16	B	2
2	B	1	17	C	1
3	B	1	18	B	1
4	C	2	19	C	1
5	B	1	20	B	1
6	C	2	21	C	2
7	B	1	22	B	1
8	C	2	23	C	2
9	A	1	24	A	1
10	B	1	25	B	1
11	A	1	26	C	2
12	B	1	27	C	2
13	C	2	28	A	1
14	C	2	29	B	1
15	C	2	30	B	2

a. Develop a crosstabulation for the data, with *x* as the row variable and *y* as the column variable.
b. Compute the row percentages.
c. Compute the column percentages.
d. What is the relationship, if any, between *x* and *y*?

SELF test

30. The following 20 observations are for two quantitative variables, *x* and *y*.

WEB file
Scatter

Observation	*x*	*y*	Observation	*x*	*y*
1	−22	22	11	−37	48
2	−33	49	12	34	−29
3	2	8	13	9	−18
4	29	−16	14	−33	31
5	−13	10	15	20	−16
6	21	−28	16	−3	14
7	−13	27	17	−15	18
8	−23	35	18	12	17
9	14	−5	19	−20	−11
10	3	−3	20	−7	−22

a. Develop a scatter diagram for the relationship between *x* and *y*.
b. What is the relationship, if any, between *x* and *y*?

Applications

31. The following crosstabulation shows household income by educational level of the head of household (*Statistical Abstract of the United States: 2008*).

	Household Income ($1000s)					
Educational Level	**Under 25**	**25.0–49.9**	**50.0–74.9**	**75.0–99.9**	**100 or more**	**Total**
Not H.S. graduate	4207	3459	1389	539	367	9961
H.S. graduate	4917	6850	5027	2637	2668	22099
Some college	2807	5258	4678	3250	4074	20067
Bachelor's degree	885	2094	2848	2581	5379	13787
Beyond bach. deg.	290	829	1274	1241	4188	7822
Total	13106	18490	15216	10248	16676	73736

a. Compute the row percentages and identify the percent frequency distributions of income for households in which the head is a high school graduate and in which the head holds a bachelor's degree.
b. What percentage of households headed by high school graduates earn $75,000 or more? What percentage of households headed by bachelor's degree recipients earn $75,000 or more?
c. Construct percent frequency histograms of income for households headed by persons with a high school degree and for those headed by persons with a bachelor's degree. Is any relationship evident between household income and educational level?

32. Refer again to the crosstabulation of household income by educational level shown in exercise 31.
a. Compute column percentages and identify the percent frequency distributions displayed. What percentage of the heads of households did not graduate from high school?
b. What percentage of the households earning $100,000 or more were headed by a person having schooling beyond a bachelor's degree? What percentage of the households headed by a person with schooling beyond a bachelor's degree earned over $100,000? Why are these two percentages different?
c. Compare the percent frequency distributions for those households earning "Under 25," "100 or more," and for "Total." Comment on the relationship between household income and educational level of the head of household.

33. Recently, management at Oak Tree Golf Course received a few complaints about the condition of the greens. Several players complained that the greens are too fast. Rather than react to the comments of just a few, the Golf Association conducted a survey of 100 male and 100 female golfers. The survey results are summarized here.

Male Golfers

	Greens Condition	
Handicap	**Too Fast**	**Fine**
Under 15	10	40
15 or more	25	25

Female Golfers

	Greens Condition	
Handicap	**Too Fast**	**Fine**
Under 15	1	9
15 or more	39	51

a. Combine these two crosstabulations into one with Male and Female as the row labels and Too Fast and Fine as the column labels. Which group shows the highest percentage saying that the greens are too fast?

b. Refer to the initial crosstabulations. For those players with low handicaps (better players), which group (male or female) shows the highest percentage saying the greens are too fast?
c. Refer to the initial crosstabulations. For those players with higher handicaps, which group (male or female) shows the highest percentage saying the greens are too fast?
d. What conclusions can you draw about the preferences of men and women concerning the speed of the greens? Are the conclusions you draw from part (a) as compared with parts (b) and (c) consistent? Explain any apparent inconsistencies.

34. Table 2.13 shows a data set containing information for 45 mutual funds that are part of the *Morningstar Funds500* for 2008. The data set includes the following five variables:

Fund Type: The type of fund, labeled DE (Domestic Equity), IE (International Equity), and FI (Fixed Income)

Net Asset Value ($): The closing price per share

5-Year Average Return (%): The average annual return for the fund over the past 5 years

Expense Ratio (%): The percentage of assets deducted each fiscal year for fund expenses

Morningstar Rank: The risk adjusted star rating for each fund; Morningstar ranks go from a low of 1-Star to a high of 5-Stars

a. Prepare a crosstabulation of the data on Fund Type (rows) and the average annual return over the past 5 years (columns). Use classes of 0–9.99, 10–19.99, 20–29.99, 30–39.99, 40–49.99, and 50–59.99 for the 5-Year Average Return (%).
b. Prepare a frequency distribution for the data on Fund Type.
c. Prepare a frequency distribution for the data on 5-Year Average Return (%).
d. How has the crosstabulation helped in preparing the frequency distributions in parts (b) and (c)?
e. What conclusions can you draw about the fund type and the average return over the past 5 years?

35. Refer to the data in Table 2.13.
a. Prepare a crosstabulation of the data on Fund Type (rows) and the expense ratio (columns). Use classes of .25–.49, .50–.74, .75–.99, 1.00–1.24, and 1.25–1.49 for Expense Ratio (%).
b. Prepare a percent frequency distribution for Expense Ratio (%).
c. What conclusions can you draw about fund type and the expense ratio?

36. Refer to the data in Table 2.13.
a. Prepare a scatter diagram with 5-Year Average Return (%) on the horizontal axis and Net Asset Value ($) on the vertical axis.
b. Comment on the relationship, if any, between the variables.

37. The U.S. Department of Energy's Fuel Economy Guide provides fuel efficiency data for cars and trucks (Fuel Economy website, February 22, 2008). A portion of the data for 311 compact, midsize, and large cars is shown in Table 2.14. The data set contains the following variables:

Size: Compact, Midsize, and Large

Displacement: Engine size in liters

Cylinders: Number of cylinders in the engine

Drive: Front wheel (F), rear wheel (R), and four wheel (4)

Fuel Type: Premium (P) or regular (R) fuel

City MPG: Fuel efficiency rating for city driving in terms of miles per gallon

Hwy MPG: Fuel efficiency rating for highway driving in terms of miles per gallon

The complete data set is contained in the file named FuelData08.

a. Prepare a crosstabulation of the data on Size (rows) and Hwy MPG (columns). Use classes of 15–19, 20–24, 25–29, 30–34, and 35–39 for Hwy MPG.
b. Comment on the relationship beween Size and Hwy MPG.

WEB file MutualFunds

TABLE 2.13 FINANCIAL DATA FOR A SAMPLE OF 45 MUTUAL FUNDS

Fund Name	Fund Type	Net Asset Value ($)	5-Year Average Return (%)	Expense Ratio (%)	Morningstar Rank
Amer Cent Inc & Growth Inv	DE	28.88	12.39	0.67	2-Star
American Century Intl. Disc	IE	14.37	30.53	1.41	3-Star
American Century Tax-Free Bond	FI	10.73	3.34	0.49	4-Star
American Century Ultra	DE	24.94	10.88	0.99	3-Star
Ariel	DE	46.39	11.32	1.03	2-Star
Artisan Intl Val	IE	25.52	24.95	1.23	3-Star
Artisan Small Cap	DE	16.92	15.67	1.18	3-Star
Baron Asset	DE	50.67	16.77	1.31	5-Star
Brandywine	DE	36.58	18.14	1.08	4-Star
Brown Cap Small	DE	35.73	15.85	1.20	4-Star
Buffalo Mid Cap	DE	15.29	17.25	1.02	3-Star
Delafield	DE	24.32	17.77	1.32	4-Star
DFA U.S. Micro Cap	DE	13.47	17.23	0.53	3-Star
Dodge & Cox Income	FI	12.51	4.31	0.44	4-Star
Fairholme	DE	31.86	18.23	1.00	5-Star
Fidelity Contrafund	DE	73.11	17.99	0.89	5-Star
Fidelity Municipal Income	FI	12.58	4.41	0.45	5-Star
Fidelity Overseas	IE	48.39	23.46	0.90	4-Star
Fidelity Sel Electronics	DE	45.60	13.50	0.89	3-Star
Fidelity Sh-Term Bond	FI	8.60	2.76	0.45	3-Star
Fidelity	DE	39.85	14.40	0.56	4-Star
FPA New Income	FI	10.95	4.63	0.62	3-Star
Gabelli Asset AAA	DE	49.81	16.70	1.36	4-Star
Greenspring	DE	23.59	12.46	1.07	3-Star
Janus	DE	32.26	12.81	0.90	3-Star
Janus Worldwide	IE	54.83	12.31	0.86	2-Star
Kalmar Gr Val Sm Cp	DE	15.30	15.31	1.32	3-Star
Managers Freemont Bond	FI	10.56	5.14	0.60	5-Star
Marsico 21st Century	DE	17.44	15.16	1.31	5-Star
Mathews Pacific Tiger	IE	27.86	32.70	1.16	3-Star
Meridan Value	DE	31.92	15.33	1.08	4-Star
Oakmark I	DE	40.37	9.51	1.05	2-Star
PIMCO Emerg Mkts Bd D	FI	10.68	13.57	1.25	3-Star
RS Value A	DE	26.27	23.68	1.36	4-Star
T. Rowe Price Latin Am.	IE	53.89	51.10	1.24	4-Star
T. Rowe Price Mid Val	DE	22.46	16.91	0.80	4-Star
Templeton Growth A	IE	24.07	15.91	1.01	3-Star
Thornburg Value A	DE	37.53	15.46	1.27	4-Star
USAA Income	FI	12.10	4.31	0.62	3-Star
Vanguard Equity-Inc	DE	24.42	13.41	0.29	4-Star
Vanguard Global Equity	IE	23.71	21.77	0.64	5-Star
Vanguard GNMA	FI	10.37	4.25	0.21	5-Star
Vanguard Sht-Tm TE	FI	15.68	2.37	0.16	3-Star
Vanguard Sm Cp Idx	DE	32.58	17.01	0.23	3-Star
Wasatch Sm Cp Growth	DE	35.41	13.98	1.19	4-Star

TABLE 2.14 FUEL EFFICIENCY DATA FOR 311 CARS

WEB file

FuelData08

Car	Size	Displacement	Cylinders	Drive	Fuel Type	City MPG	Hwy MPG
1	Compact	3.1	6	4	P	15	25
2	Compact	3.1	6	4	P	17	25
3	Compact	3.0	6	4	P	17	25
•	•	•	•	•	•	•	•
•	•	•	•	•	•	•	•
•	•	•	•	•	•	•	•
161	Midsize	2.4	4	F	R	22	30
162	Midsize	2.0	4	F	P	19	29
•	•	•	•	•	•	•	•
•	•	•	•	•	•	•	•
•	•	•	•	•	•	•	•
310	Large	3.0	6	F	R	17	25
311	Large	3.0	6	F	R	18	25

c. Prepare a crosstabulation of the data on Drive (rows) and City MPG (columns). Use classes of 5–9, 10–14, 15–19, 20–24, 25–29, 30–34, and 35–39 for City MPG.
d. Comment on the relationship between Drive and City MPG.
e. Prepare a crosstabulation of the data on Fuel Type (rows) and City MPG (columns). Use classes of 5–9, 10–14, 15–19, 20–24, 25–29, 30–34, and 35–39 for City MPG.
f. Comment on the relationship between Fuel Type and City MPG.

38. Refer to exercise 37 and the data in the file named FuelData08.
   a. Prepare a crosstabulation of the data on Displacement (rows) and Hwy MPG (columns). Use classes of 1.0–2.9, 3.0–4.9, and 5.0–6.9 for Displacement. Use classes of 15–19, 20–24, 25–29, 30–34, and 35–39 for Hwy MPG.
   b. Comment on the relationship, if any, between Displacement and Hwy MPG.
   c. Develop a scatter diagram of the data on Displacement and Hwy MPG. Use the vertical axis for Hwy MPG.
   d. What does the scatter diagram developed in part (c) indicate about the relationship, if any, between Displacement and Hwy MPG?
   e. In investigating the relationship between Displacement and Hwy MPG you developed a tabular summary of the data (crosstabulation) and a graphical summary (scatter diagram). In this case which approach do you prefer? Explain.

Summary

A set of data, even if modest in size, is often difficult to interpret directly in the form in which it is gathered. Tabular and graphical methods provide procedures for organizing and summarizing data so that patterns are revealed and the data are more easily interpreted. Frequency distributions, relative frequency distributions, percent frequency distributions, bar charts, and pie charts were presented as tabular and graphical procedures for summarizing categorical data. Frequency distributions, relative frequency distributions, percent frequency distributions, histograms, cumulative frequency distributions, cumulative relative frequency distributions, cumulative percent frequency distributions, and ogives were presented as ways of summarizing quantitative data. A stem-and-leaf display provides an exploratory data analysis technique that can be used to summarize quantitative data. Crosstabulation was presented as a tabular method for summarizing data for two variables. The scatter diagram was introduced as a graphical method for showing the relationship between two quantitative variables. Figure 2.9 shows the tabular and graphical methods presented in this chapter.

FIGURE 2.9 TABULAR AND GRAPHICAL METHODS FOR SUMMARIZING DATA

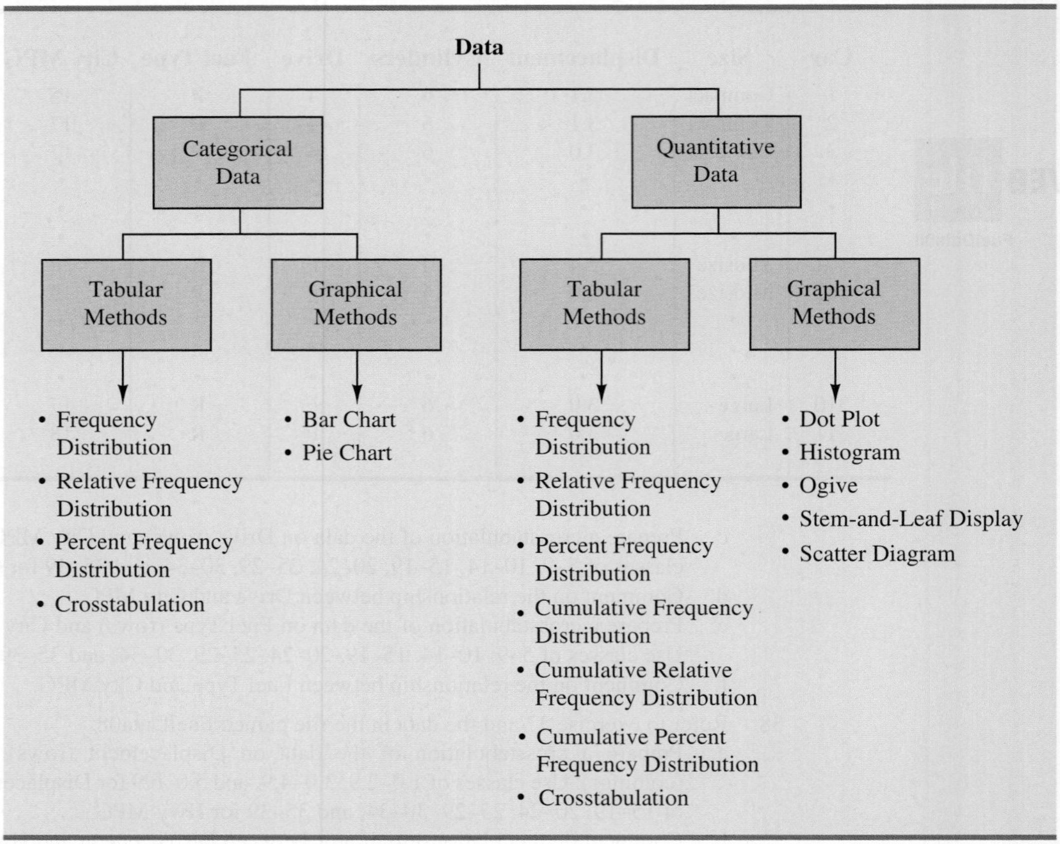

With large data sets, computer software packages are essential in constructing tabular and graphical summaries of data. In the chapter appendixes, we show how Minitab, Excel, and StatTools can be used for this purpose.

Glossary

Categorical data Labels or names used to identify categories of like items.
Quantitative data Numerical values that indicate how much or how many.
Frequency distribution A tabular summary of data showing the number (frequency) of data values in each of several nonoverlapping classes.
Relative frequency distribution A tabular summary of data showing the fraction or proportion of data values in each of several nonoverlapping classes.
Percent frequency distribution A tabular summary of data showing the percentage of data values in each of several nonoverlapping classes.
Bar chart A graphical device for depicting categorical data that have been summarized in a frequency, relative frequency, or percent frequency distribution.
Pie chart A graphical device for presenting data summaries based on subdivision of a circle into sectors that correspond to the relative frequency for each class.
Class midpoint The value halfway between the lower and upper class limits.
Dot plot A graphical device that summarizes data by the number of dots above each data value on the horizontal axis.

Histogram A graphical presentation of a frequency distribution, relative frequency distribution, or percent frequency distribution of quantitative data constructed by placing the class intervals on the horizontal axis and the frequencies, relative frequencies, or percent frequencies on the vertical axis.
Cumulative frequency distribution A tabular summary of quantitative data showing the number of data values that are less than or equal to the upper class limit of each class.
Cumulative relative frequency distribution A tabular summary of quantitative data showing the fraction or proportion of data values that are less than or equal to the upper class limit of each class.
Cumulative percent frequency distribution A tabular summary of quantitative data showing the percentage of data values that are less than or equal to the upper class limit of each class.
Ogive A graph of a cumulative distribution.
Exploratory data analysis Methods that use simple arithmetic and easy-to-draw graphs to summarize data quickly.
Stem-and-leaf display An exploratory data analysis technique that simultaneously rank orders quantitative data and provides insight about the shape of the distribution.
Crosstabulation A tabular summary of data for two variables. The classes for one variable are represented by the rows; the classes for the other variable are represented by the columns.
Simpson's paradox Conclusions drawn from two or more separate crosstabulations that can be reversed when the data are aggregated into a single crosstabulation.
Scatter diagram A graphical presentation of the relationship between two quantitative variables. One variable is shown on the horizontal axis and the other variable is shown on the vertical axis.
Trendline A line that provides an approximation of the relationship between two variables.

Key Formulas

Relative Frequency

$$\frac{\text{Frequency of the class}}{n} \tag{2.1}$$

Approximate Class Width

$$\frac{\text{Largest data value} - \text{Smallest data value}}{\text{Number of classes}} \tag{2.2}$$

Supplementary Exercises

39. The Higher Education Research Institute at UCLA provides statistics on the most popular majors among incoming college freshmen. The five most popular majors are Arts and Humanities (A), Business Administration (B), Engineering (E), Professional (P), and Social Science (S) (*The New York Times Almanac,* 2006). A broad range of other (O) majors, including biological science, physical science, computer science, and education, are grouped together. The majors selected for a sample of 64 college freshmen follow.

WEB file

Major

S	P	P	O	B	E	O	E	P	O	O	B	O	O	O	A
O	E	E	B	S	O	B	O	A	O	E	O	E	O	B	P
B	A	S	O	E	A	B	O	S	S	O	O	E	B	O	B
A	E	B	E	A	A	P	O	O	E	O	B	B	O	P	B

a. Show a frequency distribution and percent frequency distribution.
b. Show a bar chart.

c. What percentage of freshmen select one of the five most popular majors?
d. What is the most popular major for incoming freshmen? What percentage of freshmen select this major?

WEB file GMSales

40. General Motors had a 23% share of the automobile industry with sales coming from eight divisions: Buick, Cadillac, Chevrolet, GMC, Hummer, Pontiac, Saab, and Saturn (*Forbes,* December 22, 2008). The data set GMSales shows the sales for a sample of 200 General Motors vehicles. The division for the vehicle is provided for each sale.
a. Show the frequency distribution and the percent frequency distribution of sales by division for General Motors.
b. Show a bar chart of the percent frequency distribution.
c. Which General Motors division was the company leader in sales? What was the percentage of sales for this division? Was this General Motors' most important division? Explain.
d. Due to the ongoing recession, high gasoline prices, and the decline in automobile sales, General Motors was facing bankruptcy in 2009. A government "bail-out" loan and a restructuring of the company were anticipated. Expectations were that General Motors could not continue to operate all eight divisions. Based on the percentage of sales, which of the eight divisions looked to be the best candidates for General Motors to discontinue? Which divisions looked to be the least likely candidates for General Motors to discontinue?

41. Dividend yield is the annual dividend paid by a company expressed as a percentage of the price of the stock (Dividend/Stock Price × 100). The dividend yield for the Dow Jones Industrial Average companies is shown in Table 2.15 (*The Wall Street Journal,* June 8, 2009).
a. Construct a frequency distribution and percent frequency distribution.
b. Construct a histogram.
c. Comment on the shape of the distribution.
d. What do the tabular and graphical summaries tell about the dividend yields among the Dow Jones Industrial Average companies?
e. What company has the highest dividend yield? If the stock for this company currently sells for $20 per share and you purchase 500 shares, how much dividend income will this investment generate in one year?

42. Approximately 1.5 million high school students take the Scholastic Aptitude Test (SAT) each year and nearly 80% of the college and universities without open admissions policies use SAT scores in making admission decisions (College Board, March 2009). The current

TABLE 2.15 DIVIDEND YIELD FOR DOW JONES INDUSTRIAL AVERAGE COMPANIES

WEB file DYield

Company	Dividend Yield %	Company	Dividend Yield %
3M	3.6	IBM	2.1
Alcoa	1.3	Intel	3.4
American Express	2.9	J.P. Morgan Chase	0.5
AT&T	6.6	Johnson & Johnson	3.6
Bank of America	0.4	Kraft Foods	4.4
Boeing	3.8	McDonald's	3.4
Caterpillar	4.7	Merck	5.5
Chevron	3.9	Microsoft	2.5
Cisco Systems	0.0	Pfizer	4.2
Coca-Cola	3.3	Procter & Gamble	3.4
DuPont	5.8	Travelers	3.0
ExxonMobil	2.4	United Technologies	2.9
General Electric	9.2	Verizon	6.3
Hewlett-Packard	0.9	Wal-Mart Stores	2.2
Home Depot	3.9	Walt Disney	1.5

version of the SAT includes three parts: reading comprehension, mathematics, and writing. A perfect combined score for all three parts is 2400. A sample of SAT scores for the combined three-part SAT are as follows:

WEB file
NewSAT

1665	1525	1355	1645	1780
1275	2135	1280	1060	1585
1650	1560	1150	1485	1990
1590	1880	1420	1755	1375
1475	1680	1440	1260	1730
1490	1560	940	1390	1175

a. Show a frequency distribution and histogram. Begin with the first class starting at 800 and use a class width of 200.

b. Comment on the shape of the distribution.

c. What other observations can be made about the SAT scores based on the tabular and graphical summaries?

43. The Pittsburgh Steelers defeated the Arizona Cardinals 27 to 23 in professional football's 43rd Super Bowl. With this win, its sixth championship, the Pittsburgh Steelers became the team with the most wins in the 43-year history of the event (*Tampa Tribune,* February 2, 2009). The Super Bowl has been played in eight different states: Arizona (AZ), California (CA), Florida (FL), Georgia (GA), Louisiana (LA), Michigan (MI), Minnesota (MN), and Texas (TX). Data in the following table show the state where the Super Bowls were played and the point margin of victory for the winning team.

WEB file
SuperBowl

Super Bowl	State	Won By Points	Super Bowl	State	Won By Points	Super Bowl	State	Won By Points
1	CA	25	16	MI	5	31	LA	14
2	FL	19	17	CA	10	32	CA	7
3	FL	9	18	FL	19	33	FL	15
4	LA	16	19	CA	22	34	GA	7
5	FL	3	20	LA	36	35	FL	27
6	FL	21	21	CA	19	36	LA	3
7	CA	7	22	CA	32	37	CA	27
8	TX	17	23	FL	4	38	TX	3
9	LA	10	24	LA	45	39	FL	3
10	FL	4	25	FL	1	40	MI	11
11	CA	18	26	MN	13	41	FL	12
12	LA	17	27	CA	35	42	AZ	3
13	FL	4	28	GA	17	43	FL	4
14	CA	12	29	FL	23			
15	LA	17	30	AZ	10			

a. Show a frequency distribution and bar chart for the state where the Super Bowl was played.

b. What conclusions can you draw from your summary in part (a)? What percentage of Super Bowls were played in the states of Florida or California? What percentage of Super Bowls were played in northern or cold-weather states?

c. Show a stretched stem-and-leaf display for the point margin of victory for the winning team. Show a histogram.

d. What conclusions can you draw from your summary in part (c)? What percentage of Super Bowls have been close games with the margin of victory less than 5 points? What percentage of Super Bowls have been won by 20 or more points?

e. The closest Super Bowl occurred when the New York Giants beat the Buffalo Bills. Where was this game played and what was the winning margin of victory? The biggest point margin in Super Bowl history occurred when the San Francisco 49ers beat the Denver Broncos. Where was this game played and what was the winning margin of victory?

44. Data from the U.S. Census Bureau provides the population by state in millions of people (*The World Almanac,* 2006).

WEB file Population

State	Population	State	Population	State	Population
Alabama	4.5	Louisiana	4.5	Ohio	11.5
Alaska	0.7	Maine	1.3	Oklahoma	3.5
Arizona	5.7	Maryland	5.6	Oregon	3.6
Arkansas	2.8	Massachusetts	6.4	Pennsylvania	12.4
California	35.9	Michigan	10.1	Rhode Island	1.1
Colorado	4.6	Minnesota	5.1	South Carolina	4.2
Connecticut	3.5	Mississippi	2.9	South Dakota	0.8
Delaware	0.8	Missouri	5.8	Tennessee	5.9
Florida	17.4	Montana	0.9	Texas	22.5
Georgia	8.8	Nebraska	1.7	Utah	2.4
Hawaii	1.3	Nevada	2.3	Vermont	0.6
Idaho	1.4	New Hampshire	1.3	Virginia	7.5
Illinois	12.7	New Jersey	8.7	Washington	6.2
Indiana	6.2	New Mexico	1.9	West Virginia	1.8
Iowa	3.0	New York	19.2	Wisconsin	5.5
Kansas	2.7	North Carolina	8.5	Wyoming	0.5
Kentucky	4.1	North Dakota	0.6		

a. Develop a frequency distribution, a percent frequency distribution, and a histogram. Use a class width of 2.5 million.
b. Discuss the skewness in the distribution.
c. What observations can you make about the population of the 50 states?

45. *Drug Store News* (September 2002) provided data on annual pharmacy sales for the leading pharmacy retailers in the United States. The following data are annual sales in millions.

Retailer	Sales	Retailer	Sales
Ahold USA	$ 1700	Medicine Shoppe	$ 1757
CVS	12700	Rite-Aid	8637
Eckerd	7739	Safeway	2150
Kmart	1863	Walgreens	11660
Kroger	3400	Wal-Mart	7250

a. Show a stem-and-leaf display.
b. Identify the annual sales levels for the smallest, medium, and largest drug retailers.
c. What are the two largest drug retailers?

46. The daily high and low temperatures for 20 cities follow (*USA Today,* March 3, 2006).

WEB file CityTemp

City	High	Low	City	High	Low
Albuquerque	66	39	Los Angeles	60	46
Atlanta	61	35	Miami	84	65
Baltimore	42	26	Minneapolis	30	11
Charlotte	60	29	New Orleans	68	50
Cincinnati	41	21	Oklahoma City	62	40
Dallas	62	47	Phoenix	77	50
Denver	60	31	Portland	54	38
Houston	70	54	St. Louis	45	27
Indianapolis	42	22	San Francisco	55	43
Las Vegas	65	43	Seattle	52	36

a. Prepare a stem-and-leaf display of the high temperatures.
b. Prepare a stem-and-leaf display of the low temperatures.
c. Compare the two stem-and-leaf displays and make comments about the difference between the high and low temperatures.
d. Provide a frequency distribution for both high and low temperatures.

47. Refer to the data set for high and low temperatures for 20 cities in exercise 46.
a. Develop a scatter diagram to show the relationship between the two variables, high temperature and low temperature.
b. Comment on the relationship between high and low temperatures.

48. One of the questions in a *Financial Times*/Harris Poll was, "How much do you favor or oppose a higher tax on higher carbon emission cars?" Possible responses were strongly favor, favor more than oppose, oppose more than favor, and strongly oppose. The following crosstabulation shows the responses obtained for 5372 adults surveyed in four countries in Europe and the United States (Harris Interactive website, February 27, 2008).

	Country					
Level of Support	Great Britain	Italy	Spain	Germany	United States	Total
Strongly favor	337	334	510	222	214	1617
Favor more than oppose	370	408	355	411	327	1871
Oppose more than favor	250	188	155	267	275	1135
Strongly oppose	130	115	89	211	204	749
Total	1087	1045	1109	1111	1020	5372

a. Construct a percent frequency distribution for the level of support variable. Do you think the results show support for a higher tax on higher carbon emission cars?
b. Construct a percent frequency distribution for the country variable.
c. Does the level of support among adults in the European countries appear to be different than the level of support among adults in the United States? Explain.

49. Western University has only one women's softball scholarship remaining for the coming year. The final two players that Western is considering are Allison Fealey and Emily Janson. The coaching staff has concluded that the speed and defensive skills are virtually identical for the two players, and that the final decision will be based on which player has the best batting average. Crosstabulations of each player's batting performance in their junior and senior years of high school are as follows:

	Allison Fealey	
Outcome	Junior	Senior
Hit	15	75
No Hit	25	175
Total At-Bats	40	250

	Emily Janson	
Outcome	Junior	Senior
Hit	70	35
No Hit	130	85
Total At Bats	200	120

A player's batting average is computed by dividing the number of hits a player has by the total number of at-bats. Batting averages are represented as a decimal number with three places after the decimal.

a. Calculate the batting average for each player in her junior year. Then calculate the batting average of each player in her senior year. Using this analysis, which player should be awarded the scholarship? Explain.

b. Combine or aggregate the data for the junior and senior years into one crosstabulation as follows:

	Player	
Outcome	**Fealey**	**Janson**
Hit		
No Hit		
Total At-Bats		

Calculate each player's batting average for the combined two years. Using this analysis, which player should be awarded the scholarship? Explain.

c. Are the recommendations you made in parts (a) and (b) consistent? Explain any apparent inconsistencies.

50. A survey of commercial buildings served by the Cincinnati Gas & Electric Company asked what main heating fuel was used and what year the building was constructed. A partial crosstabulation of the findings follows.

Year	Fuel Type				
Constructed	**Electricity**	**Natural Gas**	**Oil**	**Propane**	**Other**
1973 or before	40	183	12	5	7
1974–1979	24	26	2	2	0
1980–1986	37	38	1	0	6
1987–1991	48	70	2	0	1

a. Complete the crosstabulation by showing the row totals and column totals.
b. Show the frequency distributions for year constructed and for fuel type.
c. Prepare a crosstabulation showing column percentages.
d. Prepare a crosstabulation showing row percentages.
e. Comment on the relationship between year constructed and fuel type.

51. Table 2.16 contains a portion of the data in the file named Fortune. Data on stockholders' equity, market value, and profits for a sample of 50 *Fortune* 500 companies are shown.

WEB file
Fortune

TABLE 2.16 DATA FOR A SAMPLE OF 50 *FORTUNE* 500 COMPANIES

Company	Stockholders' Equity ($1000s)	Market Value ($1000s)	Profit ($1000s)
AGCO	982.1	372.1	60.6
AMP	2698.0	12017.6	2.0
Apple Computer	1642.0	4605.0	309.0
Baxter International	2839.0	21743.0	315.0
Bergen Brunswick	629.1	2787.5	3.1
Best Buy	557.7	10376.5	94.5
Charles Schwab	1429.0	35340.6	348.5
.	.	.	.
.	.	.	.
.	.	.	.
Walgreen	2849.0	30324.7	511.0
Westvaco	2246.4	2225.6	132.0
Whirlpool	2001.0	3729.4	325.0
Xerox	5544.0	35603.7	395.0

a. Prepare a crosstabulation for the variables Stockholders' Equity and Profit. Use classes of 0–200, 200–400, . . . , 1000–1200 for Profit, and classes of 0–1200, 1200–2400, . . . , 4800–6000 for Stockholders' Equity.
b. Compute the row percentages for your crosstabulation in part (a).
c. What relationship, if any, do you notice between Profit and Stockholders' Equity?

52. Refer to the data set in Table 2.16.
a. Prepare a crosstabulation for the variables Market Value and Profit.
b. Compute the row percentages for your crosstabulation in part (a).
c. Comment on any relationship between the variables.

53. Refer to the data set in Table 2.16.
a. Prepare a scatter diagram to show the relationship between the variables Profit and Stockholders' Equity.
b. Comment on any relationship between the variables.

54. Refer to the data set in Table 2.16.
a. Prepare a scatter diagram to show the relationship between the variables Market Value and Stockholders' Equity.
b. Comment on any relationship between the variables.

Case Problem 1 Pelican Stores

Pelican Stores, a division of National Clothing, is a chain of women's apparel stores operating throughout the country. The chain recently ran a promotion in which discount coupons were sent to customers of other National Clothing stores. Data collected for a sample of 100 in-store credit card transactions at Pelican Stores during one day while the promotion was running are contained in the file named PelicanStores. Table 2.17 shows a portion of the data set. The Proprietary Card method of payment refers to charges made using a National Clothing charge card. Customers who made a purchase using a discount coupon are referred to as promotional customers and customers who made a purchase but did not use a discount coupon are referred to as regular customers. Because the promotional coupons were not sent to regular Pelican Stores customers, management considers the sales made to people presenting the promotional coupons as sales it would not otherwise make. Of course, Pelican also hopes that the promotional customers will continue to shop at its stores.

WEB file
PelicanStores

TABLE 2.17 DATA FOR A SAMPLE OF 100 CREDIT CARD PURCHASES AT PELICAN STORES

Customer	Type of Customer	Items	Net Sales	Method of Payment	Gender	Marital Status	Age
1	Regular	1	39.50	Discover	Male	Married	32
2	Promotional	1	102.40	Proprietary Card	Female	Married	36
3	Regular	1	22.50	Proprietary Card	Female	Married	32
4	Promotional	5	100.40	Proprietary Card	Female	Married	28
5	Regular	2	54.00	MasterCard	Female	Married	34
.	.	.	.	.	.	.	.
.	.	.	.	.	.	.	.
.	.	.	.	.	.	.	.
96	Regular	1	39.50	MasterCard	Female	Married	44
97	Promotional	9	253.00	Proprietary Card	Female	Married	30
98	Promotional	10	287.59	Proprietary Card	Female	Married	52
99	Promotional	2	47.60	Proprietary Card	Female	Married	30
100	Promotional	1	28.44	Proprietary Card	Female	Married	44

Most of the variables shown in Table 2.17 are self-explanatory, but two of the variables require some clarification.

Items	The total number of items purchased
Net Sales	The total amount ($) charged to the credit card

Pelican's management would like to use this sample data to learn about its customer base and to evaluate the promotion involving discount coupons.

Managerial Report

Use the tabular and graphical methods of descriptive statistics to help management develop a customer profile and to evaluate the promotional campaign. At a minimum, your report should include the following:

1. Percent frequency distribution for key variables.
2. A bar chart or pie chart showing the number of customer purchases attributable to the method of payment.
3. A crosstabulation of type of customer (regular or promotional) versus net sales. Comment on any similarities or differences present.
4. A scatter diagram to explore the relationship between net sales and customer age.

Case Problem 2 Motion Picture Industry

The motion picture industry is a competitive business. More than 50 studios produce a total of 300 to 400 new motion pictures each year, and the financial success of each motion picture varies considerably. The opening weekend gross sales ($millions), the total gross sales ($millions), the number of theaters the movie was shown in, and the number of weeks the motion picture was in the top 60 for gross sales are common variables used to measure the success of a motion picture. Data collected for a sample of 100 motion pictures produced in 2005 are contained in the file named Movies. Table 2.18 shows the data for the first 10 motion pictures in this file.

Managerial Report

Use the tabular and graphical methods of descriptive statistics to learn how these variables contribute to the success of a motion picture. Include the following in your report.

TABLE 2.18 PERFORMANCE DATA FOR 10 MOTION PICTURES

WEB file

Movies

Motion Picture	Opening Gross Sales ($millions)	Total Gross Sales ($millions)	Number of Theaters	Weeks in Top 60
Coach Carter	29.17	67.25	2574	16
Ladies in Lavender	0.15	6.65	119	22
Batman Begins	48.75	205.28	3858	18
Unleashed	10.90	24.47	1962	8
Pretty Persuasion	0.06	0.23	24	4
Fever Pitch	12.40	42.01	3275	14
Harry Potter and the Goblet of Fire	102.69	287.18	3858	13
Monster-in-Law	23.11	82.89	3424	16
White Noise	24.11	55.85	2279	7
Mr. and Mrs. Smith	50.34	186.22	3451	21

1. Tabular and graphical summaries for each of the four variables along with a discussion of what each summary tells us about the motion picture industry.
2. A scatter diagram to explore the relationship between Total Gross Sales and Opening Weekend Gross Sales. Discuss.
3. A scatter diagram to explore the relationship between Total Gross Sales and Number of Theaters. Discuss.
4. A scatter diagram to explore the relationship between Total Gross Sales and Number of Weeks in the Top 60. Discuss.

Appendix 2.1 Using Minitab for Tabular and Graphical Presentations

Minitab offers extensive capabilities for constructing tabular and graphical summaries of data. In this appendix we show how Minitab can be used to construct several graphical summaries and the tabular summary of a crosstabulation. The graphical methods presented include the dot plot, the histogram, the stem-and-leaf display, and the scatter diagram.

Dot Plot

WEB file Audit

We use the audit time data in Table 2.4 to demonstrate. The data are in column C1 of a Minitab worksheet. The following steps will generate a dot plot.

Step 1. Select the **Graph** menu and choose **Dotplot**
Step 2. Select **One Y, Simple** and click **OK**
Step 3. When the Dotplot-One Y, Simple dialog box appears:
Enter C1 in the **Graph Variables** box
Click **OK**

Histogram

WEB file Audit

We show how to construct a histogram with frequencies on the vertical axis using the audit time data in Table 2.4. The data are in column C1 of a Minitab worksheet. The following steps will generate a histogram for audit times.

Step 1. Select the **Graph** menu
Step 2. Choose **Histogram**
Step 3. When the Histograms dialog box appears:
Choose **Simple**
Step 4. When the Histogram-Simple dialog box appears:
Enter C1 in the **Graph Variables** box
Click **OK**
Step 5. When the Histogram appears:*
Position the mouse pointer over any one of the bars
Double-click
Step 6. When the Edit Bars dialog box appears:
Click the **Binning** tab
Select **Cutpoint** for Interval Type
Select **Midpoint/Cutpoint positions** for Interval Definition
Enter 10:35/5 in the **Midpoint/Cutpoint positions** box
Click **OK**

*Steps 5 and 6 are optional, but are shown here to demonstrate user flexibility in displaying the histogram. The entry 10:35/5 in step 6 indicates that 10 is the starting value for the histogram, 35 is the ending value for the histogram, and 5 is the class width.

Note that Minitab also provides the option of scaling the *x*-axis so that the numerical values appear at the midpoints of the histogram rectangles. If this option is desired, modify step 6 to include Select **Midpoint** for Interval Type and Enter 12:32/5 in the **Midpoint/Cutpoint positions** box. These steps provide the same histogram with the midpoints of the histogram rectangles labeled 12, 17, 22, 27, and 32.

Stem-and-Leaf Display

WEB file
ApTest

We use the aptitude test data in Table 2.8 to demonstrate the construction of a stem-and-leaf display. The data are in column C1 of a Minitab worksheet. The following steps will generate the stretched stem-and-leaf display shown in Section 2.3.

Step 1. Select the **Graph** menu
Step 2. Choose **Stem-and-Leaf**
Step 3. When the Stem-and-Leaf dialog box appears:
Enter C1 in the **Graph Variables** box
Click **OK**

Scatter Diagram

WEB file
Stereo

We use the stereo and sound equipment store data in Table 2.12 to demonstrate the construction of a scatter diagram. The weeks are numbered from 1 to 10 in column C1, the data for number of commercials are in column C2, and the data for sales are in column C3 of a Minitab worksheet. The following steps will generate the scatter diagram shown in Figure 2.7.

Step 1. Select the **Graph** menu
Step 2. Choose **Scatterplot**
Step 3. Select **Simple** and click **OK**
Step 4. When the Scatterplot-Simple dialog box appears:
Enter C3 under **Y variables** and C2 under **X variables**
Click **OK**

Crosstabulation

WEB file
Restaurant

We use the data from Zagat's restaurant review, part of which is shown in Table 2.9, to demonstrate. The restaurants are numbered from 1 to 300 in column C1 of the Minitab worksheet. The quality ratings are in column C2, and the meal prices are in column C3.

Minitab can only create a crosstabulation for qualitative variables and meal price is a quantitative variable. So we need to first code the meal price data by specifying the class to which each meal price belongs. The following steps will code the meal price data to create four classes of meal price in column C4: $10–19, $20–29, $30–39, and $40–49.

Step 1. Select the **Data** menu
Step 2. Choose **Code**
Step 3. Choose **Numeric to Text**
Step 4. When the Code-Numeric to Text dialog box appears:
Enter C3 in the **Code data from columns** box
Enter C4 in the **Store coded data in columns** box
Enter 10:19 in the first **Original values** box and $10-19 in the adjacent **New** box
Enter 20:29 in the second **Original values** box and $20-29 in the adjacent **New** box

Enter 30:39 in the third **Original values** box and $30-39 in the adjacent **New** box

Enter 40:49 in the fourth **Original values** box and $40-49 in the adjacent **New** box

Click **OK**

For each meal price in column C3 the associated meal price category will now appear in column C4. We can now develop a crosstabulation for quality rating and the meal price categories by using the data in columns C2 and C4. The following steps will create a crosstabulation containing the same information as shown in Table 2.10.

Step 1. Select the **Stat** menu
Step 2. Choose **Tables**
Step 3. Choose **Cross Tabulation and Chi-Square**
Step 4. When the Cross Tabulation and Chi-Square dialog box appears:
Enter C2 in the **For rows** box and C4 in the **For columns** box
Select **Counts** under Display
Click **OK**

Appendix 2.2 Using Excel for Tabular and Graphical Presentations

Excel offers extensive capabilities for constructing tabular and graphical summaries of data. In this appendix, we show how Excel can be used to construct a frequency distribution, bar chart, pie chart, histogram, scatter diagram, and crosstabulation. We will demonstrate three of Excel's most powerful tools for data analysis: chart tools, PivotChart Report, and PivotTable Report.

Frequency Distribution and Bar Chart for Categorical Data

In this section we show how Excel can be used to construct a frequency distribution and a bar chart for categorical data. We illustrate each using the data on soft drink purchases in Table 2.1.

Frequency distribution We begin by showing how the COUNTIF function can be used to construct a frequency distribution for the data in Table 2.1. Refer to Figure 2.10 as we describe the steps involved. The formula worksheet (showing the functions and formulas used) is set in the background, and the value worksheet (showing the results obtained using the functions and formulas) appears in the foreground.

WEB file
SoftDrink

The label "Brand Purchased" and the data for the 50 soft drink purchases are in cells A1:A51. We also entered the labels "Soft Drink" and "Frequency" in cells C1:D1. The five soft drink names are entered into cells C2:C6. Excel's COUNTIF function can now be used to count the number of times each soft drink appears in cells A2:A51. The following steps are used.

Step 1. Select cell D2
Step 2. Enter =COUNTIF($A$2:$A$51,C2)
Step 3. Copy cell D2 to cells D3:D6

The formula worksheet in Figure 2.10 shows the cell formulas inserted by applying these steps. The value worksheet shows the values computed by the cell formulas. This worksheet shows the same frequency distribution that we developed in Table 2.2.

FIGURE 2.10 FREQUENCY DISTRIBUTION FOR SOFT DRINK PURCHASES CONSTRUCTED USING EXCEL'S COUNTIF FUNCTION

	A	B	C	D	E
1	**Brand Purchased**		**Soft Drink**	**Frequency**	
2	Coke Classic		Coke Classic	=COUNTIF($A$2:$A$51,C2)	
3	Diet Coke		Diet Coke	=COUNTIF($A$2:$A$51,C3)	
4	Pepsi		Dr. Pepper	=COUNTIF($A$2:$A$51,C4)	
5	Diet Coke		Pepsi	=COUNTIF($A$2:$A$51,C5)	
6	Coke Classic		Sprite	=COUNTIF($A$2:$A$51,C6)	
7	Coke Classic				
8	Dr. Pepper				
9	Diet Coke				
10	Pepsi				
45	Pepsi				
46	Pepsi				
47	Pepsi				
48	Coke Classic				
49	Dr. Pepper				
50	Pepsi				
51	Sprite				
52					

Note: Rows 11–44 are hidden.

	A	B	C	D	E
1	**Brand Purchased**		**Soft Drink**	**Frequency**	
2	Coke Classic		Coke Classic	19	
3	Diet Coke		Diet Coke	8	
4	Pepsi		Dr. Pepper	5	
5	Diet Coke		Pepsi	13	
6	Coke Classic		Sprite	5	
7	Coke Classic				
8	Dr. Pepper				
9	Diet Coke				
10	Pepsi				
45	Pepsi				
46	Pepsi				
47	Pepsi				
48	Coke Classic				
49	Dr. Pepper				
50	Pepsi				
51	Sprite				
52					

WEB file SoftDrink

Bar chart Here we show how Excel's chart tools can be used to construct a bar chart for the soft drink data. Refer to the frequency distribution shown in the value worksheet of Figure 2.10. The bar chart that we are going to develop is an extension of this worksheet. The worksheet and the bar chart developed are shown in Figure 2.11. The steps are as follows:

Step 1. Select cells C2:D6
Step 2. Click the **Insert** tab on the Ribbon
Step 3. In the **Charts** group, click **Column**
Step 4. When the list of column chart subtypes appears:
Go to the **2-D Column** section
Click **Clustered Column** (the leftmost chart)
Step 5. In the **Chart Layouts** group, click the **More** button (the downward-pointing arrow with a line over it) to display all the options
Step 6. Choose **Layout 9**
Step 7. Select the **Chart Title** and replace it with **Bar Chart of Soft Drink Purchases**
Step 8. Select the **Horizontal (Category) Axis Title** and replace it with **Soft Drink**
Step 9. Select the **Vertical (Value) Axis Title** and replace it with **Frequency**
Step 10. Right-click the **Series 1 Legend Entry**
Click **Delete**
Step 11. Right-click the vertical axis
Click **Format Axis**

FIGURE 2.11 BAR CHART OF SOFT DRINK PURCHASES CONSTRUCTED USING EXCEL'S CHART TOOLS

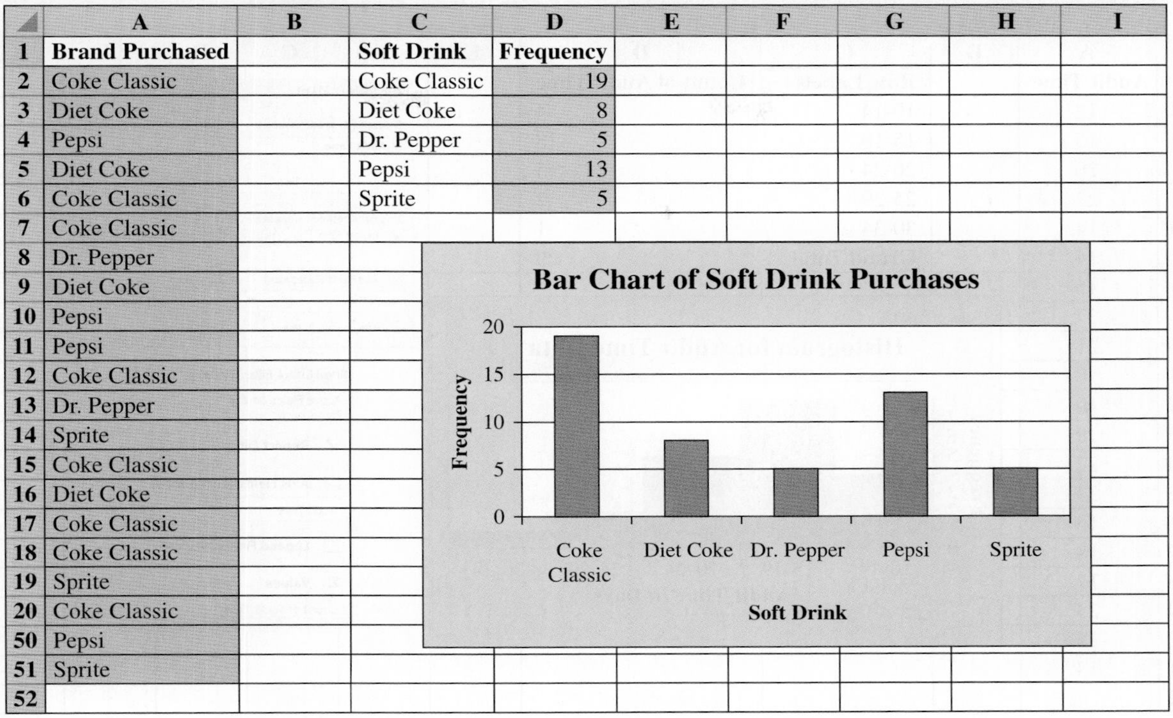

	A	B	C	D	E	F	G	H	I
1	**Brand Purchased**		**Soft Drink**	**Frequency**					
2	Coke Classic		Coke Classic	19					
3	Diet Coke		Diet Coke	8					
4	Pepsi		Dr. Pepper	5					
5	Diet Coke		Pepsi	13					
6	Coke Classic		Sprite	5					
7	Coke Classic								
8	Dr. Pepper								
9	Diet Coke								
10	Pepsi								
11	Pepsi								
12	Coke Classic								
13	Dr. Pepper								
14	Sprite								
15	Coke Classic								
16	Diet Coke								
17	Coke Classic								
18	Coke Classic								
19	Sprite								
20	Coke Classic								
50	Pepsi								
51	Sprite								
52									

Step 12. When the Format Axis dialog box appears:
Go to the **Axis Options** section
Select **Fixed** for **Major Unit** and enter 5.0 in the corresponding box
Click **Close**

The resulting bar chart is shown in Figure 2.11.*

Excel can produce a pie chart for the soft drink data in a similar fashion. The major difference is that in step 3 we would click **Pie** in the **Charts** group. Several style pie charts are available.

Frequency Distribution and Histogram for Quantitative Data

In a later section of this appendix we describe how to use Excel's PivotTable Report to construct a crosstabulation.

Excel's PivotTable Report is an interactive tool that allows you to quickly summarize data in a variety of ways, including developing a frequency distribution for quantitative data. Once a frequency distribution is created using the PivotTable Report, Excel's chart tools can then be used to construct the corresponding histogram. But, using Excel's PivotChart Report, we can construct a frequency distribution and a histogram simultaneously. We will illustrate this procedure using the audit time data in Table 2.4. The label "Audit Time" and the 20 audit time values are entered into cells A1:A21 of an Excel worksheet. The following steps describe how to use Excel's PivotChart Report to construct a frequency distribution and a histogram for the audit time data. Refer to Figure 2.12 as we describe the steps involved.

WEB file
Audit

*The bar chart in Figure 2.11 can be resized. Resizing an Excel chart is not difficult. First, select the chart. Sizing handles will appear on the chart border. Click on the sizing handles and drag them to resize the figure to your preference.

FIGURE 2.12 USING EXCEL'S PIVOTCHART REPORT TO CONSTRUCT A FREQUENCY DISTRIBUTION AND HISTOGRAM FOR THE AUDIT TIME DATA

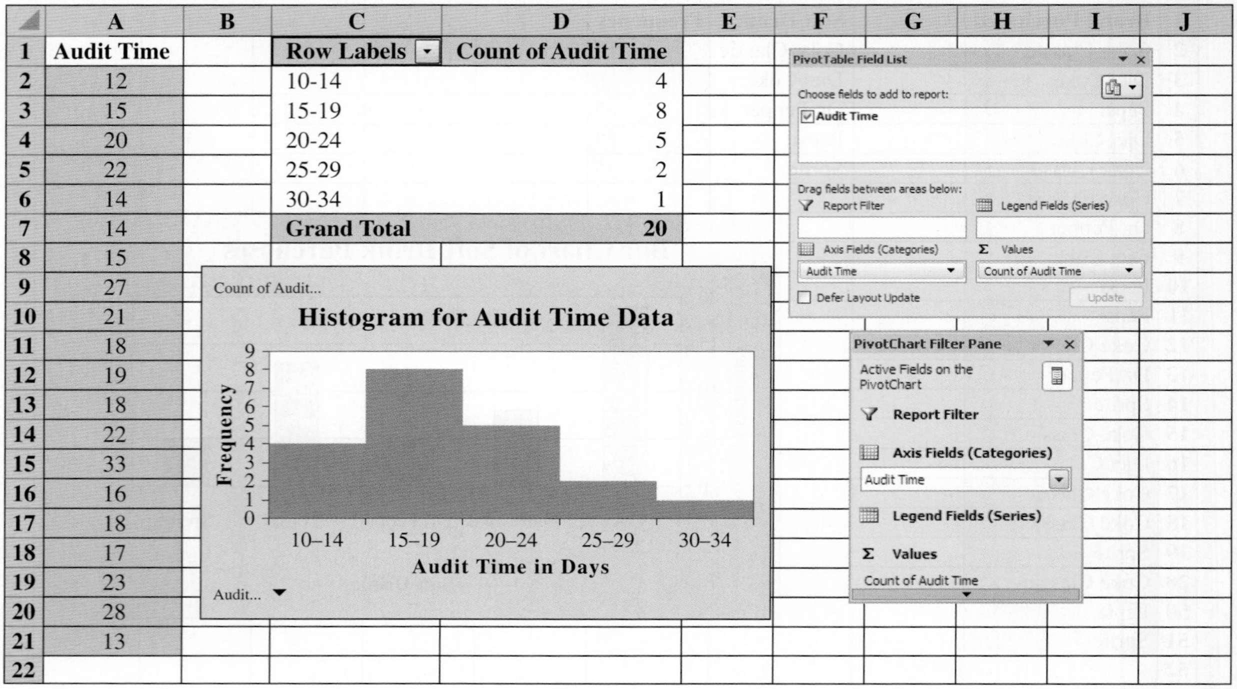

Step 1. Click the **Insert** tab on the Ribbon
Step 2. In the **Tables** group, click the word **PivotTable**
Step 3. Choose **PivotChart** from the options that appear
Step 4. When the **Create PivotTable with PivotChart** dialog box appears,
Choose **Select a table or range**
Enter A1:A21 in the **Table/Range** box
Choose **Existing Worksheet** as the location for the PivotTable and PivotChart
Enter C1 in the **Location** box
Click **OK**
Step 5. In the **PivotTable Field List**, go to **Choose Fields to add to report**
Drag the **Audit Time** field to the **Axis Fields (Categories)** area
Drag the **Audit Time** field to the **Values** area
Step 6. Click **Sum of Audit Time** in the **Values** area
Step 7. Click **Value Field Settings** from the list of options that appears
Step 8. When the Value Field Settings dialog appears,
Under **Summarize value field by**, choose **Count**
Click **OK**
Step 9. Close the **PivotTable Field List.**
Step 10. Right-click cell C2 in the PivotTable report or any other cell containing an audit time
Step 11. Choose **Group** from the list of options that appears
Step 12. When the **Grouping** dialog box appears,
Enter 10 in the **Starting at** box

Enter 34 in the **Ending at** box
Enter 5 in the **By** box
Click **OK** (a PivotChart will appear)

Step 13. Click inside the resulting PivotChart
Step 14. Click the **Design** tab on the Ribbon
Step 15. In the **Chart Layouts** group, click the **More** button (the downward pointing arrow with a line over it) to display all the options
Step 16. Choose **Layout 8**
Step 17. Select the **Chart Title** and replace it with **Histogram for Audit Time Data**
Step 18. Select the **Horizontal (Category) Axis Title** and replace it with **Audit Time in Days**
Step 19. Select the **Vertical (Value) Axis Title** and replace it with **Frequency**

The PivotChart contains a Value field button in the upper left corner of the chart and an Axis field button in the lower left corner. To remove either or both of these buttons, right-click either button and select the option to remove that button or all field buttons shown on the chart.

Figure 2.12 shows the resulting PivotTable and PivotChart. We see that the PivotTable report provides the frequency distribution for the audit time data and the PivotChart provides the corresponding histogram. If desired, we can change the labels in any cell in the frequency distribution by selecting the cell and typing in the new label.

Crosstabulation

Excel's PivotTable Report provides an excellent way to summarize the data for two or more variables simultaneously. We will illustrate the use of Excel's PivotTable Report by showing how to develop a crosstabulation of quality ratings and meal prices for the sample of 300 Los Angeles restaurants. We will use the data in the file named Restaurant; the labels "Restaurant," "Quality Rating," and "Meal Price ($)" have been entered into cells A1:C1 of the worksheet as shown in Figure 2.13. The data for each of the restaurants in the sample have been entered into cells B2:C301.

FIGURE 2.13 EXCEL WORKSHEET CONTAINING RESTAURANT DATA

WEB file
Restaurant

	A	B	C	D
1	Restaurant	Quality Rating	Meal Price ($)	
2	1	Good	18	
3	2	Very Good	22	
4	3	Good	28	
5	4	Excellent	38	
6	5	Very Good	33	
7	6	Good	28	
8	7	Very Good	19	
9	8	Very Good	11	
10	9	Very Good	23	
11	10	Good	13	
292	291	Very Good	23	
293	292	Very Good	24	
294	293	Excellent	45	
295	294	Good	14	
296	295	Good	18	
297	296	Good	17	
298	297	Good	16	
299	298	Good	15	
300	299	Very Good	38	
301	300	Very Good	31	
302				

Note: Rows 12–291 are hidden.

In order to use the Pivot Table report to create a crosstabulation, we need to perform three tasks: Display the Initial PivotTable Field List and PivotTable Report; Set Up the PivotTable Field List; and Finalize the PivotTable Report. These tasks are described as follows.

Display the Initial PivotTable Field List and PivotTable Report: Three steps are needed to display the initial PivotTable Field List and PivotTable report.

Step 1. Click the **Insert** tab on the Ribbon
Step 2. In the **Tables** group, click the icon above the word PivotTable
Step 3. When the **Create PivotTable** dialog box appears,
Choose **Select a Table or Range**
Enter A1:C301 in the **Table/Range** box
Choose **New Worksheet** as the location for the PivotTable Report
Click **OK**

The resulting initial PivotTable Field List and PivotTable Report are shown in Figure 2.14.

Set Up the PivotTable Field List: Each of the three columns in Figure 2.13 (labeled Restaurant, Quality Rating, and Meal Price ($)) is considered a field by Excel. Fields may be chosen to represent rows, columns, or values in the body of the PivotTable Report. The following steps show how to use Excel's PivotTable Field List to assign the Quality Rating field to the rows, the Meal Price ($) field to the columns, and the Restaurant field to the body of the PivotTable report.

Step 1. In the **PivotTable Field List,** go to **Choose Fields to add to report**
Drag the **Quality Rating** field to the **Row Labels** area
Drag the **Meal Price ($)** field to the **Column Labels** area
Drag the **Restaurant** field to the **Values** area

FIGURE 2.14 INITIAL PIVOTTABLE FIELD LIST AND PIVOTTABLE FIELD REPORT FOR THE RESTAURANT DATA

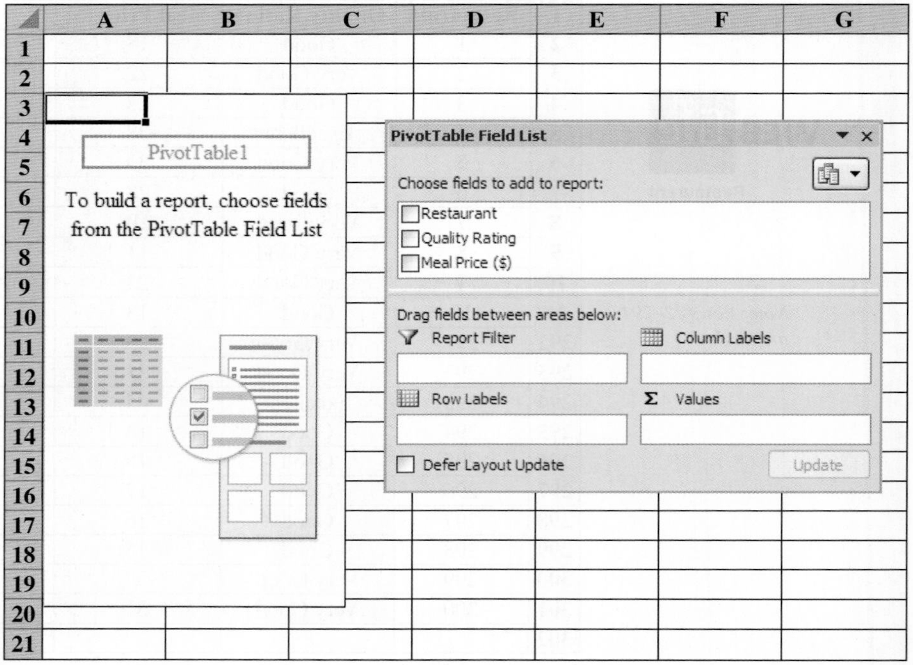

Step 2. Click on **Sum of Restaurant** in the **Values** area
Step 3. Click **Value Field Settings** from the list of options that appear
Step 4. When the Value Field Settings dialog appears,
Under **Summarize value field by**, choose **Count**
Click **OK**

Figure 2.15 shows the completed PivotTable Field List and a portion of the PivotTable worksheet as it now appears.

Finalize the PivotTable Report To complete the PivotTable Report we need to group the columns representing meal prices and place the row labels for quality rating in the proper order. The following steps accomplish this.

Step 1. Right-click in cell B4 or any cell containing meal prices
Step 2. Choose **Group** from the list of options that appears
Step 3. When the **Grouping** dialog box appears,
Enter 10 in the **Starting at** box
Enter 49 in the **Ending at** box
Enter 10 in the **By** box
Click **OK**
Step 4. Right-click on **Excellent** in cell A5
Step 5. Choose **Move** and click **Move "Excellent" to End**

The final PivotTable Report is shown in Figure 2.16. Note that it provides the same information as the crosstabulation shown in Table 2.10.

Scatter Diagram

We can use Excel's chart tools to construct a scatter diagram and a trend line for the stereo and sound equipment store data presented in Table 2.12. Refer to Figures 2.17 and 2.18 as

FIGURE 2.15 COMPLETED PIVOTTABLE FIELD LIST AND A PORTION OF THE PIVOTTABLE REPORT FOR THE RESTAURANT DATA (COLUMNS H:AK ARE HIDDEN)

	A	B	C	D	E	F	G	AL	AM	AN	AO
1											
2											
3	Count of Restaurant	Column Labels									
4	Row Labels	10	11	12	13	14	15	47	48	Grand Total	
5	Excellent				1			2	2	66	
6	Good	6	4	3	3	2	4			84	
7	Very Good	1	4	3	5	6	1		1	150	
8	Grand Total	7	8	6	9	8	5	2	3	300	
9											
10											
11											
12											
13											
14											
15											
16											
17											
18											
19											
20											

FIGURE 2.16 FINAL PIVOTTABLE REPORT FOR THE RESTAURANT DATA

	A	B	C	D	E	F	G
1							
2							
3	**Count of Restaurant**	**Column Labels**					
4	**Row Labels**	**10–19**	**20–29**	**30–39**	**40–49**	**Grand Total**	
5	Good	42	40	2		84	
6	Very Good	34	64	46	6	150	
7	Excellent	2	14	28	22	66	
8	**Grand Total**	**78**	**118**	**76**	**28**	**300**	
9							
10							
11							
12							
13							
14							
15							
16							
17							
18							
19							
20							
21							

FIGURE 2.17 SCATTER DIAGRAM FOR THE STEREO AND SOUND EQUIPMENT STORE USING EXCEL'S CHART TOOLS

	A	B	C	D	E	F	G	H
1	**Week**	**No. of Commercials**	**Sales Volume**					
2	1	2	50					
3	2	5	57					
4	3	1	41					
5	4	3	54					
6	5	4	54					
7	6	1	38					
8	7	5	63					
9	8	3	48					
10	9	4	59					
11	10	2	46					
12								
13								
14								
15								
16								
17								
18								
19								
20								

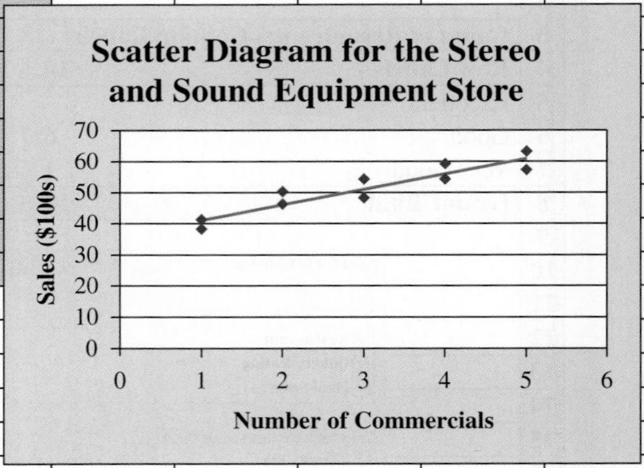

FIGURE 2.18 SCATTER DIAGRAM AND TRENDLINE FOR THE STEREO AND SOUND EQUIPMENT STORE USING EXCEL'S CHART TOOLS

	A	B	C	D	E	F	G	H
1	Week	No. of Commercials	Sales Volume					
2	1	2	50					
3	2	5	57					
4	3	1	41					
5	4	3	54					
6	5	4	54					
7	6	1	38					
8	7	5	63					
9	8	3	48					
10	9	4	59					
11	10	2	46					
12								
13								
14								
15								
16								
17								
18								
19								
20								

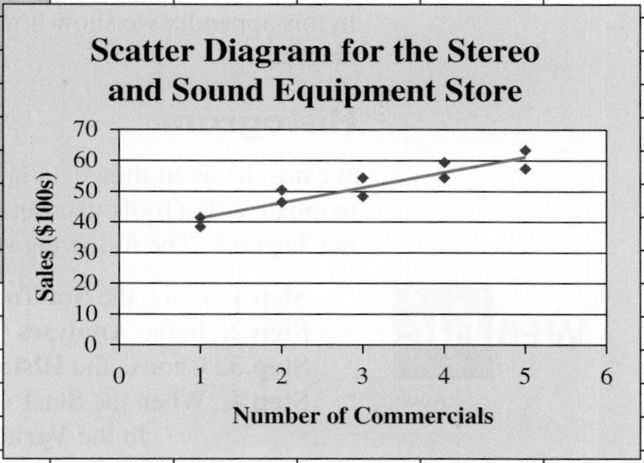

WEB file Stereo

we describe the steps involved. We will use the data in the file named Stereo; the labels Week, No. of Commercials, and Sales Volume have been entered into cells A1:C1 of the worksheet. The data for each of the 10 weeks are entered into cells B2:C11. The following steps describe how to use Excel's chart tools to produce a scatter diagram for the data.

Step 1. Select cells B2:C11
Step 2. Click the **Insert** tab on the Ribbon
Step 3. In the **Charts** group, click **Scatter**
Step 4. When the list of scatter diagram subtypes appears, click **Scatter with only Markers** (the chart in the upper left corner)
Step 5. In the **Chart Layouts** group, click **Layout 1**
Step 6. Select the **Chart Title** and replace it with **Scatter Diagram for the Stereo and Sound Equipment Store**
Step 7. Select the **Horizontal (Value) Axis Title** and replace it with **Number of Commercials**
Step 8. Select the **Vertical (Value) Axis Title** and replace it with **Sales ($100s)**
Step 9. Right-click the **Series 1 Legend Entry** and click **Delete**

The worksheet displayed in Figure 2.17 shows the scatter diagram produced by Excel. The following steps describe how to add a trend line.

Step 1. Position the mouse pointer over any data point in the scatter diagram and right-click to display a list of options
Step 2. Choose **Add Trendline**
Step 3. When the **Format Trendline** dialog box appears,
Select **Trendline Options**
Choose **Linear** from the **Trend/Regression Type** list
Click **Close**

The worksheet displayed in Figure 2.18 shows the scatter diagram with the trendline added.

Appendix 2.3 Using StatTools for Tabular and Graphical Presentations

In this appendix we show how StatTools can be used to construct a histogram and a scatter diagram.

Histogram

We use the audit time data in Table 2.4 to illustrate. Begin by using the Data Set Manager to create a StatTools data set for these data using the procedure described in the appendix in Chapter 1. The following steps will generate a histogram.

WEB file
Audit

Step 1. Click the **StatTools** tab on the Ribbon
Step 2. In the **Analyses Group,** click **Summary Graphs**
Step 3. Choose the **Histogram** option
Step 4. When the StatTools-Histogram dialog box appears,
In the **Variables** section, select **Audit Time**
In the **Options** section,
Enter 5 in the **Number of Bins** box
Enter 9.5 in the **Histogram Minimum** box
Enter 34.5 in the **Histogram Maximum** box
Choose **Categorical** in the **X-Axis** box
Choose **Frequency** in the **Y-Axis** box
Click **OK**

A histogram for the audit time data similar to the histogram shown in Figure 2.12 will appear. The only difference is the histogram developed using StatTools shows the class midpoints on the horizontal axis.

Scatter Diagram

We use the stereo and sound equipment data in Table 2.12 to demonstrate the construction of a scatter diagram. Begin by using the Data Set Manager to create a StatTools data set for these data using the procedure described in the appendix in Chapter 1. The following steps will generate a scatter diagram.

WEB file
Stereo

Step 1. Click the **StatTools** tab on the Ribbon
Step 2. In the **Analyses Group,** click **Summary Graphs**
Step 3. Choose the **Scatterplot** option
Step 4. When the StatTools-Scatterplot dialog box appears,
In the **Variables** section,
In the column labeled **X**, select **No. of Commercials**
In the column labeled **Y**, select **Sales Volume**
Click **OK**

A scatter diagram similar to the one shown in Figure 2.17 will appear.

CHAPTER 3

Descriptive Statistics: Numerical Measures

CONTENTS

STATISTICS *in* PRACTICE

SMALL FRY DESIGN*
SANTA ANA, CALIFORNIA

Founded in 1997, Small Fry Design is a toy and accessory company that designs and imports products for infants. The company's product line includes teddy bears, mobiles, musical toys, rattles, and security blankets and features high-quality soft toy designs with an emphasis on color, texture, and sound. The products are designed in the United States and manufactured in China.

Small Fry Design uses independent representatives to sell the products to infant furnishing retailers, children's accessory and apparel stores, gift shops, upscale department stores, and major catalog companies. Currently, Small Fry Design products are distributed in more than 1000 retail outlets throughout the United States.

Cash flow management is one of the most critical activities in the day-to-day operation of this company. Ensuring sufficient incoming cash to meet both current and ongoing debt obligations can mean the difference between business success and failure. A critical factor in cash flow management is the analysis and control of accounts receivable. By measuring the average age and dollar value of outstanding invoices, management can predict cash availability and monitor changes in the status of accounts receivable. The company set the following goals: the average age for outstanding invoices should not exceed 45 days, and the dollar value of invoices more than 60 days old should not exceed 5% of the dollar value of all accounts receivable.

In a recent summary of accounts receivable status, the following descriptive statistics were provided for the age of outstanding invoices:

Mean	40 days
Median	35 days
Mode	31 days

*The authors are indebted to John A. McCarthy, President of Small Fry Design, for providing this Statistics in Practice.

Small Fry Design's "King of the Jungle" mobile.

Interpretation of these statistics shows that the mean or average age of an invoice is 40 days. The median shows that half of the invoices remain outstanding 35 days or more. The mode of 31 days, the most frequent invoice age, indicates that the most common length of time an invoice is outstanding is 31 days. The statistical summary also showed that only 3% of the dollar value of all accounts receivable was more than 60 days old. Based on the statistical information, management was satisfied that accounts receivable and incoming cash flow were under control.

In this chapter, you will learn how to compute and interpret some of the statistical measures used by Small Fry Design. In addition to the mean, median, and mode, you will learn about other descriptive statistics such as the range, variance, standard deviation, percentiles, and correlation. These numerical measures will assist in the understanding and interpretation of data.

In Chapter 2 we discussed tabular and graphical presentations used to summarize data. In this chapter, we present several numerical measures that provide additional alternatives for summarizing data.

We start by developing numerical summary measures for data sets consisting of a single variable. When a data set contains more than one variable, the same numerical measures can be computed separately for each variable. However, in the two-variable case, we will also develop measures of the relationship between the variables.

Numerical measures of location, dispersion, shape, and association are introduced. If the measures are computed for data from a sample, they are called **sample statistics**. If the measures are computed for data from a population, they are called **population parameters**. In statistical inference, a sample statistic is referred to as the **point estimator** of the corresponding population parameter. In Chapter 7 we will discuss in more detail the process of point estimation.

In the three chapter appendixes we show how Minitab, Excel, and StatTools can be used to compute the numerical measures described in the chapter.

3.1 Measures of Location

Mean

Perhaps the most important measure of location is the **mean**, or average value, for a variable. The mean provides a measure of central location for the data. If the data are for a sample, the mean is denoted by $\bar{x}$; if the data are for a population, the mean is denoted by the Greek letter μ.

In statistical formulas, it is customary to denote the value of variable x for the first observation by x_1, the value of variable x for the second observation by x_2, and so on. In general, the value of variable x for the ith observation is denoted by x_i. For a sample with n observations, the formula for the sample mean is as follows.

The sample mean $\bar{x}$ is a sample statistic.

SAMPLE MEAN

$$\bar{x} = \frac{\Sigma x_i}{n} \tag{3.1}$$

In the preceding formula, the numerator is the sum of the values of the n observations. That is,

$$\Sigma x_i = x_1 + x_2 + \cdots + x_n$$

The Greek letter Σ is the summation sign.

To illustrate the computation of a sample mean, let us consider the following class size data for a sample of five college classes.

46 54 42 46 32

We use the notation x_1, x_2, x_3, x_4, x_5 to represent the number of students in each of the five classes.

$$x_1 = 46 \quad x_2 = 54 \quad x_3 = 42 \quad x_4 = 46 \quad x_5 = 32$$

Hence, to compute the sample mean, we can write

$$\bar{x} = \frac{\Sigma x_i}{n} = \frac{x_1 + x_2 + x_3 + x_4 + x_5}{5} = \frac{46 + 54 + 42 + 46 + 32}{5} = 44$$

The sample mean class size is 44 students.

Another illustration of the computation of a sample mean is given in the following situation. Suppose that a college placement office sent a questionnaire to a sample of business school graduates requesting information on monthly starting salaries. Table 3.1 shows the

TABLE 3.1 MONTHLY STARTING SALARIES FOR A SAMPLE OF 12 BUSINESS SCHOOL GRADUATES

WEB file StartSalary

Graduate	Monthly Starting Salary ($)	Graduate	Monthly Starting Salary ($)
1	3450	7	3490
2	3550	8	3730
3	3650	9	3540
4	3480	10	3925
5	3355	11	3520
6	3310	12	3480

collected data. The mean monthly starting salary for the sample of 12 business college graduates is computed as

$$\bar{x} = \frac{\Sigma x_i}{n} = \frac{x_1 + x_2 + \cdots + x_{12}}{12}$$

$$= \frac{3450 + 3550 + \cdots + 3480}{12}$$

$$= \frac{42{,}480}{12} = 3540$$

Equation (3.1) shows how the mean is computed for a sample with n observations. The formula for computing the mean of a population remains the same, but we use different notation to indicate that we are working with the entire population. The number of observations in a population is denoted by N and the symbol for a population mean is μ.

The sample mean $\bar{x}$ is a point estimator of the population mean μ.

POPULATION MEAN

$$\mu = \frac{\Sigma x_i}{N} \tag{3.2}$$

Median

The **median** is another measure of central location. The median is the value in the middle when the data are arranged in ascending order (smallest value to largest value). With an odd number of observations, the median is the middle value. An even number of observations has no single middle value. In this case, we follow convention and define the median as the average of the values for the middle two observations. For convenience the definition of the median is restated as follows.

MEDIAN

Arrange the data in ascending order (smallest value to largest value).

(a) For an odd number of observations, the median is the middle value.
(b) For an even number of observations, the median is the average of the two middle values.

Let us apply this definition to compute the median class size for the sample of five college classes. Arranging the data in ascending order provides the following list.

32 42 46 46 54

Because $n = 5$ is odd, the median is the middle value. Thus the median class size is 46 students. Even though this data set contains two observations with values of 46, each observation is treated separately when we arrange the data in ascending order.

Suppose we also compute the median starting salary for the 12 business college graduates in Table 3.1. We first arrange the data in ascending order.

$$3310 \quad 3355 \quad 3450 \quad 3480 \quad 3480 \quad \underbrace{3490 \quad 3520}_{\text{Middle Two Values}} \quad 3540 \quad 3550 \quad 3650 \quad 3730 \quad 3925$$

Because $n = 12$ is even, we identify the middle two values: 3490 and 3520. The median is the average of these values.

$$\text{Median} = \frac{3490 + 3520}{2} = 3505$$

The median is the measure of location most often reported for annual income and property value data because a few extremely large incomes or property values can inflate the mean. In such cases, the median is the preferred measure of central location.

Although the mean is the more commonly used measure of central location, in some situations the median is preferred. The mean is influenced by extremely small and large data values. For instance, suppose that one of the graduates (see Table 3.1) had a starting salary of $10,000 per month (maybe the individual's family owns the company). If we change the highest monthly starting salary in Table 3.1 from $3925 to $10,000 and recompute the mean, the sample mean changes from $3540 to $4046. The median of $3505, however, is unchanged, because $3490 and $3520 are still the middle two values. With the extremely high starting salary included, the median provides a better measure of central location than the mean. We can generalize to say that whenever a data set contains extreme values, the median is often the preferred measure of central location.

Mode

A third measure of location is the **mode**. The mode is defined as follows.

> MODE
>
> The mode is the value that occurs with greatest frequency.

To illustrate the identification of the mode, consider the sample of five class sizes. The only value that occurs more than once is 46. Because this value, occurring with a frequency of 2, has the greatest frequency, it is the mode. As another illustration, consider the sample of starting salaries for the business school graduates. The only monthly starting salary that occurs more than once is $3480. Because this value has the greatest frequency, it is the mode.

Situations can arise for which the greatest frequency occurs at two or more different values. In these instances more than one mode exists. If the data contain exactly two modes, we say that the data are *bimodal*. If data contain more than two modes, we say that the data are *multimodal*. In multimodal cases the mode is almost never reported because listing three or more modes would not be particularly helpful in describing a location for the data.

Percentiles

A **percentile** provides information about how the data are spread over the interval from the smallest value to the largest value. For data that do not contain numerous repeated values, the pth percentile divides the data into two parts. Approximately p percent of the observations have values less than the pth percentile; approximately $(100 - p)$ percent of the observations have values greater than the pth percentile. The pth percentile is formally defined as follows.

PERCENTILE

The pth percentile is a value such that *at least* p percent of the observations are less than or equal to this value and *at least* $(100 - p)$ percent of the observations are greater than or equal to this value.

Colleges and universities frequently report admission test scores in terms of percentiles. For instance, suppose an applicant obtains a raw score of 54 on the verbal portion of an admission test. How this student performed in relation to other students taking the same test may not be readily apparent. However, if the raw score of 54 corresponds to the 70th percentile, we know that approximately 70% of the students scored lower than this individual and approximately 30% of the students scored higher than this individual.

The following procedure can be used to compute the pth percentile.

CALCULATING THE pTH PERCENTILE

Following these steps makes it easy to calculate percentiles.

Step 1. Arrange the data in ascending order (smallest value to largest value).

Step 2. Compute an index i

$$i = \left(\frac{p}{100}\right)n$$

where p is the percentile of interest and n is the number of observations.

Step 3. (a) If *i is not an integer, round up.* The next integer *greater* than i denotes the position of the pth percentile.
(b) If *i is an integer,* the pth percentile is the average of the values in positions i and $i + 1$.

As an illustration of this procedure, let us determine the 85th percentile for the starting salary data in Table 3.1.

Step 1. Arrange the data in ascending order.

3310 3355 3450 3480 3480 3490 3520 3540 3550 3650 3730 3925

Step 2.

$$i = \left(\frac{p}{100}\right)n = \left(\frac{85}{100}\right)12 = 10.2$$

Step 3. Because i is not an integer, *round up.* The position of the 85th percentile is the next integer greater than 10.2, the 11th position.

Returning to the data, we see that the 85th percentile is the data value in the 11th position, or 3730.

As another illustration of this procedure, let us consider the calculation of the 50th percentile for the starting salary data. Applying step 2, we obtain

$$i = \left(\frac{50}{100}\right)12 = 6$$

Because i is an integer, step 3(b) states that the 50th percentile is the average of the sixth and seventh data values; thus the 50th percentile is (3490 + 3520)/2 = 3505. Note that the *50th percentile is also the median.*

Quartiles

Quartiles are just specific percentiles; thus, the steps for computing percentiles can be applied directly in the computation of quartiles.

It is often desirable to divide data into four parts, with each part containing approximately one-fourth, or 25% of the observations. Figure 3.1 shows a data distribution divided into four parts. The division points are referred to as the **quartiles** and are defined as

Q_1 = first quartile, or 25th percentile
Q_2 = second quartile, or 50th percentile (also the median)
Q_3 = third quartile, or 75th percentile.

The starting salary data are again arranged in ascending order. We already identified Q_2, the second quartile (median), as 3505.

3310 3355 3450 3480 3480 3490 3520 3540 3550 3650 3730 3925

The computations of quartiles Q_1 and Q_3 require the use of the rule for finding the 25th and 75th percentiles. These calculations follow.

For Q_1,

$$i = \left(\frac{p}{100}\right)n = \left(\frac{25}{100}\right)12 = 3$$

Because i is an integer, step 3(b) indicates that the first quartile, or 25th percentile, is the average of the third and fourth data values; thus, Q_1 = (3450 + 3480)/2 = 3465.

For Q_3,

$$i = \left(\frac{p}{100}\right)n = \left(\frac{75}{100}\right)12 = 9$$

Again, because i is an integer, step 3(b) indicates that the third quartile, or 75th percentile, is the average of the ninth and tenth data values; thus, Q_3 = (3550 + 3650)/2 = 3600.

FIGURE 3.1 LOCATION OF THE QUARTILES

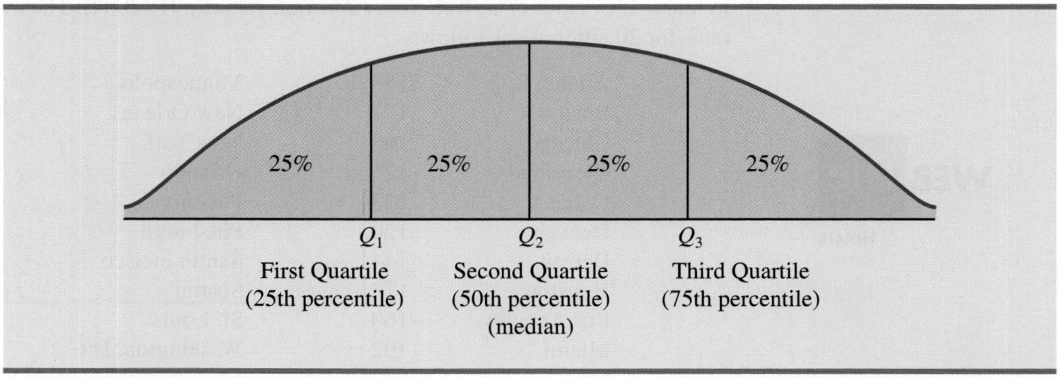

The quartiles divide the starting salary data into four parts, with each part containing 25% of the observations.

3310	3355	3450	3480	3480	3490	3520	3540	3550	3650	3730	3925

$Q_1 = 3465$ $Q_2 = 3505$ (Median) $Q_3 = 3600$

We defined the quartiles as the 25th, 50th, and 75th percentiles. Thus, we computed the quartiles in the same way as percentiles. However, other conventions are sometimes used to compute quartiles, and the actual values reported for quartiles may vary slightly depending on the convention used. Nevertheless, the objective of all procedures for computing quartiles is to divide the data into four equal parts.

NOTES AND COMMENTS

It is better to use the median than the mean as a measure of central location when a data set contains extreme values. Another measure, sometimes used when extreme values are present, is the *trimmed mean.* It is obtained by deleting a percentage of the smallest and largest values from a data set and then computing the mean of the remaining values. For example, the 5% trimmed mean is obtained by removing the smallest 5% and the largest 5% of the data values and then computing the mean of the remaining values. Using the sample with $n = 12$ starting salaries, $0.05(12) = 0.6$. Rounding this value to 1 indicates that the 5% trimmed mean would remove the 1 smallest data value and the 1 largest data value. The 5% trimmed mean using the 10 remaining observations is 3524.50.

Exercises

Methods

1. Consider a sample with data values of 10, 20, 12, 17, and 16. Compute the mean and median.
2. Consider a sample with data values of 10, 20, 21, 17, 16, and 12. Compute the mean and median.

SELF test

3. Consider a sample with data values of 27, 25, 20, 15, 30, 34, 28, and 25. Compute the 20th, 25th, 65th, and 75th percentiles.
4. Consider a sample with data values of 53, 55, 70, 58, 64, 57, 53, 69, 57, 68, and 53. Compute the mean, median, and mode.

Applications

5. The Dow Jones Travel Index reported what business travelers pay for hotel rooms per night in major U.S. cities (*The Wall Street Journal,* January 16, 2004). The average hotel room rates for 20 cities are as follows:

WEB file Hotels

Atlanta	$163	Minneapolis	$125
Boston	177	New Orleans	167
Chicago	166	New York	245
Cleveland	126	Orlando	146
Dallas	123	Phoenix	139
Denver	120	Pittsburgh	134
Detroit	144	San Francisco	167
Houston	173	Seattle	162
Los Angeles	160	St. Louis	145
Miami	192	Washington, D.C.	207

a. What is the mean hotel room rate?
b. What is the median hotel room rate?
c. What is the mode?
d. What is the first quartile?
e. What is the third quartile?

6. During the 2007–2008 NCAA college basketball season, men's basketball teams attempted an all-time high number of 3-point shots, averaging 19.07 shots per game (Associated Press Sports, January 24, 2009). In an attempt to discourage so many 3-point shots and encourage more inside play, the NCAA rules committee moved the 3-point line back from 19 feet, 9 inches to 20 feet, 9 inches at the beginning of the 2008–2009 basketball season. Shown in the following table are the 3-point shots taken and the 3-point shots made for a sample of 19 NCAA basketball games during the 2008–2009 season.

WEB file
3Points

3-Point Shots	Shots Made	3-Point Shots	Shots Made
23	4	17	7
20	6	19	10
17	5	22	7
18	8	25	11
13	4	15	6
16	4	10	5
8	5	11	3
19	8	25	8
28	5	23	7
21	7		

a. What is the mean number of 3-point shots taken per game?
b. What is the mean number of 3-point shots made per game?
c. Using the closer 3-point line, players were making 35.2% of their shots. What percentage of shots were players making from the new 3-point line?
d. What was the impact of the NCAA rules change that moved the 3-point line back to 20 feet, 9 inches for the 2008–2009 season? Would you agree with the Associated Press Sports article that stated, "Moving back the 3-point line hasn't changed the game dramatically"? Explain.

7. Endowment income is a critical part of the annual budgets at colleges and universities. A study by the National Association of College and University Business Officers reported that the 435 colleges and universities surveyed held a total of $413 billion in endowments. The 10 wealthiest universities are shown below (*The Wall Street Journal,* January 27, 2009). Amounts are in billion of dollars.

University	Endowment ($billion)	University	Endowment ($billion)
Columbia	7.2	Princeton	16.4
Harvard	36.6	Stanford	17.2
M.I.T.	10.1	Texas	16.1
Michigan	7.6	Texas A&M	6.7
Northwestern	7.2	Yale	22.9

a. What is the mean endowment for these universities?
b. What is the median endowment?
c. What is the mode endowment?
d. Compute the first and third quartiles?

e. What is the total endowment at these 10 universities? These universities represent 2.3% of the 435 colleges and universities surveyed. What percentage of the total $413 billion in endowments is held by these 10 universities?

f. *The Wall Street Journal* reported that over a recent five-month period, a downturn in the economy has caused endowments to decline 23%. What is the estimate of the dollar amount of the decline in the total endowments held by these 10 universities? Given this situation, what are some of the steps you would expect university administrators to be considering?

SELF test

8. The cost of consumer purchases such as single-family housing, gasoline, Internet services, tax preparation, and hospitalization were provided in *The Wall-Street Journal* (January 2, 2007). Sample data typical of the cost of tax-return preparation by services such as H&R Block are shown below.

WEB file
TaxCost

120	230	110	115	160
130	150	105	195	155
105	360	120	120	140
100	115	180	235	255

a. Compute the mean, median, and mode.
b. Compute the first and third quartiles.
c. Compute and interpret the 90th percentile.

9. The National Association of Realtors provided data showing that home sales were the slowest in 10 years (Associated Press, December 24, 2008). Sample data with representative sales prices for existing homes and new homes follow. Data are in thousands of dollars:

Existing Homes	315.5	202.5	140.2	181.3	470.2	169.9	112.8	230.0	177.5
New Homes	275.9	350.2	195.8	525.0	225.3	215.5	175.0	149.5	

a. What is the median sales price for existing homes?
b. What is the median sales price for new homes?
c. Do existing homes or new homes have the higher median sales price? What is the difference between the median sales prices?
d. A year earlier the median sales price for existing homes was $208.4 thousand and the median sales price for new homes was $249 thousand. Compute the percentage change in the median sales price of existing and new homes over the one-year period. Did existing homes or new homes have the larger percentage change in median sales price?

10. A panel of economists provided forecasts of the U.S. economy for the first six months of 2007 (*The Wall Street Journal,* January 2, 2007). The percent changes in the gross domestic product (GDP) forecasted by 30 economists are as follows.

WEB file
Economy

2.6	3.1	2.3	2.7	3.4	0.9	2.6	2.8	2.0	2.4
2.7	2.7	2.7	2.9	3.1	2.8	1.7	2.3	2.8	3.5
0.4	2.5	2.2	1.9	1.8	1.1	2.0	2.1	2.5	0.5

a. What is the minimum forecast for the percent change in the GDP? What is the maximum?
b. Compute the mean, median, and mode.
c. Compute the first and third quartiles.
d. Did the economists provide an optimistic or pessimistic outlook for the U.S. economy? Discuss.

11. In automobile mileage and gasoline-consumption testing, 13 automobiles were road tested for 300 miles in both city and highway driving conditions. The following data were recorded for miles-per-gallon performance.

City:	16.2	16.7	15.9	14.4	13.2	15.3	16.8	16.0	16.1	15.3	15.2	15.3	16.2
Highway:	19.4	20.6	18.3	18.6	19.2	17.4	17.2	18.6	19.0	21.1	19.4	18.5	18.7

Use the mean, median, and mode to make a statement about the difference in performance for city and highway driving.

12. Walt Disney Company bought Pixar Animation Studios, Inc., in a deal worth $7.4 billion (CNN Money website, January 24, 2006). The animated movies produced by Disney and Pixar during the previous 10 years are listed in the following table. The box office revenues are in millions of dollars. Compute the total revenue, the mean, the median, and the quartiles to compare the box office success of the movies produced by both companies. Do the statistics suggest at least one of the reasons Disney was interested in buying Pixar? Discuss.

WEB file

Disney

Disney Movies	**Revenue ($millions)**	**Pixar Movies**	**Revenue ($millions)**
Pocahontas	346	*Toy Story*	362
Hunchback of Notre Dame	325	*A Bug's Life*	363
Hercules	253	*Toy Story 2*	485
Mulan	304	*Monsters, Inc.*	525
Tarzan	448	*Finding Nemo*	865
Dinosaur	354	*The Incredibles*	631
The Emperor's New Groove	169		
Lilo & Stitch	273		
Treasure Planet	110		
The Jungle Book 2	136		
Brother Bear	250		
Home on the Range	104		
Chicken Little	249		

3.2 Measures of Variability

The variability in the delivery time creates uncertainty for production scheduling. Methods in this section help measure and understand variability.

In addition to measures of location, it is often desirable to consider measures of variability, or dispersion. For example, suppose that you are a purchasing agent for a large manufacturing firm and that you regularly place orders with two different suppliers. After several months of operation, you find that the mean number of days required to fill orders is 10 days for both of the suppliers. The histograms summarizing the number of working days required to fill orders from the suppliers are shown in Figure 3.2. Although the mean number of days is 10 for both suppliers, do the two suppliers demonstrate the same degree of reliability in terms of making deliveries on schedule? Note the dispersion, or variability, in delivery times indicated by the histograms. Which supplier would you prefer?

For most firms, receiving materials and supplies on schedule is important. The 7- or 8-day deliveries shown for J.C. Clark Distributors might be viewed favorably; however, a few of the slow 13- to 15-day deliveries could be disastrous in terms of keeping a workforce busy

FIGURE 3.2 HISTORICAL DATA SHOWING THE NUMBER OF DAYS REQUIRED TO FILL ORDERS

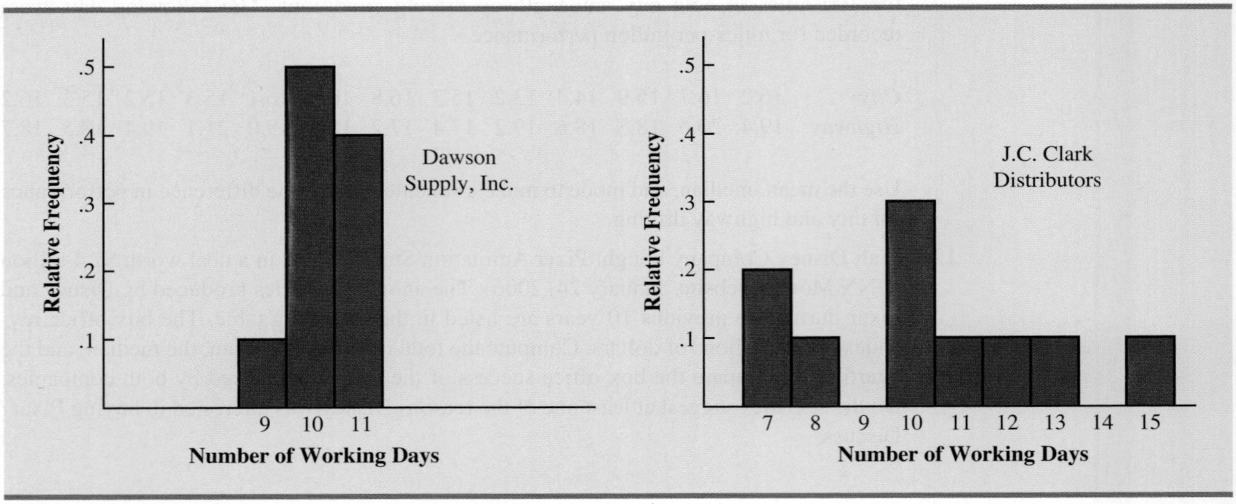

and production on schedule. This example illustrates a situation in which the variability in the delivery times may be an overriding consideration in selecting a supplier. For most purchasing agents, the lower variability shown for Dawson Supply, Inc., would make Dawson the preferred supplier.

We turn now to a discussion of some commonly used measures of variability.

Range

The simplest measure of variability is the **range**.

RANGE

$$\text{Range} = \text{Largest value} - \text{Smallest value}$$

Let us refer to the data on starting salaries for business school graduates in Table 3.1. The largest starting salary is 3925 and the smallest is 3310. The range is $3925 - 3310 = 615$.

Although the range is the easiest of the measures of variability to compute, it is seldom used as the only measure. The reason is that the range is based on only two of the observations and thus is highly influenced by extreme values. Suppose one of the graduates received a starting salary of $10,000 per month. In this case, the range would be $10,000 - 3310 = 6690$ rather than 615. This large value for the range would not be especially descriptive of the variability in the data because 11 of the 12 starting salaries are closely grouped between 3310 and 3730.

Interquartile Range

A measure of variability that overcomes the dependency on extreme values is the **interquartile range (IQR)**. This measure of variability is the difference between the third quartile, Q_3, and the first quartile, Q_1. In other words, the interquartile range is the range for the middle 50% of the data.

INTERQUARTILE RANGE

$$\text{IQR} = Q_3 - Q_1 \tag{3.3}$$

For the data on monthly starting salaries, the quartiles are $Q_3 = 3600$ and $Q_1 = 3465$. Thus, the interquartile range is $3600 - 3465 = 135$.

Variance

The **variance** is a measure of variability that utilizes all the data. The variance is based on the difference between the value of each observation (x_i) and the mean. The difference between each x_i and the mean ($\bar{x}$ for a sample, μ for a population) is called a *deviation about the mean.* For a sample, a deviation about the mean is written $(x_i - \bar{x})$; for a population, it is written $(x_i - \mu)$. In the computation of the variance, the deviations about the mean are *squared.*

If the data are for a population, the average of the squared deviations is called the *population variance.* The population variance is denoted by the Greek symbol σ^2. For a population of N observations and with μ denoting the population mean, the definition of the population variance is as follows.

POPULATION VARIANCE

$$\sigma^2 = \frac{\Sigma(x_i - \mu)^2}{N} \tag{3.4}$$

In most statistical applications, the data being analyzed are for a sample. When we compute a sample variance, we are often interested in using it to estimate the population variance σ^2. Although a detailed explanation is beyond the scope of this text, it can be shown that if the sum of the squared deviations about the sample mean is divided by $n - 1$, and not n, the resulting sample variance provides an unbiased estimate of the population variance. For this reason, the *sample variance,* denoted by s^2, is defined as follows.

The sample variance s^2 is the estimator of the population variance σ^2.

SAMPLE VARIANCE

$$s^2 = \frac{\Sigma(x_i - \bar{x})^2}{n - 1} \tag{3.5}$$

To illustrate the computation of the sample variance, we will use the data on class size for the sample of five college classes as presented in Section 3.1. A summary of the data, including the computation of the deviations about the mean and the squared deviations about the mean, is shown in Table 3.2. The sum of squared deviations about the mean is $\Sigma(x_i - \bar{x})^2 = 256$. Hence, with $n - 1 = 4$, the sample variance is

$$s^2 = \frac{\Sigma(x_i - \bar{x})^2}{n - 1} = \frac{256}{4} = 64$$

Before moving on, let us note that the units associated with the sample variance often cause confusion. Because the values being summed in the variance calculation, $(x_i - \bar{x})^2$, are squared, the units associated with the sample variance are also *squared.* For instance, the

TABLE 3.2 COMPUTATION OF DEVIATIONS AND SQUARED DEVIATIONS ABOUT THE MEAN FOR THE CLASS SIZE DATA

Number of Students in Class (x_i)	Mean Class Size ($\bar{x}$)	Deviation About the Mean ($x_i - \bar{x}$)	Squared Deviation About the Mean $(x_i - \bar{x})^2$
46	44	2	4
54	44	10	100
42	44	−2	4
46	44	2	4
32	44	−12	144
		0	256
		$\Sigma(x_i - \bar{x})$	$\Sigma(x_i - \bar{x})^2$

sample variance for the class size data is $s^2 = 64$ (students)^2. The squared units associated with variance make it difficult to obtain an intuitive understanding and interpretation of the numerical value of the variance. We recommend that you think of the variance as a measure useful in comparing the amount of variability for two or more variables. In a comparison of the variables, the one with the largest variance shows the most variability. Further interpretation of the value of the variance may not be necessary.

The variance is useful in comparing the variability of two or more variables.

As another illustration of computing a sample variance, consider the starting salaries listed in Table 3.1 for the 12 business school graduates. In Section 3.1, we showed that the sample mean starting salary was 3540. The computation of the sample variance ($s^2 = 27{,}440.91$) is shown in Table 3.3.

TABLE 3.3 COMPUTATION OF THE SAMPLE VARIANCE FOR THE STARTING SALARY DATA

Monthly Salary (x_i)	Sample Mean ($\bar{x}$)	Deviation About the Mean ($x_i - \bar{x}$)	Squared Deviation About the Mean $(x_i - \bar{x})^2$
3450	3540	−90	8,100
3550	3540	10	100
3650	3540	110	12,100
3480	3540	−60	3,600
3355	3540	−185	34,225
3310	3540	−230	52,900
3490	3540	−50	2,500
3730	3540	190	36,100
3540	3540	0	0
3925	3540	385	148,225
3520	3540	−20	400
3480	3540	−60	3,600
		0	301,850
		$\Sigma(x_i - \bar{x})$	$\Sigma(x_i - \bar{x})^2$

Using equation (3.5),

$$s^2 = \frac{\Sigma(x_i - \bar{x})^2}{n - 1} = \frac{301{,}850}{11} = 27{,}440.91$$

In Tables 3.2 and 3.3 we show both the sum of the deviations about the mean and the sum of the squared deviations about the mean. For any data set, the sum of the deviations about the mean will *always equal zero.* Note that in Tables 3.2 and 3.3, $\Sigma(x_i - \bar{x}) = 0$. The positive deviations and negative deviations cancel each other, causing the sum of the deviations about the mean to equal zero.

Standard Deviation

The **standard deviation** is defined to be the positive square root of the variance. Following the notation we adopted for a sample variance and a population variance, we use s to denote the sample standard deviation and σ to denote the population standard deviation. The standard deviation is derived from the variance in the following way.

The sample standard deviation s is the estimator of the population standard deviation σ.

STANDARD DEVIATION

$$\text{Sample standard deviation} = s = \sqrt{s^2} \tag{3.6}$$

$$\text{Population standard deviation} = \sigma = \sqrt{\sigma^2} \tag{3.7}$$

Recall that the sample variance for the sample of class sizes in five college classes is $s^2 = 64$. Thus, the sample standard deviation is $s = \sqrt{64} = 8$. For the data on starting salaries, the sample standard deviation is $s = \sqrt{27{,}440.91} = 165.65$.

The standard deviation is easier to interpret than the variance because the standard deviation is measured in the same units as the data.

What is gained by converting the variance to its corresponding standard deviation? Recall that the units associated with the variance are squared. For example, the sample variance for the starting salary data of business school graduates is $s^2 = 27{,}440.91$ (dollars)^2. Because the standard deviation is the square root of the variance, the units of the variance, dollars squared, are converted to dollars in the standard deviation. Thus, the standard deviation of the starting salary data is \$165.65. In other words, the standard deviation is measured in the same units as the original data. For this reason the standard deviation is more easily compared to the mean and other statistics that are measured in the same units as the original data.

Coefficient of Variation

The coefficient of variation is a relative measure of variability; it measures the standard deviation relative to the mean.

In some situations we may be interested in a descriptive statistic that indicates how large the standard deviation is relative to the mean. This measure is called the **coefficient of variation** and is usually expressed as a percentage.

COEFFICIENT OF VARIATION

$$\left(\frac{\text{Standard deviation}}{\text{Mean}} \times 100\right)\% \tag{3.8}$$

For the class size data, we found a sample mean of 44 and a sample standard deviation of 8. The coefficient of variation is $[(8/44) \times 100]\% = 18.2\%$. In words, the coefficient of variation tells us that the sample standard deviation is 18.2% of the value of the sample mean. For the starting salary data with a sample mean of 3540 and a sample standard deviation of 165.65, the coefficient of variation, $[(165.65/3540) \times 100]\% = 4.7\%$, tells us the sample standard deviation is only 4.7% of the value of the sample mean. In general, the coefficient of variation is a useful statistic for comparing the variability of variables that have different standard deviations and different means.

NOTES AND COMMENTS

1. Statistical software packages and spreadsheets can be used to develop the descriptive statistics presented in this chapter. After the data are entered into a worksheet, a few simple commands can be used to generate the desired output. In three chapter-ending appendixes we show how Minitab, Excel, and StatTools can be used to develop descriptive statistics.
2. The standard deviation is a commonly used measure of the risk associated with investing in stock and stock funds (*BusinessWeek,* January 17, 2000). It provides a measure of how monthly returns fluctuate around the long-run average return.
3. Rounding the value of the sample mean $\bar{x}$ and the values of the squared deviations $(x_i - \bar{x})^2$ may introduce errors when a calculator is used in the computation of the variance and standard deviation. To reduce rounding errors, we recommend carrying at least six significant digits during intermediate calculations. The resulting variance or standard deviation can then be rounded to fewer digits.
4. An alternative formula for the computation of the sample variance is

$$s^2 = \frac{\Sigma x_i^2 - n\bar{x}^2}{n - 1}$$

where $\Sigma x_i^2 = x_1^2 + x_2^2 + \cdots + x_n^2$.

Exercises

Methods

13. Consider a sample with data values of 10, 20, 12, 17, and 16. Compute the range and interquartile range.
14. Consider a sample with data values of 10, 20, 12, 17, and 16. Compute the variance and standard deviation.

SELF test

15. Consider a sample with data values of 27, 25, 20, 15, 30, 34, 28, and 25. Compute the range, interquartile range, variance, and standard deviation.

Applications

SELF test

16. A bowler's scores for six games were 182, 168, 184, 190, 170, and 174. Using these data as a sample, compute the following descriptive statistics:
    a. Range
    b. Variance
    c. Standard deviation
    d. Coefficient of variation
17. A home theater in a box is the easiest and cheapest way to provide surround sound for a home entertainment center. A sample of prices is shown here (*Consumer Reports Buying Guide,* 2004). The prices are for models with a DVD player and for models without a DVD player.

Models with DVD Player	Price	Models without DVD Player	Price
Sony HT-1800DP	$450	Pioneer HTP-230	$300
Pioneer HTD-330DV	300	Sony HT-DDW750	300
Sony HT-C800DP	400	Kenwood HTB-306	360
Panasonic SC-HT900	500	RCA RT-2600	290
Panasonic SC-MTI	400	Kenwood HTB-206	300

a. Compute the mean price for models with a DVD player and the mean price for models without a DVD player. What is the additional price paid to have a DVD player included in a home theater unit?
b. Compute the range, variance, and standard deviation for the two samples. What does this information tell you about the prices for models with and without a DVD player?

18. Car rental rates per day for a sample of seven Eastern U.S. cities are as follows (*The Wall Street Journal,* January 16, 2004).

City	Daily Rate
Boston	$43
Atlanta	35
Miami	34
New York	58
Orlando	30
Pittsburgh	30
Washington, D.C.	36

a. Compute the mean, variance, and standard deviation for the car rental rates.
b. A similar sample of seven Western U.S. cities showed a sample mean car rental rate of $38 per day. The variance and standard deviation were 12.3 and 3.5, respectively. Discuss any difference between the car rental rates in Eastern and Western U.S. cities.

19. The *Los Angeles Times* regularly reports the air quality index for various areas of Southern California. A sample of air quality index values for Pomona provided the following data: 28, 42, 58, 48, 45, 55, 60, 49, and 50.
a. Compute the range and interquartile range.
b. Compute the sample variance and sample standard deviation.
c. A sample of air quality index readings for Anaheim provided a sample mean of 48.5, a sample variance of 136, and a sample standard deviation of 11.66. What comparisons can you make between the air quality in Pomona and that in Anaheim on the basis of these descriptive statistics?

20. The following data were used to construct the histograms of the number of days required to fill orders for Dawson Supply, Inc., and J.C. Clark Distributors (see Figure 3.2).

Dawson Supply Days for Delivery:	11	10	9	10	11	11	10	11	10	10
Clark Distributors Days for Delivery:	8	10	13	7	10	11	10	7	15	12

Use the range and standard deviation to support the previous observation that Dawson Supply provides the more consistent and reliable delivery times.

21. How do grocery costs compare across the country? Using a market basket of 10 items including meat, milk, bread, eggs, coffee, potatoes, cereal, and orange juice, *Where to Retire* magazine calculated the cost of the market basket in six cities and in six retirement areas across the country (*Where to Retire,* November/December 2003). The data with market basket cost to the nearest dollar are as follows:

City	Cost	Retirement Area	Cost
Buffalo, NY	$33	Biloxi-Gulfport, MS	$29
Des Moines, IA	27	Asheville, NC	32
Hartford, CT	32	Flagstaff, AZ	32
Los Angeles, CA	38	Hilton Head, SC	34
Miami, FL	36	Fort Myers, FL	34
Pittsburgh, PA	32	Santa Fe, NM	31

a. Compute the mean, variance, and standard deviation for the sample of cities and the sample of retirement areas.
b. What observations can be made based on the two samples?

WEB file
BackToSchool

22. The National Retail Federation reported that college freshman spend more on back-to-school items than any other college group (*USA Today,* August 4, 2006). Sample data comparing the back-to-school expenditures for 25 freshmen and 20 seniors are shown in the data file BackToSchool.
 a. What is the mean back-to-school expenditure for each group? Are the data consistent with the National Retail Federation's report?
 b. What is the range for the expenditures in each group?
 c. What is the interquartile range for the expenditures in each group?
 d. What is the standard deviation for expenditures in each group?
 e. Do freshmen or seniors have more variation in back-to-school expenditures?
23. Scores turned in by an amateur golfer at the Bonita Fairways Golf Course in Bonita Springs, Florida, during 2005 and 2006 are as follows:

2005 Season:	74	78	79	77	75	73	75	77
2006 Season:	71	70	75	77	85	80	71	79

 a. Use the mean and standard deviation to evaluate the golfer's performance over the two-year period.
 b. What is the primary difference in performance between 2005 and 2006? What improvement, if any, can be seen in the 2006 scores?
24. The following times were recorded by the quarter-mile and mile runners of a university track team (times are in minutes).

Quarter-Mile Times:	.92	.98	1.04	.90	.99
Mile Times:	4.52	4.35	4.60	4.70	4.50

After viewing this sample of running times, one of the coaches commented that the quarter-milers turned in the more consistent times. Use the standard deviation and the coefficient of variation to summarize the variability in the data. Does the use of the coefficient of variation indicate that the coach's statement should be qualified?

3.3 Measures of Distribution Shape, Relative Location, and Detecting Outliers

We have described several measures of location and variability for data. In addition, it is often important to have a measure of the shape of a distribution. In Chapter 2 we noted that a histogram provides a graphical display showing the shape of a distribution. An important numerical measure of the shape of a distribution is called **skewness**.

Distribution Shape

Shown in Figure 3.3 are four histograms constructed from relative frequency distributions. The histograms in Panels A and B are moderately skewed. The one in Panel A is skewed to the left; its skewness is −.85. The histogram in Panel B is skewed to the right; its skewness is +.85. The histogram in Panel C is symmetric; its skewness is zero. The histogram in Panel D is highly skewed to the right; its skewness is 1.62. The formula used to compute skewness is somewhat complex.[1] However, the skewness can be easily

[1]The formula for the skewness of sample data:

$$\text{Skewness} = \frac{n}{(n-1)(n-2)} \sum \left(\frac{x_i - \bar{x}}{s} \right)^3$$

FIGURE 3.3 HISTOGRAMS SHOWING THE SKEWNESS FOR FOUR DISTRIBUTIONS

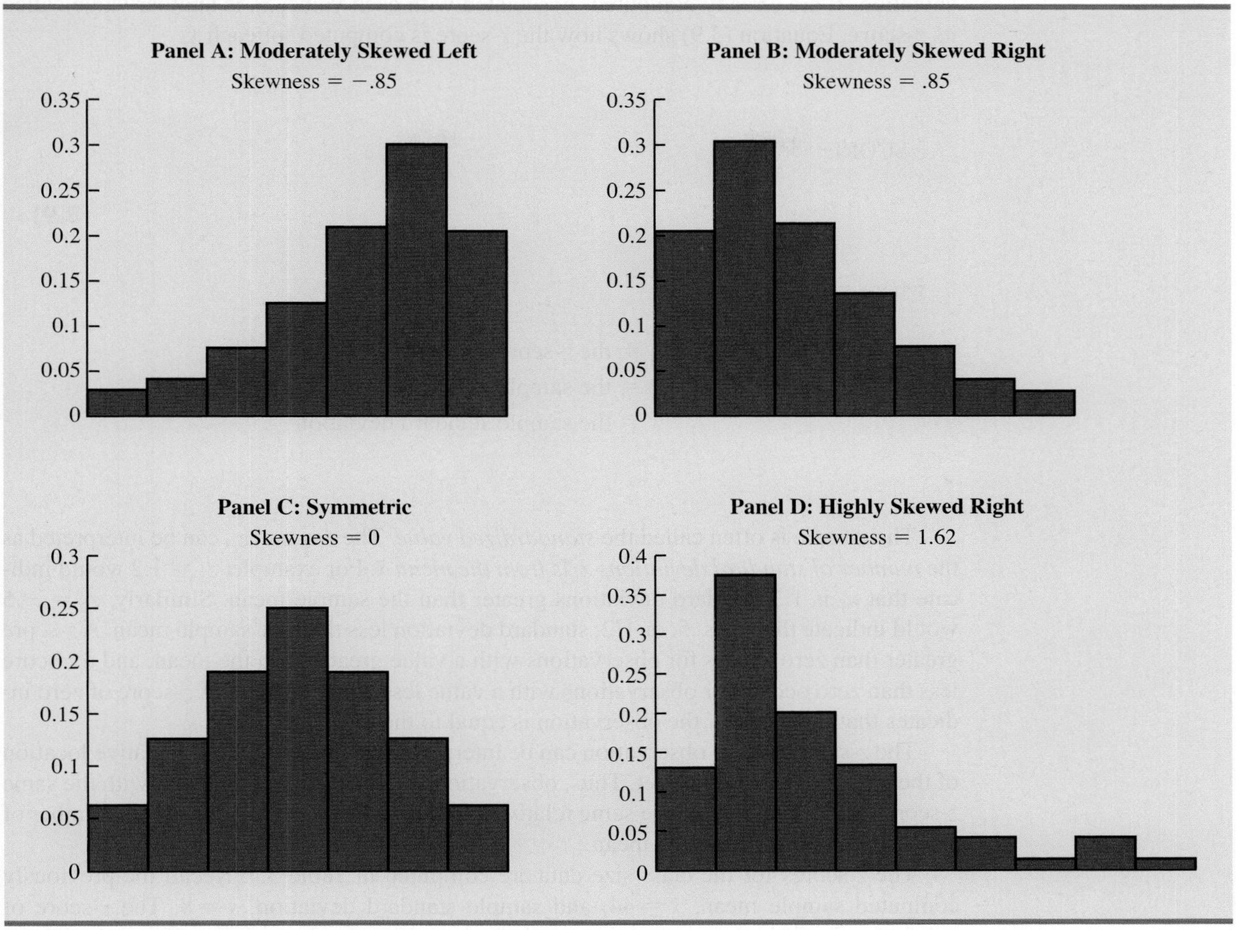

computed using statistical software. For data skewed to the left, the skewness is negative; for data skewed to the right, the skewness is positive. If the data are symmetric, the skewness is zero.

For a symmetric distribution, the mean and the median are equal. When the data are positively skewed, the mean will usually be greater than the median; when the data are negatively skewed, the mean will usually be less than the median. The data used to construct the histogram in Panel D are customer purchases at a women's apparel store. The mean purchase amount is $77.60 and the median purchase amount is $59.70. The relatively few large purchase amounts tend to increase the mean, while the median remains unaffected by the large purchase amounts. The median provides the preferred measure of location when the data are highly skewed.

z-Scores

In addition to measures of location, variability, and shape, we are also interested in the relative location of values within a data set. Measures of relative location help us determine how far a particular value is from the mean.

By using both the mean and standard deviation, we can determine the relative location of any observation. Suppose we have a sample of n observations, with the values denoted by $x_1, x_2, \ldots, x_n$. In addition, assume that the sample mean, $\bar{x}$, and the sample standard deviation, s, are already computed. Associated with each value, x_i, is another value called its **z-score**. Equation (3.9) shows how the z-score is computed for each x_i.

z-SCORE

$$z_i = \frac{x_i - \bar{x}}{s} \tag{3.9}$$

where

z_i = the z-score for x_i
$\bar{x}$ = the sample mean
s = the sample standard deviation

The z-score is often called the *standardized value*. The z-score, z_i, can be interpreted as the *number of standard deviations x_i is from the mean $\bar{x}$*. For example, $z_1 = 1.2$ would indicate that x_1 is 1.2 standard deviations greater than the sample mean. Similarly, $z_2 = -.5$ would indicate that x_2 is .5, or 1/2, standard deviation less than the sample mean. A z-score greater than zero occurs for observations with a value greater than the mean, and a z-score less than zero occurs for observations with a value less than the mean. A z-score of zero indicates that the value of the observation is equal to the mean.

The z-score for any observation can be interpreted as a measure of the relative location of the observation in a data set. Thus, observations in two different data sets with the same z-score can be said to have the same relative location in terms of being the same number of standard deviations from the mean.

The z-scores for the class size data are computed in Table 3.4. Recall the previously computed sample mean, $\bar{x} = 44$, and sample standard deviation, $s = 8$. The z-score of -1.50 for the fifth observation shows it is farthest from the mean; it is 1.50 standard deviations below the mean.

Chebyshev's Theorem

Chebyshev's theorem enables us to make statements about the proportion of data values that must be within a specified number of standard deviations of the mean.

TABLE 3.4 z-SCORES FOR THE CLASS SIZE DATA

Number of Students in Class (x_i)	Deviation About the Mean ($x_i - \bar{x}$)	z-Score $\left(\frac{x_i - \bar{x}}{s}\right)$
46	2	2/8 = .25
54	10	10/8 = 1.25
42	−2	−2/8 = −.25
46	2	2/8 = .25
32	−12	−12/8 = −1.50

CHEBYSHEV'S THEOREM

At least $(1 - 1/z^2)$ of the data values must be within z standard deviations of the mean, where z is any value greater than 1.

Some of the implications of this theorem, with $z = 2$, 3, and 4 standard deviations, follow.

- At least .75, or 75%, of the data values must be within $z = 2$ standard deviations of the mean.
- At least .89, or 89%, of the data values must be within $z = 3$ standard deviations of the mean.
- At least .94, or 94%, of the data values must be within $z = 4$ standard deviations of the mean.

For an example using Chebyshev's theorem, suppose that the midterm test scores for 100 students in a college business statistics course had a mean of 70 and a standard deviation of 5. How many students had test scores between 60 and 80? How many students had test scores between 58 and 82?

For the test scores between 60 and 80, we note that 60 is two standard deviations below the mean and 80 is two standard deviations above the mean. Using Chebyshev's theorem, we see that at least .75, or at least 75%, of the observations must have values within two standard deviations of the mean. Thus, at least 75% of the students must have scored between 60 and 80.

Chebyshev's theorem requires $z > 1$; but z need not be an integer.

For the test scores between 58 and 82, we see that $(58 - 70)/5 = -2.4$ indicates 58 is 2.4 standard deviations below the mean and that $(82 - 70)/5 = +2.4$ indicates 82 is 2.4 standard deviations above the mean. Applying Chebyshev's theorem with $z = 2.4$, we have

$$\left(1 - \frac{1}{z^2}\right) = \left(1 - \frac{1}{(2.4)^2}\right) = .826$$

At least 82.6% of the students must have test scores between 58 and 82.

Empirical Rule

The empirical rule is based on the normal probability distribution, which will be discussed in Chapter 6. The normal distribution is used extensively throughout the text.

One of the advantages of Chebyshev's theorem is that it applies to any data set regardless of the shape of the distribution of the data. Indeed, it could be used with any of the distributions in Figure 3.3. In many practical applications, however, data sets exhibit a symmetric mound-shaped or bell-shaped distribution like the one shown in Figure 3.4. When the data are believed to approximate this distribution, the **empirical rule** can be used to determine the percentage of data values that must be within a specified number of standard deviations of the mean.

EMPIRICAL RULE

For data having a bell-shaped distribution:

- Approximately 68% of the data values will be within one standard deviation of the mean.
- Approximately 95% of the data values will be within two standard deviations of the mean.
- Almost all of the data values will be within three standard deviations of the mean.

FIGURE 3.4 A SYMMETRIC MOUND-SHAPED OR BELL-SHAPED DISTRIBUTION

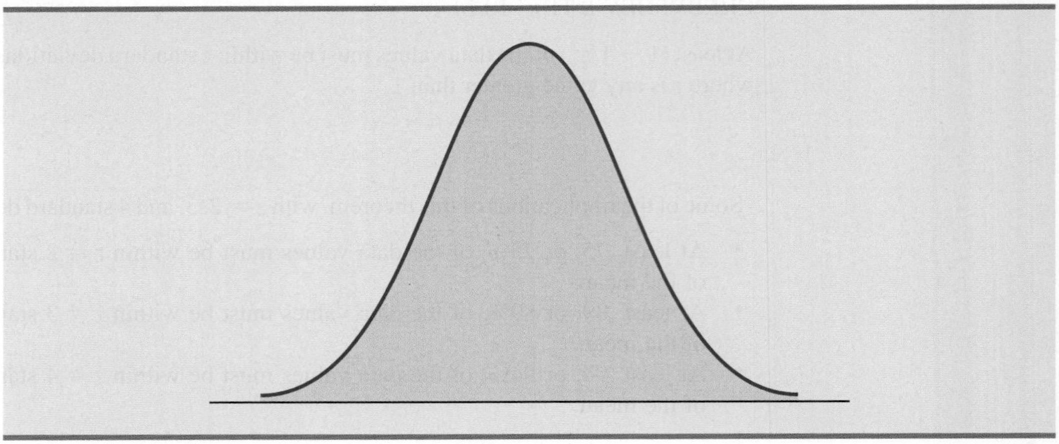

For example, liquid detergent cartons are filled automatically on a production line. Filling weights frequently have a bell-shaped distribution. If the mean filling weight is 16 ounces and the standard deviation is .25 ounces, we can use the empirical rule to draw the following conclusions.

- Approximately 68% of the filled cartons will have weights between 15.75 and 16.25 ounces (within one standard deviation of the mean).
- Approximately 95% of the filled cartons will have weights between 15.50 and 16.50 ounces (within two standard deviations of the mean).
- Almost all filled cartons will have weights between 15.25 and 16.75 ounces (within three standard deviations of the mean).

Detecting Outliers

Sometimes a data set will have one or more observations with unusually large or unusually small values. These extreme values are called **outliers**. Experienced statisticians take steps to identify outliers and then review each one carefully. An outlier may be a data value that has been incorrectly recorded. If so, it can be corrected before further analysis. An outlier may also be from an observation that was incorrectly included in the data set; if so, it can be removed. Finally, an outlier may be an unusual data value that has been recorded correctly and belongs in the data set. In such cases it should remain.

It is a good idea to check for outliers before making decisions based on data analysis. Errors are often made in recording data and entering data into the computer. Outliers should not necessarily be deleted, but their accuracy and appropriateness should be verified.

Standardized values (z-scores) can be used to identify outliers. Recall that the empirical rule allows us to conclude that for data with a bell-shaped distribution, almost all the data values will be within three standard deviations of the mean. Hence, in using z-scores to identify outliers, we recommend treating any data value with a z-score less than -3 or greater than $+3$ as an outlier. Such data values can then be reviewed for accuracy and to determine whether they belong in the data set.

Refer to the z-scores for the class size data in Table 3.4. The z-score of -1.50 shows the fifth class size is farthest from the mean. However, this standardized value is well within the -3 to $+3$ guideline for outliers. Thus, the z-scores do not indicate that outliers are present in the class size data.

NOTES AND COMMENTS

1. Chebyshev's theorem is applicable for any data set and can be used to state the minimum number of data values that will be within a certain number of standard deviations of the mean. If the data are known to be approximately bell-shaped, more can be said. For instance, the

empirical rule allows us to say that *approximately* 95% of the data values will be within two standard deviations of the mean; Chebyshev's theorem allows us to conclude only that at least 75% of the data values will be in that interval.

2. Before analyzing a data set, statisticians usually make a variety of checks to ensure the validity of data. In a large study it is not uncommon for errors to be made in recording data values or in entering the values into a computer. Identifying outliers is one tool used to check the validity of the data.

Exercises

Methods

25. Consider a sample with data values of 10, 20, 12, 17, and 16. Compute the z-score for each of the five observations.

26. Consider a sample with a mean of 500 and a standard deviation of 100. What are the z-scores for the following data values: 520, 650, 500, 450, and 280?

SELF test

27. Consider a sample with a mean of 30 and a standard deviation of 5. Use Chebyshev's theorem to determine the percentage of the data within each of the following ranges:
    a. 20 to 40
    b. 15 to 45
    c. 22 to 38
    d. 18 to 42
    e. 12 to 48

28. Suppose the data have a bell-shaped distribution with a mean of 30 and a standard deviation of 5. Use the empirical rule to determine the percentage of data within each of the following ranges:
    a. 20 to 40
    b. 15 to 45
    c. 25 to 35

Applications

SELF test

29. The results of a national survey showed that on average, adults sleep 6.9 hours per night. Suppose that the standard deviation is 1.2 hours.
    a. Use Chebyshev's theorem to calculate the percentage of individuals who sleep between 4.5 and 9.3 hours.
    b. Use Chebyshev's theorem to calculate the percentage of individuals who sleep between 3.9 and 9.9 hours.
    c. Assume that the number of hours of sleep follows a bell-shaped distribution. Use the empirical rule to calculate the percentage of individuals who sleep between 4.5 and 9.3 hours per day. How does this result compare to the value that you obtained using Chebyshev's theorem in part (a)?

30. The Energy Information Administration reported that the mean retail price per gallon of regular grade gasoline was $2.05 (Energy Information Administration, May 2009). Suppose that the standard deviation was $.10 and that the retail price per gallon has a bell-shaped distribution.
    a. What percentage of regular grade gasoline sold between $1.95 and $2.15 per gallon?
    b. What percentage of regular grade gasoline sold between $1.95 and $2.25 per gallon?
    c. What percentage of regular grade gasoline sold for more than $2.25 per gallon?

31. The national average for the math portion of the College Board's SAT test is 515 (*The World Almanac,* 2009). The College Board periodically rescales the test scores such that the standard deviation is approximately 100. Answer the following questions using a bell-shaped distribution and the empirical rule for the math test scores.

a. What percentage of students have an SAT math score greater than 615?
b. What percentage of students have an SAT math score greater than 715?
c. What percentage of students have an SAT math score between 415 and 515?
d. What percentage of students have an SAT math score between 315 and 615?

32. The high costs in the California real estate market have caused families who cannot afford to buy bigger homes to consider backyard sheds as an alternative form of housing expansion. Many are using the backyard structures for home offices, art studios, and hobby areas as well as for additional storage. The mean price of a customized wooden, shingled backyard structure is $3100 (*Newsweek,* September 29, 2003). Assume that the standard deviation is $1200.
a. What is the z-score for a backyard structure costing $2300?
b. What is the z-score for a backyard structure costing $4900?
c. Interpret the z-scores in parts (a) and (b). Comment on whether either should be considered an outlier.
d. The *Newsweek* article described a backyard shed-office combination built in Albany, California, for $13,000. Should this structure be considered an outlier? Explain.

33. Florida Power & Light (FP&L) Company has enjoyed a reputation for quickly fixing its electric system after storms. However, during the hurricane seasons of 2004 and 2005, a new reality was that the company's historical approach to emergency electric system repairs was no longer good enough (*The Wall Street Journal,* January 16, 2006). Data showing the days required to restore electric service after seven hurricanes during 2004 and 2005 follow.

Hurricane	Days to Restore Service
Charley	13
Frances	12
Jeanne	8
Dennis	3
Katrina	8
Rita	2
Wilma	18

Based on this sample of seven, compute the following descriptive statistics:
a. Mean, median, and mode
b. Range and standard deviation
c. Should Wilma be considered an outlier in terms of the days required to restore electric service?
d. The seven hurricanes resulted in 10 million service interruptions to customers. Do the statistics show that FP&L should consider updating its approach to emergency electric system repairs? Discuss.

34. A sample of 10 NCAA college basketball game scores provided the following data (*USA Today,* January 26, 2004).

WEB file
NCAA

Winning Team	Points	Losing Team	Points	Winning Margin
Arizona	90	Oregon	66	24
Duke	85	Georgetown	66	19
Florida State	75	Wake Forest	70	5
Kansas	78	Colorado	57	21
Kentucky	71	Notre Dame	63	8
Louisville	65	Tennessee	62	3
Oklahoma State	72	Texas	66	6

Winning Team	Points	Losing Team	Points	Winning Margin
Purdue	76	Michigan State	70	6
Stanford	77	Southern Cal	67	10
Wisconsin	76	Illinois	56	20

a. Compute the mean and standard deviation for the points scored by the winning team.
b. Assume that the points scored by the winning teams for all NCAA games follow a bell-shaped distribution. Using the mean and standard deviation found in part (a), estimate the percentage of all NCAA games in which the winning team scores 84 or more points. Estimate the percentage of NCAA games in which the winning team scores more than 90 points.
c. Compute the mean and standard deviation for the winning margin. Do the data contain outliers? Explain.

35. *Consumer Reports* posts reviews and ratings of a variety of products on its website. The following is a sample of 20 speaker systems and their ratings. The ratings are on a scale of 1 to 5, with 5 being best.

WEB file Speakers

Speaker	Rating	Speaker	Rating
Infinity Kappa 6.1	4.00	ACI Sapphire III	4.67
Allison One	4.12	Bose 501 Series	2.14
Cambridge Ensemble II	3.82	DCM KX-212	4.09
Dynaudio Contour 1.3	4.00	Eosone RSF1000	4.17
Hsu Rsch. HRSW12V	4.56	Joseph Audio RM7si	4.88
Legacy Audio Focus	4.32	Martin Logan Aerius	4.26
Mission 73li	4.33	Omni Audio SA 12.3	2.32
PSB 400i	4.50	Polk Audio RT12	4.50
Snell Acoustics D IV	4.64	Sunfire True Subwoofer	4.17
Thiel CS1.5	4.20	Yamaha NS-A636	2.17

a. Compute the mean and the median.
b. Compute the first and third quartiles.
c. Compute the standard deviation.
d. The skewness of this data is -1.67. Comment on the shape of the distribution.
e. What are the z-scores associated with Allison One and Omni Audio?
f. Do the data contain any outliers? Explain.

3.4 Exploratory Data Analysis

In Chapter 2 we introduced the stem-and-leaf display as a technique of exploratory data analysis. Recall that exploratory data analysis enables us to use simple arithmetic and easy-to-draw pictures to summarize data. In this section we continue exploratory data analysis by considering five-number summaries and box plots.

Five-Number Summary

In a **five-number summary**, the following five numbers are used to summarize the data:

1. Smallest value
2. First quartile (Q_1)
3. Median (Q_2)
4. Third quartile (Q_3)
5. Largest value

The easiest way to develop a five-number summary is to first place the data in ascending order. Then it is easy to identify the smallest value, the three quartiles, and the largest value. The monthly starting salaries shown in Table 3.1 for a sample of 12 business school graduates are repeated here in ascending order.

3310 3355 3450 | 3480 3480 3490 | 3520 3540 3550 | 3650 3730 3925

$Q_1 = 3465$ $\qquad$ $Q_2 = 3505$ (Median) $\qquad$ $Q_3 = 3600$

The median of 3505 and the quartiles $Q_1 = 3465$ and $Q_3 = 3600$ were computed in Section 3.1. Reviewing the data shows a smallest value of 3310 and a largest value of 3925. Thus the five-number summary for the salary data is 3310, 3465, 3505, 3600, 3925. Approximately one-fourth, or 25%, of the observations are between adjacent numbers in a five-number summary.

Box Plot

A **box plot** is a graphical summary of data that is based on a five-number summary. A key to the development of a box plot is the computation of the median and the quartiles, Q_1 and Q_3. The interquartile range, IQR $= Q_3 - Q_1$, is also used. Figure 3.5 is the box plot for the monthly starting salary data. The steps used to construct the box plot follow.

Box plots provide another way to identify outliers. But they do not necessarily identify the same values as those with a z-score less than −3 or greater than +3. Either or both procedures may be used.

1. A box is drawn with the ends of the box located at the first and third quartiles. For the salary data, $Q_1 = 3465$ and $Q_3 = 3600$. This box contains the middle 50% of the data.
2. A vertical line is drawn in the box at the location of the median (3505 for the salary data).
3. By using the interquartile range, IQR $= Q_3 - Q_1$, *limits* are located. The limits for the box plot are 1.5(IQR) below Q_1 and 1.5(IQR) above Q_3. For the salary data, IQR $= Q_3 - Q_1 = 3600 - 3465 = 135$. Thus, the limits are $3465 - 1.5(135) = 3262.5$ and $3600 + 1.5(135) = 3802.5$. Data outside these limits are considered *outliers*.
4. The dashed lines in Figure 3.5 are called *whiskers*. The whiskers are drawn from the ends of the box to the smallest and largest values *inside the limits* computed in step 3. Thus, the whiskers end at salary values of 3310 and 3730.
5. Finally, the location of each outlier is shown with the symbol *. In Figure 3.5 we see one outlier, 3925.

In Figure 3.5 we included lines showing the location of the upper and lower limits. These lines were drawn to show how the limits are computed and where they are located.

FIGURE 3.5 BOX PLOT OF THE STARTING SALARY DATA WITH LINES SHOWING THE LOWER AND UPPER LIMITS

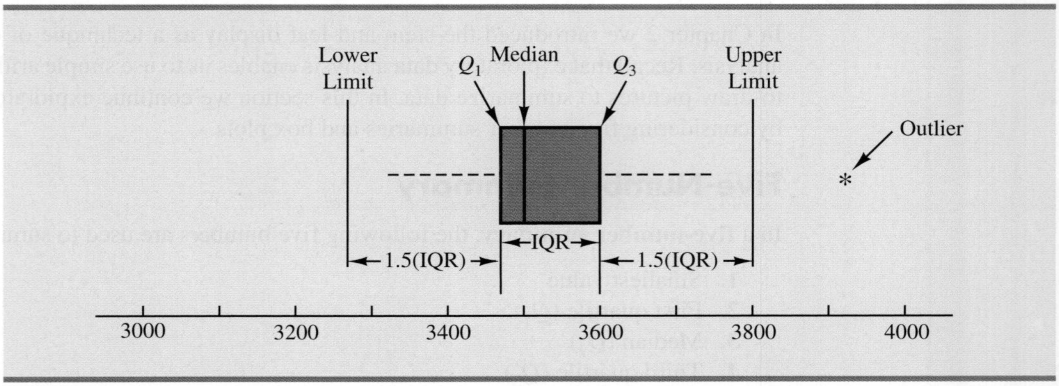

FIGURE 3.6 BOX PLOT OF MONTHLY STARTING SALARY DATA

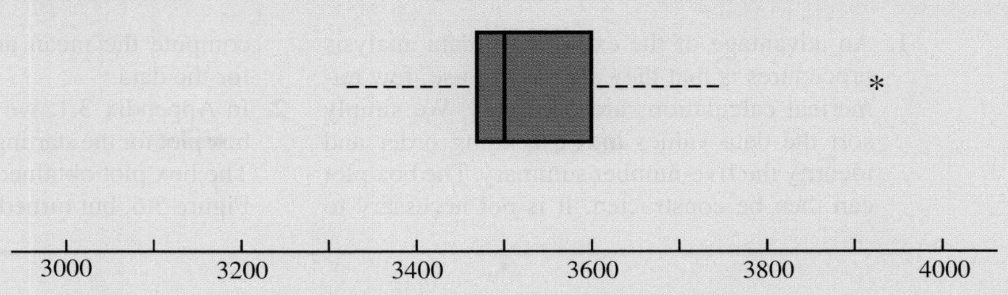

Although the limits are always computed, generally they are not drawn on the box plots. Figure 3.6 shows the usual appearance of a box plot for the salary data.

In order to compare monthly starting salaries for business school graduates by major, a sample of 111 recent graduates was selected. The major and the monthly starting salary were recorded for each graduate. Figure 3.7 shows the Minitab box plots for accounting, finance, information systems, management, and marketing majors. Note that the major is shown on the horizontal axis and each box plot is shown vertically above the corresponding major. Displaying box plots in this manner is an excellent graphical technique for making comparisons among two or more groups.

WEB file
MajorSalary

What observations can you make about monthly starting salaries by major using the box plots in Figured 3.7? Specifically, we note the following:

- The higher salaries are in accounting; the lower salaries are in management and marketing.
- Based on the medians, accounting and information systems have similar and higher median salaries. Finance is next with management and marketing showing lower median salaries.
- High salary outliers exist for accounting, finance, and marketing majors.
- Finance salaries appear to have the least variation, while accounting salaries appear to have the most variation.

Perhaps you can see additional interpretations based on these box plots.

FIGURE 3.7 MINITAB BOX PLOTS OF MONTLY STARTING SALARY BY MAJOR

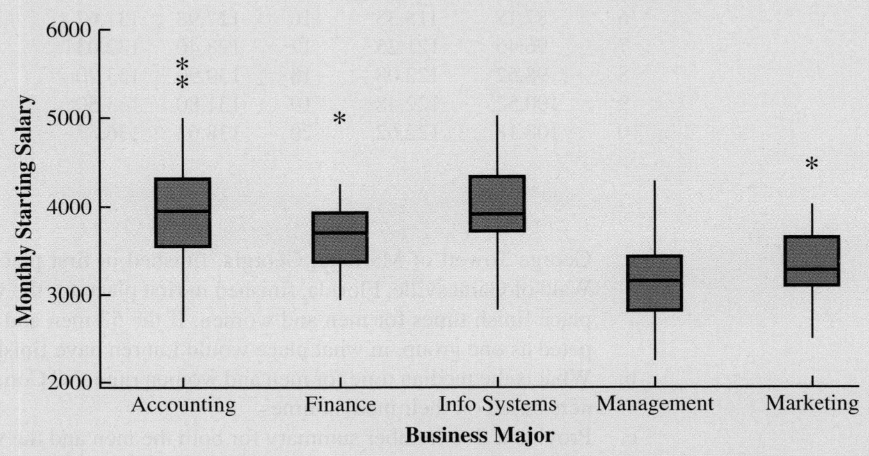

NOTES AND COMMENTS

1. An advantage of the exploratory data analysis procedures is that they are easy to use; few numerical calculations are necessary. We simply sort the data values into ascending order and identify the five-number summary. The box plot can then be constructed. It is not necessary to compute the mean and the standard deviation for the data.
2. In Appendix 3.1, we show how to construct a box plot for the starting salary data using Minitab. The box plot obtained looks just like the one in Figure 3.6, but turned on its side.

Exercises

Methods

36. Consider a sample with data values of 27, 25, 20, 15, 30, 34, 28, and 25. Provide the five-number summary for the data.
37. Show the box plot for the data in exercise 36.

SELF test

38. Show the five-number summary and the box plot for the following data: 5, 15, 18, 10, 8, 12, 16, 10, 6.
39. A data set has a first quartile of 42 and a third quartile of 50. Compute the lower and upper limits for the corresponding box plot. Should a data value of 65 be considered an outlier?

Applications

40. Naples, Florida, hosts a half-marathon (13.1-mile race) in January each year. The event attracts top runners from throughout the United States as well as from around the world. In January 2009, 22 men and 31 women entered the 19–24 age class. Finish times in minutes are as follows (*Naples Daily News,* January 19, 2009). Times are shown in order of finish.

WEB file
Runners

Finish	Men	Women	Finish	Men	Women	Finish	Men	Women
1	65.30	109.03	11	109.05	123.88	21	143.83	136.75
2	66.27	111.22	12	110.23	125.78	22	148.70	138.20
3	66.52	111.65	13	112.90	129.52	23		139.00
4	66.85	111.93	14	113.52	129.87	24		147.18
5	70.87	114.38	15	120.95	130.72	25		147.35
6	87.18	118.33	16	127.98	131.67	26		147.50
7	96.45	121.25	17	128.40	132.03	27		147.75
8	98.52	122.08	18	130.90	133.20	28		153.88
9	100.52	122.48	19	131.80	133.50	29		154.83
10	108.18	122.62	20	138.63	136.57	30		189.27
						31		189.28

a. George Towett of Marietta, Georgia, finished in first place for the men and Lauren Wald of Gainesville, Florida, finished in first place for the women. Compare the first-place finish times for men and women. If the 53 men and women runners had competed as one group, in what place would Lauren have finished?
b. What is the median time for men and women runners? Compare men and women runners based on their median times.
c. Provide a five-number summary for both the men and the women.
d. Are there outliers in either group?

e. Show the box plots for the two groups. Did men or women have the most variation in finish times? Explain.

SELF test

41. Annual sales, in millions of dollars, for 21 pharmaceutical companies follow.

8408	1374	1872	8879	2459	11413
608	14138	6452	1850	2818	1356
10498	7478	4019	4341	739	2127
3653	5794	8305			

a. Provide a five-number summary.
b. Compute the lower and upper limits.
c. Do the data contain any outliers?
d. Johnson & Johnson's sales are the largest on the list at $14,138 million. Suppose a data entry error (a transposition) had been made and the sales had been entered as $41,138 million. Would the method of detecting outliers in part (c) identify this problem and allow for correction of the data entry error?
e. Show a box plot.

42. *Consumer Reports* provided overall customer satisfaction scores for AT&T, Sprint, T-Mobile, and Verizon cell-phone services in major metropolitan areas throughout the United States. The rating for each service reflects the overall customer satisfaction considering a variety of factors such as cost, connectivity problems, dropped calls, static interference, and customer support. A satisfaction scale from 0 to 100 was used with 0 indicating completely dissatisfied and 100 indicating completely satisfied. The ratings for the four cell-phone services in 20 metropolitan areas are as shown (*Consumer Reports,* January 2009).

WEB file
CellService

Metropolitan Area	AT&T	Sprint	T-Mobile	Verizon
Atlanta	70	66	71	79
Boston	69	64	74	76
Chicago	71	65	70	77
Dallas	75	65	74	78
Denver	71	67	73	77
Detroit	73	65	77	79
Jacksonville	73	64	75	81
Las Vegas	72	68	74	81
Los Angeles	66	65	68	78
Miami	68	69	73	80
Minneapolis	68	66	75	77
Philadelphia	72	66	71	78
Phoenix	68	66	76	81
San Antonio	75	65	75	80
San Diego	69	68	72	79
San Francisco	66	69	73	75
Seattle	68	67	74	77
St. Louis	74	66	74	79
Tampa	73	63	73	79
Washington	72	68	71	76

a. Consider T-Mobile first. What is the median rating?
b. Develop a five-number summary for the T-Mobile service.
c. Are there outliers for T-Mobile? Explain.
d. Repeat parts (b) and (c) for the other three cell-phone services.

e. Show the box plots for the four cell-phone services on one graph. Discuss what a comparison of the box plots tells about the four services. Which service did *Consumer Reports* recommend as being best in terms of overall customer satisfaction?

43. The Philadelphia Phillies defeated the Tampa Bay Rays 4 to 3 to win the 2008 major league baseball World Series (*The Philadelphia Inquirer,* October 29, 2008). Earlier in the major league baseball playoffs, the Philadelphia Phillies defeated the Los Angeles Dodgers to win the National League Championship, while the Tampa Bay Rays defeated the Boston Red Sox to win the American League Championship. The file MLBSalaries contains the salaries for the 28 players on each of these four teams (USA Today Salary Database, October 2008). The data, shown in thousands of dollars, have been ordered from the highest salary to the lowest salary for each team.

WEB file
MLBSalaries

a. Analyze the salaries for the World Champion Philadelphia Phillies. What is the total payroll for the team? What is the median salary? What is the five-number summary?
b. Were there salary outliers for the Philadelphia Phillies? If so, how many and what were the salary amounts?
c. What is the total payroll for each of the other three teams? Develop the five-number summary for each team and identify any outliers.
d. Show the box plots of the salaries for all four teams. What are your interpretations? Of these four teams, does it appear that the team with the higher salaries won the league championships and the World Series?

44. A listing of 46 mutual funds and their 12-month total return percentage is shown in Table 3.5 (*Smart Money,* February 2004).

WEB file
Mutual

a. What are the mean and median return percentages for these mutual funds?
b. What are the first and third quartiles?
c. Provide a five-number summary.
d. Do the data contain any outliers? Show a box plot.

TABLE 3.5 TWELVE-MONTH RETURN FOR MUTUAL FUNDS

Mutual Fund	Return (%)	Mutual Fund	Return (%)
Alger Capital Appreciation	23.5	Nations Small Company	21.4
Alger LargeCap Growth	22.8	Nations SmallCap Index	24.5
Alger MidCap Growth	38.3	Nations Strategic Growth	10.4
Alger SmallCap	41.3	Nations Value Inv	10.8
AllianceBernstein Technology	40.6	One Group Diversified Equity	10.0
Federated American Leaders	15.6	One Group Diversified Int'l	10.9
Federated Capital Appreciation	12.4	One Group Diversified Mid Cap	15.1
Federated Equity-Income	11.5	One Group Equity Income	6.6
Federated Kaufmann	33.3	One Group Int'l Equity Index	13.2
Federated Max-Cap Index	16.0	One Group Large Cap Growth	13.6
Federated Stock	16.9	One Group Large Cap Value	12.8
Janus Adviser Int'l Growth	10.3	One Group Mid Cap Growth	18.7
Janus Adviser Worldwide	3.4	One Group Mid Cap Value	11.4
Janus Enterprise	24.2	One Group Small Cap Growth	23.6
Janus High-Yield	12.1	PBHG Growth	27.3
Janus Mercury	20.6	Putnam Europe Equity	20.4
Janus Overseas	11.9	Putnam Int'l Capital Opportunity	36.6
Janus Worldwide	4.1	Putnam International Equity	21.5
Nations Convertible Securities	13.6	Putnam Int'l New Opportunity	26.3
Nations Int'l Equity	10.7	Strong Advisor Mid Cap Growth	23.7
Nations LargeCap Enhd. Core	13.2	Strong Growth 20	11.7
Nations LargeCap Index	13.5	Strong Growth Inv	23.2
Nation MidCap Index	19.5	Strong Large Cap Growth	14.5

3.5 Measures of Association Between Two Variables

Thus far we have examined numerical methods used to summarize the data for *one variable at a time*. Often a manager or decision maker is interested in the *relationship between two variables*. In this section we present covariance and correlation as descriptive measures of the relationship between two variables.

We begin by reconsidering the application concerning a stereo and sound equipment store in San Francisco as presented in Section 2.4. The store's manager wants to determine the relationship between the number of weekend television commercials shown and the sales at the store during the following week. Sample data with sales expressed in hundreds of dollars are provided in Table 3.6. It shows 10 observations ($n = 10$), one for each week. The scatter diagram in Figure 3.8 shows a positive relationship, with higher sales (y) associated with a greater number of commercials (x). In fact, the scatter diagram suggests that a straight line could be used as an approximation of the relationship. In the following discussion, we introduce **covariance** as a descriptive measure of the linear association between two variables.

Covariance

For a sample of size n with the observations (x_1, y_1), (x_2, y_2), and so on, the sample covariance is defined as follows:

SAMPLE COVARIANCE

$$s_{xy} = \frac{\Sigma(x_i - \bar{x})(y_i - \bar{y})}{n - 1} \tag{3.10}$$

This formula pairs each x_i with a y_i. We then sum the products obtained by multiplying the deviation of each x_i from its sample mean $\bar{x}$ by the deviation of the corresponding y_i from its sample mean $\bar{y}$; this sum is then divided by $n - 1$.

TABLE 3.6 SAMPLE DATA FOR THE STEREO AND SOUND EQUIPMENT STORE

WEB file
Stereo

Week	Number of Commercials x	Sales Volume ($100s) y
1	2	50
2	5	57
3	1	41
4	3	54
5	4	54
6	1	38
7	5	63
8	3	48
9	4	59
10	2	46

FIGURE 3.8 SCATTER DIAGRAM FOR THE STEREO AND SOUND EQUIPMENT STORE

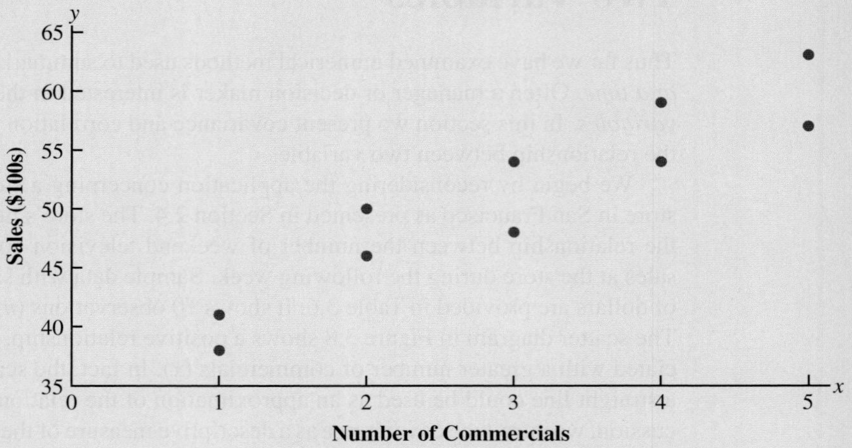

To measure the strength of the linear relationship between the number of commercials x and the sales volume y in the stereo and sound equipment store problem, we use equation (3.10) to compute the sample covariance. The calculations in Table 3.7 show the computation of $\Sigma(x_i - \bar{x})(y_i - \bar{y})$. Note that $\bar{x} = 30/10 = 3$ and $\bar{y} = 510/10 = 51$. Using equation (3.10), we obtain a sample covariance of

$$s_{xy} = \frac{\Sigma(x_i - \bar{x})(y_i - \bar{y})}{n - 1} = \frac{99}{9} = 11$$

TABLE 3.7 CALCULATIONS FOR THE SAMPLE COVARIANCE

	x_i	y_i	$x_i - \bar{x}$	$y_i - \bar{y}$	$(x_i - \bar{x})(y_i - \bar{y})$
	2	50	−1	−1	1
	5	57	2	6	12
	1	41	−2	−10	20
	3	54	0	3	0
	4	54	1	3	3
	1	38	−2	−13	26
	5	63	2	12	24
	3	48	0	−3	0
	4	59	1	8	8
	2	46	−1	−5	5
Totals	30	510	0	0	99

$$s_{xy} = \frac{\Sigma(x_i - \bar{x})(y_i - \bar{y})}{n - 1} = \frac{99}{10 - 1} = 11$$

The formula for computing the covariance of a population of size N is similar to equation (3.10), but we use different notation to indicate that we are working with the entire population.

POPULATION COVARIANCE

$$\sigma_{xy} = \frac{\Sigma(x_i - \mu_x)(y_i - \mu_y)}{N} \quad \textbf{(3.11)}$$

In equation (3.11) we use the notation μ_x for the population mean of the variable x and μ_y for the population mean of the variable y. The population covariance σ_{xy} is defined for a population of size N.

Interpretation of the Covariance

To aid in the interpretation of the sample covariance, consider Figure 3.9. It is the same as the scatter diagram of Figure 3.8 with a vertical dashed line at $\bar{x} = 3$ and a horizontal dashed line at $\bar{y} = 51$. The lines divide the graph into four quadrants. Points in quadrant I correspond to x_i greater than $\bar{x}$ and y_i greater than $\bar{y}$, points in quadrant II correspond to x_i less than $\bar{x}$ and y_i greater than $\bar{y}$, and so on. Thus, the value of $(x_i - \bar{x})(y_i - \bar{y})$ must be positive for points in quadrant I, negative for points in quadrant II, positive for points in quadrant III, and negative for points in quadrant IV.

The covariance is a measure of the linear association between two variables.

If the value of s_{xy} is positive, the points with the greatest influence on s_{xy} must be in quadrants I and III. Hence, a positive value for s_{xy} indicates a positive linear association between x and y; that is, as the value of x increases, the value of y increases. If the value of s_{xy} is negative, however, the points with the greatest influence on s_{xy} are in quadrants II and IV. Hence, a negative value for s_{xy} indicates a negative linear association between x and y; that is, as the value of x increases, the value of y decreases. Finally, if the points are evenly distributed across all four quadrants, the value of s_{xy} will be close to zero, indicating no linear association between x and y. Figure 3.10 shows the values of s_{xy} that can be expected with three different types of scatter diagrams.

FIGURE 3.9 PARTITIONED SCATTER DIAGRAM FOR THE STEREO AND SOUND EQUIPMENT STORE

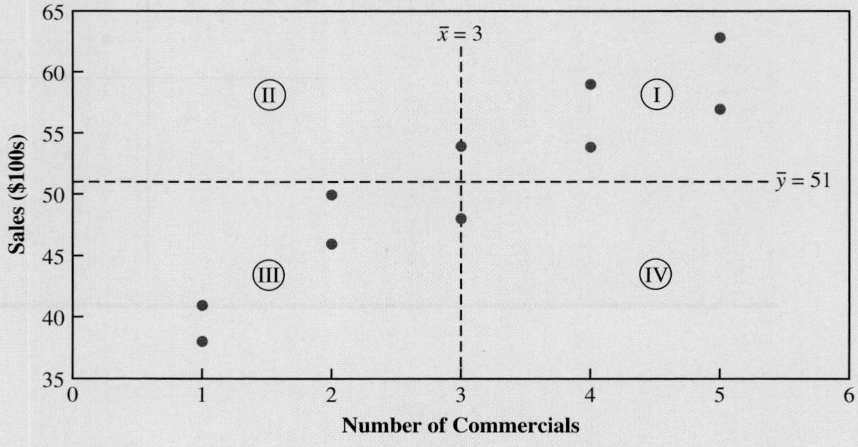

FIGURE 3.10 INTERPRETATION OF SAMPLE COVARIANCE

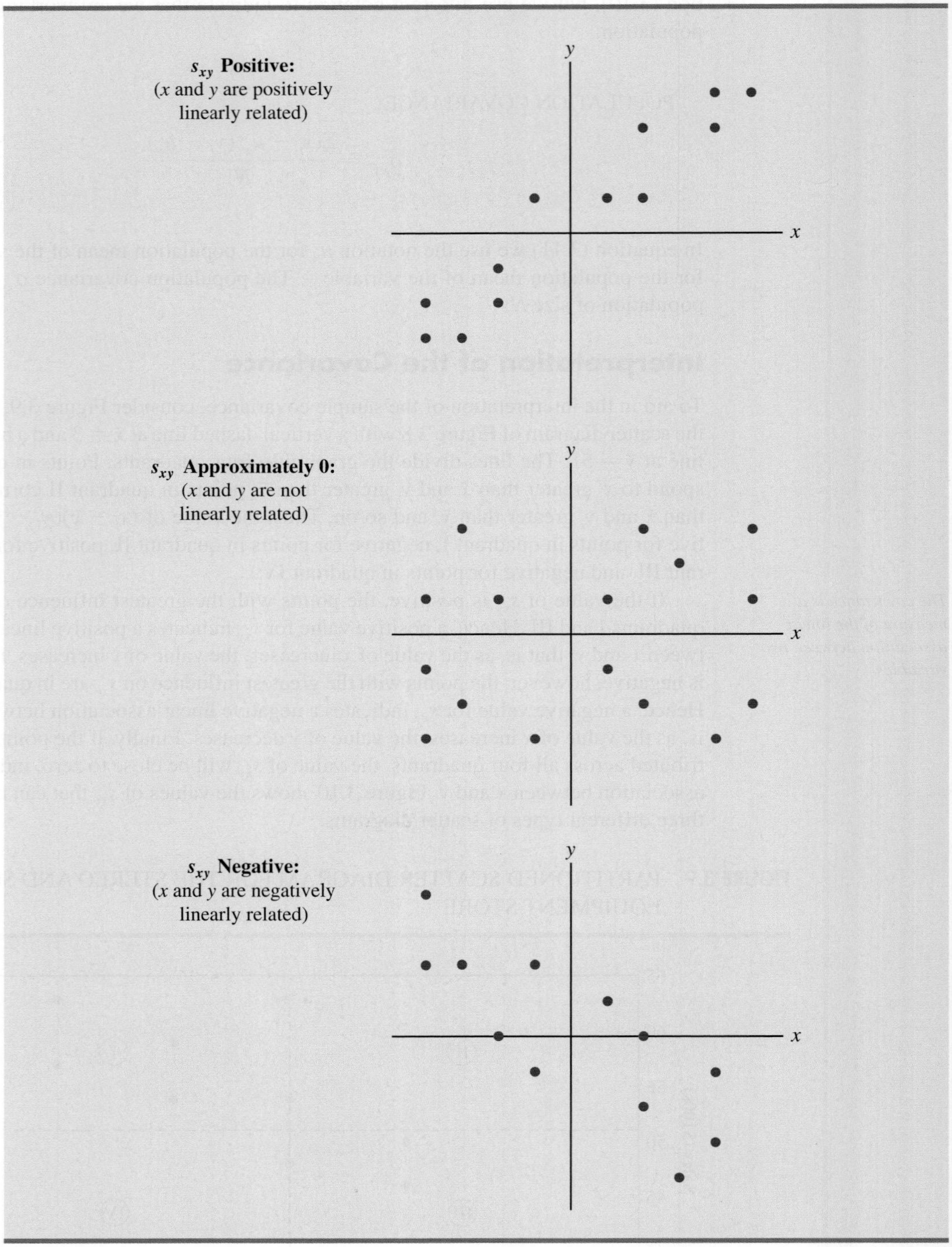

Referring again to Figure 3.9, we see that the scatter diagram for the stereo and sound equipment store follows the pattern in the top panel of Figure 3.10. As we should expect, the value of the sample covariance indicates a positive linear relationship with $s_{xy} = 11$.

From the preceding discussion, it might appear that a large positive value for the covariance indicates a strong positive linear relationship and that a large negative value indicates a strong negative linear relationship. However, one problem with using covariance as a measure of the strength of the linear relationship is that the value of the covariance depends on the units of measurement for x and y. For example, suppose we are interested in the relationship between height x and weight y for individuals. Clearly the strength of the relationship should be the same whether we measure height in feet or inches. Measuring the height in inches, however, gives us much larger numerical values for $(x_i - \bar{x})$ than when we measure height in feet. Thus, with height measured in inches, we would obtain a larger value for the numerator $\Sigma(x_i - \bar{x})(y_i - \bar{y})$ in equation (3.10)—and hence a larger covariance—when in fact the relationship does not change. A measure of the relationship between two variables that is not affected by the units of measurement for x and y is the **correlation coefficient**.

Correlation Coefficient

For sample data, the Pearson product moment correlation coefficient is defined as follows.

PEARSON PRODUCT MOMENT CORRELATION COEFFICIENT: SAMPLE DATA

$$r_{xy} = \frac{s_{xy}}{s_x s_y} \tag{3.12}$$

where

r_{xy} = sample correlation coefficient
s_{xy} = sample covariance
s_x = sample standard deviation of x
s_y = sample standard deviation of y

Equation (3.12) shows that the Pearson product moment correlation coefficient for sample data (commonly referred to more simply as the *sample correlation coefficient*) is computed by dividing the sample covariance by the product of the sample standard deviation of x and the sample standard deviation of y.

Let us now compute the sample correlation coefficient for the stereo and sound equipment store. Using the data in Table 3.7, we can compute the sample standard deviations for the two variables:

$$s_x = \sqrt{\frac{\Sigma(x_i - \bar{x})^2}{n - 1}} = \sqrt{\frac{20}{9}} = 1.49$$

$$s_y = \sqrt{\frac{\Sigma(y_i - \bar{y})^2}{n - 1}} = \sqrt{\frac{566}{9}} = 7.93$$

Now, because $s_{xy} = 11$, the sample correlation coefficient equals

$$r_{xy} = \frac{s_{xy}}{s_x s_y} = \frac{11}{(1.49)(7.93)} = .93$$

The formula for computing the correlation coefficient for a population, denoted by the Greek letter ρ_{xy} (rho, pronounced "row"), follows.

The sample correlation coefficient r_{xy} is the estimator of the population correlation coefficient ρ_{xy}.

PEARSON PRODUCT MOMENT CORRELATION COEFFICIENT: POPULATION DATA

$$\rho_{xy} = \frac{\sigma_{xy}}{\sigma_x \sigma_y} \tag{3.13}$$

where

ρ_{xy} = population correlation coefficient
σ_{xy} = population covariance
σ_x = population standard deviation for x
σ_y = population standard deviation for y

The sample correlation coefficient r_{xy} provides an estimate of the population correlation coefficient ρ_{xy}.

Interpretation of the Correlation Coefficient

First let us consider a simple example that illustrates the concept of a perfect positive linear relationship. The scatter diagram in Figure 3.11 depicts the relationship between x and y based on the following sample data.

x_i	y_i
5	10
10	30
15	50

FIGURE 3.11 SCATTER DIAGRAM DEPICTING A PERFECT POSITIVE LINEAR RELATIONSHIP

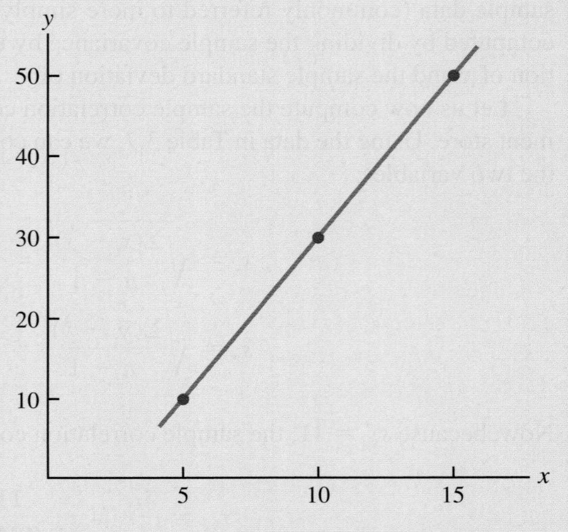

TABLE 3.8 COMPUTATIONS USED IN CALCULATING THE SAMPLE CORRELATION COEFFICIENT

	x_i	y_i	$x_i - \bar{x}$	$(x_i - \bar{x})^2$	$y_i - \bar{y}$	$(y_i - \bar{y})^2$	$(x_i - \bar{x})(y_i - \bar{y})$
	5	10	−5	25	−20	400	100
	10	30	0	0	0	0	0
	15	50	5	25	20	400	100
Totals	30	90	0	50	0	800	200
	$\bar{x} = 10$	$\bar{y} = 30$					

The straight line drawn through each of the three points shows a perfect linear relationship between x and y. In order to apply equation (3.12) to compute the sample correlation we must first compute s_{xy}, s_x, and s_y. Some of the computations are shown in Table 3.8. Using the results in this table, we find

$$s_{xy} = \frac{\Sigma(x_i - \bar{x})(y_i - \bar{y})}{n - 1} = \frac{200}{2} = 100$$

$$s_x = \sqrt{\frac{\Sigma(x_i - \bar{x})^2}{n - 1}} = \sqrt{\frac{50}{2}} = 5$$

$$s_y = \sqrt{\frac{\Sigma(y_i - \bar{y})^2}{n - 1}} = \sqrt{\frac{800}{2}} = 20$$

$$r_{xy} = \frac{s_{xy}}{s_x s_y} = \frac{100}{5(20)} = 1$$

The correlation coefficient ranges from −1 to +1. Values close to −1 or +1 indicate a strong linear relationship. The closer the correlation is to zero, the weaker the relationship.

Thus, we see that the value of the sample correlation coefficient is 1.

In general, it can be shown that if all the points in a data set fall on a positively sloped straight line, the value of the sample correlation coefficient is +1; that is, a sample correlation coefficient of +1 corresponds to a perfect positive linear relationship between x and y. Moreover, if the points in the data set fall on a straight line having negative slope, the value of the sample correlation coefficient is −1; that is, a sample correlation coefficient of −1 corresponds to a perfect negative linear relationship between x and y.

Let us now suppose that a certain data set indicates a positive linear relationship between x and y but that the relationship is not perfect. The value of r_{xy} will be less than 1, indicating that the points in the scatter diagram are not all on a straight line. As the points deviate more and more from a perfect positive linear relationship, the value of r_{xy} becomes smaller and smaller. A value of r_{xy} equal to zero indicates no linear relationship between x and y, and values of r_{xy} near zero indicate a weak linear relationship.

For the data involving the stereo and sound equipment store, $r_{xy} = .93$. Therefore, we conclude that a strong positive linear relationship occurs between the number of commercials and sales. More specifically, an increase in the number of commercials is associated with an increase in sales.

In closing, we note that correlation provides a measure of linear association and not necessarily causation. A high correlation between two variables does not mean that changes in one variable will cause changes in the other variable. For example, we may find that the quality rating and the typical meal price of restaurants are positively correlated. However, simply increasing the meal price at a restaurant will not cause the quality rating to increase.

Exercises

Methods

SELF test

45. Five observations taken for two variables follow.

x_i	4	6	11	3	16
y_i	50	50	40	60	30

a. Develop a scatter diagram with x on the horizontal axis.
b. What does the scatter diagram developed in part (a) indicate about the relationship between the two variables?
c. Compute and interpret the sample covariance.
d. Compute and interpret the sample correlation coefficient.

46. Five observations taken for two variables follow.

x_i	6	11	15	21	27
y_i	6	9	6	17	12

a. Develop a scatter diagram for these data.
b. What does the scatter diagram indicate about a relationship between x and y?
c. Compute and interpret the sample covariance.
d. Compute and interpret the sample correlation coefficient.

Applications

47. Nielsen Media Research provides two measures of the television viewing audience: a television program *rating,* which is the percentage of households with televisions watching a program, and a television program *share,* which is the percentage of households watching a program among those with televisions in use. The following data show the Nielsen television ratings and share data for the Major League Baseball World Series over a nine-year period (Associated Press, October 27, 2003).

Rating	19	17	17	14	16	12	15	12	13
Share	32	28	29	24	26	20	24	20	22

a. Develop a scatter diagram with rating on the horizontal axis.
b. What is the relationship between rating and share? Explain.
c. Compute and interpret the sample covariance.
d. Compute the sample correlation coefficient. What does this value tell us about the relationship between rating and share?

48. A department of transportation's study on driving speed and miles per gallon for midsize automobiles resulted in the following data:

Speed (Miles per Hour)	30	50	40	55	30	25	60	25	50	55
Miles per Gallon	28	25	25	23	30	32	21	35	26	25

Compute and interpret the sample correlation coefficient.

49. At the beginning of 2009, the economic downturn resulted in the loss of jobs and an increase in delinquent loans for housing. The national unemployment rate was 6.5% and the percentage of delinquent loans was 6.12% (*The Wall Street Journal,* January 27, 2009). In projecting where the real estate market was headed in the coming year, economists studied the relationship between the jobless rate and the percentage of delinquent loans. The expectation was that if the jobless rate continued to increase, there would also be an

increase in the percentage of delinquent loans. The data below show the jobless rate and the delinquent loan percentage for 27 major real estate markets.

WEB file
Housing

Metro Area	Jobless Rate (%)	Delinquent Loan (%)	Metro Area	Jobless Rate (%)	Delinquent Loan (%)
Atlanta	7.1	7.02	New York	6.2	5.78
Boston	5.2	5.31	Orange County	6.3	6.08
Charlotte	7.8	5.38	Orlando	7.0	10.05
Chicago	7.8	5.40	Philadelphia	6.2	4.75
Dallas	5.8	5.00	Phoenix	5.5	7.22
Denver	5.8	4.07	Portland	6.5	3.79
Detroit	9.3	6.53	Raleigh	6.0	3.62
Houston	5.7	5.57	Sacramento	8.3	9.24
Jacksonville	7.3	6.99	St. Louis	7.5	4.40
Las Vegas	7.6	11.12	San Diego	7.1	6.91
Los Angeles	8.2	7.56	San Francisco	6.8	5.57
Miami	7.1	12.11	Seattle	5.5	3.87
Minneapolis	6.3	4.39	Tampa	7.5	8.42
Nashville	6.6	4.78			

a. Compute the correlation coefficient. Is there a positive correlation between the jobless rate and the percentage of delinquent housing loans? What is your interpretation?
b. Show a scatter diagram of the relationship between jobless rate and the percentage of delinquent housing loans.

50. The Dow Jones Industrial Average (DJIA) and the Standard & Poor's 500 Index (S&P 500) are both used to measure the performance of the stock market. The DJIA is based on the price of stocks for 30 large companies; the S&P 500 is based on the price of stocks for 500 companies. If both the DJIA and S&P 500 measure the performance of the stock market, how are they correlated? The following data show the daily percent increase or daily percent decrease in the DJIA and S&P 500 for a sample of nine days over a three-month period (*The Wall Street Journal,* January 15 to March 10, 2006).

WEB file
StockMarket

DJIA	.20	.82	−.99	.04	−.24	1.01	.30	.55	−.25
S&P 500	.24	.19	−.91	.08	−.33	.87	.36	.83	−.16

a. Show a scatter diagram.
b. Compute the sample correlation coefficient for these data.
c. Discuss the association between the DJIA and S&P 500. Do you need to check both before having a general idea about the daily stock market performance?

51. The daily high and low temperatures for 14 cities around the world are shown (The Weather Channel, April 22, 2009).

WEB file
WorldTemp

City	High	Low	City	High	Low
Athens	68	50	London	67	45
Beijing	70	49	Moscow	44	29
Berlin	65	44	Paris	69	44
Cairo	96	64	Rio de Janeiro	76	69
Dublin	57	46	Rome	69	51
Geneva	70	45	Tokyo	70	58
Hong Kong	80	73	Toronto	44	39

a. What is the sample mean high temperature?
b. What is the sample mean low temperature?
c. What is the correlation between the high and low temperatures? Discuss.

3.6 The Weighted Mean and Working with Grouped Data

In Section 3.1, we presented the mean as one of the most important measures of central location. The formula for the mean of a sample with n observations is restated as follows.

$$\bar{x} = \frac{\Sigma x_i}{n} = \frac{x_1 + x_2 + \cdots + x_n}{n} \tag{3.14}$$

In this formula, each x_i is given equal importance or weight. Although this practice is most common, in some instances, the mean is computed by giving each observation a weight that reflects its importance. A mean computed in this manner is referred to as a **weighted mean**.

Weighted Mean

The weighted mean is computed as follows:

WEIGHTED MEAN

$$\bar{x} = \frac{\Sigma w_i x_i}{\Sigma w_i} \tag{3.15}$$

where

x_i = value of observation i
w_i = weight for observation i

When the data are from a sample, equation (3.15) provides the weighted sample mean. When the data are from a population, μ replaces $\bar{x}$ and equation (3.15) provides the weighted population mean.

As an example of the need for a weighted mean, consider the following sample of five purchases of a raw material over the past three months.

Purchase	Cost per Pound ($)	Number of Pounds
1	3.00	1200
2	3.40	500
3	2.80	2750
4	2.90	1000
5	3.25	800

Note that the cost per pound varies from \$2.80 to \$3.40, and the quantity purchased varies from 500 to 2750 pounds. Suppose that a manager asked for information about the mean cost per pound of the raw material. Because the quantities ordered vary, we must use the formula for a weighted mean. The five cost-per-pound data values are $x_1 = 3.00$, $x_2 = 3.40$, $x_3 = 2.80$, $x_4 = 2.90$, and $x_5 = 3.25$. The weighted mean cost per pound is found by weighting each cost by its corresponding quantity. For this example, the weights are $w_1 = 1200$, $w_2 = 500$, $w_3 = 2750$, $w_4 = 1000$, and $w_5 = 800$. Based on equation (3.15), the weighted mean is calculated as follows:

$$\bar{x} = \frac{1200(3.00) + 500(3.40) + 2750(2.80) + 1000(2.90) + 800(3.25)}{1200 + 500 + 2750 + 1000 + 800}$$

$$= \frac{18{,}500}{6250} = 2.96$$

Thus, the weighted mean computation shows that the mean cost per pound for the raw material is \$2.96. Note that using equation (3.14) rather than the weighted mean formula would have provided misleading results. In this case, the mean of the five cost-per-pound values is $(3.00 + 3.40 + 2.80 + 2.90 + 3.25)/5 = 15.35/5 = \$3.07$, which overstates the actual mean cost per pound purchased.

The choice of weights for a particular weighted mean computation depends upon the application. An example that is well known to college students is the computation of a grade point average (GPA). In this computation, the data values generally used are 4 for an A grade, 3 for a B grade, 2 for a C grade, 1 for a D grade, and 0 for an F grade. The weights are the number of credits hours earned for each grade. Exercise 54 at the end of this section provides an example of this weighted mean computation. In other weighted mean computations, quantities such as pounds, dollars, or volume are frequently used as weights. In any case, when observations vary in importance, the analyst must choose the weight that best reflects the importance of each observation in the determination of the mean.

Computing a grade point average is a good example of the use of a weighted mean.

Grouped Data

In most cases, measures of location and variability are computed by using the individual data values. Sometimes, however, data are available only in a grouped or frequency distribution form. In the following discussion, we show how the weighted mean formula can be used to obtain approximations of the mean, variance, and standard deviation for **grouped data**.

In Section 2.2 we provided a frequency distribution of the time in days required to complete year-end audits for the public accounting firm of Sanderson and Clifford. The frequency distribution of audit times is shown in Table 3.9. Based on this frequency distribution, what is the sample mean audit time?

To compute the mean using only the grouped data, we treat the midpoint of each class as being representative of the items in the class. Let M_i denote the midpoint for class i and let f_i denote the frequency of class i. The weighted mean formula (3.15) is then used with the data values denoted as M_i and the weights given by the frequencies f_i. In this case, the denominator of equation (3.15) is the sum of the frequencies, which is the

TABLE 3.9 FREQUENCY DISTRIBUTION OF AUDIT TIMES

Audit Time (days)	Frequency
10–14	4
15–19	8
20–24	5
25–29	2
30–34	1
Total	20

sample size n. That is, $\Sigma f_i = n$. Thus, the equation for the sample mean for grouped data is as follows.

SAMPLE MEAN FOR GROUPED DATA

$$\bar{x} = \frac{\Sigma f_i M_i}{n} \tag{3.16}$$

where

M_i = the midpoint for class i
f_i = the frequency for class i
n = the sample size

With the class midpoints, M_i, halfway between the class limits, the first class of 10–14 in Table 3.9 has a midpoint at $(10 + 14)/2 = 12$. The five class midpoints and the weighted mean computation for the audit time data are summarized in Table 3.10. As can be seen, the sample mean audit time is 19 days.

To compute the variance for grouped data, we use a slightly altered version of the formula for the variance provided in equation (3.5). In equation (3.5), the squared deviations of the data about the sample mean $\bar{x}$ were written $(x_i - \bar{x})^2$. However, with grouped data, the values are not known. In this case, we treat the class midpoint, M_i, as being representative of the x_i values in the corresponding class. Thus, the squared deviations about the sample mean, $(x_i - \bar{x})^2$, are replaced by $(M_i - \bar{x})^2$. Then, just as we did with the sample mean calculations for grouped data, we weight each value by the frequency of the class, f_i. The sum of the squared deviations about the mean for all the data is approximated by $\Sigma f_i(M_i - \bar{x})^2$. The term $n - 1$ rather than n appears in the denominator in order to make the sample variance the estimate of the population variance. Thus, the following formula is used to obtain the sample variance for grouped data.

SAMPLE VARIANCE FOR GROUPED DATA

$$s^2 = \frac{\Sigma f_i(M_i - \bar{x})^2}{n - 1} \tag{3.17}$$

TABLE 3.10 COMPUTATION OF THE SAMPLE MEAN AUDIT TIME FOR GROUPED DATA

Audit Time (days)	Class Midpoint (M_i)	Frequency (f_i)	$f_i M_i$
10–14	12	4	48
15–19	17	8	136
20–24	22	5	110
25–29	27	2	54
30–34	32	1	32
		20	380

$$\text{Sample mean } \bar{x} = \frac{\Sigma f_i M_i}{n} = \frac{380}{20} = 19 \text{ days}$$

TABLE 3.11 COMPUTATION OF THE SAMPLE VARIANCE OF AUDIT TIMES FOR GROUPED DATA (SAMPLE MEAN $\bar{x} = 19$)

Audit Time (days)	Class Midpoint (M_i)	Frequency (f_i)	Deviation ($M_i - \bar{x}$)	Squared Deviation ($(M_i - \bar{x})^2$)	$f_i(M_i - \bar{x})^2$
10–14	12	4	−7	49	196
15–19	17	8	−2	4	32
20–24	22	5	3	9	45
25–29	27	2	8	64	128
30–34	32	1	13	169	169
		20			570
					$\Sigma f_i(M_i - \bar{x})^2$

$$\text{Sample variance } s^2 = \frac{\Sigma f_i(M_i - \bar{x})^2}{n - 1} = \frac{570}{19} = 30$$

The calculation of the sample variance for audit times based on the grouped data is shown in Table 3.11. The sample variance is 30.

The standard deviation for grouped data is simply the square root of the variance for grouped data. For the audit time data, the sample standard deviation is $s = \sqrt{30} = 5.48$.

Before closing this section on computing measures of location and dispersion for grouped data, we note that formulas (3.16) and (3.17) are for a sample. Population summary measures are computed similarly. The grouped data formulas for a population mean and variance follow.

POPULATION MEAN FOR GROUPED DATA

$$\mu = \frac{\Sigma f_i M_i}{N} \tag{3.18}$$

POPULATION VARIANCE FOR GROUPED DATA

$$\sigma^2 = \frac{\Sigma f_i(M_i - \mu)^2}{N} \tag{3.19}$$

NOTES AND COMMENTS

In computing descriptive statistics for grouped data, the class midpoints are used to approximate the data values in each class. As a result, the descriptive statistics for grouped data approximate the descriptive statistics that would result from using the original data directly. We therefore recommend computing descriptive statistics from the original data rather than from grouped data whenever possible.

Exercises

Methods

52. Consider the following data and corresponding weights.

x_i	Weight (w_i)
3.2	6
2.0	3
2.5	2
5.0	8

a. Compute the weighted mean.
b. Compute the sample mean of the four data values without weighting. Note the difference in the results provided by the two computations.

SELF test

53. Consider the sample data in the following frequency distribution.

Class	Midpoint	Frequency
3–7	5	4
8–12	10	7
13–17	15	9
18–22	20	5

a. Compute the sample mean.
b. Compute the sample variance and sample standard deviation.

Applications

SELF test

54. The grade point average for college students is based on a weighted mean computation. For most colleges, the grades are given the following data values: A (4), B (3), C (2), D (1), and F (0). After 60 credit hours of course work, a student at State University earned 9 credit hours of A, 15 credit hours of B, 33 credit hours of C, and 3 credit hours of D.
a. Compute the student's grade point average.
b. Students at State University must maintain a 2.5 grade point average for their first 60 credit hours of course work in order to be admitted to the business college. Will this student be admitted?

55. Morningstar tracks the total return for a large number of mutual funds. The following table shows the total return and the number of funds for four categories of mutual funds (*Morningstar Funds500*, 2008).

Type of Fund	Number of Funds	Total Return (%)
Domestic Equity	9191	4.65
International Equity	2621	18.15
Specialty Stock	1419	11.36
Hybrid	2900	6.75

a. Using the number of funds as weights, compute the weighted average total return for the mutual funds covered by Morningstar.
b. Is there any difficulty associated with using the "number of funds" as the weights in computing the weighted average total return for Morningstar in part (a)? Discuss. What else might be used for weights?
c. Suppose you had invested \$10,000 in mutual funds at the beginning of 2007 and diversified the investment by placing \$2000 in Domestic Equity funds, \$4000 in

International Equity funds, \$3000 in Specialty Stock funds, and \$1000 in Hybrid funds. What is the expected return on the portfolio?

56. Based on a survey of 425 master's programs in business administration, the *U. S. News & World Report* ranked the Indiana University Kelley Business School as the 20th best business program in the country (*America's Best Graduate Schools,* 2009). The ranking was based in part on surveys of business school deans and corporate recruiters. Each survey respondent was asked to rate the overall academic quality of the master's program on a scale from 1 "marginal" to 5 "outstanding." Use the sample of responses shown below to compute the weighted mean score for the business school deans and the corporate recruiters. Discuss.

Quality Assessment	Business School Deans	Corporate Recruiters
5	44	31
4	66	34
3	60	43
2	10	12
1	0	0

57. The following frequency distribution shows the price per share of the 30 companies in the Dow Jones Industrial Average (*Barron's,* February 2, 2009).

Price per Share	Number of Companies
\$0–9	4
\$10–19	5
\$20–29	7
\$30–39	3
\$40–49	4
\$50–59	4
\$60–69	0
\$70–79	2
\$80–89	0
\$90–99	1

a. Compute the mean price per share and the standard deviation of the price per share for the Dow Jones Industrial Average companies.
b. On January 16, 2006, the mean price per share was \$45.83 and the standard deviation was \$18.14. Comment on the changes in the price per share over the three-year period.

Summary

In this chapter we introduced several descriptive statistics that can be used to summarize the location, variability, and shape of a data distribution. Unlike the tabular and graphical procedures introduced in Chapter 2, the measures introduced in this chapter summarize the data in terms of numerical values. When the numerical values obtained are for a sample, they are called sample statistics. When the numerical values obtained are for a population, they are called population parameters. Some of the notation used for sample statistics and population parameters follow.

In statistical inference, the sample statistic is referred to as the point estimator of the population parameter.

	Sample Statistic	Population Parameter
Mean	$\bar{x}$	μ
Variance	s^2	σ^2
Standard deviation	s	σ
Covariance	s_{xy}	σ_{xy}
Correlation	r_{xy}	ρ_{xy}

As measures of central location, we defined the mean, median, and mode. Then the concept of percentiles was used to describe other locations in the data set. Next, we presented the range, interquartile range, variance, standard deviation, and coefficient of variation as measures of variability or dispersion. Our primary measure of the shape of a data distribution was the skewness. Negative values indicate a data distribution skewed to the left. Positive values indicate a data distribution skewed to the right. We then described how the mean and standard deviation could be used, applying Chebyshev's theorem and the empirical rule, to provide more information about the distribution of data and to identify outliers.

In Section 3.4 we showed how to develop a five-number summary and a box plot to provide simultaneous information about the location, variability, and shape of the distribution. In Section 3.5 we introduced covariance and the correlation coefficient as measures of association between two variables. In the final section, we showed how to compute a weighted mean and how to calculate a mean, variance, and standard deviation for grouped data.

The descriptive statistics we discussed can be developed using statistical software packages and spreadsheets. In the chapter-ending appendixes we show how to use Minitab, Excel, and StatTools to develop the descriptive statistics introduced in this chapter.

Glossary

Sample statistic A numerical value used as a summary measure for a sample (e.g., the sample mean, $\bar{x}$, the sample variance, s^2, and the sample standard deviation, s).

Population parameter A numerical value used as a summary measure for a population (e.g., the population mean, μ, the population variance, σ^2, and the population standard deviation, σ).

Point estimator The sample statistic, such as $\bar{x}$, s^2, and s, when used to estimate the corresponding population parameter.

Mean A measure of central location computed by summing the data values and dividing by the number of observations.

Median A measure of central location provided by the value in the middle when the data are arranged in ascending order.

Mode A measure of location, defined as the value that occurs with greatest frequency.

Percentile A value such that at least p percent of the observations are less than or equal to this value and at least $(100 - p)$ percent of the observations are greater than or equal to this value. The 50th percentile is the median.

Quartiles The 25th, 50th, and 75th percentiles, referred to as the first quartile, the second quartile (median), and third quartile, respectively. The quartiles can be used to divide a data set into four parts, with each part containing approximately 25% of the data.

Range A measure of variability, defined to be the largest value minus the smallest value.

Interquartile range (IQR) A measure of variability, defined to be the difference between the third and first quartiles.

Variance A measure of variability based on the squared deviations of the data values about the mean.

Standard deviation A measure of variability computed by taking the positive square root of the variance.

Coefficient of variation A measure of relative variability computed by dividing the standard deviation by the mean and multiplying by 100.

Skewness A measure of the shape of a data distribution. Data skewed to the left result in negative skewness; a symmetric data distribution results in zero skewness; and data skewed to the right result in positive skewness.

z-score A value computed by dividing the deviation about the mean $(x_i - \bar{x})$ by the standard deviation s. A z-score is referred to as a standardized value and denotes the number of standard deviations x_i is from the mean.
Chebyshev's theorem A theorem that can be used to make statements about the proportion of data values that must be within a specified number of standard deviations of the mean.
Empirical rule A rule that can be used to compute the percentage of data values that must be within one, two, and three standard deviations of the mean for data that exhibit a bell-shaped distribution.
Outlier An unusually small or unusually large data value.
Five-number summary An exploratory data analysis technique that uses five numbers to summarize the data: smallest value, first quartile, median, third quartile, and largest value.
Box plot A graphical summary of data based on a five-number summary.
Covariance A measure of linear association between two variables. Positive values indicate a positive relationship; negative values indicate a negative relationship.
Correlation coefficient A measure of linear association between two variables that takes on values between -1 and $+1$. Values near $+1$ indicate a strong positive linear relationship; values near -1 indicate a strong negative linear relationship; and values near zero indicate the lack of a linear relationship.
Weighted mean The mean obtained by assigning each observation a weight that reflects its importance.
Grouped data Data available in class intervals as summarized by a frequency distribution. Individual values of the original data are not available.

Key Formulas

Sample Mean

$$\bar{x} = \frac{\Sigma x_i}{n} \tag{3.1}$$

Population Mean

$$\mu = \frac{\Sigma x_i}{N} \tag{3.2}$$

Interquartile Range

$$\text{IQR} = Q_3 - Q_1 \tag{3.3}$$

Population Variance

$$\sigma^2 = \frac{\Sigma(x_i - \mu)^2}{N} \tag{3.4}$$

Sample Variance

$$s^2 = \frac{\Sigma(x_i - \bar{x})^2}{n - 1} \tag{3.5}$$

Standard Deviation

$$\text{Sample standard deviation} = s = \sqrt{s^2} \tag{3.6}$$

$$\text{Population standard deviation} = \sigma = \sqrt{\sigma^2} \tag{3.7}$$

Coefficient of Variation

$$\left(\frac{\text{Standard deviation}}{\text{Mean}} \times 100\right)\% \tag{3.8}$$

***z*-Score**

$$z_i = \frac{x_i - \bar{x}}{s} \tag{3.9}$$

Sample Covariance

$$s_{xy} = \frac{\Sigma(x_i - \bar{x})(y_i - \bar{y})}{n - 1} \tag{3.10}$$

Population Covariance

$$\sigma_{xy} = \frac{\Sigma(x_i - \mu_x)(y_i - \mu_y)}{N} \tag{3.11}$$

Pearson Product Moment Correlation Coefficient: Sample Data

$$r_{xy} = \frac{s_{xy}}{s_x s_y} \tag{3.12}$$

Pearson Product Moment Correlation Coefficient: Population Data

$$\rho_{xy} = \frac{\sigma_{xy}}{\sigma_x \sigma_y} \tag{3.13}$$

Weighted Mean

$$\bar{x} = \frac{\Sigma w_i x_i}{\Sigma w_i} \tag{3.15}$$

Sample Mean for Grouped Data

$$\bar{x} = \frac{\Sigma f_i M_i}{n} \tag{3.16}$$

Sample Variance for Grouped Data

$$s^2 = \frac{\Sigma f_i (M_i - \bar{x})^2}{n - 1} \tag{3.17}$$

Population Mean for Grouped Data

$$\mu = \frac{\Sigma f_i M_i}{N} \tag{3.18}$$

Population Variance for Grouped Data

$$\sigma^2 = \frac{\Sigma f_i (M_i - \mu)^2}{N} \tag{3.19}$$

Supplementary Exercises

58. According to an annual consumer spending survey, the average monthly Bank of America Visa credit card charge was $1838 (*U.S. Airways Attaché Magazine,* December 2003). A sample of monthly credit card charges provides the following data.

WEB file Visa

236	1710	1351	825	7450
316	4135	1333	1584	387
991	3396	170	1428	1688

a. Compute the mean and median.
b. Compute the first and third quartiles.
c. Compute the range and interquartile range.
d. Compute the variance and standard deviation.
e. The skewness measure for these data is 2.12. Comment on the shape of this distribution. Is it the shape you would expect? Why or why not?
f. Do the data contain outliers?

59. The U.S. Census Bureau provides statistics on family life in the United States, including the age at the time of first marriage, current marital status, and size of household (U.S. Census Bureau website, March 20, 2006). The following data show the age at the time of first marriage for a sample of men and a sample of women.

WEB file Ages

Men	26	23	28	25	27	30	26	35	28
	21	24	27	29	30	27	32	27	25
Women	20	28	23	30	24	29	26	25	
	22	22	25	23	27	26	19		

a. Determine the median age at the time of first marriage for men and women.
b. Compute the first and third quartiles for both men and women.
c. Twenty-five years ago the median age at the time of first marriage was 25 for men and 22 for women. What insight does this information provide about the decision of when to marry among young people today?

60. Dividend yield is the annual dividend per share a company pays divided by the current market price per share expressed as a percentage. A sample of 10 large companies provided the following dividend yield data (*The Wall Street Journal,* January 16, 2004).

Company	Yield %	Company	Yield %
Altria Group	5.0	General Motors	3.7
American Express	0.8	JPMorgan Chase	3.5
Caterpillar	1.8	McDonald's	1.6
Eastman Kodak	1.9	United Technology	1.5
ExxonMobil	2.5	Wal-Mart Stores	0.7

a. What are the mean and median dividend yields?
b. What are the variance and standard deviation?
c. Which company provides the highest dividend yield?
d. What is the z-score for McDonald's? Interpret this z-score.
e. What is the z-score for General Motors? Interpret this z-score.
f. Based on z-scores, do the data contain any outliers?

61. The U.S. Department of Education reports that about 50% of all college students use a student loan to help cover college expenses (National Center for Educational Studies, January 2006). A sample of students who graduated with student loan debt is shown here. The data, in thousands of dollars, show typical amounts of debt upon graduation.

10.1	14.8	5.0	10.2	12.4	12.2	2.0	11.5	17.8	4.0

a. For those students who use a student loan, what is the mean loan debt upon graduation?
b. What is the variance? Standard deviation?

62. Small business owners often look to payroll service companies to handle their employee payroll. Reasons are that small business owners face complicated tax regulations and penalties for employment tax errors are costly. According to the Internal Revenue Service, 26% of all small business employment tax returns contained errors that resulted in a tax penalty to the owner (*The Wall Street Journal,* January 30, 2006). The tax penalty for a sample of 20 small business owners follows:

WEB file
Penalty

820	270	450	1010	890	700	1350	350	300	1200
390	730	2040	230	640	350	420	270	370	620

a. What is the mean tax penalty for improperly filed employment tax returns?
b. What is the standard deviation?
c. Is the highest penalty, $2040, an outlier?
d. What are some of the advantages of a small business owner hiring a payroll service company to handle employee payroll services, including the employment tax returns?

63. Public transportation and the automobile are two methods an employee can use to get to work each day. Samples of times recorded for each method are shown. Times are in minutes.

Public Transportation:	28	29	32	37	33	25	29	32	41	34
Automobile:	29	31	33	32	34	30	31	32	35	33

a. Compute the sample mean time to get to work for each method.
b. Compute the sample standard deviation for each method.
c. On the basis of your results from parts (a) and (b), which method of transportation should be preferred? Explain.
d. Develop a box plot for each method. Does a comparison of the box plots support your conclusion in part (c)?

64. The National Association of Realtors reported the median home price in the United States and the increase in median home price over a five-year period (*The Wall Street Journal,* January 16, 2006). Use the sample home prices shown here to answer the following questions.

WEB file
Homes

995.9	48.8	175.0	263.5	298.0	218.9	209.0
628.3	111.0	212.9	92.6	2325.0	958.0	212.5

a. What is the sample median home price?
b. In January 2001, the National Association of Realtors reported a median home price of $139,300 in the United States. What was the percentage increase in the median home price over the five-year period?
c. What are the first quartile and the third quartile for the sample data?
d. Provide a five-number summary for the home prices.
e. Do the data contain any outliers?
f. What is the mean home price for the sample? Why does the National Association of Realtors prefer to use the median home price in its reports?

65. The U.S. Census Bureau's American Community Survey reported the percentage of children under 18 years of age who had lived below the poverty level during the previous 12 months (U.S. Census Bureau website, August 2008). The region of the country, Northeast (NE), Southeast (SE), Midwest (MW), Southwest (SW), and West (W) and the percentage of children under 18 who had lived below the poverty level are shown for each state.

WEB file PovertyLevel

State	Region	Poverty %	State	Region	Poverty %
Alabama	SE	23.0	Montana	W	17.3
Alaska	W	15.1	Nebraska	MW	14.4
Arizona	SW	19.5	Nevada	W	13.9
Arkansas	SE	24.3	New Hampshire	NE	9.6
California	W	18.1	New Jersey	NE	11.8
Colorado	W	15.7	New Mexico	SW	25.6
Connecticut	NE	11.0	New York	NE	20.0
Delaware	NE	15.8	North Carolina	SE	20.2
Florida	SE	17.5	North Dakota	MW	13.0
Georgia	SE	20.2	Ohio	MW	18.7
Hawaii	W	11.4	Oklahoma	SW	24.3
Idaho	W	15.1	Oregon	W	16.8
Illinois	MW	17.1	Pennsylvania	NE	16.9
Indiana	MW	17.9	Rhode Island	NE	15.1
Iowa	MW	13.7	South Carolina	SE	22.1
Kansas	MW	15.6	South Dakota	MW	16.8
Kentucky	SE	22.8	Tennessee	SE	22.7
Louisiana	SE	27.8	Texas	SW	23.9
Maine	NE	17.6	Utah	W	11.9
Maryland	NE	9.7	Vermont	NE	13.2
Massachusetts	NE	12.4	Virginia	SE	12.2
Michigan	MW	18.3	Washington	W	15.4
Minnesota	MW	12.2	West Virginia	SE	25.2
Mississippi	SE	29.5	Wisconsin	MW	14.9
Missouri	MW	18.6	Wyoming	W	12.0

a. What is the median poverty level percentage for the 50 states?

b. What are the first and third quartiles? What is your interpretation of the quartiles?

c. Show a box plot for the data. Interpret the box plot in terms of what it tells you about the level of poverty for children in the United States. Are any states considered outliers? Discuss.

d. Identify the states in the lower quartile. What is your interpretation of this group and what region or regions are represented most in the lower quartile?

66. *Travel + Leisure* magazine presented its annual list of the 500 best hotels in the world (*Travel + Leisure,* January 2009). The magazine provides a rating for each hotel along with a brief description that includes the size of the hotel, amenities, and the cost per night for a double room. A sample of 12 of the top-rated hotels in the United States follows.

WEB file Travel

Hotel	Location	Rooms	Cost/Night
Boulders Resort & Spa	Phoenix, AZ	220	499
Disney's Wilderness Lodge	Orlando, FL	727	340
Four Seasons Hotel Beverly Hills	Los Angeles, CA	285	585
Four Seasons Hotel	Boston, MA	273	495
Hay-Adams	Washington, DC	145	495
Inn on Biltmore Estate	Asheville, NC	213	279
Loews Ventana Canyon Resort	Phoenix, AZ	398	279
Mauna Lani Bay Hotel	Island of Hawaii	343	455
Montage Laguna Beach	Laguna Beach, CA	250	595
Sofitel Water Tower	Chicago, IL	414	367
St. Regis Monarch Beach	Dana Point, CA	400	675
The Broadmoor	Colorado Springs, CO	700	420

a. What is the mean number of rooms?

b. What is the mean cost per night for a double room?

c. Develop a scatter diagram with the number of rooms on the horizontal axis and the cost per night on the vertical axis. Does there appear to be a relationship between the number of rooms and the cost per night? Discuss.
d. What is the sample correlation coefficient? What does it tell you about the relationship between the number of rooms and the cost per night for a double room? Does this appear reasonable? Discuss.

WEB file
FairValue

67. Morningstar tracks the performance of a large number of companies and publishes an evaluation of each. Along with a variety of financial data, Morningstar includes a Fair Value estimate for the price that should be paid for a share of the company's common stock. Data for 30 companies are available in the file named FairValue. The data include the Fair Value estimate per share of common stock, the most recent price per share, and the earning per share for the company (*Morningstar Stocks 500,* 2008).
   a. Develop a scatter diagram for the Fair Value and Share Price data with Share Price on the horizontal axis. What is the sample correlation coefficient, and what can you say about the relationship between the variables?
   b. Develop a scatter diagram for the Fair Value and Earnings per Share data with Earnings per Share on the horizontal axis. What is the sample correlation coefficient, and what can you say about the relationship between the variables?
68. Does a major league baseball team's record during spring training indicate how the team will play during the regular season? Over the last six years, the correlation coefficient between a team's winning percentage in spring training and its winning percentage in the regular season is .18 (*The Wall Street Journal,* March 30, 2009). Shown are the winning percentages for the 14 American League teams during the 2008 season.

WEB file
SpringTraining

Team	Spring Training	Regular Season	Team	Spring Training	Regular Season
Baltimore Orioles	.407	.422	Minnesota Twins	.500	.540
Boston Red Sox	.429	.586	New York Yankees	.577	.549
Chicago White Sox	.417	.546	Oakland A's	.692	.466
Cleveland Indians	.569	.500	Seattle Mariners	.500	.377
Detroit Tigers	.569	.457	Tampa Bay Rays	.731	.599
Kansas City Royals	.533	.463	Texas Rangers	.643	.488
Los Angeles Angels	.724	.617	Toronto Blue Jays	.448	.531

   a. What is the correlation coefficient between the spring training and the regular season winning percentages?
   b. What is your conclusion about a team's record during spring training indicating how the team will play during the regular season? What are some of the reasons why this occurs? Discuss.
69. The days to maturity for a sample of five money market funds are shown here. The dollar amounts invested in the funds are provided. Use the weighted mean to determine the mean number of days to maturity for dollars invested in these five money market funds.

Days to Maturity	Dollar Value ($millions)
20	20
12	30
7	10
5	15
6	10

70. Automobiles traveling on a road with a posted speed limit of 55 miles per hour are checked for speed by a state police radar system. Following is a frequency distribution of speeds.

Speed (miles per hour)	Frequency
45–49	10
50–54	40
55–59	150
60–64	175
65–69	75
70–74	15
75–79	10
Total	475

a. What is the mean speed of the automobiles traveling on this road?
b. Compute the variance and the standard deviation.

Case Problem 1 Pelican Stores

Pelican Stores, a division of National Clothing, is a chain of women's apparel stores operating throughout the country. The chain recently ran a promotion in which discount coupons were sent to customers of other National Clothing stores. Data collected for a sample of 100 in-store credit card transactions at Pelican Stores during one day while the promotion was running are contained in the file named PelicanStores. Table 3.12 shows a portion of the data set. The proprietary card method of payment refers to charges made using a National Clothing charge card. Customers who made a purchase using a discount

WEB file
PelicanStores

TABLE 3.12 SAMPLE OF 100 CREDIT CARD PURCHASES AT PELICAN STORES

Customer	Type of Customer	Items	Net Sales	Method of Payment	Gender	Marital Status	Age
1	Regular	1	39.50	Discover	Male	Married	32
2	Promotional	1	102.40	Proprietary Card	Female	Married	36
3	Regular	1	22.50	Proprietary Card	Female	Married	32
4	Promotional	5	100.40	Proprietary Card	Female	Married	28
5	Regular	2	54.00	MasterCard	Female	Married	34
6	Regular	1	44.50	MasterCard	Female	Married	44
7	Promotional	2	78.00	Proprietary Card	Female	Married	30
8	Regular	1	22.50	Visa	Female	Married	40
9	Promotional	2	56.52	Proprietary Card	Female	Married	46
10	Regular	1	44.50	Proprietary Card	Female	Married	36
⋮	⋮	⋮	⋮	⋮	⋮	⋮	⋮
96	Regular	1	39.50	MasterCard	Female	Married	44
97	Promotional	9	253.00	Proprietary Card	Female	Married	30
98	Promotional	10	287.59	Proprietary Card	Female	Married	52
99	Promotional	2	47.60	Proprietary Card	Female	Married	30
100	Promotional	1	28.44	Proprietary Card	Female	Married	44

coupon are referred to as promotional customers and customers who made a purchase but did not use a discount coupon are referred to as regular customers. Because the promotional coupons were not sent to regular Pelican Stores customers, management considers the sales made to people presenting the promotional coupons as sales it would not otherwise make. Of course, Pelican also hopes that the promotional customers will continue to shop at its stores.

Most of the variables shown in Table 3.12 are self-explanatory, but two of the variables require some clarification.

Items	The total number of items purchased
Net Sales	The total amount ($) charged to the credit card

Pelican's management would like to use this sample data to learn about its customer base and to evaluate the promotion involving discount coupons.

Managerial Report

Use the methods of descriptive statistics presented in this chapter to summarize the data and comment on your findings. At a minimum, your report should include the following:

1. Descriptive statistics on net sales and descriptive statistics on net sales by various classifications of customers.
2. Descriptive statistics concerning the relationship between age and net sales.

Case Problem 2 Motion Picture Industry

The motion picture industry is a competitive business. More than 50 studios produce a total of 300 to 400 new motion pictures each year, and the financial success of each motion picture varies considerably. The opening weekend gross sales, the total gross sales, the number of theaters the movie was shown in, and the number of weeks the motion picture was in the top 60 for gross sales are common variables used to measure the success of a motion picture. Data collected for a sample of 100 motion pictures produced in 2005 are contained in the file named Movies. Table 3.13 shows the data for the first 10 motion pictures in the file.

WEB file Movies

TABLE 3.13 PERFORMANCE DATA FOR 10 MOTION PICTURES

Motion Picture	Opening Gross Sales ($millions)	Total Gross Sales ($millions)	Number of Theaters	Weeks in Top 60
Coach Carter	29.17	67.25	2574	16
Ladies in Lavender	0.15	6.65	119	22
Batman Begins	48.75	205.28	3858	18
Unleashed	10.90	24.47	1962	8
Pretty Persuasion	0.06	0.23	24	4
Fever Pitch	12.40	42.01	3275	14
Harry Potter and the Goblet of Fire	102.69	287.18	3858	13
Monster-in-Law	23.11	82.89	3424	16
White Noise	24.11	55.85	2279	7
Mr. and Mrs. Smith	50.34	186.22	3451	21

Managerial Report

Use the numerical methods of descriptive statistics presented in this chapter to learn how these variables contribute to the success of a motion picture. Include the following in your report.

1. Descriptive statistics for each of the four variables along with a discussion of what the descriptive statistics tell us about the motion picture industry.
2. What motion pictures, if any, should be considered high-performance outliers? Explain.
3. Descriptive statistics showing the relationship between total gross sales and each of the other variables. Discuss.

Case Problem 3 Business Schools of Asia-Pacific

WEB file

Asian

The pursuit of a higher education degree in business is now international. A survey shows that more and more Asians choose the master of business administration (MBA) degree route to corporate success. As a result, the number of applicants for MBA courses at Asia-Pacific schools continues to increase.

Across the region, thousands of Asians show an increasing willingness to temporarily shelve their careers and spend two years in pursuit of a theoretical business qualification. Courses in these schools are notoriously tough and include economics, banking, marketing, behavioral sciences, labor relations, decision making, strategic thinking, business law, and more. The data set in Table 3.14 shows some of the characteristics of the leading Asia-Pacific business schools.

Managerial Report

Use the methods of descriptive statistics to summarize the data in Table 3.14. Discuss your findings.

1. Include a summary for each variable in the data set. Make comments and interpretations based on maximums and minimums, as well as the appropriate means and proportions. What new insights do these descriptive statistics provide concerning Asia-Pacific business schools?
2. Summarize the data to compare the following:
   a. Any difference between local and foreign tuition costs.
   b. Any difference between mean starting salaries for schools requiring and not requiring work experience.
   c. Any difference between starting salaries for schools requiring and not requiring English tests.
3. Do starting salaries appear to be related to tuition?
4. Present any additional graphical and numerical summaries that will be beneficial in communicating the data in Table 3.14 to others.

Case Problem 4 Heavenly Chocolates Website Transactions

Heavenly Chocolates manufactures and sells quality chocolate products at its plant and retail store located in Saratoga Springs, New York. Two years ago the company developed a website and began selling its products over the Internet. Website sales have exceeded the company's expectations, and mangement is now considering stragegies to increase sales even further. To learn more about the website customers, a sample of 50 Heavenly Chocolate transactions was selected from the previous month's sales. Data showing the day

TABLE 3.14 DATA FOR 25 ASIA-PACIFIC BUSINESS SCHOOLS

Business School	Full-Time Enrollment	Students per Faculty	Local Tuition ($)	Foreign Tuition ($)	Age	%Foreign	GMAT	English Test	Work Experience	Starting Salary ($)
Melbourne Business School	200	5	24,420	29,600	28	47	Yes	No	Yes	71,400
University of New South Wales (Sydney)	228	4	19,993	32,582	29	28	Yes	No	Yes	65,200
Indian Institute of Management (Ahmedabad)	392	5	4,300	4,300	22	0	No	No	No	7,100
Chinese University of Hong Kong	90	5	11,140	11,140	29	10	Yes	No	No	31,000
International University of Japan (Niigata)	126	4	33,060	33,060	28	60	Yes	Yes	No	87,000
Asian Institute of Management (Manila)	389	5	7,562	9,000	25	50	Yes	No	Yes	22,800
Indian Institute of Management (Bangalore)	380	5	3,935	16,000	23	1	Yes	No	No	7,500
National University of Singapore	147	6	6,146	7,170	29	51	Yes	Yes	Yes	43,300
Indian Institute of Management (Calcutta)	463	8	2,880	16,000	23	0	No	No	No	7,400
Australian National University (Canberra)	42	2	20,300	20,300	30	80	Yes	Yes	Yes	46,600
Nanyang Technological University (Singapore)	50	5	8,500	8,500	32	20	Yes	No	Yes	49,300
University of Queensland (Brisbane)	138	17	16,000	22,800	32	26	No	No	Yes	49,600
Hong Kong University of Science and Technology	60	2	11,513	11,513	26	37	Yes	No	Yes	34,000
Macquarie Graduate School of Management (Sydney)	12	8	17,172	19,778	34	27	No	No	Yes	60,100
Chulalongkorn University (Bangkok)	200	7	17,355	17,355	25	6	Yes	No	Yes	17,600
Monash Mt. Eliza Business School (Melbourne)	350	13	16,200	22,500	30	30	Yes	Yes	Yes	52,500
Asian Institute of Management (Bangkok)	300	10	18,200	18,200	29	90	No	Yes	Yes	25,000
University of Adelaide	20	19	16,426	23,100	30	10	No	No	Yes	66,000
Massey University (Palmerston North, New Zealand)	30	15	13,106	21,625	37	35	No	Yes	Yes	41,400
Royal Melbourne Institute of Technology Business Graduate School	30	7	13,880	17,765	32	30	No	Yes	Yes	48,900
Jamnalal Bajaj Institute of Management Studies (Mumbai)	240	9	1,000	1,000	24	0	No	No	Yes	7,000
Curtin Institute of Technology (Perth)	98	15	9,475	19,097	29	43	Yes	No	Yes	55,000
Lahore University of Management Sciences	70	14	11,250	26,300	23	2.5	No	No	No	7,500
Universiti Sains Malaysia (Penang)	30	5	2,260	2,260	32	15	No	Yes	Yes	16,000
De La Salle University (Manila)	44	17	3,300	3,600	28	3.5	Yes	No	Yes	13,100

TABLE 3.15 A SAMPLE OF 50 HEAVENLY CHOCOLATES WEBSITE TRANSACTIONS

Customer	Day	Browser	Time (min)	Pages Viewed	Amount Spent ($)
1	Mon	Internet Explorer	12.0	4	54.52
2	Wed	Other	19.5	6	94.90
3	Mon	Internet Explorer	8.5	4	26.68
4	Tue	Firefox	11.4	2	44.73
5	Wed	Internet Explorer	11.3	4	66.27
6	Sat	Firefox	10.5	6	67.80
7	Sun	Internet Explorer	11.4	2	36.04
.	.	.	.	.	.
.	.	.	.	.	.
.	.	.	.	.	.
48	Fri	Internet Explorer	9.7	5	103.15
49	Mon	Other	7.3	6	52.15
50	Fri	Internet Explorer	13.4	3	98.75

WEB file
Shoppers

of the week each transaction was made, the type of browser the customer used, the time spent on the website, the number of website pages viewed, and the amount spent by each of the 50 customers are contained in the file named Shoppers. A portion of the data are shown in Table 3.15.

Heavenly Chocolates would like to use the sample data to determine if online shoppers who spend more time and view more pages also spend more money during their visit to the website. The company would also like to investigate the effect that the day of the week and the type of browser have on sales.

Managerial Report

Use the methods of descriptive statistics to learn about the customers who visit the Heavenly Chocolates website. Include the following in your report.

1. Graphical and numerical summaries for the length of time the shopper spends on the website, the number of pages viewed, and the mean amount spent per transaction. Discuss what you learn about Heavenly Cholcolates' online shoppers from these numerical summaries.
2. Summarize the frequency, the total dollars spent, and the mean amount spent per transaction for each day of week. What observations can you make about Hevenly Chocolates' business based on the day of the week? Discuss.
3. Summarize the frequency, the total dollars spent, and the mean amount spent per transaction for each type of browser. What observations can you make about Heavenly Chocolate's business based on the type of browser? Discuss.
4. Develop a scatter diagram and compute the sample correlation coefficient to explore the relationship between the time spent on the website and the dollar amount spent. Use the horizontal axis for the time spent on the website. Discuss.
5. Develop a scatter diagram and compute the sample correlation coefficient to explore the relationship between the the number of website pages viewed and the amount spent. Use the horizontal axis for the number of website pages viewed. Discuss.
6. Develop a scatter diagram and compute the sample correlation coefficient to explore the relationship between the time spent on the website and the number of pages viewed. Use the horizontal axis to represent the number of pages viewed. Discuss.

Appendix 3.1 Descriptive Statistics Using Minitab

In this appendix, we describe how Minitab can be used to compute a variety of descriptive statistics and display box plots. We then show how Minitab can be used to obtain covariance and correlation measures for two variables.

Descriptive Statistics

WEB file
StartSalary

Table 3.1 provided the starting salaries for 12 business school graduates. These data are in column C2 of the file StartSalary. The following steps can be used to generate descriptive statistics for the starting salary data.

Step 1. Select the **Stat** menu
Step 2. Choose **Basic Statistics**
Step 3. Choose **Display Descriptive Statistics**
Step 4. When the Display Descriptive Statistics dialog box appears:
Enter C2 in the **Variables** box
Click **OK**

Figure 3.12 shows the descriptive statistics obtained using Minitab. Definitions of the headings follow.

N	number of data values	Minimum	minimum data value
N*	number of missing data values	Q1	first quartile
Mean	mean	Median	median
SE Mean	standard error of mean	Q3	third quartile
StDev	standard deviation	Maximum	maximum data value

The label SE Mean refers to the *standard error of the mean.* It is computed by dividing the standard deviation by the square root of *N*. The interpretation and use of this measure are discussed in Chapter 7 when we introduce the topics of sampling and sampling distributions.

The ten descriptive statistics shown in Figure 3.12 are the default descriptive statistics selected automatically by Minitab. These descriptive statistics are of interest to the majority of users. However, Minitab provides fifteen additional descriptive statistics that may be selected depending upon the preferences of the user. The variance, coefficient of variation, range, interquartile range, mode, and skewness are among the additional descriptive statistics available. To select one or more of these additional descriptive statistics, modify step 4 as follows.

Step 4. When the Display Descriptive Statistics dialog box appears:
Enter C2 in the **Variables** box
Click **Statistics**
Select the **descriptive statistics** you wish to obtain or choose **All** to obtain all 25 descriptive statistics
Click **OK**
Click **OK**

FIGURE 3.12 DESCRIPTIVE STATISTICS PROVIDED BY MINITAB

N	N*	Mean	SEMean	StDev
12	0	3540.0	47.8	165.7
Minimum	Q1	Median	Q3	Maximum
3310.0	3457.5	3505.0	3625.0	3925.0

Finally, note that Minitab's quartiles $Q_1 = 3457.5$ and $Q_3 = 3625$ are slightly different from the quartiles $Q_1 = 3465$ and $Q_3 = 3600$ computed in Section 3.1. The different conventions* used to identify the quartiles explain this variation. Hence, the values of Q_1 and Q_3 provided by one convention may not be identical to the values of Q_1 and Q_3 provided by another convention. Any differences tend to be negligible, however, and the results provided should not mislead the user in making the usual interpretations associated with quartiles.

Box Plot

The following steps use the file StartSalary to generate the box plot for the starting salary data.

Step 1. Select the **Graph** menu
Step 2. Choose **Boxplot**
Step 3. Select **Simple** and click **OK**
Step 4. When the Boxplot-One Y, Simple dialog box appears:
Enter C2 in the **Graph variables** box
Click **OK**

Covariance and Correlation

WEB file
Stereo

Table 3.6 provided for the number of commercials and the sales volume for a stereo and sound equipment store. These data are available in the file Stereo, with the number of commercials in column C2 and the sales volume in column C3. The following steps show how Minitab can be used to compute the covariance for the two variables.

Step 1. Select the **Stat** menu
Step 2. Choose **Basic Statistics**
Step 3. Choose **Covariance**
Step 4. When the Covariance dialog box appears:
Enter C2 C3 in the **Variables** box
Click **OK**

To obtain the correlation coefficient for the number of commercials and the sales volume, only one change is necessary in the preceding procedure. In step 3, choose the **Correlation** option.

Appendix 3.2 Descriptive Statistics Using Excel

Excel can be used to generate the descriptive statistics discussed in this chapter. We show how Excel can be used to generate several measures of location and variability for a single variable and to generate the covariance and correlation coefficient as measures of association between two variables.

Using Excel Functions

Excel provides functions for computing the mean, median, mode, sample variance, and sample standard deviation. We illustrate the use of these Excel functions by computing the mean, median,

*With the n observations arranged in ascending order (smallest value to largest value), Minitab uses the positions given by $(n + 1)/4$ and $3(n + 1)/4$ to locate Q_1 and Q_3, respectively. When a position is fractional, Minitab interpolates between the two adjacent ordered data values to determine the corresponding quartile.

FIGURE 3.13 USING EXCEL FUNCTIONS FOR COMPUTING THE MEAN, MEDIAN, MODE, VARIANCE, AND STANDARD DEVIATION

	A	B	C	D	E	F
1	Graduate	Starting Salary		Mean	=AVERAGE(B2:B13)	
2	1	3450		Median	=MEDIAN(B2:B13)	
3	2	3550		Mode	=MODE.SNGL(B2:B13)	
4	3	3650		Variance	=VAR(B2:B13)	
5	4	3480		Standard Deviation	=STDEV(B2:B13)	
6	5	3355				
7	6	3310				
8	7	3490				
9	8	3730				
10	9	3540				
11	10	3925				
12	11	3520				
13	12	3480				
14						

	A	B	C	D	E	F
1	Graduate	Starting Salary		Mean	3540	
2	1	3450		Median	3505	
3	2	3550		Mode	3480	
4	3	3650		Variance	27440.91	
5	4	3480		Standard Deviation	165.65	
6	5	3355				
7	6	3310				
8	7	3490				
9	8	3730				
10	9	3540				
11	10	3925				
12	11	3520				
13	12	3480				
14						

WEB file StartSalary

mode, sample variance, and sample standard deviation for the starting salary data in Table 3.1. Refer to Figure 3.13 as we describe the steps involved. The data are entered in column B.

Excel's AVERAGE function can be used to compute the mean by entering the following formula into cell E1:

=AVERAGE(B2:B13)

Similarly, the formulas =MEDIAN(B2:B13), =MODE.SNGL(B2:B13), =VAR(B2:B13), and =STDEV(B2:B13) are entered into cells E2:E5, respectively, to compute the median, mode, variance, and standard deviation. The worksheet in the foreground shows that the values computed using the Excel functions are the same as we computed earlier in the chapter.

WEB file Stereo

Excel also provides functions that can be used to compute the sample covariance and the sample correlation coefficient. We show here how these functions can be used to compute the sample covariance and the sample correlation coefficient for the stereo and sound equipment store data in Table 3.7. Refer to Figure 3.14 as we present the steps involved.

Excel's sample covariance function, COVAR.S, can be used to compute the sample covariance by entering the following formula into cell F1:

=COVAR.S(B2:B11,C2:C11)

Similarly, the formula =CORREL(B2:B11,C2:C11) is entered into cell F2 to compute the sample correlation coefficient. The worksheet in the foreground shows the values computed using the Excel functions. Note that the value of the sample covariance (11) is the same as

FIGURE 3.14 USING EXCEL FUNCTIONS FOR COMPUTING COVARIANCE AND CORRELATION

	A	B	C	D	E	F	G
1	**Week**	**Commercials**	**Sales**		**Population Covariance**	=COVAR.S(B2:B11,C2:C11)	
2	1	2	50		**Sample Correlation**	=CORREL(B2:B11,C2:C11)	
3	2	5	57				
4	3	1	41				
5	4	3	54				
6	5	4	54				
7	6	1	38				
8	7	5	63				
9	8	3	48				
10	9	4	59				
11	10	2	46				
12							

	A	B	C	D	E	F	G
1	**Week**	**Commercials**	**Sales**		**Sample Covariance**	11	
2	1	2	50		**Sample Correlation**	0.93	
3	2	5	57				
4	3	1	41				
5	4	3	54				
6	5	4	54				
7	6	1	38				
8	7	5	63				
9	8	3	48				
10	9	4	59				
11	10	2	46				
12							

computed using equation (3.10). And the value of the sample correlation coefficient (.93) is the same as computed using equation (3.12).

Using Excel's Descriptive Statistics Tool

WEB file

StartSalary

As we already demonstrated, Excel provides statistical functions to compute descriptive statistics for a data set. These functions can be used to compute one statistic at a time (e.g., mean, variance, etc.). Excel also provides a variety of Data Analysis Tools. One of these tools, called Descriptive Statistics, allows the user to compute a variety of descriptive statistics at once. We show here how it can be used to compute descriptive statistics for the starting salary data in Table 3.1.

Step 1. Click the **Data** tab on the Ribbon
Step 2. In the **Analysis** group, click **Data Analysis**
Step 3. When the Data Analysis dialog box appears:
Choose **Descriptive Statistics**
Step 4. When the Descriptive Statistics dialog box appears:
Enter B1:B13 in the **Input Range** box
Select **Grouped By Columns**
Select **Labels in First Row**
Select **Output Range**
Enter D1 in the **Output Range** box (to identify the upper left-hand corner of the section of the worksheet where the descriptive statistics will appear)
Select **Summary statistics**
Click **OK**

Cells D1:E15 of Figure 3.15 show the descriptive statistics provided by Excel. The boldface entries are the descriptive statistics we covered in this chapter. The descriptive statistics that are not boldface are either covered subsequently in the text or discussed in more advanced texts.

FIGURE 3.15 EXCEL'S DESCRIPTIVE STATISTICS TOOL OUTPUT

	A	B	C	D	E	F
1	**Graduate**	**Starting Salary**		*Starting Salary*		
2	1	3450				
3	2	3550		**Mean**	3540	
4	3	3650		Standard Error	47.82	
5	4	3480		**Median**	3505	
6	5	3355		**Mode**	3480	
7	6	3310		**Standard Deviation**	165.65	
8	7	3490		**Sample Variance**	27440.91	
9	8	3730		Kurtosis	1.7189	
10	9	3540		**Skewness**	1.0911	
11	10	3925		**Range**	615	
12	11	3520		**Minimum**	3310	
13	12	3480		**Maximum**	3925	
14				**Sum**	42480	
15				**Count**	12	
16						

Appendix 3.3 Descriptive Statistics Using StatTools

In this appendix, we describe how StatTools can be used to compute a variety of descriptive statistics and also display box plots. We then show how StatTools can be used to obtain covariance and correlation measures for two variables.

Descriptive Statistics

WEB file
StartSalary

We use the starting salary data in Table 3.1 to illustrate. Begin by using the Data Set Manager to create a StatTools data set for these data using the procedure described in the appendix in Chapter 1. The following steps will generate a variety of descriptive statistics.

Step 1. Click the **StatTools** tab on the Ribbon
Step 2. In the **Analyses Group,** click **Summary Statistics**
Step 3. Choose the **One-Variable Summary** option
Step 4. When the One-Variable Summary Statistics dialog box appears:
In the **Variables** section, select **Starting Salary**
Click **OK**

A variety of descriptive statistics will appear.

Box Plots

We use the starting salary data in Table 3.1 to illustrate. Begin by using the Data Set Manager to create a StatTools data set for these data using the procedure described in the appendix in Chapter 1. The following steps will create a box plot for these data.

WEB file
StartSalary

Step 1. Click the **StatTools** tab on the Ribbon
Step 2. In the **Analyses Group,** click **Summary Graphs**
Step 3. Choose the **Box-Whisker Plot** option

Step 4. When the StatTools-Box-Whisker Plot dialog box appears:
In the Variables section, select **Starting Salary**
Click **OK**

The symbol □ is used to identify an outlier and x is used to identify the mean.

Covariance and Correlation

We use the stereo and sound equipment data in Table 3.7 to demonstrate the computation of the sample covariance and the sample correlation coefficient. Begin by using the Data Set Manager to create a StatTools data set for these data using the procedure described in the appendix in Chapter 1. The following steps will provide the sample covariance and sample correlation coefficient.

WEB file
Stereo

Step 1. Click the **StatTools** tab on the Ribbon
Step 2. In the **Analyses Group,** click **Summary Statistics**
Step 3. Choose the **Correlation and Covariance** option
Step 4. When the StatTools-Correlation and Covariance dialog box appears:
In the **Variables** section
Select **No. of Commercials**
Select **Sales Volume**
In the **Tables to Create** section,
Select **Table of Correlations**
Select **Table of Covariances**
In the **Table Structure** section select **Symmetric**
Click **OK**

A table showing the correlation coefficient and the covariance will appear.

CHAPTER 4

Introduction to Probability

CONTENTS

STATISTICS *in* PRACTICE

OCEANWIDE SEAFOOD*
SPRINGBORO, OHIO

Oceanwide Seafood is the leading provider of quality seafood in southwestern Ohio. The company stocks over 90 varieties of fresh and frozen seafood products from around the world and prepares specialty cuts according to customer specifications. Customers include major restaurants and retail food stores in Ohio, Kentucky, and Indiana. Established in 2005, the company has become successful by providing superior customer service and exceptional quality seafood.

Probability and statistical information are used for both operational and marketing decisions. For instance, a time series showing monthly sales is used to track the company's growth and to set future target sales levels. Statistics such as the mean customer order size and the mean number of days a customer takes to make payments help identify the firm's best customers as well as provide benchmarks for handling accounts receivable issues. In addition, data on monthly inventory levels are used in the analysis of operating profits and trends in product sales.

Probability analysis has helped Oceanwide determine reasonable and profitable prices for its products. For example, when Oceanwide receives a whole fresh fish from one of its suppliers, the fish must be processed and cut to fill individual customer orders. A fresh 100-pound whole tuna packed in ice might cost Oceanwide \$500. At first glance, the company's cost for tuna appears to be \$500/100 = \$5 per pound. However, due to the loss in the processing and cutting operation, a 100-pound whole tuna will not provide 100 pounds of finished product. If the processing and cutting operation yields 75% of the whole tuna, the number of pounds of finished product available for sale to customers would be .75(100) = 75 pounds, not 100 pounds. In this case, the company's actual cost of tuna would be \$500/75 = \$6.67 per pound. Thus, Oceanwide would need to use a cost of \$6.67 per pound to determine a profitable price to charge its customers.

*The authors are indebted to Dale Hartlage, president of Oceanwide Seafood Company, for providing this Statistics in Practice.

Fresh bluefin tuna are shipped to Oceanwide Seafood almost everyday © Gregor Kervina, 2009/ Used under license from Shutterstock.com.

To help determine the yield percentage that is likely for processing and cutting whole tuna, data were collected on the yields from a sample of whole tunas. Let Y denote the yield percentage for whole tuna. Using the data, Oceanwide was able to determine that 5% of the time the yield for whole tuna was at least 90%. In conditional probability notation, this probability is written $P(Y \geq 90\% \mid \text{Tuna}) = .05$; in other words, the probability that the yield will be at least 90% given that the fish is a tuna is .05. If Oceanwide established the selling price for tuna based on a 90% yield, 95% of the time the company would realize a yield less than expected. As a result, the company would be understating its cost per pound and also understating the price of tuna for its customers. Additional conditional probability information for other yield percentages helped management select an 70% yield as the basis for determining the cost of tuna and the price to charge its customers. Similar conditional probabilities for other seafood products helped management establish pricing yield percentages for each type of seafood product. In this chapter, you will learn how to compute and interpret conditional probabilities and other probabilities that are helpful in the decision-making process.

Managers often base their decisions on an analysis of uncertainties such as the following:

1. What are the chances that sales will decrease if we increase prices?
2. What is the likelihood a new assembly method will increase productivity?
3. How likely is it that the project will be finished on time?
4. What is the chance that a new investment will be profitable?

Some of the earliest work on probability originated in a series of letters between Pierre de Fermat and Blaise Pascal in the 1650s.

Probability is a numerical measure of the likelihood that an event will occur. Thus, probabilities can be used as measures of the degree of uncertainty associated with the four events previously listed. If probabilities are available, we can determine the likelihood of each event occurring.

Probability values are always assigned on a scale from 0 to 1. A probability near zero indicates an event is unlikely to occur; a probability near 1 indicates an event is almost certain to occur. Other probabilities between 0 and 1 represent degrees of likelihood that an event will occur. For example, if we consider the event "rain tomorrow," we understand that when the weather report indicates "a near-zero probability of rain," it means almost no chance of rain. However, if a .90 probability of rain is reported, we know that rain is likely to occur. A .50 probability indicates that rain is just as likely to occur as not. Figure 4.1 depicts the view of probability as a numerical measure of the likelihood of an event occurring.

4.1 Experiments, Counting Rules, and Assigning Probabilities

In discussing probability, we define an **experiment** as a process that generates well-defined outcomes. On any single repetition of an experiment, one and only one of the possible experimental outcomes will occur. Several examples of experiments and their associated outcomes follow.

Experiment	Experimental Outcomes
Toss a coin	Head, tail
Select a part for inspection	Defective, nondefective
Conduct a sales call	Purchase, no purchase
Roll a die	1, 2, 3, 4, 5, 6
Play a football game	Win, lose, tie

By specifying all possible experimental outcomes, we identify the **sample space** for an experiment.

SAMPLE SPACE

The sample space for an experiment is the set of all experimental outcomes.

Experimental outcomes are also called sample points.

An experimental outcome is also called a **sample point** to identify it as an element of the sample space.

FIGURE 4.1 PROBABILITY AS A NUMERICAL MEASURE OF THE LIKELIHOOD OF AN EVENT OCCURRING

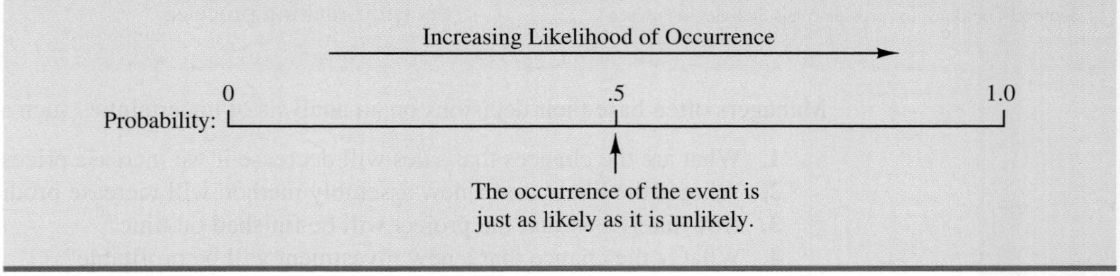

Consider the first experiment in the preceding table—tossing a coin. The upward face of the coin—a head or a tail—determines the experimental outcomes (sample points). If we let S denote the sample space, we can use the following notation to describe the sample space.

$$S = \{\text{Head, Tail}\}$$

The sample space for the second experiment in the table—selecting a part for inspection—can be described as follows:

$$S = \{\text{Defective, Nondefective}\}$$

Both of the experiments just described have two experimental outcomes (sample points). However, suppose we consider the fourth experiment listed in the table—rolling a die. The possible experimental outcomes, defined as the number of dots appearing on the upward face of the die, are the six points in the sample space for this experiment.

$$S = \{1, 2, 3, 4, 5, 6\}$$

Counting Rules, Combinations, and Permutations

Being able to identify and count the experimental outcomes is a necessary step in assigning probabilities. We now discuss three useful counting rules.

Multiple-step experiments The first counting rule applies to multiple-step experiments. Consider the experiment of tossing two coins. Let the experimental outcomes be defined in terms of the pattern of heads and tails appearing on the upward faces of the two coins. How many experimental outcomes are possible for this experiment? The experiment of tossing two coins can be thought of as a two-step experiment in which step 1 is the tossing of the first coin and step 2 is the tossing of the second coin. If we use H to denote a head and T to denote a tail, (H, H) indicates the experimental outcome with a head on the first coin and a head on the second coin. Continuing this notation, we can describe the sample space (S) for this coin-tossing experiment as follows:

$$S = \{(H, H), (H, T), (T, H), (T, T)\}$$

Thus, we see that four experimental outcomes are possible. In this case, we can easily list all of the experimental outcomes.

The counting rule for multiple-step experiments makes it possible to determine the number of experimental outcomes without listing them.

COUNTING RULE FOR MULTIPLE-STEP EXPERIMENTS

If an experiment can be described as a sequence of k steps with n_1 possible outcomes on the first step, n_2 possible outcomes on the second step, and so on, then the total number of experimental outcomes is given by $(n_1)\,(n_2)\,\ldots\,(n_k)$.

Viewing the experiment of tossing two coins as a sequence of first tossing one coin ($n_1 = 2$) and then tossing the other coin ($n_2 = 2$), we can see from the counting rule that $(2)(2) = 4$ distinct experimental outcomes are possible. As shown, they are $S = \{(H, H), (H, T), (T, H), (T, T)\}$. The number of experimental outcomes in an experiment involving tossing six coins is $(2)(2)(2)(2)(2)(2) = 64$.

FIGURE 4.2 TREE DIAGRAM FOR THE EXPERIMENT OF TOSSING TWO COINS

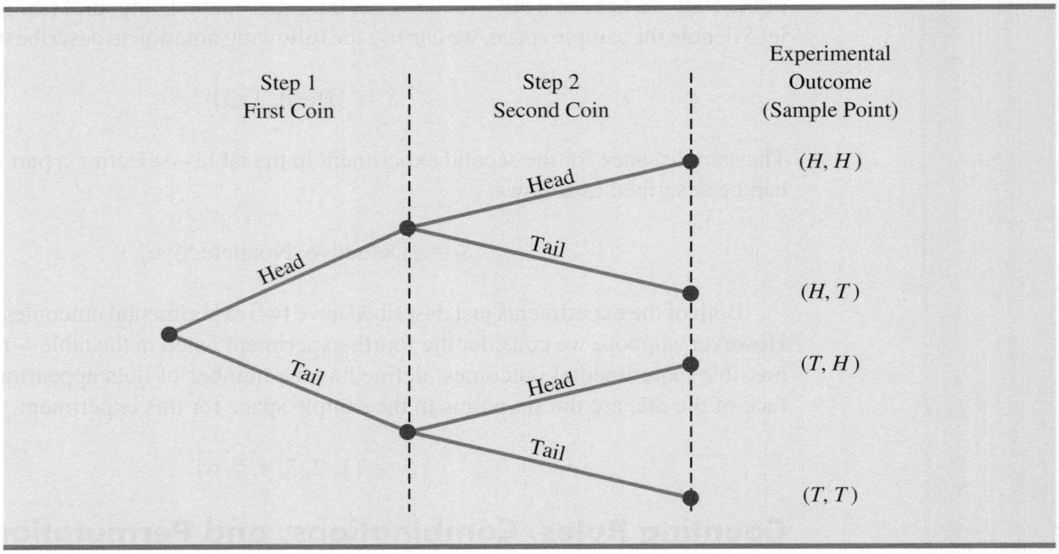

Without the tree diagram, one might think only three experimental outcomes are possible for two tosses of a coin: 0 heads, 1 head, and 2 heads.

A **tree diagram** is a graphical representation that helps in visualizing a multiple-step experiment. Figure 4.2 shows a tree diagram for the experiment of tossing two coins. The sequence of steps moves from left to right through the tree. Step 1 corresponds to tossing the first coin, and step 2 corresponds to tossing the second coin. For each step, the two possible outcomes are head or tail. Note that for each possible outcome at step 1 two branches correspond to the two possible outcomes at step 2. Each of the points on the right end of the tree corresponds to an experimental outcome. Each path through the tree from the leftmost node to one of the nodes at the right side of the tree corresponds to a unique sequence of outcomes.

Let us now see how the counting rule for multiple-step experiments can be used in the analysis of a capacity expansion project for the Kentucky Power & Light Company (KP&L). KP&L is starting a project designed to increase the generating capacity of one of its plants in northern Kentucky. The project is divided into two sequential stages or steps: stage 1 (design) and stage 2 (construction). Even though each stage will be scheduled and controlled as closely as possible, management cannot predict beforehand the exact time required to complete each stage of the project. An analysis of similar construction projects revealed possible completion times for the design stage of 2, 3, or 4 months and possible completion times for the construction stage of 6, 7, or 8 months. In addition, because of the critical need for additional electrical power, management set a goal of 10 months for the completion of the entire project.

Because this project has three possible completion times for the design stage (step 1) and three possible completion times for the construction stage (step 2), the counting rule for multiple-step experiments can be applied here to determine a total of $(3)(3) = 9$ experimental outcomes. To describe the experimental outcomes, we use a two-number notation; for instance, (2, 6) indicates that the design stage is completed in 2 months and the construction stage is completed in 6 months. This experimental outcome results in a total of $2 + 6 = 8$ months to complete the entire project. Table 4.1 summarizes the nine experimental outcomes for the KP&L problem. The tree diagram in Figure 4.3 shows how the nine outcomes (sample points) occur.

The counting rule and tree diagram help the project manager identify the experimental outcomes and determine the possible project completion times. From the information in

TABLE 4.1 EXPERIMENTAL OUTCOMES (SAMPLE POINTS) FOR THE KP&L PROJECT

Completion Time (months)			
Stage 1 Design	**Stage 2 Construction**	**Notation for Experimental Outcome**	**Total Project Completion Time (months)**
2	6	(2, 6)	8
2	7	(2, 7)	9
2	8	(2, 8)	10
3	6	(3, 6)	9
3	7	(3, 7)	10
3	8	(3, 8)	11
4	6	(4, 6)	10
4	7	(4, 7)	11
4	8	(4, 8)	12

FIGURE 4.3 TREE DIAGRAM FOR THE KP&L PROJECT

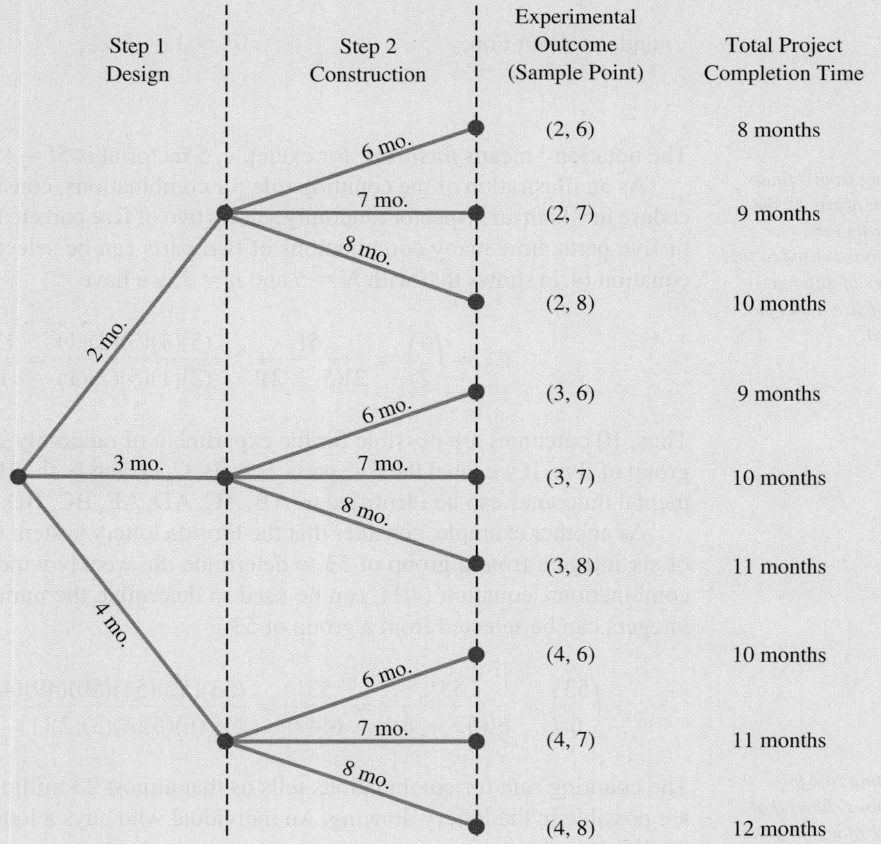

Figure 4.3, we see that the project will be completed in 8 to 12 months, with six of the nine experimental outcomes providing the desired completion time of 10 months or less. Even though identifying the experimental outcomes may be helpful, we need to consider how probability values can be assigned to the experimental outcomes before making an assessment of the probability that the project will be completed within the desired 10 months.

Combinations A second useful counting rule allows one to count the number of experimental outcomes when the experiment involves selecting n objects from a (usually larger) set of N objects. It is called the counting rule for combinations.

COUNTING RULE FOR COMBINATIONS

The number of combinations of N objects taken n at a time is

$$C_n^N = \binom{N}{n} = \frac{N!}{n!(N-n)!} \tag{4.1}$$

where

$$N! = N(N-1)(N-2)\cdots(2)(1)$$
$$n! = n(n-1)(n-2)\cdots(2)(1)$$

and, by definition,

$$0! = 1$$

In sampling from a finite population of size N, the counting rule for combinations is used to find the number of different samples of size n that can be selected.

The notation ! means *factorial;* for example, 5 factorial is $5! = (5)(4)(3)(2)(1) = 120$.

As an illustration of the counting rule for combinations, consider a quality control procedure in which an inspector randomly selects two of five parts to test for defects. In a group of five parts, how many combinations of two parts can be selected? The counting rule in equation (4.1) shows that with $N = 5$ and $n = 2$, we have

$$C_2^5 = \binom{5}{2} = \frac{5!}{2!(5-2)!} = \frac{(5)(4)(3)(2)(1)}{(2)(1)(3)(2)(1)} = \frac{120}{12} = 10$$

Thus, 10 outcomes are possible for the experiment of randomly selecting two parts from a group of five. If we label the five parts as A, B, C, D, and E, the 10 combinations or experimental outcomes can be identified as AB, AC, AD, AE, BC, BD, BE, CD, CE, and DE.

As another example, consider that the Florida lottery system uses the random selection of six integers from a group of 53 to determine the weekly winner. The counting rule for combinations, equation (4.1), can be used to determine the number of ways six different integers can be selected from a group of 53.

$$\binom{53}{6} = \frac{53!}{6!(53-6)!} = \frac{53!}{6!47!} = \frac{(53)(52)(51)(50)(49)(48)}{(6)(5)(4)(3)(2)(1)} = 22{,}957{,}480$$

The counting rule for combinations shows that the chance of winning the lottery is very unlikely.

The counting rule for combinations tells us that almost 23 million experimental outcomes are possible in the lottery drawing. An individual who buys a lottery ticket has 1 chance in 22,957,480 of winning.

Permutations A third counting rule that is sometimes useful is the counting rule for permutations. It allows one to compute the number of experimental outcomes when n objects are to be selected from a set of N objects where the order of selection is important. The same n objects selected in a different order are considered a different experimental outcome.

COUNTING RULE FOR PERMUTATIONS

The number of permutations of N objects taken n at a time is given by

$$P_n^N = n!\binom{N}{n} = \frac{N!}{(N-n)!} \quad \textbf{(4.2)}$$

The counting rule for permutations closely relates to the one for combinations; however, an experiment results in more permutations than combinations for the same number of objects because every selection of n objects can be ordered in $n!$ different ways.

As an example, consider again the quality control process in which an inspector selects two of five parts to inspect for defects. How many permutations may be selected? The counting rule in equation (4.2) shows that with $N = 5$ and $n = 2$, we have

$$P_2^5 = \frac{5!}{(5-2)!} = \frac{5!}{3!} = \frac{(5)(4)(3)(2)(1)}{(3)(2)(1)} = \frac{120}{6} = 20$$

Thus, 20 outcomes are possible for the experiment of randomly selecting two parts from a group of five when the order of selection must be taken into account. If we label the parts A, B, C, D, and E, the 20 permutations are AB, BA, AC, CA, AD, DA, AE, EA, BC, CB, BD, DB, BE, EB, CD, DC, CE, EC, DE, and ED.

Assigning Probabilities

Now let us see how probabilities can be assigned to experimental outcomes. The three approaches most frequently used are the classical, relative frequency, and subjective methods. Regardless of the method used, two **basic requirements for assigning probabilities** must be met.

BASIC REQUIREMENTS FOR ASSIGNING PROBABILITIES

1. The probability assigned to each experimental outcome must be between 0 and 1, inclusively. If we let E_i denote the ith experimental outcome and $P(E_i)$ its probability, then this requirement can be written as

$$0 \le P(E_i) \le 1 \text{ for all } i \quad \textbf{(4.3)}$$

2. The sum of the probabilities for all the experimental outcomes must equal 1.0. For n experimental outcomes, this requirement can be written as

$$P(E_1) + P(E_2) + \cdots + P(E_n) = 1 \quad \textbf{(4.4)}$$

The **classical method** of assigning probabilities is appropriate when all the experimental outcomes are equally likely. If n experimental outcomes are possible, a probability of $1/n$ is assigned to each experimental outcome. When using this approach, the two basic requirements for assigning probabilities are automatically satisfied.

For an example, consider the experiment of tossing a fair coin; the two experimental outcomes—head and tail—are equally likely. Because one of the two equally likely outcomes is a head, the probability of observing a head is 1/2, or .50. Similarly, the probability of observing a tail is also 1/2, or .50.

As another example, consider the experiment of rolling a die. It would seem reasonable to conclude that the six possible outcomes are equally likely, and hence each outcome is assigned a probability of 1/6. If $P(1)$ denotes the probability that one dot appears on the upward face of the die, then $P(1) = 1/6$. Similarly, $P(2) = 1/6$, $P(3) = 1/6$, $P(4) = 1/6$, $P(5) = 1/6$, and $P(6) = 1/6$. Note that these probabilities satisfy the two basic requirements of equations (4.3) and (4.4) because each of the probabilities is greater than or equal to zero and they sum to 1.0.

The **relative frequency method** of assigning probabilities is appropriate when data are available to estimate the proportion of the time the experimental outcome will occur if the experiment is repeated a large number of times. As an example, consider a study of waiting times in the X-ray department for a local hospital. A clerk recorded the number of patients waiting for service at 9:00 A.M. on 20 successive days and obtained the following results.

Number Waiting	Number of Days Outcome Occurred
0	2
1	5
2	6
3	4
4	3
Total	20

These data show that on 2 of the 20 days, zero patients were waiting for service; on 5 of the days, one patient was waiting for service; and so on. Using the relative frequency method, we would assign a probability of $2/20 = .10$ to the experimental outcome of zero patients waiting for service, $5/20 = .25$ to the experimental outcome of one patient waiting, $6/20 = .30$ to two patients waiting, $4/20 = .20$ to three patients waiting, and $3/20 = .15$ to four patients waiting. As with the classical method, using the relative frequency method automatically satisfies the two basic requirements of equations (4.3) and (4.4).

The **subjective method** of assigning probabilities is most appropriate when one cannot realistically assume that the experimental outcomes are equally likely and when little relevant data are available. When the subjective method is used to assign probabilities to the experimental outcomes, we may use any information available, such as our experience or intuition. After considering all available information, a probability value that expresses our *degree of belief* (on a scale from 0 to 1) that the experimental outcome will occur is specified. Because subjective probability expresses a person's degree of belief, it is personal. Using the subjective method, different people can be expected to assign different probabilities to the same experimental outcome.

The subjective method requires extra care to ensure that the two basic requirements of equations (4.3) and (4.4) are satisfied. Regardless of a person's degree of belief, the probability value assigned to each experimental outcome must be between 0 and 1, inclusive, and the sum of all the probabilities for the experimental outcomes must equal 1.0.

Consider the case in which Tom and Judy Elsbernd make an offer to purchase a house. Two outcomes are possible:

$$E_1 = \text{their offer is accepted}$$
$$E_2 = \text{their offer is rejected}$$

Judy believes that the probability their offer will be accepted is .8; thus, Judy would set $P(E_1) = .8$ and $P(E_2) = .2$. Tom, however, believes that the probability that their offer will be accepted is .6; hence, Tom would set $P(E_1) = .6$ and $P(E_2) = .4$. Note that Tom's probability estimate for E_1 reflects a greater pessimism that their offer will be accepted.

Bayes' theorem (see Section 4.5) provides a means for combining subjectively determined prior probabilities with probabilities obtained by other means to obtain revised, or posterior, probabilities.

Both Judy and Tom assigned probabilities that satisfy the two basic requirements. The fact that their probability estimates are different emphasizes the personal nature of the subjective method.

Even in business situations where either the classical or the relative frequency approach can be applied, managers may want to provide subjective probability estimates. In such cases, the best probability estimates often are obtained by combining the estimates from the classical or relative frequency approach with subjective probability estimates.

Probabilities for the KP&L Project

To perform further analysis on the KP&L project, we must develop probabilities for each of the nine experimental outcomes listed in Table 4.1. On the basis of experience and judgment, management concluded that the experimental outcomes were not equally likely. Hence, the classical method of assigning probabilities could not be used. Management then decided to conduct a study of the completion times for similar projects undertaken by KP&L over the past three years. The results of a study of 40 similar projects are summarized in Table 4.2.

After reviewing the results of the study, management decided to employ the relative frequency method of assigning probabilities. Management could have provided subjective probability estimates, but felt that the current project was quite similar to the 40 previous projects. Thus, the relative frequency method was judged best.

In using the data in Table 4.2 to compute probabilities, we note that outcome (2, 6)—stage 1 completed in 2 months and stage 2 completed in 6 months—occurred six times in the 40 projects. We can use the relative frequency method to assign a probability of 6/40 = .15 to this outcome. Similarly, outcome (2, 7) also occurred in six of the 40 projects, providing a 6/40 = .15 probability. Continuing in this manner, we obtain the probability assignments for the sample points of the KP&L project shown in Table 4.3. Note that $P(2, 6)$ represents the probability of the sample point (2, 6), $P(2, 7)$ represents the probability of the sample point (2, 7), and so on.

TABLE 4.2 COMPLETION RESULTS FOR 40 KP&L PROJECTS

Completion Time (months) Stage 1 Design	Completion Time (months) Stage 2 Construction	Sample Point	Number of Past Projects Having These Completion Times
2	6	(2, 6)	6
2	7	(2, 7)	6
2	8	(2, 8)	2
3	6	(3, 6)	4
3	7	(3, 7)	8
3	8	(3, 8)	2
4	6	(4, 6)	2
4	7	(4, 7)	4
4	8	(4, 8)	6
		Total	40

TABLE 4.3 PROBABILITY ASSIGNMENTS FOR THE KP&L PROJECT BASED ON THE RELATIVE FREQUENCY METHOD

Sample Point	Project Completion Time	Probability of Sample Point
(2, 6)	8 months	$P(2, 6) = 6/40 = .15$
(2, 7)	9 months	$P(2, 7) = 6/40 = .15$
(2, 8)	10 months	$P(2, 8) = 2/40 = .05$
(3, 6)	9 months	$P(3, 6) = 4/40 = .10$
(3, 7)	10 months	$P(3, 7) = 8/40 = .20$
(3, 8)	11 months	$P(3, 8) = 2/40 = .05$
(4, 6)	10 months	$P(4, 6) = 2/40 = .05$
(4, 7)	11 months	$P(4, 7) = 4/40 = .10$
(4, 8)	12 months	$P(4, 8) = 6/40 = .15$
		Total 1.00

NOTES AND COMMENTS

1. In statistics, the notion of an experiment differs somewhat from the notion of an experiment in the physical sciences. In the physical sciences, researchers usually conduct an experiment in a laboratory or a controlled environment in order to learn about cause and effect. In statistical experiments, probability determines outcomes. Even though the experiment is repeated in exactly the same way, an entirely different outcome may occur. Because of this influence of probability on the outcome, the experiments of statistics are sometimes called *random experiments.*

2. When drawing a random sample without replacement from a population of size N, the counting rule for combinations is used to find the number of different samples of size n that can be selected.

Exercises

Methods

1. An experiment has three steps with three outcomes possible for the first step, two outcomes possible for the second step, and four outcomes possible for the third step. How many experimental outcomes exist for the entire experiment?

SELF test

2. How many ways can three items be selected from a group of six items? Use the letters A, B, C, D, E, and F to identify the items, and list each of the different combinations of three items.

3. How many permutations of three items can be selected from a group of six? Use the letters A, B, C, D, E, and F to identify the items, and list each of the permutations of items B, D, and F.

4. Consider the experiment of tossing a coin three times.
   a. Develop a tree diagram for the experiment.
   b. List the experimental outcomes.
   c. What is the probability for each experimental outcome?

5. Suppose an experiment has five equally likely outcomes: E_1, E_2, E_3, E_4, E_5. Assign probabilities to each outcome and show that the requirements in equations (4.3) and (4.4) are satisfied. What method did you use?

SELF test

6. An experiment with three outcomes has been repeated 50 times, and it was learned that E_1 occurred 20 times, E_2 occurred 13 times, and E_3 occurred 17 times. Assign probabilities to the outcomes. What method did you use?

7. A decision maker subjectively assigned the following probabilities to the four outcomes of an experiment: $P(E_1) = .10$, $P(E_2) = .15$, $P(E_3) = .40$, and $P(E_4) = .20$. Are these probability assignments valid? Explain.

Applications

8. In the city of Milford, applications for zoning changes go through a two-step process: a review by the planning commission and a final decision by the city council. At step 1 the planning commission reviews the zoning change request and makes a positive or negative recommendation concerning the change. At step 2 the city council reviews the planning commission's recommendation and then votes to approve or to disapprove the zoning change. Suppose the developer of an apartment complex submits an application for a zoning change. Consider the application process as an experiment.
   a. How many sample points are there for this experiment? List the sample points.
   b. Construct a tree diagram for the experiment.

SELF test

9. Simple random sampling uses a sample of size *n* from a population of size *N* to obtain data that can be used to make inferences about the characteristics of a population. Suppose that, from a population of 50 bank accounts, we want to take a random sample of four accounts in order to learn about the population. How many different random samples of four accounts are possible?

SELF test

10. Many students accumulate debt by the time they graduate from college. Shown in the following table is the percentage of graduates with debt and the average amount of debt for these graduates at four universities and four liberal arts colleges (*U.S. News and World Report, America's Best Colleges,* 2008).

University	% with Debt	Amount($)	College	% with Debt	Amount($)
Pace	72	32,980	Wartburg	83	28,758
Iowa State	69	32,130	Morehouse	94	27,000
Massachusetts	55	11,227	Wellesley	55	10,206
SUNY—Albany	64	11,856	Wofford	49	11,012

   a. If you randomly choose a graduate of Morehouse College, what is the probability that this individual graduated with debt?
   b. If you randomly choose one of these eight institutions for a follow-up study on student loans, what is the probability that you will choose an institution with more than 60% of its graduates having debt?
   c. If you randomly choose one of these eight institutions for a follow-up study on student loans, what is the probability that you will choose an institution whose graduates with debts have an average debt of more than $30,000?
   d. What is the probability that a graduate of Pace University does not have debt?
   e. For graduates of Pace University with debt, the average amount of debt is $32,980. Considering all graduates from Pace University, what is the average debt per graduate?

11. The National Highway Traffic Safety Administration (NHTSA) conducted a survey to learn about how drivers throughout the United States are using seat belts (Associated Press, August 25, 2003). Sample data consistent with the NHTSA survey are as follows.

	Driver Using Seat Belt?	
Region	**Yes**	**No**
Northeast	148	52
Midwest	162	54
South	296	74
West	252	48
Total	858	228

a. For the United States, what is the probability that a driver is using a seat belt?
b. The seat belt usage probability for a U.S. driver a year earlier was .75. NHTSA chief Dr. Jeffrey Runge had hoped for a .78 probability in 2003. Would he have been pleased with the 2003 survey results?
c. What is the probability of seat belt usage by region of the country? What region has the highest seat belt usage?
d. What proportion of the drivers in the sample came from each region of the country? What region had the most drivers selected? What region had the second most drivers selected?
e. Assuming the total number of drivers in each region is the same, do you see any reason why the probability estimate in part (a) might be too high? Explain.

12. The Powerball lottery is played twice each week in 28 states, the Virgin Islands, and the District of Columbia. To play Powerball a participant must purchase a ticket and then select five numbers from the digits 1 through 55 and a Powerball number from the digits 1 through 42. To determine the winning numbers for each game, lottery officials draw five white balls out of a drum with 55 white balls, and one red ball out of a drum with 42 red balls. To win the jackpot, a participant's numbers must match the numbers on the five white balls in any order and the number on the red Powerball. Eight coworkers at the ConAgra Foods plant in Lincoln, Nebraska, claimed the record $365 million jackpot on February 18, 2006, by matching the numbers 15-17-43-44-49 and the Powerball number 29. A variety of other cash prizes are awarded each time the game is played. For instance, a prize of $200,000 is paid if the participant's five numbers match the numbers on the five white balls (Powerball website, March 19, 2006).
a. Compute the number of ways the first five numbers can be selected.
b. What is the probability of winning a prize of $200,000 by matching the numbers on the five white balls?
c. What is the probability of winning the Powerball jackpot?

13. A company that manufactures toothpaste is studying five different package designs. Assuming that one design is just as likely to be selected by a consumer as any other design, what selection probability would you assign to each of the package designs? In an actual experiment, 100 consumers were asked to pick the design they preferred. The following data were obtained. Do the data confirm the belief that one design is just as likely to be selected as another? Explain.

Design	Number of Times Preferred
1	5
2	15
3	30
4	40
5	10

4.2 Events and Their Probabilities

In the introduction to this chapter we used the term *event* much as it would be used in everyday language. Then, in Section 4.1 we introduced the concept of an experiment and its associated experimental outcomes or sample points. Sample points and events provide the foundation for the study of probability. As a result, we must now introduce the formal definition of an **event** as it relates to sample points. Doing so will provide the basis for determining the probability of an event.

EVENT

An event is a collection of sample points.

For an example, let us return to the KP&L project and assume that the project manager is interested in the event that the entire project can be completed in 10 months or less. Referring to Table 4.3, we see that six sample points—(2, 6), (2, 7), (2, 8), (3, 6), (3, 7), and (4, 6)—provide a project completion time of 10 months or less. Let C denote the event that the project is completed in 10 months or less; we write

$$C = \{(2, 6), (2, 7), (2, 8), (3, 6), (3, 7), (4, 6)\}$$

Event C is said to occur if *any one* of these six sample points appears as the experimental outcome.

Other events that might be of interest to KP&L management include the following.

L = The event that the project is completed in *less* than 10 months

M = The event that the project is completed in *more* than 10 months

Using the information in Table 4.3, we see that these events consist of the following sample points.

$$L = \{(2, 6), (2, 7), (3, 6)\}$$
$$M = \{(3, 8), (4, 7), (4, 8)\}$$

A variety of additional events can be defined for the KP&L project, but in each case the event must be identified as a collection of sample points for the experiment.

Given the probabilities of the sample points shown in Table 4.3, we can use the following definition to compute the probability of any event that KP&L management might want to consider.

PROBABILITY OF AN EVENT

The probability of any event is equal to the sum of the probabilities of the sample points in the event.

Using this definition, we calculate the probability of a particular event by adding the probabilities of the sample points (experimental outcomes) that make up the event. We can now compute the probability that the project will take 10 months or less to complete. Because this event is given by $C = \{(2, 6), (2, 7), (2, 8), (3, 6), (3, 7), (4, 6)\}$, the probability of event C, denoted $P(C)$, is given by

$$P(C) = P(2, 6) + P(2, 7) + P(2, 8) + P(3, 6) + P(3, 7) + P(4, 6)$$

Refer to the sample point probabilities in Table 4.3; we have

$$P(C) = .15 + .15 + .05 + .10 + .20 + .05 = .70$$

Similarly, because the event that the project is completed in less than 10 months is given by $L = \{(2, 6), (2, 7), (3, 6)\}$, the probability of this event is given by

$$\begin{aligned} P(L) &= P(2, 6) + P(2, 7) + P(3, 6) \\ &= .15 + .15 + .10 = .40 \end{aligned}$$

Finally, for the event that the project is completed in more than 10 months, we have $M = \{(3, 8), (4, 7), (4, 8)\}$ and thus

$$\begin{aligned} P(M) &= P(3, 8) + P(4, 7) + P(4, 8) \\ &= .05 + .10 + .15 = .30 \end{aligned}$$

Using these probability results, we can now tell KP&L management that there is a .70 probability that the project will be completed in 10 months or less, a .40 probability that the project will be completed in less than 10 months, and a .30 probability that the project will be completed in more than 10 months. This procedure of computing event probabilities can be repeated for any event of interest to the KP&L management.

Any time that we can identify all the sample points of an experiment and assign probabilities to each, we can compute the probability of an event using the definition. However, in many experiments the large number of sample points makes the identification of the sample points, as well as the determination of their associated probabilities, extremely cumbersome, if not impossible. In the remaining sections of this chapter, we present some basic probability relationships that can be used to compute the probability of an event without knowledge of all the sample point probabilities.

NOTES AND COMMENTS

1. The sample space, S, is an event. Because it contains all the experimental outcomes, it has a probability of 1; that is, $P(S) = 1$.
2. When the classical method is used to assign probabilities, the assumption is that the experimental outcomes are equally likely. In such cases, the probability of an event can be computed by counting the number of experimental outcomes in the event and dividing the result by the total number of experimental outcomes.

Exercises

Methods

14. An experiment has four equally likely outcomes: E_1, E_2, E_3, and E_4.
    a. What is the probability that E_2 occurs?
    b. What is the probability that any two of the outcomes occur (e.g., E_1 or E_3)?
    c. What is the probability that any three of the outcomes occur (e.g., E_1 or E_2 or E_4)?

SELF test

15. Consider the experiment of selecting a playing card from a deck of 52 playing cards. Each card corresponds to a sample point with a 1/52 probability.
    a. List the sample points in the event an ace is selected.
    b. List the sample points in the event a club is selected.
    c. List the sample points in the event a face card (jack, queen, or king) is selected.
    d. Find the probabilities associated with each of the events in parts (a), (b), and (c).
16. Consider the experiment of rolling a pair of dice. Suppose that we are interested in the sum of the face values showing on the dice.
    a. How many sample points are possible? (*Hint:* Use the counting rule for multiple-step experiments.)
    b. List the sample points.
    c. What is the probability of obtaining a value of 7?
    d. What is the probability of obtaining a value of 9 or greater?
    e. Because each roll has six possible even values (2, 4, 6, 8, 10, and 12) and only five possible odd values (3, 5, 7, 9, and 11), the dice should show even values more often than odd values. Do you agree with this statement? Explain.
    f. What method did you use to assign the probabilities requested?

Applications

SELF test

17. Refer to the KP&L sample points and sample point probabilities in Tables 4.2 and 4.3.
    a. The design stage (stage 1) will run over budget if it takes 4 months to complete. List the sample points in the event the design stage is over budget.
    b. What is the probability that the design stage is over budget?
    c. The construction stage (stage 2) will run over budget if it takes 8 months to complete. List the sample points in the event the construction stage is over budget.
    d. What is the probability that the construction stage is over budget?
    e. What is the probability that both stages are over budget?
18. To investigate how often families eat at home, Harris Interactive surveyed 496 adults living with children under the age of 18 (*USA Today,* January 3, 2007). The survey results are shown in the following table.

Number of Family Meals per Week	Number of Survey Responses
0	11
1	11
2	30
3	36
4	36
5	119
6	114
7 or more	139

For a randomly selected family with children under the age of 18, compute the following.
    a. The probability the family eats no meals at home during the week.
    b. The probability the family eats at least four meals at home during the week.
    c. The probability the family eats two or fewer meals at home during the week.
19. The National Sporting Goods Association conducted a survey of persons 7 years of age or older about participation in sports activities (*Statistical Abstract of the United States*, 2002). The total population in this age group was reported at 248.5 million, with 120.9 million male and 127.6 million female. The number of participants for the top five sports activities appears here.

	Participants (millions)	
Activity	**Male**	**Female**
Bicycle riding	22.2	21.0
Camping	25.6	24.3
Exercise walking	28.7	57.7
Exercising with equipment	20.4	24.4
Swimming	26.4	34.4

    a. For a randomly selected female, estimate the probability of participation in each of the sports activities.
    b. For a randomly selected male, estimate the probability of participation in each of the sports activities.
    c. For a randomly selected person, what is the probability the person participates in exercise walking?
    d. Suppose you just happen to see an exercise walker going by. What is the probability the walker is a woman? What is the probability the walker is a man?

20. *Fortune* magazine publishes an annual list of the 500 largest companies in the United States. The following data show the five states with the largest number of *Fortune* 500 companies (*The New York Times Almanac,* 2006).

State	Number of Companies
New York	54
California	52
Texas	48
Illinois	33
Ohio	30

Suppose a *Fortune* 500 company is chosen for a follow-up questionnaire. What are the probabilities of the following events?

a. Let N be the event the company is headquartered in New York. Find $P(N)$.
b. Let T be the event the company is headquartered in Texas. Find $P(T)$.
c. Let B be the event the company is headquartered in one of these five states. Find $P(B)$.

21. The U.S. adult population by age is as follows (*The World Almanac,* 2009). The data are in millions of people.

Age	Number
18 to 24	29.8
25 to 34	40.0
35 to 44	43.4
45 to 54	43.9
55 to 64	32.7
65 and over	37.8

Assume that a person will be randomly chosen from this population.

a. What is the probability the person is 18 to 24 years old?
b. What is the probability the person is 18 to 34 years old?
c. What is the probability the person is 45 or older?

4.3 Some Basic Relationships of Probability

Complement of an Event

Given an event A, the **complement of A** is defined to be the event consisting of all sample points that are *not* in A. The complement of A is denoted by A^c. Figure 4.4 is a diagram, known as a **Venn diagram**, which illustrates the concept of a complement. The rectangular area represents the sample space for the experiment and as such contains all possible sample points. The circle represents event A and contains only the sample points that belong to A. The shaded region of the rectangle contains all sample points not in event A and is by definition the complement of A.

In any probability application, either event A or its complement A^c must occur. Therefore, we have

$$P(A) + P(A^c) = 1$$

FIGURE 4.4 COMPLEMENT OF EVENT A IS SHADED

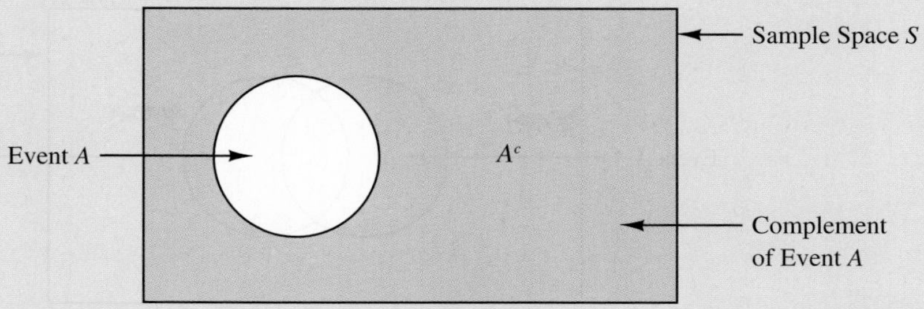

Solving for $P(A)$, we obtain the following result.

COMPUTING PROBABILITY USING THE COMPLEMENT

$$P(A) = 1 - P(A^c) \tag{4.5}$$

Equation (4.5) shows that the probability of an event A can be computed easily if the probability of its complement, $P(A^c)$, is known.

As an example, consider the case of a sales manager who, after reviewing sales reports, states that 80% of new customer contacts result in no sale. By allowing A to denote the event of a sale and A^c to denote the event of no sale, the manager is stating that $P(A^c) = .80$. Using equation (4.5), we see that

$$P(A) = 1 - P(A^c) = 1 - .80 = .20$$

We can conclude that a new customer contact has a .20 probability of resulting in a sale.

In another example, a purchasing agent states a .90 probability that a supplier will send a shipment that is free of defective parts. Using the complement, we can conclude that there is a $1 - .90 = .10$ probability that the shipment will contain defective parts.

Addition Law

The addition law is helpful when we are interested in knowing the probability that at least one of two events occurs. That is, with events A and B we are interested in knowing the probability that event A or event B or both occur.

Before we present the addition law, we need to discuss two concepts related to the combination of events: the *union* of events and the *intersection* of events. Given two events A and B, the **union of A and B** is defined as follows.

UNION OF TWO EVENTS

The *union* of A and B is the event containing *all* sample points belonging to A *or* B *or both.* The union is denoted by $A \cup B$.

The Venn diagram in Figure 4.5 depicts the union of events A and B. Note that the two circles contain all the sample points in event A as well as all the sample points in event B.

FIGURE 4.5 UNION OF EVENTS A AND B IS SHADED

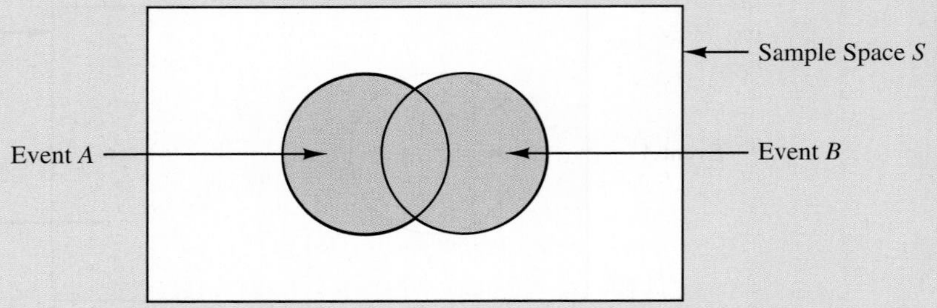

The fact that the circles overlap indicates that some sample points are contained in both A and B.

The definition of the **intersection of A and B** follows.

INTERSECTION OF TWO EVENTS

Given two events A and B, the *intersection* of A and B is the event containing the sample points belonging to *both A and B*. The intersection is denoted by $A \cap B$.

The Venn diagram depicting the intersection of events A and B is shown in Figure 4.6. The area where the two circles overlap is the intersection; it contains the sample points that are in both A and B.

Let us now continue with a discussion of the addition law. The **addition law** provides a way to compute the probability that event A or event B or both occur. In other words, the addition law is used to compute the probability of the union of two events. The addition law is written as follows.

ADDITION LAW

$$P(A \cup B) = P(A) + P(B) - P(A \cap B) \tag{4.6}$$

FIGURE 4.6 INTERSECTION OF EVENTS A AND B IS SHADED

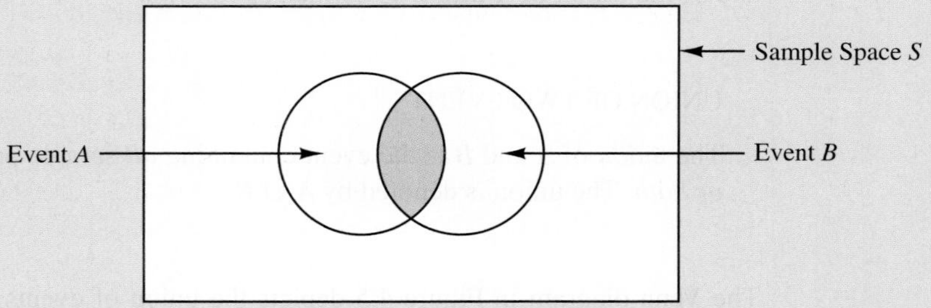

To understand the addition law intuitively, note that the first two terms in the addition law, $P(A) + P(B)$, account for all the sample points in $A \cup B$. However, because the sample points in the intersection $A \cap B$ are in both A and B, when we compute $P(A) + P(B)$, we are in effect counting each of the sample points in $A \cap B$ twice. We correct for this overcounting by subtracting $P(A \cap B)$.

As an example of an application of the addition law, let us consider the case of a small assembly plant with 50 employees. Each worker is expected to complete work assignments on time and in such a way that the assembled product will pass a final inspection. On occasion, some of the workers fail to meet the performance standards by completing work late or assembling a defective product. At the end of a performance evaluation period, the production manager found that 5 of the 50 workers completed work late, 6 of the 50 workers assembled a defective product, and 2 of the 50 workers both completed work late *and* assembled a defective product.

Let

$$L = \text{the event that the work is completed late}$$
$$D = \text{the event that the assembled product is defective}$$

The relative frequency information leads to the following probabilities.

$$P(L) = \frac{5}{50} = .10$$

$$P(D) = \frac{6}{50} = .12$$

$$P(L \cap D) = \frac{2}{50} = .04$$

After reviewing the performance data, the production manager decided to assign a poor performance rating to any employee whose work was either late or defective; thus the event of interest is $L \cup D$. What is the probability that the production manager assigned an employee a poor performance rating?

Note that the probability question is about the union of two events. Specifically, we want to know $P(L \cup D)$. Using equation (4.6), we have

$$P(L \cup D) = P(L) + P(D) - P(L \cap D)$$

Knowing values for the three probabilities on the right side of this expression, we can write

$$P(L \cup D) = .10 + .12 - .04 = .18$$

This calculation tells us that there is a .18 probability that a randomly selected employee received a poor performance rating.

As another example of the addition law, consider a recent study conducted by the personnel manager of a major computer software company. The study showed that 30% of the employees who left the firm within two years did so primarily because they were dissatisfied with their salary, 20% left because they were dissatisfied with their work assignments, and 12% of the former employees indicated dissatisfaction with *both* their salary and their work assignments. What is the probability that an employee who leaves within two years does so because of dissatisfaction with salary, dissatisfaction with the work assignment, or both?

Let

$$S = \text{the event that the employee leaves because of salary}$$
$$W = \text{the event that the employee leaves because of work assignment}$$

We have $P(S) = .30$, $P(W) = .20$, and $P(S \cap W) = .12$. Using equation (4.6), the addition law, we have

$$P(S \cup W) = P(S) + P(W) - P(S \cap W) = .30 + .20 - .12 = .38.$$

We find a .38 probability that an employee leaves for salary or work assignment reasons.

Before we conclude our discussion of the addition law, let us consider a special case that arises for **mutually exclusive events**.

MUTUALLY EXCLUSIVE EVENTS

Two events are said to be mutually exclusive if the events have no sample points in common.

Events A and B are mutually exclusive if, when one event occurs, the other cannot occur. Thus, a requirement for A and B to be mutually exclusive is that their intersection must contain no sample points. The Venn diagram depicting two mutually exclusive events A and B is shown in Figure 4.7. In this case $P(A \cap B) = 0$ and the addition law can be written as follows.

ADDITION LAW FOR MUTUALLY EXCLUSIVE EVENTS

$$P(A \cup B) = P(A) + P(B)$$

FIGURE 4.7 MUTUALLY EXCLUSIVE EVENTS

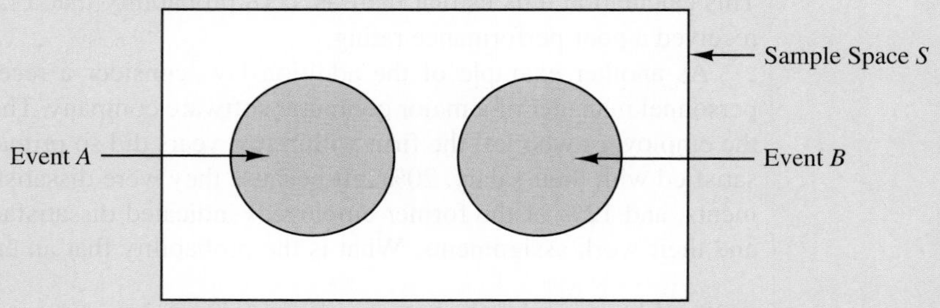

Exercises

Methods

22. Suppose that we have a sample space with five equally likely experimental outcomes: E_1, E_2, E_3, E_4, E_5. Let

$$A = \{E_1, E_2\}$$
$$B = \{E_3, E_4\}$$
$$C = \{E_2, E_3, E_5\}$$

   a. Find $P(A)$, $P(B)$, and $P(C)$.
   b. Find $P(A \cup B)$. Are A and B mutually exclusive?
   c. Find A^c, C^c, $P(A^c)$, and $P(C^c)$.
   d. Find $A \cup B^c$ and $P(A \cup B^c)$.
   e. Find $P(B \cup C)$.

SELF test

23. Suppose that we have a sample space $S = \{E_1, E_2, E_3, E_4, E_5, E_6, E_7\}$, where $E_1, E_2, \ldots, E_7$ denote the sample points. The following probability assignments apply: $P(E_1) = .05$, $P(E_2) = .20$, $P(E_3) = .20$, $P(E_4) = .25$, $P(E_5) = .15$, $P(E_6) = .10$, and $P(E_7) = .05$. Let

$$A = \{E_1, E_4, E_6\}$$
$$B = \{E_2, E_4, E_7\}$$
$$C = \{E_2, E_3, E_5, E_7\}$$

   a. Find $P(A)$, $P(B)$, and $P(C)$.
   b. Find $A \cup B$ and $P(A \cup B)$.
   c. Find $A \cap B$ and $P(A \cap B)$.
   d. Are events A and C mutually exclusive?
   e. Find B^c and $P(B^c)$.

Applications

24. Clarkson University surveyed alumni to learn more about what they think of Clarkson. One part of the survey asked respondents to indicate whether their overall experience at Clarkson fell short of expectations, met expectations, or surpassed expectations. The results showed that 4% of the respondents did not provide a response, 26% said that their experience fell short of expectations, and 65% of the respondents said that their experience met expectations.
   a. If we chose an alumnus at random, what is the probability that the alumnus would say their experience *surpassed* expectations?
   b. If we chose an alumnus at random, what is the probability that the alumnus would say their experience met or surpassed expectations?

25. The U.S. Census Bureau provides data on the number of young adults, ages 18–24, who are living in their parents' home.[1] Let

M = the event a male young adult is living in his parents' home
F = the event a female young adult is living in her parents' home

If we randomly select a male young adult and a female young adult, the Census Bureau data enable us to conclude $P(M) = .56$ and $P(F) = .42$ (*The World Almanac,* 2006). The probability that both are living in their parents' home is .24.
   a. What is the probability at least one of the two young adults selected is living in his or her parents' home?
   b. What is the probability both young adults selected are living on their own (neither is living in their parents' home)?

[1] The data include single young adults who are living in college dormitories because it is assumed these young adults will return to their parents' home when school is not in session.

26. Information about mutual funds provided by Morningstar Investment Research includes the type of mutual fund (Domestic Equity, International Equity, or Fixed Income) and the Morningstar rating for the fund. The rating is expressed from 1-star (lowest rating) to 5-star (highest rating). A sample of 25 mutual funds was selected from *Morningstar Funds500* (2008). The following counts were obtained:
    - Sixteen mutual funds were Domestic Equity funds.
    - Thirteen mutual funds were rated 3-star or less.
    - Seven of the Domestic Equity funds were rated 4-star.
    - Two of the Domestic Equity funds were rated 5-star.

    Assume that one of these 25 mutual funds will be randomly selected in order to learn more about the mutual fund and its investment strategy.
    a. What is the probability of selecting a Domestic Equity fund?
    b. What is the probability of selecting a fund with a 4-star or 5-star rating?
    c. What is the probability of selecting a fund that is both a Domestic Equity fund *and* a fund with a 4-star or 5-star rating?
    d. What is the probability of selecting a fund that is a Domestic Equity fund *or* a fund with a 4-star or 5-star rating?
27. What NCAA college basketball conferences have the higher probability of having a team play in college basketball's national championship game? Over the last 20 years, the Atlantic Coast Conference (ACC) ranks first by having a team in the championship game 10 times. The Southeastern Conference (SEC) ranks second by having a team in the championship game 8 times. However, these two conferences have both had teams in the championship game only one time, when Arkansas (SEC) beat Duke (ACC) 76–70 in 1994 (NCAA website, April 2009). Use these data to estimate the following probabilities.
    a. What is the probability the ACC will have a team in the championship game?
    b. What is the probability the SEC will have team in the championship game?
    c. What is the probability the ACC and SEC will both have teams in the championship game?
    d. What is the probability at least one team from these two conferences will be in the championship game? That is, what is the probability a team from the ACC or SEC will play in the championship game?
    e. What is the probability that the championship game will not a have team from one of these two conferences?

SELF test

28. A survey of magazine subscribers showed that 45.8% rented a car during the past 12 months for business reasons, 54% rented a car during the past 12 months for personal reasons, and 30% rented a car during the past 12 months for both business and personal reasons.
    a. What is the probability that a subscriber rented a car during the past 12 months for business or personal reasons?
    b. What is the probability that a subscriber did not rent a car during the past 12 months for either business or personal reasons?
29. High school seniors with strong academic records apply to the nation's most selective colleges in greater numbers each year. Because the number of slots remains relatively stable, some colleges reject more early applicants. The University of Pennsylvania received 2851 applications for early admission. Of this group, it admitted 1033 students early, rejected 854 outright, and deferred 964 to the regular admission pool for further consideration. In the past, Penn has admitted 18% of the deferred early admission applicants during the regular admission process. Counting the students admitted early and the students admitted during the regular admission process, the total class size was 2375 (*USA Today*, January 24, 2001). Let E, R, and D represent the events that a student who applies for early admission is admitted early, rejected outright, or deferred to the regular admissions pool.
    a. Use the data to estimate $P(E)$, $P(R)$, and $P(D)$.
    b. Are events E and D mutually exclusive? Find $P(E \cap D)$.

c. For the 2375 students admitted to Penn, what is the probability that a randomly selected student was accepted during early admission?
d. Suppose a student applies to Penn for early admission. What is the probability the student will be admitted for early admission or be deferred and later admitted during the regular admission process?

4.4 Conditional Probability

Often, the probability of an event is influenced by whether a related event already occurred. Suppose we have an event A with probability $P(A)$. If we obtain new information and learn that a related event, denoted by B, already occurred, we will want to take advantage of this information by calculating a new probability for event A. This new probability of event A is called a **conditional probability** and is written $P(A \mid B)$. We use the notation $\mid$ to indicate that we are considering the probability of event A *given* the condition that event B has occurred. Hence, the notation $P(A \mid B)$ reads "the probability of A given B."

As an illustration of the application of conditional probability, consider the situation of the promotion status of male and female officers of a major metropolitan police force in the eastern United States. The police force consists of 1200 officers, 960 men and 240 women. Over the past two years, 324 officers on the police force received promotions. The specific breakdown of promotions for male and female officers is shown in Table 4.4.

After reviewing the promotion record, a committee of female officers raised a discrimination case on the basis that 288 male officers had received promotions but only 36 female officers had received promotions. The police administration argued that the relatively low number of promotions for female officers was due not to discrimination, but to the fact that relatively few females are members of the police force. Let us show how conditional probability could be used to analyze the discrimination charge.

Let

$$M = \text{event an officer is a man}$$
$$W = \text{event an officer is a woman}$$
$$A = \text{event an officer is promoted}$$
$$A^c = \text{event an officer is not promoted}$$

Dividing the data values in Table 4.4 by the total of 1200 officers enables us to summarize the available information with the following probability values.

$P(M \cap A) = 288/1200 = .24$ probability that a randomly selected officer is a man *and* is promoted

$P(M \cap A^c) = 672/1200 = .56$ probability that a randomly selected officer is a man *and* is not promoted

TABLE 4.4 PROMOTION STATUS OF POLICE OFFICERS OVER THE PAST TWO YEARS

	Men	Women	Total
Promoted	288	36	324
Not Promoted	672	204	876
Total	960	240	1200

TABLE 4.5 JOINT PROBABILITY TABLE FOR PROMOTIONS

Joint probabilities appear in the body of the table.

	Men (M)	Women (W)	Total
Promoted (A)	.24	.03	.27
Not Promoted (A^c)	.56	.17	.73
Total	.80	.20	1.00

Marginal probabilities appear in the margins of the table.

$P(W \cap A) = 36/1200 = .03$ probability that a randomly selected officer is a woman *and* is promoted

$P(W \cap A^c) = 204/1200 = .17$ probability that a randomly selected officer is a woman *and* is not promoted

Because each of these values gives the probability of the intersection of two events, the probabilities are called **joint probabilities**. Table 4.5, which provides a summary of the probability information for the police officer promotion situation, is referred to as a *joint probability table.*

The values in the margins of the joint probability table provide the probabilities of each event separately. That is, $P(M) = .80$, $P(W) = .20$, $P(A) = .27$, and $P(A^c) = .73$. These probabilities are referred to as **marginal probabilities** because of their location in the margins of the joint probability table. We note that the marginal probabilities are found by summing the joint probabilities in the corresponding row or column of the joint probability table. For instance, the marginal probability of being promoted is $P(A) = P(M \cap A) + P(W \cap A) = .24 + .03 = .27$. From the marginal probabilities, we see that 80% of the force is male, 20% of the force is female, 27% of all officers received promotions, and 73% were not promoted.

Let us begin the conditional probability analysis by computing the probability that an officer is promoted given that the officer is a man. In conditional probability notation, we are attempting to determine $P(A \mid M)$. To calculate $P(A \mid M)$, we first realize that this notation simply means that we are considering the probability of the event A (promotion) given that the condition designated as event M (the officer is a man) is known to exist. Thus $P(A \mid M)$ tells us that we are now concerned only with the promotion status of the 960 male officers. Because 288 of the 960 male officers received promotions, the probability of being promoted given that the officer is a man is $288/960 = .30$. In other words, given that an officer is a man, that officer had a 30% chance of receiving a promotion over the past two years.

This procedure was easy to apply because the values in Table 4.4 show the number of officers in each category. We now want to demonstrate how conditional probabilities such as $P(A \mid M)$ can be computed directly from related event probabilities rather than the frequency data of Table 4.4.

We have shown that $P(A \mid M) = 288/960 = .30$. Let us now divide both the numerator and denominator of this fraction by 1200, the total number of officers in the study.

$$P(A \mid M) = \frac{288}{960} = \frac{288/1200}{960/1200} = \frac{.24}{.80} = .30$$

We now see that the conditional probability $P(A \mid M)$ can be computed as .24/.80. Refer to the joint probability table (Table 4.5). Note in particular that .24 is the joint probability of

A and M; that is, $P(A \cap M) = .24$. Also note that .80 is the marginal probability that a randomly selected officer is a man; that is, $P(M) = .80$. Thus, the conditional probability $P(A \mid M)$ can be computed as the ratio of the joint probability $P(A \cap M)$ to the marginal probability $P(M)$.

$$P(A \mid M) = \frac{P(A \cap M)}{P(M)} = \frac{.24}{.80} = .30$$

The fact that conditional probabilities can be computed as the ratio of a joint probability to a marginal probability provides the following general formula for conditional probability calculations for two events A and B.

CONDITIONAL PROBABILITY

$$P(A \mid B) = \frac{P(A \cap B)}{P(B)} \qquad \textbf{(4.7)}$$

or

$$P(B \mid A) = \frac{P(A \cap B)}{P(A)} \qquad \textbf{(4.8)}$$

The Venn diagram in Figure 4.8 is helpful in obtaining an intuitive understanding of conditional probability. The circle on the right shows that event B has occurred; the portion of the circle that overlaps with event A denotes the event $(A \cap B)$. We know that once event B has occurred, the only way that we can also observe event A is for the event $(A \cap B)$ to occur. Thus, the ratio $P(A \cap B)/P(B)$ provides the conditional probability that we will observe event A given that event B has already occurred.

Let us return to the issue of discrimination against the female officers. The marginal probability in row 1 of Table 4.5 shows that the probability of promotion of an officer is $P(A) = .27$ (regardless of whether that officer is male or female). However, the critical issue in the discrimination case involves the two conditional probabilities $P(A \mid M)$ and $P(A \mid W)$. That is, what is the probability of a promotion *given* that the officer is a man, and what is the probability of a promotion *given* that the officer is a woman? If these two probabilities are equal, a discrimination argument has no basis because the chances of a promotion are the same for male and female officers. However, a difference in the two conditional probabilities will support the position that male and female officers are treated differently in promotion decisions.

FIGURE 4.8 CONDITIONAL PROBABILITY $P(A \mid B) = P(A \cap B)/P(B)$

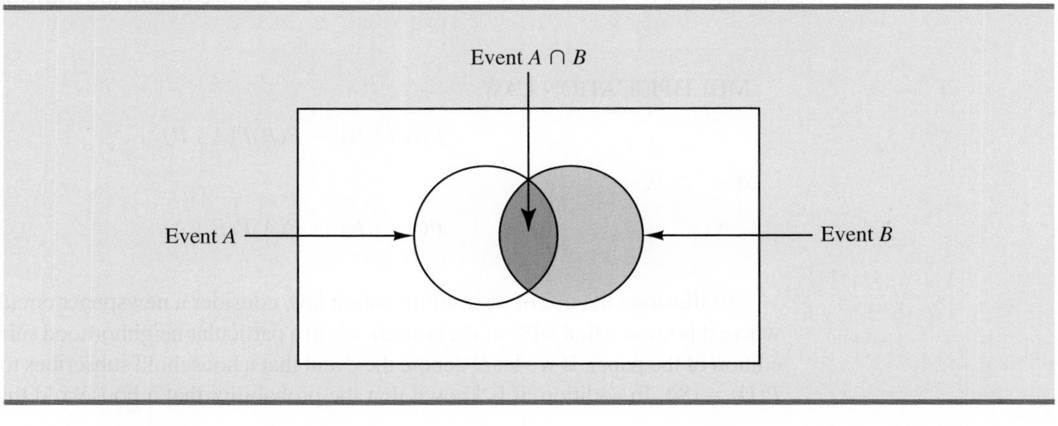

We already determined that $P(A \mid M) = .30$. Let us now use the probability values in Table 4.5 and the basic relationship of conditional probability in equation (4.7) to compute the probability that an officer is promoted given that the officer is a woman; that is, $P(A \mid W)$. Using equation (4.7), with W replacing B, we obtain

$$P(A \mid W) = \frac{P(A \cap W)}{P(W)} = \frac{.03}{.20} = .15$$

What conclusion do you draw? The probability of a promotion given that the officer is a man is .30, twice the .15 probability of a promotion given that the officer is a woman. Although the use of conditional probability does not in itself prove that discrimination exists in this case, the conditional probability values support the argument presented by the female officers.

Independent Events

In the preceding illustration, $P(A) = .27$, $P(A \mid M) = .30$, and $P(A \mid W) = .15$. We see that the probability of a promotion (event A) is affected or influenced by whether the officer is a man or a woman. Particularly, because $P(A \mid M) \neq P(A)$, we would say that events A and M are dependent events. That is, the probability of event A (promotion) is altered or affected by knowing that event M (the officer is a man) exists. Similarly, with $P(A \mid W) \neq P(A)$, we would say that events A and W are *dependent events.* However, if the probability of event A is not changed by the existence of event M—that is, $P(A \mid M) = P(A)$—we would say that events A and M are **independent events**. This situation leads to the following definition of the independence of two events.

INDEPENDENT EVENTS

Two events A and B are independent if

$$P(A \mid B) = P(A) \tag{4.9}$$

or

$$P(B \mid A) = P(B) \tag{4.10}$$

Otherwise, the events are dependent.

Multiplication Law

Whereas the addition law of probability is used to compute the probability of a union of two events, the multiplication law is used to compute the probability of the intersection of two events. The multiplication law is based on the definition of conditional probability. Using equations (4.7) and (4.8) and solving for $P(A \cap B)$, we obtain the **multiplication law**.

MULTIPLICATION LAW

$$P(A \cap B) = P(B)P(A \mid B) \tag{4.11}$$

or

$$P(A \cap B) = P(A)P(B \mid A) \tag{4.12}$$

To illustrate the use of the multiplication law, consider a newspaper circulation department where it is known that 84% of the households in a particular neighborhood subscribe to the daily edition of the paper. If we let D denote the event that a household subscribes to the daily edition, $P(D) = .84$. In addition, it is known that the probability that a household that already holds a daily subscription also subscribes to the Sunday edition (event S) is .75; that is, $P(S \mid D) = .75$. What is the probability that a household subscribes to both the Sunday and daily editions of the newspaper? Using the multiplication law, we compute the desired $P(S \cap D)$ as

$$P(S \cap D) = P(D)P(S \mid D) = .84(.75) = .63$$

We now know that 63% of the households subscribe to both the Sunday and daily editions.

Before concluding this section, let us consider the special case of the multiplication law when the events involved are independent. Recall that events A and B are independent whenever $P(A \mid B) = P(A)$ or $P(B \mid A) = P(B)$. Hence, using equations (4.11) and (4.12) for the special case of independent events, we obtain the following multiplication law.

MULTIPLICATION LAW FOR INDEPENDENT EVENTS

$$P(A \cap B) = P(A)P(B) \tag{4.13}$$

To compute the probability of the intersection of two independent events, we simply multiply the corresponding probabilities. Note that the multiplication law for independent events provides another way to determine whether A and B are independent. That is, if $P(A \cap B) = P(A)P(B)$, then A and B are independent; if $P(A \cap B) \neq P(A)P(B)$, then A and B are dependent.

As an application of the multiplication law for independent events, consider the situation of a service station manager who knows from past experience that 80% of the customers use a credit card when they purchase gasoline. What is the probability that the next two customers purchasing gasoline will each use a credit card? If we let

A = the event that the first customer uses a credit card

B = the event that the second customer uses a credit card

then the event of interest is $A \cap B$. Given no other information, we can reasonably assume that A and B are independent events. Thus,

$$P(A \cap B) = P(A)P(B) = (.80)(.80) = .64$$

To summarize this section, we note that our interest in conditional probability is motivated by the fact that events are often related. In such cases, we say the events are dependent and the conditional probability formulas in equations (4.7) and (4.8) must be used to compute the event probabilities. If two events are not related, they are independent; in this case neither event's probability is affected by whether the other event occurred.

NOTES AND COMMENTS

Do not confuse the notion of mutually exclusive events with that of independent events. Two events with nonzero probabilities cannot be both mutually exclusive and independent. If one mutually exclusive event is known to occur, the other cannot occur; thus, the probability of the other event occurring is reduced to zero. They are therefore dependent.

Exercises

Methods

SELF test

30. Suppose that we have two events, A and B, with $P(A) = .50$, $P(B) = .60$, and $P(A \cap B) = .40$.
    a. Find $P(A \mid B)$.
    b. Find $P(B \mid A)$.
    c. Are A and B independent? Why or why not?

31. Assume that we have two events, A and B, that are mutually exclusive. Assume further that we know $P(A) = .30$ and $P(B) = .40$.
   a. What is $P(A \cap B)$?
   b. What is $P(A \mid B)$?
   c. A student in statistics argues that the concepts of mutually exclusive events and independent events are really the same, and that if events are mutually exclusive they must be independent. Do you agree with this statement? Use the probability information in this problem to justify your answer.
   d. What general conclusion would you make about mutually exclusive and independent events given the results of this problem?

Applications

32. The automobile industry sold 657,000 vehicles in the United States during January 2009 (*The Wall Street Journal,* February 4, 2009). This volume was down 37% from January 2008 as economic conditions continued to decline. The Big Three U.S. automakers—General Motors, Ford, and Chrysler—sold 280,500 vehicles, down 48% from January 2008. A summary of sales by automobile manufacturer and type of vehicle sold is shown in the following table. Data are in thousands of vehicles. The non-U.S. manufacturers are led by Toyota, Honda, and Nissan. The category Light Truck includes pickup, minivan, SUV, and crossover models.

		Type of Vehicle	
		Car	**Light Truck**
Manufacturer	**U.S.**	87.4	193.1
	Non-U.S.	228.5	148.0

   a. Develop a joint probability table for these data and use the table to answer the remaining questions.
   b. What are the marginal probabilities? What do they tell you about the probabilities associated with the manufacturer and the type of vehicle sold?
   c. If a vehicle was manufactured by one of the U.S. automakers, what is the probability that the vehicle was a car? What is the probability it was a light truck?
   d. If a vehicle was not manufactured by one of the U.S. automakers, what is the probability that the vehicle was a car? What is the probability it was a light truck?
   e. If the vehicle was a light truck, what is the probability that it was manufactured by one of the U.S. automakers?
   f. What does the probability information tell you about sales?

SELF test

33. In a survey of MBA students, the following data were obtained on "students' first reason for application to the school in which they matriculated."

		Reason for Application			
		School Quality	**School Cost or Convenience**	**Other**	**Totals**
Enrollment Status	**Full Time**	421	393	76	890
	Part Time	400	593	46	1039
	Totals	821	986	122	1929

   a. Develop a joint probability table for these data.
   b. Use the marginal probabilities of school quality, school cost or convenience, and other to comment on the most important reason for choosing a school.

c. If a student goes full time, what is the probability that school quality is the first reason for choosing a school?
d. If a student goes part time, what is the probability that school quality is the first reason for choosing a school?
e. Let A denote the event that a student is full time and let B denote the event that the student lists school quality as the first reason for applying. Are events A and B independent? Justify your answer.

34. The U.S. Department of Transportation reported that during November, 83.4% of Southwest Airlines' flights, 75.1% of US Airways' flights, and 70.1% of JetBlue's flights arrived on time (*USA Today,* January 4, 2007). Assume that this on-time performance is applicable for flights arriving at concourse A of the Rochester International Airport, and that 40% of the arrivals at concourse A are Southwest Airlines flights, 35% are US Airways flights, and 25% are JetBlue flights.
a. Develop a joint probability table with three rows (airlines) and two columns (on-time arrivals vs. late arrivals).
b. An announcement has just been made that Flight 1424 will be arriving at gate 20 in concourse A. What is the most likely airline for this arrival?
c. What is the probability that Flight 1424 will arrive on time?
d. Suppose that an announcement is made saying that Flight 1424 will be arriving late. What is the most likely airline for this arrival? What is the least likely airline?

35. According to the Ameriprise Financial Money Across Generations study, 9 out of 10 parents with adult children ages 20 to 35 have helped their adult children with some type of financial assistance ranging from college, a car, rent, utilities, credit-card debt, and/or down payments for houses (*Money,* January 2009). The following table with sample data consistent with the study shows the number of times parents have given their adult children financial assistance to buy a car and to pay rent.

		Pay Rent	
		Yes	**No**
Buy a Car	**Yes**	56	52
	No	14	78

a. Develop a joint probability table and use it to answer the remaining questions.
b. Using the marginal probabilities for buy a car and pay rent, are parents more likely to assist their adult children with buying a car or paying rent? What is your interpretation of the marginal probabilities?
c. If parents provided financial assistance to buy a car, what it the probability that the parents assisted with paying rent?
d. If parents did not provide financial assistance to buy a car, what is the probability the parents assisted with paying rent?
e. Is financial assistance to buy a car independent of financial assistance to pay rent? Use probabilities to justify your answer.
f. What is the probability that parents provided financial assistance for their adult children by either helping buy a car or pay rent?

36. Jerry Stackhouse of the National Basketball Association's Dallas Mavericks is the best free-throw shooter on the team, making 89% of his shots (ESPN website, July, 2008). Assume that late in a basketball game, Jerry Stackhouse is fouled and is awarded two shots.
a. What is the probability that he will make both shots?
b. What is the probability that he will make at least one shot?
c. What is the probability that he will miss both shots?

d. Late in a basketball game, a team often intentionally fouls an opposing player in order to stop the game clock. The usual strategy is to intentionally foul the other team's worst free-throw shooter. Assume that the Dallas Mavericks' center makes 58% of his free-throw shots. Calculate the probabilities for the center as shown in parts (a), (b), and (c), and show that intentionally fouling the Dallas Mavericks' center is a better strategy than intentionally fouling Jerry Stackhouse.

37. Visa Card USA studied how frequently young consumers, ages 18 to 24, use plastic (debit and credit) cards in making purchases (Associated Press, January 16, 2006). The results of the study provided the following probabilities.
    - The probability that a consumer uses a plastic card when making a purchase is .37.
    - Given that the consumer uses a plastic card, there is a .19 probability that the consumer is 18 to 24 years old.
    - Given that the consumer uses a plastic card, there is a .81 probability that the consumer is more than 24 years old.

    U.S. Census Bureau data show that 14% of the consumer population is 18 to 24 years old.
    a. Given the consumer is 18 to 24 years old, what is the probability that the consumer use a plastic card?
    b. Given the consumer is over 24 years old, what is the probability that the consumer uses a plastic card?
    c. What is the interpretation of the probabilities shown in parts (a) and (b)?
    d. Should companies such as Visa, MasterCard, and Discover make plastic cards available to the 18 to 24 year old age group before these consumers have had time to establish a credit history? If no, why? If yes, what restrictions might the companies place on this age group?

38. A Morgan Stanley Consumer Research Survey sampled men and women and asked each whether they preferred to drink plain bottled water or a sports drink such as Gatorade or Propel Fitness water (*The Atlanta Journal-Constitution*, December 28, 2005). Suppose 200 men and 200 women participated in the study, and 280 reported they preferred plain bottled water. Of the group preferring a sports drink, 80 were men and 40 were women.
    Let

    M = the event the consumer is a man
    W = the event the consumer is a woman
    B = the event the consumer preferred plain bottled water
    S = the event the consumer preferred sports drink

    a. What is the probability a person in the study preferred plain bottled water?
    b. What is the probability a person in the study preferred a sports drink?
    c. What are the conditional probabilities $P(M \mid S)$ and $P(W \mid S)$?
    d. What are the joint probabilities $P(M \cap S)$ and $P(W \cap S)$?
    e. Given a consumer is a man, what is the probability he will prefer a sports drink?
    f. Given a consumer is a woman, what is the probability she will prefer a sports drink?
    g. Is preference for a sports drink independent of whether the consumer is a man or a woman? Explain using probability information.

4.5 Bayes' Theorem

In the discussion of conditional probability, we indicated that revising probabilities when new information is obtained is an important phase of probability analysis. Often, we begin the analysis with initial or **prior probability** estimates for specific events of interest. Then, from sources such as a sample, a special report, or a product test, we obtain additional information about the events. Given this new information, we update the prior probability values by calculating revised probabilities, referred to as **posterior probabilities**. **Bayes' theorem** provides a means for making these probability calculations. The steps in this probability revision process are shown in Figure 4.9.

FIGURE 4.9 PROBABILITY REVISION USING BAYES' THEOREM

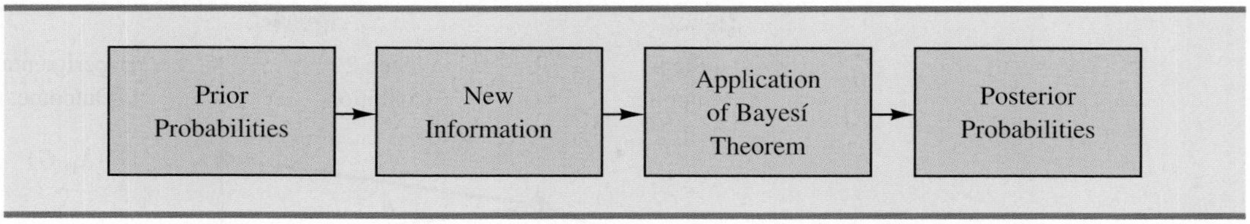

As an application of Bayes' theorem, consider a manufacturing firm that receives shipments of parts from two different suppliers. Let A_1 denote the event that a part is from supplier 1 and A_2 denote the event that a part is from supplier 2. Currently, 65% of the parts purchased by the company are from supplier 1 and the remaining 35% are from supplier 2. Hence, if a part is selected at random, we would assign the prior probabilities $P(A_1) = .65$ and $P(A_2) = .35$.

The quality of the purchased parts varies with the source of supply. Historical data suggest that the quality ratings of the two suppliers are as shown in Table 4.6. If we let G denote the event that a part is good and B denote the event that a part is bad, the information in Table 4.6 provides the following conditional probability values.

$$P(G \mid A_1) = .98 \quad P(B \mid A_1) = .02$$
$$P(G \mid A_2) = .95 \quad P(B \mid A_2) = .05$$

The tree diagram in Figure 4.10 depicts the process of the firm receiving a part from one of the two suppliers and then discovering that the part is good or bad as a two-step experiment. We see that four experimental outcomes are possible; two correspond to the part being good and two correspond to the part being bad.

Each of the experimental outcomes is the intersection of two events, so we can use the multiplication rule to compute the probabilities. For instance,

$$P(A_1, G) = P(A_1 \cap G) = P(A_1)P(G \mid A_1)$$

The process of computing these joint probabilities can be depicted in what is called a probability tree (see Figure 4.11). From left to right through the tree, the probabilities for each branch at step 1 are prior probabilities and the probabilities for each branch at step 2 are conditional probabilities. To find the probabilities of each experimental outcome, we simply multiply the probabilities on the branches leading to the outcome. Each of these joint probabilities is shown in Figure 4.11 along with the known probabilities for each branch.

Suppose now that the parts from the two suppliers are used in the firm's manufacturing process and that a machine breaks down because it attempts to process a bad part. Given the information that the part is bad, what is the probability that it came from supplier 1 and

TABLE 4.6 HISTORICAL QUALITY LEVELS OF TWO SUPPLIERS

	Percentage Good Parts	Percentage Bad Parts
Supplier 1	98	2
Supplier 2	95	5

FIGURE 4.10 TREE DIAGRAM FOR TWO-SUPPLIER EXAMPLE

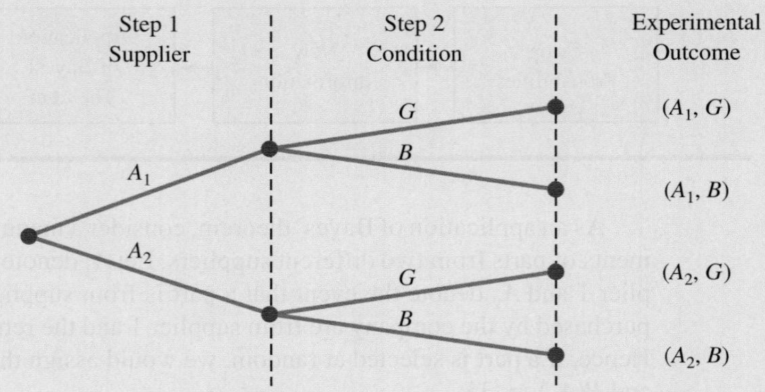

Note: Step 1 shows that the part comes from one of two suppliers, and step 2 shows whether the part is good or bad.

what is the probability that it came from supplier 2? With the information in the probability tree (Figure 4.11), Bayes' theorem can be used to answer these questions.

Letting B denote the event that the part is bad, we are looking for the posterior probabilities $P(A_1 \mid B)$ and $P(A_2 \mid B)$. From the law of conditional probability, we know that

$$P(A_1 \mid B) = \frac{P(A_1 \cap B)}{P(B)} \tag{4.14}$$

Referring to the probability tree, we see that

$$P(A_1 \cap B) = P(A_1)P(B \mid A_1) \tag{4.15}$$

FIGURE 4.11 PROBABILITY TREE FOR TWO-SUPPLIER EXAMPLE

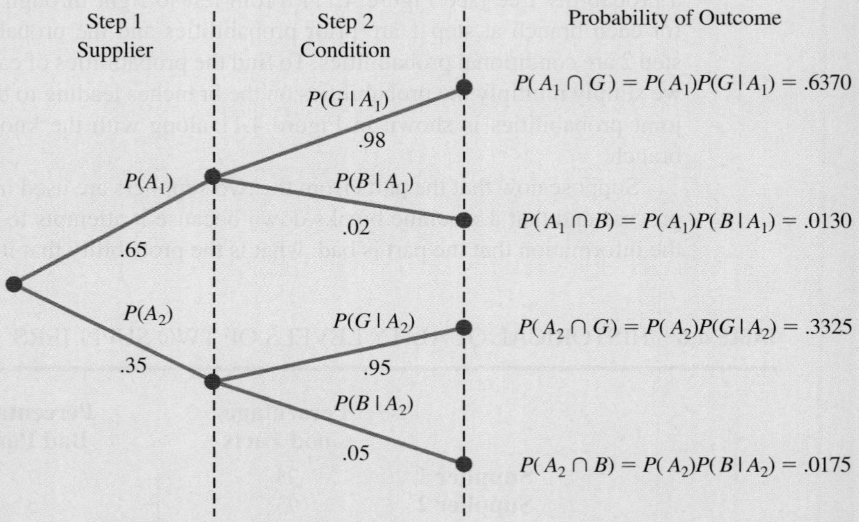

To find $P(B)$, we note that event B can occur in only two ways: $(A_1 \cap B)$ and $(A_2 \cap B)$. Therefore, we have

$$\begin{aligned} P(B) &= P(A_1 \cap B) + P(A_2 \cap B) \\ &= P(A_1)P(B \mid A_1) + P(A_2)P(B \mid A_2) \end{aligned} \quad \textbf{(4.16)}$$

Substituting from equations (4.15) and (4.16) into equation (4.14) and writing a similar result for $P(A_2 \mid B)$, we obtain Bayes' theorem for the case of two events.

The Reverend Thomas Bayes (1702–1761), a Presbyterian minister, is credited with the original work leading to the version of Bayes' theorem in use today.

BAYES' THEOREM (TWO-EVENT CASE)

$$P(A_1 \mid B) = \frac{P(A_1)P(B \mid A_1)}{P(A_1)P(B \mid A_1) + P(A_2)P(B \mid A_2)} \quad \textbf{(4.17)}$$

$$P(A_2 \mid B) = \frac{P(A_2)P(B \mid A_2)}{P(A_1)P(B \mid A_1) + P(A_2)P(B \mid A_2)} \quad \textbf{(4.18)}$$

Using equation (4.17) and the probability values provided in the example, we have

$$\begin{aligned} P(A_1 \mid B) &= \frac{P(A_1)P(B \mid A_1)}{P(A_1)P(B \mid A_1) + P(A_2)P(B \mid A_2)} \\ &= \frac{(.65)(.02)}{(.65)(.02) + (.35)(.05)} = \frac{.0130}{.0130 + .0175} \\ &= \frac{.0130}{.0305} = .4262 \end{aligned}$$

In addition, using equation (4.18), we find $P(A_2 \mid B)$.

$$\begin{aligned} P(A_2 \mid B) &= \frac{(.35)(.05)}{(.65)(.02) + (.35)(.05)} \\ &= \frac{.0175}{.0130 + .0175} = \frac{.0175}{.0305} = .5738 \end{aligned}$$

Note that in this application we started with a probability of .65 that a part selected at random was from supplier 1. However, given information that the part is bad, the probability that the part is from supplier 1 drops to .4262. In fact, if the part is bad, it has better than a 50–50 chance that it came from supplier 2; that is, $P(A_2 \mid B) = .5738$.

Bayes' theorem is applicable when the events for which we want to compute posterior probabilities are mutually exclusive and their union is the entire sample space.[2] For the case of n mutually exclusive events $A_1, A_2, \ldots, A_n$, whose union is the entire sample space, Bayes' theorem can be used to compute any posterior probability $P(A_i \mid B)$ as shown here.

BAYES' THEOREM

$$P(A_i \mid B) = \frac{P(A_i)P(B \mid A_i)}{P(A_1)P(B \mid A_1) + P(A_2)P(B \mid A_2) + \cdots + P(A_n)P(B \mid A_n)} \quad \textbf{(4.19)}$$

[2]If the union of events is the entire sample space, the events are said to be *collectively exhaustive.*

With prior probabilities $P(A_1), P(A_2), \ldots, P(A_n)$ and the appropriate conditional probabilities $P(B \mid A_1), P(B \mid A_2), \ldots, P(B \mid A_n)$, equation (4.19) can be used to compute the posterior probability of the events $A_1, A_2, \ldots, A_n$.

Tabular Approach

A tabular approach is helpful in conducting the Bayes' theorem calculations. Such an approach is shown in Table 4.7 for the parts supplier problem. The computations shown there are done in the following steps.

Step 1. Prepare the following three columns:
Column 1—The mutually exclusive events A_i for which posterior probabilities are desired
Column 2—The prior probabilities $P(A_i)$ for the events
Column 3—The conditional probabilities $P(B \mid A_i)$ of the new information B given each event

Step 2. In column 4, compute the joint probabilities $P(A_i \cap B)$ for each event and the new information B by using the multiplication law. These joint probabilities are found by multiplying the prior probabilities in column 2 by the corresponding conditional probabilities in column 3; that is, $P(A_i \cap B) = P(A_i)P(B \mid A_i)$.

Step 3. Sum the joint probabilities in column 4. The sum is the probability of the new information, $P(B)$. Thus we see in Table 4.7 that there is a .0130 probability that the part came from supplier 1 and is bad and a .0175 probability that the part came from supplier 2 and is bad. Because these are the only two ways in which a bad part can be obtained, the sum .0130 + .0175 shows an overall probability of .0305 of finding a bad part from the combined shipments of the two suppliers.

Step 4. In column 5, compute the posterior probabilities using the basic relationship of conditional probability.

$$P(A_i \mid B) = \frac{P(A_i \cap B)}{P(B)}$$

Note that the joint probabilities $P(A_i \cap B)$ are in column 4 and the probability $P(B)$ is the sum of column 4.

TABLE 4.7 TABULAR APPROACH TO BAYES' THEOREM CALCULATIONS FOR THE TWO-SUPPLIER PROBLEM

(1) Events A_i	(2) Prior Probabilities $P(A_i)$	(3) Conditional Probabilities $P(B \mid A_i)$	(4) Joint Probabilities $P(A_i \cap B)$	(5) Posterior Probabilities $P(A_i \mid B)$
A_1	.65	.02	.0130	.0130/.0305 = .4262
A_2	.35	.05	.0175	.0175/.0305 = .5738
	1.00		$P(B)$ = .0305	1.0000

NOTES AND COMMENTS

1. Bayes' theorem is used extensively in decision analysis. The prior probabilities are often subjective estimates provided by a decision maker. Sample information is obtained and posterior probabilities are computed for use in choosing the best decision.
2. An event and its complement are mutually exclusive, and their union is the entire sample space. Thus, Bayes' theorem is always applicable for computing posterior probabilities of an event and its complement.

Exercises

Methods

SELF test

39. The prior probabilities for events A_1 and A_2 are $P(A_1) = .40$ and $P(A_2) = .60$. It is also known that $P(A_1 \cap A_2) = 0$. Suppose $P(B \mid A_1) = .20$ and $P(B \mid A_2) = .05$.
    a. Are A_1 and A_2 mutually exclusive? Explain.
    b. Compute $P(A_1 \cap B)$ and $P(A_2 \cap B)$.
    c. Compute $P(B)$.
    d. Apply Bayes' theorem to compute $P(A_1 \mid B)$ and $P(A_2 \mid B)$.
40. The prior probabilities for events A_1, A_2, and A_3 are $P(A_1) = .20$, $P(A_2) = .50$, and $P(A_3) = .30$. The conditional probabilities of event B given A_1, A_2, and A_3 are $P(B \mid A_1) = .50$, $P(B \mid A_2) = .40$, and $P(B \mid A_3) = .30$.
    a. Compute $P(B \cap A_1)$, $P(B \cap A_2)$, and $P(B \cap A_3)$.
    b. Apply Bayes' theorem, equation (4.19), to compute the posterior probability $P(A_2 \mid B)$.
    c. Use the tabular approach to applying Bayes' theorem to compute $P(A_1 \mid B)$, $P(A_2 \mid B)$, and $P(A_3 \mid B)$.

Applications

41. A consulting firm submitted a bid for a large research project. The firm's management initially felt they had a 50–50 chance of getting the project. However, the agency to which the bid was submitted subsequently requested additional information on the bid. Past experience indicates that for 75% of the successful bids and 40% of the unsuccessful bids the agency requested additional information.
    a. What is the prior probability of the bid being successful (that is, prior to the request for additional information)?
    b. What is the conditional probability of a request for additional information given that the bid will ultimately be successful?
    c. Compute the posterior probability that the bid will be successful given a request for additional information.

SELF test

42. A local bank reviewed its credit card policy with the intention of recalling some of its credit cards. In the past approximately 5% of cardholders defaulted, leaving the bank unable to collect the outstanding balance. Hence, management established a prior probability of .05 that any particular cardholder will default. The bank also found that the probability of missing a monthly payment is .20 for customers who do not default. Of course, the probability of missing a monthly payment for those who default is 1.
    a. Given that a customer missed one or more monthly payments, compute the posterior probability that the customer will default.
    b. The bank would like to recall its card if the probability that a customer will default is greater than .20. Should the bank recall its card if the customer misses a monthly payment? Why or why not?

43. Small cars get better gas mileage, but they are not as safe as bigger cars. Small cars accounted for 18% of the vehicles on the road, but accidents involving small cars led to 11,898 fatalities during a recent year (*Reader's Digest,* May 2000). Assume the probability a small car is involved in an accident is .18. The probability of an accident involving a small car leading to a fatality is .128 and the probability of an accident not involving a small car leading to a fatality is .05. Suppose you learn of an accident involving a fatality. What is the probability a small car was involved? Assume that the likelihood of getting into an accident is independent of car size.

44. The American Council of Education reported that 47% of college freshmen earn a degree and graduate within five years (Associated Press, May 6, 2002). Assume that graduation records show women make up 50% of the students who graduated within five years, but only 45% of the students who did not graduate within five years. The students who had not graduated within five years either dropped out or were still working on their degrees.
    a. Let A_1 = the student graduated within five years
       A_2 = the student did not graduate within five years
       W = the student is a female student
       Using the given information, what are the values for $P(A_1)$, $P(A_2)$, $P(W \mid A_1)$, and $P(W \mid A_2)$?
    b. What is the probability that a female student will graduate within five years?
    c. What is the probability that a male student will graduate within five years?
    d. Given the preceding results, what are the percentage of women and the percentage of men in the entering freshman class?

45. In an article about investment alternatives, *Money* magazine reported that drug stocks provide a potential for long-term growth, with over 50% of the adult population of the United States taking prescription drugs on a regular basis. For adults age 65 and older, 82% take prescription drugs regularly. For adults age 18 to 64, 49% take prescription drugs regularly. The age 18–64 age group accounts for 83.5% of the adult population (*Statistical Abstract of the United States*, 2008).
    a. What is the probability that a randomly selected adult is 65 or older?
    b. Given an adult takes prescription drugs regularly, what is the probability that the adult is 65 or older?

Summary

In this chapter we introduced basic probability concepts and illustrated how probability analysis can be used to provide helpful information for decision making. We described how probability can be interpreted as a numerical measure of the likelihood that an event will occur. In addition, we saw that the probability of an event can be computed either by summing the probabilities of the experimental outcomes (sample points) comprising the event or by using the relationships established by the addition, conditional probability, and multiplication laws of probability. For cases in which additional information is available, we showed how Bayes' theorem can be used to obtain revised or posterior probabilities.

Glossary

Probability A numerical measure of the likelihood that an event will occur.
Experiment A process that generates well-defined outcomes.
Sample space The set of all experimental outcomes.
Sample point An element of the sample space. A sample point represents an experimental outcome.
Tree diagram A graphical representation that helps in visualizing a multiple-step experiment.

Basic requirements for assigning probabilities Two requirements that restrict the manner in which probability assignments can be made: (1) for each experimental outcome E_i we must have $0 \leq P(E_i) \leq 1$; (2) considering all experimental outcomes, we must have $P(E_1) + P(E_2) + \cdots + P(E_n) = 1.0$.

Classical method A method of assigning probabilities that is appropriate when all the experimental outcomes are equally likely.

Relative frequency method A method of assigning probabilities that is appropriate when data are available to estimate the proportion of the time the experimental outcome will occur if the experiment is repeated a large number of times.

Subjective method A method of assigning probabilities on the basis of judgment.

Event A collection of sample points.

Complement of *A* The event consisting of all sample points that are not in *A*.

Venn diagram A graphical representation for showing symbolically the sample space and operations involving events in which the sample space is represented by a rectangle and events are represented as circles within the sample space.

Union of *A* and *B* The event containing all sample points belonging to *A* or *B* or both. The union is denoted $A \cup B$.

Intersection of *A* and *B* The event containing the sample points belonging to both *A* and *B*. The intersection is denoted $A \cap B$.

Addition law A probability law used to compute the probability of the union of two events. It is $P(A \cup B) = P(A) + P(B) - P(A \cap B)$. For mutually exclusive events, $P(A \cap B) = 0$; in this case the addition law reduces to $P(A \cup B) = P(A) + P(B)$.

Mutually exclusive events Events that have no sample points in common; that is, $A \cap B$ is empty and $P(A \cap B) = 0$.

Conditional probability The probability of an event given that another event already occurred. The conditional probability of *A* given *B* is $P(A \mid B) = P(A \cap B)/P(B)$.

Joint probability The probability of two events both occurring; that is, the probability of the intersection of two events.

Marginal probability The values in the margins of a joint probability table that provide the probabilities of each event separately.

Independent events Two events *A* and *B* where $P(A \mid B) = P(A)$ or $P(B \mid A) = P(B)$; that is, the events have no influence on each other.

Multiplication law A probability law used to compute the probability of the intersection of two events. It is $P(A \cap B) = P(B)P(A \mid B)$ or $P(A \cap B) = P(A)P(B \mid A)$. For independent events it reduces to $P(A \cap B) = P(A)P(B)$.

Prior probabilities Initial estimates of the probabilities of events.

Posterior probabilities Revised probabilities of events based on additional information.

Bayes' theorem A method used to compute posterior probabilities.

Key Formulas

Counting Rule for Combinations

$$C_n^N = \binom{N}{n} = \frac{N!}{n!(N-n)!} \tag{4.1}$$

Counting Rule for Permutations

$$P_n^N = n!\binom{N}{n} = \frac{N!}{(N-n)!} \tag{4.2}$$

Computing Probability Using the Complement

$$P(A) = 1 - P(A^c) \tag{4.5}$$

Addition Law

$$P(A \cup B) = P(A) + P(B) - P(A \cap B) \tag{4.6}$$

Conditional Probability

$$P(A \mid B) = \frac{P(A \cap B)}{P(B)} \tag{4.7}$$

$$P(B \mid A) = \frac{P(A \cap B)}{P(A)} \tag{4.8}$$

Multiplication Law

$$P(A \cap B) = P(B)P(A \mid B) \tag{4.11}$$

$$P(A \cap B) = P(A)P(B \mid A) \tag{4.12}$$

Multiplication Law for Independent Events

$$P(A \cap B) = P(A)P(B) \tag{4.13}$$

Bayes' Theorem

$$P(A_i \mid B) = \frac{P(A_i)P(B \mid A_i)}{P(A_1)P(B \mid A_1) + P(A_2)P(B \mid A_2) + \cdots + P(A_n)P(B \mid A_n)} \tag{4.19}$$

Supplementary Exercises

46. *The Wall Street Journal*/Harris Personal Finance poll asked 2082 adults if they owned a home (All Business website, January 23, 2008). A total of 1249 survey respondents answered Yes. Of the 450 respondents in the 18–34 age group, 117 responded Yes.
    a. What is the probability that a respondent to the poll owned a home?
    b. What is the probability that a respondent in the 18–34 age group owned a home?
    c. What is the probability that a respondent to the poll did not own a home?
    d. What is the probability that a respondent in the 18–34 age group did not own a home?

47. A financial manager made two new investments—one in the oil industry and one in municipal bonds. After a one-year period, each of the investments will be classified as either successful or unsuccessful. Consider the making of the two investments as an experiment.
    a. How many sample points exist for this experiment?
    b. Show a tree diagram and list the sample points.
    c. Let O = the event that the oil industry investment is successful and M = the event that the municipal bond investment is successful. List the sample points in O and in M.
    d. List the sample points in the union of the events ($O \cup M$).
    e. List the sample points in the intersection of the events ($O \cap M$).
    f. Are events O and M mutually exclusive? Explain.

48. In early 2003, President Bush proposed eliminating the taxation of dividends to shareholders on the grounds that it was double taxation. Corporations pay taxes on the earnings that are later paid out in dividends. In a poll of 671 Americans, TechnoMetrica Market Intelligence found that 47% favored the proposal, 44% opposed it, and 9% were not sure (*Investor's Business Daily,* January 13, 2003). In looking at the responses across party lines

the poll showed that 29% of Democrats were in favor, 64% of Republicans were in favor, and 48% of Independents were in favor.

a. How many of those polled favored elimination of the tax on dividends?
b. What is the conditional probability in favor of the proposal given the person polled is a Democrat?
c. Is party affiliation independent of whether one is in favor of the proposal?
d. If we assume people's responses were consistent with their own self-interest, which group do you believe will benefit most from passage of the proposal?

49. A study of 31,000 hospital admissions in New York State found that 4% of the admissions led to treatment-caused injuries. One-seventh of these treatment-caused injuries resulted in death, and one-fourth were caused by negligence. Malpractice claims were filed in one out of 7.5 cases involving negligence, and payments were made in one out of every two claims.
a. What is the probability a person admitted to the hospital will suffer a treatment-caused injury due to negligence?
b. What is the probability a person admitted to the hospital will die from a treatment-caused injury?
c. In the case of a negligent treatment-caused injury, what is the probability a malpractice claim will be paid?

50. A telephone survey to determine viewer response to a new television show obtained the following data.

Rating	Frequency
Poor	4
Below average	8
Average	11
Above average	14
Excellent	13

a. What is the probability that a randomly selected viewer will rate the new show as average or better?
b. What is the probability that a randomly selected viewer will rate the new show below average or worse?

51. The following crosstabulation shows household income by educational level of the head of household (*Statistical Abstract of the United States*, 2008).

	Household Income ($1000s)					
Education Level	**Under 25**	**25.0–49.9**	**50.0–74.9**	**75.0–99.9**	**100 or more**	**Total**
Not H.S. Graduate	4,207	3,459	1,389	539	367	9,961
H.S. Graduate	4,917	6,850	5,027	2,637	2,668	22,099
Some College	2,807	5,258	4,678	3,250	4,074	20,067
Bachelor's Degree	885	2,094	2,848	2,581	5,379	13,787
Beyond Bach. Deg.	290	829	1,274	1,241	4,188	7,822
Total	13,106	18,490	15,216	10,248	16,676	73,736

a. Develop a joint probability table.
b. What is the probability of a head of household not being a high school graduate?
c. What is the probability of a head of household having a bachelor's degree or more education?
d. What is the probability of a household headed by someone with a bachelor's degree earning $100,000 or more?

e. What is the probability of a household having income below $25,000?
f. What is the probability of a household headed by someone with a bachelor's degree earning less than $25,000?
g. Is household income independent of educational level?

52. An MBA new-matriculants survey provided the following data for 2018 students.

		Applied to More Than One School	
		Yes	No
Age Group	23 and under	207	201
	24–26	299	379
	27–30	185	268
	31–35	66	193
	36 and over	51	169

a. For a randomly selected MBA student, prepare a joint probability table for the experiment consisting of observing the student's age and whether the student applied to one or more schools.
b. What is the probability that a randomly selected applicant is 23 or under?
c. What is the probability that a randomly selected applicant is older than 26?
d. What is the probability that a randomly selected applicant applied to more than one school?

53. Refer again to the data from the MBA new-matriculants survey in exercise 52.
a. Given that a person applied to more than one school, what is the probability that the person is 24–26 years old?
b. Given that a person is in the 36-and-over age group, what is the probability that the person applied to more than one school?
c. What is the probability that a person is 24–26 years old or applied to more than one school?
d. Suppose a person is known to have applied to only one school. What is the probability that the person is 31 or more years old?
e. Is the number of schools applied to independent of age? Explain.

54. An IBD/TIPP poll conducted to learn about attitudes toward investment and retirement (*Investor's Business Daily,* May 5, 2000) asked male and female respondents how important they felt level of risk was in choosing a retirement investment. The following joint probability table was constructed from the data provided. "Important" means the respondent said level of risk was either important or very important.

	Male	Female	Total
Important	.22	.27	.49
Not Important	.28	.23	.51
Total	.50	.50	1.00

a. What is the probability a survey respondent will say level of risk is important?
b. What is the probability a male respondent will say level of risk is important?
c. What is the probability a female respondent will say level of risk is important?
d. Is the level of risk independent of the gender of the respondent? Why or why not?
e. Do male and female attitudes toward risk differ?

55. A large consumer goods company ran a television advertisement for one of its soap products. On the basis of a survey that was conducted, probabilities were assigned to the following events.

B = individual purchased the product
S = individual recalls seeing the advertisement
$B \cap S$ = individual purchased the product and recalls seeing the advertisement

The probabilities assigned were $P(B) = .20$, $P(S) = .40$, and $P(B \cap S) = .12$.

a. What is the probability of an individual's purchasing the product given that the individual recalls seeing the advertisement? Does seeing the advertisement increase the probability that the individual will purchase the product? As a decision maker, would you recommend continuing the advertisement (assuming that the cost is reasonable)?
b. Assume that individuals who do not purchase the company's soap product buy from its competitors. What would be your estimate of the company's market share? Would you expect that continuing the advertisement will increase the company's market share? Why or why not?
c. The company also tested another advertisement and assigned it values of $P(S) = .30$ and $P(B \cap S) = .10$. What is $P(B \mid S)$ for this other advertisement? Which advertisement seems to have had the bigger effect on customer purchases?

56. Cooper Realty is a small real estate company located in Albany, New York, specializing primarily in residential listings. They recently became interested in determining the likelihood of one of their listings being sold within a certain number of days. An analysis of company sales of 800 homes in previous years produced the following data.

		Days Listed Until Sold			
		Under 30	**31–90**	**Over 90**	**Total**
Initial Asking Price	**Under $150,000**	50	40	10	100
	$150,000–$199,999	20	150	80	250
	$200,000–$250,000	20	280	100	400
	Over $250,000	10	30	10	50
	Total	100	500	200	800

a. If A is defined as the event that a home is listed for more than 90 days before being sold, estimate the probability of A.
b. If B is defined as the event that the initial asking price is under $150,000, estimate the probability of B.
c. What is the probability of $A \cap B$?
d. Assuming that a contract was just signed to list a home with an initial asking price of less than $150,000, what is the probability that the home will take Cooper Realty more than 90 days to sell?
e. Are events A and B independent?

57. A company studied the number of lost-time accidents occurring at its Brownsville, Texas, plant. Historical records show that 6% of the employees suffered lost-time accidents last year. Management believes that a special safety program will reduce such accidents to 5% during the current year. In addition, it estimates that 15% of employees who had lost-time accidents last year will experience a lost-time accident during the current year.

a. What percentage of the employees will experience lost-time accidents in both years?
b. What percentage of the employees will suffer at least one lost-time accident over the two-year period?

58. A survey showed that 8% of Internet users age 18 and older report keeping a blog. Referring to the 18–29 age group as young adults, the survey showed that for bloggers 54% are young adults and for nonbloggers 24% are young adults (Pew Internet & American Life Project, July 19, 2006).
   a. Develop a joint probability table for these data with two rows (bloggers vs. non-bloggers) and two columns (young adults vs. older adults).
   b. What is the probability that an Internet user is a young adult?
   c. What is the probability that an Internet user keeps a blog and is a young adult?
   d. Suppose that in a follow-up phone survey we contact someone who is 24 years old. What is the probability that this person keeps a blog?

59. An oil company purchased an option on land in Alaska. Preliminary geologic studies assigned the following prior probabilities.

$$P(\text{high-quality oil}) = .50$$
$$P(\text{medium-quality oil}) = .20$$
$$P(\text{no oil}) = .30$$

   a. What is the probability of finding oil?
   b. After 200 feet of drilling on the first well, a soil test is taken. The probabilities of finding the particular type of soil identified by the test follow.

$$P(\text{soil} \mid \text{high-quality oil}) = .20$$
$$P(\text{soil} \mid \text{medium-quality oil}) = .80$$
$$P(\text{soil} \mid \text{no oil}) = .20$$

   How should the firm interpret the soil test? What are the revised probabilities, and what is the new probability of finding oil?

60. Companies that do business over the Internet can often obtain probability information about website visitors from previous websites visited. The article "Internet Marketing" (*Interfaces,* March/April 2001) described how clickstream data on websites visited could be used in conjunction with a Bayesian updating scheme to determine the gender of a website visitor. Par Fore created a website to market golf equipment and apparel. Management would like a certain offer to appear for female visitors and a different offer to appear for male visitors. From a sample of past website visits, management learned that 60% of the visitors to the website ParFore are male and 40% are female.
   a. What is the prior probability that the next visitor to the website will be female?
   b. Suppose you know that the current visitor to the website ParFore previously visited the Dillard's website, and that women are three times as likely to visit the Dillard's website as men. What is the revised probability that the current visitor to the website ParFore is female? Should you display the offer that appeals more to female visitors or the one that appeals more to male visitors?

Case Problem Hamilton County Judges

Hamilton County judges try thousands of cases per year. In an overwhelming majority of the cases disposed, the verdict stands as rendered. However, some cases are appealed, and of those appealed, some of the cases are reversed. Kristen DelGuzzi of *The Cincinnati Enquirer* conducted a study of cases handled by Hamilton County judges over a three-year period. Shown in Table 4.8 are the results for 182,908 cases handled (disposed) by 38 judges in Common Pleas Court, Domestic Relations Court, and Municipal Court. Two of the judges (Dinkelacker and Hogan) did not serve in the same court for the entire three-year period.

WEB file
Judge

TABLE 4.8 TOTAL CASES DISPOSED, APPEALED, AND REVERSED IN HAMILTON COUNTY COURTS

Common Pleas Court

Judge	Total Cases Disposed	Appealed Cases	Reversed Cases
Fred Cartolano	3,037	137	12
Thomas Crush	3,372	119	10
Patrick Dinkelacker	1,258	44	8
Timothy Hogan	1,954	60	7
Robert Kraft	3,138	127	7
William Mathews	2,264	91	18
William Morrissey	3,032	121	22
Norbert Nadel	2,959	131	20
Arthur Ney, Jr.	3,219	125	14
Richard Niehaus	3,353	137	16
Thomas Nurre	3,000	121	6
John O'Connor	2,969	129	12
Robert Ruehlman	3,205	145	18
J. Howard Sundermann	955	60	10
Ann Marie Tracey	3,141	127	13
Ralph Winkler	3,089	88	6
Total	43,945	1762	199

Domestic Relations Court

Judge	Total Cases Disposed	Appealed Cases	Reversed Cases
Penelope Cunningham	2,729	7	1
Patrick Dinkelacker	6,001	19	4
Deborah Gaines	8,799	48	9
Ronald Panioto	12,970	32	3
Total	30,499	106	17

Municipal Court

Judge	Total Cases Disposed	Appealed Cases	Reversed Cases
Mike Allen	6,149	43	4
Nadine Allen	7,812	34	6
Timothy Black	7,954	41	6
David Davis	7,736	43	5
Leslie Isaiah Gaines	5,282	35	13
Karla Grady	5,253	6	0
Deidra Hair	2,532	5	0
Dennis Helmick	7,900	29	5
Timothy Hogan	2,308	13	2
James Patrick Kenney	2,798	6	1
Joseph Luebbers	4,698	25	8
William Mallory	8,277	38	9
Melba Marsh	8,219	34	7
Beth Mattingly	2,971	13	1
Albert Mestemaker	4,975	28	9
Mark Painter	2,239	7	3
Jack Rosen	7,790	41	13
Mark Schweikert	5,403	33	6
David Stockdale	5,371	22	4
John A. West	2,797	4	2
Total	108,464	500	104

The purpose of the newspaper's study was to evaluate the performance of the judges. Appeals are often the result of mistakes made by judges, and the newspaper wanted to know which judges were doing a good job and which were making too many mistakes. You are called in to assist in the data analysis. Use your knowledge of probability and conditional probability to help with the ranking of the judges. You also may be able to analyze the likelihood of appeal and reversal for cases handled by different courts.

Managerial Report

Prepare a report with your rankings of the judges. Also, include an analysis of the likelihood of appeal and case reversal in the three courts. At a minimum, your report should include the following:

1. The probability of cases being appealed and reversed in the three different courts.
2. The probability of a case being appealed for each judge.
3. The probability of a case being reversed for each judge.
4. The probability of reversal given an appeal for each judge.
5. Rank the judges within each court. State the criteria you used and provide a rationale for your choice.

CHAPTER 5

Discrete Probability Distributions

CONTENTS

STATISTICS *in* PRACTICE

CITIBANK*
LONG ISLAND CITY, NEW YORK

Citibank, the retail banking division of Citigroup, offers a wide range of financial services including checking and saving accounts, loans and mortgages, insurance, and investment services. It delivers these services through a unique system referred to as Citibanking.

Citibank was one of the first banks in the United States to introduce automatic teller machines (ATMs). Citibank's ATMs, located in Citicard Banking Centers (CBCs), let customers do all of their banking in one place with the touch of a finger, 24 hours a day, 7 days a week. More than 150 different banking functions—from deposits to managing investments—can be performed with ease. Citibank customers use ATMs for 80% of their transactions.

Each Citibank CBC operates as a waiting line system with randomly arriving customers seeking service at one of the ATMs. If all ATMs are busy, the arriving customers wait in line. Periodic CBC capacity studies are used to analyze customer waiting times and to determine whether additional ATMs are needed.

Data collected by Citibank showed that the random customer arrivals followed a probability distribution known as the Poisson distribution. Using the Poisson distribution, Citibank can compute probabilities for the number of customers arriving at a CBC during any time period and make decisions concerning the number of ATMs needed. For example, let x = the number of customers arriving during a one-minute period. Assuming that a particular CBC has a mean arrival rate of two customers per minute, the following table shows the probabilities for the number of customers arriving during a one-minute period.

A Citibank state-of-the-art ATM. © Jeff Greenberg/Photo Edit.

x	**Probability**
0	.1353
1	.2707
2	.2707
3	.1804
4	.0902
5 or more	.0527

Discrete probability distributions, such as the one used by Citibank, are the topic of this chapter. In addition to the Poisson distribution, you will learn about the binomial and hypergeometric distributions and how they can be used to provide helpful probability information.

*The authors are indebted to Ms. Stacey Karter, Citibank, for providing this Statistics in Practice.

In this chapter we continue the study of probability by introducing the concepts of random variables and probability distributions. The focus of this chapter is discrete probability distributions. Three special discrete probability distributions—the binomial, Poisson, and hypergeometric—are covered.

5.1 Random Variables

In Chapter 4 we defined the concept of an experiment and its associated experimental outcomes. A random variable provides a means for describing experimental outcomes using numerical values. Random variables must assume numerical values.

RANDOM VARIABLE

Random variables must have numerical values.

A **random variable** is a numerical description of the outcome of an experiment.

In effect, a random variable associates a numerical value with each possible experimental outcome. The particular numerical value of the random variable depends on the outcome of the experiment. A random variable can be classified as being either *discrete* or *continuous* depending on the numerical values it assumes.

Discrete Random Variables

A random variable that may assume either a finite number of values or an infinite sequence of values such as 0, 1, 2, . . . is referred to as a **discrete random variable**. For example, consider the experiment of an accountant taking the certified public accountant (CPA) examination. The examination has four parts. We can define a random variable as x = the number of parts of the CPA examination passed. It is a discrete random variable because it may assume the finite number of values 0, 1, 2, 3, or 4.

As another example of a discrete random variable, consider the experiment of cars arriving at a tollbooth. The random variable of interest is x = the number of cars arriving during a one-day period. The possible values for x come from the sequence of integers 0, 1, 2, and so on. Hence, x is a discrete random variable assuming one of the values in this infinite sequence.

Although the outcomes of many experiments can naturally be described by numerical values, others cannot. For example, a survey question might ask an individual to recall the message in a recent television commercial. This experiment would have two possible outcomes: The individual cannot recall the message and the individual can recall the message. We can still describe these experimental outcomes numerically by defining the discrete random variable x as follows: let $x = 0$ if the individual cannot recall the message and $x = 1$ if the individual can recall the message. The numerical values for this random variable are arbitrary (we could use 5 and 10), but they are acceptable in terms of the definition of a random variable—namely, x is a random variable because it provides a numerical description of the outcome of the experiment.

Table 5.1 provides some additional examples of discrete random variables. Note that in each example the discrete random variable assumes a finite number of values or an infinite sequence of values such as 0, 1, 2, ... These types of discrete random variables are discussed in detail in this chapter.

TABLE 5.1 EXAMPLES OF DISCRETE RANDOM VARIABLES

Experiment	Random Variable (x)	Possible Values for the Random Variable
Contact five customers	Number of customers who place an order	0, 1, 2, 3, 4, 5
Inspect a shipment of 50 radios	Number of defective radios	0, 1, 2, . . . , 49, 50
Operate a restaurant for one day	Number of customers	0, 1, 2, 3, . . .
Sell an automobile	Gender of the customer	0 if male; 1 if female

Continuous Random Variables

A random variable that may assume any numerical value in an interval or collection of intervals is called a **continuous random variable**. Experimental outcomes based on measurement scales such as time, weight, distance, and temperature can be described by continuous random variables. For example, consider an experiment of monitoring incoming telephone calls to the claims office of a major insurance company. Suppose the random variable of interest is x = the time between consecutive incoming calls in minutes. This random variable may assume any value in the interval $x \geq 0$. Actually, an infinite number of values are possible for x, including values such as 1.26 minutes, 2.751 minutes, 4.3333 minutes, and so on. As another example, consider a 90-mile section of interstate highway I-75 north of Atlanta, Georgia. For an emergency ambulance service located in Atlanta, we might define the random variable as x = number of miles to the location of the next traffic accident along this section of I-75. In this case, x would be a continuous random variable assuming any value in the interval $0 \leq x \leq 90$. Additional examples of continuous random variables are listed in Table 5.2. Note that each example describes a random variable that may assume any value in an interval of values. Continuous random variables and their probability distributions will be the topic of Chapter 6.

TABLE 5.2 EXAMPLES OF CONTINUOUS RANDOM VARIABLES

Experiment	Random Variable (x)	Possible Values for the Random Variable
Operate a bank	Time between customer arrivals in minutes	$x \geq 0$
Fill a soft drink can (max = 12.1 ounces)	Number of ounces	$0 \leq x \leq 12.1$
Construct a new library	Percentage of project complete after six months	$0 \leq x \leq 100$
Test a new chemical process	Temperature when the desired reaction takes place (min 150° F; max 212° F)	$150 \leq x \leq 212$

NOTES AND COMMENTS

One way to determine whether a random variable is discrete or continuous is to think of the values of the random variable as points on a line segment. Choose two points representing values of the random variable. If the entire line segment between the two points also represents possible values for the random variable, then the random variable is continuous.

Exercises

Methods

SELF test

1. Consider the experiment of tossing a coin twice.
   a. List the experimental outcomes.
   b. Define a random variable that represents the number of heads occurring on the two tosses.
   c. Show what value the random variable would assume for each of the experimental outcomes.
   d. Is this random variable discrete or continuous?

2. Consider the experiment of a worker assembling a product.
   a. Define a random variable that represents the time in minutes required to assemble the product.
   b. What values may the random variable assume?
   c. Is the random variable discrete or continuous?

Applications

SELF test

3. Three students scheduled interviews for summer employment at the Brookwood Institute. In each case the interview results in either an offer for a position or no offer. Experimental outcomes are defined in terms of the results of the three interviews.
   a. List the experimental outcomes.
   b. Define a random variable that represents the number of offers made. Is the random variable continuous?
   c. Show the value of the random variable for each of the experimental outcomes.
4. In November the U.S. unemployment rate was 4.5% (*USA Today,* January 4, 2007). The Census Bureau includes nine states in the Northeast region. Assume that the random variable of interest is the number of Northeastern states with an unemployment rate in November that was less than 4.5%. What values may this random variable have?
5. To perform a certain type of blood analysis, lab technicians must perform two procedures. The first procedure requires either one or two separate steps, and the second procedure requires either one, two, or three steps.
   a. List the experimental outcomes associated with performing the blood analysis.
   b. If the random variable of interest is the total number of steps required to do the complete analysis (both procedures), show what value the random variable will assume for each of the experimental outcomes.
6. Listed is a series of experiments and associated random variables. In each case, identify the values that the random variable can assume and state whether the random variable is discrete or continuous.

Experiment	Random Variable (x)
a. Take a 20-question examination	Number of questions answered correctly
b. Observe cars arriving at a tollbooth for 1 hour	Number of cars arriving at tollbooth
c. Audit 50 tax returns	Number of returns containing errors
d. Observe an employee's work	Number of nonproductive hours in an eight-hour workday
e. Weigh a shipment of goods	Number of pounds

5.2 Discrete Probability Distributions

The **probability distribution** for a random variable describes how probabilities are distributed over the values of the random variable. For a discrete random variable x, the probability distribution is defined by a **probability function**, denoted by $f(x)$. The probability function provides the probability for each value of the random variable.

As an illustration of a discrete random variable and its probability distribution, consider the sales of automobiles at DiCarlo Motors in Saratoga, New York. Over the past 300 days of operation, sales data show 54 days with no automobiles sold, 117 days with 1 automobile sold, 72 days with 2 automobiles sold, 42 days with 3 automobiles sold, 12 days with 4 automobiles sold, and 3 days with 5 automobiles sold. Suppose we consider the experiment of selecting a day of operation at DiCarlo Motors and define the random variable of interest as x = the number of automobiles sold during a day. From historical data, we know

x is a discrete random variable that can assume the values 0, 1, 2, 3, 4, or 5. In probability function notation, $f(0)$ provides the probability of 0 automobiles sold, $f(1)$ provides the probability of 1 automobile sold, and so on. Because historical data show 54 of 300 days with 0 automobiles sold, we assign the value $54/300 = .18$ to $f(0)$, indicating that the probability of 0 automobiles being sold during a day is .18. Similarly, because 117 of 300 days had 1 automobile sold, we assign the value $117/300 = .39$ to $f(1)$, indicating that the probability of exactly 1 automobile being sold during a day is .39. Continuing in this way for the other values of the random variable, we compute the values for $f(2)$, $f(3)$, $f(4)$, and $f(5)$ as shown in Table 5.3, the probability distribution for the number of automobiles sold during a day at DiCarlo Motors.

A primary advantage of defining a random variable and its probability distribution is that once the probability distribution is known, it is relatively easy to determine the probability of a variety of events that may be of interest to a decision maker. For example, using the probability distribution for DiCarlo Motors as shown in Table 5.3, we see that the most probable number of automobiles sold during a day is 1 with a probability of $f(1) = .39$. In addition, there is an $f(3) + f(4) + f(5) = .14 + .04 + .01 = .19$ probability of selling 3 or more automobiles during a day. These probabilities, plus others the decision maker may ask about, provide information that can help the decision maker understand the process of selling automobiles at DiCarlo Motors.

In the development of a probability function for any discrete random variable, the following two conditions must be satisfied.

These conditions are the analogs to the two basic requirements for assigning probabilities to experimental outcomes presented in Chapter 4.

REQUIRED CONDITIONS FOR A DISCRETE PROBABILITY FUNCTION

$$f(x) \geq 0 \quad \text{(5.1)}$$

$$\Sigma f(x) = 1 \quad \text{(5.2)}$$

Table 5.3 shows that the probabilities for the random variable x satisfy equation (5.1); $f(x)$ is greater than or equal to 0 for all values of x. In addition, because the probabilities sum to 1, equation (5.2) is satisfied. Thus, the DiCarlo Motors probability function is a valid discrete probability function.

We can also present probability distributions graphically. In Figure 5.1 the values of the random variable x for DiCarlo Motors are shown on the horizontal axis and the probability associated with these values is shown on the vertical axis.

In addition to tables and graphs, a formula that gives the probability function, $f(x)$, for every value of x is often used to describe probability distributions. The simplest example of

TABLE 5.3 PROBABILITY DISTRIBUTION FOR THE NUMBER OF AUTOMOBILES SOLD DURING A DAY AT DICARLO MOTORS

x	$f(x)$
0	.18
1	.39
2	.24
3	.14
4	.04
5	.01
Total	1.00

FIGURE 5.1 GRAPHICAL REPRESENTATION OF THE PROBABILITY DISTRIBUTION FOR THE NUMBER OF AUTOMOBILES SOLD DURING A DAY AT DICARLO MOTORS

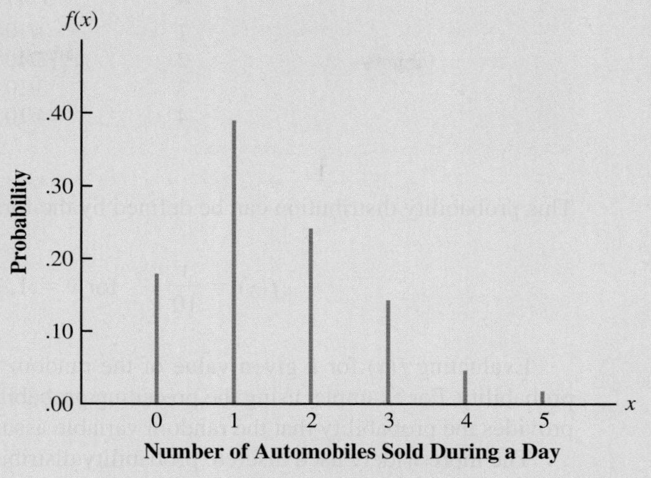

a discrete probability distribution given by a formula is the **discrete uniform probability distribution**. Its probability function is defined by equation (5.3).

DISCRETE UNIFORM PROBABILITY FUNCTION

$$f(x) = 1/n \tag{5.3}$$

where

n = the number of values the random variable may have

For example, suppose that for the experiment of rolling a die we define the random variable x to be the number of dots on the upward face. For this experiment, $n = 6$ values are possible for the random variable; $x = 1, 2, 3, 4, 5, 6$. Thus, the probability function for this discrete uniform random variable is

$$f(x) = 1/6 \qquad x = 1, 2, 3, 4, 5, 6$$

The possible values of the random variable and the associated probabilities are shown.

x	$f(x)$
1	1/6
2	1/6
3	1/6
4	1/6
5	1/6
6	1/6

As another example, consider the random variable x with the following discrete probability distribution.

x	$f(x)$
1	1/10
2	2/10
3	3/10
4	4/10

This probability distribution can be defined by the formula

$$f(x) = \frac{x}{10} \qquad \text{for } x = 1, 2, 3, \text{ or } 4$$

Evaluating $f(x)$ for a given value of the random variable will provide the associated probability. For example, using the preceding probability function, we see that $f(2) = 2/10$ provides the probability that the random variable assumes a value of 2.

The more widely used discrete probability distributions generally are specified by formulas. Three important cases are the binomial, Poisson, and hypergeometric distributions; these distributions are discussed later in the chapter.

Exercises

Methods

SELF test

7. The probability distribution for the random variable x follows.

x	$f(x)$
20	.20
25	.15
30	.25
35	.40

   a. Is this probability distribution valid? Explain.
   b. What is the probability that $x = 30$?
   c. What is the probability that x is less than or equal to 25?
   d. What is the probability that x is greater than 30?

Applications

SELF test

8. The following data were collected by counting the number of operating rooms in use at Tampa General Hospital over a 20-day period: On three of the days only one operating room was used, on five of the days two were used, on eight of the days three were used, and on four days all four of the hospital's operating rooms were used.
   a. Use the relative frequency approach to construct a probability distribution for the number of operating rooms in use on any given day.
   b. Draw a graph of the probability distribution.
   c. Show that your probability distribution satisfies the required conditions for a valid discrete probability distribution.

9. Nationally, 38% of fourth-graders cannot read an age-appropriate book. The following data show the number of children, by age, identified as learning disabled under special education. Most of these children have reading problems that should be identified and corrected before third grade. Current federal law prohibits most children from receiving extra help from special education programs until they fall behind by approximately two years' worth of learning, and that typically means third grade or later (*USA Today,* September 6, 2001).

Age	Number of Children
6	37,369
7	87,436
8	160,840
9	239,719
10	286,719
11	306,533
12	310,787
13	302,604
14	289,168

Suppose that we want to select a sample of children identified as learning disabled under special education for a program designed to improve reading ability. Let x be a random variable indicating the age of one randomly selected child.

a. Use the data to develop a probability distribution for x. Specify the values for the random variable and the corresponding values for the probability function $f(x)$.
b. Draw a graph of the probability distribution.
c. Show that the probability distribution satisfies equations (5.1) and (5.2).

10. The percent frequency distributions of job satisfaction scores for a sample of information systems (IS) senior executives and middle managers are as follows. The scores range from a low of 1 (very dissatisfied) to a high of 5 (very satisfied).

Job Satisfaction Score	IS Senior Executives (%)	IS Middle Managers (%)
1	5	4
2	9	10
3	3	12
4	42	46
5	41	28

a. Develop a probability distribution for the job satisfaction score of a senior executive.
b. Develop a probability distribution for the job satisfaction score of a middle manager.
c. What is the probability a senior executive will report a job satisfaction score of 4 or 5?
d. What is the probability a middle manager is very satisfied?
e. Compare the overall job satisfaction of senior executives and middle managers.

11. A technician services mailing machines at companies in the Phoenix area. Depending on the type of malfunction, the service call can take 1, 2, 3, or 4 hours. The different types of malfunctions occur at about the same frequency.

a. Develop a probability distribution for the duration of a service call.
b. Draw a graph of the probability distribution.
c. Show that your probability distribution satisfies the conditions required for a discrete probability function.

d. What is the probability a service call will take three hours?
e. A service call has just come in, but the type of malfunction is unknown. It is 3:00 P.M. and service technicians usually get off at 5:00 P.M. What is the probability the service technician will have to work overtime to fix the machine today?

12. The two largest cable providers are Comcast Cable Communications, with 21.5 million subscribers, and Time Warner Cable, with 11.0 million subscribers (*The New York Times Almanac*, 2007). Suppose that the management of Time Warner Cable subjectively assesses a probability distribution for the number of new subscribers next year in the state of New York as follows.

x	$f(x)$
100,000	.10
200,000	.20
300,000	.25
400,000	.30
500,000	.10
600,000	.05

a. Is this probability distribution valid? Explain.
b. What is the probability Time Warner will obtain more than 400,000 new subscribers?
c. What is the probability Time Warner will obtain fewer than 200,000 new subscribers?

13. A psychologist determined that the number of sessions required to obtain the trust of a new patient is either 1, 2, or 3. Let x be a random variable indicating the number of sessions required to gain the patient's trust. The following probability function has been proposed.

$$f(x) = \frac{x}{6} \qquad \text{for } x = 1, 2, \text{ or } 3$$

a. Is this probability function valid? Explain.
b. What is the probability that it takes exactly 2 sessions to gain the patient's trust?
c. What is the probability that it takes at least 2 sessions to gain the patient's trust?

14. The following table is a partial probability distribution for the MRA Company's projected profits (x = profit in \$1000s) for the first year of operation (the negative value denotes a loss).

x	$f(x)$
−100	.10
0	.20
50	.30
100	.25
150	.10
200	

a. What is the proper value for $f(200)$? What is your interpretation of this value?
b. What is the probability that MRA will be profitable?
c. What is the probability that MRA will make at least \$100,000?

5.3 Expected Value and Variance

Expected Value

The **expected value**, or mean, of a random variable is a measure of the central location for the random variable. The formula for the expected value of a discrete random variable x follows.

The expected value is a weighted average of the values the random variable where the weights are the probabilities.

EXPECTED VALUE OF A DISCRETE RANDOM VARIABLE

$$E(x) = \mu = \Sigma x f(x) \tag{5.4}$$

Both the notations $E(x)$ and μ are used to denote the expected value of a random variable.

Equation (5.4) shows that to compute the expected value of a discrete random variable, we must multiply each value of the random variable by the corresponding probability $f(x)$ and then add the resulting products. Using the DiCarlo Motors automobile sales example from Section 5.2, we show the calculation of the expected value for the number of automobiles sold during a day in Table 5.4. The sum of the entries in the $xf(x)$ column shows that the expected value is 1.50 automobiles per day. We therefore know that although sales of 0, 1, 2, 3, 4, or 5 automobiles are possible on any one day, over time DiCarlo can anticipate selling an average of 1.50 automobiles per day. Assuming 30 days of operation during a month, we can use the expected value of 1.50 to forecast average monthly sales of $30(1.50) = 45$ automobiles.

The expected value does not have to be a value the random variable can assume.

Variance

Even though the expected value provides the mean value for the random variable, we often need a measure of variability, or dispersion. Just as we used the variance in Chapter 3 to summarize the variability in data, we now use **variance** to summarize the variability in the values of a random variable. The formula for the variance of a discrete random variable follows.

The variance is a weighted average of the squared deviations of a random variable from its mean. The weights are the probabilities.

VARIANCE OF A DISCRETE RANDOM VARIABLE

$$\text{Var}(x) = \sigma^2 = \Sigma(x - \mu)^2 f(x) \tag{5.5}$$

As equation (5.5) shows, an essential part of the variance formula is the deviation, $x - \mu$, which measures how far a particular value of the random variable is from the expected value, or mean, μ. In computing the variance of a random variable, the deviations are squared and then weighted by the corresponding value of the probability function. The sum of these weighted squared deviations for all values of the random variable is referred to as the *variance*. The notations $\text{Var}(x)$ and σ^2 are both used to denote the variance of a random variable.

TABLE 5.4 CALCULATION OF THE EXPECTED VALUE FOR THE NUMBER OF AUTOMOBILES SOLD DURING A DAY AT DICARLO MOTORS

x	$f(x)$	$xf(x)$
0	.18	0(.18) = .00
1	.39	1(.39) = .39
2	.24	2(.24) = .48
3	.14	3(.14) = .42
4	.04	4(.04) = .16
5	.01	5(.01) = .05
		1.50

$E(x) = \mu = \Sigma x f(x)$

TABLE 5.5 CALCULATION OF THE VARIANCE FOR THE NUMBER OF AUTOMOBILES SOLD DURING A DAY AT DICARLO MOTORS

x	$x - \mu$	$(x - \mu)^2$	$f(x)$	$(x - \mu)^2 f(x)$
0	$0 - 1.50 = -1.50$	2.25	.18	$2.25(.18) = .4050$
1	$1 - 1.50 = -.50$	.25	.39	$.25(.39) = .0975$
2	$2 - 1.50 = .50$	.25	.24	$.25(.24) = .0600$
3	$3 - 1.50 = 1.50$	2.25	.14	$2.25(.14) = .3150$
4	$4 - 1.50 = 2.50$	6.25	.04	$6.25(.04) = .2500$
5	$5 - 1.50 = 3.50$	12.25	.01	$12.25(.01) = .1225$
				1.2500

$$\sigma^2 = \Sigma(x - \mu)^2 f(x)$$

The calculation of the variance for the probability distribution of the number of automobiles sold during a day at DiCarlo Motors is summarized in Table 5.5. We see that the variance is 1.25. The **standard deviation,** σ, is defined as the positive square root of the variance. Thus, the standard deviation for the number of automobiles sold during a day is

$$\sigma = \sqrt{1.25} = 1.118$$

The standard deviation is measured in the same units as the random variable ($\sigma = 1.118$ automobiles) and therefore is often preferred in describing the variability of a random variable. The variance σ^2 is measured in squared units and is thus more difficult to interpret.

Exercises

Methods

15. The following table provides a probability distribution for the random variable x.

x	$f(x)$
3	.25
6	.50
9	.25

a. Compute $E(x)$, the expected value of x.
b. Compute σ^2, the variance of x.
c. Compute σ, the standard deviation of x.

SELF test

16. The following table provides a probability distribution for the random variable y.

y	$f(y)$
2	.20
4	.30
7	.40
8	.10

a. Compute $E(y)$.
b. Compute $\text{Var}(y)$ and σ.

Applications

17. The number of students taking the Scholastic Aptitude Test (SAT) has risen to an all-time high of more than 1.5 million (College Board, August 26, 2008). Students are allowed to repeat the test in hopes of improving the score that is sent to college and university admission offices. The number of times the SAT was taken and the number of students are as follows.

Number of Times	Number of Students
1	721,769
2	601,325
3	166,736
4	22,299
5	6,730

a. Let x be a random variable indicating the number of times a student takes the SAT. Show the probability distribution for this random variable.
b. What is the probability that a student takes the SAT more than one time?
c. What is the probability that a student takes the SAT three or more times?
d. What is the expected value of the number of times the SAT is taken? What is your interpretation of the expected value?
e. What is the variance and standard deviation for the number of times the SAT is taken?

SELF test

18. The American Housing Survey reported the following data on the number of bedrooms in owner-occupied and renter-occupied houses in central cities (U.S. Census Bureau website, March 31, 2003).

	Number of Houses (1000s)	
Bedrooms	**Renter-Occupied**	**Owner-Occupied**
0	547	23
1	5012	541
2	6100	3832
3	2644	8690
4 or more	557	3783

a. Define a random variable x = number of bedrooms in renter-occupied houses and develop a probability distribution for the random variable. (Let $x = 4$ represent 4 or more bedrooms.)
b. Compute the expected value and variance for the number of bedrooms in renter-occupied houses.
c. Define a random variable y = number of bedrooms in owner-occupied houses and develop a probability distribution for the random variable. (Let $y = 4$ represent 4 or more bedrooms.)
d. Compute the expected value and variance for the number of bedrooms in owner-occupied houses.
e. What observations can you make from a comparison of the number of bedrooms in renter-occupied versus owner-occupied homes?

19. The National Basketball Association (NBA) records a variety of statistics for each team. Two of these statistics are the percentage of field goals made by the team and the percentage of three-point shots made by the team. For a portion of the 2004 season, the shooting records of the 29 teams in the NBA showed the probability of scoring two points by making

a field goal was .44, and the probability of scoring three points by making a three-point shot was .34 (NBA website, January 3, 2004).

a. What is the expected value of a two-point shot for these teams?
b. What is the expected value of a three-point shot for these teams?
c. If the probability of making a two-point shot is greater than the probability of making a three-point shot, why do coaches allow some players to shoot the three-point shot if they have the opportunity? Use expected value to explain your answer.

20. The probability distribution for damage claims paid by the Newton Automobile Insurance Company on collision insurance follows.

Payment ($)	Probability
0	.85
500	.04
1000	.04
3000	.03
5000	.02
8000	.01
10000	.01

a. Use the expected collision payment to determine the collision insurance premium that would enable the company to break even.
b. The insurance company charges an annual rate of $520 for the collision coverage. What is the expected value of the collision policy for a policyholder? (*Hint:* It is the expected payments from the company minus the cost of coverage.) Why does the policyholder purchase a collision policy with this expected value?

21. The following probability distributions of job satisfaction scores for a sample of information systems (IS) senior executives and middle managers range from a low of 1 (very dissatisfied) to a high of 5 (very satisfied).

	Probability	
Job Satisfaction Score	**IS Senior Executives**	**IS Middle Managers**
1	.05	.04
2	.09	.10
3	.03	.12
4	.42	.46
5	.41	.28

a. What is the expected value of the job satisfaction score for senior executives?
b. What is the expected value of the job satisfaction score for middle managers?
c. Compute the variance of job satisfaction scores for executives and middle managers.
d. Compute the standard deviation of job satisfaction scores for both probability distributions.
e. Compare the overall job satisfaction of senior executives and middle managers.

22. The demand for a product of Carolina Industries varies greatly from month to month. The probability distribution in the following table, based on the past two years of data, shows the company's monthly demand.

Unit Demand	Probability
300	.20
400	.30
500	.35
600	.15

a. If the company bases monthly orders on the expected value of the monthly demand, what should Carolina's monthly order quantity be for this product?

b. Assume that each unit demanded generates $70 in revenue and that each unit ordered costs $50. How much will the company gain or lose in a month if it places an order based on your answer to part (a) and the actual demand for the item is 300 units?

23. The New York City Housing and Vacancy Survey showed a total of 59,324 rent-controlled housing units and 236,263 rent-stabilized units built in 1947 or later. For these rental units, the probability distributions for the number of persons living in the unit are given (U.S. Census Bureau website, January 12, 2004).

Number of Persons	Rent-Controlled	Rent-Stabilized
1	.61	.41
2	.27	.30
3	.07	.14
4	.04	.11
5	.01	.03
6	.00	.01

a. What is the expected value of the number of persons living in each type of unit?

b. What is the variance of the number of persons living in each type of unit?

c. Make some comparisons between the number of persons living in rent-controlled units and the number of persons living in rent-stabilized units.

24. The J. R. Ryland Computer Company is considering a plant expansion to enable the company to begin production of a new computer product. The company's president must determine whether to make the expansion a medium- or large-scale project. Demand for the new product is uncertain, which for planning purposes may be low demand, medium demand, or high demand. The probability estimates for demand are .20, .50, and .30, respectively. Letting x and y indicate the annual profit in thousands of dollars, the firm's planners developed the following profit forecasts for the medium- and large-scale expansion projects.

		Medium-Scale Expansion Profit		Large-Scale Expansion Profit	
		x	$f(x)$	y	$f(y)$
Demand	Low	50	.20	0	.20
	Medium	150	.50	100	.50
	High	200	.30	300	.30

a. Compute the expected value for the profit associated with the two expansion alternatives. Which decision is preferred for the objective of maximizing the expected profit?

b. Compute the variance for the profit associated with the two expansion alternatives. Which decision is preferred for the objective of minimizing the risk or uncertainty?

5.4 Binomial Probability Distribution

The binomial probability distribution is a discrete probability distribution that provides many applications. It is associated with a multiple-step experiment that we call the binomial experiment.

A Binomial Experiment

A **binomial experiment** exhibits the following four properties.

PROPERTIES OF A BINOMIAL EXPERIMENT

1. The experiment consists of a sequence of n identical trials.
2. Two outcomes are possible on each trial. We refer to one outcome as a *success* and the other outcome as a *failure.*
3. The probability of a success, denoted by p, does not change from trial to trial. Consequently, the probability of a failure, denoted by $1 - p$, does not change from trial to trial.
4. The trials are independent.

Jakob Bernoulli (1654–1705), the first of the Bernoulli family of Swiss mathematicians, published a treatise on probability that contained the theory of permutations and combinations, as well as the binomial theorem.

If properties 2, 3, and 4 are present, we say the trials are generated by a Bernoulli process. If, in addition, property 1 is present, we say we have a binomial experiment. Figure 5.2 depicts one possible sequence of successes and failures for a binomial experiment involving eight trials.

In a binomial experiment, our interest is in the *number of successes occurring in the n trials*. If we let x denote the number of successes occurring in the n trials, we see that x can assume the values of $0, 1, 2, 3, \ldots, n$. Because the number of values is finite, x is a *discrete* random variable. The probability distribution associated with this random variable is called the **binomial probability distribution**. For example, consider the experiment of tossing a coin five times and on each toss observing whether the coin lands with a head or a tail on its upward face. Suppose we want to count the number of heads appearing over the five tosses. Does this experiment show the properties of a binomial experiment? What is the random variable of interest? Note that:

1. The experiment consists of five identical trials; each trial involves the tossing of one coin.
2. Two outcomes are possible for each trial: a head or a tail. We can designate head a success and tail a failure.
3. The probability of a head and the probability of a tail are the same for each trial, with $p = .5$ and $1 - p = .5$.
4. The trials or tosses are independent because the outcome on any one trial is not affected by what happens on other trials or tosses.

FIGURE 5.2 ONE POSSIBLE SEQUENCE OF SUCCESSES AND FAILURES FOR AN EIGHT-TRIAL BINOMIAL EXPERIMENT

Property 1: The experiment consists of $n = 8$ identical trials.

Property 2: Each trial results in either success (S) or failure (F).

Trials ⟶	1	2	3	4	5	6	7	8
Outcomes ⟶	S	F	F	S	S	F	S	S

Thus, the properties of a binomial experiment are satisfied. The random variable of interest is x = the number of heads appearing in the five trials. In this case, x can assume the values of 0, 1, 2, 3, 4, or 5.

As another example, consider an insurance salesperson who visits 10 randomly selected families. The outcome associated with each visit is classified as a success if the family purchases an insurance policy and a failure if the family does not. From past experience, the salesperson knows the probability that a randomly selected family will purchase an insurance policy is .10. Checking the properties of a binomial experiment, we observe that:

1. The experiment consists of 10 identical trials; each trial involves contacting one family.
2. Two outcomes are possible on each trial: the family purchases a policy (success) or the family does not purchase a policy (failure).
3. The probabilities of a purchase and a nonpurchase are assumed to be the same for each sales call, with $p = .10$ and $1 - p = .90$.
4. The trials are independent because the families are randomly selected.

Because the four assumptions are satisfied, this example is a binomial experiment. The random variable of interest is the number of sales obtained in contacting the 10 families. In this case, x can assume the values of 0, 1, 2, 3, 4, 5, 6, 7, 8, 9, and 10.

Property 3 of the binomial experiment is called the *stationarity assumption* and is sometimes confused with property 4, independence of trials. To see how they differ, consider again the case of the salesperson calling on families to sell insurance policies. If, as the day wore on, the salesperson got tired and lost enthusiasm, the probability of success (selling a policy) might drop to .05, for example, by the tenth call. In such a case, property 3 (stationarity) would not be satisfied, and we would not have a binomial experiment. Even if property 4 held—that is, the purchase decisions of each family were made independently—it would not be a binomial experiment if property 3 was not satisfied.

In applications involving binomial experiments, a special mathematical formula, called the *binomial probability function,* can be used to compute the probability of x successes in the n trials. Using probability concepts introduced in Chapter 4, we will show in the context of an illustrative problem how the formula can be developed.

Martin Clothing Store Problem

Let us consider the purchase decisions of the next three customers who enter the Martin Clothing Store. On the basis of past experience, the store manager estimates the probability that any one customer will make a purchase is .30. What is the probability that two of the next three customers will make a purchase?

Using a tree diagram (Figure 5.3), we can see that the experiment of observing the three customers each making a purchase decision has eight possible outcomes. Using S to denote success (a purchase) and F to denote failure (no purchase), we are interested in experimental outcomes involving two successes in the three trials (purchase decisions). Next, let us verify that the experiment involving the sequence of three purchase decisions can be viewed as a binomial experiment. Checking the four requirements for a binomial experiment, we note that:

1. The experiment can be described as a sequence of three identical trials, one trial for each of the three customers who will enter the store.
2. Two outcomes—the customer makes a purchase (success) or the customer does not make a purchase (failure)—are possible for each trial.
3. The probability that the customer will make a purchase (.30) or will not make a purchase (.70) is assumed to be the same for all customers.
4. The purchase decision of each customer is independent of the decisions of the other customers.

FIGURE 5.3 TREE DIAGRAM FOR THE MARTIN CLOTHING STORE PROBLEM

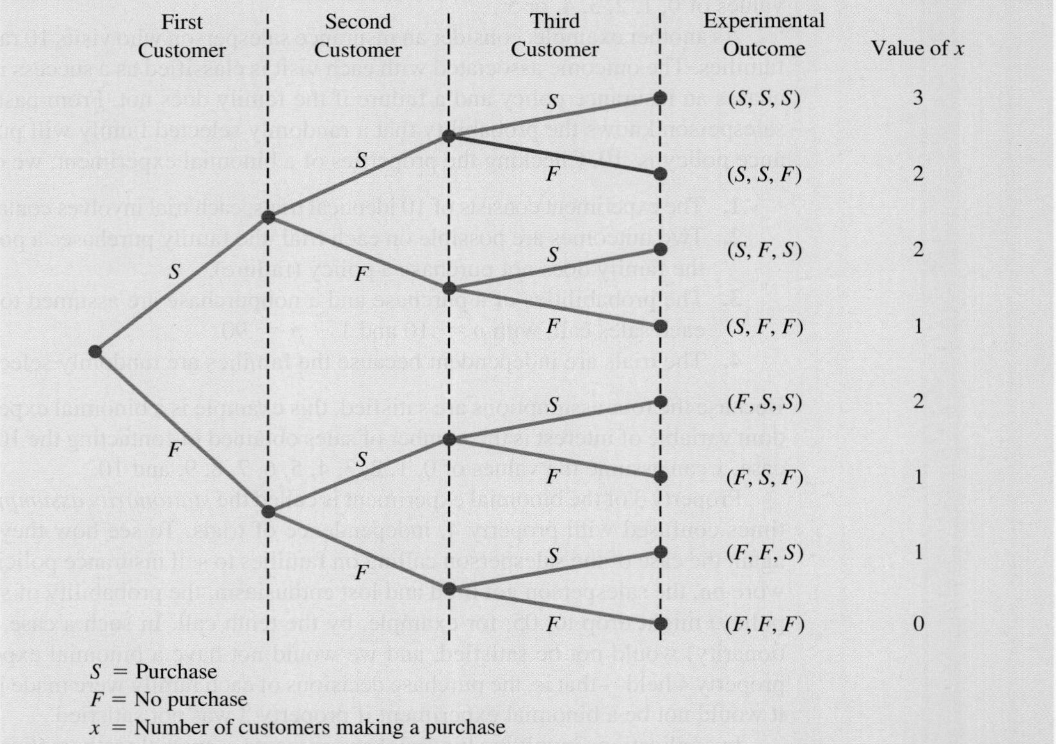

Hence, the properties of a binomial experiment are present.

The number of experimental outcomes resulting in exactly x successes in n trials can be computed using the following formula.[1]

NUMBER OF EXPERIMENTAL OUTCOMES PROVIDING EXACTLY x SUCCESSES IN n TRIALS

$$\binom{n}{x} = \frac{n!}{x!(n-x)!} \tag{5.6}$$

where

$$n! = n(n-1)(n-2) \cdots (2)(1)$$

and, by definition,

$$0! = 1$$

Now let us return to the Martin Clothing Store experiment involving three customer purchase decisions. Equation (5.6) can be used to determine the number of experimental

[1]This formula, introduced in Chapter 4, determines the number of combinations of n objects selected x at a time. For the binomial experiment, this combinatorial formula provides the number of experimental outcomes (sequences of n trials) resulting in x successes.

outcomes involving two purchases; that is, the number of ways of obtaining $x = 2$ successes in the $n = 3$ trials. From equation (5.6) we have

$$\binom{n}{x} = \binom{3}{2} = \frac{3!}{2!(3-2)!} = \frac{(3)(2)(1)}{(2)(1)(1)} = \frac{6}{2} = 3$$

Equation (5.6) shows that three of the experimental outcomes yield two successes. From Figure 5.3 we see these three outcomes are denoted by (S, S, F), (S, F, S), and (F, S, S).

Using equation (5.6) to determine how many experimental outcomes have three successes (purchases) in the three trials, we obtain

$$\binom{n}{x} = \binom{3}{3} = \frac{3!}{3!(3-3)!} = \frac{3!}{3!0!} = \frac{(3)(2)(1)}{3(2)(1)(1)} = \frac{6}{6} = 1$$

From Figure 5.3 we see that the one experimental outcome with three successes is identified by (S, S, S).

We know that equation (5.6) can be used to determine the number of experimental outcomes that result in x successes. If we are to determine the probability of x successes in n trials, however, we must also know the probability associated with each of these experimental outcomes. Because the trials of a binomial experiment are independent, we can simply multiply the probabilities associated with each trial outcome to find the probability of a particular sequence of successes and failures.

The probability of purchases by the first two customers and no purchase by the third customer, denoted (S, S, F), is given by

$$pp(1-p)$$

With a .30 probability of a purchase on any one trial, the probability of a purchase on the first two trials and no purchase on the third is given by

$$(.30)(.30)(.70) = (.30)^2(.70) = .063$$

Two other experimental outcomes also result in two successes and one failure. The probabilities for all three experimental outcomes involving two successes follow.

Trial Outcomes				
1st Customer	**2nd Customer**	**3rd Customer**	**Experimental Outcome**	**Probability of Experimental Outcome**
Purchase	Purchase	No purchase	(S, S, F)	$pp(1-p) = p^2(1-p)$ $= (.30)^2(.70) = .063$
Purchase	No purchase	Purchase	(S, F, S)	$p(1-p)p = p^2(1-p)$ $= (.30)^2(.70) = .063$
No purchase	Purchase	Purchase	(F, S, S)	$(1-p)pp = p^2(1-p)$ $= (.30)^2(.70) = .063$

Observe that all three experimental outcomes with two successes have exactly the same probability. This observation holds in general. In any binomial experiment, all sequences of trial outcomes yielding x successes in n trials have the *same probability* of occurrence. The probability of each sequence of trials yielding x successes in n trials follows.

$$\text{Probability of a particular sequence of trial outcomes with } x \text{ successes in } n \text{ trials} = p^x(1-p)^{(n-x)} \tag{5.7}$$

For the Martin Clothing Store, this formula shows that any experimental outcome with two successes has a probability of $p^2(1-p)^{(3-2)} = p^2(1-p)^1 = (.30)^2(.70)^1 = .063$.

Because equation (5.6) shows the number of outcomes in a binomial experiment with x successes and equation (5.7) gives the probability for each sequence involving x successes, we combine equations (5.6) and (5.7) to obtain the following **binomial probability function**.

BINOMIAL PROBABILITY FUNCTION

$$f(x) = \binom{n}{x} p^x(1-p)^{(n-x)} \tag{5.8}$$

where

x = the number of successes
p = the probability of a success on one trial
n = the number of trials
$f(x)$ = the probability of x successes in n trials

$$\binom{n}{x} = \frac{n!}{x!(n-x)!}$$

For the binomial probability distribution, x is a discrete random variable with the probability function $f(x)$ applicable for values of $x = 0, 1, 2, \ldots, n$.

In the Martin Clothing Store example, let use equation (5.8) to compute the probability that no customer makes a purchase, exactly one customer makes a purchase, exactly two customers make a purchase, and all three customers make a purchase. The calculations are summarized in Table 5.6, which gives the probability distribution of the number of customers making a purchase. Figure 5.4 is a graph of this probability distribution.

The binomial probability function can be applied to *any* binomial experiment. If we are satisfied that a situation demonstrates the properties of a binomial experiment and if we know the values of n and p, we can use equation (5.8) to compute the probability of x successes in the n trials.

TABLE 5.6 PROBABILITY DISTRIBUTION FOR THE NUMBER OF CUSTOMERS MAKING A PURCHASE

x	$f(x)$
0	$\frac{3!}{0!3!}(.30)^0(.70)^3 = .343$
1	$\frac{3!}{1!2!}(.30)^1(.70)^2 = .441$
2	$\frac{3!}{2!1!}(.30)^2(.70)^1 = .189$
3	$\frac{3!}{3!0!}(.30)^3(.70)^0 = .027$
	1.000

FIGURE 5.4 GRAPHICAL REPRESENTATION OF THE PROBABILITY DISTRIBUTION FOR THE NUMBER OF CUSTOMERS MAKING A PURCHASE

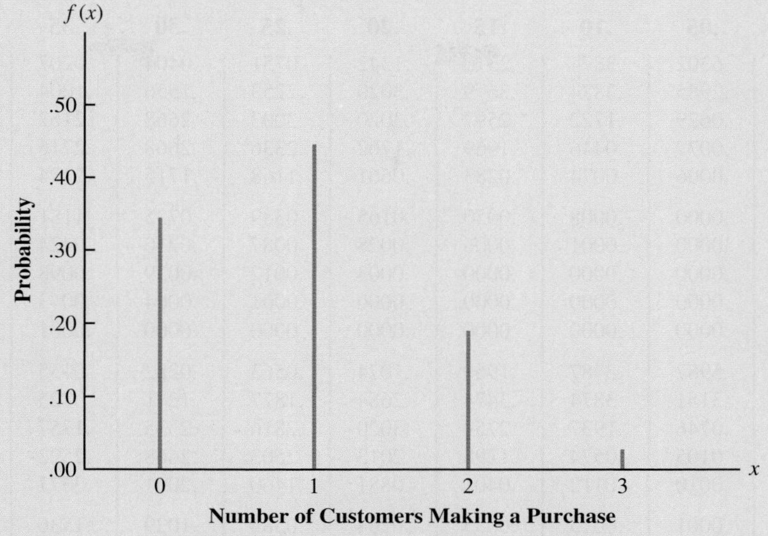

If we consider variations of the Martin experiment, such as 10 customers rather than three entering the store, the binomial probability function given by equation (5.8) is still applicable. Suppose we have a binomial experiment with $n = 10$, $x = 4$, and $p = .30$. The probability of making exactly four sales to 10 customers entering the store is

$$f(4) = \frac{10!}{4!6!}(.30)^4(.70)^6 = .2001$$

Using Tables of Binomial Probabilities

Tables have been developed that give the probability of x successes in n trials for a binomial experiment. The tables are generally easy to use and quicker than equation (5.8). Table 5 of Appendix B provides such a table of binomial probabilities. A portion of this table appears in Table 5.7. To use this table, we must specify the values of n, p, and x for the binomial experiment of interest. In the example at the top of Table 5.7, we see that the probability of $x = 3$ successes in a binomial experiment with $n = 10$ and $p = .40$ is .2150. You can use equation (5.8) to verify that you would obtain the same answer if you used the binomial probability function directly.

Now let us use Table 5.7 to verify the probability of four successes in 10 trials for the Martin Clothing Store problem. Note that the value of $f(4) = .2001$ can be read directly from the table of binomial probabilities, with $n = 10$, $x = 4$, and $p = .30$.

With modern calculators, these tables are almost unnecessary. It is easy to evaluate equation (5.8) directly.

Even though the tables of binomial probabilities are relatively easy to use, it is impossible to have tables that show all possible values of n and p that might be encountered in a binomial experiment. However, with today's calculators, using equation (5.8) to calculate the desired probability is not difficult, especially if the number of trials is not large. In the exercises, you should practice using equation (5.8) to compute the binomial probabilities unless the problem specifically requests that you use the binomial probability table.

TABLE 5.7 SELECTED VALUES FROM THE BINOMIAL PROBABILITY TABLE
EXAMPLE: $n = 10, x = 3, p = .40; f(3) = .2150$

						p					
n	*x*	.05	.10	.15	.20	.25	.30	.35	.40	.45	.50
9	0	.6302	.3874	.2316	.1342	.0751	.0404	.0207	.0101	.0046	.0020
	1	.2985	.3874	.3679	.3020	.2253	.1556	.1004	.0605	.0339	.0176
	2	.0629	.1722	.2597	.3020	.3003	.2668	.2162	.1612	.1110	.0703
	3	.0077	.0446	.1069	.1762	.2336	.2668	.2716	.2508	.2119	.1641
	4	.0006	.0074	.0283	.0661	.1168	.1715	.2194	.2508	.2600	.2461
	5	.0000	.0008	.0050	.0165	.0389	.0735	.1181	.1672	.2128	.2461
	6	.0000	.0001	.0006	.0028	.0087	.0210	.0424	.0743	.1160	.1641
	7	.0000	.0000	.0000	.0003	.0012	.0039	.0098	.0212	.0407	.0703
	8	.0000	.0000	.0000	.0000	.0001	.0004	.0013	.0035	.0083	.0176
	9	.0000	.0000	.0000	.0000	.0000	.0000	.0001	.0003	.0008	.0020
10	0	.5987	.3487	.1969	.1074	.0563	.0282	.0135	.0060	.0025	.0010
	1	.3151	.3874	.3474	.2684	.1877	.1211	.0725	.0403	.0207	.0098
	2	.0746	.1937	.2759	.3020	.2816	.2335	.1757	.1209	.0763	.0439
	3	.0105	.0574	.1298	.2013	.2503	.2668	.2522	**.2150**	.1665	.1172
	4	.0010	.0112	.0401	.0881	.1460	.2001	.2377	.2508	.2384	.2051
	5	.0001	.0015	.0085	.0264	.0584	.1029	.1536	.2007	.2340	.2461
	6	.0000	.0001	.0012	.0055	.0162	.0368	.0689	.1115	.1596	.2051
	7	.0000	.0000	.0001	.0008	.0031	.0090	.0212	.0425	.0746	.1172
	8	.0000	.0000	.0000	.0001	.0004	.0014	.0043	.0106	.0229	.0439
	9	.0000	.0000	.0000	.0000	.0000	.0001	.0005	.0016	.0042	.0098
	10	.0000	.0000	.0000	.0000	.0000	.0000	.0000	.0001	.0003	.0010

Statistical software packages such as Minitab and spreadsheet packages such as Excel also provide a capability for computing binomial probabilities. Consider the Martin Clothing Store example with $n = 10$ and $p = .30$. Figure 5.5 shows the binomial probabilities generated by Minitab for all possible values of x. Note that these values are the same as those found in the $p = .30$ column of Table 5.7. Appendix 5.1 gives the step-by-step procedure for using Minitab to generate the output in Figure 5.5. Appendix 5.2 describes how Excel can be used to compute binomial probabilities.

Expected Value and Variance for the Binomial Distribution

In Section 5.3 we provided formulas for computing the expected value and variance of a discrete random variable. In the special case where the random variable has a binomial distribution with a known number of trials n and a known probability of success p, the general formulas for the expected value and variance can be simplified. The results follow.

EXPECTED VALUE AND VARIANCE FOR THE BINOMIAL DISTRIBUTION

$$E(x) = \mu = np \tag{5.9}$$

$$\text{Var}(x) = \sigma^2 = np(1 - p) \tag{5.10}$$

FIGURE 5.5 MINITAB OUTPUT SHOWING BINOMIAL PROBABILITIES FOR THE MARTIN CLOTHING STORE PROBLEM

x	P(X = x)
0	0.0282
1	0.1211
2	0.2335
3	0.2668
4	0.2001
5	0.1029
6	0.0368
7	0.0090
8	0.0014
9	0.0001
10	0.0000

For the Martin Clothing Store problem with three customers, we can use equation (5.9) to compute the expected number of customers who will make a purchase.

$$E(x) = np = 3(.30) = .9$$

Suppose that for the next month the Martin Clothing Store forecasts 1000 customers will enter the store. What is the expected number of customers who will make a purchase? The answer is $\mu = np = (1000)(.3) = 300$. Thus, to increase the expected number of purchases, Martin's must induce more customers to enter the store and/or somehow increase the probability that any individual customer will make a purchase after entering.

For the Martin Clothing Store problem with three customers, we see that the variance and standard deviation for the number of customers who will make a purchase are

$$\sigma^2 = np(1 - p) = 3(.3)(.7) = .63$$
$$\sigma = \sqrt{.63} = .79$$

For the next 1000 customers entering the store, the variance and standard deviation for the number of customers who will make a purchase are

$$\sigma^2 = np(1 - p) = 1000(.3)(.7) = 210$$
$$\sigma = \sqrt{210} = 14.49$$

NOTES AND COMMENTS

1. The binomial table in Appendix B shows values of p up to and including $p = .95$. Some sources of the binomial table only show values of p up to and including $p = .50$. It would appear that such a table cannot be used when the probability of success exceeds $p = .50$. However, the table can be used by noting that the probability of $n - x$ failures is also the probability of x successes. Thus, when the probability of success is greater than $p = .50$, we can compute the probability of $n - x$ failures instead. The probability of failure, $1 - p$, will be less than .50 when $p > .50$.

2. Some sources present the binomial table in a cumulative form. In using such a table, one must subtract entries in the table to find the probability of exactly x success in n trials. For example, $f(2) = P(x \leq 2) - P(x \leq 1)$. The binomial table we provide in Appendix B provides $f(2)$ directly. To compute cumulative probabilities using the binomial table in Appendix B, sum the entries in the table. For example, to determine the cumulative probability $P(x \leq 2)$, compute the sum $f(0) + f(1) + f(2)$.

Exercises

Methods

SELF test

25. Consider a binomial experiment with two trials and $p = .4$.
    a. Draw a tree diagram for this experiment (see Figure 5.3).
    b. Compute the probability of one success, $f(1)$.
    c. Compute $f(0)$.
    d. Compute $f(2)$.
    e. Compute the probability of at least one success.
    f. Compute the expected value, variance, and standard deviation.

26. Consider a binomial experiment with $n = 10$ and $p = .10$.
    a. Compute $f(0)$.
    b. Compute $f(2)$.
    c. Compute $P(x \leq 2)$.
    d. Compute $P(x \geq 1)$.
    e. Compute $E(x)$.
    f. Compute $\text{Var}(x)$ and σ.

27. Consider a binomial experiment with $n = 20$ and $p = .70$.
    a. Compute $f(12)$.
    b. Compute $f(16)$.
    c. Compute $P(x \geq 16)$.
    d. Compute $P(x \leq 15)$.
    e. Compute $E(x)$.
    f. Compute $\text{Var}(x)$ and σ.

Applications

28. A Harris Interactive survey for InterContinental Hotels & Resorts asked respondents, "When traveling internationally, do you generally venture out on your own to experience culture, or stick with your tour group and itineraries?" The survey found that 23% of the respondents stick with their tour group (*USA Today,* January 21, 2004).
    a. In a sample of six international travelers, what is the probability that two will stick with their tour group?
    b. In a sample of six international travelers, what is the probability that at least two will stick with their tour group?
    c. In a sample of 10 international travelers, what is the probability that none will stick with the tour group?

29. In San Francisco, 30% of workers take public transportation daily (*USA Today,* December 21, 2005).
    a. In a sample of 10 workers, what is the probability that exactly three workers take public transportation daily?
    b. In a sample of 10 workers, what is the probability that at least three workers take public transportation daily?

SELF test

30. When a new machine is functioning properly, only 3% of the items produced are defective. Assume that we will randomly select two parts produced on the machine and that we are interested in the number of defective parts found.
    a. Describe the conditions under which this situation would be a binomial experiment.
    b. Draw a tree diagram similar to Figure 5.3 showing this problem as a two-trial experiment.
    c. How many experimental outcomes result in exactly one defect being found?
    d. Compute the probabilities associated with finding no defects, exactly one defect, and two defects.

31. Nine percent of undergraduate students carry credit card balances greater than $7000 (*Reader's Digest,* July 2002). Suppose 10 undergraduate students are selected randomly to be interviewed about credit card usage.
    a. Is the selection of 10 students a binomial experiment? Explain.
    b. What is the probability that two of the students will have a credit card balance greater than $7000?
    c. What is the probability that none will have a credit card balance greater than $7000?
    d. What is the probability that at least three will have a credit card balance greater than $7000?
32. Military radar and missile detection systems are designed to warn a country of an enemy attack. A reliability question is whether a detection system will be able to identify an attack and issue a warning. Assume that a particular detection system has a .90 probability of detecting a missile attack. Use the binomial probability distribution to answer the following questions.
    a. What is the probability that a single detection system will detect an attack?
    b. If two detection systems are installed in the same area and operate independently, what is the probability that at least one of the systems will detect the attack?
    c. If three systems are installed, what is the probability that at least one of the systems will detect the attack?
    d. Would you recommend that multiple detection systems be used? Explain.
33. Fifty percent of Americans believed the country was in a recession, even though technically the economy had not shown two straight quarters of negative growth (*BusinessWeek,* July 30, 2001). For a sample of 20 Americans, make the following calculations.
    a. Compute the probability that exactly 12 people believed the country was in a recession.
    b. Compute the probability that no more than five people believed the country was in a recession.
    c. How many people would you expect to say the country was in a recession?
    d. Compute the variance and standard deviation of the number of people who believed the country was in a recession.
34. The Census Bureau's Current Population Survey shows 28% of individuals, ages 25 and older, have completed four years of college (*The New York Times Almanac,* 2006). For a sample of 15 individuals, ages 25 and older, answer the following questions:
    a. What is the probability four will have completed four years of college?
    b. What is the probability three or more will have completed four years of college?
35. A university found that 20% of its students withdraw without completing the introductory statistics course. Assume that 20 students registered for the course.
    a. Compute the probability that two or fewer will withdraw.
    b. Compute the probability that exactly four will withdraw.
    c. Compute the probability that more than three will withdraw.
    d. Compute the expected number of withdrawals.
36. According to a survey conducted by TD Ameritrade, one out of four investors have exchange-traded funds in their portfolios (*USA Today,* January 11, 2007). Consider a sample of 20 investors.
    a. Compute the probability that exactly 4 investors have exchange-traded funds in their portfolios.
    b. Compute the probability that at least 2 of the investors have exchange-traded funds in their portfolios.
    c. If you found that exactly 12 of the investors have exchange-traded funds in their portfolios, would you doubt the accuracy of the survey results?
    d. Compute the expected number of investors who have exchange-traded funds in their portfolios.
37. Twenty-three percent of automobiles are not covered by insurance (CNN, February 23, 2006). On a particular weekend, 35 automobiles are involved in traffic accidents.
    a. What is the expected number of these automobiles that are not covered by insurance?
    b. What are the variance and standard deviation?

5.5 Poisson Probability Distribution

The Poisson probability distribution is often used to model random arrivals in waiting line situations.

In this section we consider a discrete random variable that is often useful in estimating the number of occurrences over a specified interval of time or space. For example, the random variable of interest might be the number of arrivals at a car wash in one hour, the number of repairs needed in 10 miles of highway, or the number of leaks in 100 miles of pipeline. If the following two properties are satisfied, the number of occurrences is a random variable described by the **Poisson probability distribution**.

PROPERTIES OF A POISSON EXPERIMENT

1. The probability of an occurrence is the same for any two intervals of equal length.
2. The occurrence or nonoccurrence in any interval is independent of the occurrence or nonoccurrence in any other interval.

The **Poisson probability function** is defined by equation (5.11).

Siméon Poisson taught mathematics at the Ecole Polytechnique in Paris from 1802 to 1808. In 1837, he published a work entitled, "Researches on the Probability of Criminal and Civil Verdicts," which includes a discussion of what later became known as the Poisson distribution.

POISSON PROBABILITY FUNCTION

$$f(x) = \frac{\mu^x e^{-\mu}}{x!} \quad \textbf{(5.11)}$$

where

$f(x)$ = the probability of x occurrences in an interval

μ = expected value or mean number of occurrences in an interval

e = 2.71828

For the Poisson probability distribution, x is a discrete random variable indicating the number of occurrences in the interval. Since there is no stated upper limit for the number of occurrences, the probability function $f(x)$ is applicable for values $x = 0, 1, 2, \ldots$ without limit. In practical applications, x will eventually become large enough so that $f(x)$ is approximately zero and the probability of any larger values of x becomes negligible.

An Example Involving Time Intervals

Bell Labs used the Poisson distribution to model the arrival of telephone calls.

Suppose that we are interested in the number of arrivals at the drive-up teller window of a bank during a 15-minute period on weekday mornings. If we can assume that the probability of a car arriving is the same for any two time periods of equal length and that the arrival or nonarrival of a car in any time period is independent of the arrival or nonarrival in any other time period, the Poisson probability function is applicable. Suppose these assumptions are satisfied and an analysis of historical data shows that the average number of cars arriving in a 15-minute period of time is 10; in this case, the following probability function applies.

$$f(x) = \frac{10^x e^{-10}}{x!}$$

The random variable here is x = number of cars arriving in any 15-minute period.

If management wanted to know the probability of exactly five arrivals in 15 minutes, we would set $x = 5$ and thus obtain

$$\begin{array}{c}\text{Probability of exactly} \\ \text{5 arrivals in 15 minutes}\end{array} = f(5) = \frac{10^5 e^{-10}}{5!} = .0378$$

Although this probability was determined by evaluating the probability function with $\mu = 10$ and $x = 5$, it is often easier to refer to a table for the Poisson distribution. The table provides probabilities for specific values of x and μ. We included such a table as Table 7 of Appendix B. For convenience, we reproduced a portion of this table as Table 5.8. Note that to use the table of Poisson probabilities, we need know only the values of x and μ. From Table 5.8 we see that the probability of five arrivals in a 15-minute period is found by locating the value in the row of the table corresponding to $x = 5$ and the column of the table corresponding to $\mu = 10$. Hence, we obtain $f(5) = .0378$.

A property of the Poisson distribution is that the mean and variance are equal.

In the preceding example, the mean of the Poisson distribution is $\mu = 10$ arrivals per 15-minute period. A property of the Poisson distribution is that the mean of the distribution and the variance of the distribution are *equal.* Thus, the variance for the number of arrivals during 15-minute periods is $\sigma^2 = 10$. The standard deviation is $\sigma = \sqrt{10} = 3.16$.

Our illustration involves a 15-minute period, but other time periods can be used. Suppose we want to compute the probability of one arrival in a 3-minute period. Because 10 is the expected number of arrivals in a 15-minute period, we see that $10/15 = 2/3$ is the expected number of arrivals in a 1-minute period and that $(2/3)(3 \text{ minutes}) = 2$ is the expected number of arrivals in a 3-minute period. Thus, the probability of x arrivals in a 3-minute time period with $\mu = 2$ is given by the following Poisson probability function.

$$f(x) = \frac{2^x e^{-2}}{x!}$$

TABLE 5.8 SELECTED VALUES FROM THE POISSON PROBABILITY TABLES EXAMPLE: $\mu = 10$, $x = 5$; $f(5) = .0378$

					μ					
x	**9.1**	**9.2**	**9.3**	**9.4**	**9.5**	**9.6**	**9.7**	**9.8**	**9.9**	**10**
0	.0001	.0001	.0001	.0001	.0001	.0001	.0001	.0001	.0001	.0000
1	.0010	.0009	.0009	.0008	.0007	.0007	.0006	.0005	.0005	.0005
2	.0046	.0043	.0040	.0037	.0034	.0031	.0029	.0027	.0025	.0023
3	.0140	.0131	.0123	.0115	.0107	.0100	.0093	.0087	.0081	.0076
4	.0319	.0302	.0285	.0269	.0254	.0240	.0226	.0213	.0201	.0189
5	.0581	.0555	.0530	.0506	.0483	.0460	.0439	.0418	.0398	**.0378**
6	.0881	.0851	.0822	.0793	.0764	.0736	.0709	.0682	.0656	.0631
7	.1145	.1118	.1091	.1064	.1037	.1010	.0982	.0955	.0928	.0901
8	.1302	.1286	.1269	.1251	.1232	.1212	.1191	.1170	.1148	.1126
9	.1317	.1315	.1311	.1306	.1300	.1293	.1284	.1274	.1263	.1251
10	.1198	.1210	.1219	.1228	.1235	.1241	.1245	.1249	.1250	.1251
11	.0991	.1012	.1031	.1049	.1067	.1083	.1098	.1112	.1125	.1137
12	.0752	.0776	.0799	.0822	.0844	.0866	.0888	.0908	.0928	.0948
13	.0526	.0549	.0572	.0594	.0617	.0640	.0662	.0685	.0707	.0729
14	.0342	.0361	.0380	.0399	.0419	.0439	.0459	.0479	.0500	.0521
15	.0208	.0221	.0235	.0250	.0265	.0281	.0297	.0313	.0330	.0347
16	.0118	.0127	.0137	.0147	.0157	.0168	.0180	.0192	.0204	.0217
17	.0063	.0069	.0075	.0081	.0088	.0095	.0103	.0111	.0119	.0128
18	.0032	.0035	.0039	.0042	.0046	.0051	.0055	.0060	.0065	.0071
19	.0015	.0017	.0019	.0021	.0023	.0026	.0028	.0031	.0034	.0037
20	.0007	.0008	.0009	.0010	.0011	.0012	.0014	.0015	.0017	.0019
21	.0003	.0003	.0004	.0004	.0005	.0006	.0006	.0007	.0008	.0009
22	.0001	.0001	.0002	.0002	.0002	.0002	.0003	.0003	.0004	.0004
23	.0000	.0001	.0001	.0001	.0001	.0001	.0001	.0001	.0002	.0002
24	.0000	.0000	.0000	.0000	.0000	.0000	.0000	.0001	.0001	.0001

The probability of one arrival in a 3-minute period is calculated as follows:

$$\text{Probability of exactly 1 arrival in 3 minutes} = f(1) = \frac{2^1 e^{-2}}{1!} = .2707$$

Earlier we computed the probability of five arrivals in a 15-minute period; it was .0378. Note that the probability of one arrival in a three-minute period (.2707) is not the same. When computing a Poisson probability for a different time interval, we must first convert the mean arrival rate to the time period of interest and then compute the probability.

An Example Involving Length or Distance Intervals

Let us illustrate an application not involving time intervals in which the Poisson distribution is useful. Suppose we are concerned with the occurrence of major defects in a highway one month after resurfacing. We will assume that the probability of a defect is the same for any two highway intervals of equal length and that the occurrence or nonoccurrence of a defect in any one interval is independent of the occurrence or nonoccurrence of a defect in any other interval. Hence, the Poisson distribution can be applied.

Suppose we learn that major defects one month after resurfacing occur at the average rate of two per mile. Let us find the probability of no major defects in a particular three-mile section of the highway. Because we are interested in an interval with a length of three miles, $\mu = (2 \text{ defects/mile})(3 \text{ miles}) = 6$ represents the expected number of major defects over the three-mile section of highway. Using equation (5.11), the probability of no major defects is $f(0) = 6^0 e^{-6}/0! = .0025$. Thus, it is unlikely that no major defects will occur in the three-mile section. In fact, this example indicates a $1 - .0025 = .9975$ probability of at least one major defect in the three-mile highway section.

Exercises

Methods

38. Consider a Poisson distribution with $\mu = 3$.
    a. Write the appropriate Poisson probability function.
    b. Compute $f(2)$.
    c. Compute $f(1)$.
    d. Compute $P(x \geq 2)$.

SELF test

39. Consider a Poisson distribution with a mean of two occurrences per time period.
    a. Write the appropriate Poisson probability function.
    b. What is the expected number of occurrences in three time periods?
    c. Write the appropriate Poisson probability function to determine the probability of x occurrences in three time periods.
    d. Compute the probability of two occurrences in one time period.
    e. Compute the probability of six occurrences in three time periods.
    f. Compute the probability of five occurrences in two time periods.

Applications

40. Phone calls arrive at the rate of 48 per hour at the reservation desk for Regional Airways.
    a. Compute the probability of receiving three calls in a 5-minute interval of time.
    b. Compute the probability of receiving exactly 10 calls in 15 minutes.
    c. Suppose no calls are currently on hold. If the agent takes 5 minutes to complete the current call, how many callers do you expect to be waiting by that time? What is the probability that none will be waiting?
    d. If no calls are currently being processed, what is the probability that the agent can take 3 minutes for personal time without being interrupted by a call?

41. During the period of time that a local university takes phone-in registrations, calls come in at the rate of one every two minutes.
    a. What is the expected number of calls in one hour?
    b. What is the probability of three calls in five minutes?
    c. What is the probability of no calls in a five-minute period?

SELF test

42. More than 50 million guests stay at bed and breakfasts (B&Bs) each year. The website for the Bed and Breakfast Inns of North America, which averages seven visitors per minute, enables many B&Bs to attract guests (*Time,* September 2001).
    a. Compute the probability of no website visitors in a one-minute period.
    b. Compute the probability of two or more website visitors in a one-minute period.
    c. Compute the probability of one or more website visitors in a 30-second period.
    d. Compute the probability of five or more website visitors in a one-minute period.
43. Airline passengers arrive randomly and independently at the passenger-screening facility at a major international airport. The mean arrival rate is 10 passengers per minute.
    a. Compute the probability of no arrivals in a one-minute period.
    b. Compute the probability that three or fewer passengers arrive in a one-minute period.
    c. Compute the probability of no arrivals in a 15-second period.
    d. Compute the probability of at least one arrival in a 15-second period.
44. An average of 15 aircraft accidents occur each year (*The World Almanac and Book of Facts,* 2004).
    a. Compute the mean number of aircraft accidents per month.
    b. Compute the probability of no accidents during a month.
    c. Compute the probability of exactly one accident during a month.
    d. Compute the probability of more than one accident during a month.
45. The National Safety Council (NSC) estimates that off-the-job accidents cost U.S. businesses almost $200 billion annually in lost productivity (National Safety Council, March 2006). Based on NSC estimates, companies with 50 employees are expected to average three employee off-the-job accidents per year. Answer the following questions for companies with 50 employees.
    a. What is the probability of no off-the-job accidents during a one-year period?
    b. What is the probability of at least two off-the-job accidents during a one-year period?
    c. What is the expected number of off-the-job accidents during six months?
    d. What is the probability of no off-the-job accidents during the next six months?

5.6 Hypergeometric Probability Distribution

The **hypergeometric probability distribution** is closely related to the binomial distribution. The two probability distributions differ in two key ways. With the hypergeometric distribution, the trials are not independent; and the probability of success changes from trial to trial.

In the usual notation for the hypergeometric distribution, r denotes the number of elements in the population of size N labeled success, and $N - r$ denotes the number of elements in the population labeled failure. The **hypergeometric probability function** is used to compute the probability that in a random selection of n elements, selected without replacement, we obtain x elements labeled success and $n - x$ elements labeled failure. For this outcome to occur, we must obtain x successes from the r successes in the population and $n - x$ failures from the $N - r$ failures. The following hypergeometric probability function provides $f(x)$, the probability of obtaining x successes in n trials.

HYPERGEOMETRIC PROBABILITY FUNCTION

$$f(x) = \frac{\binom{r}{x}\binom{N-r}{n-x}}{\binom{N}{n}} \tag{5.12}$$

where

x = the number of successes
n = the number of trials
$f(x)$ = the probability of x successes in n trials
N = the number of elements in the population
r = the number of elements in the population labeled success

Note that $\binom{N}{n}$ represents the number of ways n elements can be selected from a population of size N; $\binom{r}{x}$ represents the number of ways that x successes can be selected from a total of r successes in the population; and $\binom{N-r}{n-x}$ represents the number of ways that $n - x$ failures can be selected from a total of $N - r$ failures in the population.

For the hypergeometric probability distribution, x is a discrete random variable and the probability function $f(x)$ given by equation (5.12) is usually applicable for values of $x = 0, 1, 2, \ldots, n$. However, only values of x where the number of observed successes is *less than or equal* to the number of successes in the population ($x \le r$) and where the number of observed failures is *less than or equal to* the number of failures in the population ($n - x \le N - r$) are valid. If these two conditions do not hold for one or more values of x, the corresponding $f(x) = 0$ indicating that the probability of this value of x is zero.

To illustrate the computations involved in using equation (5.12), let us consider the following quality control application. Electric fuses produced by Ontario Electric are packaged in boxes of 12 units each. Suppose an inspector randomly selects three of the 12 fuses in a box for testing. If the box contains exactly five defective fuses, what is the probability that the inspector will find exactly one of the three fuses defective? In this application, $n = 3$ and $N = 12$. With $r = 5$ defective fuses in the box the probability of finding $x = 1$ defective fuse is

$$f(1) = \frac{\binom{5}{1}\binom{7}{2}}{\binom{12}{3}} = \frac{\left(\frac{5!}{1!4!}\right)\left(\frac{7!}{2!5!}\right)}{\left(\frac{12!}{3!9!}\right)} = \frac{(5)(21)}{220} = .4773$$

Now suppose that we wanted to know the probability of finding *at least* 1 defective fuse. The easiest way to answer this question is to first compute the probability that the inspector does not find any defective fuses. The probability of $x = 0$ is

$$f(0) = \frac{\binom{5}{0}\binom{7}{3}}{\binom{12}{3}} = \frac{\left(\frac{5!}{0!5!}\right)\left(\frac{7!}{3!4!}\right)}{\left(\frac{12!}{3!9!}\right)} = \frac{(1)(35)}{220} = .1591$$

With a probability of zero defective fuses $f(0) = .1591$, we conclude that the probability of finding at least one defective fuse must be $1 - .1591 = .8409$. Thus, there is a reasonably high probability that the inspector will find at least 1 defective fuse.

The mean and variance of a hypergeometric distribution are as follows.

$$E(x) = \mu = n\left(\frac{r}{N}\right) \tag{5.13}$$

$$\text{Var}(x) = \sigma^2 = n\left(\frac{r}{N}\right)\left(1 - \frac{r}{N}\right)\left(\frac{N-n}{N-1}\right) \tag{5.14}$$

In the preceding example $n = 3$, $r = 5$, and $N = 12$. Thus, the mean and variance for the number of defective fuses are

$$\mu = n\left(\frac{r}{N}\right) = 3\left(\frac{5}{12}\right) = 1.25$$

$$\sigma^2 = n\left(\frac{r}{N}\right)\left(1 - \frac{r}{N}\right)\left(\frac{N-n}{N-1}\right) = 3\left(\frac{5}{12}\right)\left(1 - \frac{5}{12}\right)\left(\frac{12-3}{12-1}\right) = .60$$

The standard deviation is $\sigma = \sqrt{.60} = .77$.

NOTES AND COMMENTS

Consider a hypergeometric distribution with n trials. Let $p = (r/N)$ denote the probability of a success on the first trial. If the population size is large, the term $(N - n)/(N - 1)$ in equation (5.14) approaches 1. As a result, the expected value and variance can be written $E(x) = np$ and $\text{Var}(x) = np(1 - p)$. Note that these expressions are the same as the expressions used to compute the expected value and variance of a binomial distribution, as in equations (5.9) and (5.10). When the population size is large, a hypergeometric distribution can be approximated by a binomial distribution with n trials and a probability of success $p = (r/N)$.

Exercises

Methods

SELF test

46. Suppose $N = 10$ and $r = 3$. Compute the hypergeometric probabilities for the following values of n and x.
    a. $n = 4, x = 1$.
    b. $n = 2, x = 2$.
    c. $n = 2, x = 0$.
    d. $n = 4, x = 2$.
    e. $n = 4, x = 4$.
47. Suppose $N = 15$ and $r = 4$. What is the probability of $x = 3$ for $n = 10$?

Applications

48. In a survey conducted by the Gallup Organization, respondents were asked, "What is your favorite sport to watch?" Football and basketball ranked number one and two in terms of preference (Gallup website, January 3, 2004). Assume that in a group of 10 individuals, seven prefer football and three prefer basketball. A random sample of three of these individuals is selected.
    a. What is the probability that exactly two prefer football?
    b. What is the probability that the majority (either two or three) prefer football?

49. Blackjack, or twenty-one as it is frequently called, is a popular gambling game played in Las Vegas casinos. A player is dealt two cards. Face cards (jacks, queens, and kings) and tens have a point value of 10. Aces have a point value of 1 or 11. A 52-card deck contains 16 cards with a point value of 10 (jacks, queens, kings, and tens) and four aces.
   a. What is the probability that both cards dealt are aces or 10-point cards?
   b. What is the probability that both of the cards are aces?
   c. What is the probability that both of the cards have a point value of 10?
   d. A blackjack is a 10-point card and an ace for a value of 21. Use your answers to parts (a), (b), and (c) to determine the probability that a player is dealt blackjack. (*Hint:* Part (d) is not a hypergeometric problem. Develop your own logical relationship as to how the hypergeometric probabilities from parts (a), (b), and (c) can be combined to answer this question.)

SELF test

50. Axline Computers manufactures personal computers at two plants, one in Texas and the other in Hawaii. The Texas plant has 40 employees; the Hawaii plant has 20. A random sample of 10 employees is to be asked to fill out a benefits questionnaire.
   a. What is the probability that none of the employees in the sample work at the plant in Hawaii?
   b. What is the probability that one of the employees in the sample works at the plant in Hawaii?
   c. What is the probability that two or more of the employees in the sample work at the plant in Hawaii?
   d. What is the probability that nine of the employees in the sample work at the plant in Texas?

51. The Zagat Restaurant Survey provides food, decor, and service ratings for some of the top restaurants across the United States. For 15 restaurants located in Boston, the average price of a dinner, including one drink and tip, was \$48.60. You are leaving for a business trip to Boston and will eat dinner at three of these restaurants. Your company will reimburse you for a maximum of \$50 per dinner. Business associates familiar with these restaurants have told you that the meal cost at one-third of these restaurants will exceed \$50. Suppose that you randomly select three of these restaurants for dinner.
   a. What is the probability that none of the meals will exceed the cost covered by your company?
   b. What is the probability that one of the meals will exceed the cost covered by your company?
   c. What is the probability that two of the meals will exceed the cost covered by your company?
   d. What is the probability that all three of the meals will exceed the cost covered by your company?

52. The Troubled Asset Relief Program (TARP), passed by the U.S. Congress in October 2008, provided \$700 billion in assistance for the struggling U.S. economy. Over \$200 billion was given to troubled financial institutions with the hope that there would be an increase in lending to help jump-start the economy. But three months later, a Federal Reserve survey found that two-thirds of the banks that had received TARP funds had tightened terms for business loans (*The Wall Street Journal,* February 3, 2009). Of the ten banks that were the biggest recipients of TARP funds, only three had actually increased lending during this period.

Increased Lending	Decreased Lending
BB&T	Bank of America
Sun Trust Banks	Capital One
U.S. Bancorp	Citigroup
	Fifth Third Bancorp
	J.P. Morgan Chase
	Regions Financial
	U.S. Bancorp

For the purposes of this exercise, assume that you will randomly select three of these ten banks for a study that will continue to monitor bank lending practices. Let x be a random variable indicating the number of banks in the study that had increased lending.

a. What is $f(0)$? What is your interpretation of this value?
b. What is $f(3)$? What is your interpretation of this value?
c. Compute $f(1)$ and $f(2)$. Show the probability distribution for the number of banks in the study that had increased lending. What value of x has the highest probability?
d. What is the probability that the study will have at least one bank that had increased lending?
e. Compute the expected value, variance, and standard deviation for the random variable.

Summary

A random variable provides a numerical description of the outcome of an experiment. The probability distribution for a random variable describes how the probabilities are distributed over the values the random variable can assume. For any discrete random variable x, the probability distribution is defined by a probability function, denoted by $f(x)$, which provides the probability associated with each value of the random variable. Once the probability function is defined, we can compute the expected value, variance, and standard deviation for the random variable.

The binomial distribution can be used to determine the probability of x successes in n trials whenever the experiment has the following properties:

1. The experiment consists of a sequence of n identical trials.
2. Two outcomes are possible on each trial, one called success and the other failure.
3. The probability of a success p does not change from trial to trial. Consequently, the probability of failure, $1 - p$, does not change from trial to trial.
4. The trials are independent.

When the four properties hold, the binomial probability function can be used to determine the probability of obtaining x successes in n trials. Formulas were also presented for the mean and variance of the binomial distribution.

The Poisson distribution is used when it is desirable to determine the probability of obtaining x occurrences over an interval of time or space. The following assumptions are necessary for the Poisson distribution to be applicable.

1. The probability of an occurrence of the event is the same for any two intervals of equal length.
2. The occurrence or nonoccurrence of the event in any interval is independent of the occurrence or nonoccurrence of the event in any other interval.

A third discrete probability distribution, the hypergeometric, was introduced in Section 5.6. Like the binomial, it is used to compute the probability of x successes in n trials. But, in contrast to the binomial, the probability of success changes from trial to trial.

Glossary

Random variable A numerical description of the outcome of an experiment.
Discrete random variable A random variable that may assume either a finite number of values or an infinite sequence of values.
Continuous random variable A random variable that may assume any numerical value in an interval or collection of intervals.

Probability distribution A description of how the probabilities are distributed over the values of the random variable.

Probability function A function, denoted by $f(x)$, that provides the probability that x assumes a particular value for a discrete random variable.

Discrete uniform probability distribution A probability distribution for which each possible value of the random variable has the same probability.

Expected value A measure of the central location of a random variable.

Variance A measure of the variability, or dispersion, of a random variable.

Standard deviation The positive square root of the variance.

Binomial experiment An experiment having the four properties stated at the beginning of Section 5.4.

Binomial probability distribution A probability distribution showing the probability of x successes in n trials of a binomial experiment.

Binomial probability function The function used to compute binomial probabilities.

Poisson probability distribution A probability distribution showing the probability of x occurrences of an event over a specified interval of time or space.

Poisson probability function The function used to compute Poisson probabilities.

Hypergeometric probability distribution A probability distribution showing the probability of x successes in n trials from a population with r successes and $N - r$ failures.

Hypergeometric probability function The function used to compute hypergeometric probabilities.

Key Formulas

Discrete Uniform Probability Function

$$f(x) = 1/n \tag{5.3}$$

Expected Value of a Discrete Random Variable

$$E(x) = \mu = \Sigma x f(x) \tag{5.4}$$

Variance of a Discrete Random Variable

$$\text{Var}(x) = \sigma^2 = \Sigma(x - \mu)^2 f(x) \tag{5.5}$$

Number of Experimental Outcomes Providing Exactly x Successes in n Trials

$$\binom{n}{x} = \frac{n!}{x!(n - x)!} \tag{5.6}$$

Binomial Probability Function

$$f(x) = \binom{n}{x} p^x (1 - p)^{(n-x)} \tag{5.8}$$

Expected Value for the Binomial Distribution

$$E(x) = \mu = np \tag{5.9}$$

Variance for the Binomial Distribution

$$\text{Var}(x) = \sigma^2 = np(1 - p) \tag{5.10}$$

Poisson Probability Function

$$f(x) = \frac{\mu^x e^{-\mu}}{x!} \tag{5.11}$$

Hypergeometric Probability Function

$$f(x) = \frac{\binom{r}{x}\binom{N-r}{n-x}}{\binom{N}{n}} \tag{5.12}$$

Expected Value for the Hypergeometric Distribution

$$E(x) = \mu = n\left(\frac{r}{N}\right) \tag{5.13}$$

Variance for the Hypergeometric Distribution

$$\text{Var}(x) = \sigma^2 = n\left(\frac{r}{N}\right)\left(1 - \frac{r}{N}\right)\left(\frac{N-n}{N-1}\right) \tag{5.14}$$

Supplementary Exercises

53. The *Barron's* Big Money Poll asked 131 investment managers across the United States about their short-term investment outlook (*Barron's,* October 28, 2002). Their responses showed 4% were very bullish, 39% were bullish, 29% were neutral, 21% were bearish, and 7% were very bearish. Let x be the random variable reflecting the level of optimism about the market. Set $x = 5$ for very bullish down through $x = 1$ for very bearish.
    a. Develop a probability distribution for the level of optimism of investment managers.
    b. Compute the expected value for the level of optimism.
    c. Compute the variance and standard deviation for the level of optimism.
    d. Comment on what your results imply about the level of optimism and its variability.
54. The American Association of Individual Investors publishes an annual guide to the top mutual funds (*The Individual Investor's Guide to the Top Mutual Funds,* 22e, American Association of Individual Investors, 2003). The total risk ratings for 29 categories of mutual funds are as follows.

Total Risk	Number of Fund Categories
Low	7
Below Average	6
Average	3
Above Average	6
High	7

    a. Let $x = 1$ for low risk up through $x = 5$ for high risk, and develop a probability distribution for level of risk.
    b. What are the expected value and variance for total risk?
    c. It turns out that 11 of the fund categories were bond funds. For the bond funds, seven categories were rated low and four were rated below average. Compare the total risk of the bond funds with the 18 categories of stock funds.

55. The budgeting process for a midwestern college resulted in expense forecasts for the coming year (in $ millions) of $9, $10, $11, $12, and $13. Because the actual expenses are unknown, the following respective probabilities are assigned: .3, .2, .25, .05, and .2.
    a. Show the probability distribution for the expense forecast.
    b. What is the expected value of the expense forecast for the coming year?
    c. What is the variance of the expense forecast for the coming year?
    d. If income projections for the year are estimated at $12 million, comment on the financial position of the college.

56. A survey showed that the average commuter spends about 26 minutes on a one-way door-to-door trip from home to work. In addition, 5% of commuters reported a one-way commute of more than one hour (Bureau of Transportation Statistics website, January 12, 2004).
    a. If 20 commuters are surveyed on a particular day, what is the probability that three will report a one-way commute of more than one hour?
    b. If 20 commuters are surveyed on a particular day, what is the probability that none will report a one-way commute of more than one hour?
    c. If a company has 2000 employees, what is the expected number of employees that have a one-way commute of more than one hour?
    d. If a company has 2000 employees, what is the variance and standard deviation of the number of employees that have a one-way commute of more than one hour?

57. A political action group is planning to interview home owners to assess the impact caused by a recent slump in housing prices. According to a *Wall Street Journal*/Harris Interactive Personal Finance poll, 26% of individuals aged 18–34, 50% of individuals aged 35–44, and 88% of individuals aged 55 and over are home owners (All Business website, January 23, 2008).
    a. How many people from the 18–34 age group must be sampled to find an expected number of at least 20 home owners?
    b. How many people from the 35–44 age group must be sampled to find an expected number of at least 20 home owners?
    c. How many people from the 55 and over age group must be sampled to find an expected number of at least 20 home owners?
    d. If the number of 18–34 year olds sampled is equal to the value identified in part (a), what is the standard deviation of the number who will be home owners?
    e. If the number of 35–44 year olds sampled is equal to the value identified in part (b), what is the standard deviation of the number who will be home owners?

58. Many companies use a quality control technique called acceptance sampling to monitor incoming shipments of parts, raw materials, and so on. In the electronics industry, component parts are commonly shipped from suppliers in large lots. Inspection of a sample of n components can be viewed as the n trials of a binomial experiment. The outcome for each component tested (trial) will be that the component is classified as good or defective. Reynolds Electronics accepts a lot from a particular supplier if the defective components in the lot do not exceed 1%. Suppose a random sample of five items from a recent shipment is tested.
    a. Assume that 1% of the shipment is defective. Compute the probability that no items in the sample are defective.
    b. Assume that 1% of the shipment is defective. Compute the probability that exactly one item in the sample is defective.
    c. What is the probability of observing one or more defective items in the sample if 1% of the shipment is defective?
    d. Would you feel comfortable accepting the shipment if one item was found to be defective? Why or why not?

59. The unemployment rate in the state of Arizona is 4.1% (CNN Money website, May 2, 2007). Assume that 100 employable people in Arizona are selected randomly.
    a. What is the expected number of people who are unemployed?
    b. What are the variance and standard deviation of the number of people who are unemployed?
60. A poll conducted by Zogby International showed that of those Americans who said music plays a "very important" role in their lives, 30% said their local radio stations "always" play the kind of music they like (Zogby website, January 12, 2004). Suppose a sample of 800 people who say music plays an important role in their lives is taken.
    a. How many would you expect to say that their local radio stations always play the kind of music they like?
    b. What is the standard deviation of the number of respondents who think their local radio stations always play the kind of music they like?
    c. What is the standard deviation of the number of respondents who do not think their local radio stations always play the kind of music they like?
61. Cars arrive at a car wash randomly and independently; the probability of an arrival is the same for any two time intervals of equal length. The mean arrival rate is 15 cars per hour. What is the probability that 20 or more cars will arrive during any given hour of operation?
62. A new automated production process averages 1.5 breakdowns per day. Because of the cost associated with a breakdown, management is concerned about the possibility of having three or more breakdowns during a day. Assume that breakdowns occur randomly, that the probability of a breakdown is the same for any two time intervals of equal length, and that breakdowns in one period are independent of breakdowns in other periods. What is the probability of having three or more breakdowns during a day?
63. A regional director responsible for business development in the state of Pennsylvania is concerned about the number of small business failures. If the mean number of small business failures per month is 10, what is the probability that exactly four small businesses will fail during a given month? Assume that the probability of a failure is the same for any two months and that the occurrence or nonoccurrence of a failure in any month is independent of failures in any other month.
64. Customer arrivals at a bank are random and independent; the probability of an arrival in any one-minute period is the same as the probability of an arrival in any other one-minute period. Answer the following questions, assuming a mean arrival rate of three customers per minute.
    a. What is the probability of exactly three arrivals in a one-minute period?
    b. What is the probability of at least three arrivals in a one-minute period?
65. A deck of playing cards contains 52 cards, four of which are aces. What is the probability that the deal of a five-card hand provides:
    a. A pair of aces?
    b. Exactly one ace?
    c. No aces?
    d. At least one ace?
66. Through the week ending September 16, 2001, Tiger Woods was the leading money winner on the PGA Tour, with total earnings of $5,517,777. Of the top 10 money winners, seven players used a Titleist brand golf ball (PGA Tour website). Suppose that we randomly select two of the top 10 money winners.
    a. What is the probability that exactly one uses a Titleist golf ball?
    b. What is the probability that both use Titleist golf balls?
    c. What is the probability that neither uses a Titleist golf ball?

Appendix 5.1 Discrete Probability Distributions with Minitab

Statistical packages such as Minitab offer a relatively easy and efficient procedure for computing binomial probabilities. In this appendix, we show the step-by-step procedure for determining the binomial probabilities for the Martin Clothing Store problem in Section 5.4. Recall that the desired binomial probabilities are based on $n = 10$ and $p = .30$. Before beginning the Minitab routine, the user must enter the desired values of the random variable x into a column of the worksheet. We entered the values 0, 1, 2, . . . , 10 in column 1 (see Figure 5.5) to generate the entire binomial probability distribution. The Minitab steps to obtain the desired binomial probabilities follow.

Step 1. Select the **Calc** menu
Step 2. Choose **Probability Distributions**
Step 3. Choose **Binomial**
Step 4. When the Binomial Distribution dialog box appears:
Select **Probability**
Enter 10 in the **Number of trials** box
Enter .3 in the **Event probability** box
Enter C1 in the **Input column** box
Click **OK**

The Minitab output with the binomial probabilities will appear as shown in Figure 5.5.

Minitab provides Poisson and hypergeometric probabilities in a similar manner. For instance, to compute Poisson probabilities the only differences are in step 3, where the **Poisson** option would be selected, and step 4, where the **Mean** would be entered rather than the number of trials and the probability of success.

Appendix 5.2 Discrete Probability Distributions with Excel

Excel provides functions for computing probabilities for the binomial, Poisson, and hypergeometric distributions introduced in this chapter. The Excel function for computing binomial probabilities is BINOM.DIST. It has four arguments: x (the number of successes), n (the number of trials), p (the probability of success), and cumulative. FALSE is used for the fourth argument (cumulative) if we want the probability of x successes, and TRUE is used for the fourth argument if we want the cumulative probability of x or fewer successes. Here we show how to compute the probabilities of 0 through 10 successes for the Martin Clothing Store problem in Section 5.4 (see Figure 5.5).

As we describe the worksheet development, refer to Figure 5.6; the formula worksheet is set in the background, and the value worksheet appears in the foreground. We entered the number of trials (10) into cell B1, the probability of success into cell B2, and the values for the random variable into cells B5:B15. The following steps will generate the desired probabilities:

Step 1. Use the BINOM.DIST function to compute the probability of $x = 0$ by entering the following formula into cell C5:

=BINOM.DIST(B5,$B$1,$B$2,FALSE)

Step 2. Copy the formula in cell C5 into cells C6:C15.

FIGURE 5.6 EXCEL WORKSHEET FOR COMPUTING BINOMIAL PROBABILITIES

	A	B	C	D
1	**Number of Trials (*n*)**	10		
2	**Probability of Success (*p*)**	0.3		
3				
4		*x*	*f*(*x*)	
5		0	=BINOM.DIST(B5,$B$1,$B$2,FALSE)	
6		1	=BINOM.DIST(B6,$B$1,$B$2,FALSE)	
7		2	=BINOM.DIST(B7,$B$1,$B$2,FALSE)	
8		3	=BINOM.DIST(B8,$B$1,$B$2,FALSE)	
9		4	=BINOM.DIST(B9,$B$1,$B$2,FALSE)	
10		5	=BINOM.DIST(B10,$B$1,$B$2,FALSE)	
11		6	=BINOM.DIST(B11,$B$1,$B$2,FALSE)	
12		7	=BINOM.DIST(B12,$B$1,$B$2,FALSE)	
13		8	=BINOM.DIST(B13,$B$1,$B$2,FALSE)	
14		9	=BINOM.DIST(B14,$B$1,$B$2,FALSE)	
15		10	=BINOM.DIST(B15,$B$1,$B$2,FALSE)	
16				

	A	B	C	D
1	**Number of Trials (*n*)**	10		
2	**Probability of Success (*p*)**	0.3		
3				
4		*x*	*f*(*x*)	
5		0	0.0282	
6		1	0.1211	
7		2	0.2335	
8		3	0.2668	
9		4	0.2001	
10		5	0.1029	
11		6	0.0368	
12		7	0.0090	
13		8	0.0014	
14		9	0.0001	
15		10	0.0000	
16				

The value worksheet in Figure 5.6 shows that the probabilities obtained are the same as in Figure 5.5. Poisson and hypergeometric probabilities can be computed in a similar fashion. The POISSON.DIST and HYPGEOM.DIST functions are used. Excel's Insert Function dialog box can help the user in entering the proper arguments for these functions (see Appendix E).

CHAPTER 6

Continuous Probability Distributions

CONTENTS

STATISTICS *in* PRACTICE

PROCTER & GAMBLE*
CINCINNATI, OHIO

Procter & Gamble (P&G) produces and markets such products as detergents, disposable diapers, over-the-counter pharmaceuticals, dentifrices, bar soaps, mouthwashes, and paper towels. Worldwide, it has the leading brand in more categories than any other consumer products company. Since its merger with Gillette, P&G also produces and markets razors, blades, and many other personal care products.

As a leader in the application of statistical methods in decision making, P&G employs people with diverse academic backgrounds: engineering, statistics, operations research, and business. The major quantitative technologies for which these people provide support are probabilistic decision and risk analysis, advanced simulation, quality improvement, and quantitative methods (e.g., linear programming, regression analysis, probability analysis).

The Industrial Chemicals Division of P&G is a major supplier of fatty alcohols derived from natural substances such as coconut oil and from petroleum-based derivatives. The division wanted to know the economic risks and opportunities of expanding its fatty-alcohol production facilities, so it called in P&G's experts in probabilistic decision and risk analysis to help. After structuring and modeling the problem, they determined that the key to profitability was the cost difference between the petroleum- and coconut-based raw materials. Future costs were unknown, but the analysts were able to approximate them with the following continuous random variables.

x = the coconut oil price per pound of fatty alcohol

and

y = the petroleum raw material price per pound of fatty alcohol

Because the key to profitability was the difference between these two random variables, a third random variable, $d = x - y$, was used in the analysis. Experts were interviewed to determine the probability distributions for x and y. In turn, this information was used to develop a probability distribution for the difference in prices d. This continuous probability distribution showed a .90 probability that the price difference would be $.0655 or less and a .50 probability that the price difference would be $.035 or less. In addition, there was only a .10 probability that the price difference would be $.0045 or less.†

Some of Procter & Gamble's many well-known products. © Robert Sullivan/AFP/Getty Images.

The Industrial Chemicals Division thought that being able to quantify the impact of raw material price differences was key to reaching a consensus. The probabilities obtained were used in a sensitivity analysis of the raw material price difference. The analysis yielded sufficient insight to form the basis for a recommendation to management.

The use of continuous random variables and their probability distributions was helpful to P&G in analyzing the economic risks associated with its fatty-alcohol production. In this chapter, you will gain an understanding of continuous random variables and their probability distributions, including one of the most important probability distributions in statistics, the normal distribution.

*The authors are indebted to Joel Kahn of Procter & Gamble for providing this Statistics in Practice.

†The price differences stated here have been modified to protect proprietary data.

In the preceding chapter we discussed discrete random variables and their probability distributions. In this chapter we turn to the study of continuous random variables. Specifically, we discuss three continuous probability distributions: the uniform, the normal, and the exponential.

A fundamental difference separates discrete and continuous random variables in terms of how probabilities are computed. For a discrete random variable, the probability function $f(x)$ provides the probability that the random variable assumes a particular value. With continuous random variables, the counterpart of the probability function is the **probability density function**, also denoted by $f(x)$. The difference is that the probability density function does not directly provide probabilities. However, the area under the graph of $f(x)$ corresponding to a given interval does provide the probability that the continuous random variable x assumes a value in that interval. So when we compute probabilities for continuous random variables we are computing the probability that the random variable assumes any value in an interval.

Because the area under the graph of $f(x)$ at any particular point is zero, one of the implications of the definition of probability for continuous random variables is that the probability of any particular value of the random variable is zero. In Section 6.1 we demonstrate these concepts for a continuous random variable that has a uniform distribution.

Much of the chapter is devoted to describing and showing applications of the normal distribution. The normal distribution is of major importance because of its wide applicability and its extensive use in statistical inference. The chapter closes with a discussion of the exponential distribution. The exponential distribution is useful in applications involving such factors as waiting times and service times.

6.1 Uniform Probability Distribution

Whenever the probability is proportional to the length of the interval, the random variable is uniformly distributed.

Consider the random variable x representing the flight time of an airplane traveling from Chicago to New York. Suppose the flight time can be any value in the interval from 120 minutes to 140 minutes. Because the random variable x can assume any value in that interval, x is a continuous rather than a discrete random variable. Let us assume that sufficient actual flight data are available to conclude that the probability of a flight time within any 1-minute interval is the same as the probability of a flight time within any other 1-minute interval contained in the larger interval from 120 to 140 minutes. With every 1-minute interval being equally likely, the random variable x is said to have a **uniform probability distribution**. The probability density function, which defines the uniform distribution for the flight-time random variable, is

$$f(x) = \begin{cases} 1/20 & \text{for } 120 \leq x \leq 140 \\ 0 & \text{elsewhere} \end{cases}$$

Figure 6.1 is a graph of this probability density function. In general, the uniform probability density function for a random variable x is defined by the following formula.

UNIFORM PROBABILITY DENSITY FUNCTION

$$f(x) = \begin{cases} \dfrac{1}{b - a} & \text{for } a \leq x \leq b \\ 0 & \text{elsewhere} \end{cases} \tag{6.1}$$

For the flight-time random variable, $a = 120$ and $b = 140$.

FIGURE 6.1 UNIFORM PROBABILITY DISTRIBUTION FOR FLIGHT TIME

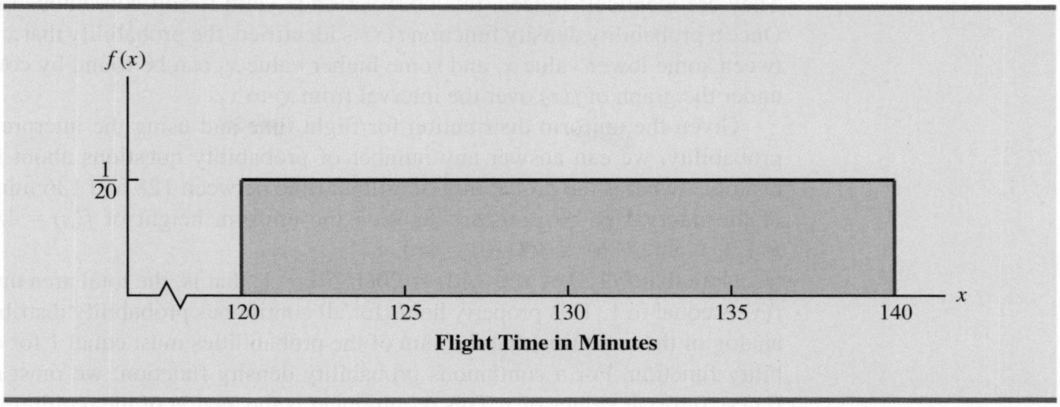

As noted in the introduction, for a continuous random variable, we consider probability only in terms of the likelihood that a random variable assumes a value within a specified interval. In the flight time example, an acceptable probability question is: What is the probability that the flight time is between 120 and 130 minutes? That is, what is $P(120 \leq x \leq 130)$? Because the flight time must be between 120 and 140 minutes and because the probability is described as being uniform over this interval, we feel comfortable saying $P(120 \leq x \leq 130) = .50$. In the following subsection we show that this probability can be computed as the area under the graph of $f(x)$ from 120 to 130 (see Figure 6.2).

Area as a Measure of Probability

Let us make an observation about the graph in Figure 6.2. Consider the area under the graph of $f(x)$ in the interval from 120 to 130. The area is rectangular, and the area of a rectangle is simply the width multiplied by the height. With the width of the interval equal to $130 - 120 = 10$ and the height equal to the value of the probability density function $f(x) = 1/20$, we have area $=$ width $\times$ height $= 10(1/20) = 10/20 = .50$.

FIGURE 6.2 AREA PROVIDES PROBABILITY OF A FLIGHT TIME BETWEEN 120 AND 130 MINUTES

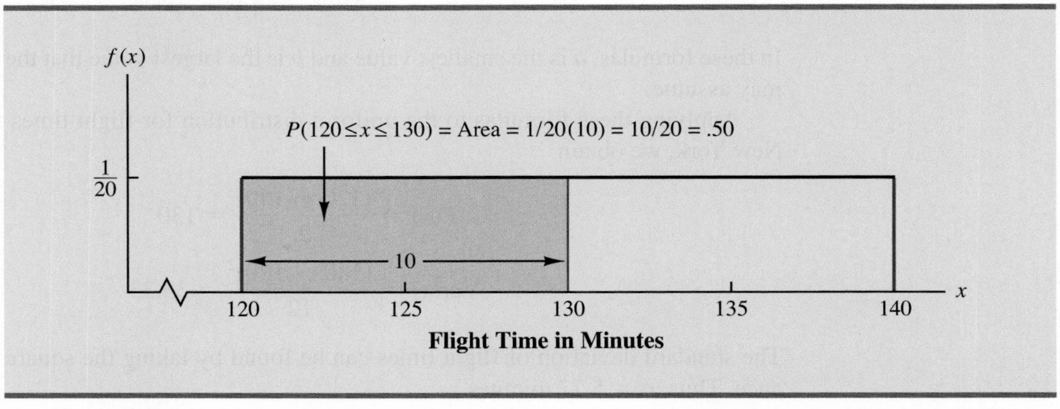

What observation can you make about the area under the graph of $f(x)$ and probability? They are identical! Indeed, this observation is valid for all continuous random variables. Once a probability density function $f(x)$ is identified, the probability that x takes a value between some lower value x_1 and some higher value x_2 can be found by computing the area under the graph of $f(x)$ over the interval from x_1 to x_2.

Given the uniform distribution for flight time and using the interpretation of area as probability, we can answer any number of probability questions about flight times. For example, what is the probability of a flight time between 128 and 136 minutes? The width of the interval is $136 - 128 = 8$. With the uniform height of $f(x) = 1/20$, we see that $P(128 \leq x \leq 136) = 8(1/20) = .40$.

Note that $P(120 \leq x \leq 140) = 20(1/20) = 1$; that is, the total area under the graph of $f(x)$ is equal to 1. This property holds for all continuous probability distributions and is the analog of the condition that the sum of the probabilities must equal 1 for a discrete probability function. For a continuous probability density function, we must also require that $f(x) \geq 0$ for all values of x. This requirement is the analog of the requirement that $f(x) \geq 0$ for discrete probability functions.

Two major differences stand out between the treatment of continuous random variables and the treatment of their discrete counterparts.

To see that the probability of any single point is 0, refer to Figure 6.2 and compute the probability of a single point, say, $x = 125$. $P(x = 125) = P(125 \leq x \leq 125) = 0(1/20) = 0$.

1. We no longer talk about the probability of the random variable assuming a particular value. Instead, we talk about the probability of the random variable assuming a value within some given interval.
2. The probability of a continuous random variable assuming a value within some given interval from x_1 to x_2 is defined to be the area under the graph of the probability density function between x_1 and x_2. Because a single point is an interval of zero width, this implies that the probability of a continuous random variable assuming any particular value exactly is zero. It also means that the probability of a continuous random variable assuming a value in any interval is the same whether or not the endpoints are included.

The calculation of the expected value and variance for a continuous random variable is analogous to that for a discrete random variable. However, because the computational procedure involves integral calculus, we leave the derivation of the appropriate formulas to more advanced texts.

For the uniform continuous probability distribution introduced in this section, the formulas for the expected value and variance are

$$E(x) = \frac{a + b}{2}$$

$$\text{Var}(x) = \frac{(b - a)^2}{12}$$

In these formulas, a is the smallest value and b is the largest value that the random variable may assume.

Applying these formulas to the uniform distribution for flight times from Chicago to New York, we obtain

$$E(x) = \frac{(120 + 140)}{2} = 130$$

$$\text{Var}(x) = \frac{(140 - 120)^2}{12} = 33.33$$

The standard deviation of flight times can be found by taking the square root of the variance. Thus, $\sigma = 5.77$ minutes.

NOTES AND COMMENTS

To see more clearly why the height of a probability density function is not a probability, think about a random variable with the following uniform probability distribution.

$$f(x) = \begin{cases} 2 & \text{for } 0 \leq x \leq .5 \\ 0 & \text{elsewhere} \end{cases}$$

The height of the probability density function, $f(x)$, is 2 for values of x between 0 and .5. However, we know probabilities can never be greater than 1. Thus, we see that $f(x)$ cannot be interpreted as the probability of x.

Exercises

Methods

SELF test

1. The random variable x is known to be uniformly distributed between 1.0 and 1.5.
   a. Show the graph of the probability density function.
   b. Compute $P(x = 1.25)$.
   c. Compute $P(1.0 \leq x \leq 1.25)$.
   d. Compute $P(1.20 < x < 1.5)$.
2. The random variable x is known to be uniformly distributed between 10 and 20.
   a. Show the graph of the probability density function.
   b. Compute $P(x < 15)$.
   c. Compute $P(12 \leq x \leq 18)$.
   d. Compute $E(x)$.
   e. Compute $\text{Var}(x)$.

Applications

3. Delta Airlines quotes a flight time of 2 hours, 5 minutes for its flights from Cincinnati to Tampa. Suppose we believe that actual flight times are uniformly distributed between 2 hours and 2 hours, 20 minutes.
   a. Show the graph of the probability density function for flight time.
   b. What is the probability that the flight will be no more than 5 minutes late?
   c. What is the probability that the flight will be more than 10 minutes late?
   d. What is the expected flight time?

SELF test

4. Most computer languages include a function that can be used to generate random numbers. In Excel, the RAND function can be used to generate random numbers between 0 and 1. If we let x denote a random number generated using RAND, then x is a continuous random variable with the following probability density function.

$$f(x) = \begin{cases} 1 & \text{for } 0 \leq x \leq 1 \\ 0 & \text{elsewhere} \end{cases}$$

   a. Graph the probability density function.
   b. What is the probability of generating a random number between .25 and .75?
   c. What is the probability of generating a random number with a value less than or equal to .30?
   d. What is the probability of generating a random number with a value greater than .60?
   e. Generate 50 random numbers by entering =RAND() into 50 cells of an Excel worksheet.
   f. Compute the mean and standard deviation for the random numbers in part (e).

5. The driving distance for the top 100 golfers on the PGA tour is between 284.7 and 310.6 yards (*Golfweek,* March 29, 2003). Assume that the driving distance for these golfers is uniformly distributed over this interval.
   a. Give a mathematical expression for the probability density function of driving distance.
   b. What is the probability the driving distance for one of these golfers is less than 290 yards?
   c. What is the probability the driving distance for one of these golfers is at least 300 yards?
   d. What is the probability the driving distance for one of these golfers is between 290 and 305 yards?
   e. How many of these golfers drive the ball at least 290 yards?
6. On average, 30-minute television sitcoms have 22 minutes of programming (CNBC, February 23, 2006). Assume that the probability distribution for minutes of programming can be approximated by a uniform distribution from 18 minutes to 26 minutes.
   a. What is the probability a sitcom will have 25 or more minutes of programming?
   b. What is the probability a sitcom will have between 21 and 25 minutes of programming?
   c. What is the probability a sitcom will have more than 10 minutes of commercials or other nonprogramming interruptions?
7. Suppose we are interested in bidding on a piece of land and we know one other bidder is interested.[1] The seller announced that the highest bid in excess of \$10,000 will be accepted. Assume that the competitor's bid x is a random variable that is uniformly distributed between \$10,000 and \$15,000.
   a. Suppose you bid \$12,000. What is the probability that your bid will be accepted?
   b. Suppose you bid \$14,000. What is the probability that your bid will be accepted?
   c. What amount should you bid to maximize the probability that you get the property?
   d. Suppose you know someone who is willing to pay you \$16,000 for the property. Would you consider bidding less than the amount in part (c)? Why or why not?

6.2 Normal Probability Distribution

Abraham de Moivre, a French mathematician, published The Doctrine of Chances *in 1733. He derived the normal distribution.*

The most important probability distribution for describing a continuous random variable is the **normal probability distribution**. The normal distribution has been used in a wide variety of practical applications in which the random variables are heights and weights of people, test scores, scientific measurements, amounts of rainfall, and other similar values. It is also widely used in statistical inference, which is the major topic of the remainder of this book. In such applications, the normal distribution provides a description of the likely results obtained through sampling.

Normal Curve

The form, or shape, of the normal distribution is illustrated by the bell-shaped normal curve in Figure 6.3. The probability density function that defines the bell-shaped curve of the normal distribution follows.

[1]This exercise is based on a problem suggested to us by Professor Roger Myerson of Northwestern University.

FIGURE 6.3 BELL-SHAPED CURVE FOR THE NORMAL DISTRIBUTION

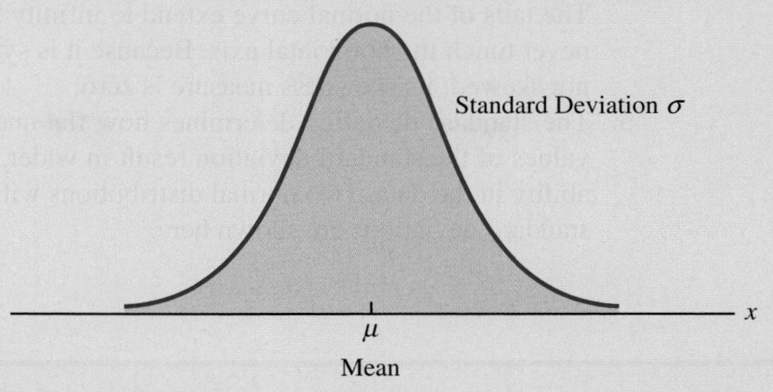

NORMAL PROBABILITY DENSITY FUNCTION

$$f(x) = \frac{1}{\sigma\sqrt{2\pi}} e^{-(x-\mu)^2/2\sigma^2} \qquad (6.2)$$

where

μ = mean
σ = standard deviation
π = 3.14159
e = 2.71828

We make several observations about the characteristics of the normal distribution.

The normal curve has two parameters, μ and σ. They determine the location and shape of the normal distribution.

1. The entire family of normal distributions is differentiated by two parameters: the mean μ and the standard deviation σ.
2. The highest point on the normal curve is at the mean, which is also the median and mode of the distribution.
3. The mean of the distribution can be any numerical value: negative, zero, or positive. Three normal distributions with the same standard deviation but three different means (−10, 0, and 20) are shown here.

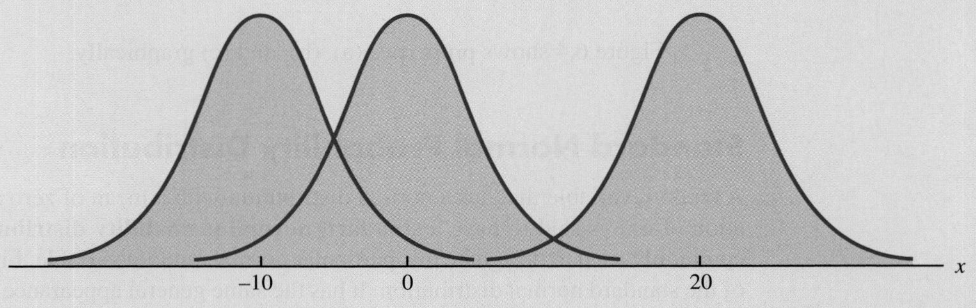

4. The normal distribution is symmetric, with the shape of the normal curve to the left of the mean a mirror image of the shape of the normal curve to the right of the mean. The tails of the normal curve extend to infinity in both directions and theoretically never touch the horizontal axis. Because it is symmetric, the normal distribution is not skewed; its skewness measure is zero.
5. The standard deviation determines how flat and wide the normal curve is. Larger values of the standard deviation result in wider, flatter curves, showing more variability in the data. Two normal distributions with the same mean but with different standard deviations are shown here.

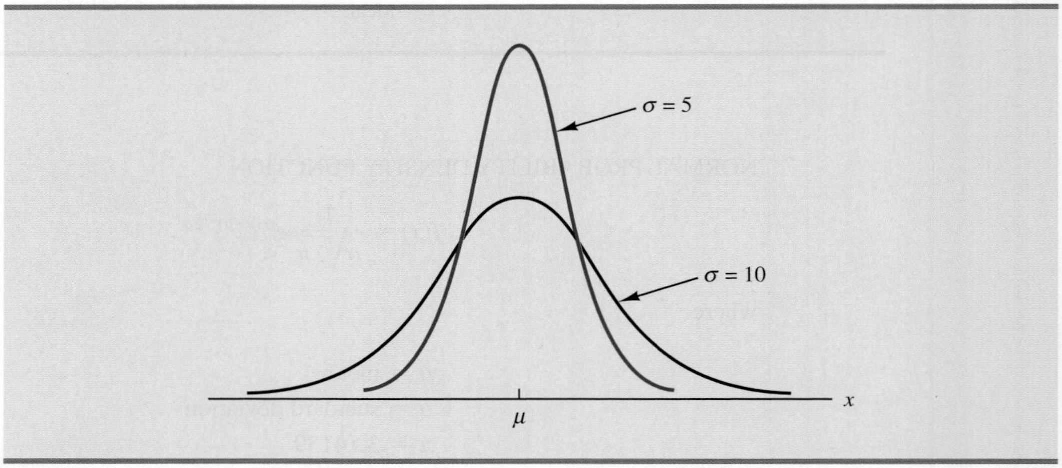

6. Probabilities for the normal random variable are given by areas under the normal curve. The total area under the curve for the normal distribution is 1. Because the distribution is symmetric, the area under the curve to the left of the mean is .50 and the area under the curve to the right of the mean is .50.
7. The percentage of values in some commonly used intervals are
   a. 68.3% of the values of a normal random variable are within plus or minus one standard deviation of its mean.
   b. 95.4% of the values of a normal random variable are within plus or minus two standard deviations of its mean.
   c. 99.7% of the values of a normal random variable are within plus or minus three standard deviations of its mean.

These percentages are the basis for the empirical rule introduced in Section 3.3.

Figure 6.4 shows properties (a), (b), and (c) graphically.

Standard Normal Probability Distribution

A random variable that has a normal distribution with a mean of zero and a standard deviation of one is said to have a **standard normal probability distribution**. The letter z is commonly used to designate this particular normal random variable. Figure 6.5 is the graph of the standard normal distribution. It has the same general appearance as other normal distributions, but with the special properties of $\mu = 0$ and $\sigma = 1$.

FIGURE 6.4 AREAS UNDER THE CURVE FOR ANY NORMAL DISTRIBUTION

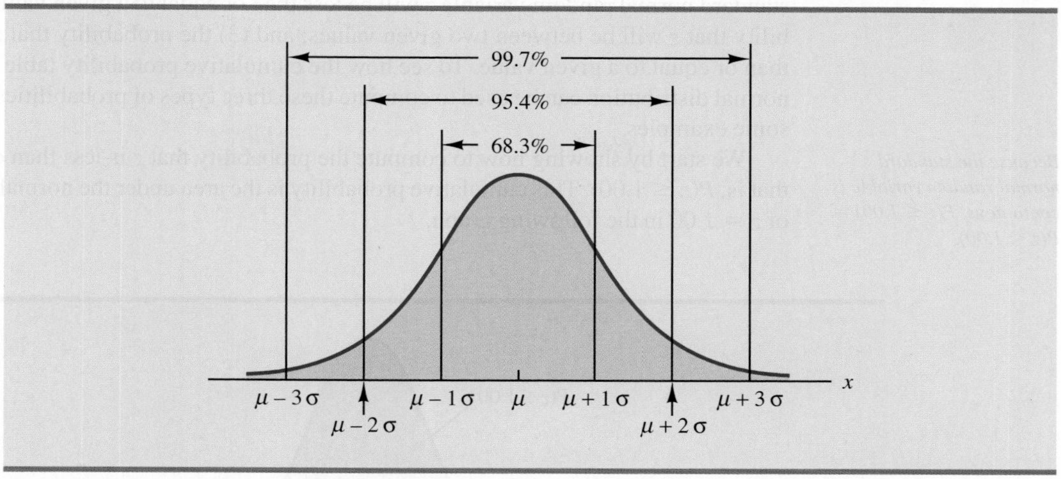

FIGURE 6.5 THE STANDARD NORMAL DISTRIBUTION

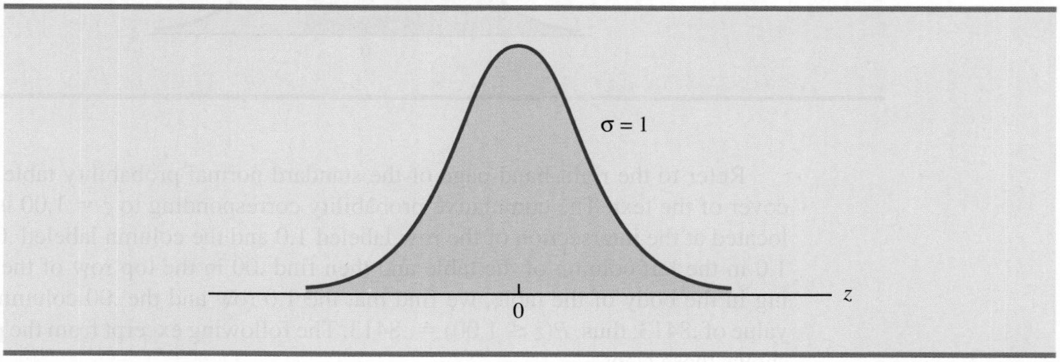

Because $\mu = 0$ and $\sigma = 1$, the formula for the standard normal probability density function is a simpler version of equation (6.2).

STANDARD NORMAL DENSITY FUNCTION

$$f(z) = \frac{1}{\sqrt{2\pi}} e^{-z^2/2}$$

As with other continuous random variables, probability calculations with any normal distribution are made by computing areas under the graph of the probability density function. Thus, to find the probability that a normal random variable is within any specific interval, we must compute the area under the normal curve over that interval.

For the normal probability density function, the height of the normal curve varies and more advanced mathematics is required to compute the areas that represent probability.

For the standard normal distribution, areas under the normal curve have been computed and are available in tables that can be used to compute probabilities. Such a table appears on the two pages inside the front cover of the text. The table on the left-hand page contains areas, or cumulative probabilities, for z values less than or equal to the mean of zero. The table on the right-hand page contains areas, or cumulative probabilities, for z values greater than or equal to the mean of zero.

The three types of probabilities we need to compute include (1) the probability that the standard normal random variable z will be less than or equal to a given value; (2) the probability that z will be between two given values; and (3) the probability that z will be greater than or equal to a given value. To see how the cumulative probability table for the standard normal distribution can be used to compute these three types of probabilities, let us consider some examples.

Because the standard normal random variable is continuous, $P(z \leq 1.00) = P(z < 1.00)$.

We start by showing how to compute the probability that z is less than or equal to 1.00; that is, $P(z \leq 1.00)$. This cumulative probability is the area under the normal curve to the left of $z = 1.00$ in the following graph.

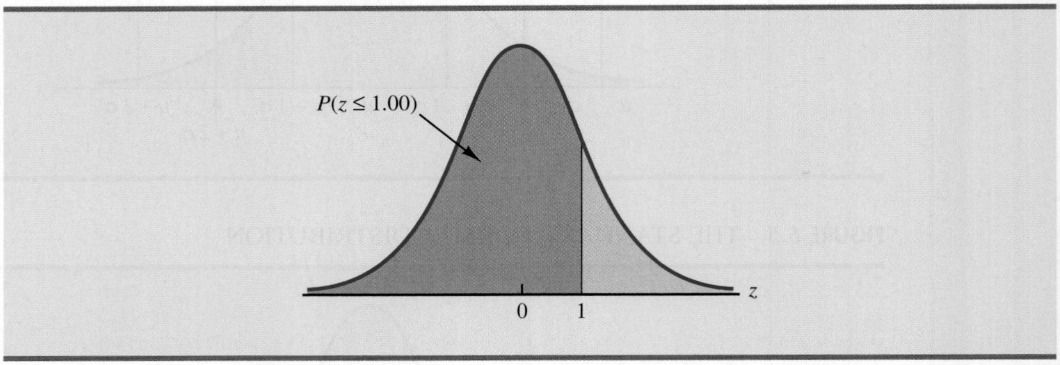

Refer to the right-hand page of the standard normal probability table inside the front cover of the text. The cumulative probability corresponding to $z = 1.00$ is the table value located at the intersection of the row labeled 1.0 and the column labeled .00. First we find 1.0 in the left column of the table and then find .00 in the top row of the table. By looking in the body of the table, we find that the 1.0 row and the .00 column intersect at the value of .8413; thus, $P(z \leq 1.00) = .8413$. The following excerpt from the probability table shows these steps.

z	.00	.01	.02
•			
•			
•			
.9	.8159	.8186	.8212
1.0	**.8413**	.8438	.8461
1.1	.8643	.8665	.8686
1.2	.8849	.8869	.8888
•			
•			
•			

$P(z \leq 1.00)$

To illustrate the second type of probability calculation we show how to compute the probability that z is in the interval between $-.50$ and 1.25; that is, $P(-.50 \leq z \leq 1.25)$. The following graph shows this area, or probability.

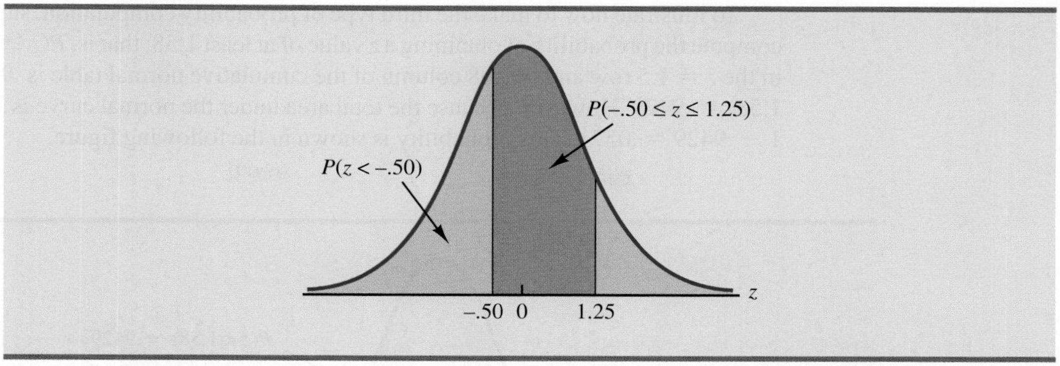

Three steps are required to compute this probability. First, we find the area under the normal curve to the left of $z = 1.25$. Second, we find the area under the normal curve to the left of $z = -.50$. Finally, we subtract the area to the left of $z = -.50$ from the area to the left of $z = 1.25$ to find $P(-.50 \leq z \leq 1.25)$.

To find the area under the normal curve to the left of $z = 1.25$, we first locate the 1.2 row in the standard normal probability table and then move across to the .05 column. Because the table value in the 1.2 row and the .05 column is .8944, $P(z \leq 1.25) = .8944$. Similarly, to find the area under the curve to the left of $z = -.50$, we use the left-hand page of the table to locate the table value in the $-.5$ row and the .00 column; with a table value of .3085, $P(z \leq -.50) = .3085$. Thus, $P(-.50 \leq z \leq 1.25) = P(z \leq 1.25) - P(z \leq -.50) = .8944 - .3085 = .5859$.

Let us consider another example of computing the probability that z is in the interval between two given values. Often it is of interest to compute the probability that a normal random variable assumes a value within a certain number of standard deviations of the mean. Suppose we want to compute the probability that the standard normal random variable is within one standard deviation of the mean; that is, $P(-1.00 \leq z \leq 1.00)$. To compute this probability we must find the area under the curve between -1.00 and 1.00. Earlier we found that $P(z \leq 1.00) = .8413$. Referring again to the table inside the front cover of the book, we find that the area under the curve to the left of $z = -1.00$ is .1587, so $P(z \leq -1.00) = .1587$. Therefore, $P(-1.00 \leq z \leq 1.00) = P(z \leq 1.00) - P(z \leq -1.00) = .8413 - .1587 = .6826$. This probability is shown graphically in the following figure.

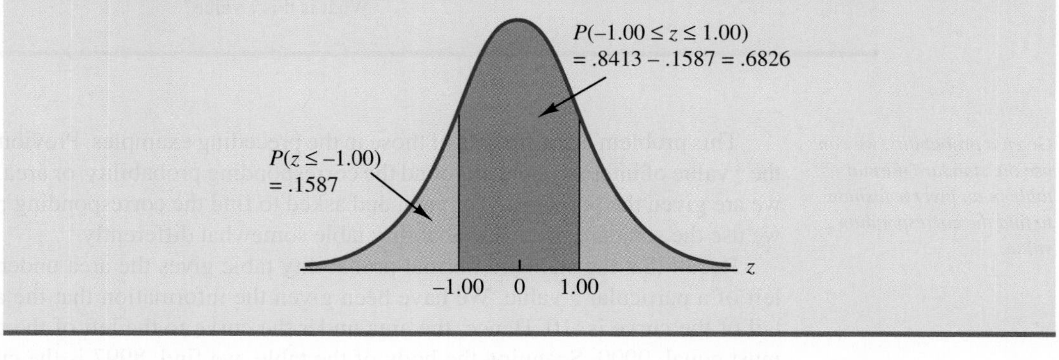

To illustrate how to make the third type of probability computation, suppose we want to compute the probability of obtaining a z value of at least 1.58; that is, $P(z \geq 1.58)$. The value in the $z = 1.5$ row and the .08 column of the cumulative normal table is .9429; thus, $P(z < 1.58) = .9429$. However, because the total area under the normal curve is 1, $P(z \geq 1.58) = 1 - .9429 = .0571$. This probability is shown in the following figure.

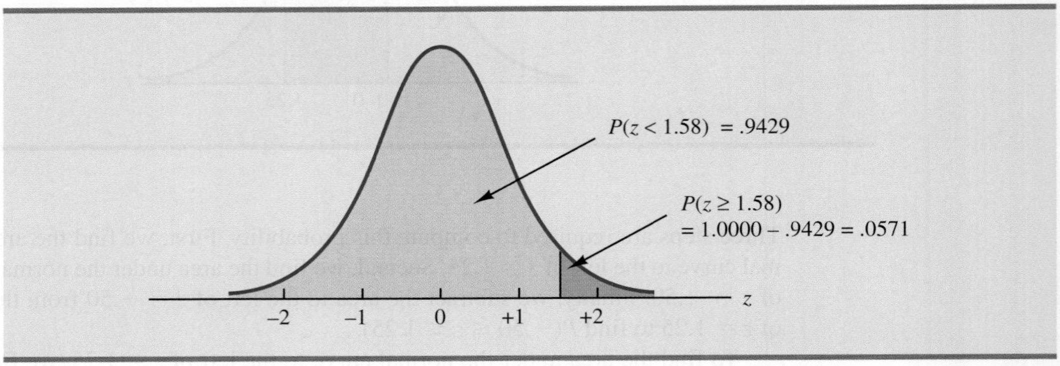

In the preceding illustrations, we showed how to compute probabilities given specified z values. In some situations, we are given a probability and are interested in working backward to find the corresponding z value. Suppose we want to find a z value such that the probability of obtaining a larger z value is .10. The following figure shows this situation graphically.

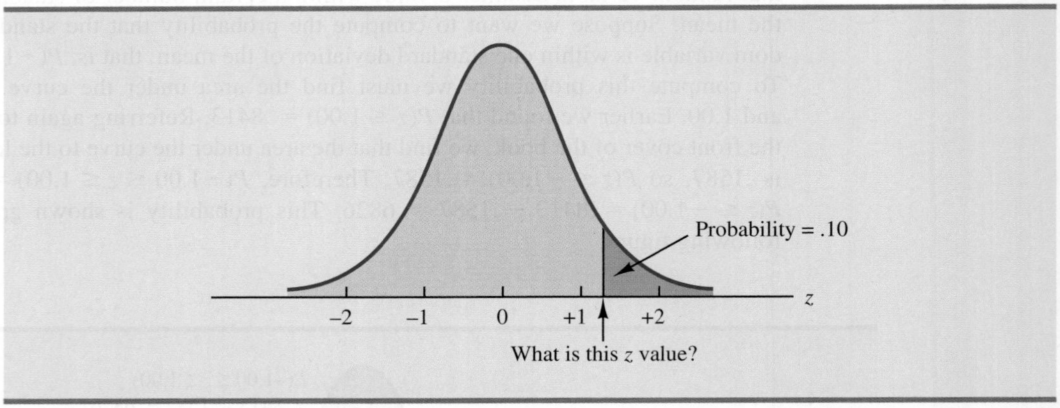

Given a probability, we can use the standard normal table in an inverse fashion to find the corresponding z value.

This problem is the inverse of those in the preceding examples. Previously, we specified the z value of interest and then found the corresponding probability, or area. In this example, we are given the probability, or area, and asked to find the corresponding z value. To do so, we use the standard normal probability table somewhat differently.

Recall that the standard normal probability table gives the area under the curve to the left of a particular z value. We have been given the information that the area in the upper tail of the curve is .10. Hence, the area under the curve to the left of the unknown z value must equal .9000. Scanning the body of the table, we find .8997 is the cumulative probability value closest to .9000. The section of the table providing this result follows.

z	.06	.07	.08	.09
.				
.				
.				
1.0	.8554	.8577	.8599	.8621
1.1	.8770	.8790	.8810	.8830
1.2	.8962	.8980	.8997	.9015
1.3	.9131	.9147	.9162	.9177
1.4	.9279	.9292	.9306	.9319
.				
.				
.				

Cumulative probability value closest to .9000

Reading the z value from the left-most column and the top row of the table, we find that the corresponding z value is 1.28. Thus, an area of approximately .9000 (actually .8997) will be to the left of $z = 1.28$.[2] In terms of the question originally asked, there is an approximately .10 probability of a z value larger than 1.28.

The examples illustrate that the table of cumulative probabilities for the standard normal probability distribution can be used to find probabilities associated with values of the standard normal random variable z. Two types of questions can be asked. The first type of question specifies a value, or values, for z and asks us to use the table to determine the corresponding areas or probabilities. The second type of question provides an area, or probability, and asks us to use the table to determine the corresponding z value. Thus, we need to be flexible in using the standard normal probability table to answer the desired probability question. In most cases, sketching a graph of the standard normal probability distribution and shading the appropriate area will help to visualize the situation and aid in determining the correct answer.

Computing Probabilities for Any Normal Probability Distribution

The reason for discussing the standard normal distribution so extensively is that probabilities for all normal distributions are computed by using the standard normal distribution. That is, when we have a normal distribution with any mean μ and any standard deviation σ, we answer probability questions about the distribution by first converting to the standard normal distribution. Then we can use the standard normal probability table and the appropriate z values to find the desired probabilities. The formula used to convert any normal random variable x with mean μ and standard deviation σ to the standard normal random variable z follows.

The formula for the standard normal random variable is similar to the formula we introduced in Chapter 3 for computing z-scores for a data set.

CONVERTING TO THE STANDARD NORMAL RANDOM VARIABLE

$$z = \frac{x - \mu}{\sigma} \tag{6.3}$$

[2] We could use interpolation in the body of the table to get a better approximation of the z value that corresponds to an area of .9000. Doing so to provide one more decimal place of accuracy would yield a z value of 1.282. However, in most practical situations, sufficient accuracy is obtained by simply using the table value closest to the desired probability.

A value of x equal to its mean μ results in $z = (\mu - \mu)/\sigma = 0$. Thus, we see that a value of x equal to its mean μ corresponds to $z = 0$. Now suppose that x is one standard deviation above its mean; that is, $x = \mu + \sigma$. Applying equation (6.3), we see that the corresponding z value is $z = [(\mu + \sigma) - \mu]/\sigma = \sigma/\sigma = 1$. Thus, an x value that is one standard deviation above its mean corresponds to $z = 1$. In other words, *we can interpret z as the number of standard deviations that the normal random variable x is from its mean μ.*

To see how this conversion enables us to compute probabilities for any normal distribution, suppose we have a normal distribution with $\mu = 10$ and $\sigma = 2$. What is the probability that the random variable x is between 10 and 14? Using equation (6.3), we see that at $x = 10$, $z = (x - \mu)/\sigma = (10 - 10)/2 = 0$ and that at $x = 14$, $z = (14 - 10)/2 = 4/2 = 2$. Thus, the answer to our question about the probability of x being between 10 and 14 is given by the equivalent probability that z is between 0 and 2 for the standard normal distribution. In other words, the probability that we are seeking is the probability that the random variable x is between its mean and two standard deviations above the mean. Using $z = 2.00$ and the standard normal probability table inside the front cover of the text, we see that $P(z \leq 2) = .9772$. Because $P(z \leq 0) = .5000$, we can compute $P(.00 \leq z \leq 2.00) = P(z \leq 2) - P(z \leq 0) = .9772 - .5000 = .4772$. Hence the probability that x is between 10 and 14 is .4772.

Grear Tire Company Problem

We turn now to an application of the normal probability distribution. Suppose the Grear Tire Company developed a new steel-belted radial tire to be sold through a national chain of discount stores. Because the tire is a new product, Grear's managers believe that the mileage guarantee offered with the tire will be an important factor in the acceptance of the product. Before finalizing the tire mileage guarantee policy, Grear's managers want probability information about x = number of miles the tires will last.

From actual road tests with the tires, Grear's engineering group estimated that the mean tire mileage is $\mu = 36{,}500$ miles and that the standard deviation is $\sigma = 5000$. In addition, the data collected indicate that a normal distribution is a reasonable assumption. What percentage of the tires can be expected to last more than 40,000 miles? In other words, what is the probability that the tire mileage, x, will exceed 40,000? This question can be answered by finding the area of the darkly shaded region in Figure 6.6.

FIGURE 6.6 GREAR TIRE COMPANY MILEAGE DISTRIBUTION

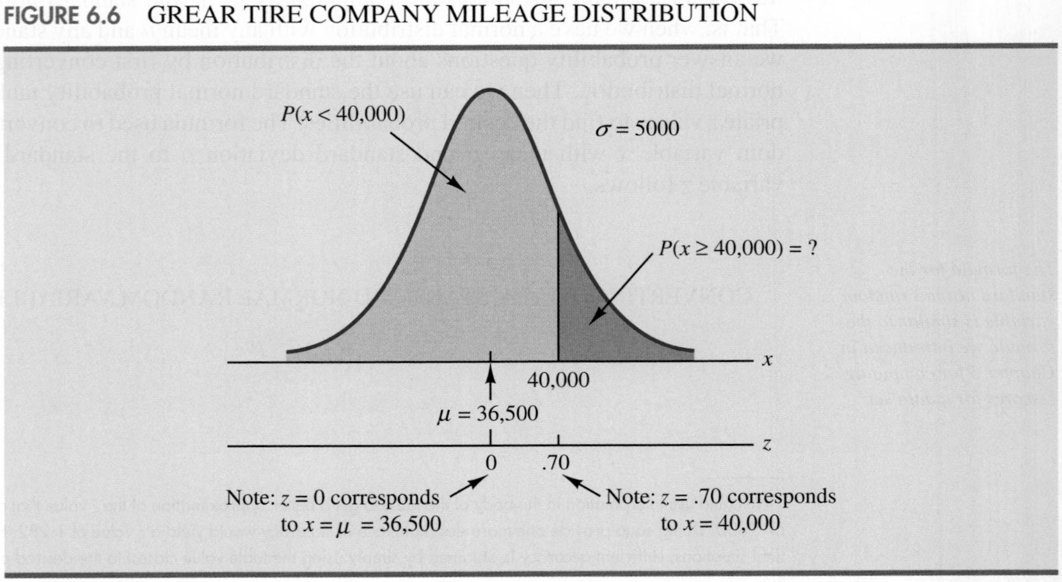

At $x = 40{,}000$, we have

$$z = \frac{x - \mu}{\sigma} = \frac{40{,}000 - 36{,}500}{5000} = \frac{3500}{5000} = .70$$

Refer now to the bottom of Figure 6.6. We see that a value of $x = 40{,}000$ on the Grear Tire normal distribution corresponds to a value of $z = .70$ on the standard normal distribution. Using the standard normal probability table, we see that the area under the standard normal curve to the left of $z = .70$ is .7580. Thus, $1.000 - .7580 = .2420$ is the probability that z will exceed .70 and hence x will exceed 40,000. We can conclude that about 24.2% of the tires will exceed 40,000 in mileage.

Let us now assume that Grear is considering a guarantee that will provide a discount on replacement tires if the original tires do not provide the guaranteed mileage. What should the guarantee mileage be if Grear wants no more than 10% of the tires to be eligible for the discount guarantee? This question is interpreted graphically in Figure 6.7.

According to Figure 6.7, the area under the curve to the left of the unknown guarantee mileage must be .10. So, we must first find the z value that cuts off an area of .10 in the left tail of a standard normal distribution. Using the standard normal probability table, we see that $z = -1.28$ cuts off an area of .10 in the lower tail. Hence, $z = -1.28$ is the value of the standard normal random variable corresponding to the desired mileage guarantee on the Grear Tire normal distribution. To find the value of x corresponding to $z = -1.28$, we have

The guarantee mileage we need to find is 1.28 standard deviations below the mean. Thus, $x = \mu - 1.28\sigma$.

$$z = \frac{x - \mu}{\sigma} = -1.28$$
$$x - \mu = -1.28\sigma$$
$$x = \mu - 1.28\sigma$$

With $\mu = 36{,}500$ and $\sigma = 5000$,

$$x = 36{,}500 - 1.28(5000) = 30{,}100$$

With the guarantee set at 30,000 miles, the actual percentage eligible for the guarantee will be 9.68%.

Thus, a guarantee of 30,100 miles will meet the requirement that approximately 10% of the tires will be eligible for the guarantee. Perhaps, with this information, the firm will set its tire mileage guarantee at 30,000 miles.

FIGURE 6.7 GREAR'S DISCOUNT GUARANTEE

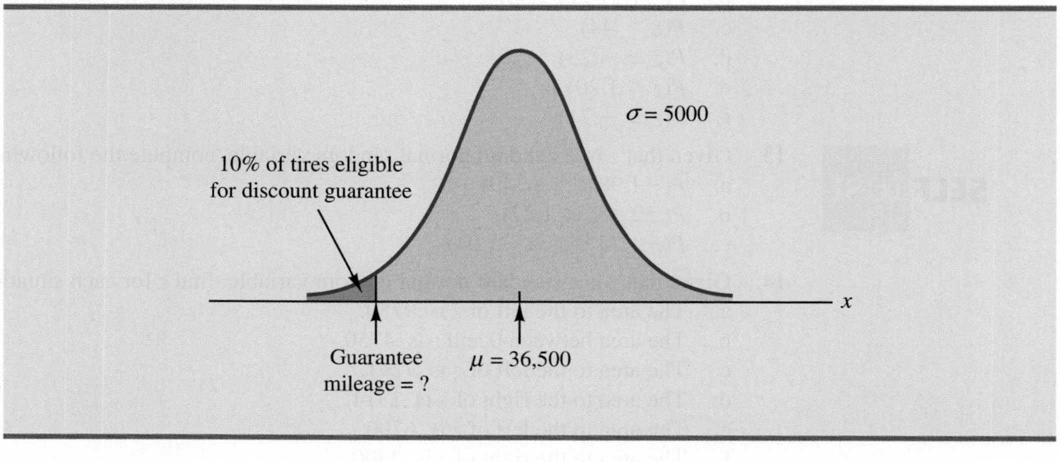

Again, we see the important role that probability distributions play in providing decision-making information. Namely, once a probability distribution is established for a particular application, it can be used to obtain probability information about the problem. Probability does not make a decision recommendation directly, but it provides information that helps the decision maker better understand the risks and uncertainties associated with the problem. Ultimately, this information may assist the decision maker in reaching a good decision.

EXERCISES

Methods

8. Using Figure 6.4 as a guide, sketch a normal curve for a random variable x that has a mean of $\mu = 100$ and a standard deviation of $\sigma = 10$. Label the horizontal axis with values of 70, 80, 90, 100, 110, 120, and 130.

9. A random variable is normally distributed with a mean of $\mu = 50$ and a standard deviation of $\sigma = 5$.
   a. Sketch a normal curve for the probability density function. Label the horizontal axis with values of 35, 40, 45, 50, 55, 60, and 65. Figure 6.4 shows that the normal curve almost touches the horizontal axis at three standard deviations below and at three standard deviations above the mean (in this case at 35 and 65).
   b. What is the probability the random variable will assume a value between 45 and 55?
   c. What is the probability the random variable will assume a value between 40 and 60?

10. Draw a graph for the standard normal distribution. Label the horizontal axis at values of −3, −2, −1, 0, 1, 2, and 3. Then use the table of probabilities for the standard normal distribution inside the front cover of the text to compute the following probabilities.
    a. $P(z \leq 1.5)$
    b. $P(z \leq 1)$
    c. $P(1 \leq z \leq 1.5)$
    d. $P(0 < z < 2.5)$

11. Given that z is a standard normal random variable, compute the following probabilities.
    a. $P(z \leq -1.0)$
    b. $P(z \geq -1)$
    c. $P(z \geq -1.5)$
    d. $P(-2.5 \leq z)$
    e. $P(-3 < z \leq 0)$

12. Given that z is a standard normal random variable, compute the following probabilities.
    a. $P(0 \leq z \leq .83)$
    b. $P(-1.57 \leq z \leq 0)$
    c. $P(z > .44)$
    d. $P(z \geq -.23)$
    e. $P(z < 1.20)$
    f. $P(z \leq -.71)$

SELF test

13. Given that z is a standard normal random variable, compute the following probabilities.
    a. $P(-1.98 \leq z \leq .49)$
    b. $P(.52 \leq z \leq 1.22)$
    c. $P(-1.75 \leq z \leq -1.04)$

14. Given that z is a standard normal random variable, find z for each situation.
    a. The area to the left of z is .9750.
    b. The area between 0 and z is .4750.
    c. The area to the left of z is .7291.
    d. The area to the right of z is .1314.
    e. The area to the left of z is .6700.
    f. The area to the right of z is .3300.

SELF test

15. Given that z is a standard normal random variable, find z for each situation.
    a. The area to the left of z is .2119.
    b. The area between $-z$ and z is .9030.
    c. The area between $-z$ and z is .2052.
    d. The area to the left of z is .9948.
    e. The area to the right of z is .6915.
16. Given that z is a standard normal random variable, find z for each situation.
    a. The area to the right of z is .01.
    b. The area to the right of z is .025.
    c. The area to the right of z is .05.
    d. The area to the right of z is .10.

Applications

17. For borrowers with good credit scores, the mean debt for revolving and installment accounts is $15,015 (*BusinessWeek,* March 20, 2006). Assume the standard deviation is $3540 and that debt amounts are normally distributed.
    a. What is the probability that the debt for a borrower with good credit is more than $18,000?
    b. What is the probability that the debt for a borrower with good credit is less than $10,000?
    c. What is the probability that the debt for a borrower with good credit is between $12,000 and $18,000?
    d. What is the probability that the debt for a borrower with good credit is no more than $14,000?

SELF test

18. The average stock price for companies making up the S&P 500 is $30, and the standard deviation is $8.20 (*BusinessWeek,* Special Annual Issue, Spring 2003). Assume the stock prices are normally distributed.
    a. What is the probability a company will have a stock price of at least $40?
    b. What is the probability a company will have a stock price no higher than $20?
    c. How high does a stock price have to be to put a company in the top 10%?
19. In an article about the cost of health care, *Money* magazine reported that a visit to a hospital emergency room for something as simple as a sore throat has a mean cost of $328 (*Money,* January 2009). Assume that the cost for this type of hospital emergency room visit is normally distributed with a standard deviation of $92. Answer the following questions about the cost of a hospital emergency room visit for this medical service.
    a. What is the probability that the cost will be more than $500?
    b. What is the probability that the cost will be less than $250?
    c. What is the probability that the cost will be between $300 and $400?
    d. If the cost to a patient is in the lower 8% of charges for this medical service, what was the cost of this patient's emergency room visit?
20. In January 2003, the American worker spent an average of 77 hours logged on to the Internet while at work (CNBC, March 15, 2003). Assume the population mean is 77 hours, the times are normally distributed, and that the standard deviation is 20 hours.
    a. What is the probability that in January 2003 a randomly selected worker spent fewer than 50 hours logged on to the Internet?
    b. What percentage of workers spent more than 100 hours in January 2003 logged on to the Internet?
    c. A person is classified as a heavy user if he or she is in the upper 20% of usage. In January 2003, how many hours did a worker have to be logged on to the Internet to be considered a heavy user?
21. A person must score in the upper 2% of the population on an IQ test to qualify for membership in Mensa, the international high-IQ society (*U.S. Airways Attaché,* September 2000). If IQ scores are normally distributed with a mean of 100 and a standard deviation of 15, what score must a person have to qualify for Mensa?

22. The mean hourly pay rate for financial managers in the East North Central region is \$32.62, and the standard deviation is \$2.32 (Bureau of Labor Statistics, September 2005). Assume that pay rates are normally distributed.
    a. What is the probability a financial manager earns between \$30 and \$35 per hour?
    b. How high must the hourly rate be to put a financial manager in the top 10% with respect to pay?
    c. For a randomly selected financial manager, what is the probability the manager earned less than \$28 per hour?
23. The time needed to complete a final examination in a particular college course is normally distributed with a mean of 80 minutes and a standard deviation of 10 minutes. Answer the following questions.
    a. What is the probability of completing the exam in one hour or less?
    b. What is the probability that a student will complete the exam in more than 60 minutes but less than 75 minutes?
    c. Assume that the class has 60 students and that the examination period is 90 minutes in length. How many students do you expect will be unable to complete the exam in the allotted time?

WEB file
Volume

24. Trading volume on the New York Stock Exchange is heaviest during the first half hour (early morning) and last half hour (late afternoon) of the trading day. The early morning trading volumes (millions of shares) for 13 days in January and February are shown here (*Barron's,* January 23, 2006; February 13, 2006; and February 27, 2006).

214	163	265	194	180
202	198	212	201	
174	171	211	211	

    The probability distribution of trading volume is approximately normal.
    a. Compute the mean and standard deviation to use as estimates of the population mean and standard deviation.
    b. What is the probability that, on a randomly selected day, the early morning trading volume will be less than 180 million shares?
    c. What is the probability that, on a randomly selected day, the early morning trading volume will exceed 230 million shares?
    d. How many shares would have to be traded for the early morning trading volume on a particular day to be among the busiest 5% of days?
25. According to the Sleep Foundation, the average night's sleep is 6.8 hours (*Fortune,* March 20, 2006). Assume the standard deviation is .6 hours and that the probability distribution is normal.
    a. What is the probability that a randomly selected person sleeps more than 8 hours?
    b. What is the probability that a randomly selected person sleeps 6 hours or less?
    c. Doctors suggest getting between 7 and 9 hours of sleep each night. What percentage of the population gets this much sleep?

6.3 Normal Approximation of Binomial Probabilities

In Section 5.4 we presented the discrete binomial distribution. Recall that a binomial experiment consists of a sequence of n identical independent trials with each trial having two possible outcomes, a success or a failure. The probability of a success on a trial is the same for all trials and is denoted by p. The binomial random variable is the number of successes in the n trials, and probability questions pertain to the probability of x successes in the n trials.

FIGURE 6.8 NORMAL APPROXIMATION TO A BINOMIAL PROBABILITY DISTRIBUTION WITH $n = 100$ AND $p = .10$ SHOWING THE PROBABILITY OF 12 ERRORS

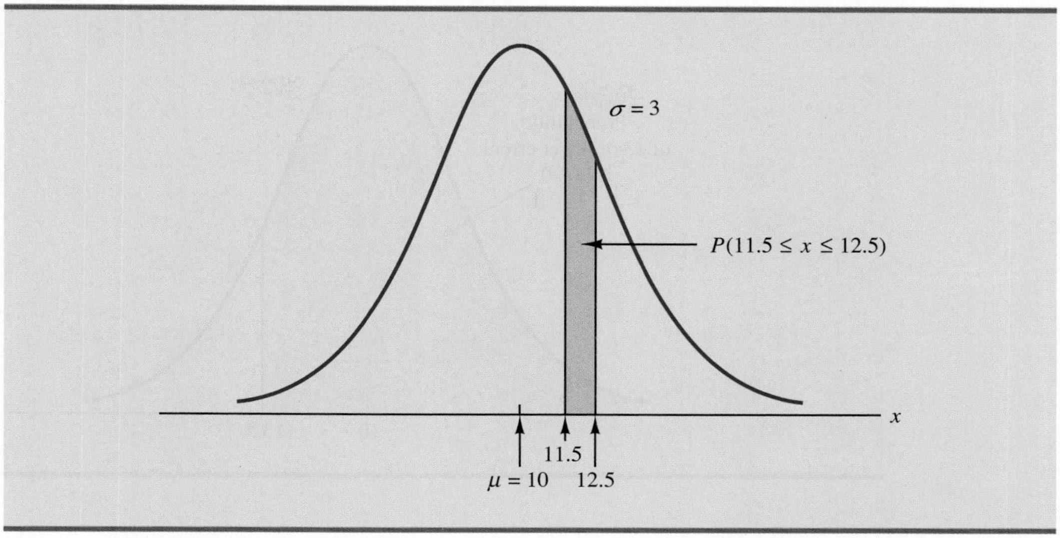

When the number of trials becomes large, evaluating the binomial probability function by hand or with a calculator is difficult. In cases where $np \geq 5$, and $n(1 - p) \geq 5$, the normal distribution provides an easy-to-use approximation of binomial probabilities. When using the normal approximation to the binomial, we set $\mu = np$ and $\sigma = \sqrt{np(1 - p)}$ in the definition of the normal curve.

Let us illustrate the normal approximation to the binomial by supposing that a particular company has a history of making errors in 10% of its invoices. A sample of 100 invoices has been taken, and we want to compute the probability that 12 invoices contain errors. That is, we want to find the binomial probability of 12 successes in 100 trials. In applying the normal approximation in this case, we set $\mu = np = (100)(.1) = 10$ and $\sigma = \sqrt{np(1 - p)} = \sqrt{(100)(.1)(.9)} = 3$. A normal distribution with $\mu = 10$ and $\sigma = 3$ is shown in Figure 6.8.

Recall that, with a continuous probability distribution, probabilities are computed as areas under the probability density function. As a result, the probability of any single value for the random variable is zero. Thus to approximate the binomial probability of 12 successes, we compute the area under the corresponding normal curve between 11.5 and 12.5. The .5 that we add and subtract from 12 is called a **continuity correction factor**. It is introduced because a continuous distribution is being used to approximate a discrete distribution. Thus, $P(x = 12)$ for the *discrete* binomial distribution is approximated by $P(11.5 \leq x \leq 12.5)$ for the *continuous* normal distribution.

Converting to the standard normal distribution to compute $P(11.5 \leq x \leq 12.5)$, we have

$$z = \frac{x - \mu}{\sigma} = \frac{12.5 - 10.0}{3} = .83 \quad \text{at } x = 12.5$$

and

$$z = \frac{x - \mu}{\sigma} = \frac{11.5 - 10.0}{3} = .50 \quad \text{at } x = 11.5$$

FIGURE 6.9 NORMAL APPROXIMATION TO A BINOMIAL PROBABILITY DISTRIBUTION WITH $n = 100$ AND $p = .10$ SHOWING THE PROBABILITY OF 13 OR FEWER ERRORS

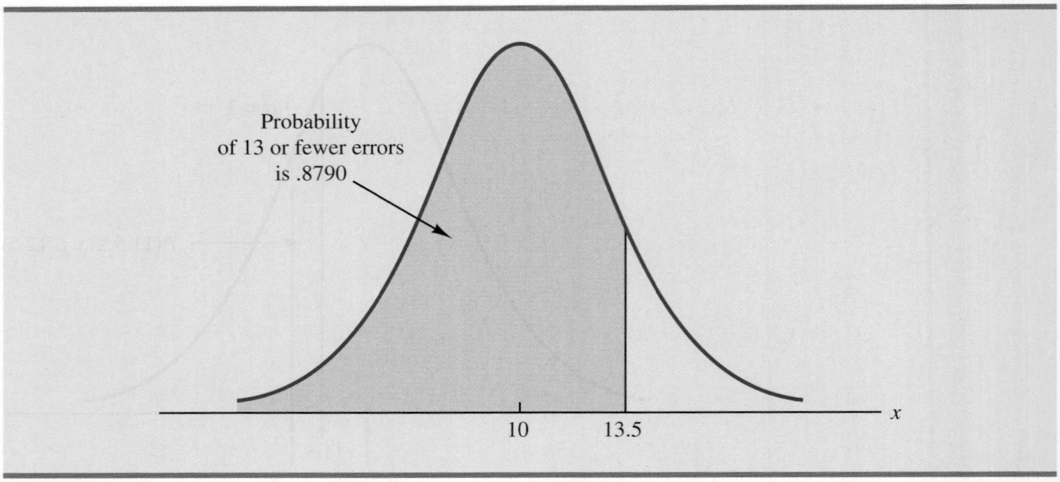

Using the standard normal probability table, we find that the area under the curve (in Figure 6.8) to the left of 12.5 is .7967. Similarly, the area under the curve to the left of 11.5 is .6915. Therefore, the area between 11.5 and 12.5 is .7967 − .6915 = .1052. The normal approximation to the probability of 12 successes in 100 trials is .1052.

For another illustration, suppose we want to compute the probability of 13 or fewer errors in the sample of 100 invoices. Figure 6.9 shows the area under the normal curve that approximates this probability. Note that the use of the continuity correction factor results in the value of 13.5 being used to compute the desired probability. The z value corresponding to $x = 13.5$ is

$$z = \frac{13.5 - 10.0}{3.0} = 1.17$$

The standard normal probability table shows that the area under the standard normal curve to the left of $z = 1.17$ is .8790. The area under the normal curve approximating the probability of 13 or fewer errors is given by the shaded portion of the graph in Figure 6.9.

Exercises

Methods

SELF test

26. A binomial probability distribution has $p = .20$ and $n = 100$.
    a. What are the mean and standard deviation?
    b. Is this situation one in which binomial probabilities can be approximated by the normal probability distribution? Explain.
    c. What is the probability of exactly 24 successes?
    d. What is the probability of 18 to 22 successes?
    e. What is the probability of 15 or fewer successes?
27. Assume a binomial probability distribution has $p = .60$ and $n = 200$.
    a. What are the mean and standard deviation?
    b. Is this situation one in which binomial probabilities can be approximated by the normal probability distribution? Explain.

c. What is the probability of 100 to 110 successes?
d. What is the probability of 130 or more successes?
e. What is the advantage of using the normal probability distribution to approximate the binomial probabilities? Use part (d) to explain the advantage.

Applications

SELF test

28. Although studies continue to show smoking leads to significant health problems, 20% of adults in the United States smoke. Consider a group of 250 adults.
    a. What is the expected number of adults who smoke?
    b. What is the probability that fewer than 40 smoke?
    c. What is the probability that from 55 to 60 smoke?
    d. What is the probability that 70 or more smoke?
29. An Internal Revenue Oversight Board survey found that 82% of taxpayers said that it was very important for the Internal Revenue Service (IRS) to ensure that high-income tax payers do not cheat on their tax returns (*The Wall Street Journal,* February 11, 2009).
    a. For a sample of eight taxpayers, what is the probability that at least six taxpayers say that it is very important to ensure that high-income tax payers do not cheat on their tax returns? Use the binomial distribution probability function shown in Section 5.4 to answer this question.
    b. For a sample of 80 taxpayers, what is the probability that at least 60 taxpayers say that it is very important to ensure that high-income tax payers do not cheat on their tax returns? Use the normal approximation of the binomial distribution to answer this question.
    c. As the number of trails in a binomial distribution application becomes large, what is the advantage of using the normal approximation of the binomial distribution to compute probabilities?
    d. When the number of trials for a binominal distribution application becomes large, would developers of statistical software packages prefer to use the binomial distribution probability function shown in Section 5.4 or the normal approximation of the binomial distribution shown in Section 6.3? Explain.
30. When you sign up for a credit card, do you read the contract carefully? In a FindLaw.com survey, individuals were asked, “How closely do you read a contract for a credit card?” (*USA Today,* October 16, 2003). The findings were that 44% read every word, 33% read enough to understand the contract, 11% just glance at it, and 4% don’t read it at all.
    a. For a sample of 500 people, how many would you expect to say that they read every word of a credit card contract?
    b. For a sample of 500 people, what is the probability that 200 or fewer will say they read every word of a credit card contract?
    c. For a sample of 500 people, what is the probability that at least 15 say they don’t read credit card contracts?
31. A Myrtle Beach resort hotel has 120 rooms. In the spring months, hotel room occupancy is approximately 75%.
    a. What is the probability that at least half of the rooms are occupied on a given day?
    b. What is the probability that 100 or more rooms are occupied on a given day?
    c. What is the probability that 80 or fewer rooms are occupied on a given day?

6.4 Exponential Probability Distribution

The **exponential probability distribution** may be used for random variables such as the time between arrivals at a car wash, the time required to load a truck, the distance between major defects in a highway, and so on. The exponential probability density function follows.

EXPONENTIAL PROBABILITY DENSITY FUNCTION

$$f(x) = \frac{1}{\mu} e^{-x/\mu} \quad \text{for } x \geq 0 \tag{6.4}$$

where μ = expected value or mean

As an example of the exponential distribution, suppose that x represents the loading time for a truck at the Schips loading dock and follows such a distribution. If the mean, or average, loading time is 15 minutes ($\mu = 15$), the appropriate probability density function for x is

$$f(x) = \frac{1}{15} e^{-x/15}$$

Figure 6.10 is the graph of this probability density function.

Computing Probabilities for the Exponential Distribution

In waiting line applications, the exponential distribution is often used for service time.

As with any continuous probability distribution, the area under the curve corresponding to an interval provides the probability that the random variable assumes a value in that interval. In the Schips loading dock example, the probability that loading a truck will take 6 minutes or less $P(x \leq 6)$ is defined to be the area under the curve in Figure 6.10 from $x = 0$ to $x = 6$. Similarly, the probability that the loading time will be 18 minutes or less $P(x \leq 18)$ is the area under the curve from $x = 0$ to $x = 18$. Note also that the probability that the loading time will be between 6 minutes and 18 minutes $P(6 \leq x \leq 18)$ is given by the area under the curve from $x = 6$ to $x = 18$.

To compute exponential probabilities such as those just described, we use the following formula. It provides the cumulative probability of obtaining a value for the exponential random variable of less than or equal to some specific value denoted by x_0.

EXPONENTIAL DISTRIBUTION: CUMULATIVE PROBABILITIES

$$P(x \leq x_0) = 1 - e^{-x_0/\mu} \tag{6.5}$$

FIGURE 6.10 EXPONENTIAL DISTRIBUTION FOR THE SCHIPS LOADING DOCK EXAMPLE

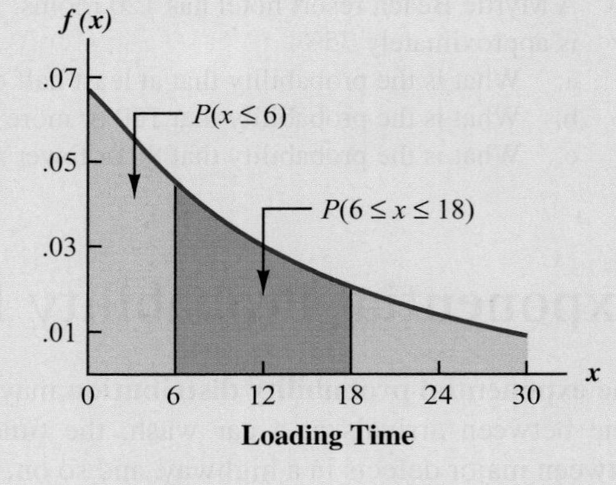

For the Schips loading dock example, x = loading time in minutes and $\mu = 15$ minutes. Using equation (6.5)

$$P(x \le x_0) = 1 - e^{-x_0/15}$$

Hence, the probability that loading a truck will take 6 minutes or less is

$$P(x \le 6) = 1 - e^{-6/15} = .3297$$

Using equation (6.5), we calculate the probability of loading a truck in 18 minutes or less.

$$P(x \le 18) = 1 - e^{-18/15} = .6988$$

Thus, the probability that loading a truck will take between 6 minutes and 18 minutes is equal to $.6988 - .3297 = .3691$. Probabilities for any other interval can be computed similarly.

A property of the exponential distribution is that the mean and standard deviation are equal.

In the preceding example, the mean time it takes to load a truck is $\mu = 15$ minutes. A property of the exponential distribution is that the mean of the distribution and the standard deviation of the distribution are *equal.* Thus, the standard deviation for the time it takes to load a truck is $\sigma = 15$ minutes. The variance is $\sigma^2 = (15)^2 = 225$.

Relationship Between the Poisson and Exponential Distributions

In Section 5.5 we introduced the Poisson distribution as a discrete probability distribution that is often useful in examining the number of occurrences of an event over a specified interval of time or space. Recall that the Poisson probability function is

$$f(x) = \frac{\mu^x e^{-\mu}}{x!}$$

where

$$\mu = \text{expected value or mean number of occurrences over a specified interval}$$

If arrivals follow a Poisson distribution, the time between arrivals must follow an exponential distribution.

The continuous exponential probability distribution is related to the discrete Poisson distribution. If the Poisson distribution provides an appropriate description of the number of occurrences per interval, the exponential distribution provides a description of the length of the interval between occurrences.

To illustrate this relationship, suppose the number of cars that arrive at a car wash during one hour is described by a Poisson probability distribution with a mean of 10 cars per hour. The Poisson probability function that gives the probability of x arrivals per hour is

$$f(x) = \frac{10^x e^{-10}}{x!}$$

Because the average number of arrivals is 10 cars per hour, the average time between cars arriving is

$$\frac{1 \text{ hour}}{10 \text{ cars}} = .1 \text{ hour/car}$$

Thus, the corresponding exponential distribution that describes the time between the arrivals has a mean of $\mu = .1$ hour per car; as a result, the appropriate exponential probability density function is

$$f(x) = \frac{1}{.1} e^{-x/.1} = 10e^{-10x}$$

NOTES AND COMMENTS

As we can see in Figure 6.10, the exponential distribution is skewed to the right. Indeed, the skewness measure for exponential distributions is 2. The exponential distribution gives us a good idea what a skewed distribution looks like.

Exercises

Methods

32. Consider the following exponential probability density function.

$$f(x) = \frac{1}{8} e^{-x/8} \quad \text{for } x \geq 0$$

a. Find $P(x \leq 6)$.
b. Find $P(x \leq 4)$.
c. Find $P(x \geq 6)$.
d. Find $P(4 \leq x \leq 6)$.

SELF test

33. Consider the following exponential probability density function.

$$f(x) = \frac{1}{3} e^{-x/3} \quad \text{for } x \geq 0$$

a. Write the formula for $P(x \leq x_0)$.
b. Find $P(x \leq 2)$.
c. Find $P(x \geq 3)$.
d. Find $P(x \leq 5)$.
e. Find $P(2 \leq x \leq 5)$.

Applications

34. The time required to pass through security screening at the airport can be annoying to travelers. The mean wait time during peak periods at Cincinnati/Northern Kentucky International Airport is 12.1 minutes (*The Cincinnati Enquirer,* February 2, 2006). Assume the time to pass through security screening follows an exponential distribution.
a. What is the probability it will take less than 10 minutes to pass through security screening during a peak period?
b. What is the probability it will take more than 20 minutes to pass through security screening during a peak period?
c. What is the probability it will take between 10 and 20 minutes to pass through security screening during a peak period?
d. It is 8:00 A.M. (a peak period) and you just entered the security line. To catch your plane you must be at the gate within 30 minutes. If it takes 12 minutes from the time you clear security until you reach your gate, what is the probability you will miss your flight?

SELF test

35. The time between arrivals of vehicles at a particular intersection follows an exponential probability distribution with a mean of 12 seconds.
a. Sketch this exponential probability distribution.
b. What is the probability that the arrival time between vehicles is 12 seconds or less?
c. What is the probability that the arrival time between vehicles is 6 seconds or less?
d. What is the probability of 30 or more seconds between vehicle arrivals?

36. Comcast Corporation is the largest cable television company, the second largest Internet service provider, and the fourth largest telephone service provider in the United States. Generally known for quality and reliable service, the company periodically experiences unexpected service interruptions. On January 14, 2009, such an interruption occurred for the Comcast customers living in southwest Florida. When customers called the Comcast office, a recorded message told them that the company was aware of the service outage and that it was anticipated that service would be restored in two hours. Assume that two hours is the mean time to do the repair and that the repair time has an exponential probability distribution.
    a. What is the probability that the cable service will be repaired in one hour or less?
    b. What is the probability that the repair will take between one hour and two hours?
    c. For a customer who calls the Comcast office at 1:00 P.M., what is the probability that the cable service will not be repaired by 5:00 P.M.?
37. Collina's Italian Café in Houston, Texas, advertises that carryout orders take about 25 minutes (Collina's website, February 27, 2008). Assume that the time required for a carryout order to be ready for customer pickup has an exponential distribution with a mean of 25 minutes.
    a. What is the probability than a carryout order will be ready within 20 minutes?
    b. If a customer arrives 30 minutes after placing an order, what is the probability that the order will not be ready?
    c. A particular customer lives 15 minutes from Collina's Italian Café. If the customer places a telephone order at 5:20 P.M., what is the probability that the customer can drive to the café, pick up the order, and return home by 6:00 P.M.?
38. Do interruptions while you are working reduce your productivity? According to a University of California–Irvine study, businesspeople are interrupted at the rate of approximately 5½ times per hour (*Fortune,* March 20, 2006). Suppose the number of interruptions follows a Poisson probability distribution.
    a. Show the probability distribution for the time between interruptions.
    b. What is the probability a businessperson will have no interruptions during a 15-minute period?
    c. What is the probability that the next interruption will occur within 10 minutes for a particular businessperson?

Summary

This chapter extended the discussion of probability distributions to the case of continuous random variables. The major conceptual difference between discrete and continuous probability distributions involves the method of computing probabilities. With discrete distributions, the probability function $f(x)$ provides the probability that the random variable x assumes various values. With continuous distributions, the probability density function $f(x)$ does not provide probability values directly. Instead, probabilities are given by areas under the curve or graph of the probability density function $f(x)$. Because the area under the curve above a single point is zero, we observe that the probability of any particular value is zero for a continuous random variable.

Three continuous probability distributions—the uniform, normal, and exponential distributions—were treated in detail. The normal distribution is used widely in statistical inference and will be used extensively throughout the remainder of the text.

Glossary

Probability density function A function used to compute probabilities for a continuous random variable. The area under the graph of a probability density function over an interval represents probability.

Uniform probability distribution A continuous probability distribution for which the probability that the random variable will assume a value in any interval is the same for each interval of equal length.

Normal probability distribution A continuous probability distribution. Its probability density function is bell-shaped and determined by its mean μ and standard deviation σ.

Standard normal probability distribution A normal distribution with a mean of zero and a standard deviation of one.

Continuity correction factor A value of .5 that is added to or subtracted from a value of x when the continuous normal distribution is used to approximate the discrete binomial distribution.

Exponential probability distribution A continuous probability distribution that is useful in computing probabilities for the time it takes to complete a task.

Key Formulas

Uniform Probability Density Function

$$f(x) = \begin{cases} \dfrac{1}{b-a} & \text{for } a \le x \le b \\ 0 & \text{elsewhere} \end{cases} \tag{6.1}$$

Normal Probability Density Function

$$f(x) = \frac{1}{\sigma\sqrt{2\pi}} e^{-(x-\mu)^2/2\sigma^2} \tag{6.2}$$

Converting to the Standard Normal Random Variable

$$z = \frac{x-\mu}{\sigma} \tag{6.3}$$

Exponential Probability Density Function

$$f(x) = \frac{1}{\mu} e^{-x/\mu} \quad \text{for } x \ge 0 \tag{6.4}$$

Exponential Distribution: Cumulative Probabilities

$$P(x \le x_0) = 1 - e^{-x_0/\mu} \tag{6.5}$$

Supplementary Exercises

39. A business executive, transferred from Chicago to Atlanta, needs to sell her house in Chicago quickly. The executive's employer has offered to buy the house for $210,000, but the offer expires at the end of the week. The executive does not currently have a better offer but can afford to leave the house on the market for another month. From conversations with

her realtor, the executive believes the price she will get by leaving the house on the market for another month is uniformly distributed between \$200,000 and \$225,000.

a. If she leaves the house on the market for another month, what is the mathematical expression for the probability density function of the sales price?
b. If she leaves it on the market for another month, what is the probability she will get at least \$215,000 for the house?
c. If she leaves it on the market for another month, what is the probability she will get less than \$210,000?
d. Should the executive leave the house on the market for another month? Why or why not?

40. The U.S. Bureau of Labor Statistics reports that the average annual expenditure on food and drink for all families is \$5700 (*Money,* December 2003). Assume that annual expenditure on food and drink is normally distributed and that the standard deviation is \$1500.
a. What is the range of expenditures of the 10% of families with the lowest annual spending on food and drink?
b. What percentage of families spend more than \$7000 annually on food and drink?
c. What is the range of expenditures for the 5% of families with the highest annual spending on food and drink?

41. Motorola used the normal distribution to determine the probability of defects and the number of defects expected in a production process. Assume a production process produces items with a mean weight of 10 ounces. Calculate the probability of a defect and the expected number of defects for a 1000-unit production run in the following situations.
a. The process standard deviation is .15, and the process control is set at plus or minus one standard deviation. Units with weights less than 9.85 or greater than 10.15 ounces will be classified as defects.
b. Through process design improvements, the process standard deviation can be reduced to .05. Assume the process control remains the same, with weights less than 9.85 or greater than 10.15 ounces being classified as defects.
c. What is the advantage of reducing process variation, thereby causing process control limits to be at a greater number of standard deviations from the mean?

42. The average annual amount American households spend for daily transportation is \$6312 (*Money,* August 2001). Assume that the amount spent is normally distributed.
a. Suppose you learn that 5% of American households spend less than \$1000 for daily transportation. What is the standard deviation of the amount spent?
b. What is the probability that a household spends between \$4000 and \$6000?
c. What is the range of spending for the 3% of households with the highest daily transportation cost?

43. *Condé Nast Traveler* publishes a Gold List of the top hotels all over the world. The Broadmoor Hotel in Colorado Springs contains 700 rooms and is on the 2004 Gold List (*Condé Nast Traveler,* January 2004). Suppose Broadmoor's marketing group forecasts a mean demand of 670 rooms for the coming weekend. Assume that demand for the upcoming weekend is normally distributed with a standard deviation of 30.
a. What is the probability all the hotel's rooms will be rented?
b. What is the probability 50 or more rooms will not be rented?
c. Would you recommend the hotel consider offering a promotion to increase demand? What considerations would be important?

44. Ward Doering Auto Sales is considering offering a special service contract that will cover the total cost of any service work required on leased vehicles. From experience, the company manager estimates that yearly service costs are approximately normally distributed, with a mean of \$150 and a standard deviation of \$25.
a. If the company offers the service contract to customers for a yearly charge of \$200, what is the probability that any one customer's service costs will exceed the contract price of \$200?
b. What is Ward's expected profit per service contract?

45. Is lack of sleep causing traffic fatalities? A study conducted under the auspices of the National Highway Traffic Safety Administration found that the average number of fatal crashes caused by drowsy drivers each year was 1550 (*BusinessWeek,* January 26, 2004). Assume the annual number of fatal crashes per year is normally distributed with a standard deviation of 300.
   a. What is the probability of fewer than 1000 fatal crashes in a year?
   b. What is the probability the number of fatal crashes will be between 1000 and 2000 for a year?
   c. For a year to be in the upper 5% with respect to the number of fatal crashes, how many fatal crashes would have to occur?

46. Assume that the test scores from a college admissions test are normally distributed, with a mean of 450 and a standard deviation of 100.
   a. What percentage of the people taking the test score between 400 and 500?
   b. Suppose someone receives a score of 630. What percentage of the people taking the test score better? What percentage score worse?
   c. If a particular university will not admit anyone scoring below 480, what percentage of the persons taking the test would be acceptable to the university?

47. According to Salary Wizard, the average base salary for a brand manager in Houston, Texas, is \$88,592 and the average base salary for a brand manager in Los Angeles, California, is \$97,417 (Salary Wizard website, February 27, 2008). Assume that salaries are normally distributed, the standard deviation for brand managers in Houston is \$19,900, and the standard deviation for brand managers in Los Angeles is \$21,800.
   a. What is the probability that a brand manager in Houston has a base salary in excess of \$100,000?
   b. What is the probability that a brand manager in Los Angeles has a base salary in excess of \$100,000?
   c. What is the probability that a brand manager in Los Angeles has a base salary of less than \$75,000?
   d. How much would a brand manager in Los Angeles have to make in order to have a higher salary than 99% of the brand managers in Houston?

48. A machine fills containers with a particular product. The standard deviation of filling weights is known from past data to be .6 ounce. If only 2% of the containers hold less than 18 ounces, what is the mean filling weight for the machine? That is, what must μ equal? Assume the filling weights have a normal distribution.

49. Consider a multiple-choice examination with 50 questions. Each question has four possible answers. Assume that a student who has done the homework and attended lectures has a 75% probability of answering any question correctly.
   a. A student must answer 43 or more questions correctly to obtain a grade of A. What percentage of the students who have done their homework and attended lectures will obtain a grade of A on this multiple-choice examination?
   b. A student who answers 35 to 39 questions correctly will receive a grade of C. What percentage of students who have done their homework and attended lectures will obtain a grade of C on this multiple-choice examination?
   c. A student must answer 30 or more questions correctly to pass the examination. What percentage of the students who have done their homework and attended lectures will pass the examination?
   d. Assume that a student has not attended class and has not done the homework for the course. Furthermore, assume that the student will simply guess at the answer to each question. What is the probability that this student will answer 30 or more questions correctly and pass the examination?

50. A blackjack player at a Las Vegas casino learned that the house will provide a free room if play is for four hours at an average bet of \$50. The player's strategy provides a

probability of .49 of winning on any one hand, and the player knows that there are 60 hands per hour. Suppose the player plays for four hours at a bet of $50 per hand.

a. What is the player's expected payoff?
b. What is the probability the player loses $1000 or more?
c. What is the probability the player wins?
d. Suppose the player starts with $1500. What is the probability of going broke?

51. The time in minutes for which a student uses a computer terminal at the computer center of a major university follows an exponential probability distribution with a mean of 36 minutes. Assume a student arrives at the terminal just as another student is beginning to work on the terminal.
    a. What is the probability that the wait for the second student will be 15 minutes or less?
    b. What is the probability that the wait for the second student will be between 15 and 45 minutes?
    c. What is the probability that the second student will have to wait an hour or more?

52. The website for the Bed and Breakfast Inns of North America gets approximately seven visitors per minute (*Time,* September 2001). Suppose the number of website visitors per minute follows a Poisson probability distribution.
    a. What is the mean time between visits to the website?
    b. Show the exponential probability density function for the time between website visits.
    c. What is the probability no one will access the website in a 1-minute period?
    d. What is the probability no one will access the website in a 12-second period?

53. The American Community Survey showed that residents of New York City have the longest travel times to get to work compared to residents of other cities in the United States (U.S. Census Bureau website, August 2008). According to the latest statistics available, the average travel time to work for residents of New York City is 38.3 minutes.
    a. Assume the exponential probability distribution is applicable and show the probability density function for the travel time to work for a resident of this city.
    b. What is the probability it will take a resident of this city between 20 and 40 minutes to travel to work?
    c. What is the probability it will take a resident of this city more than one hour to travel to work?

54. The time (in minutes) between telephone calls at an insurance claims office has the following exponential probability distribution.

$$f(x) = .50e^{-.50x} \quad \text{for } x \geq 0$$

    a. What is the mean time between telephone calls?
    b. What is the probability of having 30 seconds or less between telephone calls?
    c. What is the probability of having 1 minute or less between telephone calls?
    d. What is the probability of having 5 or more minutes without a telephone call?

Case Problem Specialty Toys

Specialty Toys, Inc., sells a variety of new and innovative children's toys. Management learned that the preholiday season is the best time to introduce a new toy, because many families use this time to look for new ideas for December holiday gifts. When Specialty discovers a new toy with good market potential, it chooses an October market entry date.

In order to get toys in its stores by October, Specialty places one-time orders with its manufacturers in June or July of each year. Demand for children's toys can be highly volatile. If a new toy catches on, a sense of shortage in the marketplace often increases the demand to high levels and large profits can be realized. However, new toys can also flop, leaving Specialty stuck with high levels of inventory that must be sold at reduced prices. The most important question the company faces is deciding how many units of a new toy should be purchased to meet anticipated sales demand. If too few are purchased, sales will be lost; if too many are purchased, profits will be reduced because of low prices realized in clearance sales.

For the coming season, Specialty plans to introduce a new product called Weather Teddy. This variation of a talking teddy bear is made by a company in Taiwan. When a child presses Teddy's hand, the bear begins to talk. A built-in barometer selects one of five responses that predict the weather conditions. The responses range from "It looks to be a very nice day! Have fun" to "I think it may rain today. Don't forget your umbrella." Tests with the product show that, even though it is not a perfect weather predictor, its predictions are surprisingly good. Several of Specialty's managers claimed Teddy gave predictions of the weather that were as good as many local television weather forecasters.

As with other products, Specialty faces the decision of how many Weather Teddy units to order for the coming holiday season. Members of the management team suggested order quantities of 15,000, 18,000, 24,000, or 28,000 units. The wide range of order quantities suggested indicates considerable disagreement concerning the market potential. The product management team asks you for an analysis of the stock-out probabilities for various order quantities, an estimate of the profit potential, and to help make an order quantity recommendation. Specialty expects to sell Weather Teddy for $24 based on a cost of $16 per unit. If inventory remains after the holiday season, Specialty will sell all surplus inventory for $5 per unit. After reviewing the sales history of similar products, Specialty's senior sales forecaster predicted an expected demand of 20,000 units with a .95 probability that demand would be between 10,000 units and 30,000 units.

Managerial Report

Prepare a managerial report that addresses the following issues and recommends an order quantity for the Weather Teddy product.

1. Use the sales forecaster's prediction to describe a normal probability distribution that can be used to approximate the demand distribution. Sketch the distribution and show its mean and standard deviation.
2. Compute the probability of a stock-out for the order quantities suggested by members of the management team.
3. Compute the projected profit for the order quantities suggested by the management team under three scenarios: worst case in which sales = 10,000 units, most likely case in which sales = 20,000 units, and best case in which sales = 30,000 units.
4. One of Specialty's managers felt that the profit potential was so great that the order quantity should have a 70% chance of meeting demand and only a 30% chance of any stock-outs. What quantity would be ordered under this policy, and what is the projected profit under the three sales scenarios?
5. Provide your own recommendation for an order quantity and note the associated profit projections. Provide a rationale for your recommendation.

Appendix 6.1 Continuous Probability Distributions with Minitab

Let us demonstrate the Minitab procedure for computing continuous probabilities by referring to the Grear Tire Company problem where tire mileage was described by a normal distribution with $\mu = 36{,}500$ and $\sigma = 5000$. One question asked was: What is the probability that the tire mileage will exceed 40,000 miles?

For continuous probability distributions, Minitab provides the cumulative probability that the random variable takes on a value less than or equal to a specified constant. For the Grear tire mileage question, Minitab can be used to determine the cumulative probability that the tire mileage will be less than or equal to 40,000 miles. After obtaining the cumulative probability, we must subtract it from 1 to determine the probability that the tire mileage will exceed 40,000 miles.

Prior to using Minitab to compute a probability, we must enter the specified constant into a column of the worksheet. For the Grear tire mileage question we enter 40,000 into column C1 of the Minitab worksheet. The steps in using Minitab to compute the cumulative probability follow.

Step 1. Select the **Calc** menu
Step 2. Choose **Probability Distributions**
Step 3. Choose **Normal**
Step 4. When the Normal Distribution dialog box appears:
Select **Cumulative probability**
Enter 36500 in the **Mean** box
Enter 5000 in the **Standard deviation** box
Enter C1 in the **Input column** box (the column containing 40,000)
Click **OK**

Minitab shows that this probability is .7580. Because we are interested in the probability that the tire mileage will be greater than 40,000, the desired probability is $1 - .7580 = .2420$.

A second question in the Grear Tire Company problem was: What mileage guarantee should Grear set to ensure that no more than 10% of the tires qualify for the guarantee? Here we are given a probability and want to find the corresponding value for the random variable. Minitab uses an inverse calculation routine to find the value of the random variable associated with a given cumulative probability. First, we must enter the cumulative probability into a column of the Minitab worksheet. In this case, the desired cumulative probability of .10 is entered into column C1. Then, the first three steps of the Minitab procedure are as already listed. In step 4, we select **Inverse cumulative probability** instead of **Cumulative probability** and complete the remaining parts of the step. Minitab then displays the mileage guarantee of 30,092 miles.

Minitab is capable of computing probabilities for other continuous probability distributions, including the exponential probability distribution. To compute exponential probabilities, follow the procedure shown previously for the normal probability distribution and choose the **Exponential** option in step 3. Step 4 is as shown, with the exception that entering the standard deviation is not required. Output for cumulative probabilities and inverse cumulative probabilities is identical to that described for the normal probability distribution.

Appendix 6.2 Continuous Probability Distributions with Excel

Excel provides the capability for computing probabilities for several continuous probability distributions, including the normal and exponential probability distributions. In this appendix, we describe how Excel can be used to compute probabilities for any normal distribution. The procedures for the exponential and other continuous distributions are similar to the one we describe for the normal distribution.

Let us return to the Grear Tire Company problem where the tire mileage was described by a normal distribution with $\mu = 36{,}500$ and $\sigma = 5000$. Assume we are interested in the probability that tire mileage will exceed 40,000 miles.

Excel's NORM.DIST function can be used to compute cumulative probabilities for a normal distribution. The general form of the function is NORM.DIST(x,μ,σ,cumulative). For the fourth argument, TRUE is specified if a cumulative probability is desired. Thus, to compute the cumulative probability that the tire mileage will be less than or equal to 40,000 miles we would enter the following formula into any cell of an Excel worksheet:

=NORM.DIST(40000,36500,5000,TRUE)

At this point, .7580 will appear in the cell where the formula was entered, indicating that the probability of tire mileage being less than or equal to 40,000 miles is .7580. Therefore, the probability that tire mileage will exceed 40,000 miles is $1 - .7580 = .2420$.

Excel's NORM.INV function uses an inverse computation to find the x value corresponding to a given cumulative probability. For instance, suppose we want to find the guaranteed mileage Grear should offer so that no more than 10% of the tires will be eligible for the guarantee. We would enter the following formula into any cell of an Excel worksheet:

=NORM.INV(.1,36500,5000)

At this point, 30092 will appear in the cell where the formula was entered, indicating that the probability of a tire lasting 30,092 miles or less is .10.

The Excel function for computing exponential probabilities is EXPON.DIST. This function requires three inputs: x, the value of the variable; lambda, which is $1/\mu$, and TRUE if you would like the cumulative probability. For example, consider an exponential probability distribution with mean $\mu = 15$. The probability that the exponential variable is less than or equal to 6 can be computed by the Excel formula

=EXPON.DIST(6,1/15,TRUE)

If you need help inserting functions in a worksheet, Excel's Insert Function dialog box may be used. See Appendix E in the back of the text.

CHAPTER 7

Sampling and Sampling Distributions

CONTENTS

STATISTICS *in* PRACTICE

MEADWESTVACO CORPORATION*
STAMFORD, CONNECTICUT

MeadWestvaco Corporation, a leading producer of packaging, coated and specialty papers, consumer and office products, and specialty chemicals, employs more than 30,000 people. It operates worldwide in 29 countries and serves customers located in approximately 100 countries. MeadWestvaco holds a leading position in paper production, with an annual capacity of 1.8 million tons. The company's products include textbook paper, glossy magazine paper, beverage packaging systems, and office products. MeadWestvaco's internal consulting group uses sampling to provide a variety of information that enables the company to obtain significant productivity benefits and remain competitive.

For example, MeadWestvaco maintains large woodland holdings, which supply the trees, or raw material, for many of the company's products. Managers need reliable and accurate information about the timberlands and forests to evaluate the company's ability to meet its future raw material needs. What is the present volume in the forests? What is the past growth of the forests? What is the projected future growth of the forests? With answers to these important questions MeadWestvaco's managers can develop plans for the future, including long-term planting and harvesting schedules for the trees.

How does MeadWestvaco obtain the information it needs about its vast forest holdings? Data collected from sample plots throughout the forests are the basis for learning about the population of trees owned by the company. To identify the sample plots, the timberland holdings are first divided into three sections based on location and types of trees. Using maps and random numbers, MeadWestvaco analysts identify random samples of 1/5- to 1/7-acre plots in each section of the forest.

Random sampling of its forest holdings enables MeadWestvaco Corporation to meet future raw material needs. © Walter Hodges/CORBIS.

MeadWestvaco foresters collect data from these sample plots to learn about the forest population.

Foresters throughout the organization participate in the field data collection process. Periodically, two-person teams gather information on each tree in every sample plot. The sample data are entered into the company's continuous forest inventory (CFI) computer system. Reports from the CFI system include a number of frequency distribution summaries containing statistics on types of trees, present forest volume, past forest growth rates, and projected future forest growth and volume. Sampling and the associated statistical summaries of the sample data provide the reports essential for the effective management of MeadWestvaco's forests and timberlands.

In this chapter you will learn about simple random sampling and the sample selection process. In addition, you will learn how statistics such as the sample mean and sample proportion are used to estimate the population mean and population proportion. The important concept of a sampling distribution is also introduced.

*The authors are indebted to Dr. Edward P. Winkofsky for providing this Statistics in Practice.

In Chapter 1 we presented the following definitions of an element, a population, and a sample.

- An *element* is the entity on which data are collected.
- A *population* is the collection of all the elements of interest.
- A *sample* is a subset of the population.

The reason we select a sample is to collect data to make an inference and answer a research question about a population.

Let us begin by citing two examples in which sampling was used to answer a research question about a population.

1. Members of a political party in Texas were considering supporting a particular candidate for election to the U.S. Senate, and party leaders wanted to estimate the proportion of registered voters in the state favoring the candidate. A sample of 400 registered voters in Texas was selected and 160 of the 400 voters indicated a preference for the candidate. Thus, an estimate of the proportion of the population of registered voters favoring the candidate is 160/400 = .40.
2. A tire manufacturer is considering producing a new tire designed to provide an increase in mileage over the firm's current line of tires. To estimate the mean useful life of the new tires, the manufacturer produced a sample of 120 tires for testing. The test results provided a sample mean of 36,500 miles. Hence, an estimate of the mean useful life for the population of new tires was 36,500 miles.

A sample mean provides an estimate of a population mean, and a sample proportion provides an estimate of a population proportion. With estimates such as these, some estimation error can be expected. This chapter provides the basis for determining how large that error might be.

It is important to realize that sample results provide only *estimates* of the values of the corresponding population characteristics. We do not expect exactly .40, or 40%, of the population of registered voters to favor the candidate, nor do we expect the sample mean of 36,500 miles to exactly equal the mean mileage for the population of all new tires produced. The reason is simply that the sample contains only a portion of the population. Some sampling error is to be expected. With proper sampling methods, the sample results will provide "good" estimates of the population parameters. But how good can we expect the sample results to be? Fortunately, statistical procedures are available for answering this question.

Let us define some of the terms used in sampling. The **sampled population** is the population from which the sample is drawn, and a **frame** is a list of the elements that the sample will be selected from. In the first example, the sampled population is all registered voters in Texas, and the frame is a list of all the registered voters. Because the number of registered voters in Texas is a finite number, the first example is an illustration of sampling from a finite population. In Section 7.2, we discuss how a simple random sample can be selected when sampling from a finite population.

The sampled population for the tire mileage example is more difficult to define because the sample of 120 tires was obtained from a production process at a particular point in time. We can think of the sampled population as the conceptual population of all the tires that could have been made by the production process at that particular point in time. In this sense the sampled population is considered infinite, making it impossible to construct a frame to draw the sample from. In Section 7.2, we discuss how to select a random sample in such a situation.

In this chapter, we show how simple random sampling can be used to select a sample from a finite population and describe how a random sample can be taken from an infinite population that is generated by an ongoing process. We then show how data obtained from a sample can be used to compute estimates of a population mean, a population standard deviation, and a population proportion. In addition, we introduce the important concept of a sampling distribution. As we will show, knowledge of the appropriate sampling distribution enables us to make statements about how close the sample estimates are to the corresponding population parameters. The last section discusses some alternatives to simple random sampling that are often employed in practice.

7.1 The Electronics Associates Sampling Problem

The director of personnel for Electronics Associates, Inc. (EAI), has been assigned the task of developing a profile of the company's 2500 managers. The characteristics to be identified include the mean annual salary for the managers and the proportion of managers having completed the company's management training program.

WEB file
EAI

Using the 2500 managers as the population for this study, we can find the annual salary and the training program status for each individual by referring to the firm's personnel records. The data set containing this information for all 2500 managers in the population is in the file named EAI.

Using the EAI data and the formulas presented in Chapter 3, we compute the population mean and the population standard deviation for the annual salary data.

$$\text{Population mean:} \quad \mu = \$51{,}800$$
$$\text{Population standard deviation:} \quad \sigma = \$4000$$

The data for the training program status show that 1500 of the 2500 managers completed the training program.

Numerical characteristics of a population are called **parameters**. Letting p denote the proportion of the population that completed the training program, we see that $p = 1500/2500 = .60$. The population mean annual salary ($\mu = \$51{,}800$), the population standard deviation of annual salary ($\sigma = \$4000$), and the population proportion that completed the training program ($p = .60$) are parameters of the population of EAI managers.

Often the cost of collecting information from a sample is substantially less than from a population, especially when personal interviews must be conducted to collect the information.

Now, suppose that the necessary information on all the EAI managers was not readily available in the company's database. The question we now consider is how the firm's director of personnel can obtain estimates of the population parameters by using a sample of managers rather than all 2500 managers in the population. Suppose that a sample of 30 managers will be used. Clearly, the time and the cost of developing a profile would be substantially less for 30 managers than for the entire population. If the personnel director could be assured that a sample of 30 managers would provide adequate information about the population of 2500 managers, working with a sample would be preferable to working with the entire population. Let us explore the possibility of using a sample for the EAI study by first considering how we can identify a sample of 30 managers.

7.2 Selecting a Sample

In this section we describe how to select a sample. We first describe how to sample from a finite population and then describe how to select a sample from an infinite population.

Sampling from a Finite Population

Other methods of probability sampling are described in Section 7.8

Statisticians recommend selecting a probability sample when sampling from a finite population because a probability sample allows them to make valid statistical inferences about the population. The simplest type of probability sample is one in which each sample of size n has the same probability of being selected. It is called a simple random sample. A simple random sample of size n from a finite population of size N is defined as follows.

> SIMPLE RANDOM SAMPLE (FINITE POPULATION)
>
> A **simple random sample** of size n from a finite population of size N is a sample selected such that each possible sample of size n has the same probability of being selected.

Computer-generated random numbers can also be used to implement the random sample selection process. Excel provides a function for generating random numbers in its worksheets.

One procedure for selecting a simple random sample from a finite population is to choose the elements for the sample one at a time in such a way that, at each step, each of the elements remaining in the population has the same probability of being selected. Sampling n elements in this way will satisfy the definition of a simple random sample from a finite population.

To select a simple random sample from the finite population of EAI managers, we first construct a frame by assigning each manager a number. For example, we can assign the

TABLE 7.1 RANDOM NUMBERS

63271	59986	71744	51102	15141	80714	58683	93108	13554	79945
88547	09896	95436	79115	08303	01041	20030	63754	08459	28364
55957	57243	83865	09911	19761	66535	40102	26646	60147	15702
46276	87453	44790	67122	45573	84358	21625	16999	13385	22782
55363	07449	34835	15290	76616	67191	12777	21861	68689	03263
69393	92785	49902	58447	42048	30378	87618	26933	40640	16281
13186	29431	88190	04588	38733	81290	89541	70290	40113	08243
17726	28652	56836	78351	47327	18518	92222	55201	27340	10493
36520	64465	05550	30157	82242	29520	69753	72602	23756	54935
81628	36100	39254	56835	37636	02421	98063	89641	64953	99337
84649	48968	75215	75498	49539	74240	03466	49292	36401	45525
63291	11618	12613	75055	43915	26488	41116	64531	56827	30825
70502	53225	03655	05915	37140	57051	48393	91322	25653	06543
06426	24771	59935	49801	11082	66762	94477	02494	88215	27191
20711	55609	29430	70165	45406	78484	31639	52009	18873	96927
41990	70538	77191	25860	55204	73417	83920	69468	74972	38712
72452	36618	76298	26678	89334	33938	95567	29380	75906	91807
37042	40318	57099	10528	09925	89773	41335	96244	29002	46453
53766	52875	15987	46962	67342	77592	57651	95508	80033	69828
90585	58955	53122	16025	84299	53310	67380	84249	25348	04332
32001	96293	37203	64516	51530	37069	40261	61374	05815	06714
62606	64324	46354	72157	67248	20135	49804	09226	64419	29457
10078	28073	85389	50324	14500	15562	64165	06125	71353	77669
91561	46145	24177	15294	10061	98124	75732	00815	83452	97355
13091	98112	53959	79607	52244	63303	10413	63839	74762	50289

managers the numbers 1 to 2500 in the order that their names appear in the EAI personnel file. Next, we refer to the table of random numbers shown in Table 7.1. Using the first row of the table, each digit, 6, 3, 2, . . . , is a random digit having an equal chance of occurring. Because the largest number in the population list of EAI managers, 2500, has four digits, we will select random numbers from the table in sets or groups of four digits. Even though we may start the selection of random numbers anywhere in the table and move systematically in a direction of our choice, we will use the first row of Table 7.1 and move from left to right. The first 7 four-digit random numbers are

The random numbers in the table are shown in groups of five for readability.

6327 1599 8671 7445 1102 1514 1807

Because the numbers in the table are random, these four-digit numbers are equally likely.

We can now use these four-digit random numbers to give each manager in the population an equal chance of being included in the random sample. The first number, 6327, is greater than 2500. It does not correspond to one of the numbered managers in the population, and hence is discarded. The second number, 1599, is between 1 and 2500. Thus the first manager selected for the random sample is number 1599 on the list of EAI managers. Continuing this process, we ignore the numbers 8671 and 7445 before identifying managers number 1102, 1514, and 1807 to be included in the random sample. This process continues until the simple random sample of 30 EAI managers has been obtained.

In implementing this simple random sample selection process, it is possible that a random number used previously may appear again in the table before the complete sample of 30 EAI managers has been selected. Because we do not want to select a manager more than one time, any previously used random numbers are ignored because the corresponding manager is already included in the sample. Selecting a sample in this manner is referred to as **sampling without replacement**. If we selected a sample such that previously used random numbers are acceptable and specific managers could be included in the sample two or more times, we would be **sampling with replacement**. Sampling with replacement is a valid way of identifying a simple random sample. However, sampling without replacement is the sampling procedure used most often. When we refer to simple random sampling, we will assume the sampling is without replacement.

Sampling from an Infinite Population

Sometimes we want to select a sample from a population, but the population is infinitely large or the elements of the population are being generated by an on-going process for which there is no limit on the number of elements that can be generated. Thus, it is not possible to develop a list of all the elements in the population. This is considered the infinite population case. With an infinite population, we cannot select a simple random sample because we cannot construct a frame consisting of all the elements. In the infinite population case, statisticians recommend selecting what is called a random sample.

RANDOM SAMPLE (INFINITE POPULATION)

A **random sample** of size n from an infinite population is a sample selected such that the following conditions are satisfied.

1. Each element selected comes from the same population.
2. Each element is selected independently.

Care and judgment must be exercised in implementing the selection process for obtaining a random sample from an infinite population. Each case may require a different selection procedure. Let us consider two examples to see what we mean by the conditions (1) each element selected comes from the same population and (2) each element is selected independently.

A common quality control application involves a production process where there is no limit on the number of elements that can be produced. The conceptual population we are sampling from is all the elements that could be produced (not just the ones that are produced) by the ongoing production process. Because we cannot develop a list of all the elements that could be produced, the population is considered infinite. To be more specific, let us consider a production line designed to fill boxes of a breakfast cereal with a mean weight of 24 ounces of breakfast cereal per box. Samples of 12 boxes filled by this process are periodically selected by a quality control inspector to determine if the process is operating properly or if, perhaps, a machine malfunction has caused the process to begin underfilling or overfilling the boxes.

With a production operation such as this, the biggest concern in selecting a random sample is to make sure that condition 1, the sampled elements are selected from the same population, is satisfied. To ensure that this condition is satisfied, the boxes must be selected at approximately the same point in time. This way the inspector avoids the possibility of selecting some boxes when the process is operating properly and other boxes when the process is not operating properly and is underfilling or overfilling the boxes. With a production process such as this, the second condition, each element is selected independently, is satisfied by designing the production process so that each box of cereal is filled independently. With this assumption, the quality control inspector only needs to worry about satisfying the same population condition.

As another example of selecting a random sample from an infinite population, consider the population of customers arriving at a fast-food restaurant. Suppose an employee is asked to select and interview a sample of customers in order to develop a profile of customers who visit the restaurant. The customer arrival process is ongoing and there is no way to obtain a list of all customers in the population. So, for practical purposes, the population for this ongoing process is considered infinite. As long as a sampling procedure is designed so that all the elements in the sample are customers of the restaurant and they are selected independently, a random sample will be obtained. In this case, the employee collecting the sample needs to select the sample from people who come into the restaurant and make a purchase to ensure that the same population condition is satisfied. If, for instance, the employee selected someone for the sample who came into the restaurant just to use the restroom, that person would not be a customer and the same population condition would be violated. So, as long as the interviewer selects the sample from people making a purchase at the restaurant, condition 1 is satisfied. Ensuring that the customers are selected independently can be more difficult.

The purpose of the second condition of the random sample selection procedure (each element is selected independently) is to prevent selection bias. In this case, selection bias would occur if the interviewer were free to select customers for the sample arbitrarily. The interviewer might feel more comfortable selecting customers in a particular age group and might avoid customers in other age groups. Selection bias would also occur if the interviewer selected a group of five customers who entered the restaurant together and asked all of them to participate in the sample. Such a group of customers would be likely to exhibit similar characteristics, which might provide misleading information about the population of customers. Selection bias such as this can be avoided by ensuring that the selection of a particular customer does not influence the selection of any other customer. In other words, the elements (customers) are selected independently.

McDonald's, the fast-food restaurant leader, implemented a random sampling procedure for this situation. The sampling procedure was based on the fact that some customers presented discount coupons. Whenever a customer presented a discount coupon, the next customer served was asked to complete a customer profile questionnaire. Because arriving customers presented discount coupons randomly and independently of other customers, this sampling procedure ensured that customers were selected independently. As a result, the sample satisfied the requirements of a random sample from an infinite population.

Situations involving sampling from an infinite population are usually associated with a process that operates over time. Examples include parts being manufactured on a production line, repeated experimental trials in a laboratory, transactions occurring at a bank, telephone calls arriving at a technical support center, and customers entering a retail store. In each case, the situation may be viewed as a process that generates elements from an infinite population. As long as the sampled elements are selected from the same population and are selected independently, the sample is considered a random sample from an infinite population.

NOTES AND COMMENTS

1. In this section we have been careful to define two types of samples: a simple random sample from a finite population and a random sample from an infinite population. In the remainder of the text, we will generally refer to both of these as either a *random sample* or simply a *sample*. We will not make a distinction of the sample being a "simple" random sample unless it is necessary for the exercise or discussion.
2. Statisticians who specialize in sample surveys from finite populations use sampling methods that provide probability samples. With a probability sample, each possible sample has a known probability of selection and a random process is used to select the elements for the sample. Simple random sampling is one of these methods. In Section 7.8, we describe some other probability sampling methods: stratified random sampling, cluster sampling, and systematic sampling. We use the term "simple" in simple random sampling to clarify that this is the probability sampling method that assures each sample of size n has the same probability of being selected.
3. The number of different simple random samples of size n that can be selected from a finite population of size N is

$$\frac{N!}{n!(N-n)!}$$

In this formula, $N!$ and $n!$ are the factorial formulas discussed in Chapter 4. For the EAI problem with $N = 2500$ and $n = 30$, this expression can be used to show that approximately 2.75×10^{69} different simple random samples of 30 EAI managers can be obtained.

4. Computer software packages can be used to select a random sample. In the chapter appendixes, we show how Minitab and Excel can be used to select a simple random sample from a finite population.

Exercises

Methods

SELF test

1. Consider a finite population with five elements labeled A, B, C, D, and E. Ten possible simple random samples of size 2 can be selected.
   a. List the 10 samples beginning with AB, AC, and so on.
   b. Using simple random sampling, what is the probability that each sample of size 2 is selected?
   c. Assume random number 1 corresponds to A, random number 2 corresponds to B, and so on. List the simple random sample of size 2 that will be selected by using the random digits 8 0 5 7 5 3 2.
2. Assume a finite population has 350 elements. Using the last three digits of each of the following five-digit random numbers (e.g., 601, 022, 448, . . .), determine the first four elements that will be selected for the simple random sample.

   98601 73022 83448 02147 34229 27553 84147 93289 14209

Applications

SELF test

3. *Fortune* publishes data on sales, profits, assets, stockholders' equity, market value, and earnings per share for the 500 largest U.S. industrial corporations (*Fortune* 500, 2006). Assume that you want to select a simple random sample of 10 corporations from the *Fortune* 500 list. Use the last three digits in column 9 of Table 7.1, beginning with 554. Read down the column and identify the numbers of the 10 corporations that would be selected.
4. The 10 most active stocks on the New York Stock Exchange on March 6, 2006, are shown here (*The Wall Street Journal,* March 7, 2006).

AT&T	Lucent	Nortel	Qwest	Bell South
Pfizer	Texas Instruments	Gen. Elect.	iShrMSJpn	LSI Logic

   Exchange authorities decided to investigate trading practices using a sample of three of these stocks.
   a. Beginning with the first random digit in column 6 of Table 7.1, read down the column to select a simple random sample of three stocks for the exchange authorities.
   b. Using the information in the third Note and Comment, determine how many different simple random samples of size 3 can be selected from the list of 10 stocks.
5. A student government organization is interested in estimating the proportion of students who favor a mandatory "pass-fail" grading policy for elective courses. A list of names and addresses of the 645 students enrolled during the current quarter is available from the registrar's office. Using three-digit random numbers in row 10 of Table 7.1 and moving across the row from left to right, identify the first 10 students who would be selected using simple random sampling. The three-digit random numbers begin with 816, 283, and 610.
6. The *County and City Data Book,* published by the Census Bureau, lists information on 3139 counties throughout the United States. Assume that a national study will collect data from 30 randomly selected counties. Use four-digit random numbers from the last column of Table 7.1 to identify the numbers corresponding to the first five counties selected for the sample. Ignore the first digits and begin with the four-digit random numbers 9945, 8364, 5702, and so on.

7. Assume that we want to identify a simple random sample of 12 of the 372 doctors practicing in a particular city. The doctors' names are available from a local medical organization. Use the eighth column of five-digit random numbers in Table 7.1 to identify the 12 doctors for the sample. Ignore the first two random digits in each five-digit grouping of the random numbers. This process begins with random number 108 and proceeds down the column of random numbers.
8. The following stocks make up the Dow Jones Industrial Average (*Barron's*, March 23, 2009).

1. 3M	11. Disney	21. McDonald's
2. AT&T	12. DuPont	22. Merck
3. Alcoa	13. ExxonMobil	23. Microsoft
4. American Express	14. General Electric	24. J.P. Morgan
5. Bank of America	15. Hewlett-Packard	25. Pfizer
6. Boeing	16. Home Depot	26. Procter & Gamble
7. Caterpillar	17. IBM	27. Travelers
8. Chevron	18. Intel	28. United Technologies
9. Cisco Systems	19. Johnson & Johnson	29. Verizon
10. Coca-Cola	20. Kraft Foods	30. Wal-Mart

Suppose you would like to select a sample of six of these companies to conduct an in-depth study of management practices. Use the first two digits in each row of the ninth column of Table 7.1 to select a simple random sample of six companies.
9. *The Wall Street Journal* provides the net asset value, the year-to-date percent return, and the three-year percent return for 555 mutual funds (*The Wall Street Journal,* April 25, 2003). Assume that a simple random sample of 12 of the 555 mutual funds will be selected for a follow-up study on the size and performance of mutual funds. Use the fourth column of the random numbers in Table 7.1, beginning with 51102, to select the simple random sample of 12 mutual funds. Begin with mutual fund 102 and use the *last* three digits in each row of the fourth column for your selection process. What are the numbers of the 12 mutual funds in the simple random sample?
10. Indicate which of the following situations involve sampling from a finite population and which involve sampling from an infinite population. In cases where the sampled population is finite, describe how you would construct a frame.
    a. Obtain a sample of licensed drivers in the state of New York.
    b. Obtain a sample of boxes of cereal produced by the Breakfast Choice company.
    c. Obtain a sample of cars crossing the Golden Gate Bridge on a typical weekday.
    d. Obtain a sample of students in a statistics course at Indiana University.
    e. Obtain a sample of the orders that are processed by a mail-order firm.

7.3 Point Estimation

Now that we have described how to select a simple random sample, let us return to the EAI problem. A simple random sample of 30 managers and the corresponding data on annual salary and management training program participation are as shown in Table 7.2. The notation x_1, x_2, and so on is used to denote the annual salary of the first manager in the sample, the annual salary of the second manager in the sample, and so on. Participation in the management training program is indicated by Yes in the management training program column.

To estimate the value of a population parameter, we compute a corresponding characteristic of the sample, referred to as a **sample statistic**. For example, to estimate the population mean μ and the population standard deviation σ for the annual salary of EAI managers, we use the data in Table 7.2 to calculate the corresponding sample statistics: the

TABLE 7.2 ANNUAL SALARY AND TRAINING PROGRAM STATUS FOR A SIMPLE RANDOM SAMPLE OF 30 EAI MANAGERS

Annual Salary ($)	Management Training Program	Annual Salary ($)	Management Training Program
$x_1 = 49{,}094.30$	Yes	$x_{16} = 51{,}766.00$	Yes
$x_2 = 53{,}263.90$	Yes	$x_{17} = 52{,}541.30$	No
$x_3 = 49{,}643.50$	Yes	$x_{18} = 44{,}980.00$	Yes
$x_4 = 49{,}894.90$	Yes	$x_{19} = 51{,}932.60$	Yes
$x_5 = 47{,}621.60$	No	$x_{20} = 52{,}973.00$	Yes
$x_6 = 55{,}924.00$	Yes	$x_{21} = 45{,}120.90$	Yes
$x_7 = 49{,}092.30$	Yes	$x_{22} = 51{,}753.00$	Yes
$x_8 = 51{,}404.40$	Yes	$x_{23} = 54{,}391.80$	No
$x_9 = 50{,}957.70$	Yes	$x_{24} = 50{,}164.20$	No
$x_{10} = 55{,}109.70$	Yes	$x_{25} = 52{,}973.60$	No
$x_{11} = 45{,}922.60$	Yes	$x_{26} = 50{,}241.30$	No
$x_{12} = 57{,}268.40$	No	$x_{27} = 52{,}793.90$	No
$x_{13} = 55{,}688.80$	Yes	$x_{28} = 50{,}979.40$	Yes
$x_{14} = 51{,}564.70$	No	$x_{29} = 55{,}860.90$	Yes
$x_{15} = 56{,}188.20$	No	$x_{30} = 57{,}309.10$	No

sample mean and the sample standard deviation s. Using the formulas for a sample mean and a sample standard deviation presented in Chapter 3, the sample mean is

$$\bar{x} = \frac{\Sigma x_i}{n} = \frac{1{,}554{,}420}{30} = \$51{,}814$$

and the sample standard deviation is

$$s = \sqrt{\frac{\Sigma(x_i - \bar{x})^2}{n - 1}} = \sqrt{\frac{325{,}009{,}260}{29}} = \$3348$$

To estimate p, the proportion of managers in the population who completed the management training program, we use the corresponding sample proportion $\bar{p}$. Let x denote the number of managers in the sample who completed the management training program. The data in Table 7.2 show that $x = 19$. Thus, with a sample size of $n = 30$, the sample proportion is

$$\bar{p} = \frac{x}{n} = \frac{19}{30} = .63$$

By making the preceding computations, we perform the statistical procedure called *point estimation*. We refer to the sample mean $\bar{x}$ as the **point estimator** of the population mean μ, the sample standard deviation s as the point estimator of the population standard deviation σ, and the sample proportion $\bar{p}$ as the point estimator of the population proportion p. The numerical value obtained for $\bar{x}$, s, or $\bar{p}$ is called the **point estimate**. Thus, for the simple random sample of 30 EAI managers shown in Table 7.2, \$51,814 is the point estimate of μ, \$3348 is the point estimate of σ, and .63 is the point estimate of p. Table 7.3 summarizes the sample results and compares the point estimates to the actual values of the population parameters.

As is evident from Table 7.3, the point estimates differ somewhat from the corresponding population parameters. This difference is to be expected because a sample, and not a census of the entire population, is being used to develop the point estimates. In the next chapter, we will show how to construct an interval estimate in order to provide information about how close the point estimate is to the population parameter.

TABLE 7.3 SUMMARY OF POINT ESTIMATES OBTAINED FROM A SIMPLE RANDOM SAMPLE OF 30 EAI MANAGERS

Population Parameter	Parameter Value	Point Estimator	Point Estimate
μ = Population mean annual salary	\$51,800	$\bar{x}$ = Sample mean annual salary	\$51,814
σ = Population standard deviation for annual salary	\$4000	s = Sample standard deviation for annual salary	\$3348
p = Population proportion having completed the management training program	.60	$\bar{p}$ = Sample proportion having completed the management training program	.63

Practical Advice

The subject matter of most of the rest of the book is concerned with statistical inference. Point estimation is a form of statistical inference. We use a sample statistic to make an inference about a population parameter. When making inferences about a population based on a sample, it is important to have a close correspondence between the sampled population and the target population. The **target population** is the population we want to make inferences about, while the sampled population is the population from which the sample is actually taken. In this section, we have described the process of drawing a simple random sample from the population of EAI managers and making point estimates of characteristics of that same population. So the sampled population and the target population are indentical, which is the desired situation. But in other cases, it is not as easy to obtain a close correspondence between the sampled and target populations.

Consider the case of an amusement park selecting a sample of its customers to learn about characteristics such as age and time spent at the park. Suppose all the sample elements were selected on a day when park attendance was restricted to employees of a large company. Then the sampled population would be composed of employees of that company and members of their families. If the target population we wanted to make inferences about were typical park customers over a typical summer, then we might encounter a significant difference between the sampled population and the target population. In such a case, we would question the validity of the point estimates being made. Park management would be in the best position to know whether a sample taken on a particular day was likely to be representative of the target population.

In summary, whenever a sample is used to make inferences about a population, we should make sure that the study is designed so that the sampled population and the target population are in close agreement. Good judgment is a necessary ingredient of sound statistical practice.

Exercises

Methods

SELF test

11. The following data are from a simple random sample.

    5 8 10 7 10 14

    a. What is the point estimate of the population mean?
    b. What is the point estimate of the population standard deviation?

12. A survey question for a sample of 150 individuals yielded 75 Yes responses, 55 No responses, and 20 No Opinions.
    a. What is the point estimate of the proportion in the population who respond Yes?
    b. What is the point estimate of the proportion in the population who respond No?

Applications

SELF test

13. A simple random sample of 5 months of sales data provided the following information:

Month:	1	2	3	4	5
Units Sold:	94	100	85	94	92

a. Develop a point estimate of the population mean number of units sold per month.
b. Develop a point estimate of the population standard deviation.

WEB file
MutualFund

14. *BusinessWeek* published information on 283 equity mutual funds (*BusinessWeek,* January 26, 2004). A sample of 40 of those funds is contained in the data set MutualFund. Use the data set to answer the following questions.
a. Develop a point estimate of the proportion of the *BusinessWeek* equity funds that are load funds.
b. Develop a point estimate of the proportion of funds that are classified as high risk.
c. Develop a point estimate of the proportion of funds that have a below-average risk rating.

15. Many drugs used to treat cancer are expensive. *BusinessWeek* reported on the cost per treatment of Herceptin, a drug used to treat breast cancer (*BusinessWeek,* January 30, 2006). Typical treatment costs (in dollars) for Herceptin are provided by a simple random sample of 10 patients.

4376	5578	2717	4920	4495
4798	6446	4119	4237	3814

a. Develop a point estimate of the mean cost per treatment with Herceptin.
b. Develop a point estimate of the standard deviation of the cost per treatment with Herceptin.

16. A sample of 50 *Fortune* 500 companies (*Fortune,* April 14, 2003) showed 5 were based in New York, 6 in California, 2 in Minnesota, and 1 in Wisconsin.
a. Develop an estimate of the proportion of *Fortune* 500 companies based in New York.
b. Develop an estimate of the number of *Fortune* 500 companies based in Minnesota.
c. Develop an estimate of the proportion of *Fortune* 500 companies that are not based in these four states.

17. The American Association of Individual Investors (AAII) polls its subscribers on a weekly basis to determine the number who are bullish, bearish, or neutral on the short-term prospects for the stock market. Their findings for the week ending March 2, 2006, are consistent with the following sample results (AAII website, March 7, 2006).

Bullish	409	Neutral	299	Bearish	291

Develop a point estimate of the following population parameters.
a. The proportion of all AAII subscribers who are bullish on the stock market.
b. The proportion of all AAII subscribers who are neutral on the stock market.
c. The proportion of all AAII subscribers who are bearish on the stock market.

7.4 Introduction to Sampling Distributions

In the preceding section we said that the sample mean $\bar{x}$ is the point estimator of the population mean μ, and the sample proportion $\bar{p}$ is the point estimator of the population proportion p. For the simple random sample of 30 EAI managers shown in Table 7.2, the point estimate of μ is $\bar{x} = \$51,814$ and the point estimate of p is $\bar{p} = .63$. Suppose we select another simple random sample of 30 EAI managers and obtain the following point estimates:

$$\text{Sample mean: } \bar{x} = \$52,670$$
$$\text{Sample proportion: } \bar{p} = .70$$

TABLE 7.4 VALUES OF $\bar{x}$ AND $\bar{p}$ FROM 500 SIMPLE RANDOM SAMPLES OF 30 EAI MANAGERS

Sample Number	Sample Mean ($\bar{x}$)	Sample Proportion ($\bar{p}$)
1	51,814	.63
2	52,670	.70
3	51,780	.67
4	51,588	.53
.	.	.
.	.	.
.	.	.
500	51,752	.50

Note that different values of $\bar{x}$ and $\bar{p}$ were obtained. Indeed, a second simple random sample of 30 EAI managers cannot be expected to provide the same point estimates as the first sample.

Now, suppose we repeat the process of selecting a simple random sample of 30 EAI managers over and over again, each time computing the values of $\bar{x}$ and $\bar{p}$. Table 7.4 contains a portion of the results obtained for 500 simple random samples, and Table 7.5 shows the frequency and relative frequency distributions for the 500 $\bar{x}$ values. Figure 7.1 shows the relative frequency histogram for the $\bar{x}$ values.

The ability to understand the material in subsequent chapters depends heavily on the ability to understand and use the sampling distributions presented in this chapter.

In Chapter 5 we defined a random variable as a numerical description of the outcome of an experiment. If we consider the process of selecting a simple random sample as an experiment, the sample mean $\bar{x}$ is the numerical description of the outcome of the experiment. Thus, the sample mean $\bar{x}$ is a random variable. As a result, just like other random variables, $\bar{x}$ has a mean or expected value, a standard deviation, and a probability distribution. Because the various possible values of $\bar{x}$ are the result of different simple random samples, the probability distribution of $\bar{x}$ is called the **sampling distribution** of $\bar{x}$. Knowledge of this sampling distribution and its properties will enable us to make probability statements about how close the sample mean $\bar{x}$ is to the population mean μ.

Let us return to Figure 7.1. We would need to enumerate every possible sample of 30 managers and compute each sample mean to completely determine the sampling distribution of $\bar{x}$. However, the histogram of 500 $\bar{x}$ values gives an approximation of this sampling distribution. From the approximation we observe the bell-shaped appearance of

TABLE 7.5 FREQUENCY AND RELATIVE FREQUENCY DISTRIBUTIONS OF $\bar{x}$ FROM 500 SIMPLE RANDOM SAMPLES OF 30 EAI MANAGERS

Mean Annual Salary ($)	Frequency	Relative Frequency
49,500.00–49,999.99	2	.004
50,000.00–50,499.99	16	.032
50,500.00–50,999.99	52	.104
51,000.00–51,499.99	101	.202
51,500.00–51,999.99	133	.266
52,000.00–52,499.99	110	.220
52,500.00–52,999.99	54	.108
53,000.00–53,499.99	26	.052
53,500.00–53,999.99	6	.012
	Totals 500	1.000

FIGURE 7.1 RELATIVE FREQUENCY HISTOGRAM OF $\bar{x}$ VALUES FROM 500 SIMPLE RANDOM SAMPLES OF SIZE 30 EACH

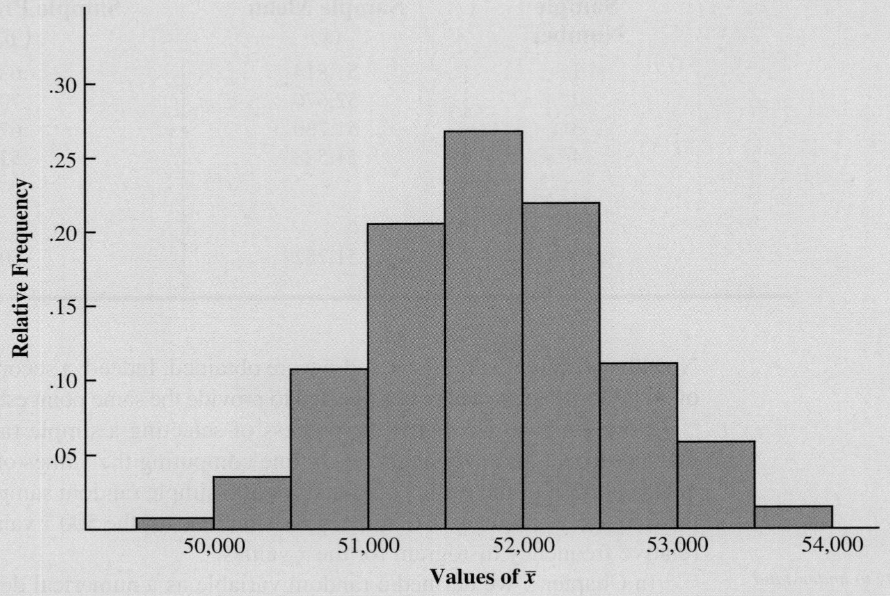

the distribution. We note that the largest concentration of the $\bar{x}$ values and the mean of the 500 $\bar{x}$ values is near the population mean $\mu = \$51{,}800$. We will describe the properties of the sampling distribution of $\bar{x}$ more fully in the next section.

The 500 values of the sample proportion $\bar{p}$ are summarized by the relative frequency histogram in Figure 7.2. As in the case of $\bar{x}$, $\bar{p}$ is a random variable. If every possible sample of size 30 were selected from the population and if a value of $\bar{p}$ were computed for each sample, the resulting probability distribution would be the sampling distribution of $\bar{p}$. The relative frequency histogram of the 500 sample values in Figure 7.2 provides a general idea of the appearance of the sampling distribution of $\bar{p}$.

In practice, we select only one simple random sample from the population. We repeated the sampling process 500 times in this section simply to illustrate that many different samples are possible and that the different samples generate a variety of values for the sample statistics $\bar{x}$ and $\bar{p}$. The probability distribution of any particular sample statistic is called the sampling distribution of the statistic. In Section 7.5 we show the characteristics of the sampling distribution of $\bar{x}$. In Section 7.6 we show the characteristics of the sampling distribution of $\bar{p}$.

7.5 Sampling Distribution of $\bar{x}$

In the previous section we said that the sample mean $\bar{x}$ is a random variable and its probability distribution is called the sampling distribution of $\bar{x}$.

SAMPLING DISTRIBUTION OF $\bar{x}$

The sampling distribution of $\bar{x}$ is the probability distribution of all possible values of the sample mean $\bar{x}$.

FIGURE 7.2 RELATIVE FREQUENCY HISTOGRAM OF $\bar{p}$ VALUES FROM 500 SIMPLE RANDOM SAMPLES OF SIZE 30 EACH

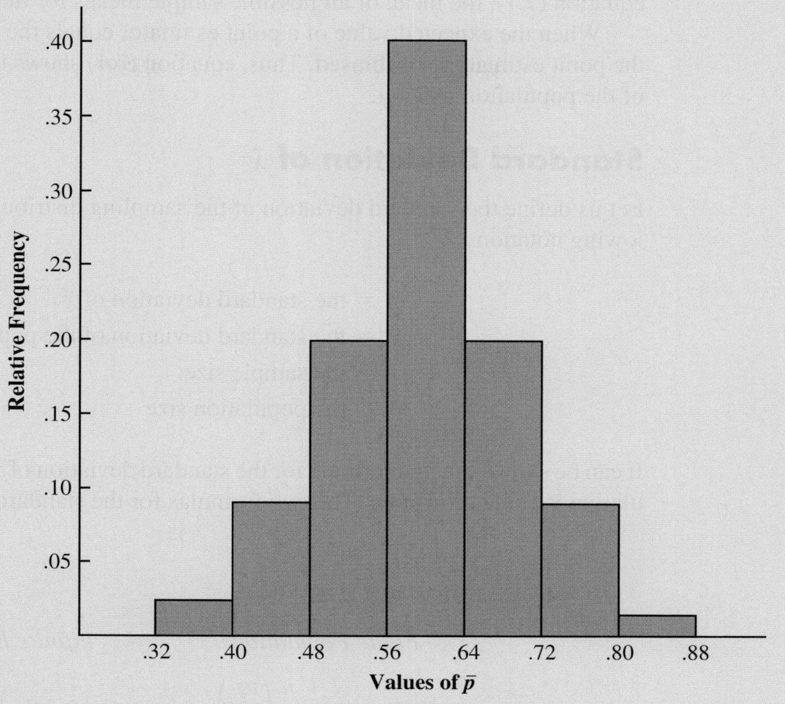

This section describes the properties of the sampling distribution of $\bar{x}$. Just as with other probability distributions we studied, the sampling distribution of $\bar{x}$ has an expected value or mean, a standard deviation, and a characteristic shape or form. Let us begin by considering the mean of all possible $\bar{x}$ values, which is referred to as the expected value of $\bar{x}$.

Expected Value of $\bar{x}$

In the EAI sampling problem we saw that different simple random samples result in a variety of values for the sample mean $\bar{x}$. Because many different values of the random variable $\bar{x}$ are possible, we are often interested in the mean of all possible values of $\bar{x}$ that can be generated by the various simple random samples. The mean of the $\bar{x}$ random variable is the expected value of $\bar{x}$. Let $E(\bar{x})$ represent the expected value of $\bar{x}$ and μ represent the mean of the population from which we are selecting a simple random sample. It can be shown that with simple random sampling, $E(\bar{x})$ and μ are equal.

The expected value of $\bar{x}$ equals the mean of the population from which the sample is selected.

EXPECTED VALUE OF $\bar{x}$

$$E(\bar{x}) = \mu \tag{7.1}$$

where

$E(\bar{x})$ = the expected value of $\bar{x}$

μ = the population mean

This result shows that with simple random sampling, the expected value or mean of the sampling distribution of $\bar{x}$ is equal to the mean of the population. In Section 7.1 we saw that the mean annual salary for the population of EAI managers is $\mu = \$51{,}800$. Thus, according to equation (7.1), the mean of all possible sample means for the EAI study is also $51,800.

When the expected value of a point estimator equals the population parameter, we say the point estimator is **unbiased**. Thus, equation (7.1) shows that $\bar{x}$ is an unbiased estimator of the population mean μ.

Standard Deviation of $\bar{x}$

Let us define the standard deviation of the sampling distribution of $\bar{x}$. We will use the following notation.

$$\begin{aligned} \sigma_{\bar{x}} &= \text{the standard deviation of } \bar{x} \\ \sigma &= \text{the standard deviation of the population} \\ n &= \text{the sample size} \\ N &= \text{the population size} \end{aligned}$$

It can be shown that the formula for the standard deviation of $\bar{x}$ depends on whether the population is finite or infinite. The two formulas for the standard deviation of $\bar{x}$ follow.

STANDARD DEVIATION OF $\bar{x}$

Finite Population *Infinite Population*

$$\sigma_{\bar{x}} = \sqrt{\frac{N-n}{N-1}}\left(\frac{\sigma}{\sqrt{n}}\right) \qquad \sigma_{\bar{x}} = \frac{\sigma}{\sqrt{n}} \tag{7.2}$$

In comparing the two formulas in (7.2), we see that the factor $\sqrt{(N-n)/(N-1)}$ is required for the finite population case but not for the infinite population case. This factor is commonly referred to as the **finite population correction factor**. In many practical sampling situations, we find that the population involved, although finite, is "large," whereas the sample size is relatively "small." In such cases the finite population correction factor $\sqrt{(N-n)/(N-1)}$ is close to 1. As a result, the difference between the values of the standard deviation of $\bar{x}$ for the finite and infinite population cases becomes negligible. Then, $\sigma_{\bar{x}} = \sigma/\sqrt{n}$ becomes a good approximation to the standard deviation of $\bar{x}$ even though the population is finite. This observation leads to the following general guideline, or rule of thumb, for computing the standard deviation of $\bar{x}$.

USE THE FOLLOWING EXPRESSION TO COMPUTE THE STANDARD DEVIATION OF $\bar{x}$

$$\sigma_{\bar{x}} = \frac{\sigma}{\sqrt{n}} \tag{7.3}$$

whenever

1. The population is infinite; or
2. The population is finite *and* the sample size is less than or equal to 5% of the population size; that is, $n/N \le .05$.

Problem 21 shows that when $n/N \le .05$, the finite population correction factor has little effect on the value of $\sigma_{\bar{x}}$.

The term standard error is used throughout statistical inference to refer to the standard deviation of a point estimator.

In cases where $n/N > .05$, the finite population version of formula (7.2) should be used in the computation of $\sigma_{\bar{x}}$. Unless otherwise noted, throughout the text we will assume that the population size is "large," $n/N \le .05$, and expression (7.3) can be used to compute $\sigma_{\bar{x}}$.

To compute $\sigma_{\bar{x}}$, we need to know σ, the standard deviation of the population. To further emphasize the difference between $\sigma_{\bar{x}}$ and σ, we refer to the standard deviation of $\bar{x}$, $\sigma_{\bar{x}}$, as the **standard error** of the mean. In general, the term *standard error* refers to the standard deviation of a point estimator. Later we will see that the value of the standard error of the mean is helpful in determining how far the sample mean may be from the population mean. Let us now return to the EAI example and compute the standard error of the mean associated with simple random samples of 30 EAI managers.

In Section 7.1 we saw that the standard deviation of annual salary for the population of 2500 EAI managers is $\sigma = 4000$. In this case, the population is finite, with $N = 2500$. However, with a sample size of 30, we have $n/N = 30/2500 = .012$. Because the sample size is less than 5% of the population size, we can ignore the finite population correction factor and use equation (7.3) to compute the standard error.

$$\sigma_{\bar{x}} = \frac{\sigma}{\sqrt{n}} = \frac{4000}{\sqrt{30}} = 730.3$$

Form of the Sampling Distribution of $\bar{x}$

The preceding results concerning the expected value and standard deviation for the sampling distribution of $\bar{x}$ are applicable for any population. The final step in identifying the characteristics of the sampling distribution of $\bar{x}$ is to determine the form or shape of the sampling distribution. We will consider two cases: (1) The population has a normal distribution; and (2) the population does not have a normal distribution.

Population has a normal distribution. In many situations it is reasonable to assume that the population from which we are selecting a random sample has a normal, or nearly normal, distribution. When the population has a normal distribution, the sampling distribution of $\bar{x}$ is normally distributed for any sample size.

Population does not have a normal distribution. When the population from which we are selecting a random sample does not have a normal distribution, the **central limit theorem** is helpful in identifying the shape of the sampling distribution of $\bar{x}$. A statement of the central limit theorem as it applies to the sampling distribution of $\bar{x}$ follows.

> CENTRAL LIMIT THEOREM
>
> In selecting random samples of size n from a population, the sampling distribution of the sample mean $\bar{x}$ can be approximated by a *normal distribution* as the sample size becomes large.

Figure 7.3 shows how the central limit theorem works for three different populations; each column refers to one of the populations. The top panel of the figure shows that none of the populations are normally distributed. Population I follows a uniform distribution. Population II is often called the rabbit-eared distribution. It is symmetric, but the more likely values fall in the tails of the distribution. Population III is shaped like the exponential distribution; it is skewed to the right.

The bottom three panels of Figure 7.3 show the shape of the sampling distribution for samples of size $n = 2$, $n = 5$, and $n = 30$. When the sample size is 2, we see that the shape of each sampling distribution is different from the shape of the corresponding population

FIGURE 7.3 ILLUSTRATION OF THE CENTRAL LIMIT THEOREM FOR THREE POPULATIONS

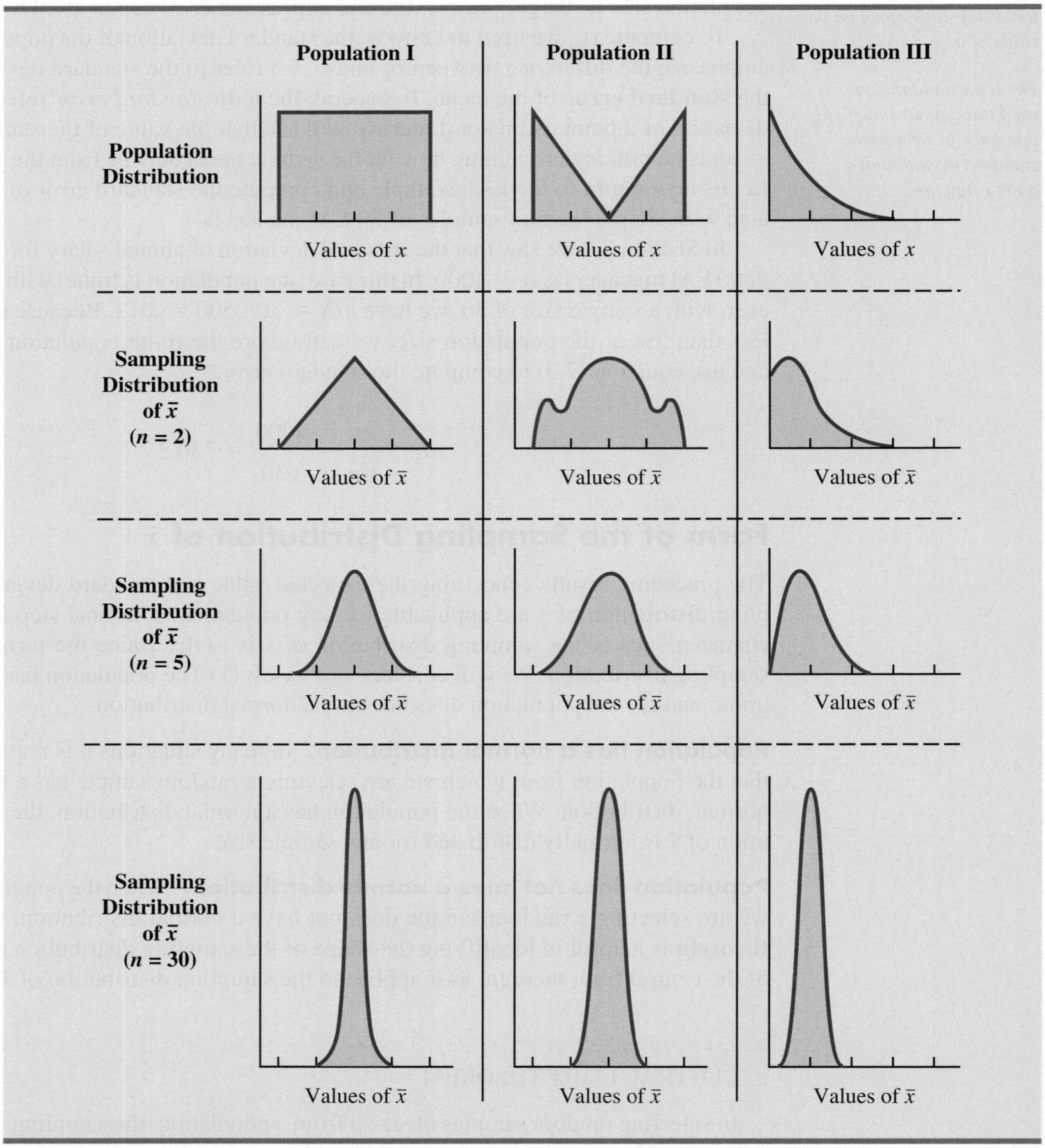

distribution. For samples of size 5, we see that the shapes of the sampling distributions for populations I and II begin to look similar to the shape of a normal distribution. Even though the shape of the sampling distribution for population III begins to look similar to the shape of a normal distribution, some skewness to the right is still present. Finally, for samples of size 30, the shapes of each of the three sampling distributions are approximately normal.

From a practitioner standpoint, we often want to know how large the sample size needs to be before the central limit theorem applies and we can assume that the shape of the sampling distribution is approximately normal. Statistical researchers have investigated this question by studying the sampling distribution of $\bar{x}$ for a variety of populations and a variety of sample sizes. General statistical practice is to assume that, for most applications, the sampling distribution of $\bar{x}$ can be approximated by a normal distribution whenever the sample is size 30 or more. In cases where the population is highly skewed or outliers are present, samples of size 50 may be needed. Finally, if the population is discrete, the sample size needed for a normal approximation often depends on the population proportion. We say more about this issue when we discuss the sampling distribution of $\bar{p}$ in Section 7.6.

Sampling Distribution of $\bar{x}$ for the EAI Problem

Let us return to the EAI problem where we previously showed that $E(\bar{x}) = \$51,800$ and $\sigma_{\bar{x}} = 730.3$. At this point, we do not have any information about the population distribution; it may or may not be normally distributed. If the population has a normal distribution, the sampling distribution of $\bar{x}$ is normally distributed. If the population does not have a normal distribution, the simple random sample of 30 managers and the central limit theorem enable us to conclude that the sampling distribution of $\bar{x}$ can be approximated by a normal distribution. In either case, we are comfortable proceeding with the conclusion that the sampling distribution of $\bar{x}$ can be described by the normal distribution shown in Figure 7.4.

Practical Value of the Sampling Distribution of $\bar{x}$

Whenever a simple random sample is selected and the value of the sample mean is used to estimate the value of the population mean μ, we cannot expect the sample mean to exactly equal the population mean. The practical reason we are interested in the sampling distribution of $\bar{x}$ is that it can be used to provide probability information about the difference between the sample mean and the population mean. To demonstrate this use, let us return to the EAI problem.

Suppose the personnel director believes the sample mean will be an acceptable estimate of the population mean if the sample mean is within \$500 of the population mean. However, it is not possible to guarantee that the sample mean will be within \$500 of the population mean. Indeed, Table 7.5 and Figure 7.1 show that some of the 500 sample means differed by more than \$2000 from the population mean. So we must think of the personnel director's request in probability terms. That is, the personnel director is concerned with the following question: What is the probability that the sample mean computed using a simple random sample of 30 EAI managers will be within \$500 of the population mean?

FIGURE 7.4 SAMPLING DISTRIBUTION OF $\bar{x}$ FOR THE MEAN ANNUAL SALARY OF A SIMPLE RANDOM SAMPLE OF 30 EAI MANAGERS

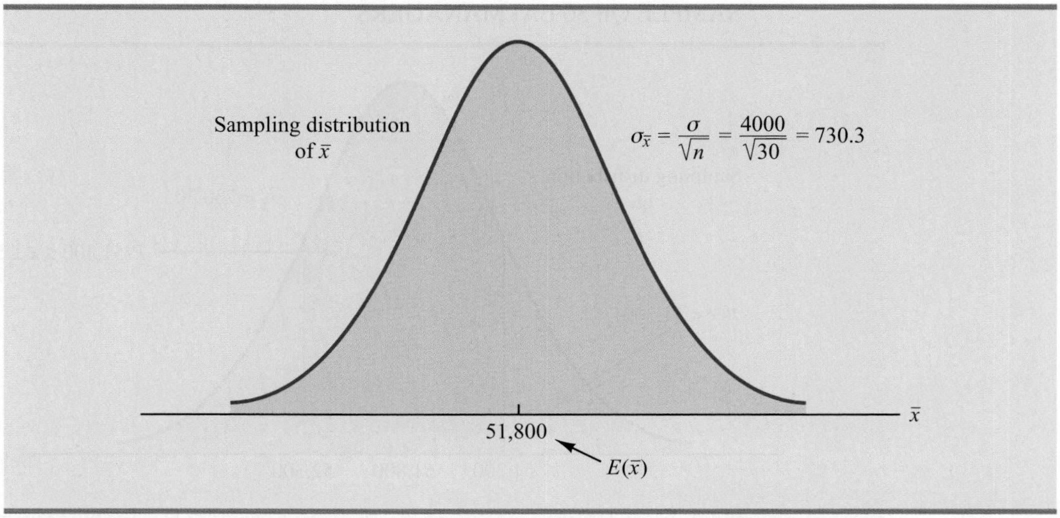

Because we have identified the properties of the sampling distribution of $\bar{x}$ (see Figure 7.4), we will use this distribution to answer the probability question. Refer to the sampling distribution of $\bar{x}$ shown again in Figure 7.5. With a population mean of \$51,800, the personnel director wants to know the probability that $\bar{x}$ is between \$51,300 and \$52,300. This probability is given by the darkly shaded area of the sampling distribution shown in Figure 7.5. Because the sampling distribution is normally distributed, with mean 51,800 and standard error of the mean 730.3, we can use the standard normal probability table to find the area or probability.

We first calculate the z value at the upper endpoint of the interval (52,300) and use the table to find the area under the curve to the left of that point (left tail area). Then we compute the z value at the lower endpoint of the interval (51,300) and use the table to find the area under the curve to the left of that point (another left tail area). Subtracting the second tail area from the first gives us the desired probability.

At $\bar{x} = 52{,}300$, we have

$$z = \frac{52{,}300 - 51{,}800}{730.30} = .68$$

Referring to the standard normal probability table, we find a cumulative probability (area to the left of $z = .68$) of .7517.

At $\bar{x} = 51{,}300$, we have

$$z = \frac{51{,}300 - 51{,}800}{730.30} = -.68$$

The area under the curve to the left of $z = -.68$ is .2483. Therefore, $P(51{,}300 \le \bar{x} \le 52{,}300) = P(z \le .68) - P(z < -.68) = .7517 - .2483 = .5034$.

The sampling distribution of $\bar{x}$ can be used to provide probability information about how close the sample mean $\bar{x}$ is to the population mean μ.

The preceding computations show that a simple random sample of 30 EAI managers has a .5034 probability of providing a sample mean $\bar{x}$ that is within \$500 of the population mean. Thus, there is a $1 - .5034 = .4966$ probability that the difference between $\bar{x}$ and $\mu = \$51{,}800$ will be more than \$500. In other words, a simple random sample of 30 EAI managers has roughly a 50/50 chance of providing a sample mean within the allowable

FIGURE 7.5 PROBABILITY OF A SAMPLE MEAN BEING WITHIN \$500 OF THE POPULATION MEAN FOR A SIMPLE RANDOM SAMPLE OF 30 EAI MANAGERS

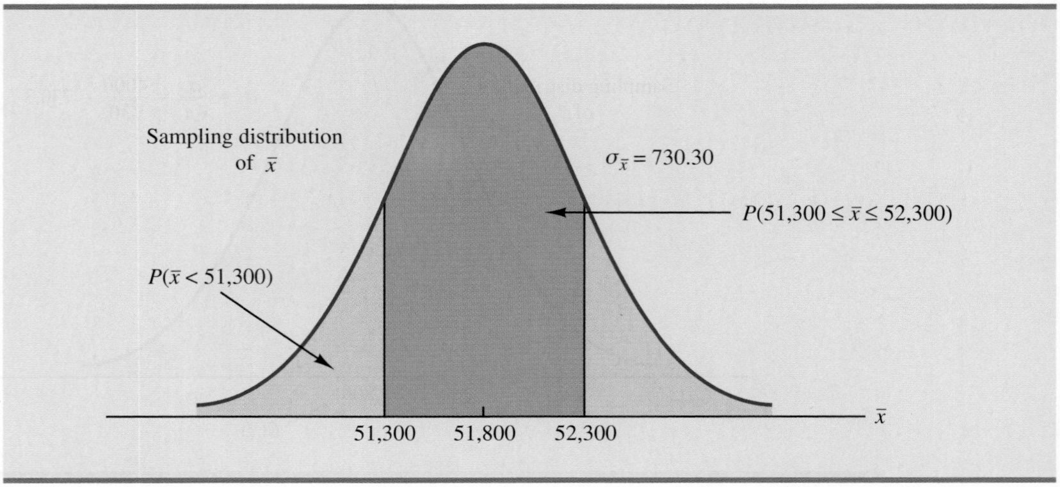

\$500. Perhaps a larger sample size should be considered. Let us explore this possibility by considering the relationship between the sample size and the sampling distribution of $\bar{x}$.

Relationship Between the Sample Size and the Sampling Distribution of $\bar{x}$

Suppose that in the EAI sampling problem we select a simple random sample of 100 EAI managers instead of the 30 originally considered. Intuitively, it would seem that with more data provided by the larger sample size, the sample mean based on $n = 100$ should provide a better estimate of the population mean than the sample mean based on $n = 30$. To see how much better, let us consider the relationship between the sample size and the sampling distribution of $\bar{x}$.

First note that $E(\bar{x}) = \mu$ regardless of the sample size. Thus, the mean of all possible values of $\bar{x}$ is equal to the population mean μ regardless of the sample size n. However, note that the standard error of the mean, $\sigma_{\bar{x}} = \sigma/\sqrt{n}$, is related to the square root of the sample size. Whenever the sample size is increased, the standard error of the mean $\sigma_{\bar{x}}$ decreases. With $n = 30$, the standard error of the mean for the EAI problem is 730.3. However, with the increase in the sample size to $n = 100$, the standard error of the mean is decreased to

$$\sigma_{\bar{x}} = \frac{\sigma}{\sqrt{n}} = \frac{4000}{\sqrt{100}} = 400$$

The sampling distributions of $\bar{x}$ with $n = 30$ and $n = 100$ are shown in Figure 7.6. Because the sampling distribution with $n = 100$ has a smaller standard error, the values of $\bar{x}$ have less variation and tend to be closer to the population mean than the values of $\bar{x}$ with $n = 30$.

We can use the sampling distribution of $\bar{x}$ for the case with $n = 100$ to compute the probability that a simple random sample of 100 EAI managers will provide a sample mean that is within \$500 of the population mean. Because the sampling distribution is normal, with mean 51,800 and standard error of the mean 400, we can use the standard normal probability table to find the area or probability.

At $\bar{x} = 52{,}300$ (see Figure 7.7), we have

$$z = \frac{52{,}300 - 51{,}800}{400} = 1.25$$

FIGURE 7.6 A COMPARISON OF THE SAMPLING DISTRIBUTIONS OF $\bar{x}$ FOR SIMPLE RANDOM SAMPLES OF $n = 30$ AND $n = 100$ EAI MANAGERS

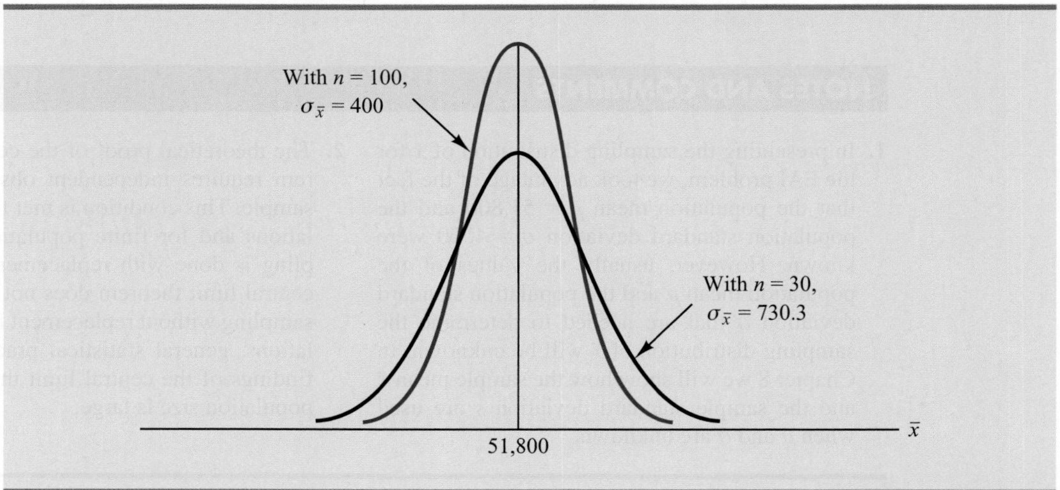

FIGURE 7.7 PROBABILITY OF A SAMPLE MEAN BEING WITHIN $500 OF THE POPULATION MEAN FOR A SIMPLE RANDOM SAMPLE OF 100 EAI MANAGERS

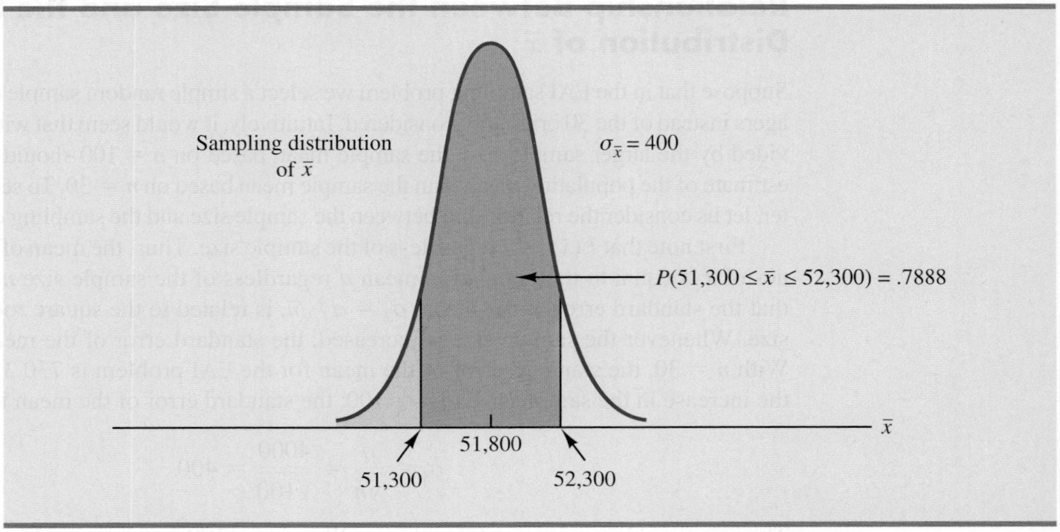

Referring to the standard normal probability table, we find a cumulative probability corresponding to $z = 1.25$ of .8944.

At $\bar{x} = 51,300$, we have

$$z = \frac{51,300 - 51,800}{400} = -1.25$$

The cumulative probability corresponding to $z = -1.25$ is .1056. Therefore, $P(51,300 \le \bar{x} \le 52,300) = P(z \le 1.25) - P(z \le -1.25) = .8944 - .1056 = .7888$. Thus, by increasing the sample size from 30 to 100 EAI managers, we increase the probability of obtaining a sample mean within $500 of the population mean from .5034 to .7888.

The important point in this discussion is that as the sample size is increased, the standard error of the mean decreases. As a result, the larger sample size provides a higher probability that the sample mean is within a specified distance of the population mean.

NOTES AND COMMENTS

1. In presenting the sampling distribution of $\bar{x}$ for the EAI problem, we took advantage of the fact that the population mean $\mu = 51,800$ and the population standard deviation $\sigma = 4000$ were known. However, usually the values of the population mean μ and the population standard deviation σ that are needed to determine the sampling distribution of $\bar{x}$ will be unknown. In Chapter 8 we will show how the sample mean $\bar{x}$ and the sample standard deviation s are used when μ and σ are unknown.
2. The theoretical proof of the central limit theorem requires independent observations in the sample. This condition is met for infinite populations and for finite populations where sampling is done with replacement. Although the central limit theorem does not directly address sampling without replacement from finite populations, general statistical practice applies the findings of the central limit theorem when the population size is large.

Exercises

Methods

18. A population has a mean of 200 and a standard deviation of 50. A simple random sample of size 100 will be taken and the sample mean $\bar{x}$ will be used to estimate the population mean.
    a. What is the expected value of $\bar{x}$?
    b. What is the standard deviation of $\bar{x}$?
    c. Show the sampling distribution of $\bar{x}$.
    d. What does the sampling distribution of $\bar{x}$ show?

SELF test

19. A population has a mean of 200 and a standard deviation of 50. Suppose a simple random sample of size 100 is selected and $\bar{x}$ is used to estimate μ.
    a. What is the probability that the sample mean will be within ± 5 of the population mean?
    b. What is the probability that the sample mean will be within ± 10 of the population mean?

20. Assume the population standard deviation is $\sigma = 25$. Compute the standard error of the mean, $\sigma_{\bar{x}}$, for sample sizes of 50, 100, 150, and 200. What can you say about the size of the standard error of the mean as the sample size is increased?

21. Suppose a simple random sample of size 50 is selected from a population with $\sigma = 10$. Find the value of the standard error of the mean in each of the following cases (use the finite population correction factor if appropriate).
    a. The population size is infinite.
    b. The population size is $N = 50{,}000$.
    c. The population size is $N = 5000$.
    d. The population size is $N = 500$.

Applications

22. Refer to the EAI sampling problem. Suppose a simple random sample of 60 managers is used.
    a. Sketch the sampling distribution of $\bar{x}$ when simple random samples of size 60 are used.
    b. What happens to the sampling distribution of $\bar{x}$ if simple random samples of size 120 are used?
    c. What general statement can you make about what happens to the sampling distribution of $\bar{x}$ as the sample size is increased? Does this generalization seem logical? Explain.

SELF test

23. In the EAI sampling problem (see Figure 7.5), we showed that for $n = 30$, there was .5034 probability of obtaining a sample mean within $\pm\$500$ of the population mean.
    a. What is the probability that $\bar{x}$ is within \$500 of the population mean if a sample of size 60 is used?
    b. Answer part (a) for a sample of size 120.

24. *Barron's* reported that the average number of weeks an individual is unemployed is 17.5 weeks (*Barron's*, February 18, 2008). Assume that for the population of all unemployed individuals the population mean length of unemployment is 17.5 weeks and that the population standard deviation is 4 weeks. Suppose you would like to select a random sample of 50 unemployed individuals for a follow-up study.
    a. Show the sampling distribution of $\bar{x}$, the sample mean average for a sample of 50 unemployed individuals.
    b. What is the probability that a simple random sample of 50 unemployed individuals will provide a sample mean within 1 week of the population mean?
    c. What is the probability that a simple random sample of 50 unemployed individuals will provide a sample mean within 1/2 week of the population mean?

25. The College Board reported the following mean scores for the three parts of the Scholastic Aptitude Test (SAT) (*The World Almanac*, 2009):

Critical Reading	502
Mathematics	515
Writing	494

Assume that the population standard deviation on each part of the test is $\sigma = 100$.

a. What is the probability a random sample of 90 test takers will provide a sample mean test score within 10 points of the population mean of 502 on the Critical Reading part of the test?
b. What is the probability a random sample of 90 test takers will provide a sample mean test score within 10 points of the population mean of 515 on the Mathematics part of the test? Compare this probability to the value computed in part (a).
c. What is the probability a random sample of 100 test takers will provide a sample mean test score within 10 of the population mean of 494 on the writing part of the test? Comment on the differences between this probability and the values computed in parts (a) and (b).

26. The mean annual cost of automobile insurance is $939 (*CNBC*, February 23, 2006). Assume that the standard deviation is $\sigma =$ $245.

a. What is the probability that a simple random sample of automobile insurance policies will have a sample mean within $25 of the population mean for each of the following sample sizes: 30, 50, 100, and 400?
b. What is the advantage of a larger sample size when attempting to estimate the population mean?

27. *BusinessWeek* conducted a survey of graduates from 30 top MBA programs (*BusinessWeek*, September 22, 2003). On the basis of the survey, assume that the mean annual salary for male and female graduates 10 years after graduation is $168,000 and $117,000, respectively. Assume the standard deviation for the male graduates is $40,000, and for the female graduates it is $25,000.

a. What is the probability that a simple random sample of 40 male graduates will provide a sample mean within $10,000 of the population mean, $168,000?
b. What is the probability that a simple random sample of 40 female graduates will provide a sample mean within $10,000 of the population mean, $117,000?
c. In which of the preceding two cases, part (a) or part (b), do we have a higher probability of obtaining a sample estimate within $10,000 of the population mean? Why?
d. What is the probability that a simple random sample of 100 male graduates will provide a sample mean more than $4000 below the population mean?

28. The average score for male golfers is 95 and the average score for female golfers is 106 (*Golf Digest,* April 2006). Use these values as the population means for men and women and assume that the population standard deviation is $\sigma = 14$ strokes for both. A simple random sample of 30 male golfers and another simple random sample of 45 female golfers will be taken.

a. Show the sampling distribution of $\bar{x}$ for male golfers.
b. What is the probability that the sample mean is within 3 strokes of the population mean for the sample of male golfers?
c. What is the probability that the sample mean is within 3 strokes of the population mean for the sample of female golfers?
d. In which case, part (b) or part (c), is the probability of obtaining a sample mean within 3 strokes of the population mean higher? Why?

29. The average price of a gallon of unleaded regular gasoline was reported to be $2.34 in northern Kentucky (*The Cincinnati Enquirer,* January 21, 2006). Use this price as the population mean, and assume the population standard deviation is $.20.

a. What is the probability that the mean price for a sample of 30 service stations is within \$.03 of the population mean?

b. What is the probability that the mean price for a sample of 50 service stations is within \$.03 of the population mean?

c. What is the probability that the mean price for a sample of 100 service stations is within \$.03 of the population mean?

d. Which, if any, of the sample sizes in parts (a), (b), and (c) would you recommend to have at least a .95 probability that the sample mean is within \$.03 of the population mean?

30. To estimate the mean age for a population of 4000 employees, a simple random sample of 40 employees is selected.

a. Would you use the finite population correction factor in calculating the standard error of the mean? Explain.

b. If the population standard deviation is $\sigma = 8.2$ years, compute the standard error both with and without the finite population correction factor. What is the rationale for ignoring the finite population correction factor whenever $n/N \leq .05$?

c. What is the probability that the sample mean age of the employees will be within ± 2 years of the population mean age?

7.6 Sampling Distribution of $\bar{p}$

The sample proportion $\bar{p}$ is the point estimator of the population proportion p. The formula for computing the sample proportion is

$$\bar{p} = \frac{x}{n}$$

where

x = the number of elements in the sample that possess the characteristic of interest
n = sample size

As noted in Section 7.4, the sample proportion $\bar{p}$ is a random variable and its probability distribution is called the sampling distribution of $\bar{p}$.

SAMPLING DISTRIBUTION OF $\bar{p}$

The sampling distribution of $\bar{p}$ is the probability distribution of all possible values of the sample proportion $\bar{p}$.

To determine how close the sample proportion $\bar{p}$ is to the population proportion p, we need to understand the properties of the sampling distribution of $\bar{p}$: the expected value of $\bar{p}$, the standard deviation of $\bar{p}$, and the shape or form of the sampling distribution of $\bar{p}$.

Expected Value of $\bar{p}$

The expected value of $\bar{p}$, the mean of all possible values of $\bar{p}$, is equal to the population proportion p.

EXPECTED VALUE OF $\bar{p}$

$$E(\bar{p}) = p \tag{7.4}$$

where

$$E(\bar{p}) = \text{the expected value of } \bar{p}$$
$$p = \text{the population proportion}$$

Because $E(\bar{p}) = p$, $\bar{p}$ is an unbiased estimator of p. Recall from Section 7.1 we noted that $p = .60$ for the EAI population, where p is the proportion of the population of managers who participated in the company's management training program. Thus, the expected value of $\bar{p}$ for the EAI sampling problem is .60.

Standard Deviation of $\bar{p}$

Just as we found for the standard deviation of $\bar{x}$, the standard deviation of $\bar{p}$ depends on whether the population is finite or infinite. The two formulas for computing the standard deviation of $\bar{p}$ follow.

STANDARD DEVIATION OF $\bar{p}$

Finite Population *Infinite Population*

$$\sigma_{\bar{p}} = \sqrt{\frac{N-n}{N-1}}\sqrt{\frac{p(1-p)}{n}} \qquad \sigma_{\bar{p}} = \sqrt{\frac{p(1-p)}{n}} \tag{7.5}$$

Comparing the two formulas in (7.5), we see that the only difference is the use of the finite population correction factor $\sqrt{(N-n)/(N-1)}$.

As was the case with the sample mean $\bar{x}$, the difference between the expressions for the finite population and the infinite population becomes negligible if the size of the finite population is large in comparison to the sample size. We follow the same rule of thumb that we recommended for the sample mean. That is, if the population is finite with $n/N \leq .05$, we will use $\sigma_{\bar{p}} = \sqrt{p(1-p)/n}$. However, if the population is finite with $n/N > .05$, the finite population correction factor should be used. Again, unless specifically noted, throughout the text we will assume that the population size is large in relation to the sample size and thus the finite population correction factor is unnecessary.

In Section 7.5 we used the term standard error of the mean to refer to the standard deviation of $\bar{x}$. We stated that in general the term standard error refers to the standard deviation of a point estimator. Thus, for proportions we use *standard error of the proportion* to refer to the standard deviation of $\bar{p}$. Let us now return to the EAI example and compute the standard error of the proportion associated with simple random samples of 30 EAI managers.

For the EAI study we know that the population proportion of managers who participated in the management training program is $p = .60$. With $n/N = 30/2500 = .012$, we can ignore the finite population correction factor when we compute the standard error of the proportion. For the simple random sample of 30 managers, $\sigma_{\bar{p}}$ is

$$\sigma_{\bar{p}} = \sqrt{\frac{p(1-p)}{n}} = \sqrt{\frac{.60(1-.60)}{30}} = .0894$$

Form of the Sampling Distribution of $\bar{p}$

Now that we know the mean and standard deviation of the sampling distribution of $\bar{p}$, the final step is to determine the form or shape of the sampling distribution. The sample proportion is $\bar{p} = x/n$. For a simple random sample from a large population, the value of x is a binomial random variable indicating the number of elements in the sample with the characteristic of interest. Because n is a constant, the probability of x/n is the same as the binomial probability of x, which means that the sampling distribution of $\bar{p}$ is also a discrete probability distribution and that the probability for each value of x/n is the same as the probability of x.

In Chapter 6 we also showed that a binomial distribution can be approximated by a normal distribution whenever the sample size is large enough to satisfy the following two conditions:

$$np \geq 5 \quad \text{and} \quad n(1 - p) \geq 5$$

Assuming these two conditions are satisfied, the probability distribution of x in the sample proportion, $\bar{p} = x/n$, can be approximated by a normal distribution. And because n is a constant, the sampling distribution of $\bar{p}$ can also be approximated by a normal distribution. This approximation is stated as follows:

> The sampling distribution of $\bar{p}$ can be approximated by a normal distribution whenever $np \geq 5$ and $n(1 - p) \geq 5$.

In practical applications, when an estimate of a population proportion is desired, we find that sample sizes are almost always large enough to permit the use of a normal approximation for the sampling distribution of $\bar{p}$.

Recall that for the EAI sampling problem we know that the population proportion of managers who participated in the training program is $p = .60$. With a simple random sample of size 30, we have $np = 30(.60) = 18$ and $n(1 - p) = 30(.40) = 12$. Thus, the sampling distribution of $\bar{p}$ can be approximated by a normal distribution shown in Figure 7.8.

Practical Value of the Sampling Distribution of $\bar{p}$

The practical value of the sampling distribution of $\bar{p}$ is that it can be used to provide probability information about the difference between the sample proportion and the population proportion. For instance, suppose that in the EAI problem the personnel director wants to know the probability of obtaining a value of $\bar{p}$ that is within .05 of the population proportion of EAI managers who participated in the training program. That is, what is the probability of obtaining a sample with a sample proportion $\bar{p}$ between .55 and .65? The darkly shaded area in Figure 7.9 shows this probability. Using the fact that the sampling distribution of $\bar{p}$ can be approximated by a normal distribution with a mean of .60 and a standard error of the proportion of $\sigma_{\bar{p}} = .0894$, we find that the standard normal random variable corresponding to $\bar{p} = .65$ has a value of $z = (.65 - .60)/.0894 = .56$. Referring to the standard normal probability table, we see that the cumulative probability corresponding to $z = .56$ is .7123. Similarly, at $\bar{p} = .55$, we find $z = (.55 - .60)/.0894 = -.56$. From the standard normal probability table, we find the cumulative probability corresponding to $z = -.56$ is .2877. Thus, the probability of selecting a sample that provides a sample proportion $\bar{p}$ within .05 of the population proportion p is given by $.7123 - .2877 = .4246$.

FIGURE 7.8 SAMPLING DISTRIBUTION OF $\bar{p}$ FOR THE PROPORTION OF EAI MANAGERS WHO PARTICIPATED IN THE MANAGEMENT TRAINING PROGRAM

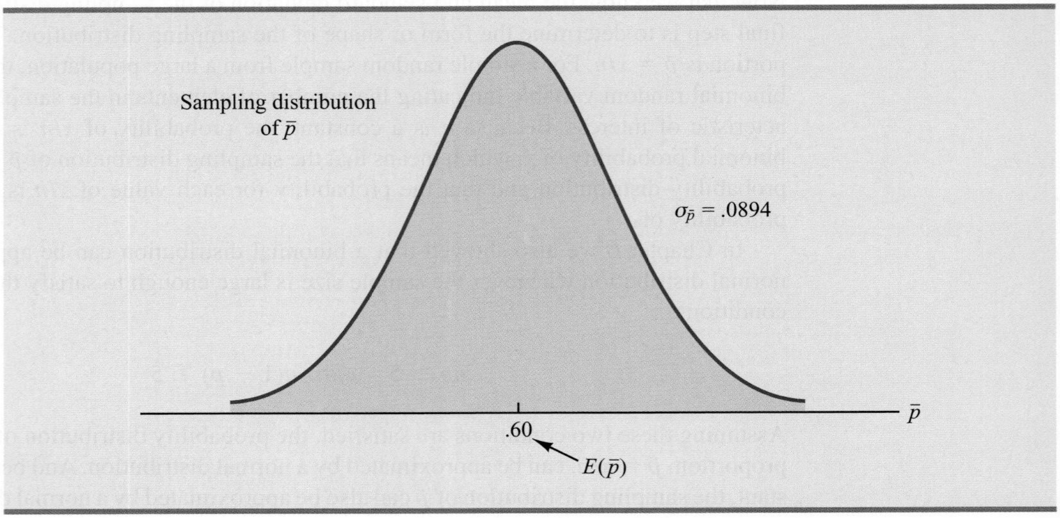

If we consider increasing the sample size to $n = 100$, the standard error of the proportion becomes

$$\sigma_{\bar{p}} = \sqrt{\frac{.60(1 - .60)}{100}} = .049$$

With a sample size of 100 EAI managers, the probability of the sample proportion having a value within .05 of the population proportion can now be computed. Because the sampling distribution is approximately normal, with mean .60 and standard deviation .049, we can use the standard normal probability table to find the area or probability. At $\bar{p} = .65$, we have $z = (.65 - .60)/.049 = 1.02$. Referring to the standard normal probability table, we see that the cumulative probability corresponding to $z = 1.02$ is .8461. Similarly, at

FIGURE 7.9 PROBABILITY OF OBTAINING $\bar{p}$ BETWEEN .55 AND .65

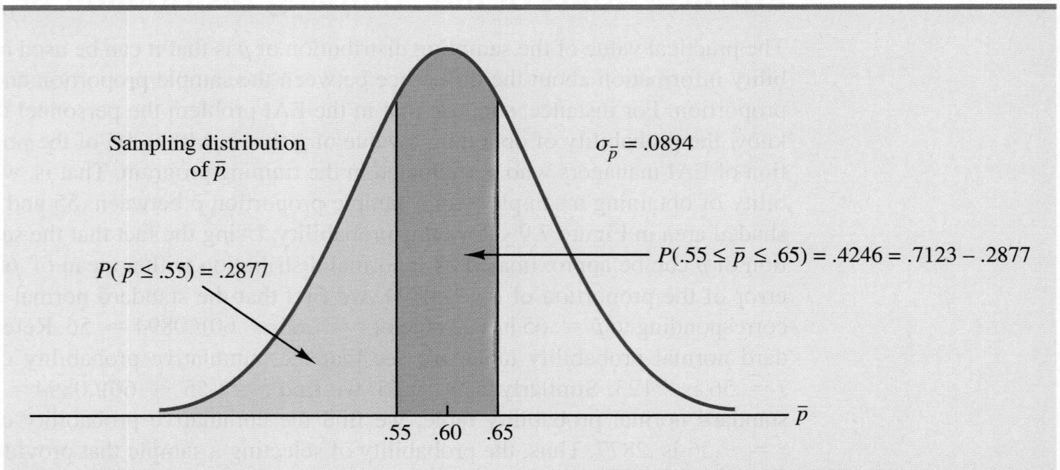

$\bar{p} = .55$, we have $z = (.55 - .60)/.049 = -1.02$. We find the cumulative probability corresponding to $z = -1.02$ is .1539. Thus, if the sample size is increased from 30 to 100, the probability that the sample proportion $\bar{p}$ is within .05 of the population proportion p will increase to $.8461 - .1539 = .6922$.

Exercises

Methods

31. A simple random sample of size 100 is selected from a population with $p = .40$.
    a. What is the expected value of $\bar{p}$?
    b. What is the standard error of $\bar{p}$?
    c. Show the sampling distribution of $\bar{p}$.
    d. What does the sampling distribution of $\bar{p}$ show?

SELF test

32. A population proportion is .40. A simple random sample of size 200 will be taken and the sample proportion $\bar{p}$ will be used to estimate the population proportion.
    a. What is the probability that the sample proportion will be within $\pm.03$ of the population proportion?
    b. What is the probability that the sample proportion will be within $\pm.05$ of the population proportion?

33. Assume that the population proportion is .55. Compute the standard error of the proportion, $\sigma_{\bar{p}}$, for sample sizes of 100, 200, 500, and 1000. What can you say about the size of the standard error of the proportion as the sample size is increased?

34. The population proportion is .30. What is the probability that a sample proportion will be within $\pm.04$ of the population proportion for each of the following sample sizes?
    a. $n = 100$
    b. $n = 200$
    c. $n = 500$
    d. $n = 1000$
    e. What is the advantage of a larger sample size?

Applications

SELF test

35. The president of Doerman Distributors, Inc., believes that 30% of the firm's orders come from first-time customers. A random sample of 100 orders will be used to estimate the proportion of first-time customers.
    a. Assume that the president is correct and $p = .30$. What is the sampling distribution of $\bar{p}$ for this study?
    b. What is the probability that the sample proportion $\bar{p}$ will be between .20 and .40?
    c. What is the probability that the sample proportion will be between .25 and .35?

36. *The Cincinnati Enquirer* reported that, in the United States, 66% of adults and 87% of youths ages 12 to 17 use the Internet (*The Cincinnati Enquirer*, February 7, 2006). Use the reported numbers as the population proportions and assume that samples of 300 adults and 300 youths will be used to learn about attitudes toward Internet security.
    a. Show the sampling distribution of $\bar{p}$ where $\bar{p}$ is the sample proportion of adults using the Internet.
    b. What is the probability that the sample proportion of adults using the Internet will be within $\pm.04$ of the population proportion?
    c. What is the probability that the sample proportion of youths using the Internet will be within $\pm.04$ of the population proportion?

d. Is the probability different in parts (b) and (c)? If so, why?
e. Answer part (b) for a sample of size 600. Is the probability smaller? Why?

37. People end up tossing 12% of what they buy at the grocery store (*Reader's Digest*, March, 2009). Assume this is the true population proportion and that you plan to take a sample survey of 540 grocery shoppers to further investigate their behavior.
a. Show the sampling distribution of $\bar{p}$, the proportion of groceries thrown out by your sample respondents.
b. What is the probability that your survey will provide a sample proportion within $\pm.03$ of the population proportion?
c. What is the probability that your survey will provide a sample proportion within $\pm.015$ of the population proportion?

38. Roper ASW conducted a survey to learn about American adults' attitudes toward money and happiness (*Money,* October 2003). Fifty-six percent of the respondents said they balance their checkbook at least once a month.
a. Suppose a sample of 400 American adults were taken. Show the sampling distribution of the proportion of adults who balance their checkbook at least once a month.
b. What is the probability that the sample proportion will be within $\pm.02$ of the population proportion?
c. What is the probability that the sample proportion will be within $\pm.04$ of the population proportion?

39. In 2008 the Better Business Bureau settled 75% of complaints they received (*USA Today*, March 2, 2009). Suppose you have been hired by the Better Business Bureau to investigate the complaints they received this year involving new car dealers. You plan to select a sample of new car dealer complaints to estimate the proportion of complaints the Better Business Bureau is able to settle. Assume the population proportion of complaints settled for new car dealers is .75, the same as the overall proportion of complaints settled in 2008.
a. Suppose you select a sample of 450 complaints involving new car dealers. Show the sampling distribution of $\bar{p}$.
b. Based upon a sample of 450 complaints, what is the probability that the sample proportion will be within .04 of the population proportion?
c. Suppose you select a sample of 200 complaints involving new car dealers. Show the sampling distribution of $\bar{p}$.
d. Based upon the smaller sample of only 200 complaints, what is the probability that the sample proportion will be within .04 of the population proportion?
e. As measured by the increase in probability, how much do you gain in precision by taking the larger sample in part (b)?

40. The Grocery Manufacturers of America reported that 76% of consumers read the ingredients listed on a product's label. Assume the population proportion is $p = .76$ and a sample of 400 consumers is selected from the population.
a. Show the sampling distribution of the sample proportion $\bar{p}$ where $\bar{p}$ is the proportion of the sampled consumers who read the ingredients listed on a product's label.
b. What is the probability that the sample proportion will be within $\pm.03$ of the population proportion?
c. Answer part (b) for a sample of 750 consumers.

41. The Food Marketing Institute shows that 17% of households spend more than \$100 per week on groceries. Assume the population proportion is $p = .17$ and a simple random sample of 800 households will be selected from the population.
a. Show the sampling distribution of $\bar{p}$, the sample proportion of households spending more than \$100 per week on groceries.
b. What is the probability that the sample proportion will be within $\pm.02$ of the population proportion?
c. Answer part (b) for a sample of 1600 households.

7.7 Properties of Point Estimators

In this chapter we showed how sample statistics such as a sample mean $\bar{x}$, a sample standard deviation s, and a sample proportion $\bar{p}$ can be used as point estimators of their corresponding population parameters μ, σ, and p. It is intuitively appealing that each of these sample statistics is the point estimator of its corresponding population parameter. However, before using a sample statistic as a point estimator, statisticians check to see whether the sample statistic demonstrates certain properties associated with good point estimators. In this section we discuss three properties of good point estimators: unbiased, efficiency, and consistency.

Because several different sample statistics can be used as point estimators of different population parameters, we use the following general notation in this section.

$$\theta = \text{the population parameter of interest}$$
$$\hat{\theta} = \text{the sample statistic or point estimator of } \theta$$

The notation θ is the Greek letter theta, and the notation $\hat{\theta}$ is pronounced "theta-hat." In general, θ represents any population parameter such as a population mean, population standard deviation, population proportion, and so on; $\hat{\theta}$ represents the corresponding sample statistic such as the sample mean, sample standard deviation, and sample proportion.

Unbiased

If the expected value of the sample statistic is equal to the population parameter being estimated, the sample statistic is said to be an *unbiased estimator* of the population parameter.

UNBIASED

The sample statistic $\hat{\theta}$ is an unbiased estimator of the population parameter θ if

$$E(\hat{\theta}) = \theta$$

where

$$E(\hat{\theta}) = \text{the expected value of the sample statistic } \hat{\theta}$$

Hence, the expected value, or mean, of all possible values of an unbiased sample statistic is equal to the population parameter being estimated.

Figure 7.10 shows the cases of unbiased and biased point estimators. In the illustration showing the unbiased estimator, the mean of the sampling distribution is equal to the value of the population parameter. The estimation errors balance out in this case, because sometimes the value of the point estimator $\hat{\theta}$ may be less than θ and other times it may be greater than θ. In the case of a biased estimator, the mean of the sampling distribution is less than or greater than the value of the population parameter. In the illustration in Panel B of Figure 7.10, $E(\hat{\theta})$ is greater than θ; thus, the sample statistic has a high probability of overestimating the value of the population parameter. The amount of the bias is shown in the figure.

In discussing the sampling distributions of the sample mean and the sample proportion, we stated that $E(\bar{x}) = \mu$ and $E(\bar{p}) = p$. Thus, both $\bar{x}$ and $\bar{p}$ are unbiased estimators of their corresponding population parameters μ and p.

In the case of the sample standard deviation s and the sample variance s^2, it can be shown that $E(s^2) = \sigma^2$. Thus, we conclude that the sample variance s^2 is an unbiased estimator of the population variance σ^2. In fact, when we first presented the formulas for the

FIGURE 7.10 EXAMPLES OF UNBIASED AND BIASED POINT ESTIMATORS

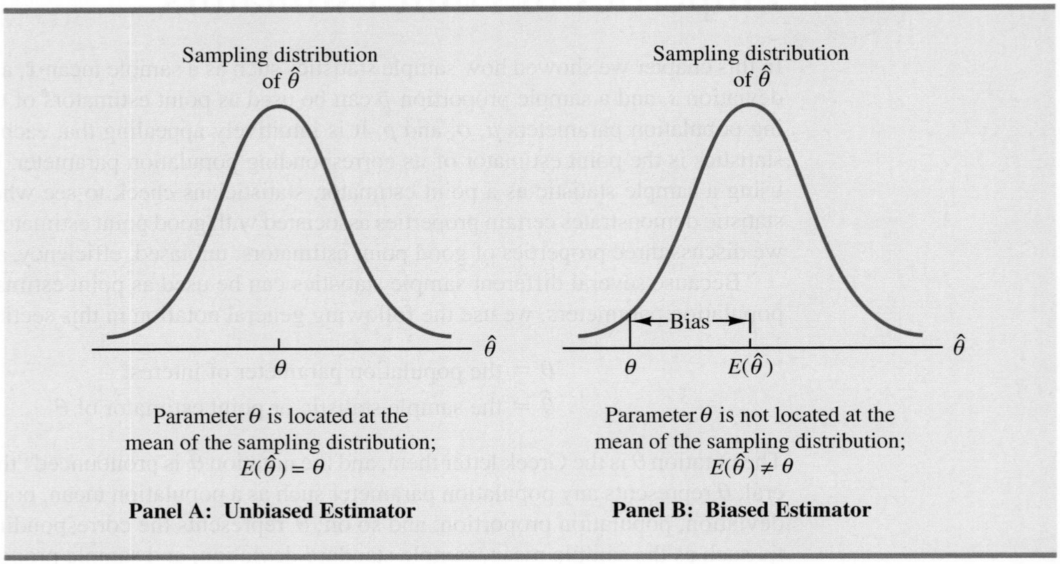

sample variance and the sample standard deviation in Chapter 3, $n - 1$ rather than n was used in the denominator. The reason for using $n - 1$ rather than n is to make the sample variance an unbiased estimator of the population variance.

Efficiency

Assume that a simple random sample of n elements can be used to provide two unbiased point estimators of the same population parameter. In this situation, we would prefer to use the point estimator with the smaller standard error, because it tends to provide estimates closer to the population parameter. The point estimator with the smaller standard error is said to have greater **relative efficiency** than the other.

Figure 7.11 shows the sampling distributions of two unbiased point estimators, $\hat{\theta}_1$ and $\hat{\theta}_2$. Note that the standard error of $\hat{\theta}_1$ is less than the standard error of $\hat{\theta}_2$; thus, values

FIGURE 7.11 SAMPLING DISTRIBUTIONS OF TWO UNBIASED POINT ESTIMATORS

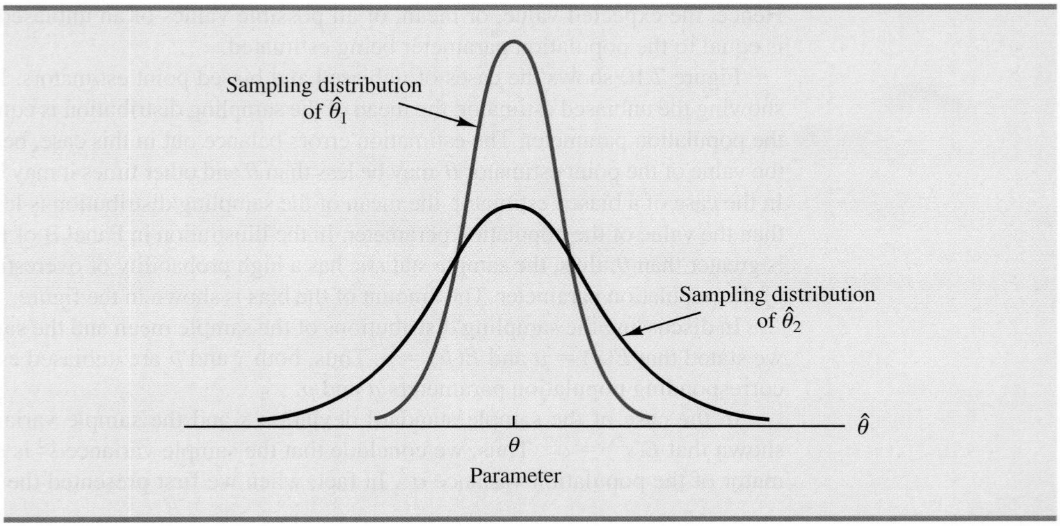

When sampling from a normal population, the standard error of the sample mean is less than the standard error of the sample median. Thus, the sample mean is more efficient than the sample median.

of $\hat{\theta}_1$ have a greater chance of being close to the parameter θ than do values of $\hat{\theta}_2$. Because the standard error of point estimator $\hat{\theta}_1$ is less than the standard error of point estimator $\hat{\theta}_2$, $\hat{\theta}_1$ is relatively more efficient than $\hat{\theta}_2$ and is the preferred point estimator.

Consistency

A third property associated with good point estimators is **consistency**. Loosely speaking, a point estimator is consistent if the values of the point estimator tend to become closer to the population parameter as the sample size becomes larger. In other words, a large sample size tends to provide a better point estimate than a small sample size. Note that for the sample mean $\bar{x}$, we showed that the standard error of $\bar{x}$ is given by $\sigma_{\bar{x}} = \sigma/\sqrt{n}$. Because $\sigma_{\bar{x}}$ is related to the sample size such that larger sample sizes provide smaller values for $\sigma_{\bar{x}}$, we conclude that a larger sample size tends to provide point estimates closer to the population mean μ. In this sense, we can say that the sample mean $\bar{x}$ is a consistent estimator of the population mean μ. Using a similar rationale, we can also conclude that the sample proportion $\bar{p}$ is a consistent estimator of the population proportion p.

NOTES AND COMMENTS

In Chapter 3 we stated that the mean and the median are two measures of central location. In this chapter we discussed only the mean. The reason is that in sampling from a normal population, where the population mean and population median are identical, the standard error of the median is approximately 25% larger than the standard error of the mean. Recall that in the EAI problem where $n = 30$, the standard error of the mean is $\sigma_{\bar{x}} = 730.3$. The standard error of the median for this problem would be $1.25 \times (730.3) = 913$. As a result, the sample mean is more efficient and will have a higher probability of being within a specified distance of the population mean.

7.8 Other Sampling Methods

We described simple random sampling as a procedure for sampling from a finite population and discussed the properties of the sampling distributions of $\bar{x}$ and $\bar{p}$ when simple random sampling is used. Other methods such as stratified random sampling, cluster sampling, and systematic sampling provide advantages over simple random sampling in some of these situations. In this section we briefly introduce these alternative sampling methods. A more in-depth treatment is provided in Chapter 22, which is located on the website that accompanies the text.

This section provides a brief introduction to survey sampling methods other than simple random sampling.

Stratified Random Sampling

Stratified random sampling works best when the variance among elements in each stratum is relatively small.

In **stratified random sampling**, the elements in the population are first divided into groups called *strata*, such that each element in the population belongs to one and only one stratum. The basis for forming the strata, such as department, location, age, industry type, and so on, is at the discretion of the designer of the sample. However, the best results are obtained when the elements within each stratum are as much alike as possible. Figure 7.12 is a diagram of a population divided into H strata.

After the strata are formed, a simple random sample is taken from each stratum. Formulas are available for combining the results for the individual stratum samples into one estimate of the population parameter of interest. The value of stratified random sampling depends on how homogeneous the elements are within the strata. If elements within strata

FIGURE 7.12 DIAGRAM FOR STRATIFIED RANDOM SAMPLING

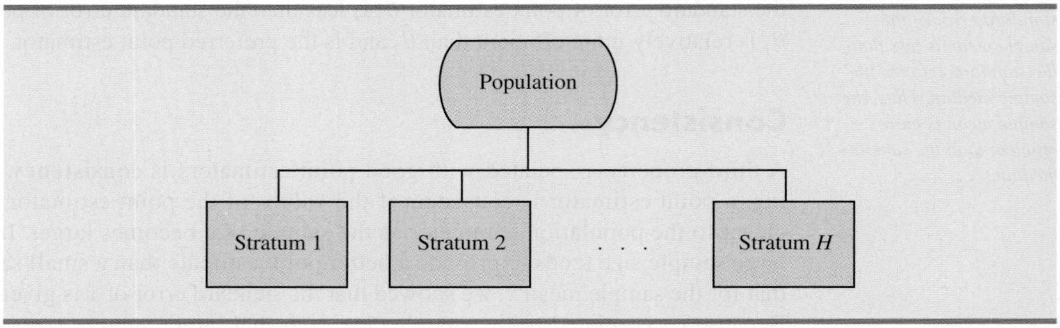

are alike, the strata will have low variances. Thus relatively small sample sizes can be used to obtain good estimates of the strata characteristics. If strata are homogeneous, the stratified random sampling procedure provides results just as precise as those of simple random sampling by using a smaller total sample size.

Cluster Sampling

Cluster sampling works best when each cluster provides a small-scale representation of the population.

In **cluster sampling**, the elements in the population are first divided into separate groups called *clusters*. Each element of the population belongs to one and only one cluster (see Figure 7.13). A simple random sample of the clusters is then taken. All elements within each sampled cluster form the sample. Cluster sampling tends to provide the best results when the elements within the clusters are not alike. In the ideal case, each cluster is a representative small-scale version of the entire population. The value of cluster sampling depends on how representative each cluster is of the entire population. If all clusters are alike in this regard, sampling a small number of clusters will provide good estimates of the population parameters.

One of the primary applications of cluster sampling is area sampling, where clusters are city blocks or other well-defined areas. Cluster sampling generally requires a larger total sample size than either simple random sampling or stratified random sampling. However, it can result in cost savings because of the fact that when an interviewer is sent to a sampled cluster (e.g., a city-block location), many sample observations can be obtained in a relatively short time. Hence, a larger sample size may be obtainable with a significantly lower total cost.

Systematic Sampling

In some sampling situations, especially those with large populations, it is time-consuming to select a simple random sample by first finding a random number and then counting or

FIGURE 7.13 DIAGRAM FOR CLUSTER SAMPLING

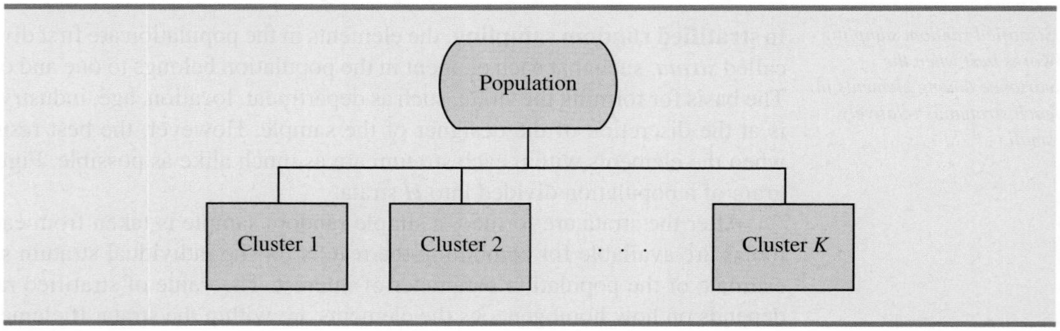

searching through the list of the population until the corresponding element is found. An alternative to simple random sampling is **systematic sampling**. For example, if a sample size of 50 is desired from a population containing 5000 elements, we will sample one element for every 5000/50 = 100 elements in the population. A systematic sample for this case involves selecting randomly one of the first 100 elements from the population list. Other sample elements are identified by starting with the first sampled element and then selecting every 100th element that follows in the population list. In effect, the sample of 50 is identified by moving systematically through the population and identifying every 100th element after the first randomly selected element. The sample of 50 usually will be easier to identify in this way than it would be if simple random sampling were used. Because the first element selected is a random choice, a systematic sample is usually assumed to have the properties of a simple random sample. This assumption is especially applicable when the list of elements in the population is a random ordering of the elements.

Convenience Sampling

The sampling methods discussed thus far are referred to as *probability sampling* techniques. Elements selected from the population have a known probability of being included in the sample. The advantage of probability sampling is that the sampling distribution of the appropriate sample statistic generally can be identified. Formulas such as the ones for simple random sampling presented in this chapter can be used to determine the properties of the sampling distribution. Then the sampling distribution can be used to make probability statements about the error associated with using the sample results to make inferences about the population.

Convenience sampling is a *nonprobability sampling* technique. As the name implies, the sample is identified primarily by convenience. Elements are included in the sample without prespecified or known probabilities of being selected. For example, a professor conducting research at a university may use student volunteers to constitute a sample simply because they are readily available and will participate as subjects for little or no cost. Similarly, an inspector may sample a shipment of oranges by selecting oranges haphazardly from among several crates. Labeling each orange and using a probability method of sampling would be impractical. Samples such as wildlife captures and volunteer panels for consumer research are also convenience samples.

Convenience samples have the advantage of relatively easy sample selection and data collection; however, it is impossible to evaluate the "goodness" of the sample in terms of its representativeness of the population. A convenience sample may provide good results or it may not; no statistically justified procedure allows a probability analysis and inference about the quality of the sample results. Sometimes researchers apply statistical methods designed for probability samples to a convenience sample, arguing that the convenience sample can be treated as though it were a probability sample. However, this argument cannot be supported, and we should be cautious in interpreting the results of convenience samples that are used to make inferences about populations.

Judgment Sampling

One additional nonprobability sampling technique is **judgment sampling**. In this approach, the person most knowledgeable on the subject of the study selects elements of the population that he or she feels are most representative of the population. Often this method is a relatively easy way of selecting a sample. For example, a reporter may sample two or three senators, judging that those senators reflect the general opinion of all senators. However, the quality of the sample results depends on the judgment of the person selecting the sample. Again, great caution is warranted in drawing conclusions based on judgment samples used to make inferences about populations.

NOTES AND COMMENTS

We recommend using probability sampling methods when sampling from finite populations: simple random sampling, stratified random sampling, cluster sampling, or systematic sampling. For these methods, formulas are available for evaluating the "goodness" of the sample results in terms of the closeness of the results to the population parameters being estimated. An evaluation of the goodness cannot be made with convenience or judgment sampling. Thus, great care should be used in interpreting the results based on nonprobability sampling methods.

Summary

In this chapter we presented the concepts of sampling and sampling distributions. We demonstrated how a simple random sample can be selected from a finite population and how a random sample can be collected from an infinite population. The data collected from such samples can be used to develop point estimates of population parameters. Because different samples provide different values for the point estimators, point estimators such as $\bar{x}$ and $\bar{p}$ are random variables. The probability distribution of such a random variable is called a sampling distribution. In particular, we described the sampling distributions of the sample mean $\bar{x}$ and the sample proportion $\bar{p}$.

In considering the characteristics of the sampling distributions of $\bar{x}$ and $\bar{p}$, we stated that $E(\bar{x}) = \mu$ and $E(\bar{p}) = p$. After developing the standard deviation or standard error formulas for these estimators, we described the conditions necessary for the sampling distributions of $\bar{x}$ and $\bar{p}$ to follow a normal distribution. Other sampling methods including stratified random sampling, cluster sampling, systematic sampling, convenience sampling, and judgment sampling were discussed.

Glossary

Sampled population The population from which the sample is taken.

Frame A listing of the elements the sample will be selected from.

Parameter A numerical characteristic of a population, such as a population mean μ, a population standard deviation σ, a population proportion p, and so on.

Simple random sample A simple random sample of size n from a finite population of size N is a sample selected such that each possible sample of size n has the same probability of being selected.

Random sample A random sample from an infinite population is a sample selected such that the following conditions are satisfied: (1) Each element selected comes from the same population; (2) each element is selected independently.

Sampling without replacement Once an element has been included in the sample, it is removed from the population and cannot be selected a second time.

Sampling with replacement Once an element has been included in the sample, it is returned to the population. A previously selected element can be selected again and therefore may appear in the sample more than once.

Sample statistic A sample characteristic, such as a sample mean $\bar{x}$, a sample standard deviation s, a sample proportion $\bar{p}$, and so on. The value of the sample statistic is used to estimate the value of the corresponding population parameter.

Point estimator The sample statistic, such as $\bar{x}$, s, or $\bar{p}$, that provides the point estimate of the population parameter.

Point estimate The value of a point estimator used in a particular instance as an estimate of a population parameter.

Target population The population for which statistical inference such as point estimates are made. It is important for the target population to correspond as closely as possible to the sampled population.

Sampling distribution A probability distribution consisting of all possible values of a sample statistic.

Unbiased A property of a point estimator that is present when the expected value of the point estimator is equal to the population parameter it estimates.

Finite population correction factor The term $\sqrt{(N - n)/(N - 1)}$ that is used in the formulas for $\sigma_{\bar{x}}$ and $\sigma_{\bar{p}}$ whenever a finite population, rather than an infinite population, is being sampled. The generally accepted rule of thumb is to ignore the finite population correction factor whenever $n/N \leq .05$.

Standard error The standard deviation of a point estimator.

Central limit theorem A theorem that enables one to use the normal probability distribution to approximate the sampling distribution of $\bar{x}$ whenever the sample size is large.

Relative efficiency Given two unbiased point estimators of the same population parameter, the point estimator with the smaller standard error is more efficient.

Consistency A property of a point estimator that is present whenever larger sample sizes tend to provide point estimates closer to the population parameter.

Stratified random sampling A probability sampling method in which the population is first divided into strata and a simple random sample is then taken from each stratum.

Cluster sampling A probability sampling method in which the population is first divided into clusters and then a simple random sample of the clusters is taken.

Systematic sampling A probability sampling method in which we randomly select one of the first k elements and then select every kth element thereafter.

Convenience sampling A nonprobability method of sampling whereby elements are selected for the sample on the basis of convenience.

Judgment sampling A nonprobability method of sampling whereby elements are selected for the sample based on the judgment of the person doing the study.

Key Formulas

Expected Value of $\bar{x}$

$$E(\bar{x}) = \mu \tag{7.1}$$

Standard Deviation of $\bar{x}$ (Standard Error)

Finite Population *Infinite Population*

$$\sigma_{\bar{x}} = \sqrt{\frac{N - n}{N - 1}}\left(\frac{\sigma}{\sqrt{n}}\right) \qquad \sigma_{\bar{x}} = \frac{\sigma}{\sqrt{n}} \tag{7.2}$$

Expected Value of $\bar{p}$

$$E(\bar{p}) = p \tag{7.4}$$

Standard Deviation of $\bar{p}$ (Standard Error)

Finite Population *Infinite Population*

$$\sigma_{\bar{p}} = \sqrt{\frac{N-n}{N-1}}\sqrt{\frac{p(1-p)}{n}} \qquad \sigma_{\bar{p}} = \sqrt{\frac{p(1-p)}{n}} \tag{7.5}$$

Supplementary Exercises

42. *U.S. News & World Report* publishes comprehensive information on America's best colleges (*America's Best Colleges*, 2009 ed.). Among other things, they provide a listing of their 133 best national universities. You would like to take a sample of these universities for a follow-up study on their students. Begin at the bottom of the third column of random digits in Table 7.1. Ignoring the first two digits in each five-number group and using the three-digit random numbers beginning with 959 read *up* the column to identify the number (from 1 to 133) of the first seven universities to be included in a simple random sample. Continue by starting at the bottom of the fourth and fifth columns and reading up if necessary.

43. Americans have become increasingly concerned about the rising cost of Medicare. In 1990, the average annual Medicare spending per enrollee was \$3267; in 2003, the average annual Medicare spending per enrollee was \$6883 (*Money,* Fall 2003). Suppose you hired a consulting firm to take a sample of fifty 2003 Medicare enrollees to further investigate the nature of expenditures. Assume the population standard deviation for 2003 was \$2000.
    a. Show the sampling distribution of the mean amount of Medicare spending for a sample of fifty 2003 enrollees.
    b. What is the probability the sample mean will be within ±\$300 of the population mean?
    c. What is the probability the sample mean will be greater than \$7500? If the consulting firm tells you the sample mean for the Medicare enrollees they interviewed was \$7500, would you question whether they followed correct simple random sampling procedures? Why or why not?

44. *BusinessWeek* surveyed MBA alumni 10 years after graduation (*BusinessWeek,* September 22, 2003). One finding was that alumni spend an average of \$115.50 per week eating out socially. You have been asked to conduct a follow-up study by taking a sample of 40 of these MBA alumni. Assume the population standard deviation is \$35.
    a. Show the sampling distribution of $\bar{x}$, the sample mean weekly expenditure for the 40 MBA alumni.
    b. What is the probability the sample mean will be within \$10 of the population mean?
    c. Suppose you find a sample mean of \$100. What is the probability of finding a sample mean of \$100 or less? Would you consider this sample to be an unusually low spending group of alumni? Why or why not?

45. The mean television viewing time for Americans is 15 hours per week (*Money,* November 2003). Suppose a sample of 60 Americans is taken to further investigate viewing habits. Assume the population standard deviation for weekly viewing time is $\sigma = 4$ hours.
    a. What is the probability the sample mean will be within 1 hour of the population mean?
    b. What is the probability the sample mean will be within 45 minutes of the population mean?

46. After deducting grants based on need, the average cost to attend the University of Southern California (USC) is \$27,175 (*U.S. News & World Report, America's Best Colleges,* 2009 ed.). Assume the population standard deviation is \$7400. Suppose that a random sample of 60 USC students will be taken from this population.
    a. What is the value of the standard error of the mean?
    b. What is the probability that the sample mean will be more than \$27,175?

c. What is the probability that the sample mean will be within \$1000 of the population mean?

d. How would the probability in part (c) change if the sample size were increased to 100?

47. Three firms carry inventories that differ in size. Firm A's inventory contains 2000 items, firm B's inventory contains 5000 items, and firm C's inventory contains 10,000 items. The population standard deviation for the cost of the items in each firm's inventory is $\sigma = 144$. A statistical consultant recommends that each firm take a sample of 50 items from its inventory to provide statistically valid estimates of the average cost per item. Managers of the small firm state that because it has the smallest population, it should be able to make the estimate from a much smaller sample than that required by the larger firms. However, the consultant states that to obtain the same standard error and thus the same precision in the sample results, all firms should use the same sample size regardless of population size.

a. Using the finite population correction factor, compute the standard error for each of the three firms given a sample of size 50.

b. What is the probability that for each firm the sample mean $\bar{x}$ will be within ± 25 of the population mean μ?

48. A researcher reports survey results by stating that the standard error of the mean is 20. The population standard deviation is 500.

a. How large was the sample used in this survey?

b. What is the probability that the point estimate was within ± 25 of the population mean?

49. A production process is checked periodically by a quality control inspector. The inspector selects simple random samples of 30 finished products and computes the sample mean product weights $\bar{x}$. If test results over a long period of time show that 5% of the $\bar{x}$ values are over 2.1 pounds and 5% are under 1.9 pounds, what are the mean and the standard deviation for the population of products produced with this process?

50. About 28% of private companies are owned by women (*The Cincinnati Enquirer,* January 26, 2006). Answer the following questions based on a sample of 240 private companies.

a. Show the sampling distribution of $\bar{p}$, the sample proportion of companies that are owned by women.

b. What is the probability the sample proportion will be within $\pm .04$ of the population proportion?

c. What is the probability the sample proportion will be within $\pm .02$ of the population proportion?

51. A market research firm conducts telephone surveys with a 40% historical response rate. What is the probability that in a new sample of 400 telephone numbers, at least 150 individuals will cooperate and respond to the questions? In other words, what is the probability that the sample proportion will be at least $150/400 = .375$?

52. Advertisers contract with Internet service providers and search engines to place ads on websites. They pay a fee based on the number of potential customers who click on their ad. Unfortunately, click fraud—the practice of someone clicking on an ad solely for the purpose of driving up advertising revenue—has become a problem. Forty percent of advertisers claim they have been a victim of click fraud (*BusinessWeek,* March 13, 2006). Suppose a simple random sample of 380 advertisers will be taken to learn more about how they are affected by this practice.

a. What is the probability that the sample proportion will be within $\pm .04$ of the population proportion experiencing click fraud?

b. What is the probability that the sample proportion will be greater than .45?

53. The proportion of individuals insured by the All-Driver Automobile Insurance Company who received at least one traffic ticket during a five-year period is .15.

a. Show the sampling distribution of $\bar{p}$ if a random sample of 150 insured individuals is used to estimate the proportion having received at least one ticket.

b. What is the probability that the sample proportion will be within $\pm .03$ of the population proportion?

54. Lori Jeffrey is a successful sales representative for a major publisher of college textbooks. Historically, Lori obtains a book adoption on 25% of her sales calls. Viewing her sales calls for one month as a sample of all possible sales calls, assume that a statistical analysis of the data yields a standard error of the proportion of .0625.
    a. How large was the sample used in this analysis? That is, how many sales calls did Lori make during the month?
    b. Let $\bar{p}$ indicate the sample proportion of book adoptions obtained during the month. Show the sampling distribution of $\bar{p}$.
    c. Using the sampling distribution of $\bar{p}$, compute the probability that Lori will obtain book adoptions on 30% or more of her sales calls during a one-month period.

Appendix 7.1 The Expected Value and Standard Deviation of $\bar{x}$

In this appendix we present the mathematical basis for the expressions for $E(\bar{x})$, the expected value of $\bar{x}$ as given by equation (7.1), and $\sigma_{\bar{x}}$, the standard deviation of $\bar{x}$ as given by equation (7.2).

Expected Value of $\bar{x}$

Assume a population with mean μ and variance σ^2. A simple random sample of size n is selected with individual observations denoted $x_1, x_2, \ldots, x_n$. A sample mean $\bar{x}$ is computed as follows.

$$\bar{x} = \frac{\Sigma x_i}{n}$$

With repeated simple random samples of size n, $\bar{x}$ is a random variable that assumes different numerical values depending on the specific n items selected. The expected value of the random variable $\bar{x}$ is the mean of all possible $\bar{x}$ values.

$$\begin{aligned}\text{Mean of } \bar{x} = E(\bar{x}) &= E\left(\frac{\Sigma x_i}{n}\right)\\ &= \frac{1}{n}[E(x_1 + x_2 + \cdots + x_n)]\\ &= \frac{1}{n}[E(x_1) + E(x_2) + \cdots + E(x_n)]\end{aligned}$$

For any x_i we have $E(x_i) = \mu$; therefore we can write

$$\begin{aligned}E(\bar{x}) &= \frac{1}{n}(\mu + \mu + \cdots + \mu)\\ &= \frac{1}{n}(n\mu) = \mu\end{aligned}$$

This result shows that the mean of all possible $\bar{x}$ values is the same as the population mean μ. That is, $E(\bar{x}) = \mu$.

Standard Deviation of $\bar{x}$

Again assume a population with mean μ, variance σ^2, and a sample mean given by

$$\bar{x} = \frac{\Sigma x_i}{n}$$

With repeated simple random samples of size n, we know that $\bar{x}$ is a random variable that takes different numerical values depending on the specific n items selected. What follows is the derivation of the expression for the standard deviation of the $\bar{x}$ values, $\sigma_{\bar{x}}$, for the case of an infinite population. The derivation of the expression for $\sigma_{\bar{x}}$ for a finite population when sampling is done without replacement is more difficult and is beyond the scope of this text.

Returning to the infinite population case, recall that a simple random sample from an infinite population consists of observations $x_1, x_2, \ldots, x_n$ that are independent. The following two expressions are general formulas for the variance of random variables.

$$\text{Var}(ax) = a^2\,\text{Var}(x)$$

where a is a constant and x is a random variable, and

$$\text{Var}(x + y) = \text{Var}(x) + \text{Var}(y)$$

where x and y are *independent* random variables. Using the two preceding equations, we can develop the expression for the variance of the random variable $\bar{x}$ as follows.

$$\text{Var}(\bar{x}) = \text{Var}\left(\frac{\Sigma x_i}{n}\right) = \text{Var}\left(\frac{1}{n}\Sigma x_i\right)$$

Then, with $1/n$ a constant, we have

$$\text{Var}(\bar{x}) = \left(\frac{1}{n}\right)^2 \text{Var}(\Sigma x_i)$$
$$= \left(\frac{1}{n}\right)^2 \text{Var}(x_1 + x_2 + \cdots + x_n)$$

In the infinite population case, the random variables $x_1, x_2, \ldots, x_n$ are independent, which enables us to write

$$\text{Var}(\bar{x}) = \left(\frac{1}{n}\right)^2 [\text{Var}(x_1) + \text{Var}(x_2) + \cdots + \text{Var}(x_n)]$$

For any x_i, we have $\text{Var}(x_i) = \sigma^2$; therefore we have

$$\text{Var}(\bar{x}) = \left(\frac{1}{n}\right)^2 (\sigma^2 + \sigma^2 + \cdots + \sigma^2)$$

With n values of σ^2 in this expression, we have

$$\text{Var}(\bar{x}) = \left(\frac{1}{n}\right)^2 (n\sigma^2) = \frac{\sigma^2}{n}$$

Taking the square root provides the formula for the standard deviation of $\bar{x}$.

$$\sigma_{\bar{x}} = \sqrt{\text{Var}(\bar{x})} = \frac{\sigma}{\sqrt{n}}$$

Appendix 7.2 Random Sampling with Minitab

If a list of the elements in a population is available in a Minitab file, Minitab can be used to select a simple random sample. For example, a list of the top 100 metropolitan areas in the United States and Canada is provided in column 1 of the data set MetAreas (*Places Rated Almanac—The Millennium Edition 2000*). Column 2 contains the overall rating of each metropolitan area. The first 10 metropolitan areas in the data set and their corresponding ratings are shown in Table 7.6.

Suppose that you would like to select a simple random sample of 30 metropolitan areas in order to do an in-depth study of the cost of living in the United States and Canada. The following steps can be used to select the sample.

Step 1. Select the **Calc** pull-down menu
Step 2. Choose **Random Data**
Step 3. Choose **Sample From Columns**
Step 4. When the Sample From Columns dialog box appears:
Enter 30 in the **Number of rows to sample** box
Enter C1 C2 in the **From columns** box below
Enter C3 C4 in the **Store samples in** box
Step 5. Click **OK**

The random sample of 30 metropolitan areas appears in columns C3 and C4.

Appendix 7.3 Random Sampling with Excel

If a list of the elements in a population is available in an Excel file, Excel can be used to select a simple random sample. For example, a list of the top 100 metropolitan areas in the United States and Canada is provided in column A of the data set MetAreas (*Places Rated Almanac—The Millennium Edition 2000*). Column B contains the overall rating of each metropolitan area. The first 10 metropolitan areas in the data set and their corresponding ratings are shown in Table 7.6. Assume that you would like to select a simple random sample of 30 metropolitan areas in order to do an in-depth study of the cost of living in the United States and Canada.

TABLE 7.6 OVERALL RATING FOR THE FIRST 10 METROPOLITAN AREAS IN THE DATA SET METAREAS

WEB file
MetAreas

Metropolitan Area	Rating
Albany, NY	64.18
Albuquerque, NM	66.16
Appleton, WI	60.56
Atlanta, GA	69.97
Austin, TX	71.48
Baltimore, MD	69.75
Birmingham, AL	69.59
Boise City, ID	68.36
Boston, MA	68.99
Buffalo, NY	66.10

The rows of any Excel data set can be placed in a random order by adding an extra column to the data set and filling the column with random numbers using the =RAND() function. Then, using Excel's sort ascending capability on the random number column, the rows of the data set will be reordered randomly. The random sample of size n appears in the first n rows of the reordered data set.

In the MetAreas data set, labels are in row 1 and the 100 metropolitan areas are in rows 2 to 101. The following steps can be used to select a simple random sample of 30 metropolitan areas.

Step 1. Enter =RAND() in cell C2
Step 2. Copy cell C2 to cells C3:C101
Step 3. Select any cell in Column C
Step 4. Click the **Home** tab on the Ribbon
Step 5. In the **Editing** group, click **Sort & Filter**
Step 6. Click **Sort Smallest to Largest**

The random sample of 30 metropolitan areas appears in rows 2 to 31 of the reordered data set. The random numbers in column C are no longer necessary and can be deleted if desired.

Appendix 7.4 Random Sampling with StatTools

WEB file
MetAreas

If a list of the elements in a population is available in an Excel file, StatTools Random Sample Utility can be used to select a simple random sample. For example, a list of the top 100 metropolitan areas in the United States and Canada is provided in column A of the data set MetAreas (*Places Rated Almanac—The Millennium Edition 2000*). Column B contains the overall rating of each metropolitan area. Assume that you would like to select a simple random sample of 30 metropolitan areas in order to do an in-depth study of the cost of living in the United States and Canada.

Begin by using the Data Set Manager to create a StatTools data set for these data using the procedure described in the appendix to Chapter 1. The following steps will generate a simple random sample of 30 metropolitan areas.

Step 1. Click the **StatTools** tab on the Ribbon
Step 2. In the **Data Group** click **Data Utilities**
Step 3. Choose the **Random Sample** option
Step 4. When the StatTools—Random Sample Utility dialog box appears:
In the **Variables** section:
Select **Metropolitan Area**
Select **Rating**
In the **Options** section:
Enter 1 in the **Number of Samples** box
Enter 30 in the **Sample Size** box
Click **OK**

The random sample of 30 metropolitan areas will appear in columns A and B of the worksheet entitled Random Sample.

CHAPTER 8

Interval Estimation

CONTENTS

STATISTICS *in* PRACTICE

FOOD LION*
SALISBURY, NORTH CAROLINA

Founded in 1957 as Food Town, Food Lion is one of the largest supermarket chains in the United States, with 1300 stores in 11 Southeastern and Mid-Atlantic states. The company sells more than 24,000 different products and offers nationally and regionally advertised brand-name merchandise, as well as a growing number of high-quality private label products manufactured especially for Food Lion. The company maintains its low price leadership and quality assurance through operating efficiencies such as standard store formats, innovative warehouse design, energy-efficient facilities, and data synchronization with suppliers. Food Lion looks to a future of continued innovation, growth, price leadership, and service to its customers.

Fresh bread arriving at a Food Lion Store. © Jeff Greenberg/PhotoEdit.

Being in an inventory-intense business, Food Lion made the decision to adopt the LIFO (last-in, first-out) method of inventory valuation. This method matches current costs against current revenues, which minimizes the effect of radical price changes on profit and loss results. In addition, the LIFO method reduces net income thereby reducing income taxes during periods of inflation.

Food Lion establishes a LIFO index for each of seven inventory pools: Grocery, Paper/Household, Pet Supplies, Health & Beauty Aids, Dairy, Cigarette/Tobacco, and Beer/Wine. For example, a LIFO index of 1.008 for the Grocery pool would indicate that the company's grocery inventory value at current costs reflects a 0.8% increase due to inflation over the most recent one-year period.

A LIFO index for each inventory pool requires that the year-end inventory count for each product be valued at the current year-end cost and at the preceding year-end cost. To avoid excessive time and expense associated with counting the inventory in all 1200 store locations, Food Lion selects a random sample of 50 stores. Year-end physical inventories are taken in each of the sample stores. The current-year and preceding-year costs for each item are then used to construct the required LIFO indexes for each inventory pool.

For a recent year, the sample estimate of the LIFO index for the Health & Beauty Aids inventory pool was 1.015. Using a 95% confidence level, Food Lion computed a margin of error of .006 for the sample estimate. Thus, the interval from 1.009 to 1.021 provided a 95% confidence interval estimate of the population LIFO index. This level of precision was judged to be very good.

In this chapter you will learn how to compute the margin of error associated with sample estimates. You will also learn how to use this information to construct and interpret interval estimates of a population mean and a population proportion.

*The authors are indebted to Keith Cunningham, Tax Director, and Bobby Harkey, Staff Tax Accountant, at Food Lion for providing this Statistics in Practice.

In Chapter 7, we stated that a point estimator is a sample statistic used to estimate a population parameter. For instance, the sample mean $\bar{x}$ is a point estimator of the population mean μ and the sample proportion $\bar{p}$ is a point estimator of the population proportion p. Because a point estimator cannot be expected to provide the exact value of the population parameter, an **interval estimate** is often computed by adding and subtracting a value, called the **margin of error**, to the point estimate. The general form of an interval estimate is as follows:

$$\text{Point estimate} \pm \text{Margin of error}$$

The purpose of an interval estimate is to provide information about how close the point estimate, provided by the sample, is to the value of the population parameter.

In this chapter we show how to compute interval estimates of a population mean μ and a population proportion p. The general form of an interval estimate of a population mean is

$$\bar{x} \pm \text{Margin of error}$$

Similarly, the general form of an interval estimate of a population proportion is

$$\bar{p} \pm \text{Margin of error}$$

The sampling distributions of $\bar{x}$ and $\bar{p}$ play key roles in computing these interval estimates.

8.1 Population Mean: σ Known

In order to develop an interval estimate of a population mean, either the population standard deviation σ or the sample standard deviation s must be used to compute the margin of error. In most applications σ is not known, and s is used to compute the margin of error. In some applications, however, large amounts of relevant historical data are available and can be used to estimate the population standard deviation prior to sampling. Also, in quality control applications where a process is assumed to be operating correctly, or "in control," it is appropriate to treat the population standard deviation as known. We refer to such cases as the **σ known** case. In this section we introduce an example in which it is reasonable to treat σ as known and show how to construct an interval estimate for this case.

Each week Lloyd's Department Store selects a simple random sample of 100 customers in order to learn about the amount spent per shopping trip. With x representing the amount spent per shopping trip, the sample mean $\bar{x}$ provides a point estimate of μ, the mean amount spent per shopping trip for the population of all Lloyd's customers. Lloyd's has been using the weekly survey for several years. Based on the historical data, Lloyd's now assumes a known value of $\sigma = \$20$ for the population standard deviation. The historical data also indicate that the population follows a normal distribution.

WEB file
Lloyd's

During the most recent week, Lloyd's surveyed 100 customers ($n = 100$) and obtained a sample mean of $\bar{x} = \$82$. The sample mean amount spent provides a point estimate of the population mean amount spent per shopping trip, μ. In the discussion that follows, we show how to compute the margin of error for this estimate and develop an interval estimate of the population mean.

Margin of Error and the Interval Estimate

In Chapter 7 we showed that the sampling distribution of $\bar{x}$ can be used to compute the probability that $\bar{x}$ will be within a given distance of μ. In the Lloyd's example, the historical data show that the population of amounts spent is normally distributed with a standard deviation of $\sigma = 20$. So, using what we learned in Chapter 7, we can conclude that the sampling distribution of $\bar{x}$ follows a normal distribution with a standard error of $\sigma_{\bar{x}} = \sigma/\sqrt{n} = 20/\sqrt{100} = 2$. This sampling distribution is shown in Figure 8.1.[1] Because

[1]We use the fact that the population of amounts spent has a normal distribution to conclude that the sampling distribution of $\bar{x}$ has a normal distribution. If the population did not have a normal distribution, we could rely on the central limit theorem and the sample size of $n = 100$ to conclude that the sampling distribution of $\bar{x}$ is approximately normal. In either case, the sampling distribution of $\bar{x}$ would appear as shown in Figure 8.1.

FIGURE 8.1 SAMPLING DISTRIBUTION OF THE SAMPLE MEAN AMOUNT SPENT FROM SIMPLE RANDOM SAMPLES OF 100 CUSTOMERS

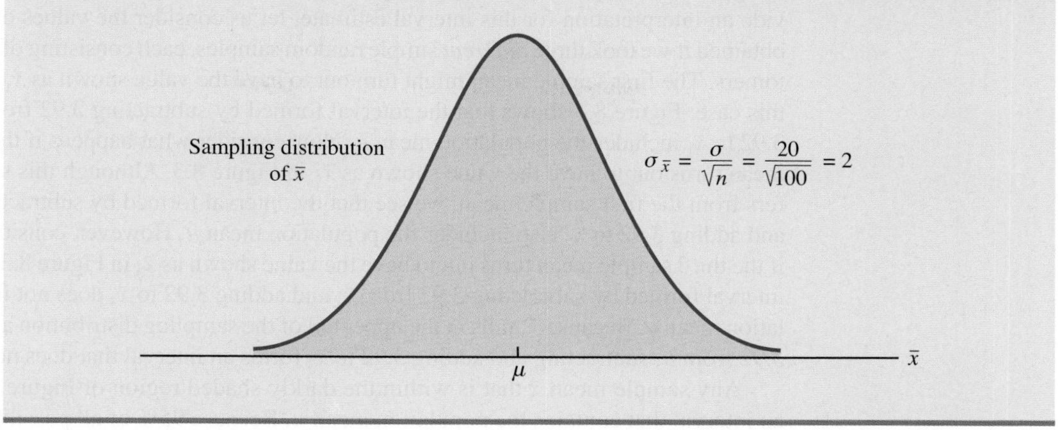

the sampling distribution shows how values of $\bar{x}$ are distributed around the population mean μ, the sampling distribution of $\bar{x}$ provides information about the possible differences between $\bar{x}$ and μ.

Using the standard normal probability table, we find that 95% of the values of any normally distributed random variable are within ± 1.96 standard deviations of the mean. Thus, when the sampling distribution of $\bar{x}$ is normally distributed, 95% of the $\bar{x}$ values must be within $\pm 1.96\sigma_{\bar{x}}$ of the mean μ. In the Lloyd's example we know that the sampling distribution of $\bar{x}$ is normally distributed with a standard error of $\sigma_{\bar{x}} = 2$. Because $\pm 1.96\sigma_{\bar{x}} = 1.96(2) = 3.92$, we can conclude that 95% of all $\bar{x}$ values obtained using a sample size of $n = 100$ will be within ± 3.92 of the population mean μ. See Figure 8.2.

FIGURE 8.2 SAMPLING DISTRIBUTION OF $\bar{x}$ SHOWING THE LOCATION OF SAMPLE MEANS THAT ARE WITHIN 3.92 OF μ

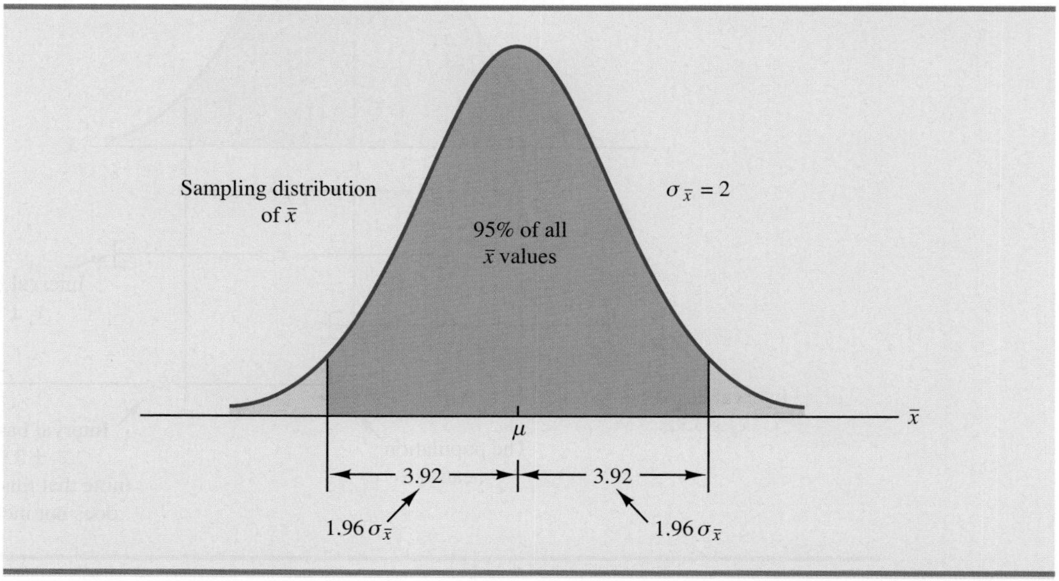

In the introduction to this chapter we said that the general form of an interval estimate of the population mean μ is $\bar{x} \pm$ margin of error. For the Lloyd's example, suppose we set the margin of error equal to 3.92 and compute the interval estimate of μ using $\bar{x} \pm 3.92$. To provide an interpretation for this interval estimate, let us consider the values of $\bar{x}$ that could be obtained if we took three *different* simple random samples, each consisting of 100 Lloyd's customers. The first sample mean might turn out to have the value shown as $\bar{x}_1$ in Figure 8.3. In this case, Figure 8.3 shows that the interval formed by subtracting 3.92 from $\bar{x}_1$ and adding 3.92 to $\bar{x}_1$ includes the population mean μ. Now consider what happens if the second sample mean turns out to have the value shown as $\bar{x}_2$ in Figure 8.3. Although this sample mean differs from the first sample mean, we see that the interval formed by subtracting 3.92 from $\bar{x}_2$ and adding 3.92 to $\bar{x}_2$ also includes the population mean μ. However, consider what happens if the third sample mean turns out to have the value shown as $\bar{x}_3$ in Figure 8.3. In this case, the interval formed by subtracting 3.92 from $\bar{x}_3$ and adding 3.92 to $\bar{x}_3$ does not include the population mean μ. Because $\bar{x}_3$ falls in the upper tail of the sampling distribution and is farther than 3.92 from μ, subtracting and adding 3.92 to $\bar{x}_3$ forms an interval that does not include μ.

Any sample mean $\bar{x}$ that is within the darkly shaded region of Figure 8.3 will provide an interval that contains the population mean μ. Because 95% of all possible sample means are in the darkly shaded region, 95% of all intervals formed by subtracting 3.92 from $\bar{x}$ and adding 3.92 to $\bar{x}$ will include the population mean μ.

Recall that during the most recent week, the quality assurance team at Lloyd's surveyed 100 customers and obtained a sample mean amount spent of $\bar{x} = 82$. Using $\bar{x} \pm 3.92$ to

FIGURE 8.3 INTERVALS FORMED FROM SELECTED SAMPLE MEANS AT LOCATIONS $\bar{x}_1$, $\bar{x}_2$, AND $\bar{x}_3$

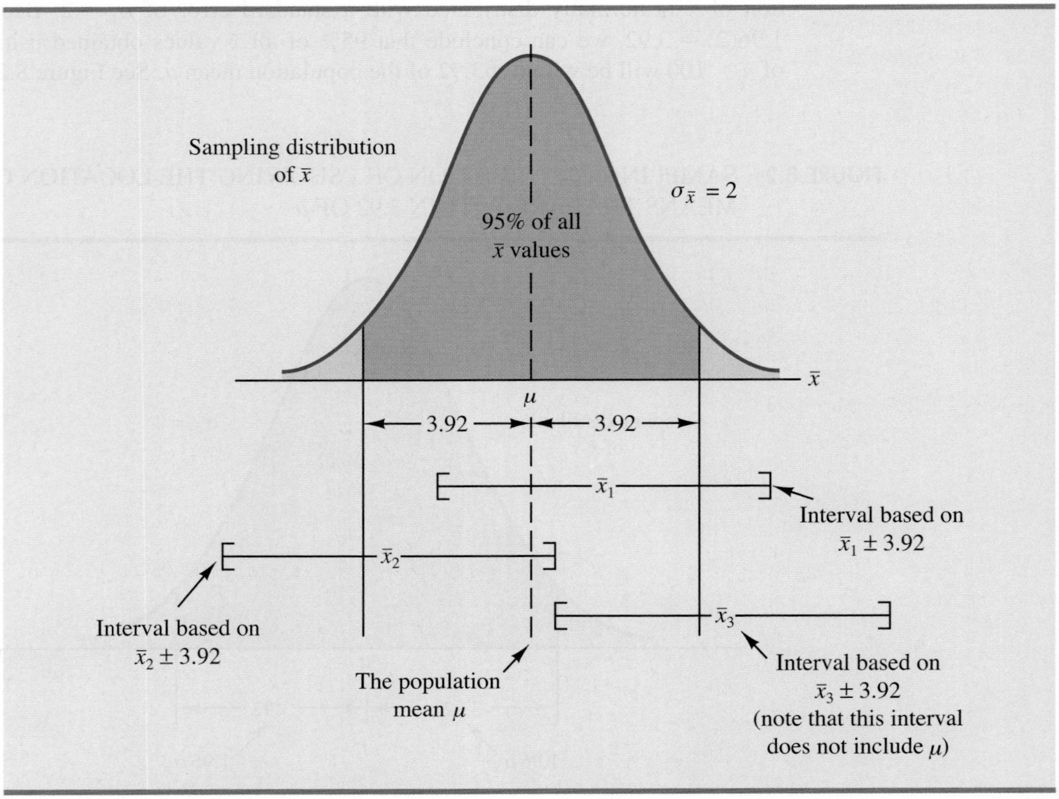

construct the interval estimate, we obtain 82 ± 3.92. Thus, the specific interval estimate of μ based on the data from the most recent week is $82 - 3.92 = 78.08$ to $82 + 3.92 = 85.92$. Because 95% of all the intervals constructed using $\bar{x} \pm 3.92$ will contain the population mean, we say that we are 95% confident that the interval 78.08 to 85.92 includes the population mean μ. We say that this interval has been established at the 95% **confidence level**. The value .95 is referred to as the **confidence coefficient**, and the interval 78.08 to 85.92 is called the 95% **confidence interval**.

This discussion provides insight as to why the interval is called a 95% confidence interval.

With the margin of error given by $z_{\alpha/2}(\sigma/\sqrt{n})$, the general form of an interval estimate of a population mean for the σ known case follows.

INTERVAL ESTIMATE OF A POPULATION MEAN: σ KNOWN

$$\bar{x} \pm z_{\alpha/2}\frac{\sigma}{\sqrt{n}} \tag{8.1}$$

where $(1 - \alpha)$ is the confidence coefficient and $z_{\alpha/2}$ is the z value providing an area of $\alpha/2$ in the upper tail of the standard normal probability distribution.

Let us use expression (8.1) to construct a 95% confidence interval for the Lloyd's example. For a 95% confidence interval, the confidence coefficient is $(1 - \alpha) = .95$ and thus, $\alpha = .05$. Using the standard normal probability table, an area of $\alpha/2 = .05/2 = .025$ in the upper tail provides $z_{.025} = 1.96$. With the Lloyd's sample mean $\bar{x} = 82$, $\sigma = 20$, and a sample size $n = 100$, we obtain

$$82 \pm 1.96\frac{20}{\sqrt{100}}$$

$$82 \pm 3.92$$

Thus, using expression (8.1), the margin of error is 3.92 and the 95% confidence interval is $82 - 3.92 = 78.08$ to $82 + 3.92 = 85.92$.

Although a 95% confidence level is frequently used, other confidence levels such as 90% and 99% may be considered. Values of $z_{\alpha/2}$ for the most commonly used confidence levels are shown in Table 8.1. Using these values and expression (8.1), the 90% confidence interval for the Lloyd's example is

$$82 \pm 1.645\frac{20}{\sqrt{100}}$$

$$82 \pm 3.29$$

TABLE 8.1 VALUES OF $z_{\alpha/2}$ FOR THE MOST COMMONLY USED CONFIDENCE LEVELS

Confidence Level	α	$\alpha/2$	$z_{\alpha/2}$
90%	.10	.05	1.645
95%	.05	.025	1.960
99%	.01	.005	2.576

Thus, at 90% confidence, the margin of error is 3.29 and the confidence interval is 82 − 3.29 = 78.71 to 82 + 3.29 = 85.29. Similarly, the 99% confidence interval is

$$82 \pm 2.576 \frac{20}{\sqrt{100}}$$

$$82 \pm 5.15$$

Thus, at 99% confidence, the margin of error is 5.15 and the confidence interval is 82 − 5.15 = 76.85 to 82 + 5.15 = 87.15.

Comparing the results for the 90%, 95%, and 99% confidence levels, we see that in order to have a higher degree of confidence, the margin of error and thus the width of the confidence interval must be larger.

Practical Advice

If the population follows a normal distribution, the confidence interval provided by expression (8.1) is exact. In other words, if expression (8.1) were used repeatedly to generate 95% confidence intervals, exactly 95% of the intervals generated would contain the population mean. If the population does not follow a normal distribution, the confidence interval provided by expression (8.1) will be approximate. In this case, the quality of the approximation depends on both the distribution of the population and the sample size.

In most applications, a sample size of $n \geq 30$ is adequate when using expression (8.1) to develop an interval estimate of a population mean. If the population is not normally distributed, but is roughly symmetric, sample sizes as small as 15 can be expected to provide good approximate confidence intervals. With smaller sample sizes, expression (8.1) should only be used if the analyst believes, or is willing to assume, that the population distribution is at least approximately normal.

NOTES AND COMMENTS

1. The interval estimation procedure discussed in this section is based on the assumption that the population standard deviation σ is known. By σ known we mean that historical data or other information are available that permit us to obtain a good estimate of the population standard deviation prior to taking the sample that will be used to develop an estimate of the population mean. So technically we don't mean that σ is actually known with certainty. We just mean that we obtained a good estimate of the standard deviation prior to sampling and thus we won't be using the same sample to estimate both the population mean and the population standard deviation.

2. The sample size n appears in the denominator of the interval estimation expression (8.1). Thus, if a particular sample size provides too wide an interval to be of any practical use, we may want to consider increasing the sample size. With n in the denominator, a larger sample size will provide a smaller margin of error, a narrower interval, and greater precision. The procedure for determining the size of a simple random sample necessary to obtain a desired precision is discussed in Section 8.3.

Exercises

Methods

1. A simple random sample of 40 items resulted in a sample mean of 25. The population standard deviation is $\sigma = 5$.
   a. What is the standard error of the mean, $\sigma_{\bar{x}}$?
   b. At 95% confidence, what is the margin of error?

SELF test

2. A simple random sample of 50 items from a population with $\sigma = 6$ resulted in a sample mean of 32.
   a. Provide a 90% confidence interval for the population mean.
   b. Provide a 95% confidence interval for the population mean.
   c. Provide a 99% confidence interval for the population mean.

3. A simple random sample of 60 items resulted in a sample mean of 80. The population standard deviation is $\sigma = 15$.
   a. Compute the 95% confidence interval for the population mean.
   b. Assume that the same sample mean was obtained from a sample of 120 items. Provide a 95% confidence interval for the population mean.
   c. What is the effect of a larger sample size on the interval estimate?

4. A 95% confidence interval for a population mean was reported to be 152 to 160. If $\sigma = 15$, what sample size was used in this study?

Applications

SELF test

5. In an effort to estimate the mean amount spent per customer for dinner at a major Atlanta restaurant, data were collected for a sample of 49 customers. Assume a population standard deviation of $5.
   a. At 95% confidence, what is the margin of error?
   b. If the sample mean is $24.80, what is the 95% confidence interval for the population mean?

WEB file
Nielsen

6. Nielsen Media Research conducted a study of household television viewing times during the 8 P.M. to 11 P.M. time period. The data contained in the file named Nielsen are consistent with the findings reported (*The World Almanac,* 2003). Based upon past studies the population standard deviation is assumed known with $\sigma = 3.5$ hours. Develop a 95% confidence interval estimate of the mean television viewing time per week during the 8 P.M. to 11 P.M. time period.

7. *The Wall Street Journal* reported that automobile crashes cost the United States $162 billion annually (*The Wall Street Journal,* March 5, 2008). The average cost per person for crashes in the Tampa, Florida, area was reported to be $1599. Suppose this average cost was based on a sample of 50 persons who had been involved in car crashes and that the population standard deviation is $\sigma = \$600$. What is the margin of error for a 95% confidence interval? What would you recommend if the study required a margin of error of $150 or less?

8. The National Quality Research Center at the University of Michigan provides a quarterly measure of consumer opinions about products and services (*The Wall Street Journal,* February 18, 2003). A survey of 10 restaurants in the Fast Food/Pizza group showed a sample mean customer satisfaction index of 71. Past data indicate that the population standard deviation of the index has been relatively stable with $\sigma = 5$.
   a. What assumption should the researcher be willing to make if a margin of error is desired?
   b. Using 95% confidence, what is the margin of error?
   c. What is the margin of error if 99% confidence is desired?

WEB file
TaxReturn

9. AARP reported on a study conducted to learn how long it takes individuals to prepare their federal income tax return (*AARP Bulletin,* April 2008). The data contained in the file named TaxReturn are consistent with the study results. These data provide the time in hours required for 40 individuals to complete their federal income tax returns. Using past years' data, the population standard deviation can be assumed known with $\sigma = 9$ hours. What is the 95% confidence interval estimate of the mean time it takes an individual to complete a federal income tax return?

10. *Playbill* magazine reported that the mean annual household income of its readers is $119,155 (*Playbill,* January 2006). Assume this estimate of the mean annual household income is based on a sample of 80 households, and based on past studies, the population standard deviation is known to be $\sigma = \$30,000$.

a. Develop a 90% confidence interval estimate of the population mean.
b. Develop a 95% confidence interval estimate of the population mean.
c. Develop a 99% confidence interval estimate of the population mean.
d. Discuss what happens to the width of the confidence interval as the confidence level is increased. Does this result seem reasonable? Explain.

8.2 Population Mean: σ Unknown

When developing an interval estimate of a population mean we usually do not have a good estimate of the population standard deviation either. In these cases, we must use the same sample to estimate both μ and σ. This situation represents the **σ unknown** case. When s is used to estimate σ, the margin of error and the interval estimate for the population mean are based on a probability distribution known as the ***t* distribution**. Although the mathematical development of the t distribution is based on the assumption of a normal distribution for the population we are sampling from, research shows that the t distribution can be successfully applied in many situations where the population deviates significantly from normal. Later in this section we provide guidelines for using the t distribution if the population is not normally distributed.

William Sealy Gosset, writing under the name "Student," is the founder of the t distribution. Gosset, an Oxford graduate in mathematics, worked for the Guinness Brewery in Dublin, Ireland. He developed the t distribution while working on small-scale materials and temperature experiments.

The t distribution is a family of similar probability distributions, with a specific t distribution depending on a parameter known as the **degrees of freedom**. The t distribution with one degree of freedom is unique, as is the t distribution with two degrees of freedom, with three degrees of freedom, and so on. As the number of degrees of freedom increases, the difference between the t distribution and the standard normal distribution becomes smaller and smaller. Figure 8.4 shows t distributions with 10 and 20 degrees of freedom and their relationship to the standard normal probability distribution. Note that a t distribution with more degrees of freedom exhibits less variability and more

FIGURE 8.4 COMPARISON OF THE STANDARD NORMAL DISTRIBUTION WITH t DISTRIBUTIONS HAVING 10 AND 20 DEGREES OF FREEDOM

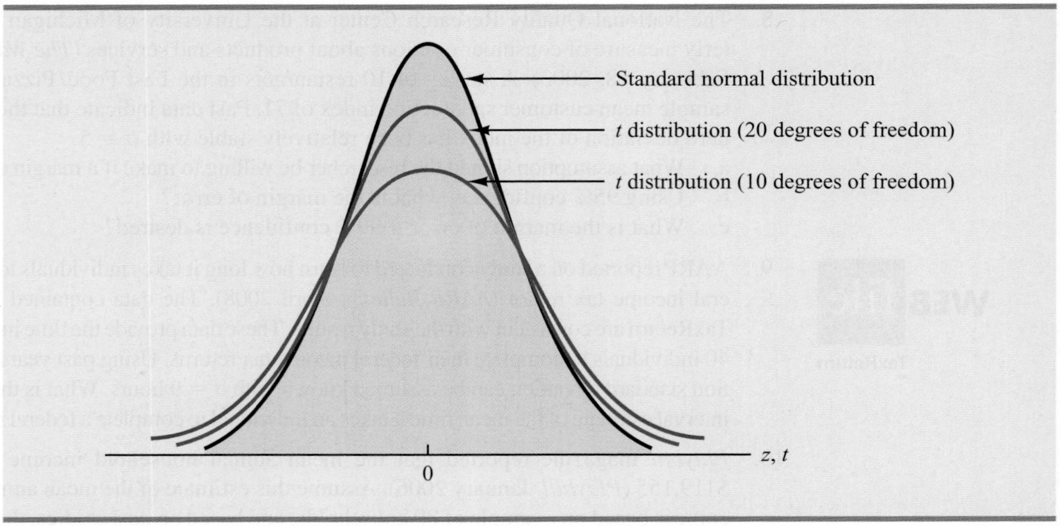

closely resembles the standard normal distribution. Note also that the mean of the t distribution is zero.

We place a subscript on t to indicate the area in the upper tail of the t distribution. For example, just as we used $z_{.025}$ to indicate the z value providing a .025 area in the upper tail of a standard normal distribution, we will use $t_{.025}$ to indicate a .025 area in the upper tail of a t distribution. In general, we will use the notation $t_{\alpha/2}$ to represent a t value with an area of $\alpha/2$ in the upper tail of the t distribution. See Figure 8.5.

As the degrees of freedom increase, the t distribution approaches the standard normal distribution.

Table 2 in Appendix B contains a table for the t distribution. A portion of this table is shown in Table 8.2. Each row in the table corresponds to a separate t distribution with the degrees of freedom shown. For example, for a t distribution with 9 degrees of freedom, $t_{.025} = 2.262$. Similarly, for a t distribution with 60 degrees of freedom, $t_{.025} = 2.000$. As the degrees of freedom continue to increase, $t_{.025}$ approaches $z_{.025} = 1.96$. In fact, the standard normal distribution z values can be found in the infinite degrees of freedom row (labeled ∞) of the t distribution table. If the degrees of freedom exceed 100, the infinite degrees of freedom row can be used to approximate the actual t value; in other words, for more than 100 degrees of freedom, the standard normal z value provides a good approximation to the t value.

Margin of Error and the Interval Estimate

In Section 8.1 we showed that an interval estimate of a population mean for the σ known case is

$$\bar{x} \pm z_{\alpha/2} \frac{\sigma}{\sqrt{n}}$$

To compute an interval estimate of μ for the σ unknown case, the sample standard deviation s is used to estimate σ, and $z_{\alpha/2}$ is replaced by the t distribution value $t_{\alpha/2}$. The margin

FIGURE 8.5 t DISTRIBUTION WITH $\alpha/2$ AREA OR PROBABILITY IN THE UPPER TAIL

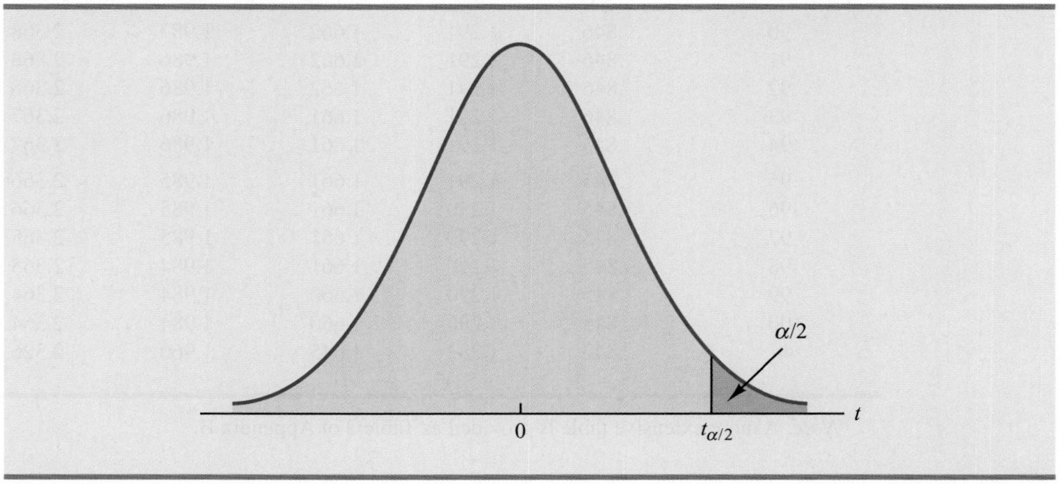

TABLE 8.2 SELECTED VALUES FROM THE *t* DISTRIBUTION TABLE*

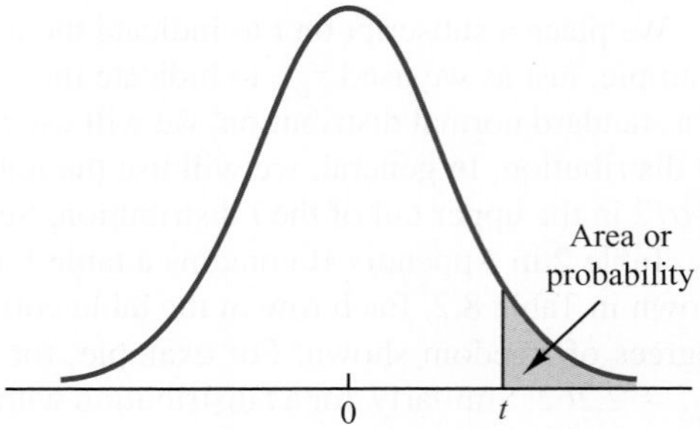

Degrees of Freedom	Area in Upper Tail					
	.20	**.10**	**.05**	**.025**	**.01**	**.005**
1	1.376	3.078	6.314	12.706	31.821	63.656
2	1.061	1.886	2.920	4.303	6.965	9.925
3	.978	1.638	2.353	3.182	4.541	5.841
4	.941	1.533	2.132	2.776	3.747	4.604
5	.920	1.476	2.015	2.571	3.365	4.032
6	.906	1.440	1.943	2.447	3.143	3.707
7	.896	1.415	1.895	2.365	2.998	3.499
8	.889	1.397	1.860	2.306	2.896	3.355
9	.883	1.383	1.833	2.262	2.821	3.250
⋮	⋮	⋮	⋮	⋮	⋮	⋮
60	.848	1.296	1.671	2.000	2.390	2.660
61	.848	1.296	1.670	2.000	2.389	2.659
62	.847	1.295	1.670	1.999	2.388	2.657
63	.847	1.295	1.669	1.998	2.387	2.656
64	.847	1.295	1.669	1.998	2.386	2.655
65	.847	1.295	1.669	1.997	2.385	2.654
66	.847	1.295	1.668	1.997	2.384	2.652
67	.847	1.294	1.668	1.996	2.383	2.651
68	.847	1.294	1.668	1.995	2.382	2.650
69	.847	1.294	1.667	1.995	2.382	2.649
⋮	⋮	⋮	⋮	⋮	⋮	⋮
90	.846	1.291	1.662	1.987	2.368	2.632
91	.846	1.291	1.662	1.986	2.368	2.631
92	.846	1.291	1.662	1.986	2.368	2.630
93	.846	1.291	1.661	1.986	2.367	2.630
94	.845	1.291	1.661	1.986	2.367	2.629
95	.845	1.291	1.661	1.985	2.366	2.629
96	.845	1.290	1.661	1.985	2.366	2.628
97	.845	1.290	1.661	1.985	2.365	2.627
98	.845	1.290	1.661	1.984	2.365	2.627
99	.845	1.290	1.660	1.984	2.364	2.626
100	.845	1.290	1.660	1.984	2.364	2.626
∞	.842	1.282	1.645	1.960	2.326	2.576

**Note:* A more extensive table is provided as Table 2 of Appendix B.

of error is then given by $t_{\alpha/2} s/\sqrt{n}$. With this margin of error, the general expression for an interval estimate of a population mean when σ is unknown follows.

INTERVAL ESTIMATE OF A POPULATION MEAN: σ UNKNOWN

$$\bar{x} \pm t_{\alpha/2} \frac{s}{\sqrt{n}} \tag{8.2}$$

where s is the sample standard deviation, $(1 - \alpha)$ is the confidence coefficient, and $t_{\alpha/2}$ is the t value providing an area of $\alpha/2$ in the upper tail of the t distribution with $n - 1$ degrees of freedom.

The reason the number of degrees of freedom associated with the t value in expression (8.2) is $n - 1$ concerns the use of s as an estimate of the population standard deviation σ. The expression for the sample standard deviation is

$$s = \sqrt{\frac{\Sigma(x_i - \bar{x})^2}{n - 1}}$$

Degrees of freedom refer to the number of independent pieces of information that go into the computation of $\Sigma(x_i - \bar{x})^2$. The n pieces of information involved in computing $\Sigma(x_i - \bar{x})^2$ are as follows: $x_1 - \bar{x}, x_2 - \bar{x}, \ldots, x_n - \bar{x}$. In Section 3.2 we indicated that $\Sigma(x_i - \bar{x}) = 0$ for any data set. Thus, only $n - 1$ of the $x_i - \bar{x}$ values are independent; that is, if we know $n - 1$ of the values, the remaining value can be determined exactly by using the condition that the sum of the $x_i - \bar{x}$ values must be 0. Thus, $n - 1$ is the number of degrees of freedom associated with $\Sigma(x_i - \bar{x})^2$ and hence the number of degrees of freedom for the t distribution in expression (8.2).

To illustrate the interval estimation procedure for the σ unknown case, we will consider a study designed to estimate the mean credit card debt for the population of U.S. households. A sample of $n = 70$ households provided the credit card balances shown in Table 8.3. For this situation, no previous estimate of the population standard deviation σ is available. Thus, the sample data must be used to estimate both the population mean and the population standard deviation. Using the data in Table 8.3, we compute the sample mean $\bar{x} = \$9312$ and the sample standard deviation $s = \$4007$. With 95% confidence and $n - 1 = 69$ degrees of

TABLE 8.3 CREDIT CARD BALANCES FOR A SAMPLE OF 70 HOUSEHOLDS

WEB file

NewBalance

9430	14661	7159	9071	9691	11032
7535	12195	8137	3603	11448	6525
4078	10544	9467	16804	8279	5239
5604	13659	12595	13479	5649	6195
5179	7061	7917	14044	11298	12584
4416	6245	11346	6817	4353	15415
10676	13021	12806	6845	3467	15917
1627	9719	4972	10493	6191	12591
10112	2200	11356	615	12851	9743
6567	10746	7117	13627	5337	10324
13627	12744	9465	12557	8372	
18719	5742	19263	6232	7445	

freedom, Table 8.2 can be used to obtain the appropriate value for $t_{.025}$. We want the t value in the row with 69 degrees of freedom, and the column corresponding to .025 in the upper tail. The value shown is $t_{.025} = 1.995$.

We use expression (8.2) to compute an interval estimate of the population mean credit card balance.

$$9312 \pm 1.995 \frac{4007}{\sqrt{70}}$$

$$9312 \pm 955$$

The point estimate of the population mean is \$9312, the margin of error is \$955, and the 95% confidence interval is 9312 − 955 = \$8357 to 9312 + 955 = \$10,267. Thus, we are 95% confident that the mean credit card balance for the population of all households is between \$8357 and \$10,267.

The procedures used by Minitab, Excel and StatTools to develop confidence intervals for a population mean are described in Appendixes 8.1, 8.2 and 8.3. For the household credit card balances study, the results of the Minitab interval estimation procedure are shown in Figure 8.6. The sample of 70 households provides a sample mean credit card balance of \$9312, a sample standard deviation of \$4007, a standard error of the mean of \$479, and a 95% confidence interval of \$8357 to \$10,267.

Practical Advice

If the population follows a normal distribution, the confidence interval provided by expression (8.2) is exact and can be used for any sample size. If the population does not follow a normal distribution, the confidence interval provided by expression (8.2) will be approximate. In this case, the quality of the approximation depends on both the distribution of the population and the sample size.

Larger sample sizes are needed if the distribution of the population is highly skewed or includes outliers.

In most applications, a sample size of $n \geq 30$ is adequate when using expression (8.2) to develop an interval estimate of a population mean. However, if the population distribution is highly skewed or contains outliers, most statisticians would recommend increasing the sample size to 50 or more. If the population is not normally distributed but is roughly symmetric, sample sizes as small as 15 can be expected to provide good approximate confidence intervals. With smaller sample sizes, expression (8.2) should only be used if the analyst believes, or is willing to assume, that the population distribution is at least approximately normal.

Using a Small Sample

In the following example we develop an interval estimate for a population mean when the sample size is small. As we already noted, an understanding of the distribution of the population becomes a factor in deciding whether the interval estimation procedure provides acceptable results.

Scheer Industries is considering a new computer-assisted program to train maintenance employees to do machine repairs. In order to fully evaluate the program, the director of

FIGURE 8.6 MINITAB CONFIDENCE INTERVAL FOR THE CREDIT CARD BALANCE SURVEY

Variable	N	Mean	StDev	SE Mean	95% CI
NewBalance	70	9312	4007	479	(8357, 10267)

TABLE 8.4 TRAINING TIME IN DAYS FOR A SAMPLE OF 20 SCHEER INDUSTRIES EMPLOYEES

WEB file
Scheer

52	59	54	42
44	50	42	48
55	54	60	55
44	62	62	57
45	46	43	56

manufacturing requested an estimate of the population mean time required for maintenance employees to complete the computer-assisted training.

A sample of 20 employees is selected, with each employee in the sample completing the training program. Data on the training time in days for the 20 employees are shown in Table 8.4. A histogram of the sample data appears in Figure 8.7. What can we say about the distribution of the population based on this histogram? First, the sample data do not support the conclusion that the distribution of the population is normal, yet we do not see any evidence of skewness or outliers. Therefore, using the guidelines in the previous subsection, we conclude that an interval estimate based on the t distribution appears acceptable for the sample of 20 employees.

We continue by computing the sample mean and sample standard deviation as follows.

$$\bar{x} = \frac{\Sigma x_i}{n} = \frac{1030}{20} = 51.5 \text{ days}$$

$$s = \sqrt{\frac{\Sigma(x_i - \bar{x})^2}{n - 1}} = \sqrt{\frac{889}{20 - 1}} = 6.84 \text{ days}$$

FIGURE 8.7 HISTOGRAM OF TRAINING TIMES FOR THE SCHEER INDUSTRIES SAMPLE

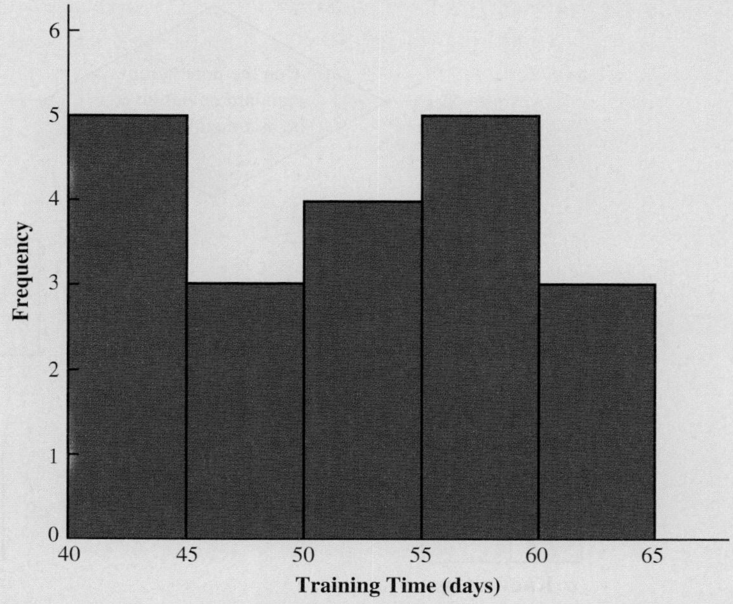

For a 95% confidence interval, we use Table 2 of Appendix B and $n - 1 = 19$ degrees of freedom to obtain $t_{.025} = 2.093$. Expression (8.2) provides the interval estimate of the population mean.

$$51.5 \pm 2.093\left(\frac{6.84}{\sqrt{20}}\right)$$

$$51.5 \pm 3.2$$

The point estimate of the population mean is 51.5 days. The margin of error is 3.2 days and the 95% confidence interval is $51.5 - 3.2 = 48.3$ days to $51.5 + 3.2 = 54.7$ days.

Using a histogram of the sample data to learn about the distribution of a population is not always conclusive, but in many cases it provides the only information available. The histogram, along with judgment on the part of the analyst, can often be used to decide whether expression (8.2) can be used to develop the interval estimate.

Summary of Interval Estimation Procedures

We provided two approaches to developing an interval estimate of a population mean. For the σ known case, σ and the standard normal distribution are used in expression (8.1) to compute the margin of error and to develop the interval estimate. For the σ unknown case, the sample standard deviation s and the t distribution are used in expression (8.2) to compute the margin of error and to develop the interval estimate.

A summary of the interval estimation procedures for the two cases is shown in Figure 8.8. In most applications, a sample size of $n \geq 30$ is adequate. If the population has a normal or approximately normal distribution, however, smaller sample sizes may be used.

FIGURE 8.8 SUMMARY OF INTERVAL ESTIMATION PROCEDURES FOR A POPULATION MEAN

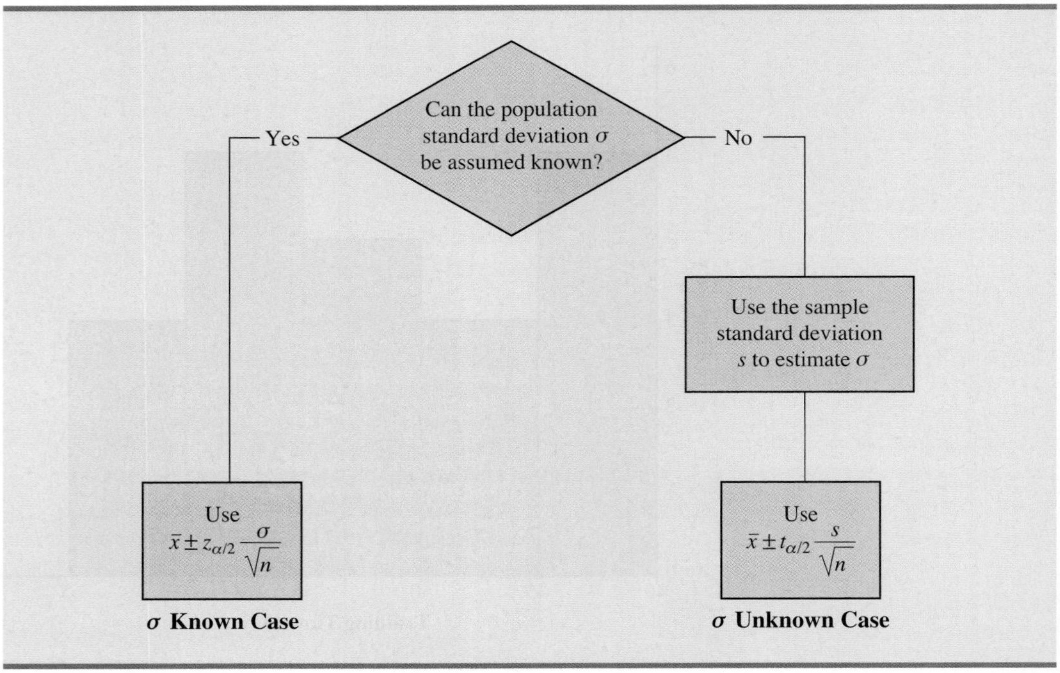

For the σ unknown case a sample size of $n \geq 50$ is recommended if the population distribution is believed to be highly skewed or has outliers.

NOTES AND COMMENTS

1. When σ is known, the margin of error, $z_{\alpha/2}(\sigma/\sqrt{n})$, is fixed and is the same for all samples of size n. When σ is unknown, the margin of error, $t_{\alpha/2}(s/\sqrt{n})$, varies from sample to sample. This variation occurs because the sample standard deviation s varies depending upon the sample selected. A large value for s provides a larger margin of error, while a small value for s provides a smaller margin of error.
2. What happens to confidence interval estimates when the population is skewed? Consider a population that is skewed to the right with large data values stretching the distribution to the right. When such skewness exists, the sample mean $\bar{x}$ and the sample standard deviation s are positively correlated. Larger values of s tend to be associated with larger values of $\bar{x}$. Thus, when $\bar{x}$ is larger than the population mean, s tends to be larger than σ. This skewness causes the margin of error, $t_{\alpha/2}(s/\sqrt{n})$, to be larger than it would be with σ known. The confidence interval with the larger margin of error tends to include the population mean μ more often than it would if the true value of σ were used. But when $\bar{x}$ is smaller than the population mean, the correlation between $\bar{x}$ and s causes the margin of error to be small. In this case, the confidence interval with the smaller margin of error tends to miss the population mean more than it would if we knew σ and used it. For this reason, we recommend using larger sample sizes with highly skewed population distributions.

Exercises

Methods

11. For a t distribution with 16 degrees of freedom, find the area, or probability, in each region.
    a. To the right of 2.120
    b. To the left of 1.337
    c. To the left of -1.746
    d. To the right of 2.583
    e. Between -2.120 and 2.120
    f. Between -1.746 and 1.746
12. Find the t value(s) for each of the following cases.
    a. Upper tail area of .025 with 12 degrees of freedom
    b. Lower tail area of .05 with 50 degrees of freedom
    c. Upper tail area of .01 with 30 degrees of freedom
    d. Where 90% of the area falls between these two t values with 25 degrees of freedom
    e. Where 95% of the area falls between these two t values with 45 degrees of freedom

SELF test

13. The following sample data are from a normal population: 10, 8, 12, 15, 13, 11, 6, 5.
    a. What is the point estimate of the population mean?
    b. What is the point estimate of the population standard deviation?
    c. With 95% confidence, what is the margin of error for the estimation of the population mean?
    d. What is the 95% confidence interval for the population mean?
14. A simple random sample with $n = 54$ provided a sample mean of 22.5 and a sample standard deviation of 4.4.
    a. Develop a 90% confidence interval for the population mean.
    b. Develop a 95% confidence interval for the population mean.

c. Develop a 99% confidence interval for the population mean.
d. What happens to the margin of error and the confidence interval as the confidence level is increased?

Applications

SELF test

15. Sales personnel for Skillings Distributors submit weekly reports listing the customer contacts made during the week. A sample of 65 weekly reports showed a sample mean of 19.5 customer contacts per week. The sample standard deviation was 5.2. Provide 90% and 95% confidence intervals for the population mean number of weekly customer contacts for the sales personnel.

16. The mean number of hours of flying time for pilots at Continental Airlines is 49 hours per month (*The Wall Street Journal,* February 25, 2003). Assume that this mean was based on actual flying times for a sample of 100 Continental pilots and that the sample standard deviation was 8.5 hours.
    a. At 95% confidence, what is the margin of error?
    b. What is the 95% confidence interval estimate of the population mean flying time for the pilots?
    c. The mean number of hours of flying time for pilots at United Airlines is 36 hours per month. Use your results from part (b) to discuss differences between the flying times for the pilots at the two airlines. *The Wall Street Journal* reported United Airlines as having the highest labor cost among all airlines. Does the information in this exercise provide insight as to why United Airlines might expect higher labor costs?

17. The International Air Transport Association surveys business travelers to develop quality ratings for transatlantic gateway airports. The maximum possible rating is 10. Suppose a simple random sample of 50 business travelers is selected and each traveler is asked to provide a rating for the Miami International Airport. The ratings obtained from the sample of 50 business travelers follow.

WEB file
Miami

6	4	6	8	7	7	6	3	3	8	10	4	8
7	8	7	5	9	5	8	4	3	8	5	5	4
4	4	8	4	5	6	2	5	9	9	8	4	8
9	9	5	9	7	8	3	10	8	9	6		

Develop a 95% confidence interval estimate of the population mean rating for Miami.

WEB file
JobSearch

18. Older people often have a hard time finding work. AARP reported on the number of weeks it takes a worker aged 55 plus to find a job. The data on number of weeks spent searching for a job contained in the file JobSearch are consistent with the AARP findings (*AARP Bulletin,* April 2008).
    a. Provide a point estimate of the population mean number of weeks it takes a worker aged 55 plus to find a job.
    b. At 95% confidence, what is the margin of error?
    c. What is the 95% confidence interval estimate of the mean?
    d. Discuss the degree of skewness found in the sample data. What suggestion would you make for a repeat of this study?

19. The average cost per night of a hotel room in New York City is $273 (*SmartMoney,* March 2009). Assume this estimate is based on a sample of 45 hotels and that the sample standard deviation is $65.
    a. With 95% confidence, what is the margin of error?
    b. What is the 95% confidence interval estimate of the population mean?
    c. Two years ago the average cost of a hotel room in New York City was $229. Discuss the change in cost over the two-year period.

WEB file Program

20. Is your favorite TV program often interrupted by advertising? CNBC presented statistics on the average number of programming minutes in a half-hour sitcom (CNBC, February 23, 2006). The following data (in minutes) are representative of their findings.

21.06	22.24	20.62
21.66	21.23	23.86
23.82	20.30	21.52
21.52	21.91	23.14
20.02	22.20	21.20
22.37	22.19	22.34
23.36	23.44	

Assume the population is approximately normal. Provide a point estimate and a 95% confidence interval for the mean number of programming minutes during a half-hour television sitcom.

WEB file Alcohol

21. Consumption of alcoholic beverages by young women of drinking age has been increasing in the United Kingdom, the United States, and Europe (*The Wall Street Journal,* February 15, 2006). Data (annual consumption in liters) consistent with the findings reported in *The Wall Street Journal* article are shown for a sample of 20 European young women.

266	82	199	174	97
170	222	115	130	169
164	102	113	171	0
93	0	93	110	130

Assuming the population is roughly symmetric, construct a 95% confidence interval for the mean annual consumption of alcoholic beverages by European young women.

22. Disney's *Hannah Montana: The Movie* opened on Easter weekend in April 2009. Over the three-day weekend, the movie became the number-one box office attraction (*The Wall Street Journal,* April 13, 2009). The ticket sales revenue in dollars for a sample of 25 theaters is as follows.

WEB file TicketSales

20,200	10,150	13,000	11,320	9700
8350	7300	14,000	9940	11,200
10,750	6240	12,700	7430	13,500
13,900	4200	6750	6700	9330
13,185	9200	21,400	11,380	10,800

a. What is the 95% confidence interval estimate for the mean ticket sales revenue per theater? Interpret this result.
b. Using the movie ticket price of $7.16 per ticket, what is the estimate of the mean number of customers per theater?
c. The movie was shown in 3118 theaters. Estimate the total number of customers who saw *Hannah Montana: The Movie* and the total box office ticket sales for the three-day weekend.

8.3 Determining the Sample Size

If a desired margin of error is selected prior to sampling, the procedures in this section can be used to determine the sample size necessary to satisfy the margin of error requirement.

In providing practical advice in the two preceding sections, we commented on the role of the sample size in providing good approximate confidence intervals when the population is not normally distributed. In this section, we focus on another aspect of the sample size issue. We describe how to choose a sample size large enough to provide a desired margin of error. To understand how this process works, we return to the σ known case presented in Section 8.1. Using expression (8.1), the interval estimate is

$$\bar{x} \pm z_{\alpha/2}\frac{\sigma}{\sqrt{n}}$$

The quantity $z_{\alpha/2}(\sigma/\sqrt{n})$ is the margin of error. Thus, we see that $z_{\alpha/2}$, the population standard deviation σ, and the sample size n combine to determine the margin of error. Once we select a confidence coefficient $1 - \alpha$, $z_{\alpha/2}$ can be determined. Then, if we have a value for σ, we can determine the sample size n needed to provide any desired margin of error. Development of the formula used to compute the required sample size n follows.

Let E = the desired margin of error:

$$E = z_{\alpha/2} \frac{\sigma}{\sqrt{n}}$$

Solving for $\sqrt{n}$, we have

$$\sqrt{n} = \frac{z_{\alpha/2}\sigma}{E}$$

Squaring both sides of this equation, we obtain the following expression for the sample size.

Equation (8.3) can be used to provide a good sample size recommendation. However, judgment on the part of the analyst should be used to determine whether the final sample size should be adjusted upward.

SAMPLE SIZE FOR AN INTERVAL ESTIMATE OF A POPULATION MEAN

$$n = \frac{(z_{\alpha/2})^2\sigma^2}{E^2} \tag{8.3}$$

This sample size provides the desired margin of error at the chosen confidence level.

In equation (8.3), E is the margin of error that the user is willing to accept, and the value of $z_{\alpha/2}$ follows directly from the confidence level to be used in developing the interval estimate. Although user preference must be considered, 95% confidence is the most frequently chosen value ($z_{.025} = 1.96$).

Finally, use of equation (8.3) requires a value for the population standard deviation σ. However, even if σ is unknown, we can use equation (8.3) provided we have a preliminary or *planning value* for σ. In practice, one of the following procedures can be chosen.

A planning value for the population standard deviation σ must be specified before the sample size can be determined. Three methods of obtaining a planning value for σ are discussed here.

1. Use the estimate of the population standard deviation computed from data of previous studies as the planning value for σ.
2. Use a pilot study to select a preliminary sample. The sample standard deviation from the preliminary sample can be used as the planning value for σ.
3. Use judgment or a "best guess" for the value of σ. For example, we might begin by estimating the largest and smallest data values in the population. The difference between the largest and smallest values provides an estimate of the range for the data. Finally, the range divided by 4 is often suggested as a rough approximation of the standard deviation and thus an acceptable planning value for σ.

Let us demonstrate the use of equation (8.3) to determine the sample size by considering the following example. A previous study that investigated the cost of renting automobiles in the United States found a mean cost of approximately \$55 per day for renting a midsize automobile. Suppose that the organization that conducted this study would like to conduct a new study in order to estimate the population mean daily rental cost for a midsize automobile in the United States. In designing the new study, the project director specifies that the population mean daily rental cost be estimated with a margin of error of \$2 and a 95% level of confidence.

The project director specified a desired margin of error of $E = 2$, and the 95% level of confidence indicates $z_{.025} = 1.96$. Thus, we only need a planning value for the population standard deviation σ in order to compute the required sample size. At this point, an analyst reviewed the sample data from the previous study and found that the sample standard deviation for the daily rental cost was \$9.65. Using 9.65 as the planning value for σ, we obtain

Equation (8.3) provides the minimum sample size needed to satisfy the desired margin of error requirement. If the computed sample size is not an integer, rounding up to the next integer value will provide a margin of error slightly smaller than required.

$$n = \frac{(z_{\alpha/2})^2\sigma^2}{E^2} = \frac{(1.96)^2(9.65)^2}{2^2} = 89.43$$

Thus, the sample size for the new study needs to be at least 89.43 midsize automobile rentals in order to satisfy the project director's \$2 margin-of-error requirement. In cases where the computed n is not an integer, we round up to the next integer value; hence, the recommended sample size is 90 midsize automobile rentals.

Exercises

Methods

23. How large a sample should be selected to provide a 95% confidence interval with a margin of error of 10? Assume that the population standard deviation is 40.

SELF test

24. The range for a set of data is estimated to be 36.
    a. What is the planning value for the population standard deviation?
    b. At 95% confidence, how large a sample would provide a margin of error of 3?
    c. At 95% confidence, how large a sample would provide a margin of error of 2?

Applications

SELF test

25. Refer to the Scheer Industries example in Section 8.2. Use 6.84 days as a planning value for the population standard deviation.
    a. Assuming 95% confidence, what sample size would be required to obtain a margin of error of 1.5 days?
    b. If the precision statement was made with 90% confidence, what sample size would be required to obtain a margin of error of 2 days?
26. The average cost of a gallon of unleaded gasoline in Greater Cincinnati was reported to be \$2.41 (*The Cincinnati Enquirer*, February 3, 2006). During periods of rapidly changing prices, the newspaper samples service stations and prepares reports on gasoline prices frequently. Assume the standard deviation is \$.15 for the price of a gallon of unleaded regular gasoline, and recommend the appropriate sample size for the newspaper to use if they wish to report a margin of error at 95% confidence.
    a. Suppose the desired margin of error is \$.07.
    b. Suppose the desired margin of error is \$.05.
    c. Suppose the desired margin of error is \$.03.
27. Annual starting salaries for college graduates with degrees in business administration are generally expected to be between \$30,000 and \$45,000. Assume that a 95% confidence interval estimate of the population mean annual starting salary is desired. What is the planning value for the population standard deviation? How large a sample should be taken if the desired margin of error is
    a. \$500?
    b. \$200?
    c. \$100?
    d. Would you recommend trying to obtain the \$100 margin of error? Explain.
28. An online survey by ShareBuilder, a retirement plan provider, and Harris Interactive reported that 60% of female business owners are not confident they are saving enough for retirement (*SmallBiz*, Winter 2006). Suppose we would like to do a follow-up study to determine how much female business owners are saving each year toward retirement and want to use \$100 as the desired margin of error for an interval estimate of the population mean. Use \$1100 as a planning value for the standard deviation and recommend a sample size for each of the following situations.
    a. A 90% confidence interval is desired for the mean amount saved.
    b. A 95% confidence interval is desired for the mean amount saved.

c. A 99% confidence interval is desired for the mean amount saved.
d. When the desired margin of error is set, what happens to the sample size as the confidence level is increased? Would you recommend using a 99% confidence interval in this case? Discuss.

29. The travel-to-work time for residents of the 15 largest cities in the United States is reported in the *2003 Information Please Almanac.* Suppose that a preliminary simple random sample of residents of San Francisco is used to develop a planning value of 6.25 minutes for the population standard deviation.
   a. If we want to estimate the population mean travel-to-work time for San Francisco residents with a margin of error of 2 minutes, what sample size should be used? Assume 95% confidence.
   b. If we want to estimate the population mean travel-to-work time for San Francisco residents with a margin of error of 1 minute, what sample size should be used? Assume 95% confidence.

30. During the first quarter of 2003, the price/earnings (P/E) ratio for stocks listed on the New York Stock Exchange generally ranged from 5 to 60 (*The Wall Street Journal,* March 7, 2003). Assume that we want to estimate the population mean P/E ratio for all stocks listed on the exchange. How many stocks should be included in the sample if we want a margin of error of 3? Use 95% confidence.

8.4 Population Proportion

In the introduction to this chapter we said that the general form of an interval estimate of a population proportion p is

$$\bar{p} \pm \text{Margin of error}$$

The sampling distribution of $\bar{p}$ plays a key role in computing the margin of error for this interval estimate.

In Chapter 7 we said that the sampling distribution of $\bar{p}$ can be approximated by a normal distribution whenever $np \geq 5$ and $n(1 - p) \geq 5$. Figure 8.9 shows the normal approximation

FIGURE 8.9 NORMAL APPROXIMATION OF THE SAMPLING DISTRIBUTION OF $\bar{p}$

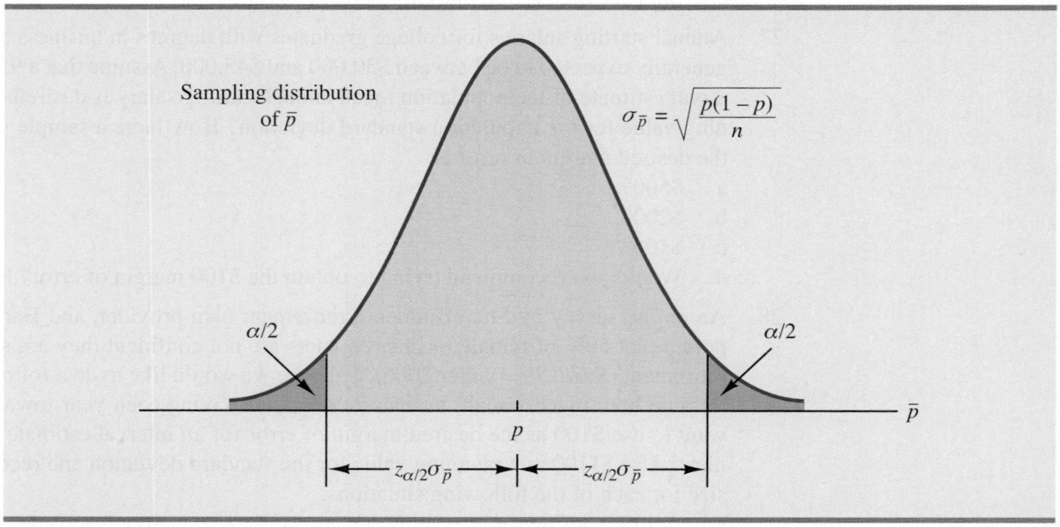

of the sampling distribution of $\bar{p}$. The mean of the sampling distribution of $\bar{p}$ is the population proportion p, and the standard error of $\bar{p}$ is

$$\sigma_{\bar{p}} = \sqrt{\frac{p(1-p)}{n}} \tag{8.4}$$

Because the sampling distribution of $\bar{p}$ is normally distributed, if we choose $z_{\alpha/2}\sigma_{\bar{p}}$ as the margin of error in an interval estimate of a population proportion, we know that $100(1-\alpha)\%$ of the intervals generated will contain the true population proportion. But $\sigma_{\bar{p}}$ cannot be used directly in the computation of the margin of error because p will not be known; p is what we are trying to estimate. So $\bar{p}$ is substituted for p and the margin of error for an interval estimate of a population proportion is given by

$$\text{Margin of error} = z_{\alpha/2}\sqrt{\frac{\bar{p}(1-\bar{p})}{n}} \tag{8.5}$$

With this margin of error, the general expression for an interval estimate of a population proportion is as follows.

When developing confidence intervals for proportions, the quantity $z_{\alpha/2}\sqrt{\bar{p}(1-\bar{p})/n}$ provides the margin of error.

INTERVAL ESTIMATE OF A POPULATION PROPORTION

$$\bar{p} \pm z_{\alpha/2}\sqrt{\frac{\bar{p}(1-\bar{p})}{n}} \tag{8.6}$$

where $1-\alpha$ is the confidence coefficient and $z_{\alpha/2}$ is the z value providing an area of $\alpha/2$ in the upper tail of the standard normal distribution.

WEB file
TeeTimes

The following example illustrates the computation of the margin of error and interval estimate for a population proportion. A national survey of 900 women golfers was conducted to learn how women golfers view their treatment at golf courses in the United States. The survey found that 396 of the women golfers were satisfied with the availability of tee times. Thus, the point estimate of the proportion of the population of women golfers who are satisfied with the availability of tee times is 396/900 = .44. Using expression (8.6) and a 95% confidence level,

$$\bar{p} \pm z_{\alpha/2}\sqrt{\frac{\bar{p}(1-\bar{p})}{n}}$$

$$.44 \pm 1.96\sqrt{\frac{.44(1-.44)}{900}}$$

$$.44 \pm .0324$$

Thus, the margin of error is .0324 and the 95% confidence interval estimate of the population proportion is .4076 to .4724. Using percentages, the survey results enable us to state with 95% confidence that between 40.76% and 47.24% of all women golfers are satisfied with the availability of tee times.

Determining the Sample Size

Let us consider the question of how large the sample size should be to obtain an estimate of a population proportion at a specified level of precision. The rationale for the sample size determination in developing interval estimates of p is similar to the rationale used in Section 8.3 to determine the sample size for estimating a population mean.

Previously in this section we said that the margin of error associated with an interval estimate of a population proportion is $z_{\alpha/2}\sqrt{\bar{p}(1-\bar{p})/n}$. The margin of error is based on the value of $z_{\alpha/2}$, the sample proportion $\bar{p}$, and the sample size n. Larger sample sizes provide a smaller margin of error and better precision.

Let E denote the desired margin of error.

$$E = z_{\alpha/2}\sqrt{\frac{\bar{p}(1-\bar{p})}{n}}$$

Solving this equation for n provides a formula for the sample size that will provide a margin of error of size E.

$$n = \frac{(z_{\alpha/2})^2\bar{p}(1-\bar{p})}{E^2}$$

Note, however, that we cannot use this formula to compute the sample size that will provide the desired margin of error because $\bar{p}$ will not be known until after we select the sample. What we need, then, is a planning value for $\bar{p}$ that can be used to make the computation. Using p^* to denote the planning value for $\bar{p}$, the following formula can be used to compute the sample size that will provide a margin of error of size E.

SAMPLE SIZE FOR AN INTERVAL ESTIMATE OF A POPULATION PROPORTION

$$n = \frac{(z_{\alpha/2})^2p^*(1-p^*)}{E^2} \qquad \textbf{(8.7)}$$

In practice, the planning value p^* can be chosen by one of the following procedures.

1. Use the sample proportion from a previous sample of the same or similar units.
2. Use a pilot study to select a preliminary sample. The sample proportion from this sample can be used as the planning value, p^*.
3. Use judgment or a "best guess" for the value of p^*.
4. If none of the preceding alternatives apply, use a planning value of $p^* = .50$.

Let us return to the survey of women golfers and assume that the company is interested in conducting a new survey to estimate the current proportion of the population of women golfers who are satisfied with the availability of tee times. How large should the sample be if the survey director wants to estimate the population proportion with a margin of error of .025 at 95% confidence? With $E = .025$ and $z_{\alpha/2} = 1.96$, we need a planning value p^* to answer the sample size question. Using the previous survey result of $\bar{p} = .44$ as the planning value p^*, equation (8.7) shows that

$$n = \frac{(z_{\alpha/2})^2p^*(1-p^*)}{E^2} = \frac{(1.96)^2(.44)(1-.44)}{(.025)^2} = 1514.5$$

TABLE 8.5 SOME POSSIBLE VALUES FOR $p^*(1 - p^*)$

p^*	$p^*(1 - p^*)$	
.10	(.10)(.90) = .09	
.30	(.30)(.70) = .21	
.40	(.40)(.60) = .24	
.50	(.50)(.50) = .25	← Largest value for $p^*(1 - p^*)$
.60	(.60)(.40) = .24	
.70	(.70)(.30) = .21	
.90	(.90)(.10) = .09	

Thus, the sample size must be at least 1514.5 women golfers to satisfy the margin of error requirement. Rounding up to the next integer value indicates that a sample of 1515 women golfers is recommended to satisfy the margin of error requirement.

The fourth alternative suggested for selecting a planning value p^* is to use $p^* = .50$. This value of p^* is frequently used when no other information is available. To understand why, note that the numerator of equation (8.7) shows that the sample size is proportional to the quantity $p^*(1 - p^*)$. A larger value for the quantity $p^*(1 - p^*)$ will result in a larger sample size. Table 8.5 gives some possible values of $p^*(1 - p^*)$. Note that the largest value of $p^*(1 - p^*)$ occurs when $p^* = .50$. Thus, in case of any uncertainty about an appropriate planning value, we know that $p^* = .50$ will provide the largest sample size recommendation. In effect, we play it safe by recommending the largest necessary sample size. If the sample proportion turns out to be different from the .50 planning value, the margin of error will be smaller than anticipated. Thus, in using $p^* = .50$, we guarantee that the sample size will be sufficient to obtain the desired margin of error.

In the survey of women golfers example, a planning value of $p^* = .50$ would have provided the sample size

$$n = \frac{(z_{\alpha/2})^2 p^*(1 - p^*)}{E^2} = \frac{(1.96)^2(.50)(1 - .50)}{(.025)^2} = 1536.6$$

Thus, a slightly larger sample size of 1537 women golfers would be recommended.

NOTES AND COMMENTS

The desired margin of error for estimating a population proportion is almost always .10 or less. In national public opinion polls conducted by organizations such as Gallup and Harris, a .03 or .04 margin of error is common. With such margins of error, equation (8.7) will almost always provide a sample size that is large enough to satisfy the requirements of $np \geq 5$ and $n(1 - p) \geq 5$ for using a normal distribution as an approximation for the sampling distribution of $\bar{x}$.

Exercises

Methods

SELF test

31. A simple random sample of 400 individuals provides 100 Yes responses.
    a. What is the point estimate of the proportion of the population that would provide Yes responses?
    b. What is your estimate of the standard error of the proportion, $\sigma_{\bar{p}}$?
    c. Compute the 95% confidence interval for the population proportion.

32. A simple random sample of 800 elements generates a sample proportion $\bar{p} = .70$.
    a. Provide a 90% confidence interval for the population proportion.
    b. Provide a 95% confidence interval for the population proportion.
33. In a survey, the planning value for the population proportion is $p^* = .35$. How large a sample should be taken to provide a 95% confidence interval with a margin of error of .05?
34. At 95% confidence, how large a sample should be taken to obtain a margin of error of .03 for the estimation of a population proportion? Assume that past data are not available for developing a planning value for p^*.

Applications

SELF test

35. The Consumer Reports National Research Center conducted a telephone survey of 2000 adults to learn about the major economic concerns for the future (*Consumer Reports,* January 2009). The survey results showed that 1760 of the respondents think the future health of Social Security is a major economic concern.
    a. What is the point estimate of the population proportion of adults who think the future health of Social Security is a major economic concern.
    b. At 90% confidence, what is the margin of error?
    c. Develop a 90% confidence interval for the population proportion of adults who think the future health of Social Security is a major economic concern.
    d. Develop a 95% confidence interval for this population proportion.
36. According to statistics reported on CNBC, a surprising number of motor vehicles are not covered by insurance (CNBC, February 23, 2006). Sample results, consistent with the CNBC report, showed 46 of 200 vehicles were not covered by insurance.
    a. What is the point estimate of the proportion of vehicles not covered by insurance?
    b. Develop a 95% confidence interval for the population proportion.
37. Towers Perrin, a New York human resources consulting firm, conducted a survey of 1100 employees at medium-sized and large companies to determine how dissatisfied employees were with their jobs (*The Wall Street Journal,* January 29, 2003). Representative data are shown in the file JobSatisfaction. A response of Yes indicates the employee strongly disliked the current work experience.

WEB file
JobSatisfaction

    a. What is the point estimate of the proportion of the population of employees who strongly dislike their current work experience?
    b. At 95% confidence, what is the margin of error?
    c. What is the 95% confidence interval for the proportion of the population of employees who strongly dislike their current work experience?
    d. Towers Perrin estimates that it costs employers one-third of an hourly employee's annual salary to find a successor and as much as 1.5 times the annual salary to find a successor for a highly compensated employee. What message did this survey send to employers?
38. According to Thomson Financial, through January 25, 2006, the majority of companies reporting profits had beaten estimates (*BusinessWeek,* February 6, 2006). A sample of 162 companies showed 104 beat estimates, 29 matched estimates, and 29 fell short.
    a. What is the point estimate of the proportion that fell short of estimates?
    b. Determine the margin of error and provide a 95% confidence interval for the proportion that beat estimates.
    c. How large a sample is needed if the desired margin of error is .05?

SELF test

39. The percentage of people not covered by health care insurance in 2003 was 15.6% (*Statistical Abstract of the United States*, 2006). A congressional committee has been charged with conducting a sample survey to obtain more current information.
    a. What sample size would you recommend if the committee's goal is to estimate the current proportion of individuals without health care insurance with a margin of error of .03? Use a 95% confidence level.
    b. Repeat part (a) using a 99% confidence level.

40. For many years businesses have struggled with the rising cost of health care. But recently, the increases have slowed due to less inflation in health care prices and employees paying for a larger portion of health care benefits. A recent Mercer survey showed that 52% of U.S. employers were likely to require higher employee contributions for health care coverage in 2009 (*BusinessWeek,* February 16, 2009). Suppose the survey was based on a sample of 800 companies. Compute the margin of error and a 95% confidence interval for the proportion of companies likely to require higher employee contributions for health care coverage in 2009.

41. America's young people are heavy Internet users; 87% of Americans ages 12 to 17 are Internet users (*The Cincinnati Enquirer,* February 7, 2006). MySpace was voted the most popular website by 9% in a sample survey of Internet users in this age group. Suppose 1400 youths participated in the survey. What is the margin of error, and what is the interval estimate of the population proportion for which MySpace is the most popular website? Use a 95% confidence level.

42. A poll for the presidential campaign sampled 491 potential voters in June. A primary purpose of the poll was to obtain an estimate of the proportion of potential voters who favored each candidate. Assume a planning value of $p^* = .50$ and a 95% confidence level.
    a. For $p^* = .50$, what was the planned margin of error for the June poll?
    b. Closer to the November election, better precision and smaller margins of error are desired. Assume the following margins of error are requested for surveys to be conducted during the presidential campaign. Compute the recommended sample size for each survey.

Survey	Margin of Error
September	.04
October	.03
Early November	.02
Pre-Election Day	.01

43. A Phoenix Wealth Management/Harris Interactive survey of 1500 individuals with net worth of $1 million or more provided a variety of statistics on wealthy people (*BusinessWeek,* September 22, 2003). The previous three-year period had been bad for the stock market, which motivated some of the questions asked.
    a. The survey reported that 53% of the respondents lost 25% or more of their portfolio value over the past three years. Develop a 95% confidence interval for the proportion of wealthy people who lost 25% or more of their portfolio value over the past three years.
    b. The survey reported that 31% of the respondents feel they have to save more for retirement to make up for what they lost. Develop a 95% confidence interval for the population proportion.
    c. Five percent of the respondents gave $25,000 or more to charity over the previous year. Develop a 95% confidence interval for the proportion who gave $25,000 or more to charity.
    d. Compare the margin of error for the interval estimates in parts (a), (b), and (c). How is the margin of error related to $\bar{p}$? When the same sample is being used to estimate a variety of proportions, which of the proportions should be used to choose the planning value p^*? Why do you think $p^* = .50$ is often used in these cases?

Summary

In this chapter we presented methods for developing interval estimates of a population mean and a population proportion. A point estimator may or may not provide a good estimate of a population parameter. The use of an interval estimate provides a measure of the precision of an estimate. Both the interval estimate of the population mean and the population proportion are of the form: point estimate ± margin of error.

We presented interval estimates for a population mean for two cases. In the σ known case, historical data or other information is used to develop an estimate of σ prior to taking a sample. Analysis of new sample data then proceeds based on the assumption that σ is known. In the σ unknown case, the sample data are used to estimate both the population mean and the population standard deviation. The final choice of which interval estimation procedure to use depends upon the analyst's understanding of which method provides the best estimate of σ.

In the σ known case, the interval estimation procedure is based on the assumed value of σ and the use of the standard normal distribution. In the σ unknown case, the interval estimation procedure uses the sample standard deviation s and the t distribution. In both cases the quality of the interval estimates obtained depends on the distribution of the population and the sample size. If the population is normally distributed the interval estimates will be exact in both cases, even for small sample sizes. If the population is not normally distributed, the interval estimates obtained will be approximate. Larger sample sizes will provide better approximations, but the more highly skewed the population is, the larger the sample size needs to be to obtain a good approximation. Practical advice about the sample size necessary to obtain good approximations was included in Sections 8.1 and 8.2. In most cases a sample of size 30 or more will provide good approximate confidence intervals.

The general form of the interval estimate for a population proportion is $\bar{p} \pm$ margin of error. In practice the sample sizes used for interval estimates of a population proportion are generally large. Thus, the interval estimation procedure is based on the standard normal distribution.

Often a desired margin of error is specified prior to developing a sampling plan. We showed how to choose a sample size large enough to provide the desired precision.

Glossary

Interval estimate An estimate of a population parameter that provides an interval believed to contain the value of the parameter. For the interval estimates in this chapter, it has the form: point estimate $\pm$ margin of error.

Margin of error The $\pm$ value added to and subtracted from a point estimate in order to develop an interval estimate of a population parameter.

σ known The case when historical data or other information provides a good value for the population standard deviation prior to taking a sample. The interval estimation procedure uses this known value of σ in computing the margin of error.

Confidence level The confidence associated with an interval estimate. For example, if an interval estimation procedure provides intervals such that 95% of the intervals formed using the procedure will include the population parameter, the interval estimate is said to be constructed at the 95% confidence level.

Confidence coefficient The confidence level expressed as a decimal value. For example, .95 is the confidence coefficient for a 95% confidence level.

Confidence interval Another name for an interval estimate.

σ unknown The more common case when no good basis exists for estimating the population standard deviation prior to taking the sample. The interval estimation procedure uses the sample standard deviation s in computing the margin of error.

***t* distribution** A family of probability distributions that can be used to develop an interval estimate of a population mean whenever the population standard deviation σ is unknown and is estimated by the sample standard deviation s.

Degrees of freedom A parameter of the t distribution. When the t distribution is used in the computation of an interval estimate of a population mean, the appropriate t distribution has $n - 1$ degrees of freedom, where n is the size of the simple random sample.

Key Formulas

Interval Estimate of a Population Mean: σ Known

$$\bar{x} \pm z_{\alpha/2} \frac{\sigma}{\sqrt{n}} \tag{8.1}$$

Interval Estimate of a Population Mean: σ Unknown

$$\bar{x} \pm t_{\alpha/2} \frac{s}{\sqrt{n}} \tag{8.2}$$

Sample Size for an Interval Estimate of a Population Mean

$$n = \frac{(z_{\alpha/2})^2 \sigma^2}{E^2} \tag{8.3}$$

Interval Estimate of a Population Proportion

$$\bar{p} \pm z_{\alpha/2} \sqrt{\frac{\bar{p}(1 - \bar{p})}{n}} \tag{8.6}$$

Sample Size for an Interval Estimate of a Population Proportion

$$n = \frac{(z_{\alpha/2})^2 p^*(1 - p^*)}{E^2} \tag{8.7}$$

Supplementary Exercises

44. A sample survey of 54 discount brokers showed that the mean price charged for a trade of 100 shares at \$50 per share was \$33.77 (*AAII Journal,* February 2006). The survey is conducted annually. With the historical data available, assume a known population standard deviation of \$15.
    a. Using the sample data, what is the margin of error associated with a 95% confidence interval?
    b. Develop a 95% confidence interval for the mean price charged by discount brokers for a trade of 100 shares at \$50 per share.
45. A survey conducted by the American Automobile Association showed that a family of four spends an average of \$215.60 per day while on vacation. Suppose a sample of 64 families of four vacationing at Niagara Falls resulted in a sample mean of \$252.45 per day and a sample standard deviation of \$74.50.
    a. Develop a 95% confidence interval estimate of the mean amount spent per day by a family of four visiting Niagara Falls.
    b. Based on the confidence interval from part (a), does it appear that the population mean amount spent per day by families visiting Niagara Falls differs from the mean reported by the American Automobile Association? Explain.
46. The 92 million Americans of age 50 and over control 50 percent of all discretionary income (*AARP Bulletin,* March 2008). AARP estimated that the average annual expenditure on restaurants and carryout food was \$1873 for individuals in this age group. Suppose this estimate is based on a sample of 80 persons and that the sample standard deviation is \$550.
    a. At 95% confidence, what is the margin of error?
    b. What is the 95% confidence interval for the population mean amount spent on restaurants and carryout food?
    c. What is your estimate of the total amount spent by Americans of age 50 and over on restaurants and carryout food?
    d. If the amount spent on restaurants and carryout food is skewed to the right, would you expect the median amount spent to be greater or less than \$1873?

47. Many stock market observers say that when the P/E ratio for stocks gets over 20 the market is overvalued. The P/E ratio is the stock price divided by the most recent 12 months of earnings. Suppose you are interested in seeing whether the current market is overvalued and would also like to know what proportion of companies pay dividends. A random sample of 30 companies listed on the New York Stock Exchange (NYSE) is provided (*Barron's,* January 19, 2004).

WEB file NYSEStocks

Company	Dividend	P/E Ratio	Company	Dividend	P/E Ratio
Albertsons	Yes	14	NY Times A	Yes	25
BRE Prop	Yes	18	Omnicare	Yes	25
CityNtl	Yes	16	PallCp	Yes	23
DelMonte	No	21	PubSvcEnt	Yes	11
EnrgzHldg	No	20	SensientTch	Yes	11
Ford Motor	Yes	22	SmtProp	Yes	12
Gildan A	No	12	TJX Cos	Yes	21
HudsnUtdBcp	Yes	13	Thomson	Yes	30
IBM	Yes	22	USB Hldg	Yes	12
JeffPilot	Yes	16	US Restr	Yes	26
KingswayFin	No	6	Varian Med	No	41
Libbey	Yes	13	Visx	No	72
MasoniteIntl	No	15	Waste Mgt	No	23
Motorola	Yes	68	Wiley A	Yes	21
Ntl City	Yes	10	Yum Brands	No	18

a. What is a point estimate of the P/E ratio for the population of stocks listed on the New York Stock Exchange? Develop a 95% confidence interval.
b. Based on your answer to part (a), do you believe that the market is overvalued?
c. What is a point estimate of the proportion of companies on the NYSE that pay dividends? Is the sample size large enough to justify using the normal distribution to construct a confidence interval for this proportion? Why or why not?

WEB file Flights

48. US Airways conducted a number of studies that indicated a substantial savings could be obtained by encouraging Dividend Miles frequent flyer customers to redeem miles and schedule award flights online (*US Airways Attaché,* February 2003). One study collected data on the amount of time required to redeem miles and schedule an award flight over the telephone. A sample showing the time in minutes required for each of 150 award flights scheduled by telephone is contained in the data set Flights. Use Minitab or Excel to help answer the following questions.
a. What is the sample mean number of minutes required to schedule an award flight by telephone?
b. What is the 95% confidence interval for the population mean time to schedule an award flight by telephone?
c. Assume a telephone ticket agent works 7.5 hours per day. How many award flights can one ticket agent be expected to handle a day?
d. Discuss why this information supported US Airways' plans to use an online system to reduce costs.

WEB file ActTemps

49. A survey by Accountemps asked a sample of 200 executives to provide data on the number of minutes per day office workers waste trying to locate mislabeled, misfiled, or misplaced items. Data consistent with this survey are contained in the data file ActTemps.
a. Use ActTemps to develop a point estimate of the number of minutes per day office workers waste trying to locate mislabeled, misfiled, or misplaced items.
b. What is the sample standard deviation?
c. What is the 95% confidence interval for the mean number of minutes wasted per day?

50. Mileage tests are conducted for a particular model of automobile. If a 98% confidence interval with a margin of error of 1 mile per gallon is desired, how many automobiles should be used in the test? Assume that preliminary mileage tests indicate the standard deviation is 2.6 miles per gallon.

51. In developing patient appointment schedules, a medical center wants to estimate the mean time that a staff member spends with each patient. How large a sample should be taken if the desired margin of error is two minutes at a 95% level of confidence? How large a sample should be taken for a 99% level of confidence? Use a planning value for the population standard deviation of eight minutes.

52. Annual salary plus bonus data for chief executive officers are presented in the *BusinessWeek* Annual Pay Survey. A preliminary sample showed that the standard deviation is $675 with data provided in thousands of dollars. How many chief executive officers should be in a sample if we want to estimate the population mean annual salary plus bonus with a margin of error of $100,000? (*Note:* The desired margin of error would be $E = 100$ if the data are in thousands of dollars.) Use 95% confidence.

53. The National Center for Education Statistics reported that 47% of college students work to pay for tuition and living expenses. Assume that a sample of 450 college students was used in the study.
    a. Provide a 95% confidence interval for the population proportion of college students who work to pay for tuition and living expenses.
    b. Provide a 99% confidence interval for the population proportion of college students who work to pay for tuition and living expenses.
    c. What happens to the margin of error as the confidence is increased from 95% to 99%?

54. A *USA Today*/CNN/Gallup survey of 369 working parents found 200 who said they spend too little time with their children because of work commitments.
    a. What is the point estimate of the proportion of the population of working parents who feel they spend too little time with their children because of work commitments?
    b. At 95% confidence, what is the margin of error?
    c. What is the 95% confidence interval estimate of the population proportion of working parents who feel they spend too little time with their children because of work commitments?

55. Which would be hardest for you to give up: Your computer or your television? In a recent survey of 1677 U.S. Internet users, 74% of the young tech elite (average age of 22) say their computer would be very hard to give up (*PC Magazine,* February 3, 2004). Only 48% say their television would be very hard to give up.
    a. Develop a 95% confidence interval for the proportion of the young tech elite that would find it very hard to give up their computer.
    b. Develop a 99% confidence interval for the proportion of the young tech elite that would find it very hard to give up their television.
    c. In which case, part (a) or part (b), is the margin of error larger? Explain why.

56. Cincinnati/Northern Kentucky International Airport had the second highest on-time arrival rate for 2005 among the nation's busiest airports (*The Cincinnati Enquirer,* February 3, 2006). Assume the findings were based on 455 on-time arrivals out of a sample of 550 flights.
    a. Develop a point estimate of the on-time arrival rate (proportion of flights arriving on time) for the airport.
    b. Construct a 95% confidence interval for the on-time arrival rate of the population of all flights at the airport during 2005.

57. The *2003 Statistical Abstract of the United States* reported the percentage of people 18 years of age and older who smoke. Suppose that a study designed to collect new data on smokers and nonsmokers uses a preliminary estimate of the proportion who smoke of .30.
    a. How large a sample should be taken to estimate the proportion of smokers in the population with a margin of error of .02? Use 95% confidence.
    b. Assume that the study uses your sample size recommendation in part (a) and finds 520 smokers. What is the point estimate of the proportion of smokers in the population?
    c. What is the 95% confidence interval for the proportion of smokers in the population?

58. A well-known bank credit card firm wishes to estimate the proportion of credit card holders who carry a nonzero balance at the end of the month and incur an interest charge. Assume that the desired margin of error is .03 at 98% confidence.
    a. How large a sample should be selected if it is anticipated that roughly 70% of the firm's card holders carry a nonzero balance at the end of the month?
    b. How large a sample should be selected if no planning value for the proportion could be specified?
59. In a survey, 200 people were asked to identify their major source of news information; 110 stated that their major source was television news.
    a. Construct a 95% confidence interval for the proportion of people in the population who consider television their major source of news information.
    b. How large a sample would be necessary to estimate the population proportion with a margin of error of .05 at 95% confidence?
60. Although airline schedules and cost are important factors for business travelers when choosing an airline carrier, a *USA Today* survey found that business travelers list an airline's frequent flyer program as the most important factor. From a sample of $n = 1993$ business travelers who responded to the survey, 618 listed a frequent flyer program as the most important factor.
    a. What is the point estimate of the proportion of the population of business travelers who believe a frequent flyer program is the most important factor when choosing an airline carrier?
    b. Develop a 95% confidence interval estimate of the population proportion.
    c. How large a sample would be required to report the margin of error of .01 at 95% confidence? Would you recommend that *USA Today* attempt to provide this degree of precision? Why or why not?

Case Problem 1 Young Professional Magazine

Young Professional magazine was developed for a target audience of recent college graduates who are in their first 10 years in a business/professional career. In its two years of publication, the magazine has been fairly successful. Now the publisher is interested in expanding the magazine's advertising base. Potential advertisers continually ask about the demographics and interests of subscribers to *Young Professional*. To collect this information, the magazine commissioned a survey to develop a profile of its subscribers. The survey results will be used to help the magazine choose articles of interest and provide advertisers with a profile of subscribers. As a new employee of the magazine, you have been asked to help analyze the survey results.

Some of the survey questions follow:

WEB file
Professional

1. What is your age?
2. Are you: Male_________ Female___________
3. Do you plan to make any real estate purchases in the next two years? Yes______ No______
4. What is the approximate total value of financial investments, exclusive of your home, owned by you or members of your household?
5. How many stock/bond/mutual fund transactions have you made in the past year?
6. Do you have broadband access to the Internet at home? Yes______ No______
7. Please indicate your total household income last year.
8. Do you have children? Yes______ No______

The file entitled Professional contains the responses to these questions. Table 8.6 shows the portion of the file pertaining to the first five survey respondents.

TABLE 8.6 PARTIAL SURVEY RESULTS FOR *YOUNG PROFESSIONAL* MAGAZINE

Age	Gender	Real Estate Purchases	Value of Investments($)	Number of Transactions	Broadband Access	Household Income($)	Children
38	Female	No	12200	4	Yes	75200	Yes
30	Male	No	12400	4	Yes	70300	Yes
41	Female	No	26800	5	Yes	48200	No
28	Female	Yes	19600	6	No	95300	No
31	Female	Yes	15100	5	No	73300	Yes
⋮	⋮	⋮	⋮	⋮	⋮	⋮	⋮

Managerial Report

Prepare a managerial report summarizing the results of the survey. In addition to statistical summaries, discuss how the magazine might use these results to attract advertisers. You might also comment on how the survey results could be used by the magazine's editors to identify topics that would be of interest to readers. Your report should address the following issues, but do not limit your analysis to just these areas.

1. Develop appropriate descriptive statistics to summarize the data.
2. Develop 95% confidence intervals for the mean age and household income of subscribers.
3. Develop 95% confidence intervals for the proportion of subscribers who have broadband access at home and the proportion of subscribers who have children.
4. Would *Young Professional* be a good advertising outlet for online brokers? Justify your conclusion with statistical data.
5. Would this magazine be a good place to advertise for companies selling educational software and computer games for young children?
6. Comment on the types of articles you believe would be of interest to readers of *Young Professional*.

Case Problem 2 Gulf Real Estate Properties

Gulf Real Estate Properties, Inc., is a real estate firm located in southwest Florida. The company, which advertises itself as "expert in the real estate market," monitors condominium sales by collecting data on location, list price, sale price, and number of days it takes to sell each unit. Each condominium is classified as *Gulf View* if it is located directly on the Gulf of Mexico or *No Gulf View* if it is located on the bay or a golf course, near but not on the Gulf. Sample data from the Multiple Listing Service in Naples, Florida, provided recent sales data for 40 Gulf View condominiums and 18 No Gulf View condominiums.* Prices are in thousands of dollars. The data are shown in Table 8.7.

Managerial Report

1. Use appropriate descriptive statistics to summarize each of the three variables for the 40 Gulf View condominiums.
2. Use appropriate descriptive statistics to summarize each of the three variables for the 18 No Gulf View condominiums.
3. Compare your summary results. Discuss any specific statistical results that would help a real estate agent understand the condominium market.

*Data based on condominium sales reported in the Naples MLS (Coldwell Banker, June 2000).

TABLE 8.7 SALES DATA FOR GULF REAL ESTATE PROPERTIES

Gulf View Condominiums			No Gulf View Condominiums		
List Price	**Sale Price**	**Days to Sell**	**List Price**	**Sale Price**	**Days to Sell**
495.0	475.0	130	217.0	217.0	182
379.0	350.0	71	148.0	135.5	338
529.0	519.0	85	186.5	179.0	122
552.5	534.5	95	239.0	230.0	150
334.9	334.9	119	279.0	267.5	169
550.0	505.0	92	215.0	214.0	58
169.9	165.0	197	279.0	259.0	110
210.0	210.0	56	179.9	176.5	130
975.0	945.0	73	149.9	144.9	149
314.0	314.0	126	235.0	230.0	114
315.0	305.0	88	199.8	192.0	120
885.0	800.0	282	210.0	195.0	61
975.0	975.0	100	226.0	212.0	146
469.0	445.0	56	149.9	146.5	137
329.0	305.0	49	160.0	160.0	281
365.0	330.0	48	322.0	292.5	63
332.0	312.0	88	187.5	179.0	48
520.0	495.0	161	247.0	227.0	52
425.0	405.0	149			
675.0	669.0	142			
409.0	400.0	28			
649.0	649.0	29			
319.0	305.0	140			
425.0	410.0	85			
359.0	340.0	107			
469.0	449.0	72			
895.0	875.0	129			
439.0	430.0	160			
435.0	400.0	206			
235.0	227.0	91			
638.0	618.0	100			
629.0	600.0	97			
329.0	309.0	114			
595.0	555.0	45			
339.0	315.0	150			
215.0	200.0	48			
395.0	375.0	135			
449.0	425.0	53			
499.0	465.0	86			
439.0	428.5	158			

WEB file

GulfProp

4. Develop a 95% confidence interval estimate of the population mean sales price and population mean number of days to sell for Gulf View condominiums. Interpret your results.
5. Develop a 95% confidence interval estimate of the population mean sales price and population mean number of days to sell for No Gulf View condominiums. Interpret your results.
6. Assume the branch manager requested estimates of the mean selling price of Gulf View condominiums with a margin of error of $40,000 and the mean selling price

of No Gulf View condominiums with a margin of error of $15,000. Using 95% confidence, how large should the sample sizes be?

7. Gulf Real Estate Properties just signed contracts for two new listings: a Gulf View condominium with a list price of $589,000 and a No Gulf View condominium with a list price of $285,000. What is your estimate of the final selling price and number of days required to sell each of these units?

Case Problem 3 Metropolitan Research, Inc.

Metropolitan Research, Inc., a consumer research organization, conducts surveys designed to evaluate a wide variety of products and services available to consumers. In one particular study, Metropolitan looked at consumer satisfaction with the performance of automobiles produced by a major Detroit manufacturer. A questionnaire sent to owners of one of the manufacturer's full-sized cars revealed several complaints about early transmission problems. To learn more about the transmission failures, Metropolitan used a sample of actual transmission repairs provided by a transmission repair firm in the Detroit area. The following data show the actual number of miles driven for 50 vehicles at the time of transmission failure.

WEB file
Auto

85,092	32,609	59,465	77,437	32,534	64,090	32,464	59,902
39,323	89,641	94,219	116,803	92,857	63,436	65,605	85,861
64,342	61,978	67,998	59,817	101,769	95,774	121,352	69,568
74,276	66,998	40,001	72,069	25,066	77,098	69,922	35,662
74,425	67,202	118,444	53,500	79,294	64,544	86,813	116,269
37,831	89,341	73,341	85,288	138,114	53,402	85,586	82,256
77,539	88,798						

Managerial Report

1. Use appropriate descriptive statistics to summarize the transmission failure data.
2. Develop a 95% confidence interval for the mean number of miles driven until transmission failure for the population of automobiles with transmission failure. Provide a managerial interpretation of the interval estimate.
3. Discuss the implication of your statistical findings in terms of the belief that some owners of the automobiles experienced early transmission failures.
4. How many repair records should be sampled if the research firm wants the population mean number of miles driven until transmission failure to be estimated with a margin of error of 5000 miles? Use 95% confidence.
5. What other information would you like to gather to evaluate the transmission failure problem more fully?

Appendix 8.1 Interval Estimation with Minitab

We describe the use of Minitab in constructing confidence intervals for a population mean and a population proportion.

Population Mean: σ Known

WEB file
Lloyd's

We illustrate interval estimation using the Lloyd's example in Section 8.1. The amounts spent per shopping trip for the sample of 100 customers are in column C1 of a Minitab worksheet. The population standard deviation $\sigma = 20$ is assumed known. The following steps can be used to compute a 95% confidence interval estimate of the population mean.

Step 1. Select the **Stat** menu
Step 2. Choose **Basic Statistics**
Step 3. Choose **1-Sample Z**
Step 4. When the 1-Sample Z dialog box appears:
Enter C1 in the **Samples in columns** box
Enter 20 in the **Standard deviation** box
Step 5. Click **OK**

The Minitab default is a 95% confidence level. In order to specify a different confidence level such as 90%, add the following to step 4.

Select **Options**
When the 1-Sample Z-Options dialog box appears:
Enter 90 in the **Confidence level** box
Click **OK**

Population Mean: σ Unknown

WEB file
NewBalance

We illustrate interval estimation using the data in Table 8.3 showing the credit card balances for a sample of 70 households. The data are in column C1 of a Minitab worksheet. In this case the population standard deviation σ will be estimated by the sample standard deviation s. The following steps can be used to compute a 95% confidence interval estimate of the population mean.

Step 1. Select the **Stat** menu
Step 2. Choose **Basic Statistics**
Step 3. Choose **1-Sample t**
Step 4. When the 1-Sample t dialog box appears:
Enter C1 in the **Samples in columns** box
Step 5. Click **OK**

The Minitab default is a 95% confidence level. In order to specify a different confidence level such as 90%, add the following to step 4.

Select **Options**
When the 1-Sample t-Options dialog box appears:
Enter 90 in the **Confidence level** box
Click **OK**

Population Proportion

WEB file
TeeTimes

We illustrate interval estimation using the survey data for women golfers presented in Section 8.4. The data are in column C1 of a Minitab worksheet. Individual responses are recorded as Yes if the golfer is satisfied with the availability of tee times and No otherwise. The following steps can be used to compute a 95% confidence interval estimate of the proportion of women golfers who are satisfied with the availability of tee times.

Step 1. Select the **Stat** menu
Step 2. Choose **Basic Statistics**
Step 3. Choose **1 Proportion**
Step 4. When the 1 Proportion dialog box appears:
Enter C1 in the **Samples in columns** box
Step 5. Select **Options**
Step 6. When the 1 Proportion-Options dialog box appears:
Select **Use test and interval based on normal distribution**
Click **OK**
Step 7. Click **OK**

The Minitab default is a 95% confidence level. In order to specify a different confidence level such as 90%, enter 90 in the **Confidence Level** box when the 1 Proportion-Options dialog box appears in step 6.

Note: Minitab's 1 Proportion routine uses an alphabetical ordering of the responses and selects the *second response* for the population proportion of interest. In the women golfers example, Minitab used the alphabetical ordering No-Yes and then provided the confidence interval for the proportion of Yes responses. Because Yes was the response of interest, the Minitab output was fine. However, if Minitab's alphabetical ordering does not provide the response of interest, select any cell in the column and use the sequence: Editor > Column > Value Order. It will provide you with the option of entering a user-specified order, but you must list the response of interest second in the define-an-order box.

Appendix 8.2 Interval Estimation Using Excel

We describe the use of Excel in constructing confidence intervals for a population mean and a population proportion.

Population Mean: σ Known

WEB file
Lloyd's

We illustrate interval estimation using the Lloyd's example in Section 8.1. The population standard deviation $\sigma = 20$ is assumed known. The amounts spent for the sample of 100 customers are in column A of an Excel worksheet. Excel's AVERAGE and CONFIDENCE.NORM functions can be used to compute the point estimate and the margin of error for an estimate of the population mean.

Step 1. Select cell C1 and enter the Excel formula =AVERAGE(A2:A101)
Step 2. Select cell C2 and enter the Excel formula =CONFIDENCE.NORM(.05,20,100)

The three inputs of the CONFIDENCE.NORM function are

Alpha = 1 − confidence coefficient = 1 − .95 = .05
The population standard deviation = 20
The sample size = 100

The point estimate of the population mean (82) in cell C1 and the margin of error (3.92) in cell C2 allow the confidence interval for the population mean to be easily computed.

Population Mean: σ Unknown

WEB file
NewBalance

We illustrate interval estimation using the data in Table 8.3, which show the credit card balances for a sample of 70 households. The data are in column A of an Excel worksheet. The following steps can be used to compute the point estimate and the margin of error for an interval estimate of a population mean. We will use Excel's Descriptive Statistics Tool described in Chapter 3.

Step 1. Click the **Data** tab on the Ribbon
Step 2. In the **Analysis** group, click **Data Analysis**
Step 3. Choose **Descriptive Statistics** from the list of Analysis Tools
Step 4. When the Descriptive Statistics dialog box appears:
Enter A1:A71 in the **Input Range** box
Select **Grouped by Columns**

FIGURE 8.10 INTERVAL ESTIMATION OF THE POPULATION MEAN CREDIT CARD BALANCE USING EXCEL

	A	B	C	D	E	F
1	**NewBalance**		***NewBalance***			
2	9430					
3	7535		Mean	9312	Point Estimate	
4	4078		Standard Error	478.9281		
5	5604		Median	9466		
6	5179		Mode	13627		
7	4416		Standard Deviation	4007		
8	10676		Sample Variance	16056048		
9	1627		Kurtosis	−0.296		
10	10112		Skewness	0.18792		
11	6567		Range	18648		
12	13627		Minimum	615		
13	18719		Maximum	19263		
14	14661		Sum	651840		
15	12195		Count	70		
16	10544		Confidence Level(95.0%)	955.4354	Margin of Error	
17	13659					
70	9743					
71	10324					
71						

Note: Rows 18 to 69 are hidden.

Select **Labels in First Row**
Select **Output Range**
Enter C1 in the Output Range box
Select **Summary Statistics**
Select **Confidence Level for Mean**
    Enter 95 in the Confidence Level for Mean box
Click **OK**

The summary statistics will appear in columns C and D. The point estimate of the population mean appears in cell D3. The margin of error, labeled "Confidence Level(95.0%)," appears in cell D16. The point estimate ($9312) and the margin of error ($955) allow the confidence interval for the population mean to be easily computed. The output from this Excel procedure is shown in Figure 8.10.

Population Proportion

WEB file

Interval p

We illustrate interval estimation using the survey data for women golfers presented in Section 8.4. The data are in column A of an Excel worksheet. Individual responses are recorded as Yes if the golfer is satisfied with the availability of tee times and No otherwise. Excel does not offer a built-in routine to handle the estimation of a population proportion; however, it is relatively easy to develop an Excel template that can be used for this purpose. The template shown in Figure 8.11 provides the 95% confidence interval estimate of the proportion of women golfers who are satisfied with the availability of tee times. Note that the background worksheet in Figure 8.11 shows the cell formulas that provide the interval

FIGURE 8.11 EXCEL TEMPLATE FOR INTERVAL ESTIMATION OF A POPULATION PROPORTION

	A	B	C	D	E
1	**Response**		**Interval Estimate of a Population Proportion**		
2	Yes				
3	No		**Sample Size**	=COUNTA(A2:A901)	
4	Yes		**Response of Interest**	Yes	
5	Yes		**Count for Response**	=COUNTIF(A2:A901,D4)	
6	No		**Sample Proportion**	=D5/D3	
7	No				
8	No		**Confidence Coefficient**	0.95	
9	Yes		***z* Value**	=NORM.S.INV(0.5+D8/2)	
10	Yes				
11	Yes		**Standard Error**	=SQRT(D6*(1-D6)/D3)	
12	No		**Margin of Error**	=D9*D11	
13	No				
14	Yes		**Point Estimate**	=D6	
15	No		**Lower Limit**	=D14-D12	
16	No		**Upper Limit**	=D14+D12	
17	Yes				
18	No				
901	Yes				
902					

	A	B	C	D	E	F	G
1	**Response**		**Interval Estimate of a Population Proportion**				
2	Yes						
3	No		**Sample Size**	900			
4	Yes		**Response of Interest**	Yes			
5	Yes		**Count for Response**	396			
6	No		**Sample Proportion**	0.4400			
7	No						
8	No		**Confidence Coefficient**	0.95			
9	Yes		***z* Value**	1.960			
10	Yes						
11	Yes		**Standard Error**	0.0165			
12	No		**Margin of Error**	0.0324			
13	No						
14	Yes		**Point Estimate**	0.4400			
15	No		**Lower Limit**	0.4076			
16	No		**Upper Limit**	0.4724			
17	Yes						
18	No						
901	Yes						
902							

Enter the response of interest

Enter the confidence coefficient

Note: Rows 19 to 900 are hidden.

estimation results shown in the foreground worksheet. The following steps are necessary to use the template for this data set.

Step 1. Enter the data range A2:A901 into the =COUNTA cell formula in cell D3
Step 2. Enter Yes as the response of interest in cell D4
Step 3. Enter the data range A2:A901 into the =COUNTIF cell formula in cell D5
Step 4. Enter .95 as the confidence coefficient in cell D8

The template automatically provides the confidence interval in cells D15 and D16.

This template can be used to compute the confidence interval for a population proportion for other applications. For instance, to compute the interval estimate for a new data set, enter the new sample data into column A of the worksheet and then make the changes to the four cells as shown. If the new sample data have already been summarized, the sample data do not have to be entered into the worksheet. In this case, enter the sample size into cell D3 and the sample proportion into cell D6; the worksheet template will then provide the confidence interval for the population proportion. The worksheet in Figure 8.11 is available in the file Interval p on the website that accompanies this book.

Appendix 8.3 Interval Estimation with StatTools

In this appendix we show how StatTools can be used to develop an interval estimate of a population mean for the σ unknown case and determine the sample size needed to provide a desired margin of error.

Population Mean: σ Unknown Case

In this case the population standard deviation σ will be estimated by the sample standard deviation s. We use the credit card balance data in Table 8.3 to illustrate. Begin by using the Data Set Manager to create a StatTools data set for these data using the procedure described in the appendix to Chapter 1. The following steps can be used to compute a 95% confidence interval estimate of the population mean.

WEB file
NewBalance

Step 1. Click the **StatTools** tab on the Ribbon
Step 2. In the **Analyses** group, click **Statistical Inference**
Step 3. Choose the **Confidence Interval** option
Step 4. Choose Mean/Std. Deviation
Step 5. When the StatTools-Confidence Interval for Mean/Std. Deviation dialog box appears:
For **Analysis Type** choose **One-Sample Analysis**
In the **Variables** section, select **NewBalance**
In the **Confidence Intervals to Calculate** section:
Select the **For the Mean** option
Select 95% for the **Confidence Level**
Click **OK**

Some descriptive statistics and the confidence interval will appear.

Determining the Sample Size

In Section 8.3 we showed how to determine the sample size needed to provide a desired margin of error. The example used involved a study designed to estimate the population mean daily rental cost for a midsize automobile in the United States. The project director specified that the population mean daily rental cost be estimated with a margin of error of \$2 and a 95% level of confidence. Sample data from a previous study provided a sample standard deviation of \$9.65; this value was used as the planning value for the population standard deviation. The following steps can be used to compute the recommended sample size required to provide a 95% confidence interval estimate of the population mean with a margin of error of \$2.

Step 1. Click the **StatTools** tab on the Ribbon
Step 2. In the **Analyses** group, click **Statistical Inference**
Step 3. Choose the **Sample Size Selection** option

Step 4. When the StatTools-Sample Size Selection dialog box appears:
In the **Parameter to Estimate** section, select **Mean**
In the **Confidence Interval Specification** section:
Select **95%** for the **Confidence Level**
Enter **2** in the **Half-Length of Interval** box
Enter **9.65** in the **Estimated Std Dev** box
Click **OK**

The half-length of interval is the margin of error.

The output showing a recommended sample size of 90 will appear.

Population Proportion

We illustrate using the survey data for women golfers presented in Section 8.4. Begin by using the Data Set Manager to create a StatTools data set for these data using the procedure described in the appendix to Chapter 1. The following steps can be used to compute a 95% confidence interval estimate of the population mean.

WEB file
Tee Times

Step 1. Click the **StatTools** tab on the Ribbon
Step 2. In the **Analyses** group, click **Statistical Inference**
Step 3. Choose **Confidence Interval**
Step 4. Choose **Proportion**
Step 5. When the StatTools-Confidence Interval for Proportion dialog box appears:
For **Analysis Type** choose **One-Sample Analysis**
In the **Variables** section, select **Response**
In the **Categories to Analyze** section, select **Yes**
In the **Options** section, enter 95% in the **Confidence Level** box
Click **OK**

Some descriptive statistics and the confidence interval will appear.

StatTools also provides a capability for determining the appropriate sample size to provide a desired margin of error. The steps are similar to those for determining the sample size in the previous subsection.

CHAPTER 9

Hypothesis Tests

CONTENTS

STATISTICS *in* PRACTICE

JOHN MORRELL & COMPANY*
CINCINNATI, OHIO

John Morrell & Company, which began in England in 1827, is considered the oldest continuously operating meat manufacturer in the United States. It is a wholly owned and independently managed subsidiary of Smithfield Foods, Smithfield, Virginia. John Morrell & Company offers an extensive product line of processed meats and fresh pork to consumers under 13 regional brands including John Morrell, E-Z-Cut, Tobin's First Prize, Dinner Bell, Hunter, Kretschmar, Rath, Rodeo, Shenson, Farmers Hickory Brand, Iowa Quality, and Peyton's. Each regional brand enjoys high brand recognition and loyalty among consumers.

Market research at Morrell provides management with up-to-date information on the company's various products and how the products compare with competing brands of similar products. A recent study compared a Beef Pot Roast made by Morrell to similar beef products from two major competitors. In the three-product comparison test, a sample of consumers was used to indicate how the products rated in terms of taste, appearance, aroma, and overall preference.

One research question concerned whether the Beef Pot Roast made by Morrell was the preferred choice of more than 50% of the consumer population. Letting p indicate the population proportion preferring Morrell's product, the hypothesis test for the research question is as follows:

$$H_0: p \leq .50$$
$$H_a: p > .50$$

The null hypothesis H_0 indicates the preference for Morrell's product is less than or equal to 50%. If the sample data support rejecting H_0 in favor of the alternative hypothesis H_a, Morrell will draw the research conclusion that in a three-product comparison, their Beef Pot Roast is preferred by more than 50% of the consumer population.

Fully cooked entrees allow consumers to heat and serve in the same microwaveable tray. © Courtesy of John Morrell's Convenient Cuisine products.

In an independent taste test study using a sample of 224 consumers in Cincinnati, Milwaukee, and Los Angeles, 150 consumers selected the Beef Pot Roast made by Morrell as the preferred product. Using statistical hypothesis testing procedures, the null hypothesis H_0 was rejected. The study provided statistical evidence supporting H_a and the conclusion that the Morrell product is preferred by more than 50% of the consumer population.

The point estimate of the population proportion was $\bar{p} = 150/224 = .67$. Thus, the sample data provided support for a food magazine advertisement showing that in a three-product taste comparison, Beef Pot Roast made by Morrell was "preferred 2 to 1 over the competition."

In this chapter we will discuss how to formulate hypotheses and how to conduct tests like the one used by Morrell. Through the analysis of sample data, we will be able to determine whether a hypothesis should or should not be rejected.

*The authors are indebted to Marty Butler, Vice President of Marketing, John Morrell, for providing this Statistics in Practice.

In Chapters 7 and 8 we showed how a sample could be used to develop point and interval estimates of population parameters. In this chapter we continue the discussion of statistical inference by showing how hypothesis testing can be used to determine whether a statement about the value of a population parameter should or should not be rejected.

In hypothesis testing we begin by making a tentative assumption about a population parameter. This tentative assumption is called the **null hypothesis** and is denoted by H_0. We then define another hypothesis, called the **alternative hypothesis**, which is the opposite of what is stated in the null hypothesis. The alternative hypothesis is denoted by H_a.

The hypothesis testing procedure uses data from a sample to test the two competing statements indicated by H_0 and H_a.

This chapter shows how hypothesis tests can be conducted about a population mean and a population proportion. We begin by providing examples that illustrate approaches to developing null and alternative hypotheses.

9.1 Developing Null and Alternative Hypotheses

It is not always obvious how the null and alternative hypotheses should be formulated. Care must be taken to structure the hypotheses appropriately so that the hypothesis testing conclusion provides the information the researcher or decision maker wants. The context of the situation is very important in determining how the hypotheses should be stated. All hypothesis testing applications involve collecting a sample and using the sample results to provide evidence for drawing a conclusion. Good questions to consider when formulating the null and alternative hypotheses are, What is the purpose of collecting the sample? What conclusions are we hoping to make?

Learning to correctly formulate hypotheses will take some practice. Expect some initial confusion over the proper choice of the null and alternative hypotheses. The examples in this section are intended to provide guidelines.

In the chapter introduction, we stated that the null hypothesis H_0 is a tentative assumption about a population parameter such as a population mean or a population proportion. The alternative hypothesis H_a is a statement that is the opposite of what is stated in the null hypothesis. In some situations it is easier to identify the alternative hypothesis first and then develop the null hypothesis. In other situations it is easier to identify the null hypothesis first and then develop the alternative hypothesis. We will illustrate these situations in the following examples.

The Alternative Hypothesis as a Research Hypothesis

Many applications of hypothesis testing involve an attempt to gather evidence in support of a research hypothesis. In these situations, it is often best to begin with the alternative hypothesis and make it the conclusion that the researcher hopes to support. Consider a particular automobile that currently attains a fuel efficiency of 24 miles per gallon in city driving. A product research group has developed a new fuel injection system designed to increase the miles-per-gallon rating. The group will run controlled tests with the new fuel injection system looking for statistical support for the conclusion that the new fuel injection system provides more miles per gallon than the current system.

Several new fuel injection units will be manufactured, installed in test automobiles, and subjected to research-controlled driving conditions. The sample mean miles per gallon for these automobiles will be computed and used in a hypothesis test to determine if it can be concluded that the new system provides more than 24 miles per gallon. In terms of the population mean miles per gallon μ, the research hypothesis $\mu > 24$ becomes the alternative hypothesis. Since the current system provides an average or mean of 24 miles per gallon, we will make the tentative assumption that the new system is not any better than the current system and choose $\mu \le 24$ as the null hypothesis. The null and alternative hypotheses are:

$$H_0\colon \mu \le 24$$
$$H_a\colon \mu > 24$$

If the sample results lead to the conclusion to reject H_0, the inference can be made that $H_a\colon \mu > 24$ is true. The researchers have the statistical support to state that the new fuel injection system increases the mean number of miles per gallon. The production of automobiles with the new fuel injection system should be considered. However, if the sample results lead to the conclusion that H_0 cannot be rejected, the researchers cannot conclude

The conclusion that the research hypothesis is true is made if the sample data provide sufficient evidence to show that the null hypothesis can be rejected.

that the new fuel injection system is better than the current system. Production of automobiles with the new fuel injection system on the basis of better gas mileage cannot be justified. Perhaps more research and further testing can be conducted.

Successful companies stay competitive by developing new products, new methods, new systems, and the like, that are better than what is currently available. Before adopting something new, it is desirable to conduct research to determine if there is statistical support for the conclusion that the new approach is indeed better. In such cases, the research hypothesis is stated as the alternative hypothesis. For example, a new teaching method is developed that is believed to be better than the current method. The alternative hypothesis is that the new method is better. The null hypothesis is that the new method is no better than the old method. A new sales force bonus plan is developed in an attempt to increase sales. The alternative hypothesis is that the new bonus plan increases sales. The null hypothesis is that the new bonus plan does not increase sales. A new drug is developed with the goal of lowering blood pressure more than an existing drug. The alternative hypothesis is that the new drug lowers blood pressure more than the existing drug. The null hypothesis is that the new drug does not provide lower blood pressure than the existing drug. In each case, rejection of the null hypothesis H_0 provides statistical support for the research hypothesis. We will see many examples of hypothesis tests in research situations such as these throughout this chapter and in the remainder of the text.

The Null Hypothesis as an Assumption to Be Challenged

Of course, not all hypothesis tests involve research hypotheses. In the following discussion we consider applications of hypothesis testing where we begin with a belief or an assumption that a statement about the value of a population parameter is true. We will then use a hypothesis test to challenge the assumption and determine if there is statistical evidence to conclude that the assumption is incorrect. In these situations, it is helpful to develop the null hypothesis first. The null hypothesis H_0 expresses the belief or assumption about the value of the population parameter. The alternative hypothesis H_a is that the belief or assumption is incorrect.

As an example, consider the situation of a manufacturer of soft drink products. The label on a soft drink bottle states that it contains 67.6 fluid ounces. We consider the label correct provided the population mean filling weight for the bottles is *at least* 67.6 fluid ounces. Without any reason to believe otherwise, we would give the manufacturer the benefit of the doubt and assume that the statement provided on the label is correct. Thus, in a hypothesis test about the population mean fluid weight per bottle, we would begin with the assumption that the label is correct and state the null hypothesis as $\mu \geq 67.6$. The challenge to this assumption would imply that the label is incorrect and the bottles are being underfilled. This challenge would be stated as the alternative hypothesis $\mu < 67.6$. Thus, the null and alternative hypotheses are:

$$H_0\colon \mu \geq 67.6$$
$$H_a\colon \mu < 67.6$$

A manufacturer's product information is usually assumed to be true and stated as the null hypothesis. The conclusion that the information is incorrect can be made if the null hypothesis is rejected.

A government agency with the responsibility for validating manufacturing labels could select a sample of soft drinks bottles, compute the sample mean filling weight, and use the sample results to test the preceding hypotheses. If the sample results lead to the conclusion to reject H_0, the inference that $H_a\colon \mu < 67.6$ is true can be made. With this statistical support, the agency is justified in concluding that the label is incorrect and underfilling of the bottles is occurring. Appropriate action to force the manufacturer to comply with labeling standards would be considered. However, if the sample results indicate H_0 cannot be rejected, the assumption that the manufacturer's labeling is correct cannot be rejected. With this conclusion, no action would be taken.

Let us now consider a variation of the soft drink bottle filling example by viewing the same situation from the manufacturer's point of view. The bottle-filling operation has been designed to fill soft drink bottles with 67.6 fluid ounces as stated on the label. The company does not want to underfill the containers because that could result in an underfilling complaint from customers or, perhaps, a government agency. However, the company does not want to overfill containers either because putting more soft drink than necessary into the containers would be an unnecessary cost. The company's goal would be to adjust the bottle-filling operation so that the population mean filling weight per bottle is 67.6 fluid ounces as specified on the label.

Although this is the company's goal, from time to time any production process can get out of adjustment. If this occurs in our example, underfilling or overfilling of the soft drink bottles will occur. In either case, the company would like to know about it in order to correct the situation by readjusting the bottle-filling operation to the designed 67.6 fluid ounces. In a hypothesis testing application, we would again begin with the assumption that the production process is operating correctly and state the null hypothesis as $\mu = 67.6$ fluid ounces. The alternative hypothesis that challenges this assumption is that $\mu \neq 67.6$, which indicates either overfilling or underfilling is occurring. The null and alternative hypotheses for the manufacturer's hypothesis test are:

$$H_0\colon \mu = 67.6$$
$$H_a\colon \mu \neq 67.6$$

Suppose that the soft drink manufacturer uses a quality control procedure to periodically select a sample of bottles from the filling operation and computes the sample mean filling weight per bottle. If the sample results lead to the conclusion to reject H_0, the inference is made that $H_a\colon \mu \neq 67.6$ is true. We conclude that the bottles are not being filled properly and the production process should be adjusted to restore the population mean to 67.6 fluid ounces per bottle. However, if the sample results indicate H_0 cannot be rejected, the assumption that the manufacturer's bottle filling operation is functioning properly cannot be rejected. In this case, no further action would be taken and the production operation would continue to run.

The two preceding forms of the soft drink manufacturing hypothesis test show that the null and alternative hypotheses may vary depending upon the point of view of the researcher or decision maker. To correctly formulate hypotheses it is important to understand the context of the situation and structure the hypotheses to provide the information the researcher or decision maker wants.

Summary of Forms for Null and Alternative Hypotheses

The hypothesis tests in this chapter involve two population parameters: the population mean and the population proportion. Depending on the situation, hypothesis tests about a population parameter may take one of three forms: two use inequalities in the null hypothesis; the third uses an equality in the null hypothesis. For hypothesis tests involving a population mean, we let μ_0 denote the hypothesized value and we must choose one of the following three forms for the hypothesis test.

The three possible forms of hypotheses H_0 and H_a are shown here. Note that the equality *always appears in the null hypothesis H_0.*

$$H_0\colon \mu \geq \mu_0 \qquad H_0\colon \mu \leq \mu_0 \qquad H_0\colon \mu = \mu_0$$
$$H_a\colon \mu < \mu_0 \qquad H_a\colon \mu > \mu_0 \qquad H_a\colon \mu \neq \mu_0$$

For reasons that will be clear later, the first two forms are called one-tailed tests. The third form is called a two-tailed test.

In many situations, the choice of H_0 and H_a is not obvious and judgment is necessary to select the proper form. However, as the preceding forms show, the equality part of the expression (either $\geq$, $\leq$, or $=$) *always* appears in the null hypothesis. In selecting the proper form of H_0 and H_a, keep in mind that the alternative hypothesis is often what the test is attempting to establish. Hence, asking whether the user is looking for evidence to support $\mu < \mu_0$, $\mu > \mu_0$, or $\mu \neq \mu_0$ will help determine H_a. The following exercises are designed to provide practice in choosing the proper form for a hypothesis test involving a population mean.

Exercises

1. The manager of the Danvers-Hilton Resort Hotel stated that the mean guest bill for a weekend is \$600 or less. A member of the hotel's accounting staff noticed that the total charges for guest bills have been increasing in recent months. The accountant will use a sample of future weekend guest bills to test the manager's claim.
   a. Which form of the hypotheses should be used to test the manager's claim? Explain.

$$H_0: \mu \geq 600 \qquad H_0: \mu \leq 600 \qquad H_0: \mu = 600$$
$$H_a: \mu < 600 \qquad H_a: \mu > 600 \qquad H_a: \mu \neq 600$$

   b. What conclusion is appropriate when H_0 cannot be rejected?
   c. What conclusion is appropriate when H_0 can be rejected?

SELF test

2. The manager of an automobile dealership is considering a new bonus plan designed to increase sales volume. Currently, the mean sales volume is 14 automobiles per month. The manager wants to conduct a research study to see whether the new bonus plan increases sales volume. To collect data on the plan, a sample of sales personnel will be allowed to sell under the new bonus plan for a one-month period.
   a. Develop the null and alternative hypotheses most appropriate for this situation.
   b. Comment on the conclusion when H_0 cannot be rejected.
   c. Comment on the conclusion when H_0 can be rejected.
3. A production line operation is designed to fill cartons with laundry detergent to a mean weight of 32 ounces. A sample of cartons is periodically selected and weighed to determine whether underfilling or overfilling is occurring. If the sample data lead to a conclusion of underfilling or overfilling, the production line will be shut down and adjusted to obtain proper filling.
   a. Formulate the null and alternative hypotheses that will help in deciding whether to shut down and adjust the production line.
   b. Comment on the conclusion and the decision when H_0 cannot be rejected.
   c. Comment on the conclusion and the decision when H_0 can be rejected.
4. Because of high production-changeover time and costs, a director of manufacturing must convince management that a proposed manufacturing method reduces costs before the new method can be implemented. The current production method operates with a mean cost of \$220 per hour. A research study will measure the cost of the new method over a sample production period.
   a. Develop the null and alternative hypotheses most appropriate for this study.
   b. Comment on the conclusion when H_0 cannot be rejected.
   c. Comment on the conclusion when H_0 can be rejected.

9.2 Type I and Type II Errors

The null and alternative hypotheses are competing statements about the population. Either the null hypothesis H_0 is true or the alternative hypothesis H_a is true, but not both. Ideally the hypothesis testing procedure should lead to the acceptance of H_0 when H_0 is true and the

TABLE 9.1 ERRORS AND CORRECT CONCLUSIONS IN HYPOTHESIS TESTING

		Population Condition	
		H_0 True	H_a True
Conclusion	Accept H_0	Correct Conclusion	Type II Error
	Reject H_0	Type I Error	Correct Conclusion

rejection of H_0 when H_a is true. Unfortunately, the correct conclusions are not always possible. Because hypothesis tests are based on sample information, we must allow for the possibility of errors. Table 9.1 illustrates the two kinds of errors that can be made in hypothesis testing.

The first row of Table 9.1 shows what can happen if the conclusion is to accept H_0. If H_0 is true, this conclusion is correct. However, if H_a is true, we make a **Type II error**; that is, we accept H_0 when it is false. The second row of Table 9.1 shows what can happen if the conclusion is to reject H_0. If H_0 is true, we make a **Type I error**; that is, we reject H_0 when it is true. However, if H_a is true, rejecting H_0 is correct.

Recall the hypothesis testing illustration discussed in Section 9.1 in which an automobile product research group developed a new fuel injection system designed to increase the miles-per-gallon rating of a particular automobile. With the current model obtaining an average of 24 miles per gallon, the hypothesis test was formulated as follows.

$$H_0\colon \mu \le 24$$
$$H_a\colon \mu > 24$$

The alternative hypothesis, $H_a\colon \mu > 24$, indicates that the researchers are looking for sample evidence to support the conclusion that the population mean miles per gallon with the new fuel injection system is greater than 24.

In this application, the Type I error of rejecting H_0 when it is true corresponds to the researchers claiming that the new system improves the miles-per-gallon rating ($\mu > 24$) when in fact the new system is not any better than the current system. In contrast, the Type II error of accepting H_0 when it is false corresponds to the researchers concluding that the new system is not any better than the current system ($\mu \le 24$) when in fact the new system improves miles-per-gallon performance.

For the miles-per-gallon rating hypothesis test, the null hypothesis is $H_0\colon \mu \le 24$. Suppose the null hypothesis is true as an equality; that is, $\mu = 24$. The probability of making a Type I error when the null hypothesis is true as an equality is called the **level of significance**. Thus, for the miles-per-gallon rating hypothesis test, the level of significance is the probability of rejecting $H_0\colon \mu \le 24$ when $\mu = 24$. Because of the importance of this concept, we now restate the definition of level of significance.

LEVEL OF SIGNIFICANCE

The level of significance is the probability of making a Type I error when the null hypothesis is true as an equality.

The Greek symbol α (alpha) is used to denote the level of significance, and common choices for α are .05 and .01.

In practice, the person responsible for the hypothesis test specifies the level of significance. By selecting α, that person is controlling the probability of making a Type I error. If the cost of making a Type I error is high, small values of α are preferred. If the cost of making a Type I error is not too high, larger values of α are typically used. Applications of hypothesis testing that only control for the Type I error are called *significance tests.* Many applications of hypothesis testing are of this type.

Although most applications of hypothesis testing control for the probability of making a Type I error, they do not always control for the probability of making a Type II error. Hence, if we decide to accept H_0, we cannot determine how confident we can be with that decision. Because of the uncertainty associated with making a Type II error when conducting significance tests, statisticians usually recommend that we use the statement "do not reject H_0" instead of "accept H_0." Using the statement "do not reject H_0" carries the recommendation to withhold both judgment and action. In effect, by not directly accepting H_0, the statistician avoids the risk of making a Type II error. Whenever the probability of making a Type II error has not been determined and controlled, we will not make the statement "accept H_0." In such cases, only two conclusions are possible: *do not reject* H_0 or *reject* H_0.

If the sample data are consistent with the null hypothesis H_0, we will follow the practice of concluding "do not reject H_0." This conclusion is preferred over "accept H_0," because the conclusion to accept H_0 puts us at risk of making a Type II error.

Although controlling for a Type II error in hypothesis testing is not common, it can be done. In Sections 9.7 and 9.8 we will illustrate procedures for determining and controlling the probability of making a Type II error. If proper controls have been established for this error, action based on the "accept H_0" conclusion can be appropriate.

NOTES AND COMMENTS

Walter Williams, syndicated columnist and professor of economics at George Mason University, points out that the possibility of making a Type I or a Type II error is always present in decision making (*The Cincinnati Enquirer,* August 14, 2005). He notes that the Food and Drug Administration runs the risk of making these errors in their drug approval process. With a Type I error, the FDA fails to approve a drug that is safe and effective. A Type II error means the FDA approves a drug that has unanticipated dangerous side effects. Regardless of the decision made, the possibility of making a costly error cannot be eliminated.

Exercises

SELF test

5. Nielsen reported that young men in the United States watch 56.2 minutes of prime-time TV daily (*The Wall Street Journal Europe,* November 18, 2003). A researcher believes that young men in Germany spend more time watching prime-time TV. A sample of German young men will be selected by the researcher and the time they spend watching TV in one day will be recorded. The sample results will be used to test the following null and alternative hypotheses.

$$H_0: \mu \leq 56.2$$
$$H_a: \mu > 56.2$$

   a. What is the Type I error in this situation? What are the consequences of making this error?
   b. What is the Type II error in this situation? What are the consequences of making this error?

6. The label on a 3-quart container of orange juice states that the orange juice contains an average of 1 gram of fat or less. Answer the following questions for a hypothesis test that could be used to test the claim on the label.
   a. Develop the appropriate null and alternative hypotheses.

b. What is the Type I error in this situation? What are the consequences of making this error?
c. What is the Type II error in this situation? What are the consequences of making this error?

7. Carpetland salespersons average \$8000 per week in sales. Steve Contois, the firm's vice president, proposes a compensation plan with new selling incentives. Steve hopes that the results of a trial selling period will enable him to conclude that the compensation plan increases the average sales per salesperson.
   a. Develop the appropriate null and alternative hypotheses.
   b. What is the Type I error in this situation? What are the consequences of making this error?
   c. What is the Type II error in this situation? What are the consequences of making this error?
8. Suppose a new production method will be implemented if a hypothesis test supports the conclusion that the new method reduces the mean operating cost per hour.
   a. State the appropriate null and alternative hypotheses if the mean cost for the current production method is \$220 per hour.
   b. What is the Type I error in this situation? What are the consequences of making this error?
   c. What is the Type II error in this situation? What are the consequences of making this error?

9.3 Population Mean: σ Known

In Chapter 8 we said that the σ known case corresponds to applications in which historical data and/or other information are available that enable us to obtain a good estimate of the population standard deviation prior to sampling. In such cases the population standard deviation can, for all practical purposes, be considered known. In this section we show how to conduct a hypothesis test about a population mean for the σ known case.

The methods presented in this section are exact if the sample is selected from a population that is normally distributed. In cases where it is not reasonable to assume the population is normally distributed, these methods are still applicable if the sample size is large enough. We provide some practical advice concerning the population distribution and the sample size at the end of this section.

One-Tailed Test

One-tailed tests about a population mean take one of the following two forms.

Lower Tail Test	Upper Tail Test
$H_0: \mu \geq \mu_0$	$H_0: \mu \leq \mu_0$
$H_a: \mu < \mu_0$	$H_a: \mu > \mu_0$

Let us consider an example involving a lower tail test.

The Federal Trade Commission (FTC) periodically conducts statistical studies designed to test the claims that manufacturers make about their products. For example, the label on a large can of Hilltop Coffee states that the can contains 3 pounds of coffee. The FTC knows that Hilltop's production process cannot place exactly 3 pounds of coffee in each can, even if the mean filling weight for the population of all cans filled is 3 pounds per can. However, as long as the population mean filling weight is at least 3 pounds per can, the rights of consumers will be protected. Thus, the FTC interprets the label information on a large can of coffee as a claim by Hilltop that the population mean filling weight is at least 3 pounds per can. We will show how the FTC can check Hilltop's claim by conducting a lower tail hypothesis test.

The first step is to develop the null and alternative hypotheses for the test. If the population mean filling weight is at least 3 pounds per can, Hilltop's claim is correct. This establishes the null hypothesis for the test. However, if the population mean weight is less than 3 pounds per can, Hilltop's claim is incorrect. This establishes the alternative hypothesis. With μ denoting the population mean filling weight, the null and alternative hypotheses are as follows:

$$H_0: \mu \geq 3$$
$$H_a: \mu < 3$$

Note that the hypothesized value of the population mean is $\mu_0 = 3$.

If the sample data indicate that H_0 cannot be rejected, the statistical evidence does not support the conclusion that a label violation has occurred. Hence, no action should be taken against Hilltop. However, if the sample data indicate H_0 can be rejected, we will conclude that the alternative hypothesis, H_a: $\mu < 3$, is true. In this case a conclusion of underfilling and a charge of a label violation against Hilltop would be justified.

Suppose a sample of 36 cans of coffee is selected and the sample mean $\bar{x}$ is computed as an estimate of the population mean μ. If the value of the sample mean $\bar{x}$ is less than 3 pounds, the sample results will cast doubt on the null hypothesis. What we want to know is how much less than 3 pounds must $\bar{x}$ be before we would be willing to declare the difference significant and risk making a Type I error by falsely accusing Hilltop of a label violation. A key factor in addressing this issue is the value the decision maker selects for the level of significance.

As noted in the preceding section, the level of significance, denoted by α, is the probability of making a Type I error by rejecting H_0 when the null hypothesis is true as an equality. The decision maker must specify the level of significance. If the cost of making a Type I error is high, a small value should be chosen for the level of significance. If the cost is not high, a larger value is more appropriate. In the Hilltop Coffee study, the director of the FTC's testing program made the following statement: "If the company is meeting its weight specifications at $\mu = 3$, I do not want to take action against them. But, I am willing to risk a 1% chance of making such an error." From the director's statement, we set the level of significance for the hypothesis test at $\alpha = .01$. Thus, we must design the hypothesis test so that the probability of making a Type I error when $\mu = 3$ is .01.

For the Hilltop Coffee study, by developing the null and alternative hypotheses and specifying the level of significance for the test, we carry out the first two steps required in conducting every hypothesis test. We are now ready to perform the third step of hypothesis testing: collect the sample data and compute the value of what is called a test statistic.

Test statistic For the Hilltop Coffee study, previous FTC tests show that the population standard deviation can be assumed known with a value of $\sigma = .18$. In addition, these tests also show that the population of filling weights can be assumed to have a normal distribution. From the study of sampling distributions in Chapter 7 we know that if the population from which we are sampling is normally distributed, the sampling distribution of $\bar{x}$ will also be normally distributed. Thus, for the Hilltop Coffee study, the sampling distribution of $\bar{x}$ is normally distributed. With a known value of $\sigma = .18$ and a sample size of $n = 36$, Figure 9.1 shows the sampling distribution of $\bar{x}$ when the null hypothesis is true as an equality; that is, when $\mu = \mu_0 = 3$.[1] Note that the standard error of $\bar{x}$ is given by $\sigma_{\bar{x}} = \sigma/\sqrt{n} = .18/\sqrt{36} = .03$.

The standard error of $\bar{x}$ is the standard deviation of the sampling distribution of $\bar{x}$.

Because the sampling distribution of $\bar{x}$ is normally distributed, the sampling distribution of

$$z = \frac{\bar{x} - \mu_0}{\sigma_{\bar{x}}} = \frac{\bar{x} - 3}{.03}$$

[1] In constructing sampling distributions for hypothesis tests, it is assumed that H_0 is satisfied as an equality.

FIGURE 9.1 SAMPLING DISTRIBUTION OF $\bar{x}$ FOR THE HILLTOP COFFEE STUDY WHEN THE NULL HYPOTHESIS IS TRUE AS AN EQUALITY ($\mu = 3$)

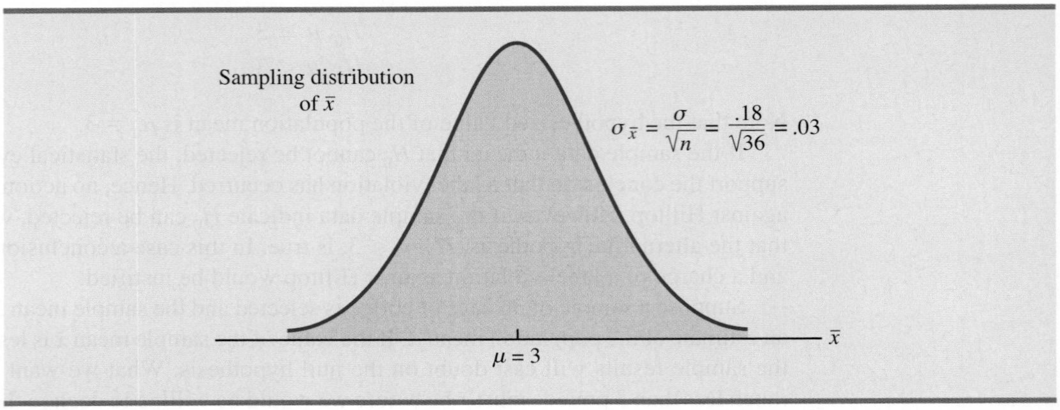

is a standard normal distribution. A value of $z = -1$ means that the value of $\bar{x}$ is one standard error below the hypothesized value of the mean, a value of $z = -2$ means that the value of $\bar{x}$ is two standard errors below the hypothesized value of the mean, and so on. We can use the standard normal probability table to find the lower tail probability corresponding to any z value. For instance, the lower tail area at $z = -3.00$ is .0013. Hence, the probability of obtaining a value of z that is three or more standard errors below the mean is .0013. As a result, the probability of obtaining a value of $\bar{x}$ that is 3 or more standard errors below the hypothesized population mean $\mu_0 = 3$ is also .0013. Such a result is unlikely if the null hypothesis is true.

For hypothesis tests about a population mean in the σ known case, we use the standard normal random variable z as a **test statistic** to determine whether $\bar{x}$ deviates from the hypothesized value of μ enough to justify rejecting the null hypothesis. With $\sigma_{\bar{x}} = \sigma/\sqrt{n}$, the test statistic is as follows.

TEST STATISTIC FOR HYPOTHESIS TESTS ABOUT A POPULATION MEAN: σ KNOWN

$$z = \frac{\bar{x} - \mu_0}{\sigma/\sqrt{n}} \tag{9.1}$$

The key question for a lower tail test is, How small must the test statistic z be before we choose to reject the null hypothesis? Two approaches can be used to answer this question: the p-value approach and the critical value approach.

***p*-value approach** The p-value approach uses the value of the test statistic z to compute a probability called a ***p*-value**.

A small p-value indicates the value of the test statistic is unusual given the assumption that H_0 is true.

p-VALUE

A p-value is a probability that provides a measure of the evidence against the null hypothesis provided by the sample. Smaller p-values indicate more evidence against H_0.

The p-value is used to determine whether the null hypothesis should be rejected.

Let us see how the p-value is computed and used. The value of the test statistic is used to compute the p-value. The method used depends on whether the test is a lower tail, an upper tail, or a two-tailed test. For a lower tail test, the p-value is the probability of obtaining a value for the test statistic as small as or smaller than that provided by the sample. Thus, to compute the p-value for the lower tail test in the σ known case, we must find the area under the standard normal curve for values of $z \leq$ the value of the test statistic. After computing the p-value, we must then decide whether it is small enough to reject the null hypothesis; as we will show, this decision involves comparing the p-value to the level of significance.

WEB file
Coffee

Let us now compute the p-value for the Hilltop Coffee lower tail test. Suppose the sample of 36 Hilltop coffee cans provides a sample mean of $\bar{x} = 2.92$ pounds. Is $\bar{x} = 2.92$ small enough to cause us to reject H_0? Because this is a lower tail test, the p-value is the area under the standard normal curve for values of $z \leq$ the value of the test statistic. Using $\bar{x} = 2.92$, $\sigma = .18$, and $n = 36$, we compute the value of the test statistic z.

$$z = \frac{\bar{x} - \mu_0}{\sigma/\sqrt{n}} = \frac{2.92 - 3}{.18/\sqrt{36}} = -2.67$$

Thus, the p-value is the probability that the test statistic z is less than or equal to -2.67 (the area under the standard normal curve to the left of the test statistic).

Using the standard normal probability table, we find that the lower tail area at $z = -2.67$ is .0038. Figure 9.2 shows that $\bar{x} = 2.92$ corresponds to $z = -2.67$ and a p-value $= .0038$. This p-value indicates a small probability of obtaining a sample mean of $\bar{x} = 2.92$ (and a test statistic of -2.67) or smaller when sampling from a population with $\mu = 3$. This

FIGURE 9.2 p-VALUE FOR THE HILLTOP COFFEE STUDY WHEN $\bar{x} = 2.92$ AND $z = -2.67$

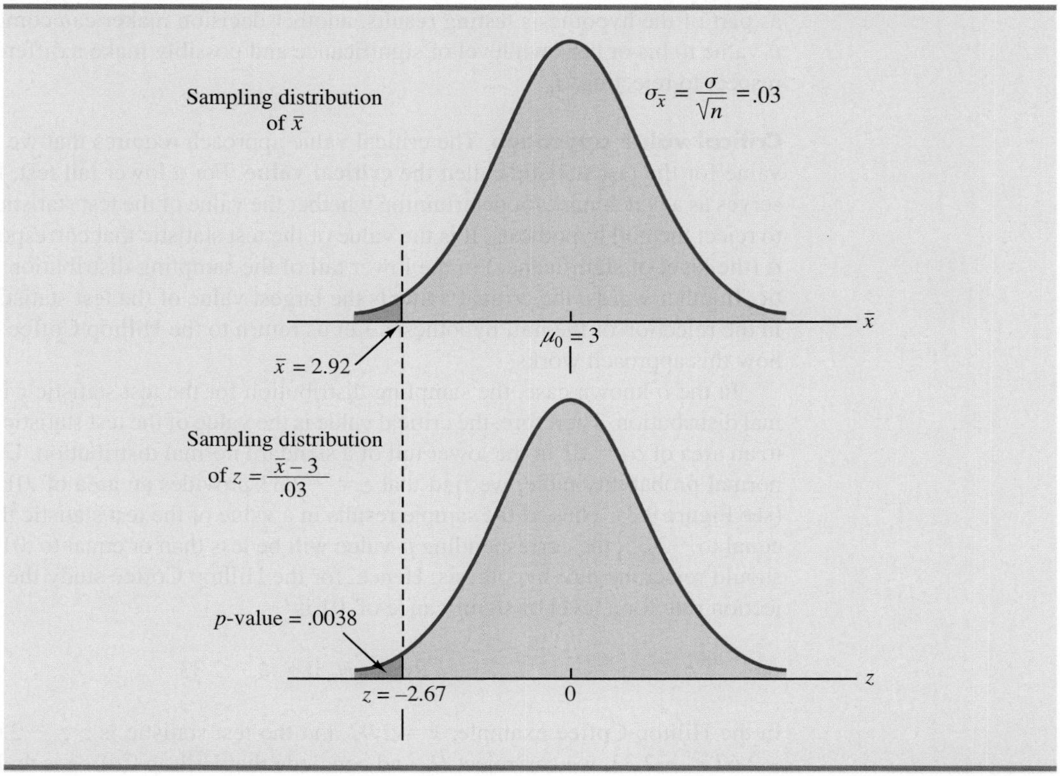

p-value does not provide much support for the null hypothesis, but is it small enough to cause us to reject H_0? The answer depends upon the level of significance for the test.

As noted previously, the director of the FTC's testing program selected a value of .01 for the level of significance. The selection of $\alpha = .01$ means that the director is willing to tolerate a probability of .01 of rejecting the null hypothesis when it is true as an equality ($\mu_0 = 3$). The sample of 36 coffee cans in the Hilltop Coffee study resulted in a p-value = .0038, which means that the probability of obtaining a value of $\bar{x} = 2.92$ or less when the null hypothesis is true as an equality is .0038. Because .0038 is less than or equal to $\alpha = .01$, we reject H_0. Therefore, we find sufficient statistical evidence to reject the null hypothesis at the .01 level of significance.

We can now state the general rule for determining whether the null hypothesis can be rejected when using the p-value approach. For a level of significance α, the rejection rule using the p-value approach is as follows:

REJECTION RULE USING p-VALUE

$$\text{Reject } H_0 \text{ if } p\text{-value} \leq \alpha$$

In the Hilltop Coffee test, the p-value of .0038 resulted in the rejection of the null hypothesis. Although the basis for making the rejection decision involves a comparison of the p-value to the level of significance specified by the FTC director, the observed p-value of .0038 means that we would reject H_0 for any value of $\alpha \geq .0038$. For this reason, the p-value is also called the *observed level of significance.*

Different decision makers may express different opinions concerning the cost of making a Type I error and may choose a different level of significance. By providing the p-value as part of the hypothesis testing results, another decision maker can compare the reported p-value to his or her own level of significance and possibly make a different decision with respect to rejecting H_0.

Critical value approach The critical value approach requires that we first determine a value for the test statistic called the **critical value**. For a lower tail test, the critical value serves as a benchmark for determining whether the value of the test statistic is small enough to reject the null hypothesis. It is the value of the test statistic that corresponds to an area of α (the level of significance) in the lower tail of the sampling distribution of the test statistic. In other words, the critical value is the largest value of the test statistic that will result in the rejection of the null hypothesis. Let us return to the Hilltop Coffee example and see how this approach works.

In the σ known case, the sampling distribution for the test statistic z is a standard normal distribution. Therefore, the critical value is the value of the test statistic that corresponds to an area of $\alpha = .01$ in the lower tail of a standard normal distribution. Using the standard normal probability table, we find that $z = -2.33$ provides an area of .01 in the lower tail (see Figure 9.3). Thus, if the sample results in a value of the test statistic that is less than or equal to -2.33, the corresponding p-value will be less than or equal to .01; in this case, we should reject the null hypothesis. Hence, for the Hilltop Coffee study the critical value rejection rule for a level of significance of .01 is

$$\text{Reject } H_0 \text{ if } z \leq -2.33$$

In the Hilltop Coffee example, $\bar{x} = 2.92$ and the test statistic is $z = -2.67$. Because $z = -2.67 < -2.33$, we can reject H_0 and conclude that Hilltop Coffee is underfilling cans.

FIGURE 9.3 CRITICAL VALUE = −2.33 FOR THE HILLTOP COFFEE HYPOTHESIS TEST

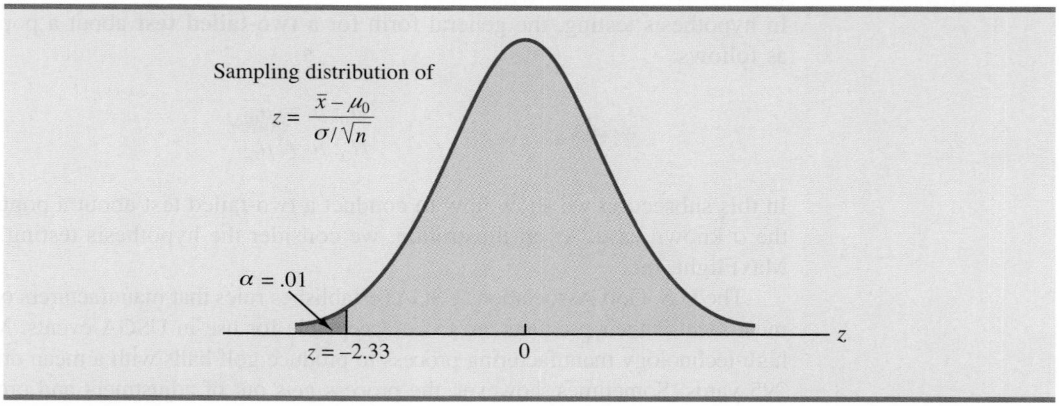

We can generalize the rejection rule for the critical value approach to handle any level of significance. The rejection rule for a lower tail test follows.

REJECTION RULE FOR A LOWER TAIL TEST: CRITICAL VALUE APPROACH

$$\text{Reject } H_0 \text{ if } z \leq -z_\alpha$$

where $-z_\alpha$ is the critical value; that is, the z value that provides an area of α in the lower tail of the standard normal distribution.

The p-value approach to hypothesis testing and the critical value approach will always lead to the same rejection decision; that is, whenever the p-value is less than or equal to α, the value of the test statistic will be less than or equal to the critical value. The advantage of the p-value approach is that the p-value tells us *how* significant the results are (the observed level of significance). If we use the critical value approach, we only know that the results are significant at the stated level of significance.

At the beginning of this section, we said that one-tailed tests about a population mean take one of the following two forms:

Lower Tail Test	Upper Tail Test
$H_0: \mu \geq \mu_0$	$H_0: \mu \leq \mu_0$
$H_a: \mu < \mu_0$	$H_a: \mu > \mu_0$

We used the Hilltop Coffee study to illustrate how to conduct a lower tail test. We can use the same general approach to conduct an upper tail test. The test statistic z is still computed using equation (9.1). But, for an upper tail test, the p-value is the probability of obtaining a value for the test statistic as large as or larger than that provided by the sample. Thus, to compute the p-value for the upper tail test in the σ known case, we must find the area under the standard normal curve to the right of the test statistic. Using the critical value approach causes us to reject the null hypothesis if the value of the test statistic is greater than or equal to the critical value z_α; in other words, we reject H_0 if $z \geq z_\alpha$.

Two-Tailed Test

In hypothesis testing, the general form for a **two-tailed test** about a population mean is as follows:

$$H_0: \mu = \mu_0$$
$$H_a: \mu \neq \mu_0$$

In this subsection we show how to conduct a two-tailed test about a population mean for the σ known case. As an illustration, we consider the hypothesis testing situation facing MaxFlight, Inc.

The U.S. Golf Association (USGA) establishes rules that manufacturers of golf equipment must meet if their products are to be acceptable for use in USGA events. MaxFlight uses a high-technology manufacturing process to produce golf balls with a mean driving distance of 295 yards. Sometimes, however, the process gets out of adjustment and produces golf balls with a mean driving distance different from 295 yards. When the mean distance falls below 295 yards, the company worries about losing sales because the golf balls do not provide as much distance as advertised. When the mean distance passes 295 yards, MaxFlight's golf balls may be rejected by the USGA for exceeding the overall distance standard concerning carry and roll.

MaxFlight's quality control program involves taking periodic samples of 50 golf balls to monitor the manufacturing process. For each sample, a hypothesis test is conducted to determine whether the process has fallen out of adjustment. Let us develop the null and alternative hypotheses. We begin by assuming that the process is functioning correctly; that is, the golf balls being produced have a mean distance of 295 yards. This assumption establishes the null hypothesis. The alternative hypothesis is that the mean distance is not equal to 295 yards. With a hypothesized value of $\mu_0 = 295$, the null and alternative hypotheses for the MaxFlight hypothesis test are as follows:

$$H_0: \mu = 295$$
$$H_a: \mu \neq 295$$

If the sample mean $\bar{x}$ is significantly less than 295 yards or significantly greater than 295 yards, we will reject H_0. In this case, corrective action will be taken to adjust the manufacturing process. On the other hand, if $\bar{x}$ does not deviate from the hypothesized mean $\mu_0 = 295$ by a significant amount, H_0 will not be rejected and no action will be taken to adjust the manufacturing process.

The quality control team selected $\alpha = .05$ as the level of significance for the test. Data from previous tests conducted when the process was known to be in adjustment show that the population standard deviation can be assumed known with a value of $\sigma = 12$. Thus, with a sample size of $n = 50$, the standard error of $\bar{x}$ is

$$\sigma_{\bar{x}} = \frac{\sigma}{\sqrt{n}} = \frac{12}{\sqrt{50}} = 1.7$$

Because the sample size is large, the central limit theorem (see Chapter 7) allows us to conclude that the sampling distribution of $\bar{x}$ can be approximated by a normal distribution. Figure 9.4 shows the sampling distribution of $\bar{x}$ for the MaxFlight hypothesis test with a hypothesized population mean of $\mu_0 = 295$.

WEB file

GolfTest

Suppose that a sample of 50 golf balls is selected and that the sample mean is $\bar{x} = 297.6$ yards. This sample mean provides support for the conclusion that the population mean is larger than 295 yards. Is this value of $\bar{x}$ enough larger than 295 to cause us to reject H_0 at the .05 level of significance? In the previous section we described two approaches that can be used to answer this question: the p-value approach and the critical value approach.

FIGURE 9.4 SAMPLING DISTRIBUTION OF $\bar{x}$ FOR THE MAXFLIGHT HYPOTHESIS TEST

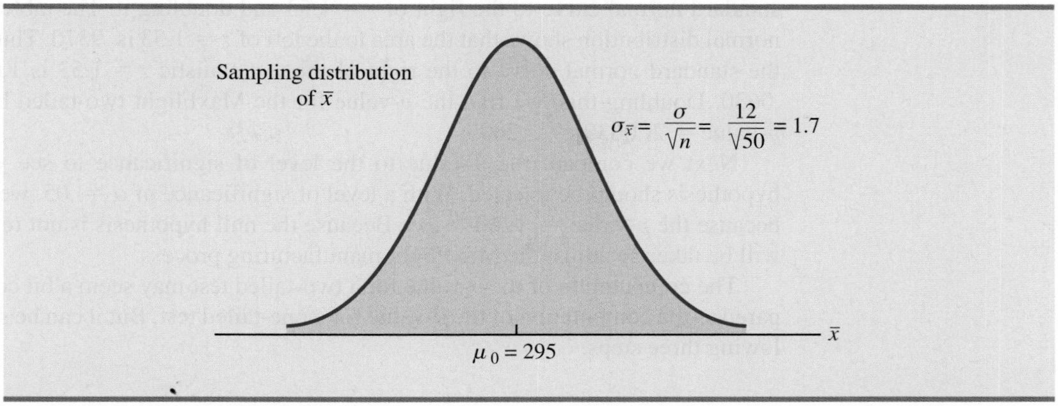

p-value approach Recall that the p-value is a probability used to determine whether the null hypothesis should be rejected. For a two-tailed test, values of the test statistic in *either* tail provide evidence against the null hypothesis. For a two-tailed test, the p-value is the probability of obtaining a value for the test statistic *as unlikely as or more unlikely than* that provided by the sample. Let us see how the p-value is computed for the MaxFlight hypothesis test.

First we compute the value of the test statistic. For the σ known case, the test statistic z is a standard normal random variable. Using equation (9.1) with $\bar{x} = 297.6$, the value of the test statistic is

$$z = \frac{\bar{x} - \mu_0}{\sigma/\sqrt{n}} = \frac{297.6 - 295}{12/\sqrt{50}} = 1.53$$

Now to compute the p-value we must find the probability of obtaining a value for the test statistic *at least as unlikely as* $z = 1.53$. Clearly values of $z \geq 1.53$ are *at least as unlikely.* But, because this is a two-tailed test, values of $z \leq -1.53$ are also *at least as unlikely as* the value of the test statistic provided by the sample. In Figure 9.5, we see that the two-tailed p-value in this case is given by $P(z \leq -1.53) + P(z \geq 1.53)$. Because the

FIGURE 9.5 p-VALUE FOR THE MAXFLIGHT HYPOTHESIS TEST

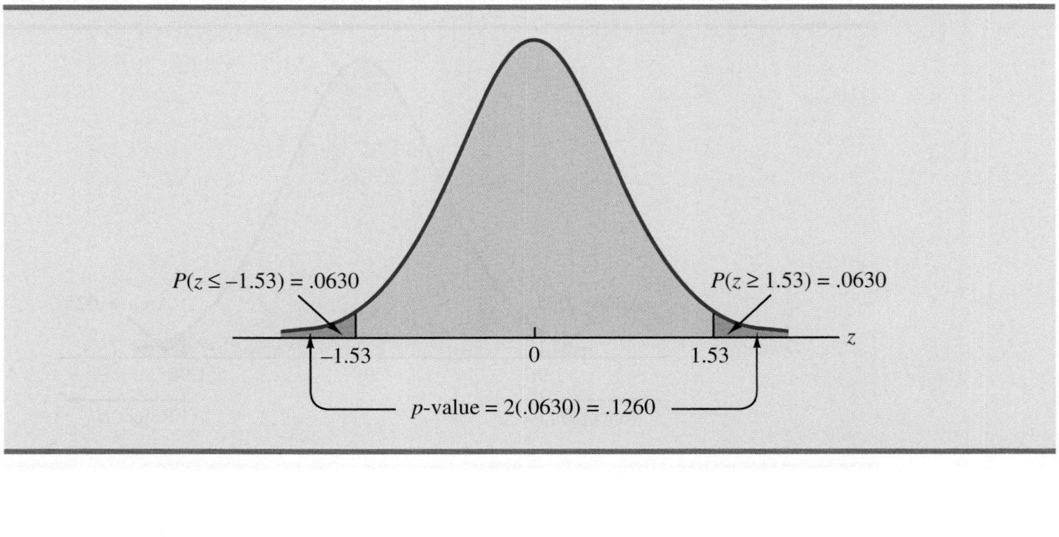

normal curve is symmetric, we can compute this probability by finding the area under the standard normal curve to the right of $z = 1.53$ and doubling it. The table for the standard normal distribution shows that the area to the left of $z = 1.53$ is .9370. Thus, the area under the standard normal curve to the right of the test statistic $z = 1.53$ is $1.0000 - .9370 = .0630$. Doubling this, we find the p-value for the MaxFlight two-tailed hypothesis test is $p\text{-value} = 2(.0630) = .1260$.

Next we compare the p-value to the level of significance to see whether the null hypothesis should be rejected. With a level of significance of $\alpha = .05$, we do not reject H_0 because the $p\text{-value} = .1260 > .05$. Because the null hypothesis is not rejected, no action will be taken to adjust the MaxFlight manufacturing process.

The computation of the p-value for a two-tailed test may seem a bit confusing as compared to the computation of the p-value for a one-tailed test. But it can be simplified by following three steps.

COMPUTATION OF p-VALUE FOR A TWO-TAILED TEST

1. Compute the value of the test statistic z.
2. If the value of the test statistic is in the upper tail ($z > 0$), find the area under the standard normal curve to the right of z. If the value of the test statistic is in the lower tail ($z < 0$), find the area under the standard normal curve to the left of z.
3. Double the tail area, or probability, obtained in step 2 to obtain the p-value.

Critical value approach Before leaving this section, let us see how the test statistic z can be compared to a critical value to make the hypothesis testing decision for a two-tailed test. Figure 9.6 shows that the critical values for the test will occur in both the lower and upper tails of the standard normal distribution. With a level of significance of $\alpha = .05$, the area in each tail beyond the critical values is $\alpha/2 = .05/2 = .025$. Using the standard normal probability table, we find the critical values for the test statistic are $-z_{.025} = -1.96$ and $z_{.025} = 1.96$. Thus, using the critical value approach, the two-tailed rejection rule is

$$\text{Reject } H_0 \text{ if } z \leq -1.96 \text{ or if } z \geq 1.96$$

Because the value of the test statistic for the MaxFlight study is $z = 1.53$, the statistical evidence will not permit us to reject the null hypothesis at the .05 level of significance.

FIGURE 9.6 CRITICAL VALUES FOR THE MAXFLIGHT HYPOTHESIS TEST

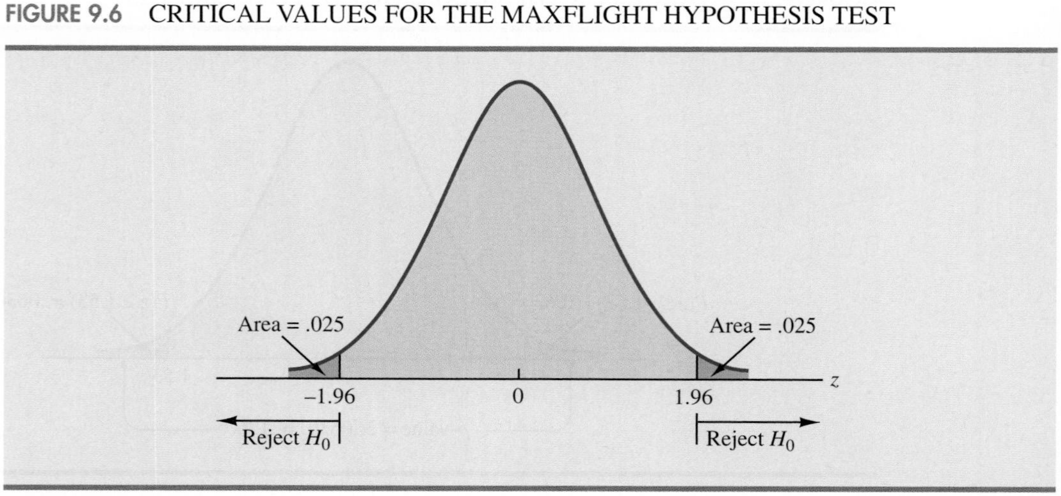

TABLE 9.2 SUMMARY OF HYPOTHESIS TESTS ABOUT A POPULATION MEAN: σ KNOWN CASE

	Lower Tail Test	Upper Tail Test	Two-Tailed Test
Hypotheses	$H_0: \mu \geq \mu_0$ $H_a: \mu < \mu_0$	$H_0: \mu \leq \mu_0$ $H_a: \mu > \mu_0$	$H_0: \mu = \mu_0$ $H_a: \mu \neq \mu_0$
Test Statistic	$z = \dfrac{\bar{x} - \mu_0}{\sigma/\sqrt{n}}$	$z = \dfrac{\bar{x} - \mu_0}{\sigma/\sqrt{n}}$	$z = \dfrac{\bar{x} - \mu_0}{\sigma/\sqrt{n}}$
Rejection Rule: *p*-Value Approach	Reject H_0 if p-value $\leq \alpha$	Reject H_0 if p-value $\leq \alpha$	Reject H_0 if p-value $\leq \alpha$
Rejection Rule: Critical Value Approach	Reject H_0 if $z \leq -z_\alpha$	Reject H_0 if $z \geq z_\alpha$	Reject H_0 if $z \leq -z_{\alpha/2}$ or if $z \geq z_{\alpha/2}$

Summary and Practical Advice

We presented examples of a lower tail test and a two-tailed test about a population mean. Based upon these examples, we can now summarize the hypothesis testing procedures about a population mean for the σ known case as shown in Table 9.2. Note that μ_0 is the hypothesized value of the population mean.

The hypothesis testing steps followed in the two examples presented in this section are common to every hypothesis test.

STEPS OF HYPOTHESIS TESTING

Step 1. Develop the null and alternative hypotheses.
Step 2. Specify the level of significance.
Step 3. Collect the sample data and compute the value of the test statistic.

p-Value Approach

Step 4. Use the value of the test statistic to compute the p-value.
Step 5. Reject H_0 if the p-value $\leq \alpha$.

Critical Value Approach

Step 4. Use the level of significance to determine the critical value and the rejection rule.
Step 5. Use the value of the test statistic and the rejection rule to determine whether to reject H_0.

Practical advice about the sample size for hypothesis tests is similar to the advice we provided about the sample size for interval estimation in Chapter 8. In most applications, a sample size of $n \geq 30$ is adequate when using the hypothesis testing procedure described in this section. In cases where the sample size is less than 30, the distribution of the population from which we are sampling becomes an important consideration. If the population is normally distributed, the hypothesis testing procedure that we described is exact and can be used for any sample size. If the population is not normally distributed but is at least roughly symmetric, sample sizes as small as 15 can be expected to provide acceptable results.

Relationship Between Interval Estimation and Hypothesis Testing

In Chapter 8 we showed how to develop a confidence interval estimate of a population mean. For the σ known case, the $(1 - \alpha)\%$ confidence interval estimate of a population mean is given by

$$\bar{x} \pm z_{\alpha/2} \frac{\sigma}{\sqrt{n}}$$

In this chapter, we showed that a two-tailed hypothesis test about a population mean takes the following form:

$$H_0: \mu = \mu_0$$
$$H_a: \mu \neq \mu_0$$

where μ_0 is the hypothesized value for the population mean.

Suppose that we follow the procedure described in Chapter 8 for constructing a $100(1 - \alpha)\%$ confidence interval for the population mean. We know that $100(1 - \alpha)\%$ of the confidence intervals generated will contain the population mean and $100\alpha\%$ of the confidence intervals generated will not contain the population mean. Thus, if we reject H_0 whenever the confidence interval does not contain μ_0, we will be rejecting the null hypothesis when it is true ($\mu = \mu_0$) with probability α. Recall that the level of significance is the probability of rejecting the null hypothesis when it is true. So constructing a $100(1 - \alpha)\%$ confidence interval and rejecting H_0 whenever the interval does not contain μ_0 is equivalent to conducting a two-tailed hypothesis test with α as the level of significance. The procedure for using a confidence interval to conduct a two-tailed hypothesis test can now be summarized.

A CONFIDENCE INTERVAL APPROACH TO TESTING A HYPOTHESIS OF THE FORM

$$H_0: \mu = \mu_0$$
$$H_a: \mu \neq \mu_0$$

1. **Select** a simple random sample from the population and use the value of the sample mean $\bar{x}$ to develop the confidence interval for the population mean μ.

$$\bar{x} \pm z_{\alpha/2} \frac{\sigma}{\sqrt{n}}$$

2. If the confidence interval contains the hypothesized value μ_0, do not reject H_0. Otherwise, reject[2] H_0.

For a two-tailed hypothesis test, the null hypothesis can be rejected if the confidence interval does not include μ_0.

Let us illustrate by conducting the MaxFlight hypothesis test using the confidence interval approach. The MaxFlight hypothesis test takes the following form:

$$H_0: \mu = 295$$
$$H_a: \mu \neq 295$$

[2]To be consistent with the rule for rejecting H_0 when the p-value $\leq \alpha$, we would also reject H_0 using the confidence interval approach if μ_0 happens to be equal to one of the end points of the $100(1 - \alpha)\%$ confidence interval.

To test these hypotheses with a level of significance of $\alpha = .05$, we sampled 50 golf balls and found a sample mean distance of $\bar{x} = 297.6$ yards. Recall that the population standard deviation is $\sigma = 12$. Using these results with $z_{.025} = 1.96$, we find that the 95% confidence interval estimate of the population mean is

$$\bar{x} \pm z_{.025}\frac{\sigma}{\sqrt{n}}$$

$$297.6 \pm 1.96\frac{12}{\sqrt{50}}$$

$$297.6 \pm 3.3$$

or

$$294.3 \text{ to } 300.9$$

This finding enables the quality control manager to conclude with 95% confidence that the mean distance for the population of golf balls is between 294.3 and 300.9 yards. Because the hypothesized value for the population mean, $\mu_0 = 295$, is in this interval, the hypothesis testing conclusion is that the null hypothesis, H_0: $\mu = 295$, cannot be rejected.

Note that this discussion and example pertain to two-tailed hypothesis tests about a population mean. However, the same confidence interval and two-tailed hypothesis testing relationship exists for other population parameters. The relationship can also be extended to one-tailed tests about population parameters. Doing so, however, requires the development of one-sided confidence intervals, which are rarely used in practice.

NOTES AND COMMENTS

We have shown how to use p-values. The smaller the p-value the greater the evidence against H_0 and the more the evidence in favor of H_a. Here are some guidelines statisticians suggest for interpreting small p-values.

- Less than .01—Overwhelming evidence to conclude H_a is true.
- Between .01 and .05—Strong evidence to conclude H_a is true.
- Between .05 and .10—Weak evidence to conclude H_a is true.
- Greater than .10—Insufficient evidence to conclude H_a is true.

Exercises

Note to Student: Some of the exercises that follow ask you to use the p-value approach and others ask you to use the critical value approach. Both methods will provide the same hypothesis testing conclusion. We provide exercises with both methods to give you practice using both. In later sections and in following chapters, we will generally emphasize the p-value approach as the preferred method, but you may select either based on personal preference.

Methods

9. Consider the following hypothesis test:

$$H_0: \mu \geq 20$$
$$H_a: \mu < 20$$

A sample of 50 provided a sample mean of 19.4. The population standard deviation is 2.
a. Compute the value of the test statistic.
b. What is the p-value?
c. Using $\alpha = .05$, what is your conclusion?
d. What is the rejection rule using the critical value? What is your conclusion?

SELF test

10. Consider the following hypothesis test:

$$H_0: \mu \leq 25$$
$$H_a: \mu > 25$$

A sample of 40 provided a sample mean of 26.4. The population standard deviation is 6.
a. Compute the value of the test statistic.
b. What is the p-value?
c. At $\alpha = .01$, what is your conclusion?
d. What is the rejection rule using the critical value? What is your conclusion?

SELF test

11. Consider the following hypothesis test:

$$H_0: \mu = 15$$
$$H_a: \mu \neq 15$$

A sample of 50 provided a sample mean of 14.15. The population standard deviation is 3.
a. Compute the value of the test statistic.
b. What is the p-value?
c. At $\alpha = .05$, what is your conclusion?
d. What is the rejection rule using the critical value? What is your conclusion?

12. Consider the following hypothesis test:

$$H_0: \mu \geq 80$$
$$H_a: \mu < 80$$

A sample of 100 is used and the population standard deviation is 12. Compute the p-value and state your conclusion for each of the following sample results. Use $\alpha = .01$.
a. $\bar{x} = 78.5$
b. $\bar{x} = 77$
c. $\bar{x} = 75.5$
d. $\bar{x} = 81$

13. Consider the following hypothesis test:

$$H_0: \mu \leq 50$$
$$H_a: \mu > 50$$

A sample of 60 is used and the population standard deviation is 8. Use the critical value approach to state your conclusion for each of the following sample results. Use $\alpha = .05$.
a. $\bar{x} = 52.5$
b. $\bar{x} = 51$
c. $\bar{x} = 51.8$

14. Consider the following hypothesis test:

$$H_0: \mu = 22$$
$$H_a: \mu \neq 22$$

A sample of 75 is used and the population standard deviation is 10. Compute the p-value and state your conclusion for each of the following sample results. Use $\alpha = .01$.

a. $\bar{x} = 23$
b. $\bar{x} = 25.1$
c. $\bar{x} = 20$

Applications

SELF test

15. Individuals filing federal income tax returns prior to March 31 received an average refund of \$1056. Consider the population of "last-minute" filers who mail their tax return during the last five days of the income tax period (typically April 10 to April 15).
    a. A researcher suggests that a reason individuals wait until the last five days is that on average these individuals receive lower refunds than do early filers. Develop appropriate hypotheses such that rejection of H_0 will support the researcher's contention.
    b. For a sample of 400 individuals who filed a tax return between April 10 and 15, the sample mean refund was \$910. Based on prior experience a population standard deviation of $\sigma = \$1600$ may be assumed. What is the p-value?
    c. At $\alpha = .05$, what is your conclusion?
    d. Repeat the preceding hypothesis test using the critical value approach.
16. In a study entitled How Undergraduate Students Use Credit Cards, it was reported that undergraduate students have a mean credit card balance of \$3173 (*Sallie Mae*, April 2009). This figure was an all-time high and had increased 44% over the previous five years. Assume that a current study is being conducted to determine if it can be concluded that the mean credit card balance for undergraduate students has continued to increase compared to the April 2009 report. Based on previous studies, use a population standard deviation $\sigma =$ \$1000.
    a. State the null and alternative hypotheses.
    b. What is the p-value for a sample of 180 undergraduate students with a sample mean credit card balance of \$3325?
    c. Using a .05 level of significance, what is your conclusion?
17. Wall Street securities firms paid out record year-end bonuses of \$125,500 per employee for 2005 (*Fortune*, February 6, 2006). Suppose we would like to take a sample of employees at the Jones & Ryan securities firm to see whether the mean year-end bonus is different from the reported mean of \$125,500 for the population.
    a. State the null and alternative hypotheses you would use to test whether the year-end bonuses paid by Jones & Ryan were different from the population mean.
    b. Suppose a sample of 40 Jones & Ryan employees showed a sample mean year-end bonus of \$118,000. Assume a population standard deviation of $\sigma = \$30,000$ and compute the p-value.
    c. With $\alpha = .05$ as the level of significance, what is your conclusion?
    d. Repeat the preceding hypothesis test using the critical value approach.
18. The average annual total return for U.S. Diversified Equity mutual funds from 1999 to 2003 was 4.1% (*BusinessWeek*, January 26, 2004). A researcher would like to conduct a hypothesis test to see whether the returns for mid-cap growth funds over the same period are significantly different from the average for U.S. Diversified Equity funds.
    a. Formulate the hypotheses that can be used to determine whether the mean annual return for mid-cap growth funds differ from the mean for U.S. Diversified Equity funds.
    b. A sample of 40 mid-cap growth funds provides a mean return of $\bar{x} = 3.4\%$. Assume the population standard deviation for mid-cap growth funds is known from previous studies to be $\sigma = 2\%$. Use the sample results to compute the test statistic and p-value for the hypothesis test.
    c. At $\alpha = .05$, what is your conclusion?

19. The U.S. Department of Labor reported the average hourly earnings for U.S. production workers to be \$14.32 per hour in 2001 (*The World Almanac,* 2003). A sample of 75 production workers during 2003 showed a sample mean of \$14.68 per hour. Assuming the population standard deviation $\sigma = \$1.45$, can we conclude that an increase occurred in the mean hourly earnings since 2001? Use $\alpha = .05$.

20. For the United States, the mean monthly Internet bill is \$32.79 per household (CNBC, January 18, 2006). A sample of 50 households in a southern state showed a sample mean of \$30.63. Use a population standard deviation of $\sigma = \$5.60$.
    a. Formulate hypotheses for a test to determine whether the sample data support the conclusion that the mean monthly Internet bill in the southern state is less than the national mean of \$32.79.
    b. What is the value of the test statistic?
    c. What is the *p*-value?
    d. At $\alpha = .01$, what is your conclusion?

WEB file
Fowle

21. Fowle Marketing Research, Inc., bases charges to a client on the assumption that telephone surveys can be completed in a mean time of 15 minutes or less. If a longer mean survey time is necessary, a premium rate is charged. A sample of 35 surveys provided the survey times shown in the file named Fowle. Based upon past studies, the population standard deviation is assumed known with $\sigma = 4$ minutes. Is the premium rate justified?
    a. Formulate the null and alternative hypotheses for this application.
    b. Compute the value of the test statistic.
    c. What is the *p*-value?
    d. At $\alpha = .01$, what is your conclusion?

22. CCN and ActMedia provided a television channel targeted to individuals waiting in supermarket checkout lines. The channel showed news, short features, and advertisements. The length of the program was based on the assumption that the population mean time a shopper stands in a supermarket checkout line is 8 minutes. A sample of actual waiting times will be used to test this assumption and determine whether actual mean waiting time differs from this standard.
    a. Formulate the hypotheses for this application.
    b. A sample of 120 shoppers showed a sample mean waiting time of 8.4 minutes. Assume a population standard deviation of $\sigma = 3.2$ minutes. What is the *p*-value?
    c. At $\alpha = .05$, what is your conclusion?
    d. Compute a 95% confidence interval for the population mean. Does it support your conclusion?

9.4 Population Mean: σ Unknown

In this section we describe how to conduct hypothesis tests about a population mean for the σ unknown case. Because the σ unknown case corresponds to situations in which an estimate of the population standard deviation cannot be developed prior to sampling, the sample must be used to develop an estimate of both μ and σ. Thus, to conduct a hypothesis test about a population mean for the σ unknown case, the sample mean $\bar{x}$ is used as an estimate of μ and the sample standard deviation s is used as an estimate of σ.

The steps of the hypothesis testing procedure for the σ unknown case are the same as those for the σ known case described in Section 9.3. But, with σ unknown, the computation of the test statistic and *p*-value is a bit different. Recall that for the σ known case, the sampling distribution of the test statistic has a standard normal distribution. For the σ unknown case, however, the sampling distribution of the test statistic follows the t distribution; it has slightly more variability because the sample is used to develop estimates of both μ and σ.

In Section 8.2 we showed that an interval estimate of a population mean for the σ unknown case is based on a probability distribution known as the *t* distribution. Hypothesis tests about a population mean for the σ unknown case are also based on the *t* distribution. For the σ unknown case, the test statistic has a *t* distribution with $n - 1$ degrees of freedom.

TEST STATISTIC FOR HYPOTHESIS TESTS ABOUT A POPULATION MEAN: σ UNKNOWN

$$t = \frac{\bar{x} - \mu_0}{s/\sqrt{n}} \tag{9.2}$$

In Chapter 8 we said that the *t* distribution is based on an assumption that the population from which we are sampling has a normal distribution. However, research shows that this assumption can be relaxed considerably when the sample size is large enough. We provide some practical advice concerning the population distribution and sample size at the end of the section.

One-Tailed Test

Let us consider an example of a one-tailed test about a population mean for the σ unknown case. A business travel magazine wants to classify transatlantic gateway airports according to the mean rating for the population of business travelers. A rating scale with a low score of 0 and a high score of 10 will be used, and airports with a population mean rating greater than 7 will be designated as superior service airports. The magazine staff surveyed a sample of 60 business travelers at each airport to obtain the ratings data. The sample for London's Heathrow Airport provided a sample mean rating of $\bar{x} = 7.25$ and a sample standard deviation of $s = 1.052$. Do the data indicate that Heathrow should be designated as a superior service airport?

WEB file
AirRating

We want to develop a hypothesis test for which the decision to reject H_0 will lead to the conclusion that the population mean rating for the Heathrow Airport is *greater* than 7. Thus, an upper tail test with H_a: $\mu > 7$ is required. The null and alternative hypotheses for this upper tail test are as follows:

$$H_0: \mu \leq 7$$
$$H_a: \mu > 7$$

We will use $\alpha = .05$ as the level of significance for the test.

Using equation (9.2) with $\bar{x} = 7.25$, $\mu_0 = 7$, $s = 1.052$, and $n = 60$, the value of the test statistic is

$$t = \frac{\bar{x} - \mu_0}{s/\sqrt{n}} = \frac{7.25 - 7}{1.052/\sqrt{60}} = 1.84$$

The sampling distribution of *t* has $n - 1 = 60 - 1 = 59$ degrees of freedom. Because the test is an upper tail test, the *p*-value is the area under the curve of the *t* distribution to the right of $t = 1.84$.

The *t* distribution table provided in most textbooks will not contain sufficient detail to determine the exact *p*-value, such as the *p*-value corresponding to $t = 1.84$. For instance, using Table 2 in Appendix B, the t distribution with 59 degrees of freedom provides the following information.

Area in Upper Tail	**.20**	**.10**	**.05**	**.025**	**.01**	**.005**
***t* Value (59 *df*)**	.848	1.296	1.671	2.001	2.391	2.662

$t = 1.84$ (between 1.671 and 2.001)

We see that $t = 1.84$ is between 1.671 and 2.001. Although the table does not provide the exact p-value, the values in the "Area in Upper Tail" row show that the p-value must be less than .05 and greater than .025. With a level of significance of $\alpha = .05$, this placement is all we need to know to make the decision to reject the null hypothesis and conclude that Heathrow should be classified as a superior service airport.

Appendix F shows how to compute p-values using Excel or Minitab.

Because it is cumbersome to use a t table to compute p-values, and only approximate values are obtained, we show how to compute the exact p-value using Excel or Minitab. The directions can be found in Appendix F at the end of this text. Using Excel or Minitab with $t = 1.84$ provides the upper tail p-value of .0354 for the Heathrow Airport hypothesis test. With $.0354 < .05$, we reject the null hypothesis and conclude that Heathrow should be classified as a superior service airport.

Two-Tailed Test

To illustrate how to conduct a two-tailed test about a population mean for the σ unknown case, let us consider the hypothesis testing situation facing Holiday Toys. The company manufactures and distributes its products through more than 1000 retail outlets. In planning production levels for the coming winter season, Holiday must decide how many units of each product to produce prior to knowing the actual demand at the retail level. For this year's most important new toy, Holiday's marketing director is expecting demand to average 40 units per retail outlet. Prior to making the final production decision based upon this estimate, Holiday decided to survey a sample of 25 retailers in order to develop more information about the demand for the new product. Each retailer was provided with information about the features of the new toy along with the cost and the suggested selling price. Then each retailer was asked to specify an anticipated order quantity.

With μ denoting the population mean order quantity per retail outlet, the sample data will be used to conduct the following two-tailed hypothesis test:

$$H_0\colon \mu = 40$$
$$H_a\colon \mu \neq 40$$

If H_0 cannot be rejected, Holiday will continue its production planning based on the marketing director's estimate that the population mean order quantity per retail outlet will be $\mu = 40$ units. However, if H_0 is rejected, Holiday will immediately reevaluate its production plan for the product. A two-tailed hypothesis test is used because Holiday wants to reevaluate the production plan if the population mean quantity per retail outlet is less than anticipated or greater than anticipated. Because no historical data are available (it's a new product), the population mean μ and the population standard deviation must both be estimated using $\bar{x}$ and s from the sample data.

WEB file
Orders

The sample of 25 retailers provided a mean of $\bar{x} = 37.4$ and a standard deviation of $s = 11.79$ units. Before going ahead with the use of the t distribution, the analyst constructed a histogram of the sample data in order to check on the form of the population distribution. The histogram of the sample data showed no evidence of skewness or any extreme outliers, so the analyst concluded that the use of the t distribution with $n - 1 = 24$ degrees of freedom was appropriate. Using equation (9.2) with $\bar{x} = 37.4$, $\mu_0 = 40$, $s = 11.79$, and $n = 25$, the value of the test statistic is

$$t = \frac{\bar{x} - \mu_0}{s/\sqrt{n}} = \frac{37.4 - 40}{11.79/\sqrt{25}} = -1.10$$

Because we have a two-tailed test, the p-value is two times the area under the curve of the t distribution for $t \leq -1.10$. Using Table 2 in Appendix B, the t distribution table for 24 degrees of freedom provides the following information.

Area in Upper Tail	**.20**	**.10**	**.05**	**.025**	**.01**	**.005**
***t*-Value (24 *df*)**	.857	1.318	1.711	2.064	2.492	2.797

$t = 1.10$

The t distribution table only contains positive t values. Because the t distribution is symmetric, however, the area under the curve to the right of $t = 1.10$ is the same as the area under the curve to the left of $t = -1.10$. We see that $t = 1.10$ is between 0.857 and 1.318. From the "Area in Upper Tail" row, we see that the area in the tail to the right of $t = 1.10$ is between .20 and .10. When we double these amounts, we see that the p-value must be between .40 and .20. With a level of significance of $\alpha = .05$, we now know that the p-value is greater than α. Therefore, H_0 cannot be rejected. Sufficient evidence is not available to conclude that Holiday should change its production plan for the coming season.

Appendix F shows how the p-value for this test can be computed using Excel or Minitab. The p-value obtained is .2822. With a level of significance of $\alpha = .05$, we cannot reject H_0 because $.2822 > .05$.

The test statistic can also be compared to the critical value to make the two-tailed hypothesis testing decision. With $\alpha = .05$ and the t distribution with 24 degrees of freedom, $-t_{.025} = -2.064$ and $t_{.025} = 2.064$ are the critical values for the two-tailed test. The rejection rule using the test statistic is

$$\text{Reject } H_0 \text{ if } t \leq -2.064 \text{ or if } t \geq 2.064$$

Based on the test statistic $t = -1.10$, H_0 cannot be rejected. This result indicates that Holiday should continue its production planning for the coming season based on the expectation that $\mu = 40$.

Summary and Practical Advice

Table 9.3 provides a summary of the hypothesis testing procedures about a population mean for the σ unknown case. The key difference between these procedures and the ones for the σ known case is that s is used, instead of σ, in the computation of the test statistic. For this reason, the test statistic follows the t distribution.

The applicability of the hypothesis testing procedures of this section is dependent on the distribution of the population being sampled from and the sample size. When the population is normally distributed, the hypothesis tests described in this section provide exact results for any sample size. When the population is not normally distributed, the procedures are approximations. Nonetheless, we find that sample sizes of 30 or greater will provide good results in most cases. If the population is approximately normal, small sample sizes (e.g., $n < 15$) can provide acceptable results. If the population is highly skewed or contains outliers, sample sizes approaching 50 are recommended.

TABLE 9.3 SUMMARY OF HYPOTHESIS TESTS ABOUT A POPULATION MEAN: σ UNKNOWN CASE

	Lower Tail Test	**Upper Tail Test**	**Two-Tailed Test**
Hypotheses	$H_0: \mu \geq \mu_0$ $H_a: \mu < \mu_0$	$H_0: \mu \leq \mu_0$ $H_a: \mu > \mu_0$	$H_0: \mu = \mu_0$ $H_a: \mu \neq \mu_0$
Test Statistic	$t = \frac{\bar{x} - \mu_0}{s/\sqrt{n}}$	$t = \frac{\bar{x} - \mu_0}{s/\sqrt{n}}$	$t = \frac{\bar{x} - \mu_0}{s/\sqrt{n}}$
Rejection Rule: *p*-Value Approach	Reject H_0 if p-value $\leq \alpha$	Reject H_0 if p-value $\leq \alpha$	Reject H_0 if p-value $\leq \alpha$
Rejection Rule: Critical Value Approach	Reject H_0 if $t \leq -t_\alpha$	Reject H_0 if $t \geq t_\alpha$	Reject H_0 if $t \leq -t_{\alpha/2}$ or if $t \geq t_{\alpha/2}$

Exercises

Methods

23. Consider the following hypothesis test:

$$H_0: \mu \leq 12$$
$$H_a: \mu > 12$$

A sample of 25 provided a sample mean $\bar{x} = 14$ and a sample standard deviation $s = 4.32$.

a. Compute the value of the test statistic.
b. Use the t distribution table (Table 2 in Appendix B) to compute a range for the p-value.
c. At $\alpha = .05$, what is your conclusion?
d. What is the rejection rule using the critical value? What is your conclusion?

SELF test

24. Consider the following hypothesis test:

$$H_0: \mu = 18$$
$$H_a: \mu \neq 18$$

A sample of 48 provided a sample mean $\bar{x} = 17$ and a sample standard deviation $s = 4.5$.

a. Compute the value of the test statistic.
b. Use the t distribution table (Table 2 in Appendix B) to compute a range for the p-value.
c. At $\alpha = .05$, what is your conclusion?
d. What is the rejection rule using the critical value? What is your conclusion?

25. Consider the following hypothesis test:

$$H_0: \mu \geq 45$$
$$H_a: \mu < 45$$

A sample of 36 is used. Identify the p-value and state your conclusion for each of the following sample results. Use $\alpha = .01$.

a. $\bar{x} = 44$ and $s = 5.2$
b. $\bar{x} = 43$ and $s = 4.6$
c. $\bar{x} = 46$ and $s = 5.0$

26. Consider the following hypothesis test:

$$H_0: \mu = 100$$
$$H_a: \mu \neq 100$$

A sample of 65 is used. Identify the p-value and state your conclusion for each of the following sample results. Use $\alpha = .05$.

a. $\bar{x} = 103$ and $s = 11.5$
b. $\bar{x} = 96.5$ and $s = 11.0$
c. $\bar{x} = 102$ and $s = 10.5$

Applications

SELF test

27. The Employment and Training Administration reported that the U.S. mean unemployment insurance benefit was \$238 per week (*The World Almanac,* 2003). A researcher in the state of Virginia anticipated that sample data would show evidence that the mean weekly unemployment insurance benefit in Virginia was below the national average.
a. Develop appropriate hypotheses such that rejection of H_0 will support the researcher's contention.
b. For a sample of 100 individuals, the sample mean weekly unemployment insurance benefit was \$231 with a sample standard deviation of \$80. What is the p-value?
c. At $\alpha = .05$, what is your conclusion?
d. Repeat the preceding hypothesis test using the critical value approach.

28. A shareholders' group, in lodging a protest, claimed that the mean tenure for a chief executive office (CEO) was at least nine years. A survey of companies reported in *The Wall Street Journal* found a sample mean tenure of $\bar{x} = 7.27$ years for CEOs with a standard deviation of $s = 6.38$ years (*The Wall Street Journal*, January 2, 2007).
a. Formulate hypotheses that can be used to challenge the validity of the claim made by the shareholders' group.
b. Assume 85 companies were included in the sample. What is the p-value for your hypothesis test?
c. At $\alpha = .01$, what is your conclusion?

WEB file

Diamonds

29. The cost of a one-carat VS2 clarity, H color diamond from Diamond Source USA is \$5600 (Diamond Source website, March 2003). A midwestern jeweler makes calls to contacts in the diamond district of New York City to see whether the mean price of diamonds there differs from \$5600.
a. Formulate hypotheses that can be used to determine whether the mean price in New York City differs from \$5600.
b. A sample of 25 New York City contacts provided the prices shown in the file named Diamonds. What is the p-value?
c. At $\alpha = .05$, can the null hypothesis be rejected? What is your conclusion?
d. Repeat the preceding hypothesis test using the critical value approach.

30. AOL Time Warner Inc.'s CNN has been the longtime ratings leader of cable television news. Nielsen Media Research indicated that the mean CNN viewing audience was 600,000 viewers per day during 2002 (*The Wall Street Journal,* March 10, 2003). Assume that for a sample of 40 days during the first half of 2003, the daily audience was 612,000 viewers with a sample standard deviation of 65,000 viewers.
a. What are the hypotheses if CNN management would like information on any change in the CNN viewing audience?
b. What is the p-value?
c. Select your own level of significance. What is your conclusion?
d. What recommendation would you make to CNN management in this application?

31. The Coca-Cola Company reported that the mean per capita annual sales of its beverages in the United States was 423 eight-ounce servings (Coca-Cola Company website, February 3,

2009). Suppose you are curious whether the consumption of Coca-Cola beverages is higher in Atlanta, Georgia, the location of Coca-Cola's corporate headquarters. A sample of 36 individuals from the Atlanta area showed a sample mean annual consumption of 460.4 eight-ounce servings with a standard deviation of $s = 101.9$ ounces. Using $\alpha = .05$, do the sample results support the conclusion that mean annual consumption of Coca-Cola beverage products is higher in Atlanta?

WEB file

UsedCars

32. According to the National Automobile Dealers Association, the mean price for used cars is \$10,192. A manager of a Kansas City used car dealership reviewed a sample of 50 recent used car sales at the dealership in an attempt to determine whether the population mean price for used cars at this particular dealership differed from the national mean. The prices for the sample of 50 cars are shown in the file named UsedCars.
    a. Formulate the hypotheses that can be used to determine whether a difference exists in the mean price for used cars at the dealership.
    b. What is the p-value?
    c. At $\alpha = .05$, what is your conclusion?
33. Annual per capita consumption of milk is 21.6 gallons (*Statistical Abstract of the United States: 2006*). Being from the Midwest, you believe milk consumption is higher there and wish to support your opinion. A sample of 16 individuals from the midwestern town of Webster City showed a sample mean annual consumption of 24.1 gallons with a standard deviation of $s = 4.8$.
    a. Develop a hypothesis test that can be used to determine whether the mean annual consumption in Webster City is higher than the national mean.
    b. What is a point estimate of the difference between mean annual consumption in Webster City and the national mean?
    c. At $\alpha = .05$, test for a significant difference. What is your conclusion?
34. Joan's Nursery specializes in custom-designed landscaping for residential areas. The estimated labor cost associated with a particular landscaping proposal is based on the number of plantings of trees, shrubs, and so on to be used for the project. For cost-estimating purposes, managers use two hours of labor time for the planting of a medium-sized tree. Actual times from a sample of 10 plantings during the past month follow (times in hours).

1.7	1.5	2.6	2.2	2.4	2.3	2.6	3.0	1.4	2.3

With a .05 level of significance, test to see whether the mean tree-planting time differs from two hours.
    a. State the null and alternative hypotheses.
    b. Compute the sample mean.
    c. Compute the sample standard deviation.
    d. What is the p-value?
    e. What is your conclusion?

9.5 Population Proportion

In this section we show how to conduct a hypothesis test about a population proportion p. Using p_0 to denote the hypothesized value for the population proportion, the three forms for a hypothesis test about a population proportion are as follows.

$$H_0\colon p \geq p_0 \qquad H_0\colon p \leq p_0 \qquad H_0\colon p = p_0$$
$$H_a\colon p < p_0 \qquad H_a\colon p > p_0 \qquad H_a\colon p \neq p_0$$

The first form is called a lower tail test, the second form is called an upper tail test, and the third form is called a two-tailed test.

Hypothesis tests about a population proportion are based on the difference between the sample proportion $\bar{p}$ and the hypothesized population proportion p_0. The methods used to conduct the hypothesis test are similar to those used for hypothesis tests about a population mean. The only difference is that we use the sample proportion and its standard error to compute the test statistic. The *p*-value approach or the critical value approach is then used to determine whether the null hypothesis should be rejected.

Let us consider an example involving a situation faced by Pine Creek golf course. Over the past year, 20% of the players at Pine Creek were women. In an effort to increase the proportion of women players, Pine Creek implemented a special promotion designed to attract women golfers. One month after the promotion was implemented, the course manager requested a statistical study to determine whether the proportion of women players at Pine Creek had increased. Because the objective of the study is to determine whether the proportion of women golfers increased, an upper tail test with $H_a\colon p > .20$ is appropriate. The null and alternative hypotheses for the Pine Creek hypothesis test are as follows:

$$H_0\colon p \le .20$$
$$H_a\colon p > .20$$

If H_0 can be rejected, the test results will give statistical support for the conclusion that the proportion of women golfers increased and the promotion was beneficial. The course manager specified that a level of significance of $\alpha = .05$ be used in carrying out this hypothesis test.

The next step of the hypothesis testing procedure is to select a sample and compute the value of an appropriate test statistic. To show how this step is done for the Pine Creek upper tail test, we begin with a general discussion of how to compute the value of the test statistic for any form of a hypothesis test about a population proportion. The sampling distribution of $\bar{p}$, the point estimator of the population parameter p, is the basis for developing the test statistic.

When the null hypothesis is true as an equality, the expected value of $\bar{p}$ equals the hypothesized value p_0; that is, $E(\bar{p}) = p_0$. The standard error of $\bar{p}$ is given by

$$\sigma_{\bar{p}} = \sqrt{\frac{p_0(1 - p_0)}{n}}$$

In Chapter 7 we said that if $np \ge 5$ and $n(1 - p) \ge 5$, the sampling distribution of $\bar{p}$ can be approximated by a normal distribution.[3] Under these conditions, which usually apply in practice, the quantity

$$z = \frac{\bar{p} - p_0}{\sigma_{\bar{p}}} \tag{9.3}$$

has a standard normal probability distribution. With $\sigma_{\bar{p}} = \sqrt{p_0(1 - p_0)/n}$, the standard normal random variable z is the test statistic used to conduct hypothesis tests about a population proportion.

[3]In most applications involving hypothesis tests of a population proportion, sample sizes are large enough to use the normal approximation. The exact sampling distribution of $\bar{p}$ is discrete with the probability for each value of $\bar{p}$ given by the binomial distribution. So hypothesis testing is a bit more complicated for small samples when the normal approximation cannot be used.

TEST STATISTIC FOR HYPOTHESIS TESTS ABOUT A POPULATION PROPORTION

$$z = \frac{\bar{p} - p_0}{\sqrt{\dfrac{p_0(1 - p_0)}{n}}} \tag{9.4}$$

WEB file
WomenGolf

We can now compute the test statistic for the Pine Creek hypothesis test. Suppose a random sample of 400 players was selected, and that 100 of the players were women. The proportion of women golfers in the sample is

$$\bar{p} = \frac{100}{400} = .25$$

Using equation (9.4), the value of the test statistic is

$$z = \frac{\bar{p} - p_0}{\sqrt{\dfrac{p_0(1 - p_0)}{n}}} = \frac{.25 - .20}{\sqrt{\dfrac{.20(1 - .20)}{400}}} = \frac{.05}{.02} = 2.50$$

Because the Pine Creek hypothesis test is an upper tail test, the p-value is the probability that z is greater than or equal to $z = 2.50$; that is, it is the area under the standard normal curve for $z \geq 2.50$. Using the standard normal probability table, we find that the area to the left of $z = 2.50$ is .9938. Thus, the p-value for the Pine Creek test is $1.0000 - .9938 = .0062$. Figure 9.7 shows this p-value calculation.

Recall that the course manager specified a level of significance of $\alpha = .05$. A p-value $= .0062 < .05$ gives sufficient statistical evidence to reject H_0 at the .05 level of significance. Thus, the test provides statistical support for the conclusion that the special promotion increased the proportion of women players at the Pine Creek golf course.

The decision whether to reject the null hypothesis can also be made using the critical value approach. The critical value corresponding to an area of .05 in the upper tail of a normal probability distribution is $z_{.05} = 1.645$. Thus, the rejection rule using the critical value approach is to reject H_0 if $z \geq 1.645$. Because $z = 2.50 > 1.645$, H_0 is rejected.

Again, we see that the p-value approach and the critical value approach lead to the same hypothesis testing conclusion, but the p-value approach provides more information. With a

FIGURE 9.7 CALCULATION OF THE p-VALUE FOR THE PINE CREEK HYPOTHESIS TEST

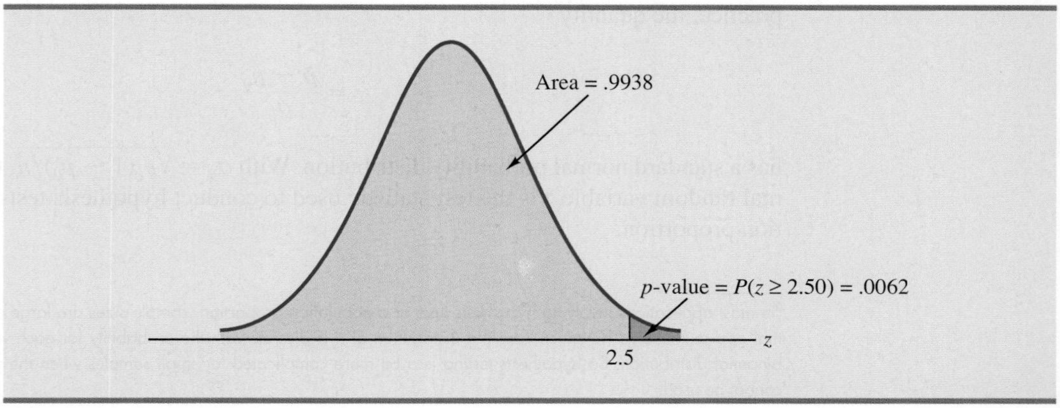

TABLE 9.4 SUMMARY OF HYPOTHESIS TESTS ABOUT A POPULATION PROPORTION

	Lower Tail Test	Upper Tail Test	Two-Tailed Test
Hypotheses	$H_0: p \geq p_0$ $H_a: p < p_0$	$H_0: p \leq p_0$ $H_a: p > p_0$	$H_0: p = p_0$ $H_a: p \neq p_0$
Test Statistic	$z = \dfrac{\bar{p} - p_0}{\sqrt{\dfrac{p_0(1 - p_0)}{n}}}$	$z = \dfrac{\bar{p} - p_0}{\sqrt{\dfrac{p_0(1 - p_0)}{n}}}$	$z = \dfrac{\bar{p} - p_0}{\sqrt{\dfrac{p_0(1 - p_0)}{n}}}$
Rejection Rule: *p*-Value Approach	Reject H_0 if p-value $\leq \alpha$	Reject H_0 if p-value $\leq \alpha$	Reject H_0 if p-value $\leq \alpha$
Rejection Rule: Critical Value Approach	Reject H_0 if $z \leq -z_{\alpha}$	Reject H_0 if $z \geq z_{\alpha}$	Reject H_0 if $z \leq -z_{\alpha/2}$ or if $z \geq z_{\alpha/2}$

p-value $= .0062$, the null hypothesis would be rejected for any level of significance greater than or equal to .0062.

Summary

The procedure used to conduct a hypothesis test about a population proportion is similar to the procedure used to conduct a hypothesis test about a population mean. Although we only illustrated how to conduct a hypothesis test about a population proportion for an upper tail test, similar procedures can be used for lower tail and two-tailed tests. Table 9.4 provides a summary of the hypothesis tests about a population proportion. We assume that $np \geq 5$ and $n(1 - p) \geq 5$; thus the normal probability distribution can be used to approximate the sampling distribution of $\bar{p}$.

Exercises

Methods

35. Consider the following hypothesis test:

$$H_0: p = .20$$
$$H_a: p \neq .20$$

A sample of 400 provided a sample proportion $\bar{p} = .175$.

a. Compute the value of the test statistic.
b. What is the p-value?
c. At $\alpha = .05$, what is your conclusion?
d. What is the rejection rule using the critical value? What is your conclusion?

SELF test

36. Consider the following hypothesis test:

$$H_0: p \geq .75$$
$$H_a: p < .75$$

A sample of 300 items was selected. Compute the p-value and state your conclusion for each of the following sample results. Use $\alpha = .05$.

a. $\bar{p} = .68$
b. $\bar{p} = .72$
c. $\bar{p} = .70$
d. $\bar{p} = .77$

Applications

37. A study found that, in 2005, 12.5% of U.S. workers belonged to unions (*The Wall Street Journal,* January 21, 2006). Suppose a sample of 400 U.S. workers is collected in 2006 to determine whether union efforts to organize have increased union membership.
    a. Formulate the hypotheses that can be used to determine whether union membership increased in 2006.
    b. If the sample results show that 52 of the workers belonged to unions, what is the p-value for your hypothesis test?
    c. At $\alpha = .05$, what is your conclusion?

SELF test

38. A study by *Consumer Reports* showed that 64% of supermarket shoppers believe supermarket brands to be as good as national name brands. To investigate whether this result applies to its own product, the manufacturer of a national name-brand ketchup asked a sample of shoppers whether they believed that supermarket ketchup was as good as the national brand ketchup.
    a. Formulate the hypotheses that could be used to determine whether the percentage of supermarket shoppers who believe that the supermarket ketchup was as good as the national brand ketchup differed from 64%.
    b. If a sample of 100 shoppers showed 52 stating that the supermarket brand was as good as the national brand, what is the p-value?
    c. At $\alpha = .05$, what is your conclusion?
    d. Should the national brand ketchup manufacturer be pleased with this conclusion? Explain.

WEB file

AgeGroup

39. According to the Pew Internet & American Life Project, 75% of American adults use the Internet (Pew Internet website, April 19, 2008). The Pew project authors also reported on the percentage of Americans who use the Internet by age group. The data in the file AgeGroup are consistent with their findings. These data were obtained from a sample of 100 Internet users in the 30–49 age group and 200 Internet users in the 50–64 age group. A Yes indicates the survey repondent had used the Internet; a No indicates the survey repondent had not.
    a. Formulate hypotheses that could be used to determine whether the percentage of Internet users in the two age groups differs from the overall average of 75%
    b. Estimate the proportion of Internet users in the 30–49 age group. Does this proportion differ significantly from the overall proportion of .75? Use $\alpha = .05$
    c. Estimate the proportion of Internet users in the 50–64 age group. Does this proportion differ significantly from the overall proportion of .75? Use $\alpha = .05$
    d. Would you expect the proportion of users in the 18–29 age group to be larger or smaller than the proportion for the 30–49 age group? Support you conclusion with the results obtained in parts (b) and (c).

40. Before the 2003 Super Bowl, ABC predicted that 22% of the Super Bowl audience would express an interest in seeing one of its forthcoming new television shows, including *8 Simple Rules, Are You Hot?,* and *Dragnet.* ABC ran commercials for these television shows during the Super Bowl. The day after the Super Bowl, Intermediate Advertising Group of New York sampled 1532 viewers who saw the commercials and found that 414 said that they would watch one of the ABC advertised television shows (*The Wall Street Journal,* January 30, 2003).
    a. What is the point estimate of the proportion of the audience that said they would watch the television shows after seeing the television commercials?
    b. At $\alpha = .05$, determine whether the intent to watch the ABC television shows significantly increased after seeing the television commercials. Formulate the appropriate hypotheses, compute the p-value, and state your conclusion.
    c. Why are such studies valuable to companies and advertising firms?

41. Speaking to a group of analysts in January 2006, a brokerage firm executive claimed that at least 70% of investors are currently confident of meeting their investment objectives. A UBS Investor Optimism Survey, conducted over the period January 2 to January 15,

found that 67% of investors were confident of meeting their investment objectives (CNBC, January 20, 2006).

a. Formulate the hypotheses that can be used to test the validity of the brokerage firm executive's claim.
b. Assume the UBS Investor Optimism Survey collected information from 300 investors. What is the p-value for the hypothesis test?
c. At $\alpha = .05$, should the executive's claim be rejected?

42. According to the University of Nevada Center for Logistics Management, 6% of all merchandise sold in the United States gets returned (*BusinessWeek*, January 15, 2007). A Houston department store sampled 80 items sold in January and found that 12 of the items were returned.
    a. Construct a point estimate of the proportion of items returned for the population of sales transactions at the Houston store.
    b. Construct a 95% confidence interval for the porportion of returns at the Houston store.
    c. Is the proportion of returns at the Houston store significantly different from the returns for the nation as a whole? Provide statistical support for your answer.

WEB file Eagle

43. Eagle Outfitters is a chain of stores specializing in outdoor apparel and camping gear. They are considering a promotion that involves mailing discount coupons to all their credit card customers. This promotion will be considered a success if more than 10% of those receiving the coupons use them. Before going national with the promotion, coupons were sent to a sample of 100 credit card customers.
    a. Develop hypotheses that can be used to test whether the population proportion of those who will use the coupons is sufficient to go national.
    b. The file Eagle contains the sample data. Develop a point estimate of the population proportion.
    c. Use $\alpha = .05$ to conduct your hypothesis test. Should Eagle go national with the promotion?

WEB file Drowsy

44. In a cover story, *BusinessWeek* published information about sleep habits of Americans (*BusinessWeek,* January 26, 2004). The article noted that sleep deprivation causes a number of problems, including highway deaths. Fifty-one percent of adult drivers admit to driving while drowsy. A researcher hypothesized that this issue was an even bigger problem for night shift workers.
    a. Formulate the hypotheses that can be used to help determine whether more than 51% of the population of night shift workers admit to driving while drowsy.
    b. A sample of 400 night shift workers identified those who admitted to driving while drowsy. See the Drowsy file. What is the sample proportion? What is the p-value?
    c. At $\alpha = .01$, what is your conclusion?

45. Many investors and financial analysts believe the Dow Jones Industrial Average (DJIA) provides a good barometer of the overall stock market. On January 31, 2006, 9 of the 30 stocks making up the DJIA increased in price (*The Wall Street Journal,* February 1, 2006). On the basis of this fact, a financial analyst claims we can assume that 30% of the stocks traded on the New York Stock Exchange (NYSE) went up the same day.
    a. Formulate null and alternative hypotheses to test the analyst's claim.
    b. A sample of 50 stocks traded on the NYSE that day showed that 24 went up. What is your point estimate of the population proportion of stocks that went up?
    c. Conduct your hypothesis test using $\alpha = .01$ as the level of significance. What is your conclusion?

9.6 Hypothesis Testing and Decision Making

In the previous sections of this chapter we have illustrated hypothesis testing applications that are considered significance tests. After formulating the null and alternative hypotheses, we selected a sample and computed the value of a test statistic and the associated p-value.

We then compared the p-value to a controlled probability of a Type I error, α, which is called the level of significance for the test. If p-value $\leq \alpha$, we made the conclusion "reject H_0" and declared the results significant; otherwise, we made the conclusion "do not reject H_0." With a significance test, we control the probability of making the Type I error, but not the Type II error. Thus, we recommended the conclusion "do not reject H_0" rather than "accept H_0" because the latter puts us at risk of making the Type II error of accepting H_0 when it is false. With the conclusion "do not reject H_0," the statistical evidence is considered inconclusive and is usually an indication to postpone a decision or action until further research and testing can be undertaken.

However, if the purpose of a hypothesis test is to make a decision when H_0 is true and a different decision when H_a is true, the decision maker may want to, and in some cases be forced to, take action with both the conclusion *do not reject* H_0 and the conclusion *reject* H_0. If this situation occurs, statisticians generally recommend controlling the probability of making a Type II error. With the probabilities of both the Type I and Type II error controlled, the conclusion from the hypothesis test is either to *accept* H_0 or *reject* H_0. In the first case, H_0 is concluded to be true, while in the second case, H_a is concluded true. Thus, a decision and appropriate action can be taken when either conclusion is reached.

A good illustration of hypothesis testing for decision making is lot-acceptance sampling, a topic we will discuss in more depth in Chapter 20. For example, a quality control manager must decide to accept a shipment of batteries from a supplier or to return the shipment because of poor quality. Assume that design specifications require batteries from the supplier to have a mean useful life of at least 120 hours. To evaluate the quality of an incoming shipment, a sample of 36 batteries will be selected and tested. On the basis of the sample, a decision must be made to accept the shipment of batteries or to return it to the supplier because of poor quality. Let μ denote the mean number of hours of useful life for batteries in the shipment. The null and alternative hypotheses about the population mean follow.

$$H_0: \mu \geq 120$$
$$H_a: \mu < 120$$

If H_0 is rejected, the alternative hypothesis is concluded to be true. This conclusion indicates that the appropriate action is to return the shipment to the supplier. However, if H_0 is not rejected, the decision maker must still determine what action should be taken. Thus, without directly concluding that H_0 is true, but merely by not rejecting it, the decision maker will have made the decision to accept the shipment as being of satisfactory quality.

In such decision-making situations, it is recommended that the hypothesis testing procedure be extended to control the probability of making a Type II error. Because a decision will be made and action taken when we do not reject H_0, knowledge of the probability of making a Type II error will be helpful. In Sections 9.7 and 9.8 we explain how to compute the probability of making a Type II error and how the sample size can be adjusted to help control the probability of making a Type II error.

9.7 Calculating the Probability of Type II Errors

In this section we show how to calculate the probability of making a Type II error for a hypothesis test about a population mean. We illustrate the procedure by using the lot-acceptance example described in Section 9.6. The null and alternative hypotheses about the mean number of hours of useful life for a shipment of batteries are $H_0: \mu \geq 120$ and $H_a: \mu < 120$. If H_0 is rejected, the decision will be to return the shipment to the supplier because the mean hours of useful life are less than the specified 120 hours. If H_0 is not rejected, the decision will be to accept the shipment.

Suppose a level of significance of $\alpha = .05$ is used to conduct the hypothesis test. The test statistic in the σ known case is

$$z = \frac{\bar{x} - \mu_0}{\sigma/\sqrt{n}} = \frac{\bar{x} - 120}{\sigma/\sqrt{n}}$$

Based on the critical value approach and $z_{.05} = 1.645$, the rejection rule for the lower tail test is

$$\text{Reject } H_0 \text{ if } z \leq -1.645$$

Suppose a sample of 36 batteries will be selected and based upon previous testing the population standard deviation can be assumed known with a value of $\sigma = 12$ hours. The rejection rule indicates that we will reject H_0 if

$$z = \frac{\bar{x} - 120}{12/\sqrt{36}} \leq -1.645$$

Solving for $\bar{x}$ in the preceding expression indicates that we will reject H_0 if

$$\bar{x} \leq 120 - 1.645\left(\frac{12}{\sqrt{36}}\right) = 116.71$$

Rejecting H_0 when $\bar{x} \leq 116.71$ means that we will make the decision to accept the shipment whenever

$$\bar{x} > 116.71$$

With this information, we are ready to compute probabilities associated with making a Type II error. First, recall that we make a Type II error whenever the true shipment mean is less than 120 hours and we make the decision to accept H_0: $\mu \geq 120$. Hence, to compute the probability of making a Type II error, we must select a value of μ less than 120 hours. For example, suppose the shipment is considered to be of poor quality if the batteries have a mean life of $\mu = 112$ hours. If $\mu = 112$ is really true, what is the probability of accepting H_0: $\mu \geq 120$ and hence committing a Type II error? Note that this probability is the probability that the sample mean $\bar{x}$ is greater than 116.71 when $\mu = 112$.

Figure 9.8 shows the sampling distribution of $\bar{x}$ when the mean is $\mu = 112$. The shaded area in the upper tail gives the probability of obtaining $\bar{x} > 116.71$. Using the standard normal distribution, we see that at $\bar{x} = 116.71$

$$z = \frac{\bar{x} - \mu}{\sigma/\sqrt{n}} = \frac{116.71 - 112}{12/\sqrt{36}} = 2.36$$

The standard normal probability table shows that with $z = 2.36$, the area in the upper tail is $1.0000 - .9909 = .0091$. Thus, .0091 is the probability of making a Type II error when $\mu = 112$. Denoting the probability of making a Type II error as β, we see that when $\mu = 112$, $\beta = .0091$. Therefore, we can conclude that if the mean of the population is 112 hours, the probability of making a Type II error is only .0091.

FIGURE 9.8 PROBABILITY OF A TYPE II ERROR WHEN $\mu = 112$

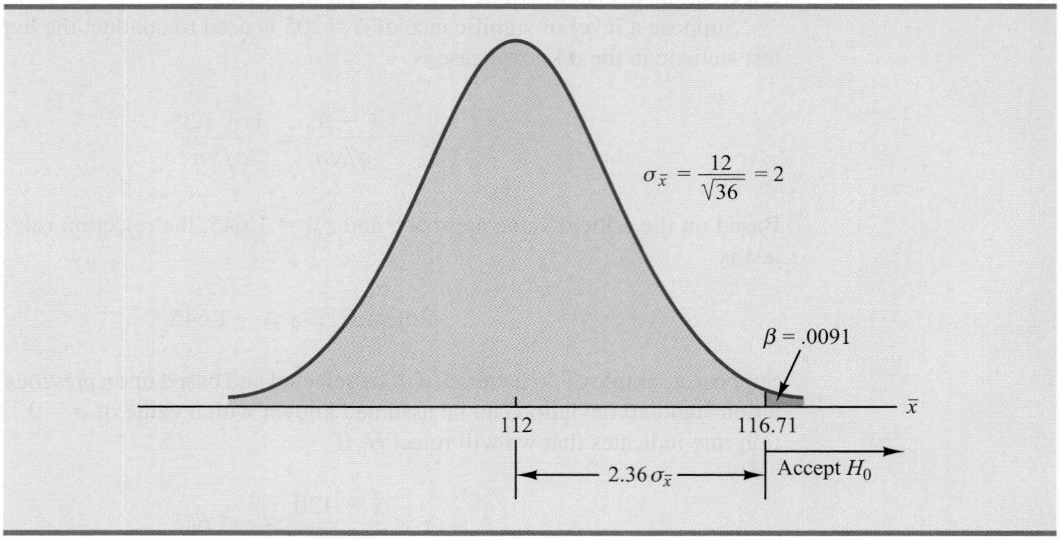

We can repeat these calculations for other values of μ less than 120. Doing so will show a different probability of making a Type II error for each value of μ. For example, suppose the shipment of batteries has a mean useful life of $\mu = 115$ hours. Because we will accept H_0 whenever $\bar{x} > 116.71$, the z value for $\mu = 115$ is given by

$$z = \frac{\bar{x} - \mu}{\sigma/\sqrt{n}} = \frac{116.71 - 115}{12/\sqrt{36}} = .86$$

From the standard normal probability table, we find that the area in the upper tail of the standard normal distribution for $z = .86$ is $1.0000 - .8051 = .1949$. Thus, the probability of making a Type II error is $\beta = .1949$ when the true mean is $\mu = 115$.

As Table 9.5 shows, the probability of a Type II error depends on the value of the population mean μ. For values of μ near μ_0, the probability of making the Type II error can be high.

In Table 9.5 we show the probability of making a Type II error for a variety of values of μ less than 120. Note that as μ increases toward 120, the probability of making a Type II error increases toward an upper bound of .95. However, as μ decreases to values farther below 120, the probability of making a Type II error diminishes. This pattern is what we should expect. When the true population mean μ is close to the null hypothesis value of $\mu = 120$, the probability is high that we will make a Type II error. However, when the true population mean μ is far below the null hypothesis value of $\mu = 120$, the probability is low that we will make a Type II error.

TABLE 9.5 PROBABILITY OF MAKING A TYPE II ERROR FOR THE LOT-ACCEPTANCE HYPOTHESIS TEST

Value of μ	$z = \dfrac{116.71 - \mu}{12/\sqrt{36}}$	**Probability of a Type II Error (β)**	**Power ($1 - \beta$)**
112	2.36	.0091	.9909
114	1.36	.0869	.9131
115	.86	.1949	.8051
116.71	.00	.5000	.5000
117	−.15	.5596	.4404
118	−.65	.7422	.2578
119.999	−1.645	.9500	.0500

FIGURE 9.9 POWER CURVE FOR THE LOT-ACCEPTANCE HYPOTHESIS TEST

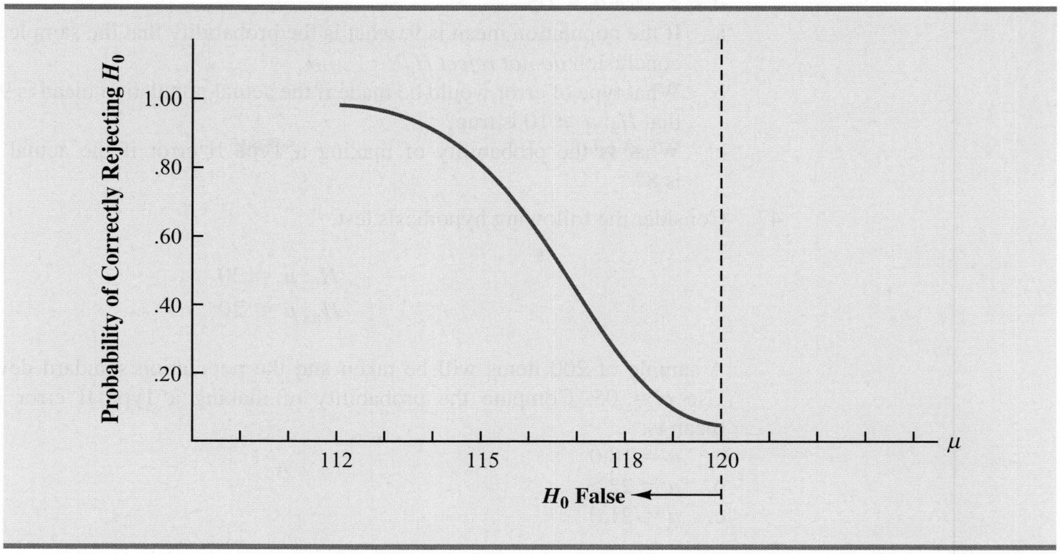

The probability of correctly rejecting H_0 when it is false is called the **power** of the test. For any particular value of μ, the power is $1 - \beta$; that is, the probability of correctly rejecting the null hypothesis is 1 minus the probability of making a Type II error. Values of power are also listed in Table 9.5. On the basis of these values, the power associated with each value of μ is shown graphically in Figure 9.9. Such a graph is called a **power curve**. Note that the power curve extends over the values of μ for which the null hypothesis is false. The height of the power curve at any value of μ indicates the probability of correctly rejecting H_0 when H_0 is false.[4]

In summary, the following step-by-step procedure can be used to compute the probability of making a Type II error in hypothesis tests about a population mean.

1. Formulate the null and alternative hypotheses.
2. Use the level of significance α and the critical value approach to determine the critical value and the rejection rule for the test.
3. Use the rejection rule to solve for the value of the sample mean corresponding to the critical value of the test statistic.
4. Use the results from step 3 to state the values of the sample mean that lead to the acceptance of H_0. These values define the acceptance region for the test.
5. Use the sampling distribution of $\bar{x}$ for a value of μ satisfying the alternative hypothesis, and the acceptance region from step 4, to compute the probability that the sample mean will be in the acceptance region. This probability is the probability of making a Type II error at the chosen value of μ.

Exercises

Methods

SELF test

46. Consider the following hypothesis test.

$$H_0: \mu \geq 10$$
$$H_a: \mu < 10$$

[4]Another graph, called the *operating characteristic curve*, is sometimes used to provide information about the probability of making a Type II error. The operating characteristic curve shows the probability of accepting H_0 and thus provides β for the values of μ where the null hypothesis is false. The probability of making a Type II error can be read directly from this graph.

The sample size is 120 and the population standard deviation is assumed known with $\sigma = 5$. Use $\alpha = .05$.

a. If the population mean is 9, what is the probability that the sample mean leads to the conclusion *do not reject* H_0?
b. What type of error would be made if the actual population mean is 9 and we conclude that $H_0: \mu \geq 10$ is true?
c. What is the probability of making a Type II error if the actual population mean is 8?

47. Consider the following hypothesis test.

$$H_0: \mu = 20$$
$$H_a: \mu \neq 20$$

A sample of 200 items will be taken and the population standard deviation is $\sigma = 10$. Use $\alpha = .05$. Compute the probability of making a Type II error if the population mean is:

a. $\mu = 18.0$
b. $\mu = 22.5$
c. $\mu = 21.0$

Applications

48. Fowle Marketing Research, Inc., bases charges to a client on the assumption that telephone surveys can be completed within 15 minutes or less. If more time is required, a premium rate is charged. With a sample of 35 surveys, a population standard deviation of 4 minutes, and a level of significance of .01, the sample mean will be used to test the null hypothesis $H_0: \mu \leq 15$.

a. What is your interpretation of the Type II error for this problem? What is its impact on the firm?
b. What is the probability of making a Type II error when the actual mean time is $\mu = 17$ minutes?
c. What is the probability of making a Type II error when the actual mean time is $\mu = 18$ minutes?
d. Sketch the general shape of the power curve for this test.

SELF test

49. A consumer research group is interested in testing an automobile manufacturer's claim that a new economy model will travel at least 25 miles per gallon of gasoline ($H_0: \mu \geq 25$).

a. With a .02 level of significance and a sample of 30 cars, what is the rejection rule based on the value of $\bar{x}$ for the test to determine whether the manufacturer's claim should be rejected? Assume that σ is 3 miles per gallon.
b. What is the probability of committing a Type II error if the actual mileage is 23 miles per gallon?
c. What is the probability of committing a Type II error if the actual mileage is 24 miles per gallon?
d. What is the probability of committing a Type II error if the actual mileage is 25.5 miles per gallon?

50. *Young Adult* magazine states the following hypotheses about the mean age of its subscribers.

$$H_0: \mu = 28$$
$$H_a: \mu \neq 28$$

a. What would it mean to make a Type II error in this situation?
b. The population standard deviation is assumed known at $\sigma = 6$ years and the sample size is 100. With $\alpha = .05$, what is the probability of accepting H_0 for μ equal to 26, 27, 29, and 30?
c. What is the power at $\mu = 26$? What does this result tell you?

51. A production line operation is tested for filling weight accuracy using the following hypotheses.

Hypothesis	Conclusion and Action
$H_0: \mu = 16$	Filling okay; keep running
$H_a: \mu \neq 16$	Filling off standard; stop and adjust machine

The sample size is 30 and the population standard deviation is $\sigma = .8$. Use $\alpha = .05$.

a. What would a Type II error mean in this situation?
b. What is the probability of making a Type II error when the machine is overfilling by .5 ounces?
c. What is the power of the statistical test when the machine is overfilling by .5 ounces?
d. Show the power curve for this hypothesis test. What information does it contain for the production manager?

52. Refer to exercise 48. Assume the firm selects a sample of 50 surveys and repeat parts (b) and (c). What observation can you make about how increasing the sample size affects the probability of making a Type II error?

53. Sparr Investments, Inc., specializes in tax-deferred investment opportunities for its clients. Recently Sparr offered a payroll deduction investment program for the employees of a particular company. Sparr estimates that the employees are currently averaging \$100 or less per month in tax-deferred investments. A sample of 40 employees will be used to test Sparr's hypothesis about the current level of investment activity among the population of employees. Assume the employee monthly tax-deferred investment amounts have a standard deviation of \$75 and that a .05 level of significance will be used in the hypothesis test.

a. What is the Type II error in this situation?
b. What is the probability of the Type II error if the actual mean employee monthly investment is \$120?
c. What is the probability of the Type II error if the actual mean employee monthly investment is \$130?
d. Assume a sample size of 80 employees is used and repeat parts (b) and (c).

9.8 Determining the Sample Size for a Hypothesis Test About a Population Mean

Assume that a hypothesis test is to be conducted about the value of a population mean. The level of significance specified by the user determines the probability of making a Type I error for the test. By controlling the sample size, the user can also control the probability of making a Type II error. Let us show how a sample size can be determined for the following lower tail test about a population mean.

$$H_0: \mu \geq \mu_0$$
$$H_a: \mu < \mu_0$$

The upper panel of Figure 9.10 is the sampling distribution of $\bar{x}$ when H_0 is true with $\mu = \mu_0$. For a lower tail test, the critical value of the test statistic is denoted $-z_\alpha$. In the upper panel of the figure the vertical line, labeled c, is the corresponding value of $\bar{x}$. Note that, if we reject H_0 when $\bar{x} \leq c$, the probability of a Type I error will be α. With z_α representing the z value corresponding to an area of α in the upper tail of the standard normal distribution, we compute c using the following formula:

$$c = \mu_0 - z_\alpha \frac{\sigma}{\sqrt{n}} \qquad \textbf{(9.5)}$$

FIGURE 9.10 DETERMINING THE SAMPLE SIZE FOR SPECIFIED LEVELS OF THE TYPE I (α) AND TYPE II (β) ERRORS

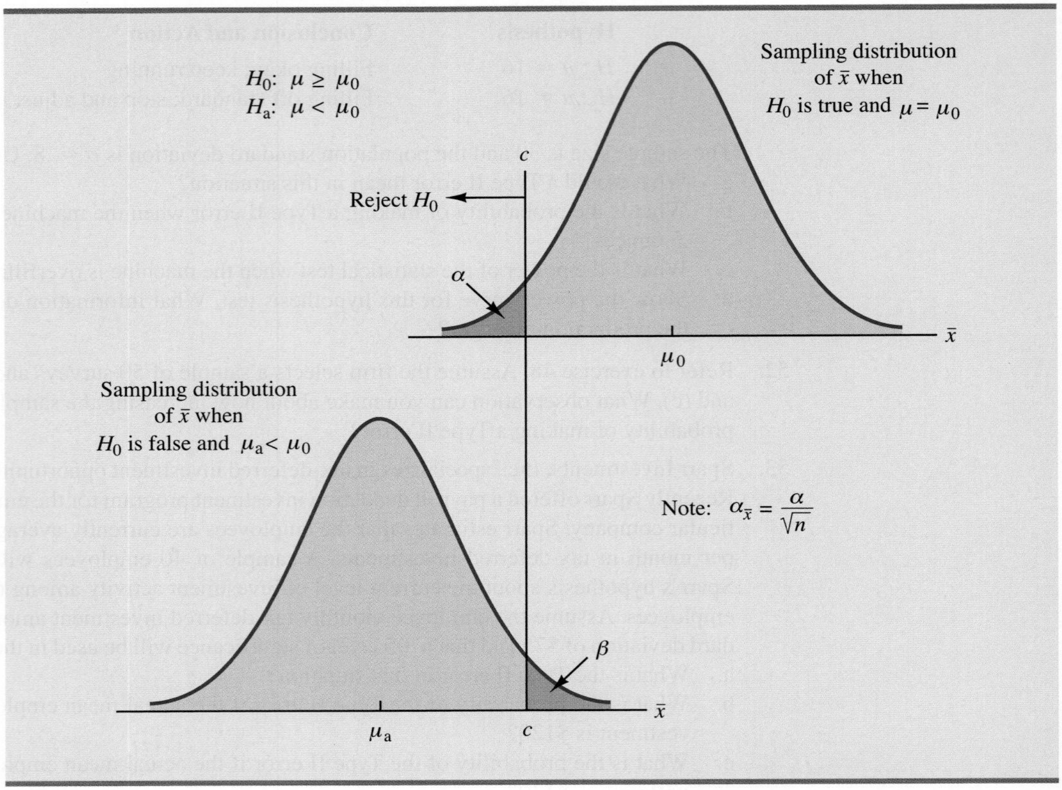

The lower panel of Figure 9.10 is the sampling distribution of $\bar{x}$ when the alternative hypothesis is true with $\mu = \mu_a < \mu_0$. The shaded region shows β, the probability of a Type II error that the decision maker will be exposed to if the null hypothesis is accepted when $\bar{x} > c$. With z_β representing the z value corresponding to an area of β in the upper tail of the standard normal distribution, we compute c using the following formula:

$$c = \mu_a + z_\beta \frac{\sigma}{\sqrt{n}} \tag{9.6}$$

Now what we want to do is to select a value for c so that when we reject H_0 and accept H_a, the probability of a Type I error is equal to the chosen value of α and the probability of a Type II error is equal to the chosen value of β. Therefore, both equations (9.5) and (9.6) must provide the same value for c, and the following equation must be true.

$$\mu_0 - z_\alpha \frac{\sigma}{\sqrt{n}} = \mu_a + z_\beta \frac{\sigma}{\sqrt{n}}$$

To determine the required sample size, we first solve for the $\sqrt{n}$ as follows.

$$\mu_0 - \mu_a = z_\alpha \frac{\sigma}{\sqrt{n}} + z_\beta \frac{\sigma}{\sqrt{n}}$$

$$\mu_0 - \mu_a = \frac{(z_\alpha + z_\beta)\sigma}{\sqrt{n}}$$

and

$$\sqrt{n} = \frac{(z_\alpha + z_\beta)\sigma}{(\mu_0 - \mu_a)}$$

Squaring both sides of the expression provides the following sample size formula for a one-tailed hypothesis test about a population mean.

SAMPLE SIZE FOR A ONE-TAILED HYPOTHESIS TEST ABOUT A POPULATION MEAN

$$n = \frac{(z_\alpha + z_\beta)^2\sigma^2}{(\mu_0 - \mu_a)^2} \tag{9.7}$$

where

z_α = z value providing an area of α in the upper tail of a standard normal distribution
z_β = z value providing an area of β in the upper tail of a standard normal distribution
σ = the population standard deviation
μ_0 = the value of the population mean in the null hypothesis
μ_a = the value of the population mean used for the Type II error

Note: In a two-tailed hypothesis test, use (9.7) with $z_{\alpha/2}$ replacing z_α.

Although the logic of equation (9.7) was developed for the hypothesis test shown in Figure 9.10, it holds for any one-tailed test about a population mean. In a two-tailed hypothesis test about a population mean, $z_{\alpha/2}$ is used instead of z_α in equation (9.7).

Let us return to the lot-acceptance example from Sections 9.6 and 9.7. The design specification for the shipment of batteries indicated a mean useful life of at least 120 hours for the batteries. Shipments were rejected if H_0: $\mu \geq 120$ was rejected. Let us assume that the quality control manager makes the following statements about the allowable probabilities for the Type I and Type II errors.

Type I error statement: If the mean life of the batteries in the shipment is $\mu = 120$, I am willing to risk an $\alpha = .05$ probability of rejecting the shipment.

Type II error statement: If the mean life of the batteries in the shipment is five hours under the specification (i.e., $\mu = 115$), I am willing to risk a $\beta = .10$ probability of accepting the shipment.

These statements are based on the judgment of the manager. Someone else might specify different restrictions on the probabilities. However, statements about the allowable probabilities of both errors must be made before the sample size can be determined.

In the example, $\alpha = .05$ and $\beta = .10$. Using the standard normal probability distribution, we have $z_{.05} = 1.645$ and $z_{.10} = 1.28$. From the statements about the error probabilities, we note that $\mu_0 = 120$ and $\mu_a = 115$. Finally, the population standard deviation was assumed known at $\sigma = 12$. By using equation (9.7), we find that the recommended sample size for the lot-acceptance example is

$$n = \frac{(1.645 + 1.28)^2(12)^2}{(120 - 115)^2} = 49.3$$

Rounding up, we recommend a sample size of 50.

Because both the Type I and Type II error probabilities have been controlled at allowable levels with $n = 50$, the quality control manager is now justified in using the *accept* H_0 and *reject* H_0 statements for the hypothesis test. The accompanying inferences are made with allowable probabilities of making Type I and Type II errors.

We can make three observations about the relationship among α, β, and the sample size n.

1. Once two of the three values are known, the other can be computed.
2. For a given level of significance α, increasing the sample size will reduce β.
3. For a given sample size, decreasing α will increase β, whereas increasing α will decrease β.

The third observation should be kept in mind when the probability of a Type II error is not being controlled. It suggests that one should not choose unnecessarily small values for the level of significance α. For a given sample size, choosing a smaller level of significance means more exposure to a Type II error. Inexperienced users of hypothesis testing often think that smaller values of α are always better. They are better if we are concerned only about making a Type I error. However, smaller values of α have the disadvantage of increasing the probability of making a Type II error.

Exercises

Methods

SELF test

54. Consider the following hypothesis test.

$$H_0: \mu \geq 10$$
$$H_a: \mu < 10$$

The sample size is 120 and the population standard deviation is 5. Use $\alpha = .05$. If the actual population mean is 9, the probability of a Type II error is .2912. Suppose the researcher wants to reduce the probability of a Type II error to .10 when the actual population mean is 9. What sample size is recommended?

55. Consider the following hypothesis test.

$$H_0: \mu = 20$$
$$H_a: \mu \neq 20$$

The population standard deviation is 10. Use $\alpha = .05$. How large a sample should be taken if the researcher is willing to accept a .05 probability of making a Type II error when the actual population mean is 22?

Applications

56. Suppose the project director for the Hilltop Coffee study (see Section 9.3) asked for a .10 probability of claiming that Hilltop was not in violation when it really was underfilling by 1 ounce ($\mu_a = 2.9375$ pounds). What sample size would have been recommended?

SELF test

57. A special industrial battery must have a life of at least 400 hours. A hypothesis test is to be conducted with a .02 level of significance. If the batteries from a particular production run have an actual mean use life of 385 hours, the production manager wants a sampling procedure that only 10% of the time would show erroneously that the batch is acceptable. What sample size is recommended for the hypothesis test? Use 30 hours as an estimate of the population standard deviation.

58. *Young Adult* magazine states the following hypotheses about the mean age of its subscribers.

$$H_0: \mu = 28$$
$$H_a: \mu \neq 28$$

If the manager conducting the test will permit a .15 probability of making a Type II error when the true mean age is 29, what sample size should be selected? Assume $\sigma = 6$ and a .05 level of significance.

59. An automobile mileage study tested the following hypotheses.

Hypothesis	Conclusion
$H_0: \mu \geq 25$ mpg	Manufacturer's claim supported
$H_a: \mu < 25$ mpg	Manufacturer's claim rejected; average mileage per gallon less than stated

For $\sigma = 3$ and a .02 level of significance, what sample size would be recommended if the researcher wants an 80% chance of detecting that μ is less than 25 miles per gallon when it is actually 24?

Summary

Hypothesis testing is a statistical procedure that uses sample data to determine whether a statement about the value of a population parameter should or should not be rejected. The hypotheses are two competing statements about a population parameter. One statement is called the null hypothesis (H_0), and the other statement is called the alternative hypothesis (H_a). In Section 9.1 we provided guidelines for developing hypotheses for situations frequently encountered in practice.

Whenever historical data or other information provides a basis for assuming that the population standard deviation is known, the hypothesis testing procedure for the population mean is based on the standard normal distribution. Whenever σ is unknown, the sample standard deviation s is used to estimate σ and the hypothesis testing procedure is based on the t distribution. In both cases, the quality of results depends on both the form of the population distribution and the sample size. If the population has a normal distribution, both hypothesis testing procedures are applicable, even with small sample sizes. If the population is not normally distributed, larger sample sizes are needed. General guidelines about the sample size were provided in Sections 9.3 and 9.4. In the case of hypothesis tests about a population proportion, the hypothesis testing procedure uses a test statistic based on the standard normal distribution.

In all cases, the value of the test statistic can be used to compute a p-value for the test. A p-value is a probability used to determine whether the null hypothesis should be rejected. If the p-value is less than or equal to the level of significance α, the null hypothesis can be rejected.

Hypothesis testing conclusions can also be made by comparing the value of the test statistic to a critical value. For lower tail tests, the null hypothesis is rejected if the value of the test statistic is less than or equal to the critical value. For upper tail tests, the null hypothesis is rejected if the value of the test statistic is greater than or equal to the critical value. Two-tailed tests consist of two critical values: one in the lower tail of the sampling distribution and one in the upper tail. In this case, the null hypothesis is rejected if the value of the test statistic is less than or equal to the critical value in the lower tail or greater than or equal to the critical value in the upper tail.

Extensions of hypothesis testing procedures to include an analysis of the Type II error were also presented. In Section 9.7 we showed how to compute the probability of making a Type II error. In Section 9.8 we showed how to determine a sample size that will control for the probability of making both a Type I error and a Type II error.

Glossary

Null hypothesis The hypothesis tentatively assumed true in the hypothesis testing procedure.
Alternative hypothesis The hypothesis concluded to be true if the null hypothesis is rejected.
Type I error The error of rejecting H_0 when it is true.
Type II error The error of accepting H_0 when it is false.
Level of significance The probability of making a Type I error when the null hypothesis is true as an equality.
One-tailed test A hypothesis test in which rejection of the null hypothesis occurs for values of the test statistic in one tail of its sampling distribution.
Test statistic A statistic whose value helps determine whether a null hypothesis should be rejected.
***p*-value** A probability that provides a measure of the evidence against the null hypothesis given by the sample. Smaller p-values indicate more evidence against H_0. For a lower tail test, the p-value is the probability of obtaining a value for the test statistic as small as or smaller than that provided by the sample. For an upper tail test, the p-value is the probability of obtaining a value for the test statistic as large as or larger than that provided by the sample. For a two-tailed test, the p-value is the probability of obtaining a value for the test statistic at least as unlikely as or more unlikely than that provided by the sample.
Critical value A value that is compared with the test statistic to determine whether H_0 should be rejected.
Two-tailed test A hypothesis test in which rejection of the null hypothesis occurs for values of the test statistic in either tail of its sampling distribution.
Power The probability of correctly rejecting H_0 when it is false.
Power Curve A graph of the probability of rejecting H_0 for all possible values of the population parameter not satisfying the null hypothesis. The power curve provides the probability of correctly rejecting the null hypothesis.

Key Formulas

Test Statistic for Hypothesis Tests About a Population Mean: σ Known

$$z = \frac{\bar{x} - \mu_0}{\sigma/\sqrt{n}} \tag{9.1}$$

Test Statistic for Hypothesis Tests About a Population Mean: σ Unknown

$$t = \frac{\bar{x} - \mu_0}{s/\sqrt{n}} \tag{9.2}$$

Test Statistic for Hypothesis Tests About a Population Proportion

$$z = \frac{\bar{p} - p_0}{\sqrt{\dfrac{p_0(1 - p_0)}{n}}} \tag{9.4}$$

Sample Size for a One-Tailed Hypothesis Test About a Population Mean

$$n = \frac{(z_\alpha + z_\beta)^2\sigma^2}{(\mu_0 - \mu_a)^2} \tag{9.7}$$

In a two-tailed test, replace z_α with $z_{\alpha/2}$.

Supplementary Exercises

60. A production line operates with a mean filling weight of 16 ounces per container. Overfilling or underfilling presents a serious problem and when detected requires the operator to shut down the production line to readjust the filling mechanism. From past data, a population standard deviation $\sigma = .8$ ounces is assumed. A quality control inspector selects a sample of 30 items every hour and at that time makes the decision of whether to shut down the line for readjustment. The level of significance is $\alpha = .05$.
    a. State the hypothesis test for this quality control application.
    b. If a sample mean of $\bar{x} = 16.32$ ounces were found, what is the p-value? What action would you recommend?
    c. If a sample mean of $\bar{x} = 15.82$ ounces were found, what is the p-value? What action would you recommend?
    d. Use the critical value approach. What is the rejection rule for the preceding hypothesis testing procedure? Repeat parts (b) and (c). Do you reach the same conclusion?

61. At Western University the historical mean of scholarship examination scores for freshman applications is 900. A historical population standard deviation $\sigma = 180$ is assumed known. Each year, the assistant dean uses a sample of applications to determine whether the mean examination score for the new freshman applications has changed.
    a. State the hypotheses.
    b. What is the 95% confidence interval estimate of the population mean examination score if a sample of 200 applications provided a sample mean $\bar{x} = 935$?
    c. Use the confidence interval to conduct a hypothesis test. Using $\alpha = .05$, what is your conclusion?
    d. What is the p-value?

62. *Playbill* is a magazine distributed around the country to people attending musicals and other theatrical productions. The mean annual household income for the population of *Playbill* readers is $119,155 (*Playbill,* January 2006). Assume the standard deviation is $\sigma = \$20,700$. A San Francisco civic group has asserted that the mean for theatergoers in the Bay Area is higher. A sample of 60 theater attendees in the Bay Area showed a sample mean household income of $126,100.
    a. Develop hypotheses that can be used to determine whether the sample data support the conclusion that theater attendees in the Bay Area have a higher mean household income than that for all *Playbill* readers.
    b. What is the p-value based on the sample of 60 theater attendees in the Bay Area?
    c. Use $\alpha = .01$ as the level of significance. What is your conclusion?

63. On Friday, Wall Street traders were anxiously awaiting the federal government's release of numbers on the January increase in nonfarm payrolls. The early consensus estimate among economists was for a growth of 250,000 new jobs (CNBC, February 3, 2006). However, a sample of 20 economists taken Thursday afternoon provided a sample mean of 266,000 with a sample standard deviation of 24,000. Financial analysts often call such a sample mean, based on late-breaking news, the *whisper number.* Treat the "consensus estimate" as the population mean. Conduct a hypothesis test to determine whether the whisper number justifies a conclusion of a statistically significant increase in the consensus estimate of economists. Use $\alpha = .01$ as the level of significance.

WEB file

FirstBirth

64. Data released by the National Center for Health Statistics showed that the mean age at which women had their first child was 25.0 in 2006 (*The Wall Street Journal*, February 4, 2009). The reporter, Sue Shellenbarger, noted that this was the first decrease in the average age at which women had their first child in several years. A recent sample of 42 women provided the data in the website file named FirstBirth concerning the age at which these women had their first child. Do the data indicate a change from 2006 in the mean age at which women had their first child? Use $\alpha = .05$.

65. An extensive study of the cost of health care in the United States presented data showing that the mean spending per Medicare enrollee in 2003 was \$6883 (*Money,* Fall 2003). To investigate differences across the country, a researcher took a sample of 40 Medicare enrollees in Indianapolis. For the Indianapolis sample, the mean 2003 Medicare spending was \$5980 and the standard deviation was \$2518.
   a. State the hypotheses that should be used if we would like to determine whether the mean annual Medicare spending in Indianapolis is lower than the national mean.
   b. Use the preceding sample results to compute the test statistic and the p-value.
   c. Use $\alpha = .05$. What is your conclusion?
   d. Repeat the hypothesis test using the critical value approach.

66. The chamber of commerce of a Florida Gulf Coast community advertises that area residential property is available at a mean cost of \$125,000 or less per lot. Suppose a sample of 32 properties provided a sample mean of \$130,000 per lot and a sample standard deviation of \$12,500. Use a .05 level of significance to test the validity of the advertising claim.

WEB file
Gasoline

67. The U.S. Energy Administration reported that the mean price for a gallon of regular gasoline in the United States was \$2.357 (U.S. Energy Administration, January 30, 2006). Data for a sample of regular gasoline prices at 50 service stations in the Lower Atlantic states are contained in the data file named Gasoline. Conduct a hypothesis test to determine whether the mean price for a gallon of gasoline in the Lower Atlantic states is different from the national mean. Use $\alpha = .05$ for the level of significance, and state your conclusion.

68. A study by the Centers for Disease Control (CDC) found that 23.3% of adults are smokers and that roughly 70% of those who do smoke indicate that they want to quit (Associated Press, July 26, 2002). CDC reported that, of people who smoked at some point in their lives, 50% have been able to kick the habit. Part of the study suggested that the success rate for quitting rose by education level. Assume that a sample of 100 college graduates who smoked at some point in their lives showed that 64 had been able to successfully stop smoking.
   a. State the hypotheses that can be used to determine whether the population of college graduates has a success rate higher than the overall population when it comes to breaking the smoking habit.
   b. Given the sample data, what is the proportion of college graduates who, having smoked at some point in their lives, were able to stop smoking?
   c. What is the p-value? At $\alpha = .01$, what is your hypothesis testing conclusion?

69. An airline promotion to business travelers is based on the assumption that two-thirds of business travelers use a laptop computer on overnight business trips.
   a. State the hypotheses that can be used to test the assumption.
   b. What is the sample proportion from an American Express sponsored survey that found 355 of 546 business travelers use a laptop computer on overnight business trips?
   c. What is the p-value?
   d. Use $\alpha = .05$. What is your conclusion?

70. Virtual call centers are staffed by individuals working out of their homes. Most home agents earn \$10 to \$15 per hour without benefits versus \$7 to \$9 per hour with benefits at a traditional call center (*BusinessWeek,* January 23, 2006). Regional Airways is considering employing home agents, but only if a level of customer satisfaction greater than 80% can be maintained. A test was conducted with home service agents. In a sample of 300 customers, 252 reported that they were satisfied with service.
   a. Develop hypotheses for a test to determine whether the sample data support the conclusion that customer service with home agents meets the Regional Airways criterion.
   b. What is your point estimate of the percentage of satisfied customers?
   c. What is the p-value provided by the sample data?
   d. What is your hypothesis testing conclusion? Use $\alpha = .05$ as the level of significance.

71. During the 2004 election year, new polling results were reported daily. In an IBD/TIPP poll of 910 adults, 503 respondents reported that they were optimistic about the national

outlook, and President Bush's leadership index jumped 4.7 points to 55.3 (*Investor's Business Daily,* January 14, 2004).

a. What is the sample proportion of respondents who are optimistic about the national outlook?

b. A campaign manager wants to claim that this poll indicates that the majority of adults are optimistic about the national outlook. Construct a hypothesis test so that rejection of the null hypothesis will permit the conclusion that the proportion optimistic is greater than 50%.

c. Use the polling data to compute the p-value for the hypothesis test in part (b). Explain to the manager what this p-value means about the level of significance of the results.

72. A radio station in Myrtle Beach announced that at least 90% of the hotels and motels would be full for the Memorial Day weekend. The station advised listeners to make reservations in advance if they planned to be in the resort over the weekend. On Saturday night a sample of 58 hotels and motels showed 49 with a no-vacancy sign and 9 with vacancies. What is your reaction to the radio station's claim after seeing the sample evidence? Use $\alpha = .05$ in making the statistical test. What is the p-value?

73. According to the federal government, 24% of workers covered by their company's health care plan were not required to contribute to the premium (*Statistical Abstract of the United States: 2006*). A recent study found that 81 out of 400 workers sampled were not required to contribute to their company's health care plan.

a. Develop hypotheses that can be used to test whether the percent of workers not required to contribute to their company's health care plan has declined.

b. What is a point estimate of the proportion receiving free company-sponsored health care insurance?

c. Has a statistically significant decline occurred in the proportion of workers receiving free company-sponsored health care insurance? Use $\alpha = .05$.

74. Shorney Construction Company bids on projects assuming that the mean idle time per worker is 72 or fewer minutes per day. A sample of 30 construction workers will be used to test this assumption. Assume that the population standard deviation is 20 minutes.

a. State the hypotheses to be tested.

b. What is the probability of making a Type II error when the population mean idle time is 80 minutes?

c. What is the probability of making a Type II error when the population mean idle time is 75 minutes?

d. What is the probability of making a Type II error when the population mean idle time is 70 minutes?

e. Sketch the power curve for this problem.

75. A federal funding program is available to low-income neighborhoods. To qualify for the funding, a neighborhood must have a mean household income of less than \$15,000 per year. Neighborhoods with mean annual household income of \$15,000 or more do not qualify. Funding decisions are based on a sample of residents in the neighborhood. A hypothesis test with a .02 level of significance is conducted. If the funding guidelines call for a maximum probability of .05 of not funding a neighborhood with a mean annual household income of \$14,000, what sample size should be used in the funding decision study? Use $\sigma = \$4000$ as a planning value.

76. H_0: $\mu = 120$ and H_a: $\mu \neq 120$ are used to test whether a bath soap production process is meeting the standard output of 120 bars per batch. Use a .05 level of significance for the test and a planning value of 5 for the standard deviation.

a. If the mean output drops to 117 bars per batch, the firm wants to have a 98% chance of concluding that the standard production output is not being met. How large a sample should be selected?

b. With your sample size from part (a), what is the probability of concluding that the process is operating satisfactorily for each of the following actual mean outputs: 117, 118, 119, 121, 122, and 123 bars per batch? That is, what is the probability of a Type II error in each case?

Case Problem 1 Quality Associates, Inc.

Quality Associates, Inc., a consulting firm, advises its clients about sampling and statistical procedures that can be used to control their manufacturing processes. In one particular application, a client gave Quality Associates a sample of 800 observations taken during a time in which that client's process was operating satisfactorily. The sample standard deviation for these data was .21; hence, with so much data, the population standard deviation was assumed to be .21. Quality Associates then suggested that random samples of size 30 be taken periodically to monitor the process on an ongoing basis. By analyzing the new samples, the client could quickly learn whether the process was operating satisfactorily. When the process was not operating satisfactorily, corrective action could be taken to eliminate the problem. The design specification indicated the mean for the process should be 12. The hypothesis test suggested by Quality Associates follows.

$$H_0\colon \mu = 12$$
$$H_a\colon \mu \neq 12$$

Corrective action will be taken any time H_0 is rejected.

The following samples were collected at hourly intervals during the first day of operation of the new statistical process control procedure. These data are available in the data set Quality.

WEB file Quality

Sample 1	Sample 2	Sample 3	Sample 4
11.55	11.62	11.91	12.02
11.62	11.69	11.36	12.02
11.52	11.59	11.75	12.05
11.75	11.82	11.95	12.18
11.90	11.97	12.14	12.11
11.64	11.71	11.72	12.07
11.80	11.87	11.61	12.05
12.03	12.10	11.85	11.64
11.94	12.01	12.16	12.39
11.92	11.99	11.91	11.65
12.13	12.20	12.12	12.11
12.09	12.16	11.61	11.90
11.93	12.00	12.21	12.22
12.21	12.28	11.56	11.88
12.32	12.39	11.95	12.03
11.93	12.00	12.01	12.35
11.85	11.92	12.06	12.09
11.76	11.83	11.76	11.77
12.16	12.23	11.82	12.20
11.77	11.84	12.12	11.79
12.00	12.07	11.60	12.30
12.04	12.11	11.95	12.27
11.98	12.05	11.96	12.29
12.30	12.37	12.22	12.47
12.18	12.25	11.75	12.03
11.97	12.04	11.96	12.17
12.17	12.24	11.95	11.94
11.85	11.92	11.89	11.97
12.30	12.37	11.88	12.23
12.15	12.22	11.93	12.25

Managerial Report

1. Conduct a hypothesis test for each sample at the .01 level of significance and determine what action, if any, should be taken. Provide the test statistic and p-value for each test.
2. Compute the standard deviation for each of the four samples. Does the assumption of .21 for the population standard deviation appear reasonable?
3. Compute limits for the sample mean $\bar{x}$ around $\mu = 12$ such that, as long as a new sample mean is within those limits, the process will be considered to be operating satisfactorily. If $\bar{x}$ exceeds the upper limit or if $\bar{x}$ is below the lower limit, corrective action will be taken. These limits are referred to as upper and lower control limits for quality control purposes.
4. Discuss the implications of changing the level of significance to a larger value. What mistake or error could increase if the level of significance is increased?

Case Problem 2 Ethical Behavior of Business Students at Bayview University

During the global recession of 2008 and 2009, there were many accusations of unethical behavior by Wall Street executives, financial managers, and other corporate officers. At that time, an article appeared that suggested that part of the reason for such unethical business behavior may stem from the fact that cheating has become more prevalent among business students (*Chronicle of Higher Education*, February 10, 2009). The article reported that 56 percent of business students admitted to cheating at some time during their academic career as compared to 47 percent of nonbusiness students.

Cheating has been a concern of the dean of the College of Business at Bayview University for several years. Some faculty members in the college believe that cheating is more widespread at Bayview than at other universities, while other faculty members think that cheating is not a major problem in the college. To resolve some of these issues, the dean commissioned a study to assess the current ethical behavior of business students at Bayview. As part of this study, an anonymous exit survey was administered to a sample of 90 business students from this year's graduating class. Responses to the following questions were used to obtain data regarding three types of cheating.

During your time at Bayview, did you ever present work copied off the Internet as your own?

Yes ________ No ________

During your time at Bayview, did you ever copy answers off another student's exam?

Yes ________ No ________

During your time at Bayview, did you ever collaborate with other students on projects that were supposed to be completed individually?

Yes ________ No ________

Any student who answered Yes to one or more of these questions was considered to have been involved in some type of cheating. A portion of the data collected follows. The complete data set is in the file named Bayview.

WEB file

Bayview

Student	Copied from Internet	Copied on Exam	Collaborated on Individual Project	Gender
1	No	No	No	Female
2	No	No	No	Male
3	Yes	No	Yes	Male
4	Yes	Yes	No	Male
5	No	No	Yes	Male
6	Yes	No	No	Female
.	.	.	.	.
.	.	.	.	.
.	.	.	.	.
88	No	No	No	Male
89	No	Yes	Yes	Male
90	No	No	No	Female

Managerial Report

Prepare a report for the dean of the college that summarizes your assessment of the nature of cheating by business students at Bayview University. Be sure to include the following items in your report.

1. Use descriptive statistics to summarize the data and comment on your findings.
2. Develop 95% confidence intervals for the proportion of all students, the proportion of male students, and the proportion of female students who were involved in some type of cheating.
3. Conduct a hypothesis test to determine if the proportion of business students at Bayview University who were involved in some type of cheating is less than that of business students at other institutions as reported by the *Chronicle of Higher Education*.
4. Conduct a hypothesis test to determine if the proportion of business students at Bayview University who were involved in some form of cheating is less than that of nonbusiness students at other institutions as reported by the *Chronicle of Higher Education*.
5. What advice would you give to the dean based upon your analysis of the data?

Appendix 9.1 Hypothesis Testing with Minitab

We describe the use of Minitab to conduct hypothesis tests about a population mean and a population proportion.

Population Mean: σ Known

We illustrate using the MaxFlight golf ball distance example in Section 9.3. The data are in column C1 of a Minitab worksheet. The population standard deviation $\sigma = 12$ is assumed known and the level of significance is $\alpha = .05$. The following steps can be used to test the hypothesis H_0: $\mu = 295$ versus H_a: $\mu \neq 295$.

WEB file

GolfTest

Step 1. Select the **Stat** menu
Step 2. Choose **Basic Statistics**
Step 3. Choose **1-Sample Z**

Step 4. When the 1-Sample Z dialog box appears:
Enter C1 in the **Samples in columns** box
Enter 12 in the **Standard deviation** box
Select **Perform Hypothesis Test**
Enter 295 in the **Hypothesized mean** box
Select **Options**
Step 5. When the 1-Sample Z-Options dialog box appears:
Enter 95 in the **Confidence level** box*
Select **not equal** in the **Alternative** box
Click **OK**
Step 6. Click **OK**

In addition to the hypothesis testing results, Minitab provides a 95% confidence interval for the population mean.

The procedure can be easily modified for a one-tailed hypothesis test by selecting the less than or greater than option in the **Alternative** box in step 5.

Population Mean: σ Unknown

WEB file
AirRating

The ratings that 60 business travelers gave for Heathrow Airport are entered in column C1 of a Minitab worksheet. The level of significance for the test is $\alpha = .05$, and the population standard deviation σ will be estimated by the sample standard deviation s. The following steps can be used to test the hypothesis H_0: $\mu \leq 7$ against H_a: $\mu > 7$.

Step 1. Select the **Stat** menu
Step 2. Choose **Basic Statistics**
Step 3. Choose **1-Sample t**
Step 4. When the 1-Sample t dialog box appears:
Enter C1 in the **Samples in columns** box
Select **Perform Hypothesis Test**
Enter 7 in the **Hypothesized mean** box
Select **Options**
Step 5. When the 1-Sample t-options dialog box appears:
Enter 95 in the **Confidence level** box
Select **greater than** in the **Alternative** box
Click **OK**
Step 6. Click **OK**

The Heathrow Airport rating study involved a greater than alternative hypothesis. The preceding steps can be easily modified for other hypothesis tests by selecting the less than or not equal options in the **Alternative** box in step 5.

Population Proportion

WEB file
WomenGolf

We illustrate using the Pine Creek golf course example in Section 9.5. The data with responses Female and Male are in column C1 of a Minitab worksheet. Minitab uses an alphabetical ordering of the responses and selects the *second response* for the population proportion of interest. In this example, Minitab uses the alphabetical ordering Female-Male to provide results for the population proportion of Male responses. Because Female is the response of interest, we change Minitab's ordering as follows: Select any cell in the column

*Minitab provides both hypothesis testing and interval estimation results simultaneously. The user may select any confidence level for the interval estimate of the population mean: 95% confidence is suggested here.

and use the sequence: Editor > Column > Value Order. Then choose the option of entering a user-specified order. Enter Male-Female in the **Define-an-order** box and click OK. Minitab's 1 Proportion routine will then provide the hypothesis test results for the population proportion of female golfers. We proceed as follows:

Step 1. Select the **Stat** menu
Step 2. Choose **Basic Statistics**
Step 3. Choose **1 Proportion**
Step 4. When the 1 Proportion dialog box appears:
  Enter C1 in the **Samples in Columns** box
  Select **Perform Hypothesis Test**
  Enter .20 in the **Hypothesized proportion** box
  Select **Options**
Step 5. When the 1 Proportion-Options dialog box appears:
  Enter 95 in the **Confidence level** box
  Select greater than in the **Alternative** box
  Select **Use test and interval based on normal distribution**
  Click **OK**
Step 6. Click **OK**

Appendix 9.2 Hypothesis Testing with Excel

Excel does not provide built-in routines for the hypothesis tests presented in this chapter. To handle these situations, we present Excel worksheets that we designed to use as templates for testing hypotheses about a population mean and a population proportion. The worksheets are easy to use and can be modified to handle any sample data. The worksheets are available on the website that accompanies this book.

Population Mean: σ Known

We illustrate using the MaxFlight golf ball distance example in Section 9.3. The data are in column A of an Excel worksheet. The population standard deviation $\sigma = 12$ is assumed known and the level of significance is $\alpha = .05$. The following steps can be used to test the hypothesis H_0: $\mu = 295$ versus H_a: $\mu \neq 295$.

Refer to Figure 9.11 as we describe the procedure. The worksheet in the background shows the cell formulas used to compute the results shown in the foreground worksheet. The data are entered into cells A2:A51. The following steps are necessary to use the template for this data set.

WEB file
Hyp Sigma Known

Step 1. Enter the data range A2:A51 into the =COUNT cell formula in cell D4
Step 2. Enter the data range A2:A51 into the =AVERAGE cell formula in cell D5
Step 3. Enter the population standard deviation $\sigma = 12$ into cell D6
Step 4. Enter the hypothesized value for the population mean 295 into cell D8

The remaining cell formulas automatically provide the standard error, the value of the test statistic z, and three p-values. Because the alternative hypothesis ($\mu_0 \neq 295$) indicates a two-tailed test, the p-value (Two Tail) in cell D15 is used to make the rejection decision. With p-value $= .1255 > \alpha = .05$, the null hypothesis cannot be rejected. The p-values in cells D13 or D14 would be used if the hypotheses involved a one-tailed test.

This template can be used to make hypothesis testing computations for other applications. For instance, to conduct a hypothesis test for a new data set, enter the new sample

FIGURE 9.11 EXCEL WORKSHEET FOR HYPOTHESIS TESTS ABOUT A POPULATION MEAN WITH σ KNOWN

	A	B	C	D	E
1	**Yards**		**Hypothesis Test About a Population Mean**		
2	303		**With σ Known**		
3	282				
4	289		**Sample Size**	=COUNT(A2:A51)	
5	298		**Sample Mean**	=AVERAGE(A2:A51)	
6	283		**Population Std. Deviation**	12	
7	317				
8	297		**Hypothesized Value**	295	
9	308				
10	317		**Standard Error**	=D6/SQRT(D4)	
11	293		**Test Statistic *z***	=(D5-D8)/D10	
12	284				
13	290		***p*-value (Lower Tail)**	=NORM.S.DIST(D11,TRUE)	
14	304		***p*-value (Upper Tail)**	=1-D13	
15	290		***p*-value (Two Tail)**	=2*MIN(D13,D14)	
16	311				
17	305				
49	303				
50	301				
51	292				
52					

	A	B	C	D	E
1	**Yards**		**Hypothesis Test About a Population Mean**		
2	303		**With σ Known**		
3	282				
4	289		**Sample Size**	50	
5	298		**Sample Mean**	297.6	
6	283		**Population Std. Deviation**	12	
7	317				
8	297		**Hypothesized Value**	295	
9	308				
10	317		**Standard Error**	1.70	
11	293		**Test Statistic *z***	1.53	
12	284				
13	290		***p*-value (Lower Tail)**	0.9372	
14	304		***p*-value (Upper Tail)**	0.0628	
15	290		***p*-value (Two Tail)**	0.1255	
16	311				
17	305				
49	303				
50	301				
51	292				
52					

Note: Rows 18 to 48 are hidden.

data into column A of the worksheet. Modify the formulas in cells D4 and D5 to correspond to the new data range. Enter the population standard deviation into cell D6 and the hypothesized value for the population mean into cell D8 to obtain the results. If the new sample data have already been summarized, the new sample data do not have to be entered into the worksheet. In this case, enter the sample size into cell D4, the sample mean into cell D5, the population standard deviation into cell D6, and the hypothesized value for the population mean into cell D8 to obtain the results. The worksheet in Figure 9.11 is available in the file Hyp Sigma Known on the website that accompanies this book.

Population Mean: σ Unknown

WEB file
Hyp Sigma Unknown

We illustrate using the Heathrow Airport rating example in Section 9.4. The data are in column A of an Excel worksheet. The population standard deviation σ is unknown and will be estimated by the sample standard deviation s. The level of significance is $\alpha = .05$. The following steps can be used to test the hypothesis H_0: $\mu \leq 7$ versus H_a: $\mu > 7$.

Refer to Figure 9.12 as we describe the procedure. The background worksheet shows the cell formulas used to compute the results shown in the foreground version of

FIGURE 9.12 EXCEL WORKSHEET FOR HYPOTHESIS TESTS ABOUT A POPULATION MEAN WITH σ UNKNOWN

	A	B	C	D	E
1	Rating		**Hypothesis Test About a Population Mean**		
2	5		**With σ Unknown**		
3	7				
4	8		**Sample Size**	=COUNT(A2:A61)	
5	7		**Sample Mean**	=AVERAGE(A2:A61)	
6	8		**Sample Std. Deviation**	=STDEV(A2:A61)	
7	8				
8	8		**Hypothesized Value**	7	
9	7				
10	8		**Standard Error**	=D6/SQRT(D4)	
11	10		**Test Statistic *t***	=(D5-D8)/D10	
12	6		**Degrees of Freedom**	=D4-1	
13	7				
14	8		***p*-value (Lower Tail)**	=T.DIST(D11,D12,TRUE)	
15	8		***p*-value (Upper Tail)**	=1-D14	
16	9		***p*-value (Two Tail)**	=2*MIN(D14,D15)	
17	7				
59	7				
60	7				
61	8				
62					

	A	B	C	D	E
1	Rating		**Hypothesis Test About a Population Mean**		
2	5		**With σ Unknown**		
3	7				
4	8		**Sample Size**	60	
5	7		**Sample Mean**	7.25	
6	8		**Sample Std. Deviation**	1.05	
7	8				
8	8		**Hypothesized Value**	7	
9	7				
10	8		**Standard Error**	0.136	
11	10		**Test Statistic *t***	1.841	
12	6		**Degrees of Freedom**	59	
13	7				
14	8		***p*-value (Lower Tail)**	0.9647	
15	8		***p*-value (Upper Tail)**	0.0353	
16	9		***p*-value (Two Tail)**	0.0706	
17	7				
59	7				
60	7				
61	8				
62					

Note: Rows 18 to 58 are hidden.

the worksheet. The data are entered into cells A2:A61. The following steps are necessary to use the template for this data set.

Step 1. Enter the data range A2:A61 into the =COUNT cell formula in cell D4
Step 2. Enter the data range A2:A61 into the =AVERAGE cell formula in cell D5
Step 3. Enter the data range A2:A61 into the =STDEV cell formula in cell D6
Step 4. Enter the hypothesized value for the population mean 7 into cell D8

The remaining cell formulas automatically provide the standard error, the value of the test statistic t, the number of degrees of freedom, and three p-values. Because the alternative hypothesis ($\mu > 7$) indicates an upper tail test, the p-value (Upper Tail) in cell D15 is used to make the decision. With p-value $= .0353 < \alpha = .05$, the null hypothesis is rejected. The p-values in cells D14 or D16 would be used if the hypotheses involved a lower tail test or a two-tailed test.

This template can be used to make hypothesis testing computations for other applications. For instance, to conduct a hypothesis test for a new data set, enter the new sample data into column A of the worksheet and modify the formulas in cells D4, D5, and D6 to correspond to the new data range. Enter the hypothesized value for the population mean into cell D8 to obtain the results. If the new sample data have already been summarized, the new sample data do not have to be entered into the worksheet. In this case, enter the sample size into cell D4, the sample mean into cell D5, the sample standard deviation into cell D6, and the hypothesized value for the population mean into cell D8 to obtain the results. The worksheet in Figure 9.12 is available in the file Hyp Sigma Unknown on the website that accompanies this book.

Population Proportion

WEB file
Hypothesis p

We illustrate using the Pine Creek golf course survey data presented in Section 9.5. The data of Male or Female golfer are in column A of an Excel worksheet. Refer to Figure 9.13 as we describe the procedure. The background worksheet shows the cell formulas used to compute the results shown in the foreground worksheet. The data are entered into cells A2:A401. The following steps can be used to test the hypothesis H_0: $p \leq .20$ versus H_a: $p > .20$.

Step 1. Enter the data range A2:A401 into the =COUNTA cell formula in cell D3
Step 2. Enter Female as the response of interest in cell D4
Step 3. Enter the data range A2:A401 into the =COUNTIF cell formula in cell D5
Step 4. Enter the hypothesized value for the population proportion .20 into cell D8

The remaining cell formulas automatically provide the standard error, the value of the test statistic z, and three p-values. Because the alternative hypothesis ($p > .20$) indicates an upper tail test, the p-value (Upper Tail) in cell D14 is used to make the decision. With p-value $= .0062 < \alpha = .05$, the null hypothesis is rejected. The p-values in cells D13 or D15 would be used if the hypothesis involved a lower tail test or a two-tailed test.

This template can be used to make hypothesis testing computations for other applications. For instance, to conduct a hypothesis test for a new data set, enter the new sample data into column A of the worksheet. Modify the formulas in cells D3 and D5 to correspond to the new data range. Enter the response of interest into cell D4 and the hypothesized value for the population proportion into cell D8 to obtain the results. If the new sample data have already been summarized, the new sample data do not have to be entered into the worksheet. In this case, enter the sample size into cell D3, the sample proportion into cell D6, and the hypothesized value for the population proportion into cell D8 to obtain the results. The worksheet in Figure 9.13 is available in the file Hypothesis p on the website that accompanies this book.

FIGURE 9.13 EXCEL WORKSHEET FOR HYPOTHESIS TESTS ABOUT A POPULATION PROPORTION

	A	B	C	D	E
1	**Golfer**		**Hypothesis Test About a Population Proportion**		
2	Female				
3	Male		**Sample Size**	=COUNTA(A2:A401)	
4	Female		**Response of Interest**	Female	
5	Male		**Count for Response**	=COUNTIF(A2:A401,D4)	
6	Male		**Sample Proportion**	=D5/D3	
7	Female				
8	Male		**Hypothesized Value**	0.20	
9	Male				
10	Female		**Standard Error**	=SQRT(D8*(1-D8)/D3)	
11	Male		**Test Statistic *z***	=(D6-D8)/D10	
12	Male				
13	Male		***p*-value (Lower Tail)**	=NORM.S.DIST(D11,TRUE)	
14	Male		***p*-value (Upper Tail)**	=1-D13	
15	Male		***p*-value (Two Tail)**	=2*MIN(D13,D14)	
16	Female				
400	Male				
401	Male				
402					

	A	B	C	D	E
1	**Golfer**		**Hypothesis Test About a Population Proportion**		
2	Female				
3	Male		**Sample Size**	400	
4	Female		**Response of Interest**	Female	
5	Male		**Count for Response**	100	
6	Male		**Sample Proportion**	0.2500	
7	Female				
8	Male		**Hypothesized Value**	0.20	
9	Male				
10	Female		**Standard Error**	0.0200	
11	Male		**Test Statistic *z***	2.50	
12	Male				
13	Male		***p*-value (Lower Tail)**	0.9938	
14	Male		***p*-value (Upper Tail)**	0.0062	
15	Male		***p*-value (Two Tail)**	0.0124	
16	Female				
400	Male				
401	Male				
402					

Note: Rows 17 to 399 are hidden.

Appendix 9.3 Hypothesis Testing with StatTools

In this appendix we show how StatTools can be used to conduct hypothesis tests about a population mean for the σ unknown case

Population Mean: σ Unknown Case

WEB file AirRating

In this case the population standard deviation σ will be estimated by the sample standard deviation s. We use the example discussed in Section 9.4 involving ratings that 60 business travelers gave for Heathrow Airport.

Begin by using the Data Set Manager to create a StatTools data set for these data using the procedure described in the appendix in Chapter 1. The following steps can be used to test the hypothesis H_0: $\mu \leq 7$ against H_a: $\mu > 7$.

Step 1. Click the **StatTools** tab on the Ribbon
Step 2. In the **Analyses** group, click **Statistical Inference**
Step 3. Choose the **Hypothesis Test** option
Step 4. Choose Mean/Std. Deviation
Step 5. When the StatTools-Hypothesis Test for Mean/Std. Deviation dialog box appears:
For **Analysis Type,** choose **One-Sample Analysis**
In the **Variables** section, select **Rating**
In the **Hypothesis Tests to Perform** section:
Select the **Mean** option
Enter 7 in the **Null Hypothesis Value** box
Select **Greater Than Null Value (One-Tailed Test)** in the **Alternative Hypothesis Type** box
If selected, remove the check in the **Standard Deviation** box
Click **OK**

The results from the hypothesis test will appear. They include the p-value and the value of the test statistic.

Population Proportion

We illustrate using the Pine Creek golf course example in Section 9.5. Begin by using the Data Set Manager to create a StatTools data set for these data using the procedure described in the appendix to Chapter 1. The following steps can be used to conduct a hypothesis test of the population proportion.

WEB file

WomenGolf

Step 1. Click the **StatTools** tab on the Ribbon
Step 2. In the **Analyses** group, click **Statistical Inference**
Step 3. Choose **Hypothesis Test**
Step 4. Choose **Proportion**
Step 5. When the StatTools-Hypothesis Test for Proportion dialog box appears:
For **Analysis Type** choose **One-Sample Analysis**
In the **Variables** section, select **Golfer**
In the **Categories to Analyze** section, select **Female**
In the **Hypotheses About Proportion** section:
Enter .20 in the **Null Hypothesis Value** box
In the **Alternaive Hypothesis Type** box, choose **Greater Than Null Value (One-Tailed Test)**
Click **OK**

The results from the hypothesis test will appear. They include the p-value and the value of the test statistic.

Index

Note: Chapter 22 can be found with the Online Content for this book. Index entries found in this chapter are denoted by chapter number 22, hyphen, and page number.

Page numbers followed by a **n** indicate a footnote.

A

B

C

D

Q

R

T

U

V

W

X

Z

PREFACE

My motivation for writing the first edition of *Introductory Econometrics: A Modern Approach* was that I saw a fairly wide gap between how econometrics is taught to undergraduates and how empirical researchers think about and apply econometric methods. I became convinced that teaching introductory econometrics from the perspective of professional users of econometrics would actually simplify the presentation, in addition to making the subject much more interesting.

Based on the positive reactions to earlier editions, it appears that my hunch was correct. Many instructors, having a variety of backgrounds and interests and teaching students with different levels of preparation, have embraced the modern approach to econometrics espoused in this text. The emphasis in this edition is still on applying econometrics to real-world problems. Each econometric method is motivated by a particular issue facing researchers analyzing nonexperimental data. The focus in the main text is on understanding and interpreting the assumptions in light of actual empirical applications: the mathematics required is no more than college algebra and basic probability and statistics.

Organized for Today's Econometrics Instructor

The fifth edition preserves the overall organization of the fourth. The most noticeable feature that distinguishes this text from most others is the separation of topics by the kind of data being analyzed. This is a clear departure from the traditional approach, which presents a linear model, lists all assumptions that may be needed at some future point in the analysis, and then proves or asserts results without clearly connecting them to the assumptions. My approach is first to treat, in Part 1, multiple regression analysis with cross-sectional data, under the assumption of random sampling. This setting is natural to students because they are familiar with random sampling from a population in their introductory statistics courses. Importantly, it allows us to distinguish assumptions made about the underlying population regression model—assumptions that can be given economic or behavioral content—from assumptions about how the data were sampled. Discussions about the consequences of nonrandom sampling can be treated in an intuitive fashion after the students have a good grasp of the multiple regression model estimated using random samples.

An important feature of a modern approach is that the explanatory variables—along with the dependent variable—are treated as outcomes of random variables. For the social sciences, allowing random explanatory variables is much more realistic than the traditional assumption of nonrandom explanatory variables. As a nontrivial benefit, the population model/random sampling approach reduces the number of assumptions that students must absorb and understand. Ironically, the classical approach to regression analysis, which treats the explanatory variables as fixed in repeated samples and is still pervasive in introductory texts, literally applies to data collected in an experimental setting. In addition, the contortions required to state and explain assumptions can be confusing to students.

My focus on the population model emphasizes that the fundamental assumptions underlying regression analysis, such as the zero mean assumption on the unobservable error term, are properly stated conditional on the explanatory variables. This leads to a clear understanding of the kinds of problems, such as heteroskedasticity (nonconstant variance), that can invalidate standard inference procedures. By focusing on the population I am also able to dispel several misconceptions that arise in econometrics texts at all levels. For example, I explain why the usual R-squared is still valid as a goodness-of-fit measure in the presence of heteroskedasticity (Chapter 8) or serially correlated errors (Chapter 12); I provide a simple demonstration that tests for functional form should not be viewed as general tests of omitted variables (Chapter 9); and I explain why one should always include in a regression model extra control variables that are uncorrelated with the explanatory variable of interest, which is often a key policy variable (Chapter 6).

Because the assumptions for cross-sectional analysis are relatively straightforward yet realistic, students can get involved early with serious cross-sectional applications without having to worry about the thorny issues of trends, seasonality, serial correlation, high persistence, and spurious regression that are ubiquitous in time series regression models. Initially, I figured that my treatment of regression with cross-sectional data followed by regression with time series data would find favor with instructors whose own research interests are in applied microeconomics, and that appears to be the case. It has been gratifying that adopters of the text with an applied time series bent have been equally enthusiastic about the structure of the text. By postponing the econometric analysis of time series data, I am able to put proper focus on the potential pitfalls in analyzing time series data that do not arise with cross-sectional data. In effect, time series econometrics finally gets the serious treatment it deserves in an introductory text.

As in the earlier editions, I have consciously chosen topics that are important for reading journal articles and for conducting basic empirical research. Within each topic, I have deliberately omitted many tests and estimation procedures that, while traditionally included in textbooks, have not withstood the empirical test of time. Likewise, I have emphasized more recent topics that have clearly demonstrated their usefulness, such as obtaining test statistics that are robust to heteroskedasticity (or serial correlation) of unknown form, using multiple years of data for policy analysis, or solving the omitted variable problem by instrumental variables methods. I appear to have made fairly good choices, as I have received only a handful of suggestions for adding or deleting material.

I take a systematic approach throughout the text, by which I mean that each topic is presented by building on the previous material in a logical fashion, and assumptions are introduced only as they are needed to obtain a conclusion. For example, empirical researchers who use econometrics in their research understand that not all of the Gauss-Markov assumptions are needed to show that the ordinary least squares (OLS) estimators are unbiased. Yet the vast majority of econometrics texts introduce a complete set of assumptions (many of which are redundant or in some cases even logically conflicting) before proving the unbiasedness of OLS. Similarly, the normality assumption is often included among the assumptions that are needed for the Gauss-Markov Theorem, even though it is fairly well known that normality plays no role in showing that the OLS estimators are the best linear unbiased estimators.

My systematic approach is illustrated by the order of assumptions that I use for multiple regression in Part 1. This structure results in a natural progression for briefly summarizing the role of each assumption:

MLR.1: Introduce the population model and interpret the population parameters (which we hope to estimate).

MLR.2: Introduce random sampling from the population and describe the data that we use to estimate the population parameters.

MLR.3: Add the assumption on the explanatory variables that allows us to compute the estimates from our sample; this is the so-called no perfect collinearity assumption.

MLR.4: Assume that, in the population, the mean of the unobservable error does not depend on the values of the explanatory variables; this is the "mean independence" assumption combined with a zero population mean for the error, and it is the key assumption that delivers unbiasedness of OLS.

After introducing Assumptions MLR.1 to MLR.3, one can discuss the algebraic properties of ordinary least squares—that is, the properties of OLS for a particular set of data. By adding Assumption MLR.4, we can show that OLS is unbiased (and consistent). Assumption MLR.5 (homoskedasticity) is added for the Gauss-Markov Theorem and for the usual OLS variance formulas to be valid. Assumption MLR.6 (normality), which is not introduced until Chapter 4, is added to round out the classical linear model assumptions. The six assumptions are used to obtain exact statistical inference and to conclude that the OLS estimators have the smallest variances among all unbiased estimators.

I use parallel approaches when I turn to the study of large-sample properties and when I treat regression for time series data in Part 2. The careful presentation and discussion of assumptions makes it relatively easy to transition to Part 3, which covers advanced topics that include using pooled cross-sectional data, exploiting panel data structures, and applying instrumental variables methods. Generally, I have strived to provide a unified view of econometrics, where all estimators and test statistics are obtained using just a few intuitively reasonable principles of estimation and testing (which, of course, also have rigorous justification). For example, regression-based tests for heteroskedasticity and serial correlation are easy for students to grasp because they already have a solid understanding of regression. This is in contrast to treatments that give a set of disjointed recipes for outdated econometric testing procedures.

Throughout the text, I emphasize ceteris paribus relationships, which is why, after one chapter on the simple regression model, I move to multiple regression analysis. The multiple regression setting motivates students to think about serious applications early. I also give prominence to policy analysis with all kinds of data structures. Practical topics, such as using proxy variables to obtain ceteris paribus effects and interpreting partial effects in models with interaction terms, are covered in a simple fashion.

New to This Edition

I have added new exercises to nearly every chapter. Some are computer exercises using existing data sets, some use new data sets, and others involve using computer simulations to study the properties of the OLS estimator. I have also added more challenging problems that require derivations.

Some of the changes to the text are worth highlighting. In Chapter 3 I have further expanded the discussion of multicollinearity and variance inflation factors, which I first introduced in the fourth edition. Also in Chapter 3 is a new section on the language that researchers should use when discussing equations estimated by ordinary least squares. It is important for beginners to understand the difference between a model and an estimation method and to remember this distinction as they learn about more sophisticated procedures and mature into empirical researchers.

Chapter 5 now includes a more intuitive discussion about how one should think about large-sample analysis, and emphasizes that it is the distribution of sample averages that changes with the sample size; population distributions, by definition, are unchanging. Chapter 6, in addition to providing more discussion of the logarithmic transformation as applied to proportions, now includes a comprehensive list of considerations when using the most common functional forms: logarithms, quadratics, and interaction terms.

Two important additions occur in Chapter 7. First, I clarify how one uses the sum of squared residual F test to obtain the Chow test when the null hypothesis allows an intercept difference across the groups. Second, I have added Section 7.7, which provides a simple yet general discussion of how to interpret linear models when the dependent variable is a discrete response.

Chapter 9 includes more discussion of using proxy variables to account for omitted, confounding factors in multiple regression analysis. My hope is that it dispels some misunderstandings about the purpose of adding proxy variables and the nature of the resulting multicollinearity. In this chapter I have also expanded the discussion of least absolute deviations estimation (LAD). New problems—one about detecting omitted variables bias and one about heteroskedasticity and LAD estimation—have been added to Chapter 9; these should be a good challenge for well-prepared students.

The appendix to Chapter 13 now includes a discussion of standard errors that are robust to both serial correlation and heteroskedasticity in the context of first-differencing estimation with panel data. Such standard errors are computed routinely now in applied microeconomic studies employing panel data methods. A discussion of the theory is beyond the scope of this text but the basic idea is easy to describe. The appendix in Chapter 14 contains a similar discussion for random effects and fixed effects estimation. Chapter 14 also contains a new Section 14.3, which introduces the reader to the "correlated random effects" approach to panel data models with unobserved heterogeneity. While this topic is more advanced, it provides a synthesis of random and fixed effects methods, and leads to important specification tests that are often reported in empirical research.

Chapter 15, on instrumental variables estimation, has been expanded in several ways. The new material includes a warning about checking the signs of coefficients on instrumental variables in reduced form equations, a discussion of how to interpret the reduced form for the dependent variable, and—as with the case of OLS in Chapter 3—emphasizes that instrumental variables is an estimation method, not a "model."

Targeted at Undergraduates, Adaptable for Master's Students

The text is designed for undergraduate economics majors who have taken college algebra and one semester of introductory probability and statistics. (Appendices A, B, and C contain the requisite background material.) A one-semester or one-quarter econometrics course would not be expected to cover all, or even any, of the more advanced material in Part 3. A typical introductory course includes Chapters 1 through 8, which cover the basics of simple and multiple regression for cross-sectional data. Provided the emphasis is on intuition and interpreting the empirical examples, the material from the first eight chapters should be accessible to undergraduates in most economics departments. Most instructors will also want to cover at least parts of the chapters on regression analysis with time series data, Chapters 10, 11, and 12, in varying degrees of depth. In the one-semester course that I teach at Michigan State, I cover Chapter 10 fairly carefully, give an overview of the material in Chapter 11, and cover the material on serial correlation in Chapter 12. I find that this basic one-semester course puts students on a solid footing to write empirical papers, such as a term paper, a senior seminar paper, or a senior thesis. Chapter 9 contains more specialized topics that arise in analyzing cross-sectional data, including data problems such as outliers and nonrandom sampling; for a one-semester course, it can be skipped without loss of continuity.

The structure of the text makes it ideal for a course with a cross-sectional or policy analysis focus: the time series chapters can be skipped in lieu of topics from Chapters 9, 13, 14, or 15. Chapter 13 is advanced only in the sense that it treats two new data structures: independently pooled cross sections and two-period panel data analysis. Such data structures are especially useful for policy analysis, and the chapter provides several examples. Students with a good grasp of Chapters 1 through 8 will have little difficulty with Chapter 13. Chapter 14 covers more advanced panel data methods and would probably be covered only in a second course. A good way to end a course on cross-sectional methods is to cover the rudiments of instrumental variables estimation in Chapter 15.

I have used selected material in Part 3, including Chapters 13, 14, 15, and 17, in a senior seminar geared to producing a serious research paper. Along with the basic one-semester course, students who have been exposed to basic panel data analysis, instrumental variables estimation, and limited dependent variable models are in a position to read large segments of the applied social sciences literature. Chapter 17 provides an introduction to the most common limited dependent variable models.

The text is also well suited for an introductory master's level course, where the emphasis is on applications rather than on derivations using matrix algebra. Several instructors have used the text to teach policy analysis at the master's level. For instructors wanting to present the material in matrix form, Appendices D and E are self-contained treatments of the matrix algebra and the multiple regression model in matrix form.

At Michigan State, PhD students in many fields that require data analysis—including accounting, agricultural economics, development economics, economics of education, finance, international economics, labor economics, macroeconomics, political science, and public finance—have found the text to be a useful bridge between the empirical work that they read and the more theoretical econometrics they learn at the PhD level.

Design Features

Numerous in-text questions are scattered throughout, with answers supplied in Appendix F. These questions are intended to provide students with immediate feedback. Each chapter contains many numbered examples. Several of these are case studies drawn from recently published papers, but where I have used my judgment to simplify the analysis, hopefully without sacrificing the main point.

The end-of-chapter problems and computer exercises are heavily oriented toward empirical work, rather than complicated derivations. The students are asked to reason carefully based on what they have learned. The computer exercises often expand on the in-text examples. Several exercises use data sets from published works or similar data sets that are motivated by published research in economics and other fields.

A pioneering feature of this introductory econometrics text is the extensive glossary. The short definitions and descriptions are a helpful refresher for students studying for exams or reading empirical research that uses econometric methods. I have added and updated several entries for the fifth edition.

Data Sets—Available in Six Formats

This edition adds R data set as an additional format for viewing and analyzing data. In response to popular demand, this edition also provides the Minitab® format. With more than 100 data sets in six different formats, including Stata®, EViews®, Minitab®, Microsoft® Excel, R, and TeX, the instructor has many options for problem sets, examples, and term projects. Because most of the data sets come from actual research, some are very large. Except for partial lists of data sets to illustrate the various data structures, the data sets are not reported in the text. This book is geared to a course where computer work plays an integral role.

Updated Data Sets Handbook

An extensive data description manual is also available online. This manual contains a list of data sources along with suggestions for ways to use the data sets that are not described in the text. This unique handbook, created by author Jeffrey M. Wooldridge, lists the source of all data sets for quick reference and how each might be used. Because the data book contains page numbers, it is easy to see how the author used the data in the text. Students may want to view the descriptions of each data set and it can help guide instructors in generating new homework exercises, exam problems or term projects. The author also provides suggestions on improving the data sets in this detailed resource that is available on the book's companion website at http://login.cengage.com and students can access it free at www.cengagebrain.com.

Instructor Supplements

Instructor's Manual with Solutions

The *Instructor's Manual with Solutions* (978-1-111-57757-5) contains answers to all problems and exercises, as well as teaching tips on how to present the material in each chapter. The instructor's manual also contains sources for each of the data files, with many suggestions for how to use them on problem sets, exams, and term papers. This supplement is available online only to instructors at http://login.cengage.com.

PowerPoint slides

Exceptional new PowerPoint® presentation slides, created specifically for this edition, help you create engaging, memorable lectures. You'll find teaching slides for each chapter in this edition, including the advanced chapters in Part 3. You can modify or customize the slides for your specific course. PowerPoint® slides are available for convenient download on the instructor-only, password-protected portion of the book's companion website at http://login.cengage.com.

Scientific Word Slides

Developed by the author, new Scientific Word® slides offer an alternative format for instructors who prefer the Scientific Word® platform, the word processor created by MacKichan Software, Inc. for composing mathematical and technical documents using LaTeX typesetting. These slides are based on the author's actual lectures and are available in PDF and TeX formats for convenient download on the instructor-only, password-protected section of the book's companion website at http://login.cengage.com.

Test Bank

In response to user requests, this edition offers a brand new Test Bank written by the author to ensure the highest quality and correspondence with the text. The author has created Test Bank questions from actual tests developed for his own courses. You will find a wealth and variety of problems, ranging from multiple-choice, to questions that require simple statistical derivations to questions that require interpreting computer output. The Test Bank is available for convenient download on the instructor-only, password-protected portion of the companion website at http://login.cengage.com.

Student Supplements

The *Student Solutions Manual* contains suggestions on how to read each chapter as well as answers to selected problems and computer exercises. The *Student Solutions Manual* can be purchased as a Printed Access Code (978-1-111-57694-3) or as an Instant Access Code (978-1-111-57693-6) and accessed online at www.cengagebrain.com.

Suggestions for Designing Your Course

I have already commented on the contents of most of the chapters as well as possible outlines for courses. Here I provide more specific comments about material in chapters that might be covered or skipped:

Chapter 9 has some interesting examples (such as a wage regression that includes IQ score as an explanatory variable). The rubric of proxy variables does not have to be formally introduced to present these kinds of examples, and I typically do so when finishing up cross-sectional analysis. In Chapter 12, for a one-semester course, I skip the material on serial correlation robust inference for ordinary least squares as well as dynamic models of heteroskedasticity.

Even in a second course I tend to spend only a little time on Chapter 16, which covers simultaneous equations analysis. I have found that instructors differ widely in their opinions on the importance of teaching simultaneous equations models to undergraduates. Some think this material is fundamental; others think it is rarely applicable. My own view is that simultaneous equations models are overused (see Chapter 16 for a discussion). If one reads applications carefully, omitted variables and measurement error are much more likely to be the reason one adopts instrumental variables estimation, and this is why I use omitted variables to motivate instrumental variables estimation in Chapter 15.

Still, simultaneous equations models are indispensable for estimating demand and supply functions, and they apply in some other important cases as well.

Chapter 17 is the only chapter that considers models inherently nonlinear in their parameters, and this puts an extra burden on the student. The first material one should cover in this chapter is on probit and logit models for binary response. My presentation of Tobit models and censored regression still appears to be novel in introductory texts. I explicitly recognize that the Tobit model is applied to corner solution outcomes on random samples, while censored regression is applied when the data collection process censors the dependent variable at essentially arbitrary thresholds.

Chapter 18 covers some recent important topics from time series econometrics, including testing for unit roots and cointegration. I cover this material only in a second-semester course at either the undergraduate or master's level. A fairly detailed introduction to forecasting is also included in Chapter 18.

Chapter 19, which would be added to the syllabus for a course that requires a term paper, is much more extensive than similar chapters in other texts. It summarizes some of the methods appropriate for various kinds of problems and data structures, points out potential pitfalls, explains in some detail how to write a term paper in empirical economics, and includes suggestions for possible projects.

Acknowledgments

I would like to thank those who reviewed the proposal for the fifth edition or provided helpful comments on the fourth edition:

Erica Johnson,
Gonzaga University

Mary Ellen Benedict,
Bowling Green State University

Yan Li,
Temple University

Melissa Tartari,
Yale University

Michael Allgrunn,
University of South Dakota

Gregory Colman,
Pace University

Yoo-Mi Chin,
Missouri University of Science and Technology

Arsen Melkumian,
Western Illinois University

Kevin J. Murphy,
Oakland University

Kristine Grimsrud,
University of New Mexico

Will Melick,
Kenyon College

Philip H. Brown,
Colby College

Argun Saatcioglu,
University of Kansas

Ken Brown,
University of Northern Iowa

Michael R. Jonas,
University of San Francisco

Melissa Yeoh,
Berry College

Nikolaos Papanikolaou,
SUNY at New Paltz

Konstantin Golyaev,
University of Minnesota

Soren Hauge,
Ripon College

Kevin Williams,
University of Minnesota

Hailong Qian,
Saint Louis University

Rod Hissong,
University of Texas at Arlington

Steven Cuellar,
Sonoma State University

Yanan Di,
Wagner College

John Fitzgerald,
Bowdoin College

Philip N. Jefferson,
Swarthmore College

Yongsheng Wang,
Washington and Jefferson College

Sheng-Kai Chang,
National Taiwan University

Damayanti Ghosh,
Binghamton University

Susan Averett,
Lafayette College

Kevin J. Mumford,
Purdue University

Nicolai V. Kuminoff,
Arizona State University

Subarna K. Samanta,
The College of New Jersey

Jing Li,
South Dakota State University

Gary Wagner,
University of Arkansas–Little Rock

Kelly Cobourn,
Boise State University

Timothy Dittmer,
Central Washington University

Daniel Fischmar,
Westminster College

Subha Mani,
Fordham University

John Maluccio,
Middlebury College

James Warner,
College of Wooster

Christopher Magee,
Bucknell University

Andrew Ewing,
Eckerd College

Debra Israel,
Indiana State University

Jay Goodliffe,
Brigham Young University

Stanley R. Thompson,
The Ohio State University

Michael Robinson,
Mount Holyoke College

Ivan Jeliazkov,
University of California, Irvine

Heather O'Neill,
Ursinus College

Leslie Papke,
Michigan State University

Timothy Vogelsang,
Michigan State University

Stephen Woodbury,
Michigan State University

Some of the changes I discussed earlier were driven by comments I received from people on this list, and I continue to mull over other specific suggestions made by one or more reviewers.

Many students and teaching assistants, too numerous to list, have caught mistakes in earlier editions or have suggested rewording some paragraphs. I am grateful to them.

As always, it was a pleasure working with the team at South-Western/Cengage Learning. Mike Worls, my longtime acquisitions editor, has learned very well how to guide me with a firm yet gentle hand. Julie Warwick has quickly mastered the difficult challenges of being the developmental editor of a dense, technical textbook. Julie's careful reading of the manuscript and fine eye for detail have improved this fifth edition considerably.

Jean Buttrom did a terrific job as production manager and Karunakaran Gunasekaran at PreMediaGlobal professionally and efficiently oversaw the project management and typesetting of the manuscript.

Special thanks to Martin Biewen at the University of Tübingen for creating the original Powerpoint slides for the text. Thanks also to Francis Smart for assisting with the creation of the R data sets.

This book is dedicated to my wife, Leslie Papke, who contributed materially to this edition by writing the initial versions of the Scientific Word slides for the chapters in Part 3; she then used the slides in her public policy course. Our children have contributed, too: Edmund has helped me keep the data handbook current, and Gwenyth keeps us entertained with her artistic talents.

Jeffrey M. Wooldridge

ABOUT THE AUTHOR

Jeffrey M. Wooldridge is University Distinguished Professor of Economics at Michigan State University, where he has taught since 1991. From 1986 to 1991, Dr. Wooldridge was an assistant professor of economics at the Massachusetts Institute of Technology. He received his bachelor of arts, with majors in computer science and economics, from the University of California, Berkeley, in 1982 and received his doctorate in economics in 1986 from the University of California, San Diego. Dr. Wooldridge has published more than three dozen articles in internationally recognized journals, as well as several book chapters. He is also the author of *Econometric Analysis of Cross Section and Panel Data*, second edition. His awards include an Alfred P. Sloan Research Fellowship, the Plura Scripsit award from *Econometric Theory*, the Sir Richard Stone prize from the *Journal of Applied Econometrics*, and three graduate teacher-of-the-year awards from MIT. He is a fellow of the Econometric Society and of the *Journal of Econometrics*. Dr. Wooldridge is currently coeditor of the *Journal of Econometric Methods*, is past editor of the *Journal of Business and Economic Statistics*, and past econometrics coeditor of *Economics Letters*. He has served on the editorial boards of *Econometric Theory*, the *Journal of Economic Literature*, the *Journal of Econometrics*, the *Review of Economics and Statistics*, and the *Stata Journal*. He has also acted as an occasional econometrics consultant for Arthur Andersen, Charles River Associates, the Washington State Institute for Public Policy, and Stratus Consulting.

CHAPTER

1

The Nature of Econometrics and Economic Data

Chapter 1 discusses the scope of econometrics and raises general issues that arise in the application of econometric methods. Section 1.1 provides a brief discussion about the purpose and scope of econometrics, and how it fits into economics analysis. Section 1.2 provides examples of how one can start with an economic theory and build a model that can be estimated using data. Section 1.3 examines the kinds of data sets that are used in business, economics, and other social sciences. Section 1.4 provides an intuitive discussion of the difficulties associated with the inference of causality in the social sciences.

1.1 What Is Econometrics?

Imagine that you are hired by your state government to evaluate the effectiveness of a publicly funded job training program. Suppose this program teaches workers various ways to use computers in the manufacturing process. The twenty-week program offers courses during nonworking hours. Any hourly manufacturing worker may participate, and enrollment in all or part of the program is voluntary. You are to determine what, if any, effect the training program has on each worker's subsequent hourly wage.

Now, suppose you work for an investment bank. You are to study the returns on different investment strategies involving short-term U.S. treasury bills to decide whether they comply with implied economic theories.

The task of answering such questions may seem daunting at first. At this point, you may only have a vague idea of the kind of data you would need to collect. By the end of this introductory econometrics course, you should know how to use econometric methods to formally evaluate a job training program or to test a simple economic theory.

Econometrics is based upon the development of statistical methods for estimating economic relationships, testing economic theories, and evaluating and implementing government and business policy. The most common application of econometrics is the forecasting of such important macroeconomic variables as interest rates, inflation rates, and gross domestic product. Whereas forecasts of economic indicators are highly visible and often widely published, econometric methods can be used in economic areas that have nothing to do with macroeconomic forecasting. For example, we will study the effects of political campaign expenditures on voting outcomes. We will consider the effect of school spending on student performance in the field of education. In addition, we will learn how to use econometric methods for forecasting economic time series.

Econometrics has evolved as a separate discipline from mathematical statistics because the former focuses on the problems inherent in collecting and analyzing nonexperimental economic data. **Nonexperimental data** are not accumulated through controlled experiments on individuals, firms, or segments of the economy. (Nonexperimental data are sometimes called **observational data**, or **retrospective data**, to emphasize the fact that the researcher is a passive collector of the data.) **Experimental data** are often collected in laboratory environments in the natural sciences, but they are much more difficult to obtain in the social sciences. Although some social experiments can be devised, it is often impossible, prohibitively expensive, or morally repugnant to conduct the kinds of controlled experiments that would be needed to address economic issues. We give some specific examples of the differences between experimental and nonexperimental data in Section 1.4.

Naturally, econometricians have borrowed from mathematical statisticians whenever possible. The method of multiple regression analysis is the mainstay in both fields, but its focus and interpretation can differ markedly. In addition, economists have devised new techniques to deal with the complexities of economic data and to test the predictions of economic theories.

1.2 Steps in Empirical Economic Analysis

Econometric methods are relevant in virtually every branch of applied economics. They come into play either when we have an economic theory to test or when we have a relationship in mind that has some importance for business decisions or policy analysis. An **empirical analysis** uses data to test a theory or to estimate a relationship.

How does one go about structuring an empirical economic analysis? It may seem obvious, but it is worth emphasizing that the first step in any empirical analysis is the careful formulation of the question of interest. The question might deal with testing a certain aspect of an economic theory, or it might pertain to testing the effects of a government policy. In principle, econometric methods can be used to answer a wide range of questions.

In some cases, especially those that involve the testing of economic theories, a formal **economic model** is constructed. An economic model consists of mathematical equations that describe various relationships. Economists are well known for their building of models to describe a vast array of behaviors. For example, in intermediate microeconomics, individual consumption decisions, subject to a budget constraint, are described by mathematical models. The basic premise underlying these models is *utility maximization*. The assumption that individuals make choices to maximize their well-being, subject to resource constraints, gives us a very powerful framework for creating tractable economic models and making clear predictions. In the context of consumption decisions, utility maximization leads to a set of *demand equations*. In a demand equation, the quantity demanded of each commodity depends on the price of the goods, the price of substitute and complementary goods, the consumer's income, and the individual's characteristics that affect taste. These equations can form the basis of an econometric analysis of consumer demand.

Economists have used basic economic tools, such as the utility maximization framework, to explain behaviors that at first glance may appear to be noneconomic in nature. A classic example is Becker's (1968) economic model of criminal behavior.

EXAMPLE 1.1 ECONOMIC MODEL OF CRIME

In a seminal article, Nobel Prize winner Gary Becker postulated a utility maximization framework to describe an individual's participation in crime. Certain crimes have clear economic rewards, but most criminal behaviors have costs. The opportunity costs of crime prevent the criminal from participating in other activities such as legal employment. In addition, there are costs associated with the possibility of being caught and then, if convicted, the costs associated with incarceration. From Becker's perspective, the decision to undertake illegal activity is one of resource allocation, with the benefits and costs of competing activities taken into account.

Under general assumptions, we can derive an equation describing the amount of time spent in criminal activity as a function of various factors. We might represent such a function as

$$y = f(x_1, x_2, x_3, x_4, x_5, x_6, x_7), \qquad [1.1]$$

where

y = hours spent in criminal activities,
x_1 = "wage" for an hour spent in criminal activity,
x_2 = hourly wage in legal employment,
x_3 = income other than from crime or employment,
x_4 = probability of getting caught,
x_5 = probability of being convicted if caught,
x_6 = expected sentence if convicted, and
x_7 = age.

Other factors generally affect a person's decision to participate in crime, but the list above is representative of what might result from a formal economic analysis. As is common in economic theory, we have not been specific about the function $f(\cdot)$ in (1.1). This function depends on an underlying utility function, which is rarely known. Nevertheless, we can use economic theory—or introspection—to predict the effect that each variable would have on criminal activity. This is the basis for an econometric analysis of individual criminal activity.

Formal economic modeling is sometimes the starting point for empirical analysis, but it is more common to use economic theory less formally, or even to rely entirely on intuition. You may agree that the determinants of criminal behavior appearing in equation (1.1) are reasonable based on common sense; we might arrive at such an equation directly, without starting from utility maximization. This view has some merit, although there are cases in which formal derivations provide insights that intuition can overlook.

Next is an example of an equation that we can derive through somewhat informal reasoning.

EXAMPLE 1.2 JOB TRAINING AND WORKER PRODUCTIVITY

Consider the problem posed at the beginning of Section 1.1. A labor economist would like to examine the effects of job training on worker productivity. In this case, there is little need for formal economic theory. Basic economic understanding is sufficient for realizing that factors such as education, experience, and training affect worker productivity. Also, economists are well aware that workers are paid commensurate with their productivity. This simple reasoning leads to a model such as

$$wage = f(educ, exper, training), \quad [1.2]$$

where

$wage$ = hourly wage,
$educ$ = years of formal education,
$exper$ = years of workforce experience, and
$training$ = weeks spent in job training.

Again, other factors generally affect the wage rate, but equation (1.2) captures the essence of the problem.

After we specify an economic model, we need to turn it into what we call an **econometric model**. Because we will deal with econometric models throughout this text, it is important to know how an econometric model relates to an economic model. Take equation (1.1) as an example. The form of the function $f(\cdot)$ must be specified before we can undertake an econometric analysis. A second issue concerning (1.1) is how to deal with variables that cannot reasonably be observed. For example, consider the wage that a person can earn in criminal activity. In principle, such a quantity is well defined, but it would be difficult if not impossible to observe this wage for a given individual. Even variables such as the probability of being arrested cannot realistically be obtained for a given individual, but at least we can observe relevant arrest statistics and derive a variable that approximates the probability of arrest. Many other factors affect criminal behavior that we cannot even list, let alone observe, but we must somehow account for them.

The ambiguities inherent in the economic model of crime are resolved by specifying a particular econometric model:

$$\begin{aligned} crime = \beta_0 + \beta_1 wage_m + \beta_2 othinc + \beta_3 freqarr + \beta_4 freqconv \\ + \beta_5 avgsen + \beta_6 age + u, \end{aligned} \quad [1.3]$$

where

$crime$ = some measure of the frequency of criminal activity,
$wage_m$ = the wage that can be earned in legal employment,
$othinc$ = the income from other sources (assets, inheritance, and so on),
$freqarr$ = the frequency of arrests for prior infractions (to approximate the probability of arrest),
$freqconv$ = the frequency of conviction, and
$avgsen$ = the average sentence length after conviction.

The choice of these variables is determined by the economic theory as well as data considerations. The term u contains unobserved factors, such as the wage for criminal activity, moral character, family background, and errors in measuring things like criminal activity and the probability of arrest. We could add family background variables to the model, such as number of siblings, parents' education, and so on, but we can never eliminate u entirely. In fact, dealing with this *error term* or *disturbance term* is perhaps the most important component of any econometric analysis.

The constants β_0, β_1, ..., β_6 are the *parameters* of the econometric model, and they describe the directions and strengths of the relationship between *crime* and the factors used to determine *crime* in the model.

A complete econometric model for Example 1.2 might be

$$wage = \beta_0 + \beta_1 educ + \beta_2 exper + \beta_3 training + u, \quad [1.4]$$

where the term u contains factors such as "innate ability," quality of education, family background, and the myriad other factors that can influence a person's wage. If we are specifically concerned about the effects of job training, then β_3 is the parameter of interest.

For the most part, econometric analysis begins by specifying an econometric model, without consideration of the details of the model's creation. We generally follow this approach, largely because careful derivation of something like the economic model of crime is time-consuming and can take us into some specialized and often difficult areas of economic theory. Economic reasoning will play a role in our examples, and we will merge any underlying economic theory into the econometric model specification. In the economic model of crime example, we would start with an econometric model such as (1.3) and use economic reasoning and common sense as guides for choosing the variables. Although this approach loses some of the richness of economic analysis, it is commonly and effectively applied by careful researchers.

Once an econometric model such as (1.3) or (1.4) has been specified, various *hypotheses* of interest can be stated in terms of the unknown parameters. For example, in equation (1.3), we might hypothesize that $wage_m$, the wage that can be earned in legal employment, has no effect on criminal behavior. In the context of this particular econometric model, the hypothesis is equivalent to $\beta_1 = 0$.

An empirical analysis, by definition, requires data. After data on the relevant variables have been collected, econometric methods are used to estimate the parameters in the econometric model and to formally test hypotheses of interest. In some cases, the econometric model is used to make predictions in either the testing of a theory or the study of a policy's impact.

Because data collection is so important in empirical work, Section 1.3 will describe the kinds of data that we are likely to encounter.

1.3 The Structure of Economic Data

Economic data sets come in a variety of types. Whereas some econometric methods can be applied with little or no modification to many different kinds of data sets, the special features of some data sets must be accounted for or should be exploited. We next describe the most important data structures encountered in applied work.

Cross-Sectional Data

A **cross-sectional data set** consists of a sample of individuals, households, firms, cities, states, countries, or a variety of other units, taken at a given point in time. Sometimes, the data on all units do not correspond to precisely the same time period. For example, several families may be surveyed during different weeks within a year. In a pure cross-sectional analysis, we would ignore any minor timing differences in collecting the data. If a set of families was surveyed during different weeks of the same year, we would still view this as a cross-sectional data set.

An important feature of cross-sectional data is that we can often assume that they have been obtained by **random sampling** from the underlying population. For example, if we obtain information on wages, education, experience, and other characteristics by randomly drawing 500 people from the working population, then we have a random sample from the population of all working people. Random sampling is the sampling scheme covered in introductory statistics courses, and it simplifies the analysis of cross-sectional data. A review of random sampling is contained in Appendix C.

Sometimes, random sampling is not appropriate as an assumption for analyzing cross-sectional data. For example, suppose we are interested in studying factors that influence the accumulation of family wealth. We could survey a random sample of families, but some families might refuse to report their wealth. If, for example, wealthier families are less likely to disclose their wealth, then the resulting sample on wealth is not a random sample from the population of all families. This is an illustration of a sample selection problem, an advanced topic that we will discuss in Chapter 17.

Another violation of random sampling occurs when we sample from units that are large relative to the population, particularly geographical units. The potential problem in such cases is that the population is not large enough to reasonably assume the observations are independent draws. For example, if we want to explain new business activity across states as a function of wage rates, energy prices, corporate and property tax rates, services provided, quality of the workforce, and other state characteristics, it is unlikely that business activities in states near one another are independent. It turns out that the econometric methods that we discuss do work in such situations, but they sometimes need to be refined. For the most part, we will ignore the intricacies that arise in analyzing such situations and treat these problems in a random sampling framework, even when it is not technically correct to do so.

Cross-sectional data are widely used in economics and other social sciences. In economics, the analysis of cross-sectional data is closely aligned with the applied microeconomics fields, such as labor economics, state and local public finance, industrial organization, urban economics, demography, and health economics. Data on individuals, households, firms, and cities at a given point in time are important for testing microeconomic hypotheses and evaluating economic policies.

The cross-sectional data used for econometric analysis can be represented and stored in computers. Table 1.1 contains, in abbreviated form, a cross-sectional data set on 526 working individuals for the year 1976. (This is a subset of the data in the file WAGE1.RAW.) The variables include *wage* (in dollars per hour), *educ* (years of education), *exper* (years of potential labor force experience), *female* (an indicator for gender), and *married* (marital status). These last two variables are binary (zero-one) in nature and serve to indicate qualitative features of the individual (the person is female or not; the person is married or not). We will have much to say about binary variables in Chapter 7 and beyond.

The variable *obsno* in Table 1.1 is the observation number assigned to each person in the sample. Unlike the other variables, it is not a characteristic of the individual. All econometrics and statistics software packages assign an observation number to each data

TABLE 1.1 A Cross-Sectional Data Set on Wages and Other Individual Characteristics

obsno	wage	educ	exper	female	married
1	3.10	11	2	1	0
2	3.24	12	22	1	1
3	3.00	11	2	0	0
4	6.00	8	44	0	1
5	5.30	12	7	0	1
.	.	.	.	.	.
.	.	.	.	.	.
.	.	.	.	.	.
525	11.56	16	5	0	1
526	3.50	14	5	1	0

unit. Intuition should tell you that, for data such as that in Table 1.1, it does not matter which person is labeled as observation 1, which person is called observation 2, and so on. The fact that the ordering of the data does not matter for econometric analysis is a key feature of cross-sectional data sets obtained from random sampling.

Different variables sometimes correspond to different time periods in cross-sectional data sets. For example, to determine the effects of government policies on long-term economic growth, economists have studied the relationship between growth in real per capita gross domestic product (GDP) over a certain period (say, 1960 to 1985) and variables determined in part by government policy in 1960 (government consumption as a percentage of GDP and adult secondary education rates). Such a data set might be represented as in Table 1.2, which constitutes part of the data set used in the study of cross-country growth rates by De Long and Summers (1991).

The variable *gpcrgdp* represents average growth in real per capita GDP over the period 1960 to 1985. The fact that *govcons60* (government consumption as a percentage of GDP) and *second60* (percentage of adult population with a secondary education) correspond to the year 1960, while *gpcrgdp* is the average growth over the period from 1960 to 1985, does not lead to any special problems in treating this information as a cross-sectional data set. The observations are listed alphabetically by country, but nothing about this ordering affects any subsequent analysis.

TABLE 1.2 A Data Set on Economic Growth Rates and Country Characteristics

obsno	country	gpcrgdp	govcons60	second60
1	Argentina	0.89	9	32
2	Austria	3.32	16	50
3	Belgium	2.56	13	69
4	Bolivia	1.24	18	12
.	.	.	.	.
.	.	.	.	.
.	.	.	.	.
61	Zimbabwe	2.30	17	6

Time Series Data

A **time series data** set consists of observations on a variable or several variables over time. Examples of time series data include stock prices, money supply, consumer price index, gross domestic product, annual homicide rates, and automobile sales figures. Because past events can influence future events and lags in behavior are prevalent in the social sciences, time is an important dimension in a time series data set. Unlike the arrangement of cross-sectional data, the chronological ordering of observations in a time series conveys potentially important information.

A key feature of time series data that makes them more difficult to analyze than cross-sectional data is that economic observations can rarely, if ever, be assumed to be independent across time. Most economic and other time series are related, often strongly related, to their recent histories. For example, knowing something about the gross domestic product from last quarter tells us quite a bit about the likely range of the GDP during this quarter, because GDP tends to remain fairly stable from one quarter to the next. Although most econometric procedures can be used with both cross-sectional and time series data, more needs to be done in specifying econometric models for time series data before standard econometric methods can be justified. In addition, modifications and embellishments to standard econometric techniques have been developed to account for and exploit the dependent nature of economic time series and to address other issues, such as the fact that some economic variables tend to display clear trends over time.

Another feature of time series data that can require special attention is the **data frequency** at which the data are collected. In economics, the most common frequencies are daily, weekly, monthly, quarterly, and annually. Stock prices are recorded at daily intervals (excluding Saturday and Sunday). The money supply in the U.S. economy is reported weekly. Many macroeconomic series are tabulated monthly, including inflation and unemployment rates. Other macro series are recorded less frequently, such as every three months (every quarter). Gross domestic product is an important example of a quarterly series. Other time series, such as infant mortality rates for states in the United States, are available only on an annual basis.

Many weekly, monthly, and quarterly economic time series display a strong seasonal pattern, which can be an important factor in a time series analysis. For example, monthly data on housing starts differ across the months simply due to changing weather conditions. We will learn how to deal with seasonal time series in Chapter 10.

Table 1.3 contains a time series data set obtained from an article by Castillo-Freeman and Freeman (1992) on minimum wage effects in Puerto Rico. The earliest year in the

TABLE 1.3 Minimum Wage, Unemployment, and Related Data for Puerto Rico

obsno	year	avgmin	avgcov	prunemp	prgnp
1	1950	0.20	20.1	15.4	878.7
2	1951	0.21	20.7	16.0	925.0
3	1952	0.23	22.6	14.8	1015.9
.	.	.	.	.	.
.	.	.	.	.	.
.	.	.	.	.	.
37	1986	3.35	58.1	18.9	4281.6
38	1987	3.35	58.2	16.8	4496.7

data set is the first observation, and the most recent year available is the last observation. When econometric methods are used to analyze time series data, the data should be stored in chronological order.

The variable *avgmin* refers to the average minimum wage for the year, *avgcov* is the average coverage rate (the percentage of workers covered by the minimum wage law), *prunemp* is the unemployment rate, and *prgnp* is the gross national product, in millions of 1954 dollars. We will use these data later in a time series analysis of the effect of the minimum wage on employment.

Pooled Cross Sections

Some data sets have both cross-sectional and time series features. For example, suppose that two cross-sectional household surveys are taken in the United States, one in 1985 and one in 1990. In 1985, a random sample of households is surveyed for variables such as income, savings, family size, and so on. In 1990, a *new* random sample of households is taken using the same survey questions. To increase our sample size, we can form a **pooled cross section** by combining the two years.

Pooling cross sections from different years is often an effective way of analyzing the effects of a new government policy. The idea is to collect data from the years before and after a key policy change. As an example, consider the following data set on housing prices taken in 1993 and 1995, before and after a reduction in property taxes in 1994. Suppose we have data on 250 houses for 1993 and on 270 houses for 1995. One way to store such a data set is given in Table 1.4.

Observations 1 through 250 correspond to the houses sold in 1993, and observations 251 through 520 correspond to the 270 houses sold in 1995. Although the order in which

TABLE 1.4 Pooled Cross Sections: Two Years of Housing Prices

obsno	year	hprice	proptax	sqrft	bdrms	bthrms
1	1993	85500	42	1600	3	2.0
2	1993	67300	36	1440	3	2.5
3	1993	134000	38	2000	4	2.5
.	.	.	.	.	.	.
.	.	.	.	.	.	.
.	.	.	.	.	.	.
250	1993	243600	41	2600	4	3.0
251	1995	65000	16	1250	2	1.0
252	1995	182400	20	2200	4	2.0
253	1995	97500	15	1540	3	2.0
.	.	.	.	.	.	.
.	.	.	.	.	.	.
.	.	.	.	.	.	.
520	1995	57200	16	1100	2	1.5

we store the data turns out not to be crucial, keeping track of the year for each observation is usually very important. This is why we enter *year* as a separate variable.

A pooled cross section is analyzed much like a standard cross section, except that we often need to account for secular differences in the variables across the time. In fact, in addition to increasing the sample size, the point of a pooled cross-sectional analysis is often to see how a key relationship has changed over time.

Panel or Longitudinal Data

A **panel data** (or *longitudinal data*) set consists of a time series for *each* cross-sectional member in the data set. As an example, suppose we have wage, education, and employment history for a set of individuals followed over a ten-year period. Or we might collect information, such as investment and financial data, about the same set of firms over a five-year time period. Panel data can also be collected on geographical units. For example, we can collect data for the same set of counties in the United States on immigration flows, tax rates, wage rates, government expenditures, and so on, for the years 1980, 1985, and 1990.

The key feature of panel data that distinguishes them from a pooled cross section is that the *same* cross-sectional units (individuals, firms, or counties in the preceding examples) are followed over a given time period. The data in Table 1.4 are not considered a panel data set because the houses sold are likely to be different in 1993 and 1995; if there are any duplicates, the number is likely to be so small as to be unimportant. In contrast, Table 1.5 contains a two-year panel data set on crime and related statistics for 150 cities in the United States.

There are several interesting features in Table 1.5. First, each city has been given a number from 1 through 150. Which city we decide to call city 1, city 2, and so on is irrelevant. As with a pure cross section, the ordering in the cross section of a panel data set does not matter. We could use the city name in place of a number, but it is often useful to have both.

TABLE 1.5 A Two-Year Panel Data Set on City Crime Statistics

obsno	city	year	murders	population	unem	police
1	1	1986	5	350000	8.7	440
2	1	1990	8	359200	7.2	471
3	2	1986	2	64300	5.4	75
4	2	1990	1	65100	5.5	75
.	.	.	.	.	.	.
.	.	.	.	.	.	.
.	.	.	.	.	.	.
297	149	1986	10	260700	9.6	286
298	149	1990	6	245000	9.8	334
299	150	1986	25	543000	4.3	520
300	150	1990	32	546200	5.2	493

A second point is that the two years of data for city 1 fill the first two rows or observations. Observations 3 and 4 correspond to city 2, and so on. Because each of the 150 cities has two rows of data, any econometrics package will view this as 300 observations. This data set can be treated as a pooled cross section, where the same cities happen to show up in each year. But, as we will see in Chapters 13 and 14, we can also use the panel structure to analyze questions that cannot be answered by simply viewing this as a pooled cross section.

In organizing the observations in Table 1.5, we place the two years of data for each city adjacent to one another, with the first year coming before the second in all cases. For just about every practical purpose, this is the preferred way for ordering panel data sets. Contrast this organization with the way the pooled cross sections are stored in Table 1.4. In short, the reason for ordering panel data as in Table 1.5 is that we will need to perform data transformations for each city across the two years.

Because panel data require replication of the same units over time, panel data sets, especially those on individuals, households, and firms, are more difficult to obtain than pooled cross sections. Not surprisingly, observing the same units over time leads to several advantages over cross-sectional data or even pooled cross-sectional data. The benefit that we will focus on in this text is that having multiple observations on the same units allows us to control for certain unobserved characteristics of individuals, firms, and so on. As we will see, the use of more than one observation can facilitate causal inference in situations where inferring causality would be very difficult if only a single cross section were available. A second advantage of panel data is that they often allow us to study the importance of lags in behavior or the result of decision making. This information can be significant because many economic policies can be expected to have an impact only after some time has passed.

Most books at the undergraduate level do not contain a discussion of econometric methods for panel data. However, economists now recognize that some questions are difficult, if not impossible, to answer satisfactorily without panel data. As you will see, we can make considerable progress with simple panel data analysis, a method that is not much more difficult than dealing with a standard cross-sectional data set.

A Comment on Data Structures

Part 1 of this text is concerned with the analysis of cross-sectional data, because this poses the fewest conceptual and technical difficulties. At the same time, it illustrates most of the key themes of econometric analysis. We will use the methods and insights from cross-sectional analysis in the remainder of the text.

Although the econometric analysis of time series uses many of the same tools as cross-sectional analysis, it is more complicated because of the trending, highly persistent nature of many economic time series. Examples that have been traditionally used to illustrate the manner in which econometric methods can be applied to time series data are now widely believed to be flawed. It makes little sense to use such examples initially, since this practice will only reinforce poor econometric practice. Therefore, we will postpone the treatment of time series econometrics until Part 2, when the important issues concerning trends, persistence, dynamics, and seasonality will be introduced.

In Part 3, we will treat pooled cross sections and panel data explicitly. The analysis of independently pooled cross sections and simple panel data analysis are fairly straightforward extensions of pure cross-sectional analysis. Nevertheless, we will wait until Chapter 13 to deal with these topics.

1.4 Causality and the Notion of Ceteris Paribus in Econometric Analysis

In most tests of economic theory, and certainly for evaluating public policy, the economist's goal is to infer that one variable (such as education) has a **causal effect** on another variable (such as worker productivity). Simply finding an association between two or more variables might be suggestive, but unless causality can be established, it is rarely compelling.

The notion of **ceteris paribus**—which means "other (relevant) factors being equal"—plays an important role in causal analysis. This idea has been implicit in some of our earlier discussion, particularly Examples 1.1 and 1.2, but thus far we have not explicitly mentioned it.

You probably remember from introductory economics that most economic questions are ceteris paribus by nature. For example, in analyzing consumer demand, we are interested in knowing the effect of changing the price of a good on its quantity demanded, while holding all other factors—such as income, prices of other goods, and individual tastes—fixed. If other factors are not held fixed, then we cannot know the causal effect of a price change on quantity demanded.

Holding other factors fixed is critical for policy analysis as well. In the job training example (Example 1.2), we might be interested in the effect of another week of job training on wages, with all other components being equal (in particular, education and experience). If we succeed in holding all other relevant factors fixed and then find a link between job training and wages, we can conclude that job training has a causal effect on worker productivity. Although this may seem pretty simple, even at this early stage it should be clear that, except in very special cases, it will not be possible to literally hold all else equal. The key question in most empirical studies is: Have enough other factors been held fixed to make a case for causality? Rarely is an econometric study evaluated without raising this issue.

In most serious applications, the number of factors that can affect the variable of interest—such as criminal activity or wages—is immense, and the isolation of any particular variable may seem like a hopeless effort. However, we will eventually see that, when carefully applied, econometric methods can simulate a ceteris paribus experiment.

At this point, we cannot yet explain how econometric methods can be used to estimate ceteris paribus effects, so we will consider some problems that can arise in trying to infer causality in economics. We do not use any equations in this discussion. For each example, the problem of inferring causality disappears if an appropriate experiment can be carried out. Thus, it is useful to describe how such an experiment might be structured, and to observe that, in most cases, obtaining experimental data is impractical. It is also helpful to think about why the available data fail to have the important features of an experimental data set.

We rely for now on your intuitive understanding of such terms as *random, independence*, and *correlation*, all of which should be familiar from an introductory probability and statistics course. (These concepts are reviewed in Appendix B.) We begin with an example that illustrates some of these important issues.

EXAMPLE 1.3 EFFECTS OF FERTILIZER ON CROP YIELD

Some early econometric studies [for example, Griliches (1957)] considered the effects of new fertilizers on crop yields. Suppose the crop under consideration is soybeans. Since fertilizer amount is only one factor affecting yields—some others include rainfall, quality of land, and presence of parasites—this issue must be posed as a ceteris paribus question. One way to determine the causal effect of fertilizer amount on soybean yield is to conduct an experiment, which might include the following steps. Choose several one-acre plots of land. Apply different amounts of fertilizer to each plot and subsequently measure the yields; this gives us a cross-sectional data set. Then, use statistical methods (to be introduced in Chapter 2) to measure the association between yields and fertilizer amounts.

As described earlier, this may not seem like a very good experiment because we have said nothing about choosing plots of land that are identical in all respects except for the amount of fertilizer. In fact, choosing plots of land with this feature is not feasible: some of the factors, such as land quality, cannot even be fully observed. How do we know the results of this experiment can be used to measure the ceteris paribus effect of fertilizer? The answer depends on the specifics of how fertilizer amounts are chosen. If the levels of fertilizer are assigned to plots independently of other plot features that affect yield—that is, other characteristics of plots are completely ignored when deciding on fertilizer amounts—then we are in business. We will justify this statement in Chapter 2.

The next example is more representative of the difficulties that arise when inferring causality in applied economics.

EXAMPLE 1.4 MEASURING THE RETURN TO EDUCATION

Labor economists and policy makers have long been interested in the "return to education." Somewhat informally, the question is posed as follows: If a person is chosen from the population and given another year of education, by how much will his or her wage increase? As with the previous examples, this is a ceteris paribus question, which implies that all other factors are held fixed while another year of education is given to the person.

We can imagine a social planner designing an experiment to get at this issue, much as the agricultural researcher can design an experiment to estimate fertilizer effects. Assume, for the moment, that the social planner has the ability to assign any level of education to any person. How would this planner emulate the fertilizer experiment in Example 1.3? The planner would choose a group of people and randomly assign each person an amount of education; some people are given an eighth-grade education, some are given a high school education, some are given two years of college, and so on. Subsequently, the planner measures wages for this group of people (where we assume that each person then works in a job). The people here are like the plots in the fertilizer example, where education plays the role of fertilizer and wage rate plays the role of soybean yield. As with Example 1.3, if levels of education are assigned independently of other characteristics that affect productivity (such as experience and innate ability), then an analysis that ignores these other factors will yield useful results. Again, it will take some effort in Chapter 2 to justify this claim; for now, we state it without support.

Unlike the fertilizer-yield example, the experiment described in Example 1.4 is unfeasible. The ethical issues, not to mention the economic costs, associated with randomly determining education levels for a group of individuals are obvious. As a logistical matter, we could not give someone only an eighth-grade education if he or she already has a college degree.

Even though experimental data cannot be obtained for measuring the return to education, we can certainly collect nonexperimental data on education levels and wages for a large group by sampling randomly from the population of working people. Such data are available from a variety of surveys used in labor economics, but these data sets have a feature that makes it difficult to estimate the ceteris paribus return to education. People *choose* their own levels of education; therefore, education levels are probably not determined independently of all other factors affecting wage. This problem is a feature shared by most nonexperimental data sets.

One factor that affects wage is experience in the workforce. Since pursuing more education generally requires postponing entering the workforce, those with more education usually have less experience. Thus, in a nonexperimental data set on wages and education, education is likely to be negatively associated with a key variable that also affects wage. It is also believed that people with more innate ability often choose higher levels of education. Since higher ability leads to higher wages, we again have a correlation between education and a critical factor that affects wage.

The omitted factors of experience and ability in the wage example have analogs in the fertilizer example. Experience is generally easy to measure and therefore is similar to a variable such as rainfall. Ability, on the other hand, is nebulous and difficult to quantify; it is similar to land quality in the fertilizer example. As we will see throughout this text, accounting for other observed factors, such as experience, when estimating the ceteris paribus effect of another variable, such as education, is relatively straightforward. We will also find that accounting for inherently unobservable factors, such as ability, is much more problematic. It is fair to say that many of the advances in econometric methods have tried to deal with unobserved factors in econometric models.

One final parallel can be drawn between Examples 1.3 and 1.4. Suppose that in the fertilizer example, the fertilizer amounts were not entirely determined at random. Instead, the assistant who chose the fertilizer levels thought it would be better to put more fertilizer on the higher-quality plots of land. (Agricultural researchers should have a rough idea about which plots of land are of better quality, even though they may not be able to fully quantify the differences.) This situation is completely analogous to the level of schooling being related to unobserved ability in Example 1.4. Because better land leads to higher yields, and more fertilizer was used on the better plots, any observed relationship between yield and fertilizer might be spurious.

Difficulty in inferring causality can also arise when studying data at fairly high levels of aggregation, as the next example on city crime rates shows.

EXAMPLE 1.5 THE EFFECT OF LAW ENFORCEMENT ON CITY CRIME LEVELS

The issue of how best to prevent crime has been, and will probably continue to be, with us for some time. One especially important question in this regard is: Does the presence of more police officers on the street deter crime?

The ceteris paribus question is easy to state: If a city is randomly chosen and given, say, ten additional police officers, by how much would its crime rates fall? Another way to state the question is: If two cities are the same in all respects, except that city A has ten more police officers than city B, by how much would the two cities' crime rates differ?

It would be virtually impossible to find pairs of communities identical in all respects except for the size of their police force. Fortunately, econometric analysis does not require this. What we do need to know is whether the data we can collect on community crime levels and the size of the police force can be viewed as experimental. We can certainly imagine a true experiment involving a large collection of cities where we dictate how many police officers each city will use for the upcoming year.

Although policies can be used to affect the size of police forces, we clearly cannot tell each city how many police officers it can hire. If, as is likely, a city's decision on how many police officers to hire is correlated with other city factors that affect crime, then the data must be viewed as nonexperimental. In fact, one way to view this problem is to see that a city's choice of police force size and the amount of crime are *simultaneously determined*. We will explicitly address such problems in Chapter 16.

The first three examples we have discussed have dealt with cross-sectional data at various levels of aggregation (for example, at the individual or city levels). The same hurdles arise when inferring causality in time series problems.

EXAMPLE 1.6 THE EFFECT OF THE MINIMUM WAGE ON UNEMPLOYMENT

An important, and perhaps contentious, policy issue concerns the effect of the minimum wage on unemployment rates for various groups of workers. Although this problem can be studied in a variety of data settings (cross-sectional, time series, or panel data), time series data are often used to look at aggregate effects. An example of a time series data set on unemployment rates and minimum wages was given in Table 1.3.

Standard supply and demand analysis implies that, as the minimum wage is increased above the market clearing wage, we slide up the demand curve for labor and total employment decreases. (Labor supply exceeds labor demand.) To quantify this effect, we can study the relationship between employment and the minimum wage over time. In addition to some special difficulties that can arise in dealing with time series data, there are possible problems with inferring causality. The minimum wage in the United States is not determined in a vacuum. Various economic and political forces impinge on the final minimum wage for any given year. (The minimum wage, once determined, is usually in place for several years, unless it is indexed for inflation.) Thus, it is probable that the amount of the minimum wage is related to other factors that have an effect on employment levels.

We can imagine the U.S. government conducting an experiment to determine the employment effects of the minimum wage (as opposed to worrying about the welfare of low-wage workers). The minimum wage could be randomly set by the government each year, and then the employment outcomes could be tabulated. The resulting experimental time series data could then be analyzed using fairly simple econometric methods. But this scenario hardly describes how minimum wages are set.

If we can control enough other factors relating to employment, then we can still hope to estimate the ceteris paribus effect of the minimum wage on employment. In this sense, the problem is very similar to the previous cross-sectional examples.

Even when economic theories are not most naturally described in terms of causality, they often have predictions that can be tested using econometric methods. The following example demonstrates this approach.

EXAMPLE 1.7 THE EXPECTATIONS HYPOTHESIS

The *expectations hypothesis* from financial economics states that, given all information available to investors at the time of investing, the *expected* return on any two investments is the same. For example, consider two possible investments with a three-month investment horizon, purchased at the same time: (1) Buy a three-month T-bill with a face value of \$10,000, for a price below \$10,000; in three months, you receive \$10,000. (2) Buy a six-month T-bill (at a price below \$10,000) and, in three months, sell it as a three-month T-bill. Each investment requires roughly the same amount of initial capital, but there is an important difference. For the first investment, you know exactly what the return is at the time of purchase because you know the initial price of the three-month T-bill, along with its face value. This is not true for the second investment: although you know the price of a six-month T-bill when you purchase it, you do not know the price you can sell it for in three months. Therefore, there is uncertainty in this investment for someone who has a three-month investment horizon.

The actual returns on these two investments will usually be different. According to the expectations hypothesis, the expected return from the second investment, given all information at the time of investment, should equal the return from purchasing a three-month T-bill. This theory turns out to be fairly easy to test, as we will see in Chapter 11.

Summary

In this introductory chapter, we have discussed the purpose and scope of econometric analysis. Econometrics is used in all applied economics fields to test economic theories, to inform government and private policy makers, and to predict economic time series. Sometimes, an econometric model is derived from a formal economic model, but in other cases, econometric models are based on informal economic reasoning and intuition. The goals of any econometric analysis are to estimate the parameters in the model and to test hypotheses about these parameters; the values and signs of the parameters determine the validity of an economic theory and the effects of certain policies.

Cross-sectional, time series, pooled cross-sectional, and panel data are the most common types of data structures that are used in applied econometrics. Data sets involving a time dimension, such as time series and panel data, require special treatment because of the correlation across time of most economic time series. Other issues, such as trends and seasonality, arise in the analysis of time series data but not cross-sectional data.

In Section 1.4, we discussed the notions of ceteris paribus and causal inference. In most cases, hypotheses in the social sciences are ceteris paribus in nature: all other relevant factors must be fixed when studying the relationship between two variables. Because of the nonexperimental nature of most data collected in the social sciences, uncovering causal relationships is very challenging.

Key Terms

Causal Effect
Ceteris Paribus
Cross-Sectional Data Set
Data Frequency
Econometric Model
Economic Model
Empirical Analysis
Experimental Data
Nonexperimental Data
Observational Data
Panel Data
Pooled Cross Section
Random Sampling
Retrospective Data
Time Series Data

Problems

1 Suppose that you are asked to conduct a study to determine whether smaller class sizes lead to improved student performance of fourth graders.
   (i) If you could conduct any experiment you want, what would you do? Be specific.
   (ii) More realistically, suppose you can collect observational data on several thousand fourth graders in a given state. You can obtain the size of their fourth-grade class and a standardized test score taken at the end of fourth grade. Why might you expect a negative correlation between class size and test score?
   (iii) Would a negative correlation necessarily show that smaller class sizes cause better performance? Explain.

2 A justification for job training programs is that they improve worker productivity. Suppose that you are asked to evaluate whethe r more job training makes workers more productive. However, rather than having data on individual workers, you have access to data on manufacturing firms in Ohio. In particular, for each firm, you have information on hours of job training per worker (*training*) and number of nondefective items produced per worker hour (*output*).
   (i) Carefully state the ceteris paribus thought experiment underlying this policy question.
   (ii) Does it seem likely that a firm's decision to train its workers will be independent of worker characteristics? What are some of those measurable and unmeasurable worker characteristics?
   (iii) Name a factor other than worker characteristics that can affect worker productivity.
   (iv) If you find a positive correlation between *output* and *training*, would you have convincingly established that job training makes workers more productive? Explain.

3 Suppose at your university you are asked to find the relationship between weekly hours spent studying (*study*) and weekly hours spent working (*work*). Does it make sense to characterize the problem as inferring whether *study* "causes" *work* or *work* "causes" *study*? Explain.

Computer Exercises

C1 Use the data in WAGE1.RAW for this exercise.
   (i) Find the average education level in the sample. What are the lowest and highest years of education?
   (ii) Find the average hourly wage in the sample. Does it seem high or low?

(iii) The wage data are reported in 1976 dollars. Using the *Economic Report of the President* (2011 or later), obtain and report the Consumer Price Index (CPI) for the years 1976 and 2010.

(iv) Use the CPI values from part (iii) to find the average hourly wage in 2010 dollars. Now does the average hourly wage seem reasonable?

(v) How many women are in the sample? How many men?

C2 Use the data in BWGHT.RAW to answer this question.

(i) How many women are in the sample, and how many report smoking during pregnancy?

(ii) What is the average number of cigarettes smoked per day? Is the average a good measure of the "typical" woman in this case? Explain.

(iii) Among women who smoked during pregnancy, what is the average number of cigarettes smoked per day? How does this compare with your answer from part (ii), and why?

(iv) Find the average of *fatheduc* in the sample. Why are only 1,192 observations used to compute this average?

(v) Report the average family income and its standard deviation in dollars.

C3 The data in MEAP01.RAW are for the state of Michigan in the year 2001. Use these data to answer the following questions.

(i) Find the largest and smallest values of *math4*. Does the range make sense? Explain.

(ii) How many schools have a perfect pass rate on the math test? What percentage is this of the total sample?

(iii) How many schools have math pass rates of exactly 50%?

(iv) Compare the average pass rates for the math and reading scores. Which test is harder to pass?

(v) Find the correlation between *math4* and *read4*. What do you conclude?

(vi) The variable *exppp* is expenditure per pupil. Find the average of *exppp* along with its standard deviation. Would you say there is wide variation in per pupil spending?

(vii) Suppose School A spends \$6,000 per student and School B spends \$5,500 per student. By what percentage does School A's spending exceed School B's? Compare this to $100 \cdot [\log(6{,}000) - \log(5{,}500)]$, which is the approximation percentage difference based on the difference in the natural logs. (See Section A.4 in Appendix A.)

C4 The data in JTRAIN2.RAW come from a job training experiment conducted for low-income men during 1976–1977; see Lalonde (1986).

(i) Use the indicator variable *train* to determine the fraction of men receiving job training.

(ii) The variable *re78* is earnings from 1978, measured in thousands of 1982 dollars. Find the averages of *re78* for the sample of men receiving job training and the sample not receiving job training. Is the difference economically large?

(iii) The variable *unem78* is an indicator of whether a man is unemployed or not in 1978. What fraction of the men who received job training are unemployed? What about for men who did not receive job training? Comment on the difference.

(iv) From parts (ii) and (iii), does it appear that the job training program was effective? What would make our conclusions more convincing?

C5 The data in FERTIL2.DTA were collected on women living in the Republic of Botswana in 1988. The variable *children* refers to the number of living children. The variable *electric* is a binary indicator equal to one if the woman's home has electricity, and zero if not.

(i) Find the smallest and largest values of *children* in the sample. What is the average of *children*?

(ii) What percentage of women have electricity in the home?

(iii) Compute the average of *children* for those without electricity and do the same for those with electricity. Comment on what you find.

(iv) From part (iii), can you infer that having electricity "causes" women to have fewer children? Explain.

PART

1

Regression Analysis with Cross-Sectional Data

Part 1 of the text covers regression analysis with cross-sectional data. It builds upon a solid base of college algebra and basic concepts in probability and statistics. Appendices A, B, and C contain complete reviews of these topics.

Chapter 2 begins with the simple linear regression model, where we explain one variable in terms of another variable. Although simple regression is not widely used in applied econometrics, it is used occasionally and serves as a natural starting point because the algebra and interpretations are relatively straightforward.

Chapters 3 and 4 cover the fundamentals of multiple regression analysis, where we allow more than one variable to affect the variable we are trying to explain. Multiple regression is still the most commonly used method in empirical research, and so these chapters deserve careful attention. Chapter 3 focuses on the algebra of the method of ordinary least squares (OLS), while also establishing conditions under which the OLS estimator is unbiased and best linear unbiased. Chapter 4 covers the important topic of statistical inference.

Chapter 5 discusses the large sample, or asymptotic, properties of the OLS estimators. This provides justification of the inference procedures in Chapter 4 when the errors in a regression model are not normally distributed. Chapter 6 covers some additional topics in regression analysis, including advanced functional form issues, data scaling, prediction, and goodness-of-fit. Chapter 7 explains how qualitative information can be incorporated into multiple regression models.

Chapter 8 illustrates how to test for and correct the problem of heteroskedasticity, or nonconstant variance, in the error terms. We show how the usual OLS statistics can be adjusted, and we also present an extension of OLS, known as *weighted least squares*, that explicitly accounts for different variances in the errors. Chapter 9 delves further into the very important problem of correlation between the error term and one or more of the explanatory variables. We demonstrate how the availability of a proxy variable can solve the omitted variables problem. In addition, we establish the bias and inconsistency in the OLS estimators in the presence of certain kinds of measurement errors in the variables. Various data problems are also discussed, including the problem of outliers.

CHAPTER 2

The Simple Regression Model

The simple regression model can be used to study the relationship between two variables. For reasons we will see, the simple regression model has limitations as a general tool for empirical analysis. Nevertheless, it is sometimes appropriate as an empirical tool. Learning how to interpret the simple regression model is good practice for studying multiple regression, which we will do in subsequent chapters.

2.1 Definition of the Simple Regression Model

Much of applied econometric analysis begins with the following premise: y and x are two variables, representing some population, and we are interested in "explaining y in terms of x," or in "studying how y varies with changes in x." We discussed some examples in Chapter 1, including: y is soybean crop yield and x is amount of fertilizer; y is hourly wage and x is years of education; and y is a community crime rate and x is number of police officers.

In writing down a model that will "explain y in terms of x," we must confront three issues. First, since there is never an exact relationship between two variables, how do we allow for other factors to affect y? Second, what is the functional relationship between y and x? And third, how can we be sure we are capturing a ceteris paribus relationship between y and x (if that is a desired goal)?

We can resolve these ambiguities by writing down an equation relating y to x. A simple equation is

$$y = \beta_0 + \beta_1 x + u. \qquad [2.1]$$

Equation (2.1), which is assumed to hold in the population of interest, defines the **simple linear regression model**. It is also called the *two-variable linear regression model* or *bivariate linear regression model* because it relates the two variables x and y. We now discuss the meaning of each of the quantities in (2.1). [Incidentally, the term "regression" has origins that are not especially important for most modern econometric applications, so we will not explain it here. See Stigler (1986) for an engaging history of regression analysis.]

When related by (2.1), the variables y and x have several different names used interchangeably, as follows: y is called the **dependent variable**, the **explained variable**, the

TABLE 2.1 Terminology for Simple Regression

y	*x*
Dependent variable	Independent variable
Explained variable	Explanatory variable
Response variable	Control variable
Predicted variable	Predictor variable
Regressand	Regressor

response variable, the **predicted variable**, or the **regressand**; x is called the **independent variable**, the **explanatory variable**, the **control variable**, the **predictor variable**, or the **regressor**. (The term **covariate** is also used for x.) The terms "dependent variable" and "independent variable" are frequently used in econometrics. But be aware that the label "independent" here does not refer to the statistical notion of independence between random variables (see Appendix B).

The terms "explained" and "explanatory" variables are probably the most descriptive. "Response" and "control" are used mostly in the experimental sciences, where the variable x is under the experimenter's control. We will not use the terms "predicted variable" and "predictor," although you sometimes see these in applications that are purely about prediction and not causality. Our terminology for simple regression is summarized in Table 2.1.

The variable u, called the **error term** or **disturbance** in the relationship, represents factors other than x that affect y. A simple regression analysis effectively treats all factors affecting y other than x as being unobserved. You can usefully think of u as standing for "unobserved."

Equation (2.1) also addresses the issue of the functional relationship between y and x. If the other factors in u are held fixed, so that the change in u is zero, $\Delta u = 0$, then x has a *linear* effect on y:

$$\Delta y = \beta_1 \Delta x \quad \text{if} \quad \Delta u = 0. \qquad [2.2]$$

Thus, the change in y is simply β_1 multiplied by the change in x. This means that β_1 is the **slope parameter** in the relationship between y and x, holding the other factors in u fixed; it is of primary interest in applied economics. The **intercept parameter** β_0, sometimes called the *constant term*, also has its uses, although it is rarely central to an analysis.

EXAMPLE 2.1 SOYBEAN YIELD AND FERTILIZER

Suppose that soybean yield is determined by the model

$$yield = \beta_0 + \beta_1 fertilizer + u, \qquad [2.3]$$

so that $y = yield$ and $x = fertilizer$. The agricultural researcher is interested in the effect of fertilizer on yield, holding other factors fixed. This effect is given by β_1. The error term u contains factors such as land quality, rainfall, and so on. The coefficient β_1 measures the effect of fertilizer on yield, holding other factors fixed: $\Delta yield = \beta_1 \Delta fertilizer$.

EXAMPLE 2.2 A SIMPLE WAGE EQUATION

A model relating a person's wage to observed education and other unobserved factors is

$$wage = \beta_0 + \beta_1 educ + u. \quad [2.4]$$

If *wage* is measured in dollars per hour and *educ* is years of education, then β_1 measures the change in hourly wage given another year of education, holding all other factors fixed. Some of those factors include labor force experience, innate ability, tenure with current employer, work ethic, and numerous other things.

The linearity of (2.1) implies that a one-unit change in x has the *same* effect on y, regardless of the initial value of x. This is unrealistic for many economic applications. For example, in the wage-education example, we might want to allow for *increasing* returns: the next year of education has a *larger* effect on wages than did the previous year. We will see how to allow for such possibilities in Section 2.4.

The most difficult issue to address is whether model (2.1) really allows us to draw ceteris paribus conclusions about how x affects y. We just saw in equation (2.2) that β_1 *does* measure the effect of x on y, holding all other factors (in u) fixed. Is this the end of the causality issue? Unfortunately, no. How can we hope to learn in general about the ceteris paribus effect of x on y, holding other factors fixed, when we are ignoring all those other factors?

Section 2.5 will show that we are only able to get reliable estimators of β_0 and β_1 from a random sample of data when we make an assumption restricting how the unobservable u is related to the explanatory variable x. Without such a restriction, we will not be able to estimate the ceteris paribus effect, β_1. Because u and x are random variables, we need a concept grounded in probability.

Before we state the key assumption about how x and u are related, we can always make one assumption about u. As long as the intercept β_0 is included in the equation, nothing is lost by assuming that the average value of u in the population is zero. Mathematically,

$$\mathrm{E}(u) = 0. \quad [2.5]$$

Assumption (2.5) says nothing about the relationship between u and x, but simply makes a statement about the distribution of the unobserved factors in the population. Using the previous examples for illustration, we can see that assumption (2.5) is not very restrictive. In Example 2.1, we lose nothing by normalizing the unobserved factors affecting soybean yield, such as land quality, to have an average of zero in the population of all cultivated plots. The same is true of the unobserved factors in Example 2.2. Without loss of generality, we can assume that things such as average ability are zero in the population of all working people. If you are not convinced, you should work through Problem 2 to see that we can always redefine the intercept in equation (2.1) to make (2.5) true.

We now turn to the crucial assumption regarding how u and x are related. A natural measure of the association between two random variables is the *correlation coefficient*. (See Appendix B for definition and properties.) If u and x are *uncorrelated*, then, as random variables, they are not *linearly* related. Assuming that u and x are uncorrelated goes a long way toward defining the sense in which u and x should be unrelated in equation (2.1). But it does not go far enough, because correlation measures only linear dependence between u and x. Correlation has a somewhat counterintuitive feature: it is possible for u to be uncorrelated with x while being correlated with functions of x, such as x^2. (See Section B.4 for further discussion.) This possibility is not acceptable for most regression purposes, as it causes problems for interpreting the model and for deriving statistical properties. A better assumption involves the *expected value of u given x*.

Because u and x are random variables, we can define the conditional distribution of u given any value of x. In particular, for any x, we can obtain the expected (or average) value of u for that slice of the population described by the value of x. The crucial assumption is that the average value of u does *not* depend on the value of x. We can write this assumption as

$$E(u|x) = E(u). \quad [2.6]$$

Equation (2.6) says that the average value of the unobservables is the same across all slices of the population determined by the value of x and that the common average is necessarily equal to the average of u over the entire population. When assumption (2.6) holds, we say that u is **mean independent** of x. (Of course, mean independence is implied by full independence between u and x, an assumption often used in basic probability and statistics.) When we combine mean independence with assumption (2.5), we obtain the **zero conditional mean assumption**, $E(u|x) = 0$. It is critical to remember that equation (2.6) is the assumption with impact; assumption (2.5) essentially defines the intercept, β_0.

Let us see what (2.6) entails in the wage example. To simplify the discussion, assume that u is the same as innate ability. Then (2.6) requires that the average level of ability is the same regardless of years of education. For example, if $E(abil|8)$ denotes the average ability for the group of all people with eight years of education, and $E(abil|16)$ denotes the average ability among people in the population with sixteen years of education, then (2.6) implies that these must be the same. In fact, the average ability level must be the same for *all* education levels. If, for example, we think that average ability increases with years of education, then (2.6) is false. (This would happen if, on average, people with more ability choose to become more educated.) As we cannot observe innate ability, we have no way of knowing whether or not average ability is the same for all education levels. But this is an issue that we must address before relying on simple regression analysis.

EXPLORING FURTHER 2.1

Suppose that a score on a final exam, *score*, depends on classes attended (*attend*) and unobserved factors that affect exam performance (such as student ability). Then

$$score = \beta_0 + \beta_1 attend + u. \quad [2.7]$$

When would you expect this model to satisfy (2.6)?

In the fertilizer example, if fertilizer amounts are chosen independently of other features of the plots, then (2.6) will hold: the average land quality will not depend on the amount of fertilizer. However, if more fertilizer is put on the higher-quality plots of land, then the expected value of u changes with the level of fertilizer, and (2.6) fails.

The zero conditional mean assumption gives β_1 another interpretation that is often useful. Taking the expected value of (2.1) conditional on x and using $E(u|x) = 0$ gives

$$E(y|x) = \beta_0 + \beta_1 x. \quad [2.8]$$

Equation (2.8) shows that the **population regression function (PRF)**, $E(y|x)$, is a linear function of x. The linearity means that a one-unit increase in x changes the *expected value* of y by the amount β_1. For any given value of x, the distribution of y is centered about $E(y|x)$, as illustrated in Figure 2.1.

It is important to understand that equation (2.8) tells us how the *average* value of y changes with x; it does not say that y equals $\beta_0 + \beta_1 x$ for all units in the population.

FIGURE 2.1 E(y|x) as a linear function of x.

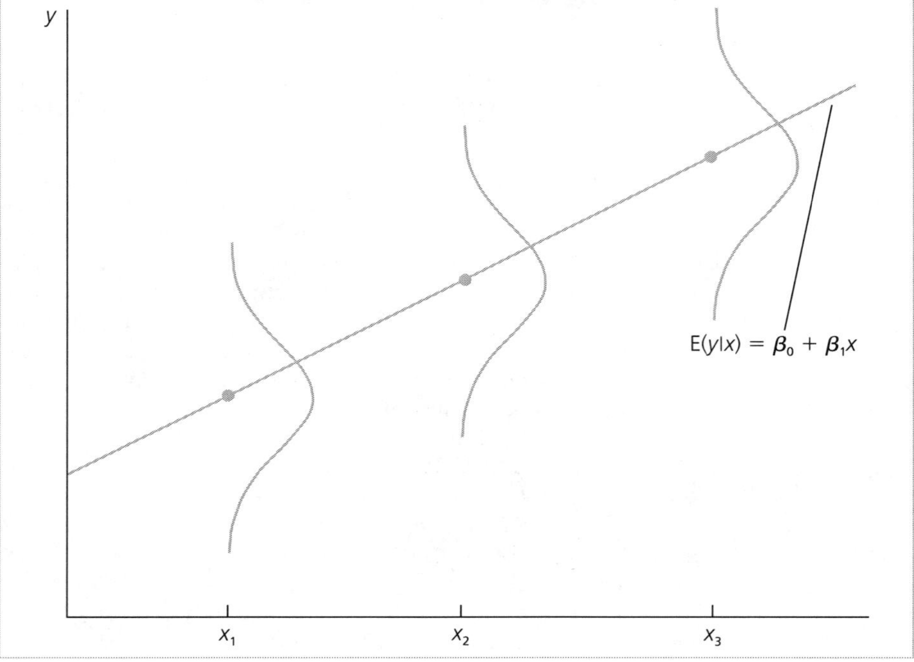

For example, suppose that x is the high school grade point average and y is the college GPA, and we happen to know that $E(colGPA|hsGPA) = 1.5 + 0.5\ hsGPA$. [Of course, in practice, we never know the population intercept and slope, but it is useful to pretend momentarily that we do to understand the nature of equation (2.8).] This GPA equation tells us the *average* college GPA among all students who have a given high school GPA. So suppose that $hsGPA = 3.6$. Then the average *colGPA* for all high school graduates who attend college with $hsGPA = 3.6$ is $1.5 + 0.5(3.6) = 3.3$. We are certainly *not* saying that every student with $hsGPA = 3.6$ will have a 3.3 college GPA; this is clearly false. The PRF gives us a relationship between the average level of y at different levels of x. Some students with $hsGPA = 3.6$ will have a college GPA higher than 3.3, and some will have a lower college GPA. Whether the actual *colGPA* is above or below 3.3 depends on the unobserved factors in u, and those differ among students even within the slice of the population with $hsGPA = 3.6$.

Given the zero conditional mean assumption $E(u|x) = 0$, it is useful to view equation (2.1) as breaking y into two components. The piece $\beta_0 + \beta_1 x$, which represents $E(y|x)$, is called the *systematic part* of y—that is, the part of y explained by x—and u is called the *unsystematic part*, or the part of y not explained by x. In Chapter 3, when we introduce more than one explanatory variable, we will discuss how to determine how large the systematic part is relative to the unsystematic part.

In the next section, we will use assumptions (2.5) and (2.6) to motivate estimators of β_0 and β_1 given a random sample of data. The zero conditional mean assumption also plays a crucial role in the statistical analysis in Section 2.6.

2.2 Deriving the Ordinary Least Squares Estimates

Now that we have discussed the basic ingredients of the simple regression model, we will address the important issue of how to estimate the parameters β_0 and β_1 in equation (2.1). To do this, we need a sample from the population. Let $\{(x_i,y_i): i = 1, ..., n\}$ denote a random sample of size n from the population. Because these data come from (2.1), we can write

$$y_i = \beta_0 + \beta_1 x_i + u_i \quad [2.9]$$

for each i. Here, u_i is the error term for observation i because it contains all factors affecting y_i other than x_i.

As an example, x_i might be the annual income and y_i the annual savings for family i during a particular year. If we have collected data on fifteen families, then $n = 15$. A scatterplot of such a data set is given in Figure 2.2, along with the (necessarily fictitious) population regression function.

We must decide how to use these data to obtain estimates of the intercept and slope in the population regression of savings on income.

There are several ways to motivate the following estimation procedure. We will use (2.5) and an important implication of assumption (2.6): in the population, u is uncorrelated with x. Therefore, we see that u has zero expected value and that the *covariance* between x and u is zero:

$$E(u) = 0 \quad [2.10]$$

FIGURE 2.2 Scatterplot of savings and income for 15 families, and the population regression E(*savings*|*income*) = $\beta_0 + \beta_1$ *income*.

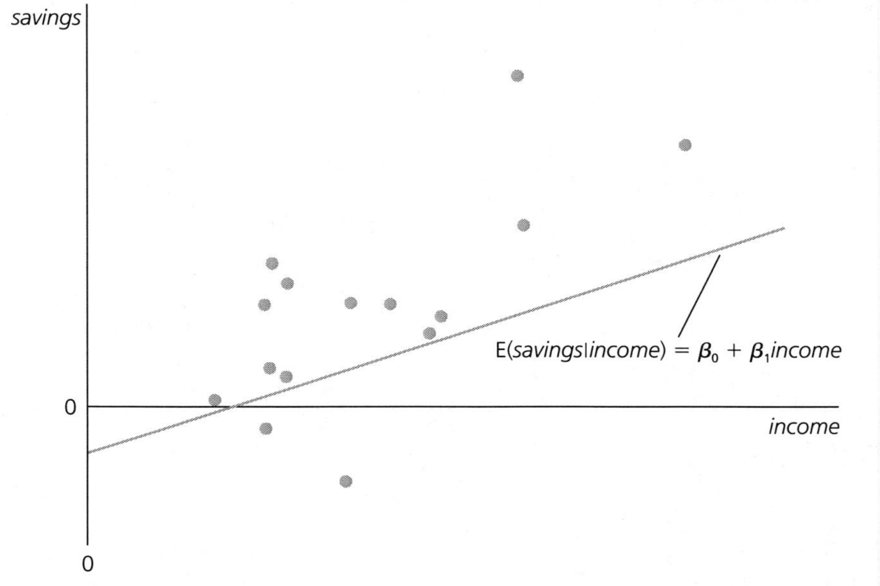

and

$$\mathrm{Cov}(x,u) = \mathrm{E}(xu) = 0, \tag{2.11}$$

where the first equality in (2.11) follows from (2.10). (See Section B.4 for the definition and properties of covariance.) In terms of the observable variables x and y and the unknown parameters β_0 and β_1, equations (2.10) and (2.11) can be written as

$$\mathrm{E}(y - \beta_0 - \beta_1 x) = 0 \tag{2.12}$$

and

$$\mathrm{E}[x(y - \beta_0 - \beta_1 x)] = 0, \tag{2.13}$$

respectively. Equations (2.12) and (2.13) imply two restrictions on the joint probability distribution of (x,y) in the population. Since there are two unknown parameters to estimate, we might hope that equations (2.12) and (2.13) can be used to obtain good estimators of β_0 and β_1. In fact, they can be. Given a sample of data, we choose estimates $\hat{\beta}_0$ and $\hat{\beta}_1$ to solve the *sample* counterparts of (2.12) and (2.13):

$$n^{-1}\sum_{i=1}^{n}(y_i - \hat{\beta}_0 - \hat{\beta}_1 x_i) = 0 \tag{2.14}$$

and

$$n^{-1}\sum_{i=1}^{n}x_i(y_i - \hat{\beta}_0 - \hat{\beta}_1 x_i) = 0. \tag{2.15}$$

This is an example of the *method of moments* approach to estimation. (See Section C.4 for a discussion of different estimation approaches.) These equations can be solved for $\hat{\beta}_0$ and $\hat{\beta}_1$.

Using the basic properties of the summation operator from Appendix A, equation (2.14) can be rewritten as

$$\bar{y} = \hat{\beta}_0 + \hat{\beta}_1\bar{x}, \tag{2.16}$$

where $\bar{y} = n^{-1}\sum_{i=1}^{n} y_i$ is the sample average of the y_i and likewise for $\bar{x}$. This equation allows us to write $\hat{\beta}_0$ in terms of $\hat{\beta}_1$, $\bar{y}$, and $\bar{x}$:

$$\hat{\beta}_0 = \bar{y} - \hat{\beta}_1\bar{x}. \tag{2.17}$$

Therefore, once we have the slope estimate $\hat{\beta}_1$, it is straightforward to obtain the intercept estimate $\hat{\beta}_0$, given $\bar{y}$ and $\bar{x}$.

Dropping the n^{-1} in (2.15) (since it does not affect the solution) and plugging (2.17) into (2.15) yields

$$\sum_{i=1}^{n}x_i[y_i - (\bar{y} - \hat{\beta}_1\bar{x}) - \hat{\beta}_1 x_i] = 0,$$

which, upon rearrangement, gives

$$\sum_{i=1}^{n}x_i(y_i - \bar{y}) = \hat{\beta}_1\sum_{i=1}^{n}x_i(x_i - \bar{x}).$$

From basic properties of the summation operator [see (A.7) and (A.8)],

$$\sum_{i=1}^{n}x_i(x_i - \bar{x}) = \sum_{i=1}^{n}(x_i - \bar{x})^2 \quad \text{and} \quad \sum_{i=1}^{n}x_i(y_i - \bar{y}) = \sum_{i=1}^{n}(x_i - \bar{x})(y_i - \bar{y}).$$

Therefore, provided that

$$\sum_{i=1}^{n}(x_i - \bar{x})^2 > 0, \quad [2.18]$$

the estimated slope is

$$\hat{\beta}_1 = \frac{\sum_{i=1}^{n}(x_i - \bar{x})(y_i - \bar{y})}{\sum_{i=1}^{n}(x_i - \bar{x})^2}. \quad [2.19]$$

Equation (2.19) is simply the sample covariance between x and y divided by the sample variance of x. (See Appendix C. Dividing both the numerator and the denominator by $n - 1$ changes nothing.) This makes sense because β_1 equals the population covariance divided by the variance of x when $E(u) = 0$ and $Cov(x,u) = 0$. An immediate implication is that if x and y are positively correlated in the sample, then $\hat{\beta}_1$ is positive; if x and y are negatively correlated, then $\hat{\beta}_1$ is negative.

Although the method for obtaining (2.17) and (2.19) is motivated by (2.6), the only assumption needed to compute the estimates for a particular sample is (2.18). This is hardly an assumption at all: (2.18) is true provided the x_i in the sample are not all equal to the same value. If (2.18) fails, then we have either been unlucky in obtaining our sample from the population or we have not specified an interesting problem (x does not vary in the population). For example, if $y = wage$ and $x = educ$, then (2.18) fails only if everyone in the sample has the same amount of education (for example, if everyone is a high school graduate; see Figure 2.3). If just one person has a different amount of education, then (2.18) holds, and the estimates can be computed.

FIGURE 2.3 A scatterplot of wage against education when $educ_i = 12$ for all i.

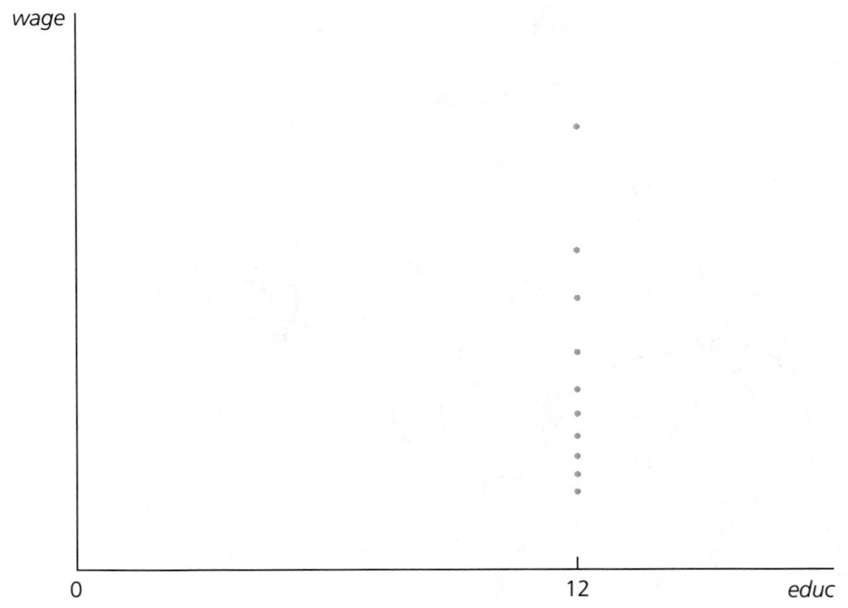

The estimates given in (2.17) and (2.19) are called the **ordinary least squares (OLS)** estimates of β_0 and β_1. To justify this name, for any $\hat{\beta}_0$ and $\hat{\beta}_1$ define a **fitted value** for y when $x = x_i$ as

$$\hat{y}_i = \hat{\beta}_0 + \hat{\beta}_1 x_i. \qquad [2.20]$$

This is the value we predict for y when $x = x_i$ for the given intercept and slope. There is a fitted value for each observation in the sample. The **residual** for observation i is the difference between the actual y_i and its fitted value:

$$\hat{u}_i = y_i - \hat{y}_i = y_i - \hat{\beta}_0 - \hat{\beta}_1 x_i. \qquad [2.21]$$

Again, there are n such residuals. [These are *not* the same as the errors in (2.9), a point we return to in Section 2.5.] The fitted values and residuals are indicated in Figure 2.4.

Now, suppose we choose $\hat{\beta}_0$ and $\hat{\beta}_1$ to make the **sum of squared residuals,**

$$\sum_{i=1}^{n} \hat{u}_i^2 = \sum_{i=1}^{n} (y_i - \hat{\beta}_0 - \hat{\beta}_1 x_i)^2, \qquad [2.22]$$

as small as possible. The appendix to this chapter shows that the conditions necessary for $(\hat{\beta}_0, \hat{\beta}_1)$ to minimize (2.22) are given exactly by equations (2.14) and (2.15), without n^{-1}. Equations (2.14) and (2.15) are often called the **first order conditions** for the OLS estimates, a term that comes from optimization using calculus (see Appendix A). From our previous calculations, we know that the solutions to the OLS first order conditions are given by (2.17) and (2.19). The name "ordinary least squares" comes from the fact that these estimates minimize the sum of squared residuals.

FIGURE 2.4 Fitted values and residuals.

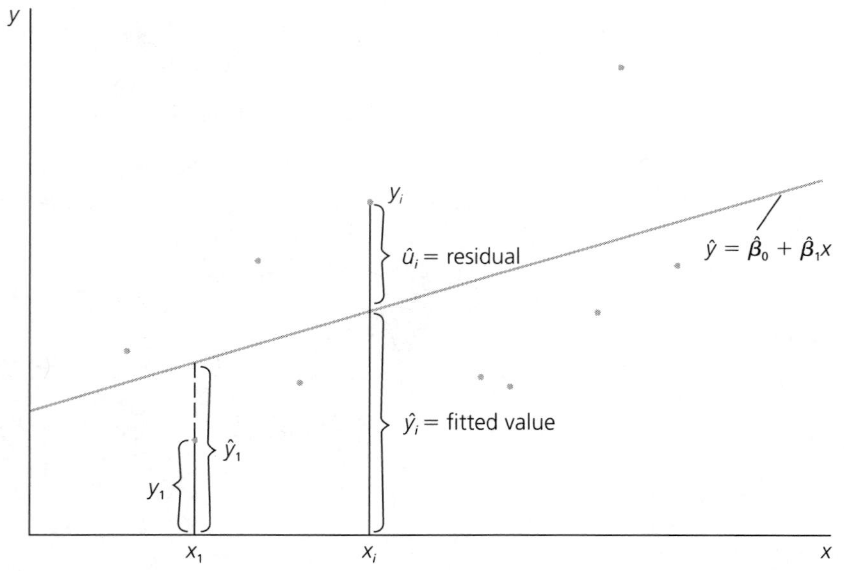

When we view ordinary least squares as minimizing the sum of squared residuals, it is natural to ask: Why not minimize some other function of the residuals, such as the absolute values of the residuals? In fact, as we will discuss in the more advanced Section 9.4, minimizing the sum of the absolute values of the residuals is sometimes very useful. But it does have some drawbacks. First, we cannot obtain formulas for the resulting estimators; given a data set, the estimates must be obtained by numerical optimization routines. As a consequence, the statistical theory for estimators that minimize the sum of the absolute residuals is very complicated. Minimizing other functions of the residuals, say, the sum of the residuals each raised to the fourth power, has similar drawbacks. (We would never choose our estimates to minimize, say, the sum of the residuals themselves, as residuals large in magnitude but with opposite signs would tend to cancel out.) With OLS, we will be able to derive unbiasedness, consistency, and other important statistical properties relatively easily. Plus, as the motivation in equations (2.13) and (2.14) suggests, and as we will see in Section 2.5, OLS is suited for estimating the parameters appearing in the conditional mean function (2.8).

Once we have determined the OLS intercept and slope estimates, we form the **OLS regression line**:

$$\hat{y} = \hat{\beta}_0 + \hat{\beta}_1 x, \qquad [2.23]$$

where it is understood that $\hat{\beta}_0$ and $\hat{\beta}_1$ have been obtained using equations (2.17) and (2.19). The notation $\hat{y}$, read as "y hat," emphasizes that the predicted values from equation (2.23) are estimates. The intercept, $\hat{\beta}_0$, is the predicted value of y when $x = 0$, although in some cases it will not make sense to set $x = 0$. In those situations, $\hat{\beta}_0$ is not, in itself, very interesting. When using (2.23) to compute predicted values of y for various values of x, we must account for the intercept in the calculations. Equation (2.23) is also called the **sample regression function (SRF)** because it is the estimated version of the population regression function $E(y|x) = \beta_0 + \beta_1 x$. It is important to remember that the PRF is something fixed, but unknown, in the population. Because the SRF is obtained for a given sample of data, a new sample will generate a different slope and intercept in equation (2.23).

In most cases, the slope estimate, which we can write as

$$\hat{\beta}_1 = \Delta\hat{y}/\Delta x, \qquad [2.24]$$

is of primary interest. It tells us the amount by which $\hat{y}$ changes when x increases by one unit. Equivalently,

$$\Delta\hat{y} = \hat{\beta}_1 \Delta x, \qquad [2.25]$$

so that given any change in x (whether positive or negative), we can compute the predicted change in y.

We now present several examples of simple regression obtained by using real data. In other words, we find the intercept and slope estimates with equations (2.17) and (2.19). Since these examples involve many observations, the calculations were done using an econometrics software package. At this point, you should be careful not to read too much into these regressions; they are not necessarily uncovering a causal relationship. We have said nothing so far about the statistical properties of OLS. In Section 2.5, we consider statistical properties after we explicitly impose assumptions on the population model equation (2.1).

EXAMPLE 2.3 CEO SALARY AND RETURN ON EQUITY

For the population of chief executive officers, let y be annual salary (*salary*) in thousands of dollars. Thus, $y = 856.3$ indicates an annual salary of \$856,300, and $y = 1{,}452.6$ indicates a salary of \$1,452,600. Let x be the average return on equity (*roe*) for the CEO's firm for the previous three years. (Return on equity is defined in terms of net income as a percentage of common equity.) For example, if $roe = 10$, then average return on equity is 10%.

To study the relationship between this measure of firm performance and CEO compensation, we postulate the simple model

$$salary = \beta_0 + \beta_1 roe + u.$$

The slope parameter β_1 measures the change in annual salary, in thousands of dollars, when return on equity increases by one percentage point. Because a higher *roe* is good for the company, we think $\beta_1 > 0$.

The data set CEOSAL1.RAW contains information on 209 CEOs for the year 1990; these data were obtained from *Business Week* (5/6/91). In this sample, the average annual salary is \$1,281,120, with the smallest and largest being \$223,000 and \$14,822,000, respectively. The average return on equity for the years 1988, 1989, and 1990 is 17.18%, with the smallest and largest values being 0.5 and 56.3%, respectively.

Using the data in CEOSAL1.RAW, the OLS regression line relating *salary* to *roe* is

$$\widehat{salary} = 963.191 + 18.501\, roe \qquad [2.26]$$

$$n = 209,$$

where the intercept and slope estimates have been rounded to three decimal places; we use "*salary* hat" to indicate that this is an estimated equation. How do we interpret the equation? First, if the return on equity is zero, $roe = 0$, then the predicted *salary* is the intercept, 963.191, which equals \$963,191 since *salary* is measured in thousands. Next, we can write the predicted change in salary as a function of the change in *roe*: $\Delta\widehat{salary} = 18.501\,(\Delta roe)$. This means that if the return on equity increases by one percentage point, $\Delta roe = 1$, then *salary* is predicted to change by about 18.5, or \$18,500. Because (2.26) is a linear equation, this is the estimated change regardless of the initial salary.

We can easily use (2.26) to compare predicted salaries at different values of *roe*. Suppose $roe = 30$. Then $\widehat{salary} = 963.191 + 18.501(30) = 1{,}518{,}221$, which is just over \$1.5 million. However, this does *not* mean that a particular CEO whose firm had a $roe = 30$ earns \$1,518,221. Many other factors affect salary. This is just our prediction from the OLS regression line (2.26). The estimated line is graphed in Figure 2.5, along with the population regression function $E(salary|roe)$. We will never know the PRF, so we cannot tell how close the SRF is to the PRF. Another sample of data will give a different regression line, which may or may not be closer to the population regression line.

FIGURE 2.5 The OLS regression line $\widehat{salary} = 963.191 + 18.501\ roe$ and the (unknown) population regression function.

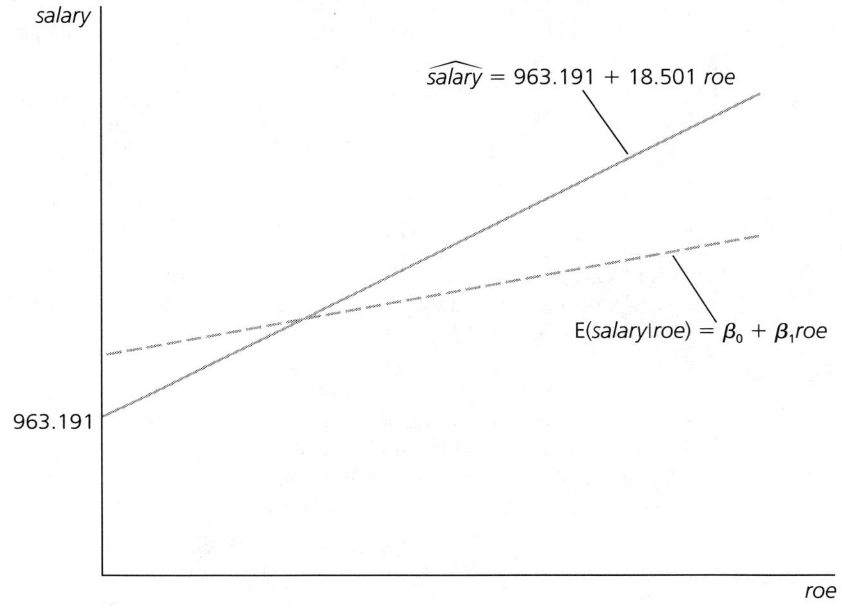

EXAMPLE 2.4 WAGE AND EDUCATION

For the population of people in the workforce in 1976, let $y = wage$, where *wage* is measured in dollars per hour. Thus, for a particular person, if $wage = 6.75$, the hourly *wage* is \$6.75. Let $x = educ$ denote years of schooling; for example, $educ = 12$ corresponds to a complete high school education. Since the average wage in the sample is \$5.90, the Consumer Price Index indicates that this amount is equivalent to \$19.06 in 2003 dollars.

Using the data in WAGE1.RAW where $n = 526$ individuals, we obtain the following OLS regression line (or sample regression function):

$$\widehat{wage} = -0.90 + 0.54\ educ \qquad [2.27]$$

$$n = 526.$$

> **EXPLORING FURTHER 2.2**
>
> The estimated wage from (2.27), when $educ = 8$, is \$3.42 in 1976 dollars. What is this value in 2003 dollars? (*Hint*: You have enough information in Example 2.4 to answer this question.)

We must interpret this equation with caution. The intercept of −0.90 literally means that a person with no education has a predicted hourly wage of −90¢ an hour. This, of course, is silly. It turns out that only 18 people in the sample of 526 have less than eight years of education. Consequently, it is not surprising that the regression line does poorly at very low levels of education. For a person with eight years of education, the predicted wage is $\widehat{wage} = -0.90 + 0.54(8) = 3.42$, or \$3.42 per hour (in 1976 dollars).

The slope estimate in (2.27) implies that one more year of education increases hourly wage by 54¢ an hour. Therefore, four more years of education increase the predicted wage by $4(0.54) = 2.16$, or \$2.16 per hour. These are fairly large effects. Because of the linear nature of (2.27), another year of education increases the wage by the same amount, regardless of the initial level of education. In Section 2.4, we discuss some methods that allow for nonconstant marginal effects of our explanatory variables.

EXAMPLE 2.5 VOTING OUTCOMES AND CAMPAIGN EXPENDITURES

The file VOTE1.RAW contains data on election outcomes and campaign expenditures for 173 two-party races for the U.S. House of Representatives in 1988. There are two candidates in each race, A and B. Let *voteA* be the percentage of the vote received by Candidate A and *shareA* be the percentage of total campaign expenditures accounted for by Candidate A. Many factors other than *shareA* affect the election outcome (including the quality of the candidates and possibly the dollar amounts spent by A and B). Nevertheless, we can estimate a simple regression model to find out whether spending more relative to one's challenger implies a higher percentage of the vote.

The estimated equation using the 173 observations is

$$\widehat{voteA} = 26.81 + 0.464\ shareA \qquad [2.28]$$

$$n = 173.$$

This means that if Candidate A's share of spending increases by one percentage point, Candidate A receives almost one-half a percentage point (0.464) more of the total vote. Whether or not this is a causal effect is unclear, but it is not unbelievable. If $shareA = 50$, *voteA* is predicted to be about 50, or half the vote.

EXPLORING FURTHER 2.3

In Example 2.5, what is the predicted vote for Candidate A if $shareA = 60$ (which means 60%)? Does this answer seem reasonable?

In some cases, regression analysis is not used to determine causality but to simply look at whether two variables are positively or negatively related, much like a standard correlation analysis. An example of this occurs in Computer Exercise C3, where you are asked to use data from Biddle and Hamermesh (1990) on time spent sleeping and working to investigate the tradeoff between these two factors.

A Note on Terminology

In most cases, we will indicate the estimation of a relationship through OLS by writing an equation such as (2.26), (2.27), or (2.28). Sometimes, for the sake of brevity, it is useful to indicate that an OLS regression has been run without actually writing out the equation. We will often indicate that equation (2.23) has been obtained by OLS in saying that we *run the regression of*

$$y \text{ on } x, \qquad [2.29]$$

or simply that we *regress* y on x. The positions of y and x in (2.29) indicate which is the dependent variable and which is the independent variable: we always regress the dependent variable on the independent variable. For specific applications, we replace y and x with their names. Thus, to obtain (2.26), we regress *salary* on *roe*, or to obtain (2.28), we regress *voteA* on *shareA*.

When we use such terminology in (2.29), we will always mean that we plan to estimate the intercept, $\hat{\beta}_0$, along with the slope, $\hat{\beta}_1$. This case is appropriate for the vast majority of applications. Occasionally, we may want to estimate the relationship between y and x *assuming* that the intercept is zero (so that $x = 0$ implies that $\hat{y} = 0$); we cover this case briefly in Section 2.6. Unless explicitly stated otherwise, we always estimate an intercept along with a slope.

2.3 Properties of OLS on Any Sample of Data

In the previous section, we went through the algebra of deriving the formulas for the OLS intercept and slope estimates. In this section, we cover some further algebraic properties of the fitted OLS regression line. The best way to think about these properties is to remember that they hold, by construction, for *any* sample of data. The harder task—considering the properties of OLS across all possible random samples of data—is postponed until Section 2.5.

Several of the algebraic properties we are going to derive will appear mundane. Nevertheless, having a grasp of these properties helps us to figure out what happens to the OLS estimates and related statistics when the data are manipulated in certain ways, such as when the measurement units of the dependent and independent variables change.

Fitted Values and Residuals

We assume that the intercept and slope estimates, $\hat{\beta}_0$ and $\hat{\beta}_1$, have been obtained for the given sample of data. Given $\hat{\beta}_0$ and $\hat{\beta}_1$, we can obtain the fitted value $\hat{y}_i$ for each observation. [This is given by equation (2.20).] By definition, each fitted value of $\hat{y}_i$ is on the OLS regression line. The OLS residual associated with observation i, $\hat{u}_i$, is the difference between y_i and its fitted value, as given in equation (2.21). If $\hat{u}_i$ is positive, the line underpredicts y_i; if $\hat{u}_i$ is negative, the line overpredicts y_i. The ideal case for observation i is when $\hat{u}_i = 0$, but in most cases, *every* residual is not equal to zero. In other words, none of the data points must actually lie on the OLS line.

EXAMPLE 2.6 CEO SALARY AND RETURN ON EQUITY

Table 2.2 contains a listing of the first 15 observations in the CEO data set, along with the fitted values, called *salaryhat*, and the residuals, called *uhat*.

The first four CEOs have lower salaries than what we predicted from the OLS regression line (2.26); in other words, given only the firm's *roe*, these CEOs make less than what we predicted. As can be seen from the positive *uhat*, the fifth CEO makes more than predicted from the OLS regression line.

TABLE 2.2 Fitted Values and Residuals for the First 15 CEOs

obsno	roe	salary	salaryhat	uhat
1	14.1	1095	1224.058	−129.0581
2	10.9	1001	1164.854	−163.8542
3	23.5	1122	1397.969	−275.9692
4	5.9	578	1072.348	−494.3484
5	13.8	1368	1218.508	149.4923
6	20.0	1145	1333.215	−188.2151
7	16.4	1078	1266.611	−188.6108
8	16.3	1094	1264.761	−170.7606
9	10.5	1237	1157.454	79.54626
10	26.3	833	1449.773	−616.7726
11	25.9	567	1442.372	−875.3721
12	26.8	933	1459.023	−526.0231
13	14.8	1339	1237.009	101.9911
14	22.3	937	1375.768	−438.7678
15	56.3	2011	2004.808	6.191895

Algebraic Properties of OLS Statistics

There are several useful algebraic properties of OLS estimates and their associated statistics. We now cover the three most important of these.

(1) The sum, and therefore the sample average of the OLS residuals, is zero. Mathematically,

$$\sum_{i=1}^{n} \hat{u}_i = 0. \qquad [2.30]$$

This property needs no proof; it follows immediately from the OLS first order condition (2.14), when we remember that the residuals are defined by $\hat{u}_i = y_i - \hat{\beta}_0 - \hat{\beta}_1 x_i$. In other words, the OLS estimates $\hat{\beta}_0$ and $\hat{\beta}_1$ are *chosen* to make the residuals add up to zero (for any data set). This says nothing about the residual for any particular observation i.

(2) The sample covariance between the regressors and the OLS residuals is zero. This follows from the first order condition (2.15), which can be written in terms of the residuals as

$$\sum_{i=1}^{n} x_i \hat{u}_i = 0. \qquad [2.31]$$

The sample average of the OLS residuals is zero, so the left-hand side of (2.31) is proportional to the sample covariance between x_i and $\hat{u}_i$.

(3) The point $(\bar{x},\bar{y})$ is always on the OLS regression line. In other words, if we take equation (2.23) and plug in $\bar{x}$ for x, then the predicted value is $\bar{y}$. This is exactly what equation (2.16) showed us.

EXAMPLE 2.7 WAGE AND EDUCATION

For the data in WAGE1.RAW, the average hourly wage in the sample is 5.90, rounded to two decimal places, and the average education is 12.56. If we plug $educ = 12.56$ into the OLS regression line (2.27), we get $\widehat{wage} = -0.90 + 0.54(12.56) = 5.8824$, which equals 5.9 when rounded to the first decimal place. These figures do not exactly agree because we have rounded the average wage and education, as well as the intercept and slope estimates. If we did not initially round any of the values, we would get the answers to agree more closely, but to little useful effect.

Writing each y_i as its fitted value, plus its residual, provides another way to interpret an OLS regression. For each i, write

$$y_i = \hat{y}_i + \hat{u}_i. \quad [2.32]$$

From property (1), the average of the residuals is zero; equivalently, the sample average of the fitted values, $\hat{y}_i$, is the same as the sample average of the y_i, or $\bar{\hat{y}} = \bar{y}$. Further, properties (1) and (2) can be used to show that the sample covariance between $\hat{y}_i$ and $\hat{u}_i$ is zero. Thus, we can view OLS as decomposing each y_i into two parts, a fitted value and a residual. The fitted values and residuals are uncorrelated in the sample.

Define the **total sum of squares (SST)**, the **explained sum of squares (SSE)**, and the **residual sum of squares (SSR)** (also known as the sum of squared residuals), as follows:

$$\text{SST} \equiv \sum_{i=1}^{n} (y_i - \bar{y})^2. \quad [2.33]$$

$$\text{SSE} \equiv \sum_{i=1}^{n} (\hat{y}_i - \bar{y})^2. \quad [2.34]$$

$$\text{SSR} \equiv \sum_{i=1}^{n} \hat{u}_i^2. \quad [2.35]$$

SST is a measure of the total sample variation in the y_i; that is, it measures how spread out the y_i are in the sample. If we divide SST by $n - 1$, we obtain the sample variance of y, as discussed in Appendix C. Similarly, SSE measures the sample variation in the $\hat{y}_i$ (where we use the fact that $\bar{\hat{y}} = \bar{y}$), and SSR measures the sample variation in the $\hat{u}_i$. The total variation in y can always be expressed as the sum of the explained variation and the unexplained variation SSR. Thus,

$$\text{SST} = \text{SSE} + \text{SSR}. \quad [2.36]$$

Proving (2.36) is not difficult, but it requires us to use all of the properties of the summation operator covered in Appendix A. Write

$$\begin{aligned}
\sum_{i=1}^{n} (y_i - \bar{y})^2 &= \sum_{i=1}^{n} [(y_i - \hat{y}_i) + (\hat{y}_i - \bar{y})]^2 \\
&= \sum_{i=1}^{n} [\hat{u}_i + (\hat{y}_i - \bar{y})]^2 \\
&= \sum_{i=1}^{n} \hat{u}_i^2 + 2\sum_{i=1}^{n} \hat{u}_i(\hat{y}_i - \bar{y}) + \sum_{i=1}^{n} (\hat{y}_i - \bar{y})^2 \\
&= \text{SSR} + 2\sum_{i=1}^{n} \hat{u}_i(\hat{y}_i - \bar{y}) + \text{SSE}.
\end{aligned}$$

Now, (2.36) holds if we show that

$$\sum_{i=1}^{n} \hat{u}_i(\hat{y}_i - \bar{y}) = 0. \qquad [2.37]$$

But we have already claimed that the sample covariance between the residuals and the fitted values is zero, and this covariance is just (2.37) divided by $n-1$. Thus, we have established (2.36).

Some words of caution about SST, SSE, and SSR are in order. There is no uniform agreement on the names or abbreviations for the three quantities defined in equations (2.33), (2.34), and (2.35). The total sum of squares is called either SST or TSS, so there is little confusion here. Unfortunately, the explained sum of squares is sometimes called the "regression sum of squares." If this term is given its natural abbreviation, it can easily be confused with the term "residual sum of squares." Some regression packages refer to the explained sum of squares as the "model sum of squares."

To make matters even worse, the residual sum of squares is often called the "error sum of squares." This is especially unfortunate because, as we will see in Section 2.5, the errors and the residuals are different quantities. Thus, we will always call (2.35) the residual sum of squares or the sum of squared residuals. We prefer to use the abbreviation SSR to denote the sum of squared residuals, because it is more common in econometric packages.

Goodness-of-Fit

So far, we have no way of measuring how well the explanatory or independent variable, x, explains the dependent variable, y. It is often useful to compute a number that summarizes how well the OLS regression line fits the data. In the following discussion, be sure to remember that we assume that an intercept is estimated along with the slope.

Assuming that the total sum of squares, SST, is not equal to zero—which is true except in the very unlikely event that all the y_i equal the same value—we can divide (2.36) by SST to get $1 = \text{SSE/SST} + \text{SSR/SST}$. The ***R*-squared** of the regression, sometimes called the **coefficient of determination**, is defined as

$$R^2 \equiv \text{SSE/SST} = 1 - \text{SSR/SST}. \qquad [2.38]$$

R^2 is the ratio of the explained variation compared to the total variation; thus, it is interpreted as the *fraction of the sample variation in y that is explained by x*. The second equality in (2.38) provides another way for computing R^2.

From (2.36), the value of R^2 is always between zero and one, because SSE can be no greater than SST. When interpreting R^2, we usually multiply it by 100 to change it into a percent: $100 \cdot R^2$ is the *percentage of the sample variation in y that is explained by x*.

If the data points all lie on the same line, OLS provides a perfect fit to the data. In this case, $R^2 = 1$. A value of R^2 that is nearly equal to zero indicates a poor fit of the OLS line: very little of the variation in the y_i is captured by the variation in the $\hat{y}_i$ (which all lie on the OLS regression line). In fact, it can be shown that R^2 is equal to the *square* of the sample correlation coefficient between y_i and $\hat{y}_i$. This is where the term "*R*-squared" came from. (The letter R was traditionally used to denote an estimate of a population correlation coefficient, and its usage has survived in regression analysis.)

EXAMPLE 2.8 CEO SALARY AND RETURN ON EQUITY

In the CEO salary regression, we obtain the following:

$$\widehat{salary} = 963.191 + 18.501\ roe \qquad [2.39]$$

$$n = 209,\ R^2 = 0.0132.$$

We have reproduced the OLS regression line and the number of observations for clarity. Using the R-squared (rounded to four decimal places) reported for this equation, we can see how much of the variation in salary is actually explained by the return on equity. The answer is: not much. The firm's return on equity explains only about 1.3% of the variation in salaries for this sample of 209 CEOs. That means that 98.7% of the salary variations for these CEOs is left unexplained! This lack of explanatory power may not be too surprising because many other characteristics of both the firm and the individual CEO should influence salary; these factors are necessarily included in the errors in a simple regression analysis.

In the social sciences, low R-squareds in regression equations are not uncommon, especially for cross-sectional analysis. We will discuss this issue more generally under multiple regression analysis, but it is worth emphasizing now that a seemingly low R-squared does not necessarily mean that an OLS regression equation is useless. It is still possible that (2.39) is a good estimate of the ceteris paribus relationship between *salary* and *roe*; whether or not this is true does *not* depend directly on the size of R-squared. Students who are first learning econometrics tend to put too much weight on the size of the R-squared in evaluating regression equations. For now, be aware that using R-squared as the main gauge of success for an econometric analysis can lead to trouble.

Sometimes, the explanatory variable explains a substantial part of the sample variation in the dependent variable.

EXAMPLE 2.9 VOTING OUTCOMES AND CAMPAIGN EXPENDITURES

In the voting outcome equation in (2.28), $R^2 = 0.856$. Thus, the share of campaign expenditures explains over 85% of the variation in the election outcomes for this sample. This is a sizable portion.

2.4 Units of Measurement and Functional Form

Two important issues in applied economics are (1) understanding how changing the units of measurement of the dependent and/or independent variables affects OLS estimates and (2) knowing how to incorporate popular functional forms used in economics into regression analysis. The mathematics needed for a full understanding of functional form issues is reviewed in Appendix A.

The Effects of Changing Units of Measurement on OLS Statistics

In Example 2.3, we chose to measure annual salary in thousands of dollars, and the return on equity was measured as a percentage (rather than as a decimal). It is crucial to know how *salary* and *roe* are measured in this example in order to make sense of the estimates in equation (2.39).

We must also know that OLS estimates change in entirely expected ways when the units of measurement of the dependent and independent variables change. In Example 2.3, suppose that, rather than measuring salary in thousands of dollars, we measure it in dollars. Let *salardol* be salary in dollars (*salardol* = 845,761 would be interpreted as $845,761). Of course, *salardol* has a simple relationship to the salary measured in thousands of dollars: *salardol* = 1,000·*salary*. We do not need to actually run the regression of *salardol* on *roe* to know that the estimated equation is:

$$\widehat{salardol} = 963{,}191 + 18{,}501\, roe. \quad [2.40]$$

We obtain the intercept and slope in (2.40) simply by multiplying the intercept and the slope in (2.39) by 1,000. This gives equations (2.39) and (2.40) the *same* interpretation. Looking at (2.40), if *roe* = 0, then $\widehat{salardol}$ = 963,191, so the predicted salary is $963,191 [the same value we obtained from equation (2.39)]. Furthermore, if *roe* increases by one, then the predicted salary increases by $18,501; again, this is what we concluded from our earlier analysis of equation (2.39).

Generally, it is easy to figure out what happens to the intercept and slope estimates when the dependent variable changes units of measurement. If the dependent variable is multiplied by the constant *c*—which means each value in the sample is multiplied by *c*—then the OLS intercept and slope estimates are also multiplied by *c*. (This assumes nothing has changed about the independent variable.) In the CEO salary example, *c* = 1,000 in moving from *salary* to *salardol*.

> **EXPLORING FURTHER 2.4**
>
> Suppose that salary is measured in hundreds of dollars, rather than in thousands of dollars, say, *salarhun*. What will be the OLS intercept and slope estimates in the regression of *salarhun* on *roe*?

We can also use the CEO salary example to see what happens when we change the units of measurement of the independent variable. Define *roedec* = *roe*/100 to be the decimal equivalent of *roe*; thus, *roedec* = 0.23 means a return on equity of 23%. To focus on changing the units of measurement of the independent variable, we return to our original dependent variable, *salary*, which is measured in thousands of dollars. When we regress *salary* on *roedec*, we obtain

$$\widehat{salary} = 963.191 + 1{,}850.1\, roedec. \quad [2.41]$$

The coefficient on *roedec* is 100 times the coefficient on *roe* in (2.39). This is as it should be. Changing *roe* by one percentage point is equivalent to $\Delta roedec = 0.01$. From (2.41), if $\Delta roedec = 0.01$, then $\Delta\widehat{salary} = 1{,}850.1(0.01) = 18.501$, which is what is obtained by using (2.39). Note that, in moving from (2.39) to (2.41), the independent variable was divided by 100, and so the OLS slope estimate was multiplied by 100, preserving the interpretation of the equation. Generally, if the independent variable is divided or multiplied by some nonzero constant, c, then the OLS slope coefficient is multiplied or divided by c, respectively.

The intercept has not changed in (2.41) because *roedec* $= 0$ still corresponds to a zero return on equity. In general, changing the units of measurement of only the independent variable does not affect the intercept.

In the previous section, we defined R-squared as a goodness-of-fit measure for OLS regression. We can also ask what happens to R^2 when the unit of measurement of either the independent or the dependent variable changes. Without doing any algebra, we should know the result: the goodness-of-fit of the model should not depend on the units of measurement of our variables. For example, the amount of variation in salary explained by the return on equity should not depend on whether salary is measured in dollars or in thousands of dollars or on whether return on equity is a percentage or a decimal. This intuition can be verified mathematically: using the definition of R^2, it can be shown that R^2 is, in fact, invariant to changes in the units of y or x.

Incorporating Nonlinearities in Simple Regression

So far, we have focused on *linear* relationships between the dependent and independent variables. As we mentioned in Chapter 1, linear relationships are not nearly general enough for all economic applications. Fortunately, it is rather easy to incorporate many nonlinearities into simple regression analysis by appropriately defining the dependent and independent variables. Here, we will cover two possibilities that often appear in applied work.

In reading applied work in the social sciences, you will often encounter regression equations where the dependent variable appears in logarithmic form. Why is this done? Recall the wage-education example, where we regressed hourly wage on years of education. We obtained a slope estimate of 0.54 [see equation (2.27)], which means that each additional year of education is predicted to increase hourly wage by 54 cents. Because of the linear nature of (2.27), 54 cents is the increase for either the first year of education or the twentieth year; this may not be reasonable.

Probably a better characterization of how wage changes with education is that each year of education increases wage by a constant *percentage*. For example, an increase in education from 5 years to 6 years increases wage by, say, 8% (ceteris paribus), and an increase in education from 11 to 12 years also increases wage by 8%. A model that gives (approximately) a constant percentage effect is

$$\log(wage) = \beta_0 + \beta_1 educ + u, \qquad [2.42]$$

where log(·) denotes the *natural* logarithm. (See Appendix A for a review of logarithms.) In particular, if $\Delta u = 0$, then

$$\%\Delta wage \approx (100 \cdot \beta_1)\Delta educ. \qquad [2.43]$$

Notice how we multiply β_1 by 100 to get the percentage change in *wage* given one additional year of education. Since the percentage change in *wage* is the same for each additional year of education, the change in *wage* for an extra year of education *increases*

FIGURE 2.6 $wage = \exp(\beta_0 + \beta_1 educ)$, with $\beta_1 > 0$.

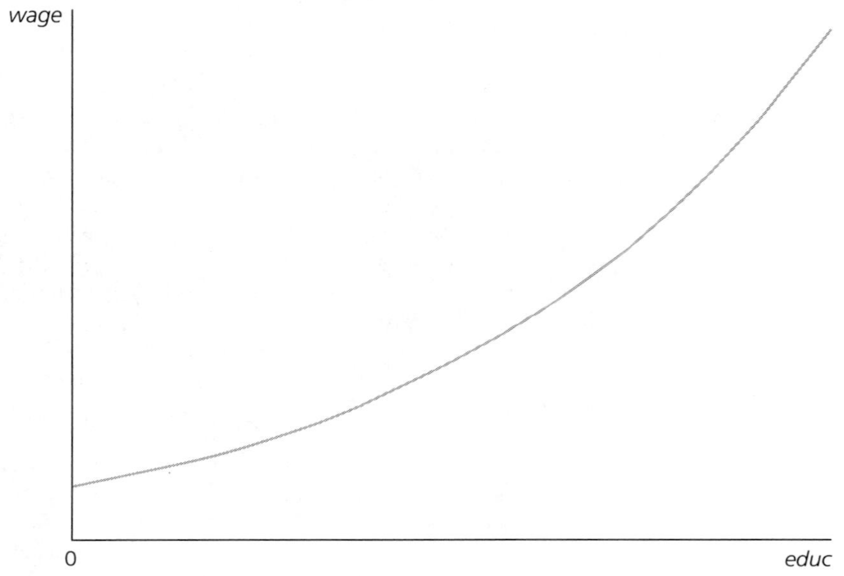

EXAMPLE 2.10 A LOG WAGE EQUATION

Using the same data as in Example 2.4, but using log(*wage*) as the dependent variable, we obtain the following relationship:

$$\widehat{\log(wage)} = 0.584 + 0.083\ educ \qquad [2.44]$$

$$n = 526, R^2 = 0.186.$$

The coefficient on *educ* has a percentage interpretation when it is multiplied by 100: $\widehat{wage}$ increases by 8.3% for every additional year of education. This is what economists mean when they refer to the "return to another year of education."

It is important to remember that the main reason for using the log of *wage* in (2.42) is to impose a constant percentage effect of education on *wage*. Once equation (2.44) is obtained, the natural log of *wage* is rarely mentioned. In particular, it is *not* correct to say that another year of education increases log(*wage*) by 8.3%.

The intercept in (2.44) is not very meaningful, because it gives the predicted log(*wage*), when *educ* = 0. The *R*-squared shows that *educ* explains about 18.6% of the variation in log(*wage*) (*not wage*). Finally, equation (2.44) might not capture all of the nonlinearity in the relationship between wage and schooling. If there are "diploma effects," then the twelfth year of education—graduation from high school—could be worth much more than the eleventh year. We will learn how to allow for this kind of nonlinearity in Chapter 7.

as education increases; in other words, (2.42) implies an *increasing* return to education. By exponentiating (2.42), we can write $wage = \exp(\beta_0 + \beta_1 educ + u)$. This equation is graphed in Figure 2.6, with $u = 0$.

Estimating a model such as (2.42) is straightforward when using simple regression. Just define the dependent variable, y, to be $y = \log(wage)$. The independent variable is represented by $x = educ$. The mechanics of OLS are the same as before: the intercept and slope estimates are given by the formulas (2.17) and (2.19). In other words, we obtain $\hat{\beta}_0$ and $\hat{\beta}_1$ from the OLS regression of log(*wage*) on *educ*.

Another important use of the natural log is in obtaining a **constant elasticity model**.

EXAMPLE 2.11 CEO SALARY AND FIRM SALES

We can estimate a constant elasticity model relating CEO salary to firm sales. The data set is the same one used in Example 2.3, except we now relate *salary* to *sales*. Let *sales* be annual firm sales, measured in millions of dollars. A constant elasticity model is

$$\log(salary) = \beta_0 + \beta_1 \log(sales) + u, \quad [2.45]$$

where β_1 is the elasticity of *salary* with respect to *sales*. This model falls under the simple regression model by defining the dependent variable to be $y = \log(salary)$ and the independent variable to be $x = \log(sales)$. Estimating this equation by OLS gives

$$\widehat{\log(salary)} = 4.822 + 0.257 \log(sales) \quad [2.46]$$

$$n = 209, R^2 = 0.211.$$

The coefficient of log(*sales*) is the estimated elasticity of *salary* with respect to *sales*. It implies that a 1% increase in firm sales increases CEO salary by about 0.257%—the usual interpretation of an elasticity.

The two functional forms covered in this section will often arise in the remainder of this text. We have covered models containing natural logarithms here because they appear so frequently in applied work. The interpretation of such models will not be much different in the multiple regression case.

It is also useful to note what happens to the intercept and slope estimates if we change the units of measurement of the dependent variable when it appears in logarithmic form. Because the change to logarithmic form approximates a proportionate change, it makes sense that *nothing* happens to the slope. We can see this by writing the rescaled variable as $c_1 y_i$ for each observation i. The original equation is $\log(y_i) = \beta_0 + \beta_1 x_i + u_i$. If we add $\log(c_1)$ to both sides, we get $\log(c_1) + \log(y_i) = [\log(c_1) + \beta_0] + \beta_1 x_i + u_i$, or $\log(c_1 y_i) = [\log(c_1) + \beta_0] + \beta_1 x_i + u_i$. (Remember that the sum of the logs is equal to the log of their product, as shown in Appendix A.) Therefore, the slope is still β_1, but the intercept is now $\log(c_1) + \beta_0$. Similarly, if the independent variable is $\log(x)$, and we change the units of measurement of x before taking the log, the slope remains the same, but the intercept changes. You will be asked to verify these claims in Problem 9.

TABLE 2.3 Summary of Functional Forms Involving Logarithms

Model	Dependent Variable	Independent Variable	Interpretation of β_1
Level-level	y	x	$\Delta y = \beta_1 \Delta x$
Level-log	y	$\log(x)$	$\Delta y = (\beta_1/100)\%\Delta x$
Log-level	$\log(y)$	x	$\%\Delta y = (100\beta_1)\Delta x$
Log-log	$\log(y)$	$\log(x)$	$\%\Delta y = \beta_1 \%\Delta x$

We end this subsection by summarizing four combinations of functional forms available from using either the original variable or its natural log. In Table 2.3, x and y stand for the variables in their original form. The model with y as the dependent variable and x as the independent variable is called the *level-level* model because each variable appears in its level form. The model with $\log(y)$ as the dependent variable and x as the independent variable is called the *log-level* model. We will not explicitly discuss the *level-log* model here, because it arises less often in practice. In any case, we will see examples of this model in later chapters.

The last column in Table 2.3 gives the interpretation of β_1. In the log-level model, $100 \cdot \beta_1$ is sometimes called the **semi-elasticity** of y with respect to x. As we mentioned in Example 2.11, in the log-log model, β_1 is the **elasticity** of y with respect to x. Table 2.3 warrants careful study, as we will refer to it often in the remainder of the text.

The Meaning of "Linear" Regression

The simple regression model that we have studied in this chapter is also called the simple *linear* regression model. Yet, as we have just seen, the general model also allows for certain *nonlinear* relationships. So what does "linear" mean here? You can see by looking at equation (2.1) that $y = \beta_0 + \beta_1 x + u$. The key is that this equation is linear in the *parameters* β_0 and β_1. There are no restrictions on how y and x relate to the original explained and explanatory variables of interest. As we saw in Examples 2.10 and 2.11, y and x can be natural logs of variables, and this is quite common in applications. But we need not stop there. For example, nothing prevents us from using simple regression to estimate a model such as $cons = \beta_0 + \beta_1 \sqrt{inc} + u$, where *cons* is annual consumption and *inc* is annual income.

Whereas the mechanics of simple regression do not depend on how y and x are defined, the interpretation of the coefficients does depend on their definitions. For successful empirical work, it is much more important to become proficient at interpreting coefficients than to become efficient at computing formulas such as (2.19). We will get much more practice with interpreting the estimates in OLS regression lines when we study multiple regression.

Plenty of models *cannot* be cast as a linear regression model because they are not linear in their parameters; an example is $cons = 1/(\beta_0 + \beta_1 inc) + u$. Estimation of such models takes us into the realm of the *nonlinear regression model*, which is beyond the scope of this text. For most applications, choosing a model that can be put into the linear regression framework is sufficient.

2.5 Expected Values and Variances of the OLS Estimators

In Section 2.1, we defined the population model $y = \beta_0 + \beta_1 x + u$, and we claimed that the key assumption for simple regression analysis to be useful is that the expected value of u given any value of x is zero. In Sections 2.2, 2.3, and 2.4, we discussed the algebraic properties of OLS estimation. We now return to the population model and study the *statistical* properties of OLS. In other words, we now view $\hat{\beta}_0$ and $\hat{\beta}_1$ as *estimators* for the parameters β_0 and β_1 that appear in the population model. This means that we will study properties of the distributions of $\hat{\beta}_0$ and $\hat{\beta}_1$ over different random samples from the population. (Appendix C contains definitions of estimators and reviews some of their important properties.)

Unbiasedness of OLS

We begin by establishing the unbiasedness of OLS under a simple set of assumptions. For future reference, it is useful to number these assumptions using the prefix "SLR" for simple linear regression. The first assumption defines the population model.

Assumption SLR.1 Linear in Parameters

In the population model, the dependent variable, y, is related to the independent variable, x, and the error (or disturbance), u, as

$$y = \beta_0 + \beta_1 x + u, \qquad [2.47]$$

where β_0 and β_1 are the population intercept and slope parameters, respectively.

To be realistic, y, x, and u are all viewed as random variables in stating the population model. We discussed the interpretation of this model at some length in Section 2.1 and gave several examples. In the previous section, we learned that equation (2.47) is not as restrictive as it initially seems; by choosing y and x appropriately, we can obtain interesting nonlinear relationships (such as constant elasticity models).

We are interested in using data on y and x to estimate the parameters β_0 and, especially, β_1. We assume that our data were obtained as a random sample. (See Appendix C for a review of random sampling.)

Assumption SLR.2 Random Sampling

We have a random sample of size n, $\{(x_i, y_i): i = 1, 2, \ldots, n\}$, following the population model in equation (2.47).

We will have to address failure of the random sampling assumption in later chapters that deal with time series analysis and sample selection problems. Not all cross-sectional samples can be viewed as outcomes of random samples, but many can be.

We can write (2.47) in terms of the random sample as

$$y_i = \beta_0 + \beta_1 x_i + u_i, \quad i = 1, 2, \ldots, n, \qquad [2.48]$$

FIGURE 2.7 Graph of $y_i = \beta_0 + \beta_1 x_i + u_i$.

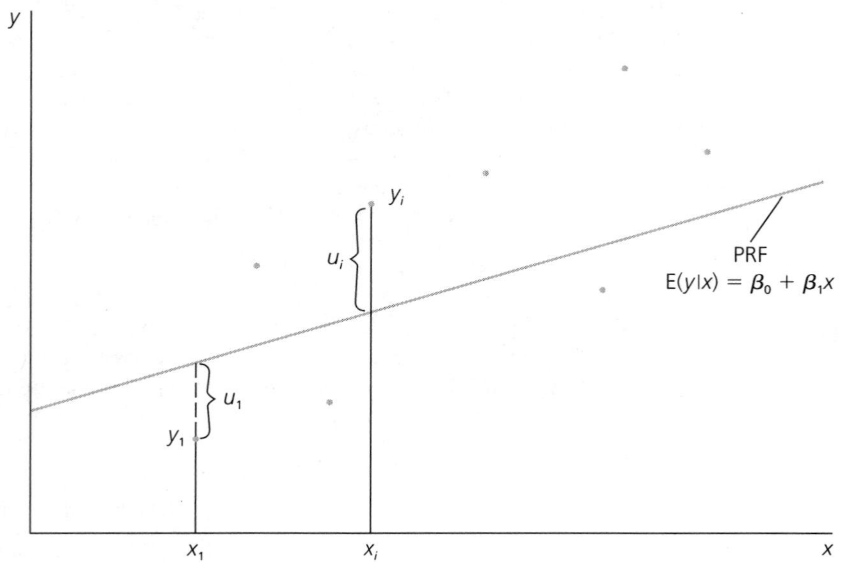

where u_i is the error or disturbance for observation i (for example, person i, firm i, city i, and so on). Thus, u_i contains the unobservables for observation i that affect y_i. The u_i should not be confused with the residuals, $\hat{u}_i$, that we defined in Section 2.3. Later on, we will explore the relationship between the errors and the residuals. For interpreting β_0 and β_1 in a particular application, (2.47) is most informative, but (2.48) is also needed for some of the statistical derivations.

The relationship (2.48) can be plotted for a particular outcome of data as shown in Figure 2.7.

As we already saw in Section 2.2, the OLS slope and intercept estimates are not defined unless we have some sample variation in the explanatory variable. We now add variation in the x_i to our list of assumptions.

Assumption SLR.3 Sample Variation in the Explanatory Variable

The sample outcomes on x, namely, $\{x_i, i = 1, \ldots, n\}$, are not all the same value.

This is a very weak assumption—certainly not worth emphasizing, but needed nevertheless. If x varies in the population, random samples on x will typically contain variation, unless the population variation is minimal or the sample size is small. Simple inspection of summary statistics on x_i reveals whether Assumption SLR.3 fails: if the sample standard deviation of x_i is zero, then Assumption SLR.3 fails; otherwise, it holds.

Finally, in order to obtain unbiased estimators of β_0 and β_1, we need to impose the zero conditional mean assumption that we discussed in some detail in Section 2.1. We now explicitly add it to our list of assumptions.

Assumption SLR.4 Zero Conditional Mean

The error u has an expected value of zero given any value of the explanatory variable. In other words,

$$\mathrm{E}(u|x) = 0.$$

For a random sample, this assumption implies that $\mathrm{E}(u_i|x_i) = 0$, for all $i = 1, 2, \ldots, n$.

In addition to restricting the relationship between u and x in the population, the zero conditional mean assumption—coupled with the random sampling assumption—allows for a convenient technical simplification. In particular, we can derive the statistical properties of the OLS estimators as *conditional* on the values of the x_i in our sample. Technically, in statistical derivations, conditioning on the sample values of the independent variable is the same as treating the x_i as *fixed in repeated samples*, which we think of as follows. We first choose n sample values for $x_1, x_2, \ldots, x_n$. (These can be repeated.) Given these values, we then obtain a sample on y (effectively by obtaining a random sample of the u_i). Next, another sample of y is obtained, using the *same* values for $x_1, x_2, \ldots, x_n$. Then another sample of y is obtained, again using the same $x_1, x_2, \ldots, x_n$. And so on.

The fixed-in-repeated-samples scenario is not very realistic in nonexperimental contexts. For instance, in sampling individuals for the wage-education example, it makes little sense to think of choosing the values of *educ* ahead of time and then sampling individuals with those particular levels of education. Random sampling, where individuals are chosen randomly and their wage and education are both recorded, is representative of how most data sets are obtained for empirical analysis in the social sciences. Once we *assume* that $\mathrm{E}(u|x) = 0$, and we have random sampling, nothing is lost in derivations by treating the x_i as nonrandom. The danger is that the fixed-in-repeated-samples assumption *always* implies that u_i and x_i are independent. In deciding when simple regression analysis is going to produce unbiased estimators, it is critical to think in terms of Assumption SLR.4.

Now, we are ready to show that the OLS estimators are unbiased. To this end, we use the fact that $\sum_{i=1}^{n}(x_i - \bar{x})(y_i - \bar{y}) = \sum_{i=1}^{n}(x_i - \bar{x})y_i$ (see Appendix A) to write the OLS slope estimator in equation (2.19) as

$$\hat{\beta}_1 = \frac{\sum_{i=1}^{n}(x_i - \bar{x})y_i}{\sum_{i=1}^{n}(x_i - \bar{x})^2}. \qquad [2.49]$$

Because we are now interested in the behavior of $\hat{\beta}_1$ across all possible samples, $\hat{\beta}_1$ is properly viewed as a random variable.

We can write $\hat{\beta}_1$ in terms of the population coefficients and errors by substituting the right-hand side of (2.48) into (2.49). We have

$$\hat{\beta}_1 = \frac{\sum_{i=1}^{n}(x_i - \bar{x})y_i}{\text{SST}_x} = \frac{\sum_{i=1}^{n}(x_i - \bar{x})(\beta_0 + \beta_1 x_i + u_i)}{\text{SST}_x}, \quad [2.50]$$

where we have defined the total variation in x_i as $\text{SST}_x = \sum_{i=1}^{n}(x_i - \bar{x})^2$ to simplify the notation. (This is not quite the sample variance of the x_i because we do not divide by $n - 1$.) Using the algebra of the summation operator, write the numerator of $\hat{\beta}_1$ as

$$\sum_{i=1}^{n}(x_i - \bar{x})\beta_0 + \sum_{i=1}^{n}(x_i - \bar{x})\beta_1 x_i + \sum_{i=1}^{n}(x_i - \bar{x})u_i$$
$$= \beta_0\sum_{i=1}^{n}(x_i - \bar{x}) + \beta_1\sum_{i=1}^{n}(x_i - \bar{x})x_i + \sum_{i=1}^{n}(x_i - \bar{x})u_i. \quad [2.51]$$

As shown in Appendix A, $\sum_{i=1}^{n}(x_i - \bar{x}) = 0$ and $\sum_{i=1}^{n}(x_i - \bar{x})x_i = \sum_{i=1}^{n}(x_i - \bar{x})^2 = \text{SST}_x$. Therefore, we can write the numerator of $\hat{\beta}_1$ as $\beta_1\text{SST}_x + \sum_{i=1}^{n}(x_i - \bar{x})u_i$. Putting this over the denominator gives

$$\hat{\beta}_1 = \beta_1 + \frac{\sum_{i=1}^{n}(x_i - \bar{x})u_i}{\text{SST}_x} = \beta_1 + (1/\text{SST}_x)\sum_{i=1}^{n} d_i u_i, \quad [2.52]$$

where $d_i = x_i - \bar{x}$. We now see that the estimator $\hat{\beta}_1$ equals the population slope, β_1, plus a term that is a linear combination in the errors $\{u_1, u_2, \ldots, u_n\}$. Conditional on the values of x_i, the randomness in $\hat{\beta}_1$ is due entirely to the errors in the sample. The fact that these errors are generally different from zero is what causes $\hat{\beta}_1$ to differ from β_1.

Using the representation in (2.52), we can prove the first important statistical property of OLS.

THEOREM 2.1

UNBIASEDNESS OF OLS:

Using Assumptions SLR.1 through SLR.4,

$$\text{E}(\hat{\beta}_0) = \beta_0, \text{ and } \text{E}(\hat{\beta}_1) = \beta_1, \quad [2.53]$$

for any values of β_0 and β_1. In other words, $\hat{\beta}_0$ is unbiased for β_0, and $\hat{\beta}_1$ is unbiased for β_1.

PROOF: In this proof, the expected values are conditional on the sample values of the independent variable. Because SST_x and d_i are functions only of the x_i, they are nonrandom in the conditioning. Therefore, from (2.52), and keeping the conditioning on $\{x_1, x_2, \ldots, x_n\}$ implicit, we have

$$\text{E}(\hat{\beta}_1) = \beta_1 + \text{E}\left[(1/\text{SST}_x)\sum_{i=1}^{n} d_i u_i\right] = \beta_1 + (1/\text{SST}_x)\sum_{i=1}^{n} \text{E}(d_i u_i)$$
$$= \beta_1 + (1/\text{SST}_x)\sum_{i=1}^{n} d_i \text{E}(u_i) = \beta_1 + (1/\text{SST}_x)\sum_{i=1}^{n} d_i \cdot 0 = \beta_1,$$

where we have used the fact that the expected value of each u_i (conditional on $\{x_1, x_2, ..., x_n\}$) is zero under Assumptions SLR.2 and SLR.4. Since unbiasedness holds for any outcome on $\{x_1, x_2, ..., x_n\}$, unbiasedness also holds without conditioning on $\{x_1, x_2, ..., x_n\}$.

The proof for $\hat{\beta}_0$ is now straightforward. Average (2.48) across i to get $\bar{y} = \beta_0 + \beta_1\bar{x} + \bar{u}$, and plug this into the formula for $\hat{\beta}_0$:

$$\hat{\beta}_0 = \bar{y} - \hat{\beta}_1\bar{x} = \beta_0 + \beta_1\bar{x} + \bar{u} - \hat{\beta}_1\bar{x} = \beta_0 + (\beta_1 - \hat{\beta}_1)\bar{x} + \bar{u}.$$

Then, conditional on the values of the x_i,

$$\mathrm{E}(\hat{\beta}_0) = \beta_0 + \mathrm{E}[(\beta_1 - \hat{\beta}_1)\bar{x}] + \mathrm{E}(\bar{u}) = \beta_0 + \mathrm{E}[(\beta_1 - \hat{\beta}_1)]\bar{x},$$

since $\mathrm{E}(\bar{u}) = 0$ by Assumptions SLR.2 and SLR.4. But, we showed that $\mathrm{E}(\hat{\beta}_1) = \beta_1$, which implies that $\mathrm{E}[(\hat{\beta}_1 - \beta_1)] = 0$. Thus, $\mathrm{E}(\hat{\beta}_0) = \beta_0$. Both of these arguments are valid for any values of β_0 and β_1, and so we have established unbiasedness.

Remember that unbiasedness is a feature of the sampling distributions of $\hat{\beta}_1$ and $\hat{\beta}_0$, which says nothing about the estimate that we obtain for a given sample. We hope that, if the sample we obtain is somehow "typical," then our estimate should be "near" the population value. Unfortunately, it is always possible that we could obtain an unlucky sample that would give us a point estimate far from β_1, and we can *never* know for sure whether this is the case. You may want to review the material on unbiased estimators in Appendix C, especially the simulation exercise in Table C.1 that illustrates the concept of unbiasedness.

Unbiasedness generally fails if any of our four assumptions fail. This means that it is important to think about the veracity of each assumption for a particular application. Assumption SLR.1 requires that y and x be linearly related, with an additive disturbance. This can certainly fail. But we also know that y and x can be chosen to yield interesting nonlinear relationships. Dealing with the failure of (2.47) requires more advanced methods that are beyond the scope of this text.

Later, we will have to relax Assumption SLR.2, the random sampling assumption, for time series analysis. But what about using it for cross-sectional analysis? Random sampling can fail in a cross section when samples are not representative of the underlying population; in fact, some data sets are constructed by intentionally oversampling different parts of the population. We will discuss problems of nonrandom sampling in Chapters 9 and 17.

As we have already discussed, Assumption SLR.3 almost always holds in interesting regression applications. Without it, we cannot even obtain the OLS estimates.

The assumption we should concentrate on for now is SLR.4. If SLR.4 holds, the OLS estimators are unbiased. Likewise, if SLR.4 fails, the OLS estimators generally will be *biased*. There are ways to determine the likely direction and size of the bias, which we will study in Chapter 3.

The possibility that x is correlated with u is almost always a concern in simple regression analysis with nonexperimental data, as we indicated with several examples in Section 2.1. Using simple regression when u contains factors affecting y that are also correlated with x can result in *spurious correlation*: that is, we find a relationship between y and x that is really due to other unobserved factors that affect y and also happen to be correlated with x.

EXAMPLE 2.12 STUDENT MATH PERFORMANCE AND THE SCHOOL LUNCH PROGRAM

Let *math10* denote the percentage of tenth graders at a high school receiving a passing score on a standardized mathematics exam. Suppose we wish to estimate the effect of the federally funded school lunch program on student performance. If anything, we expect the lunch program to have a positive ceteris paribus effect on performance: all other factors being equal, if a student who is too poor to eat regular meals becomes eligible for the school lunch program, his or her performance should improve. Let *lnchprg* denote the percentage of students who are eligible for the lunch program. Then, a simple regression model is

$$math10 = \beta_0 + \beta_1 lnchprg + u, \tag{2.54}$$

where u contains school and student characteristics that affect overall school performance. Using the data in MEAP93.RAW on 408 Michigan high schools for the 1992–1993 school year, we obtain

$$\widehat{math10} = 32.14 - 0.319\ lnchprg$$
$$n = 408,\ R^2 = 0.171.$$

This equation predicts that if student eligibility in the lunch program increases by 10 percentage points, the percentage of students passing the math exam *falls* by about 3.2 percentage points. Do we really believe that higher participation in the lunch program actually *causes* worse performance? Almost certainly not. A better explanation is that the error term u in equation (2.54) is correlated with *lnchprg*. In fact, u contains factors such as the poverty rate of children attending school, which affects student performance and is highly correlated with eligibility in the lunch program. Variables such as school quality and resources are also contained in u, and these are likely correlated with *lnchprg*. It is important to remember that the estimate -0.319 is only for this particular sample, but its sign and magnitude make us suspect that u and x are correlated, so that simple regression is biased.

In addition to omitted variables, there are other reasons for x to be correlated with u in the simple regression model. Because the same issues arise in multiple regression analysis, we will postpone a systematic treatment of the problem until then.

Variances of the OLS Estimators

In addition to knowing that the sampling distribution of $\hat{\beta}_1$ is centered about β_1 ($\hat{\beta}_1$ is unbiased), it is important to know how far we can expect $\hat{\beta}_1$ to be away from β_1 on average.

Among other things, this allows us to choose the best estimator among all, or at least a broad class of, unbiased estimators. The measure of spread in the distribution of $\hat{\beta}_1$ (and $\hat{\beta}_0$) that is easiest to work with is the variance or its square root, the standard deviation. (See Appendix C for a more detailed discussion.)

It turns out that the variance of the OLS estimators can be computed under Assumptions SLR.1 through SLR.4. However, these expressions would be somewhat complicated. Instead, we add an assumption that is traditional for cross-sectional analysis. This assumption states that the variance of the unobservable, u, conditional on x, is constant. This is known as the **homoskedasticity** or "constant variance" assumption.

Assumption SLR.5 Homoskedasticity

The error u has the same variance given any value of the explanatory variable. In other words,

$$\text{Var}(u|x) = \sigma^2.$$

We must emphasize that the homoskedasticity assumption is quite distinct from the zero conditional mean assumption, $\text{E}(u|x) = 0$. Assumption SLR.4 involves the *expected value* of u, while Assumption SLR.5 concerns the *variance* of u (both conditional on x). Recall that we established the unbiasedness of OLS without Assumption SLR.5: the homoskedasticity assumption plays *no* role in showing that $\hat{\beta}_0$ and $\hat{\beta}_1$ are unbiased. We add Assumption SLR.5 because it simplifies the variance calculations for $\hat{\beta}_0$ and $\hat{\beta}_1$ and because it implies that ordinary least squares has certain efficiency properties, which we will see in Chapter 3. If we were to assume that u and x are *independent*, then the distribution of u given x does not depend on x, and so $\text{E}(u|x) = \text{E}(u) = 0$ and $\text{Var}(u|x) = \sigma^2$. But independence is sometimes too strong of an assumption.

Because $\text{Var}(u|x) = \text{E}(u^2|x) - [\text{E}(u|x)]^2$ and $\text{E}(u|x) = 0$, $\sigma^2 = \text{E}(u^2|x)$, which means σ^2 is also the *unconditional* expectation of u^2. Therefore, $\sigma^2 = \text{E}(u^2) = \text{Var}(u)$, because $\text{E}(u) = 0$. In other words, σ^2 is the *unconditional* variance of u, and so σ^2 is often called the **error variance** or disturbance variance. The square root of σ^2, σ, is the standard deviation of the error. A larger σ means that the distribution of the unobservables affecting y is more spread out.

It is often useful to write Assumptions SLR.4 and SLR.5 in terms of the conditional mean and conditional variance of y:

$$\text{E}(y|x) = \beta_0 + \beta_1 x. \quad [2.55]$$

$$\text{Var}(y|x) = \sigma^2. \quad [2.56]$$

In other words, the conditional expectation of y given x is linear in x, but the variance of y given x is constant. This situation is graphed in Figure 2.8 where $\beta_0 > 0$ and $\beta_1 > 0$.

When $\text{Var}(u|x)$ depends on x, the error term is said to exhibit **heteroskedasticity** (or nonconstant variance). Because $\text{Var}(u|x) = \text{Var}(y|x)$, heteroskedasticity is present whenever $\text{Var}(y|x)$ is a function of x.

FIGURE 2.8 The simple regression model under homoskedasticity.

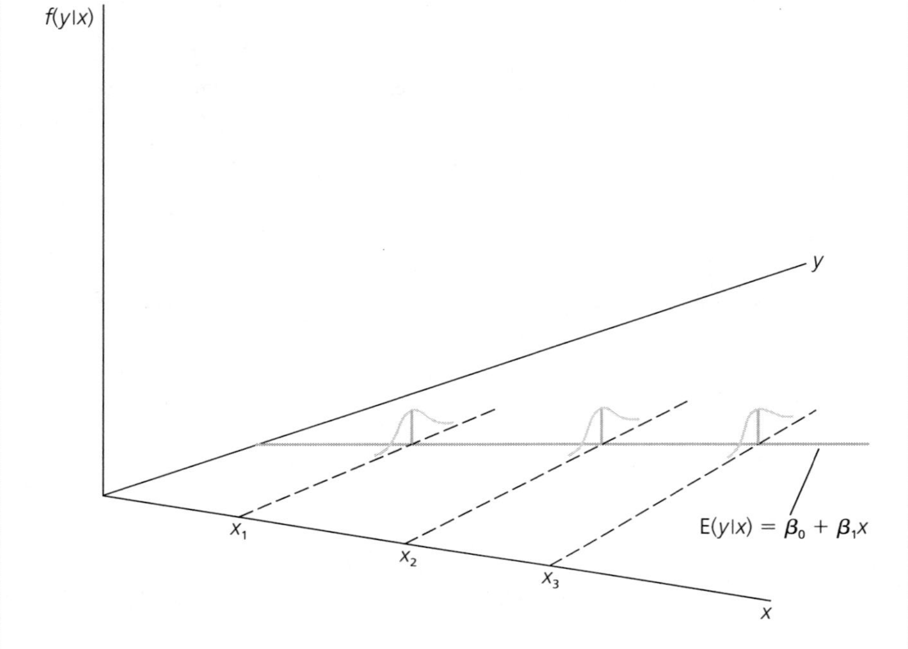

EXAMPLE 2.13 HETEROSKEDASTICITY IN A WAGE EQUATION

In order to get an unbiased estimator of the ceteris paribus effect of *educ* on *wage,* we must assume that $\text{E}(u|educ) = 0$, and this implies $\text{E}(wage|educ) = \beta_0 + \beta_1 educ$. If we also make the homoskedasticity assumption, then $\text{Var}(u|educ) = \sigma^2$ does not depend on the level of education, which is the same as assuming $\text{Var}(wage|educ) = \sigma^2$. Thus, while average wage is allowed to increase with education level—it is this rate of increase that we are interested in estimating—the *variability* in wage about its mean is assumed to be constant across all education levels. This may not be realistic. It is likely that people with more education have a wider variety of interests and job opportunities, which could lead to more wage variability at higher levels of education. People with very low levels of education have fewer opportunities and often must work at the minimum wage; this serves to reduce wage variability at low education levels. This situation is shown in Figure 2.9. Ultimately, whether Assumption SLR.5 holds is an empirical issue, and in Chapter 8 we will show how to test Assumption SLR.5.

FIGURE 2.9 Var(*wage*|*educ*) increasing with *educ*.

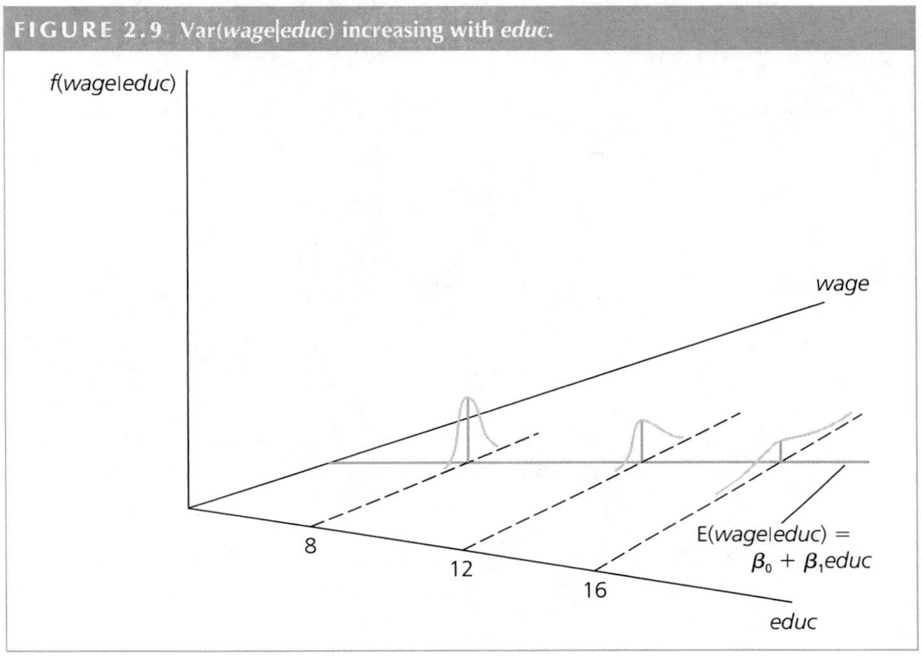

With the homoskedasticity assumption in place, we are ready to prove the following:

THEOREM 2.2

SAMPLING VARIANCES OF THE OLS ESTIMATORS

Under Assumptions SLR.1 through SLR.5,

$$\text{Var}(\hat{\beta}_1) = \frac{\sigma^2}{\sum_{i=1}^{n}(x_i - \bar{x})^2} = \sigma^2/\text{SST}_x, \quad [2.57]$$

and

$$\text{Var}(\hat{\beta}_0) = \frac{\sigma^2 n^{-1}\sum_{i=1}^{n} x_i^2}{\sum_{i=1}^{n}(x_i - \bar{x})^2}, \quad [2.58]$$

where these are conditional on the sample values $\{x_1, \ldots, x_n\}$.

PROOF: We derive the formula for $\text{Var}(\hat{\beta}_1)$, leaving the other derivation as Problem 10. The starting point is equation (2.52): $\hat{\beta}_1 = \beta_1 + (1/\text{SST}_x)\sum_{i=1}^{n} d_i u_i$. Because β_1 is just a constant, and we are conditioning on the x_i, SST_x and $d_i = x_i - \bar{x}$ are also nonrandom.

Furthermore, because the u_i are independent random variables across i (by random sampling), the variance of the sum is the sum of the variances. Using these facts, we have

$$\text{Var}(\hat{\beta}_1) = (1/\text{SST}_x)^2\text{Var}\left(\sum_{i=1}^{n} d_i u_i\right) = (1/\text{SST}_x)^2\left(\sum_{i=1}^{n} d_i^2\text{Var}(u_i)\right)$$

$$= (1/\text{SST}_x)^2\left(\sum_{i=1}^{n} d_i^2\sigma^2\right) \qquad [\text{since Var}(u_i) = \sigma^2 \text{ for all } i]$$

$$= \sigma^2(1/\text{SST}_x)^2\left(\sum_{i=1}^{n} d_i^2\right) = \sigma^2(1/\text{SST}_x)^2\text{SST}_x = \sigma^2/\text{SST}_x,$$

which is what we wanted to show.

Equations (2.57) and (2.58) are the "standard" formulas for simple regression analysis, which are invalid in the presence of heteroskedasticity. This will be important when we turn to confidence intervals and hypothesis testing in multiple regression analysis.

For most purposes, we are interested in $\text{Var}(\hat{\beta}_1)$. It is easy to summarize how this variance depends on the error variance, σ^2, and the total variation in $\{x_1, x_2, \ldots, x_n\}$, SST_x. First, the larger the error variance, the larger is $\text{Var}(\hat{\beta}_1)$. This makes sense since more variation in the unobservables affecting y makes it more difficult to precisely estimate β_1. On the other hand, more variability in the independent variable is preferred: as the variability in the x_i increases, the variance of $\hat{\beta}_1$ decreases. This also makes intuitive sense since the more spread out is the sample of independent variables, the easier it is to trace out the relationship between $\text{E}(y|x)$ and x. That is, the easier it is to estimate β_1. If there is little variation in the x_i, then it can be hard to pinpoint how $\text{E}(y|x)$ varies with x. As the sample size increases, so does the total variation in the x_i. Therefore, a larger sample size results in a smaller variance for $\hat{\beta}_1$.

EXPLORING FURTHER 2.5

Show that, when estimating β_0, it is best to have $\bar{x} = 0$. What is $\text{Var}(\hat{\beta}_0)$ in this case? [*Hint:* For any sample of numbers, $\sum_{i=1}^{n} x_i^2 \geq \sum_{i=1}^{n}(x_i - \bar{x})^2$, with equality only if $\bar{x} = 0$.]

This analysis shows that, if we are interested in β_1 and we have a choice, then we should choose the x_i to be as spread out as possible. This is sometimes possible with experimental data, but rarely do we have this luxury in the social sciences: usually, we must take the x_i that we obtain via random sampling. Sometimes, we have an opportunity to obtain larger sample sizes, although this can be costly.

For the purposes of constructing confidence intervals and deriving test statistics, we will need to work with the standard deviations of $\hat{\beta}_1$ and $\hat{\beta}_0$, $\text{sd}(\hat{\beta}_1)$ and $\text{sd}(\hat{\beta}_0)$. Recall that these are obtained by taking the square roots of the variances in (2.57) and (2.58). In particular, $\text{sd}(\hat{\beta}_1) = \sigma/\sqrt{\text{SST}_x}$, where σ is the square root of σ^2, and $\sqrt{\text{SST}_x}$ is the square root of SST_x.

Estimating the Error Variance

The formulas in (2.57) and (2.58) allow us to isolate the factors that contribute to $\text{Var}(\hat{\beta}_1)$ and $\text{Var}(\hat{\beta}_0)$. But these formulas are unknown, except in the extremely rare case that σ^2 is known.

Nevertheless, we can use the data to estimate σ^2, which then allows us to estimate $\text{Var}(\hat{\beta}_1)$ and $\text{Var}(\hat{\beta}_0)$.

This is a good place to emphasize the difference between the *errors* (or disturbances) and the *residuals*, since this distinction is crucial for constructing an estimator of σ^2. Equation (2.48) shows how to write the population model in terms of a randomly sampled observation as $y_i = \beta_0 + \beta_1 x_i + u_i$, where u_i is the error for observation i. We can also express y_i in terms of its fitted value and residual as in equation (2.32): $y_i = \hat{\beta}_0 + \hat{\beta}_1 x_i + \hat{u}_i$. Comparing these two equations, we see that the error shows up in the equation containing the *population* parameters, β_0 and β_1. On the other hand, the residuals show up in the *estimated* equation with $\hat{\beta}_0$ and $\hat{\beta}_1$. The errors are never observed, while the residuals are computed from the data.

We can use equations (2.32) and (2.48) to write the residuals as a function of the errors:

$$\hat{u}_i = y_i - \hat{\beta}_0 - \hat{\beta}_1 x_i = (\beta_0 + \beta_1 x_i + u_i) - \hat{\beta}_0 - \hat{\beta}_1 x_i,$$

or

$$\hat{u}_i = u_i - (\hat{\beta}_0 - \beta_0) - (\hat{\beta}_1 - \beta_1)x_i. \tag{2.59}$$

Although the expected value of $\hat{\beta}_0$ equals β_0, and similarly for $\hat{\beta}_1$, $\hat{u}_i$ is not the same as u_i. The difference between them does have an *expected value* of zero.

Now that we understand the difference between the errors and the residuals, we can return to estimating σ^2. First, $\sigma^2 = \text{E}(u^2)$, so an unbiased "estimator" of σ^2 is $n^{-1}\sum_{i=1}^{n} u_i^2$. Unfortunately, this is not a true estimator, because we do not observe the errors u_i. But, we do have estimates of the u_i, namely, the OLS residuals $\hat{u}_i$. If we replace the errors with the OLS residuals, we have $n^{-1}\sum_{i=1}^{n}\hat{u}_i^2 = \text{SSR}/n$. This *is* a true estimator, because it gives a computable rule for any sample of data on x and y. One slight drawback to this estimator is that it turns out to be biased (although for large n the bias is small). Because it is easy to compute an unbiased estimator, we use that instead.

The estimator SSR/n is biased essentially because it does not account for two restrictions that must be satisfied by the OLS residuals. These restrictions are given by the two OLS first order conditions:

$$\sum_{i=1}^{n}\hat{u}_i = 0, \quad \sum_{i=1}^{n} x_i\hat{u}_i = 0. \tag{2.60}$$

One way to view these restrictions is this: if we know $n - 2$ of the residuals, we can always get the other two residuals by using the restrictions implied by the first order conditions in (2.60). Thus, there are only $n - 2$ **degrees of freedom** in the OLS residuals, as opposed to n degrees of freedom in the errors. It is important to understand that if we replace $\hat{u}_i$ with u_i in (2.60), the restrictions would no longer hold.

The unbiased estimator of σ^2 that we will use makes a degrees of freedom adjustment:

$$\hat{\sigma}^2 = \frac{1}{(n-2)}\sum_{i=1}^{n}\hat{u}_i^2 = \text{SSR}/(n-2). \tag{2.61}$$

(This estimator is sometimes denoted as s^2, but we continue to use the convention of putting "hats" over estimators.)

THEOREM 2.3

UNBIASED ESTIMATION OF σ^2

Under Assumptions SLR.1 through SLR.5,

$$\mathrm{E}(\hat{\sigma}^2) = \sigma^2.$$

PROOF: If we average equation (2.59) across all i and use the fact that the OLS residuals average out to zero, we have $0 = \bar{u} - (\hat{\beta}_0 - \beta_0) - (\hat{\beta}_1 - \beta_1)\bar{x}$; subtracting this from (2.59) gives $\hat{u}_i = (u_i - \bar{u}) - (\hat{\beta}_1 - \beta_1)(x_i - \bar{x})$. Therefore, $\hat{u}_i^2 = (u_i - \bar{u})^2 + (\hat{\beta}_1 - \beta_1)^2 (x_i - \bar{x})^2 - 2(u_i - \bar{u})(\hat{\beta}_1 - \beta_1)(x_i - \bar{x})$. Summing across all i gives $\sum_{i=1}^{n} \hat{u}_i^2 = \sum_{i=1}^{n} (u_i - \bar{u})^2 + (\hat{\beta}_1 - \beta_1)^2 \sum_{i=1}^{n} (x_i - \bar{x})^2 - 2(\hat{\beta}_1 - \beta_1) \sum_{i=1}^{n} u_i(x_i - \bar{x})$. Now, the expected value of the first term is $(n - 1)\sigma^2$, something that is shown in Appendix C. The expected value of the second term is simply σ^2 because $\mathrm{E}[(\hat{\beta}_1 - \beta_1)^2] = \mathrm{Var}(\hat{\beta}_1) = \sigma^2/s_x^2$. Finally, the third term can be written as $2(\hat{\beta}_1 - \beta_1)^2 s_x^2$; taking expectations gives $2\sigma^2$. Putting these three terms together gives $\mathrm{E}\left(\sum_{i=1}^{n} \hat{u}_i^2\right) = (n - 1)\sigma^2 + \sigma^2 - 2\sigma^2 = (n - 2)\sigma^2$, so that $\mathrm{E}[\mathrm{SSR}/(n - 2)] = \sigma^2$.

If $\hat{\sigma}^2$ is plugged into the variance formulas (2.57) and (2.58), then we have unbiased estimators of $\mathrm{Var}(\hat{\beta}_1)$ and $\mathrm{Var}(\hat{\beta}_0)$. Later on, we will need estimators of the standard deviations of $\hat{\beta}_1$ and $\hat{\beta}_0$, and this requires estimating σ. The natural estimator of σ is

$$\hat{\sigma} = \sqrt{\hat{\sigma}^2} \qquad [2.62]$$

and is called the **standard error of the regression (SER)**. (Other names for $\hat{\sigma}$ are the *standard error of the estimate* and the *root mean squared error*, but we will not use these.) Although $\hat{\sigma}$ is not an unbiased estimator of σ, we can show that it is a *consistent* estimator of σ (see Appendix C), and it will serve our purposes well.

The estimate $\hat{\sigma}$ is interesting because it is an estimate of the standard deviation in the unobservables affecting y; equivalently, it estimates the standard deviation in y after the effect of x has been taken out. Most regression packages report the value of $\hat{\sigma}$ along with the R-squared, intercept, slope, and other OLS statistics (under one of the several names listed above). For now, our primary interest is in using $\hat{\sigma}$ to estimate the standard deviations of $\hat{\beta}_0$ and $\hat{\beta}_1$. Since $\mathrm{sd}(\hat{\beta}_1) = \sigma/\sqrt{\mathrm{SST}_x}$, the natural estimator of $\mathrm{sd}(\hat{\beta}_1)$ is

$$\mathrm{se}(\hat{\beta}_1) = \hat{\sigma}/\sqrt{\mathrm{SST}_x} = \hat{\sigma}\Big/\left(\sum_{i=1}^{n}(x_i - \bar{x})^2\right)^{1/2};$$

this is called the **standard error of $\hat{\beta}_1$**. Note that $\mathrm{se}(\hat{\beta}_1)$ is viewed as a random variable when we think of running OLS over different samples of y; this is true because $\hat{\sigma}$ varies with different samples. For a given sample, $\mathrm{se}(\hat{\beta}_1)$ is a number, just as $\hat{\beta}_1$ is simply a number when we compute it from the given data.

Similarly, $\mathrm{se}(\hat{\beta}_0)$ is obtained from $\mathrm{sd}(\hat{\beta}_0)$ by replacing σ with $\hat{\sigma}$. The standard error of any estimate gives us an idea of how precise the estimator is. Standard errors play a central role throughout this text; we will use them to construct test statistics and confidence intervals for every econometric procedure we cover, starting in Chapter 4.

2.6 Regression through the Origin and Regression on a Constant

In rare cases, we wish to impose the restriction that, when $x = 0$, the expected value of y is zero. There are certain relationships for which this is reasonable. For example, if income (x) is zero, then income tax revenues (y) must also be zero. In addition, there are settings where a model that originally has a nonzero intercept is transformed into a model without an intercept.

Formally, we now choose a slope estimator, which we call $\tilde{\beta}_1$, and a line of the form

$$\tilde{y} = \tilde{\beta}_1 x, \tag{2.63}$$

where the tildes over $\tilde{\beta}_1$ and $\tilde{y}$ are used to distinguish this problem from the much more common problem of estimating an intercept along with a slope. Obtaining (2.63) is called **regression through the origin** because the line (2.63) passes through the point $x = 0$, $\tilde{y} = 0$. To obtain the slope estimate in (2.63), we still rely on the method of ordinary least squares, which in this case minimizes the sum of squared residuals:

$$\sum_{i=1}^{n} (y_i - \tilde{\beta}_1 x_i)^2. \tag{2.64}$$

Using one-variable calculus, it can be shown that $\tilde{\beta}_1$ must solve the first order condition:

$$\sum_{i=1}^{n} x_i(y_i - \tilde{\beta}_1 x_i) = 0. \tag{2.65}$$

From this, we can solve for $\tilde{\beta}_1$:

$$\tilde{\beta}_1 = \frac{\sum_{i=1}^{n} x_i y_i}{\sum_{i=1}^{n} x_i^2}, \tag{2.66}$$

provided that not all the x_i are zero, a case we rule out.

Note how $\tilde{\beta}_1$ compares with the slope estimate when we also estimate the intercept (rather than set it equal to zero). These two estimates are the same if, and only if, $\bar{x} = 0$. [See equation (2.49) for $\hat{\beta}_1$.] Obtaining an estimate of β_1 using regression through the origin is not done very often in applied work, and for good reason: if the intercept $\beta_0 \neq 0$, then $\tilde{\beta}_1$ is a biased estimator of β_1. You will be asked to prove this in Problem 8.

In cases where regression through the origin is deemed appropriate, one must be careful in interpreting the R-squared that is typically reported with such regressions. Usually, unless stated otherwise, the R-squared is obtained without removing the sample average of $\{y_i : i = 1, ..., n\}$ in obtaining SST. In other words, the R-squared is computed as

$$1 - \frac{\sum_{i=1}^{n} (y_i - \tilde{\beta}_1 x_i)^2}{\sum_{i=1}^{n} y_i^2}. \tag{2.67}$$

The numerator here makes sense because it is the sum of squared residuals, but the denominator acts as if we know the average value of y in the population is zero. One reason this version of the R-squared is used is that if we use the usual total sum of squares, that is, we compute R-squared as

$$1 - \frac{\sum_{i=1}^{n}(y_i - \tilde{\beta}_1 x_i)^2}{\sum_{i=1}^{n}(y_i - \bar{y})^2}. \qquad [2.68]$$

it can actually be negative. If expression (2.68) is negative then it means that using the sample average $\bar{y}$ to predict y_i provides a better fit than using x_i in a regression through the origin. Therefore, (2.68) is actually more attractive than equation (2.67) because equation (2.68) tells us whether using x is better than ignoring x altogether.

This discussion about regression through the origin, and different ways to measure goodness-of-fit, prompts another question: what happens if we only regress on a constant? That is, we set the slope to zero (which means we need not even have an x) and estimate an intercept only? The answer is simple: the intercept is $\bar{y}$. This fact is usually shown in basic statistics, where it is shown that the constant that produces the smallest sum of squared deviations is always the sample average. In this light, equation (2.68) can be seen as comparing regression on x through the origin with regression only on a constant.

Summary

We have introduced the simple linear regression model in this chapter, and we have covered its basic properties. Given a random sample, the method of ordinary least squares is used to estimate the slope and intercept parameters in the population model. We have demonstrated the algebra of the OLS regression line, including computation of fitted values and residuals, and the obtaining of predicted changes in the dependent variable for a given change in the independent variable. In Section 2.4, we discussed two issues of practical importance: (1) the behavior of the OLS estimates when we change the units of measurement of the dependent variable or the independent variable and (2) the use of the natural log to allow for constant elasticity and constant semi-elasticity models.

In Section 2.5, we showed that, under the four Assumptions SLR.1 through SLR.4, the OLS estimators are unbiased. The key assumption is that the error term u has zero mean given any value of the independent variable x. Unfortunately, there are reasons to think this is false in many social science applications of simple regression, where the omitted factors in u are often correlated with x. When we add the assumption that the variance of the error given x is constant, we get simple formulas for the sampling variances of the OLS estimators. As we saw, the variance of the slope estimator $\hat{\beta}_1$ increases as the error variance increases, and it decreases when there is more sample variation in the independent variable. We also derived an unbiased estimator for $\sigma^2 = \mathrm{Var}(u)$.

In Section 2.6, we briefly discussed regression through the origin, where the slope estimator is obtained under the assumption that the intercept is zero. Sometimes, this is useful, but it appears infrequently in applied work.

Much work is left to be done. For example, we still do not know how to test hypotheses about the population parameters, β_0 and β_1. Thus, although we know that OLS is unbiased for the population parameters under Assumptions SLR.1 through SLR.4, we have no way of drawing inferences about the population. Other topics, such as the efficiency of OLS relative to other possible procedures, have also been omitted.

The issues of confidence intervals, hypothesis testing, and efficiency are central to multiple regression analysis as well. Since the way we construct confidence intervals and test statistics is very similar for multiple regression—and because simple regression is a special case of multiple regression—our time is better spent moving on to multiple regression, which is much more widely applicable than simple regression. Our purpose in Chapter 2 was to get you thinking about the issues that arise in econometric analysis in a fairly simple setting.

THE GAUSS-MARKOV ASSUMPTIONS FOR SIMPLE REGRESSION

For convenience, we summarize the **Gauss-Markov assumptions** that we used in this chapter. It is important to remember that only SLR.1 through SLR.4 are needed to show $\hat{\beta}_0$ and $\hat{\beta}_1$ are unbiased. We added the homoskedasticity assumption, SLR.5, to obtain the usual OLS variance formulas (2.57) and (2.58).

Assumption SLR.1 (Linear in Parameters)

In the population model, the dependent variable, y, is related to the independent variable, x, and the error (or disturbance), u, as

$$y = \beta_0 + \beta_1 x + u,$$

where β_0 and β_1 are the population intercept and slope parameters, respectively.

Assumption SLR.2 (Random Sampling)

We have a random sample of size n, $\{(x_i, y_i): i = 1, 2, \ldots, n\}$, following the population model in Assumption SLR.1.

Assumption SLR.3 (Sample Variation in the Explanatory Variable)

The sample outcomes on x, namely, $\{x_i, i = 1, \ldots, n\}$, are not all the same value.

Assumption SLR.4 (Zero Conditional Mean)

The error u has an expected value of zero given any value of the explanatory variable. In other words,

$$\mathrm{E}(u|x) = 0.$$

Assumption SLR.5 (Homoskedasticity)

The error u has the same variance given any value of the explanatory variable. In other words,

$$\mathrm{Var}(u|x) = \sigma^2.$$

Key Terms

Coefficient of Determination
Constant Elasticity Model
Control Variable
Covariate
Degrees of Freedom
Dependent Variable
Elasticity
Error Term (Disturbance)
Error Variance
Explained Sum of Squares (SSE)
Explained Variable
Explanatory Variable
First Order Conditions
Fitted Value
Gauss-Markov Assumptions
Heteroskedasticity
Homoskedasticity
Independent Variable
Intercept Parameter
Mean Independent
OLS Regression Line
Ordinary Least Squares (OLS)
Population Regression Function (PRF)
Predicted Variable
Predictor Variable

Regressand
Regression through the Origin
Regressor
Residual
Residual Sum of Squares (SSR)
Response Variable
R-squared
Sample Regression Function (SRF)
Semi-elasticity
Simple Linear Regression Model
Slope Parameter
Standard Error of $\hat{\beta}_1$
Standard Error of the Regression (SER)
Sum of Squared Residuals (SSR)
Total Sum of Squares (SST)
Zero Conditional Mean Assumption

Problems

1 Let *kids* denote the number of children ever born to a woman, and let *educ* denote years of education for the woman. A simple model relating fertility to years of education is

$$kids = \beta_0 + \beta_1 educ + u,$$

where u is the unobserved error.

(i) What kinds of factors are contained in u? Are these likely to be correlated with level of education?

(ii) Will a simple regression analysis uncover the ceteris paribus effect of education on fertility? Explain.

2 In the simple linear regression model $y = \beta_0 + \beta_1 x + u$, suppose that $\mathrm{E}(u) \neq 0$. Letting $\alpha_0 = \mathrm{E}(u)$, show that the model can always be rewritten with the same slope, but a new intercept and error, where the new error has a zero expected value.

3 The following table contains the *ACT* scores and the *GPA* (grade point average) for eight college students. Grade point average is based on a four-point scale and has been rounded to one digit after the decimal.

Student	*GPA*	*ACT*
1	2.8	21
2	3.4	24
3	3.0	26
4	3.5	27
5	3.6	29
6	3.0	25
7	2.7	25
8	3.7	30

(i) Estimate the relationship between *GPA* and *ACT* using OLS; that is, obtain the intercept and slope estimates in the equation

$$\widehat{GPA} = \hat{\beta}_0 + \hat{\beta}_1 ACT.$$

Comment on the direction of the relationship. Does the intercept have a useful interpretation here? Explain. How much higher is the *GPA* predicted to be if the *ACT* score is increased by five points?

(ii) Compute the fitted values and residuals for each observation, and verify that the residuals (approximately) sum to zero.
(iii) What is the predicted value of *GPA* when $ACT = 20$?
(iv) How much of the variation in *GPA* for these eight students is explained by *ACT*? Explain.

4 The data set BWGHT.RAW contains data on births to women in the United States. Two variables of interest are the dependent variable, infant birth weight in ounces (*bwght*), and an explanatory variable, average number of cigarettes the mother smoked per day during pregnancy (*cigs*). The following simple regression was estimated using data on $n = 1{,}388$ births:

$$\widehat{bwght} = 119.77 - 0.514\, cigs$$

(i) What is the predicted birth weight when $cigs = 0$? What about when $cigs = 20$ (one pack per day)? Comment on the difference.
(ii) Does this simple regression necessarily capture a causal relationship between the child's birth weight and the mother's smoking habits? Explain.
(iii) To predict a birth weight of 125 ounces, what would *cigs* have to be? Comment.
(iv) The proportion of women in the sample who do not smoke while pregnant is about .85. Does this help reconcile your finding from part (iii)?

5 In the linear consumption function

$$\widehat{cons} = \hat{\beta}_0 + \hat{\beta}_1 inc,$$

the (estimated) *marginal propensity to consume* (MPC) out of income is simply the slope, $\hat{\beta}_1$, while the *average propensity to consume* (APC) is $\widehat{cons}/inc = \hat{\beta}_0/inc + \hat{\beta}_1$. Using observations for 100 families on annual income and consumption (both measured in dollars), the following equation is obtained:

$$\widehat{cons} = -124.84 + 0.853\, inc$$
$$n = 100,\ R^2 = 0.692.$$

(i) Interpret the intercept in this equation, and comment on its sign and magnitude.
(ii) What is the predicted consumption when family income is \$30,000?
(iii) With *inc* on the *x*-axis, draw a graph of the estimated MPC and APC.

6 Using data from 1988 for houses sold in Andover, Massachusetts, from Kiel and McClain (1995), the following equation relates housing price (*price*) to the distance from a recently built garbage incinerator (*dist*):

$$\widehat{\log(price)} = 9.40 + 0.312 \log(dist)$$
$$n = 135,\ R^2 = 0.162.$$

(i) Interpret the coefficient on log(*dist*). Is the sign of this estimate what you expect it to be?
(ii) Do you think simple regression provides an unbiased estimator of the ceteris paribus elasticity of *price* with respect to *dist*? (Think about the city's decision on where to put the incinerator.)
(iii) What other factors about a house affect its price? Might these be correlated with distance from the incinerator?

7 Consider the savings function

$$sav = \beta_0 + \beta_1 inc + u, \; u = \sqrt{inc}\cdot e,$$

where e is a random variable with $\text{E}(e) = 0$ and $\text{Var}(e) = \sigma_e^2$. Assume that e is independent of *inc*.

(i) Show that $\text{E}(u|inc) = 0$, so that the key zero conditional mean assumption (Assumption SLR.4) is satisfied. [*Hint:* If e is independent of *inc*, then $\text{E}(e|inc) = \text{E}(e)$.]

(ii) Show that $\text{Var}(u|inc) = \sigma_e^2 inc$, so that the homoskedasticity Assumption SLR.5 is violated. In particular, the variance of *sav* increases with *inc*. [*Hint:* $\text{Var}(e|inc) = \text{Var}(e)$, if e and *inc* are independent.]

(iii) Provide a discussion that supports the assumption that the variance of savings increases with family income.

8 Consider the standard simple regression model $y = \beta_0 + \beta_1 x + u$ under the Gauss-Markov Assumptions SLR.1 through SLR.5. The usual OLS estimators $\hat{\beta}_0$ and $\hat{\beta}_1$ are unbiased for their respective population parameters. Let $\tilde{\beta}_1$ be the estimator of β_1 obtained by assuming the intercept is zero (see Section 2.6).

(i) Find $\text{E}(\tilde{\beta}_1)$ in terms of the x_i, β_0, and β_1. Verify that $\tilde{\beta}_1$ is unbiased for β_1 when the population intercept (β_0) is zero. Are there other cases where $\tilde{\beta}_1$ is unbiased?

(ii) Find the variance of $\tilde{\beta}_1$. (*Hint:* The variance does not depend on β_0.)

(iii) Show that $\text{Var}(\tilde{\beta}_1) \le \text{Var}(\hat{\beta}_1)$. [*Hint:* For any sample of data, $\sum_{i=1}^{n} x_i^2 \ge \sum_{i=1}^{n}(x_i - \bar{x})^2$, with strict inequality unless $\bar{x} = 0$.]

(iv) Comment on the tradeoff between bias and variance when choosing between $\hat{\beta}_1$ and $\tilde{\beta}_1$.

9 (i) Let $\hat{\beta}_0$ and $\hat{\beta}_1$ be the intercept and slope from the regression of y_i on x_i, using n observations. Let c_1 and c_2, with $c_2 \neq 0$, be constants. Let $\tilde{\beta}_0$ and $\tilde{\beta}_1$ be the intercept and slope from the regression of $c_1 y_i$ on $c_2 x_i$. Show that $\tilde{\beta}_1 = (c_1/c_2)\hat{\beta}_0$ and $\tilde{\beta}_0 = c_1\hat{\beta}_0$, thereby verifying the claims on units of measurement in Section 2.4. [*Hint:* To obtain $\tilde{\beta}_1$, plug the scaled versions of x and y into (2.19). Then, use (2.17) for $\tilde{\beta}_0$, being sure to plug in the scaled x and y *and* the correct slope.]

(ii) Now, let $\tilde{\beta}_0$ and $\tilde{\beta}_1$ be from the regression of $(c_1 + y_i)$ on $(c_2 + x_i)$ (with no restriction on c_1 or c_2). Show that $\tilde{\beta}_1 = \hat{\beta}_1$ and $\tilde{\beta}_0 = \hat{\beta}_0 + c_1 - c_2\hat{\beta}_1$.

(iii) Now, let $\hat{\beta}_0$ and $\hat{\beta}_1$ be the OLS estimates from the regression $\log(y_i)$ on x_i, where we must assume $y_i > 0$ for all i. For $c_1 > 0$, let $\tilde{\beta}_0$ and $\tilde{\beta}_1$ be the intercept and slope from the regression of $\log(c_1 y_i)$ on x_i. Show that $\tilde{\beta}_1 = \hat{\beta}_1$ and $\tilde{\beta}_0 = \log(c_1) + \hat{\beta}_0$.

(iv) Now, assuming that $x_i > 0$ for all i, let $\tilde{\beta}_0$ and $\tilde{\beta}_1$ be the intercept and slope from the regression of y_i on $\log(c_2 x_i)$. How do $\tilde{\beta}_0$ and $\tilde{\beta}_1$ compare with the intercept and slope from the regression of y_i on $\log(x_i)$?

10 Let $\hat{\beta}_0$ and $\hat{\beta}_1$ be the OLS intercept and slope estimators, respectively, and let $\bar{u}$ be the sample average of the errors (not the residuals!).

(i) Show that $\hat{\beta}_1$ can be written as $\hat{\beta}_1 = \beta_1 + \sum_{i=1}^{n} w_i u_i$ where $w_i = d_i/\text{SST}_x$ and $d_i = x_i - \bar{x}$.

(ii) Use part (i), along with $\sum_{i=1}^{n} w_i = 0$, to show that $\hat{\beta}_1$ and $\bar{u}$ are uncorrelated. [*Hint*: You are being asked to show that $\text{E}[(\hat{\beta}_1 - \beta_1)\cdot\bar{u}] = 0$.]

(iii) Show that $\hat{\beta}_0$ can be written as $\hat{\beta}_0 = \beta_0 + \bar{u} - (\hat{\beta}_1 - \beta_1)\bar{x}$.

(iv) Use parts (ii) and (iii) to show that $\text{Var}(\hat{\beta}_0) = \sigma^2/n + \sigma^2(\bar{x})^2/\text{SST}_x$.

(v) Do the algebra to simplify the expression in part (iv) to equation (2.58). [*Hint*: $\text{SST}_x/n = n^{-1}\sum_{i=1}^{n} x_i^2 - (\bar{x})^2$.]

11 Suppose you are interested in estimating the effect of hours spent in an SAT preparation course (*hours*) on total SAT score (*sat*). The population is all college-bound high school seniors for a particular year.

(i) Suppose you are given a grant to run a controlled experiment. Explain how you would structure the experiment in order to estimate the causal effect of *hours* on *sat*.

(ii) Consider the more realistic case where students choose how much time to spend in a preparation course, and you can only randomly sample *sat* and *hours* from the population. Write the population model as

$$sat = \beta_0 + \beta_1 hours = u$$

where, as usual in a model with an intercept, we can assume $E(u) = 0$. List at least two factors contained in u. Are these likely to have positive or negative correlation with *hours*?

(iii) In the equation from part (ii), what should be the sign of β_1 if the preparation course is effective?

(iv) In the equation from part (ii), what is the interpretation of β_0?

12 Consider the problem described at the end of Section 2.6: running a regression and only estimating an intercept.

(i) Given a sample $\{y_i : i = 1, 2, \ldots, n\}$, let $\tilde{\beta}_0$ be the solution to

$$\min_{b_0} \sum_{i=1}^{n} (y_i - b_0)^2.$$

Show that $\tilde{\beta}_0 = \bar{y}$, that is, the sample average minimizes the sum of squared residuals. (*Hint*: You may use one-variable calculus or you can show the result directly by adding and subtracting $\bar{y}$ inside the squared residual and then doing a little algebra.)

(ii) Define residuals $\tilde{u}_i = y_i - \bar{y}$. Argue that these residuals always sum to zero.

Computer Exercises

C1 The data in 401K.RAW are a subset of data analyzed by Papke (1995) to study the relationship between participation in a 401(k) pension plan and the generosity of the plan. The variable *prate* is the percentage of eligible workers with an active account; this is the variable we would like to explain. The measure of generosity is the plan match rate, *mrate*. This variable gives the average amount the firm contributes to each worker's plan for each \$1 contribution by the worker. For example, if *mrate* = 0.50, then a \$1 contribution by the worker is matched by a 50¢ contribution by the firm.

(i) Find the average participation rate and the average match rate in the sample of plans.

(ii) Now, estimate the simple regression equation

$$\widehat{prate} = \hat{\beta}_0 + \hat{\beta}_1 mrate,$$

and report the results along with the sample size and R-squared.

(iii) Interpret the intercept in your equation. Interpret the coefficient on *mrate*.

(iv) Find the predicted *prate* when *mrate* = 3.5. Is this a reasonable prediction? Explain what is happening here.

(v) How much of the variation in *prate* is explained by *mrate*? Is this a lot in your opinion?

C2 The data set in CEOSAL2.RAW contains information on chief executive officers for U.S. corporations. The variable *salary* is annual compensation, in thousands of dollars, and *ceoten* is prior number of years as company CEO.

(i) Find the average salary and the average tenure in the sample.

(ii) How many CEOs are in their first year as CEO (that is, $ceoten = 0$)? What is the longest tenure as a CEO?

(iii) Estimate the simple regression model

$$\log(salary) = \beta_0 + \beta_1 ceoten + u,$$

and report your results in the usual form. What is the (approximate) predicted percentage increase in salary given one more year as a CEO?

C3 Use the data in SLEEP75.RAW from Biddle and Hamermesh (1990) to study whether there is a tradeoff between the time spent sleeping per week and the time spent in paid work. We could use either variable as the dependent variable. For concreteness, estimate the model

$$sleep = \beta_0 + \beta_1 totwrk + u,$$

where *sleep* is minutes spent sleeping at night per week and *totwrk* is total minutes worked during the week.

(i) Report your results in equation form along with the number of observations and R^2. What does the intercept in this equation mean?

(ii) If *totwrk* increases by 2 hours, by how much is *sleep* estimated to fall? Do you find this to be a large effect?

C4 Use the data in WAGE2.RAW to estimate a simple regression explaining monthly salary (*wage*) in terms of IQ score (*IQ*).

(i) Find the average salary and average IQ in the sample. What is the sample standard deviation of IQ? (IQ scores are standardized so that the average in the population is 100 with a standard deviation equal to 15.)

(ii) Estimate a simple regression model where a one-point increase in *IQ* changes *wage* by a constant dollar amount. Use this model to find the predicted increase in wage for an increase in *IQ* of 15 points. Does *IQ* explain most of the variation in *wage*?

(iii) Now, estimate a model where each one-point increase in *IQ* has the same percentage effect on *wage*. If *IQ* increases by 15 points, what is the approximate percentage increase in predicted *wage*?

C5 For the population of firms in the chemical industry, let *rd* denote annual expenditures on research and development, and let *sales* denote annual sales (both are in millions of dollars).

(i) Write down a model (not an estimated equation) that implies a constant elasticity between *rd* and *sales*. Which parameter is the elasticity?

(ii) Now, estimate the model using the data in RDCHEM.RAW. Write out the estimated equation in the usual form. What is the estimated elasticity of *rd* with respect to *sales*? Explain in words what this elasticity means.

C6 We used the data in MEAP93.RAW for Example 2.12. Now we want to explore the relationship between the math pass rate (*math10*) and spending per student (*expend*).

(i) Do you think each additional dollar spent has the same effect on the pass rate, or does a diminishing effect seem more appropriate? Explain.

(ii) In the population model

$$math10 = \beta_0 + \beta_1 \log(expend) + u,$$

argue that $\beta_1/10$ is the percentage point change in *math10* given a 10% increase in *expend*.

(iii) Use the data in MEAP93.RAW to estimate the model from part (ii). Report the estimated equation in the usual way, including the sample size and *R*-squared.

(iv) How big is the estimated spending effect? Namely, if spending increases by 10%, what is the estimated percentage point increase in *math10*?

(v) One might worry that regression analysis can produce fitted values for *math10* that are greater than 100. Why is this not much of a worry in this data set?

C7 Use the data in CHARITY.RAW [obtained from Franses and Paap (2001)] to answer the following questions:

(i) What is the average gift in the sample of 4,268 people (in Dutch guilders)? What percentage of people gave no gift?

(ii) What is the average mailings per year? What are the minimum and maximum values?

(iii) Estimate the model

$$gift = \beta_0 + \beta_1 mailsyear + u$$

by OLS and report the results in the usual way, including the sample size and *R*-squared.

(iv) Interpret the slope coefficient. If each mailing costs one guilder, is the charity expected to make a net gain on each mailing? Does this mean the charity makes a net gain on every mailing? Explain.

(v) What is the smallest predicted charitable contribution in the sample? Using this simple regression analysis, can you ever predict zero for *gift*?

C8 To complete this exercise you need a software package that allows you to generate data from the uniform and normal distributions.

(i) Start by generating 500 observations x_i – the explanatory variable – from the uniform distribution with range [0,10]. (Most statistical packages have a command for the Uniform[0,1] distribution; just multiply those observations by 10.) What are the sample mean and sample standard deviation of the x_i?

(ii) Randomly generate 500 errors, u_i, from the Normal[0,36] distribution. (If you generate a Normal[0,1], as is commonly available, simply multiply the outcomes by six.) Is the sample average of the u_i exactly zero? Why or why not? What is the sample standard deviation of the u_i?

(iii) Now generate the y_i as

$$y_i = 1 + 2x_i + u_i \equiv \beta_0 + \beta_1 x_i + u_i;$$

that is, the population intercept is one and the population slope is two. Use the data to run the regression of y_i on x_i. What are your estimates of the intercept and slope? Are they equal to the population values in the above equation? Explain.

(iv) Obtain the OLS residuals, $\hat{u}_i$, and verify that equation (2.60) hold (subject to rounding error).

(v) Compute the same quantities in equation (2.60) but use the errors u_i in place of the residuals. Now what do you conclude?

(vi) Repeat parts (i), (ii), and (iii) with a new sample of data, starting with generating the x_i. Now what do you obtain for $\hat{\beta}_0$ and $\hat{\beta}_1$? Why are these different from what you obtained in part (iii)?

APPENDIX 2A

Minimizing the Sum of Squared Residuals

We show that the OLS estimates $\hat{\beta}_0$ and $\hat{\beta}_1$ do minimize the sum of squared residuals, as asserted in Section 2.2. Formally, the problem is to characterize the solutions $\hat{\beta}_0$ and $\hat{\beta}_1$ to the minimization problem

$$\min_{b_0, b_1} \sum_{i=1}^{n} (y_i - b_0 - b_1 x_i)^2,$$

where b_0 and b_1 are the dummy arguments for the optimization problem; for simplicity, call this function $Q(b_0, b_1)$. By a fundamental result from multivariable calculus (see Appendix A), a necessary condition for $\hat{\beta}_0$ and $\hat{\beta}_1$ to solve the minimization problem is that the partial derivatives of $Q(b_0, b_1)$ with respect to b_0 and b_1 must be zero when evaluated at $\hat{\beta}_0$, $\hat{\beta}_1$: $\partial Q(\hat{\beta}_0, \hat{\beta}_1)/\partial b_0 = 0$ and $\partial Q(\hat{\beta}_0, \hat{\beta}_1)/\partial b_1 = 0$. Using the chain rule from calculus, these two equations become

$$-2 \sum_{i=1}^{n} (y_i - \hat{\beta}_0 - \hat{\beta}_1 x_i) = 0$$

$$-2 \sum_{i=1}^{n} x_i (y_i - \hat{\beta}_0 - \hat{\beta}_1 x_i) = 0.$$

These two equations are just (2.14) and (2.15) multiplied by $-2n$ and, therefore, are solved by the same $\hat{\beta}_0$ and $\hat{\beta}_1$.

How do we know that we have actually minimized the sum of squared residuals? The first order conditions are necessary but not sufficient conditions. One way to verify that we have minimized the sum of squared residuals is to write, for any b_0 and b_1,

$$\begin{aligned} Q(b_0, b_1) &= \sum_{i=1}^{n} [y_i - \hat{\beta}_0 - \hat{\beta}_1 x_i + (\hat{\beta}_0 - b_0) + (\hat{\beta}_1 - b_1) x_i]^2 \\ &= \sum_{i=1}^{n} [\hat{u}_i + (\hat{\beta}_0 - b_0) + (\hat{\beta}_1 - b_1) x_i]^2 \\ &= \sum_{i=1}^{n} \hat{u}_i^2 + n(\hat{\beta}_0 - b_0)^2 + (\hat{\beta}_1 - b_1)^2 \sum_{i=1}^{n} x_i^2 + 2(\hat{\beta}_0 - b_0)(\hat{\beta}_1 - b_1) \sum_{i=1}^{n} x_i, \end{aligned}$$

where we have used equations (2.30) and (2.31). The first term does not depend on b_0 or b_1, while the sum of the last three terms can be written as

$$\sum_{i=1}^{n} [(\hat{\beta}_0 - b_0) + (\hat{\beta}_1 - b_1)x_i]^2,$$

as can be verified by straightforward algebra. Because this is a sum of squared terms, the smallest it can be is zero. Therefore, it is smallest when $b_0 = \hat{\beta}_0$ and $b_1 = \hat{\beta}_1$.

CHAPTER 3

Multiple Regression Analysis: Estimation

In Chapter 2, we learned how to use simple regression analysis to explain a dependent variable, y, as a function of a single independent variable, x. The primary drawback in using simple regression analysis for empirical work is that it is very difficult to draw ceteris paribus conclusions about how x affects y: the key assumption, SLR.4—that all other factors affecting y are uncorrelated with x—is often unrealistic.

Multiple regression analysis is more amenable to ceteris paribus analysis because it allows us to *explicitly* control for many other factors that simultaneously affect the dependent variable. This is important both for testing economic theories and for evaluating policy effects when we must rely on nonexperimental data. Because multiple regression models can accommodate many explanatory variables that may be correlated, we can hope to infer causality in cases where simple regression analysis would be misleading.

Naturally, if we add more factors to our model that are useful for explaining y, then more of the variation in y can be explained. Thus, multiple regression analysis can be used to build better models for predicting the dependent variable.

An additional advantage of multiple regression analysis is that it can incorporate fairly general functional form relationships. In the simple regression model, only one function of a single explanatory variable can appear in the equation. As we will see, the multiple regression model allows for much more flexibility.

Section 3.1 formally introduces the multiple regression model and further discusses the advantages of multiple regression over simple regression. In Section 3.2, we demonstrate how to estimate the parameters in the multiple regression model using the method of ordinary least squares. In Sections 3.3, 3.4, and 3.5, we describe various statistical properties of the OLS estimators, including unbiasedness and efficiency.

The multiple regression model is still the most widely used vehicle for empirical analysis in economics and other social sciences. Likewise, the method of ordinary least squares is popularly used for estimating the parameters of the multiple regression model.

3.1 Motivation for Multiple Regression

The Model with Two Independent Variables

We begin with some simple examples to show how multiple regression analysis can be used to solve problems that cannot be solved by simple regression.

The first example is a simple variation of the wage equation introduced in Chapter 2 for obtaining the effect of education on hourly wage:

$$wage = \beta_0 + \beta_1 educ + \beta_2 exper + u, \quad [3.1]$$

where *exper* is years of labor market experience. Thus, *wage* is determined by the two explanatory or independent variables, education and experience, and by other unobserved factors, which are contained in u. We are still primarily interested in the effect of *educ* on *wage*, holding fixed all other factors affecting *wage*; that is, we are interested in the parameter β_1.

Compared with a simple regression analysis relating *wage* to *educ*, equation (3.1) effectively takes *exper* out of the error term and puts it explicitly in the equation. Because *exper* appears in the equation, its coefficient, β_2, measures the ceteris paribus effect of *exper* on *wage*, which is also of some interest.

Not surprisingly, just as with simple regression, we will have to make assumptions about how u in (3.1) is related to the independent variables, *educ* and *exper*. However, as we will see in Section 3.2, there is one thing of which we can be confident: because (3.1) contains experience explicitly, we will be able to measure the effect of education on wage, holding experience fixed. In a simple regression analysis—which puts *exper* in the error term—we would have to assume that experience is uncorrelated with education, a tenuous assumption.

As a second example, consider the problem of explaining the effect of per student spending (*expend*) on the average standardized test score (*avgscore*) at the high school level. Suppose that the average test score depends on funding, average family income (*avginc*), and other unobserved factors:

$$avgscore = \beta_0 + \beta_1 expend + \beta_2 avginc + u. \quad [3.2]$$

The coefficient of interest for policy purposes is β_1, the ceteris paribus effect of *expend* on *avgscore*. By including *avginc* explicitly in the model, we are able to control for its effect on *avgscore*. This is likely to be important because average family income tends to be correlated with per student spending: spending levels are often determined by both property and local income taxes. In simple regression analysis, *avginc* would be included in the error term, which would likely be correlated with *expend*, causing the OLS estimator of β_1 in the two-variable model to be biased.

In the two previous similar examples, we have shown how observable factors other than the variable of primary interest [*educ* in equation (3.1) and *expend* in equation (3.2)] can be included in a regression model. Generally, we can write a model with two independent variables as

$$y = \beta_0 + \beta_1 x_1 + \beta_2 x_2 + u, \quad [3.3]$$

where

β_0 is the intercept.
β_1 measures the change in y with respect to x_1, holding other factors fixed.
β_2 measures the change in y with respect to x_2, holding other factors fixed.

Multiple regression analysis is also useful for generalizing functional relationships between variables. As an example, suppose family consumption (*cons*) is a quadratic function of family income (*inc*):

$$cons = \beta_0 + \beta_1 inc + \beta_2 inc^2 + u, \quad [3.4]$$

where u contains other factors affecting consumption. In this model, consumption depends on only one observed factor, income; so it might seem that it can be handled in a simple regression framework. But the model falls outside simple regression because it contains two functions of income, *inc* and inc^2 (and therefore three parameters, β_0, β_1, and β_2). Nevertheless, the consumption function is easily written as a regression model with two independent variables by letting $x_1 = inc$ and $x_2 = inc^2$.

Mechanically, there will be *no* difference in using the method of ordinary least squares (introduced in Section 3.2) to estimate equations as different as (3.1) and (3.4). Each equation can be written as (3.3), which is all that matters for computation. There is, however, an important difference in how one *interprets* the parameters. In equation (3.1), β_1 is the ceteris paribus effect of *educ* on *wage*. The parameter β_1 has no such interpretation in (3.4). In other words, it makes no sense to measure the effect of *inc* on *cons* while holding inc^2 fixed, because if *inc* changes, then so must inc^2! Instead, the change in consumption with respect to the change in income—the marginal propensity to consume—is approximated by

$$\frac{\Delta cons}{\Delta inc} \approx \beta_1 + 2\beta_2 inc.$$

See Appendix A for the calculus needed to derive this equation. In other words, the marginal effect of income on consumption depends on β_2 as well as on β_1 and the level of income. This example shows that, in any particular application, the definitions of the independent variables are crucial. But for the theoretical development of multiple regression, we can be vague about such details. We will study examples like this more completely in Chapter 6.

In the model with two independent variables, the key assumption about how u is related to x_1 and x_2 is

$$\mathrm{E}(u|x_1, x_2) = 0. \quad [3.5]$$

The interpretation of condition (3.5) is similar to the interpretation of Assumption SLR.4 for simple regression analysis. It means that, for any values of x_1 and x_2 in the population, the average of the unobserved factors is equal to zero. As with simple regression, the important part of the assumption is that the expected value of u is the same for all combinations of x_1 and x_2; that this common value is zero is no assumption at all as long as the intercept β_0 is included in the model (see Section 2.1).

How can we interpret the zero conditional mean assumption in the previous examples? In equation (3.1), the assumption is $\mathrm{E}(u|educ,exper) = 0$. This implies that other factors affecting *wage* are not related on average to *educ* and *exper*. Therefore, if we think innate ability is part of u, then we will need average ability levels to be the same across all combinations of education and experience in the working population. This may or may not be true, but, as we will see in Section 3.3, this is the question we need to ask in order to determine whether the method of ordinary least squares produces unbiased estimators.

The example measuring student performance [equation (3.2)] is similar to the wage equation. The zero conditional mean assumption is $\mathrm{E}(u|expend, avginc) = 0$, which means that other factors affecting test scores—school or student characteristics—are, on average, unrelated to per-student funding and average family income.

EXPLORING FURTHER 3.1

A simple model to explain city murder rates (*murdrate*) in terms of the probability of conviction (*prbconv*) and average sentence length (*avgsen*) is

$$murdrate = \beta_0 + \beta_1 prbconv + \beta_2 avgsen + u.$$

What are some factors contained in u? Do you think the key assumption (3.5) is likely to hold?

When applied to the quadratic consumption function in (3.4), the zero conditional mean assumption has a slightly different interpretation. Written literally, equation (3.5) becomes $E(u|inc,inc^2) = 0$. Since inc^2 is known when inc is known, including inc^2 in the expectation is redundant: $E(u|inc,inc^2) = 0$ is the same as $E(u|inc) = 0$. Nothing is wrong with putting inc^2 along with inc in the expectation when stating the assumption, but $E(u|inc) = 0$ is more concise.

The Model with *k* Independent Variables

Once we are in the context of multiple regression, there is no need to stop with two independent variables. Multiple regression analysis allows many observed factors to affect y. In the wage example, we might also include amount of job training, years of tenure with the current employer, measures of ability, and even demographic variables like the number of siblings or mother's education. In the school funding example, additional variables might include measures of teacher quality and school size.

The general **multiple linear regression model** (also called the *multiple regression model*) can be written in the population as

$$y = \beta_0 + \beta_1 x_1 + \beta_2 x_2 + \beta_3 x_3 + \ldots + \beta_k x_k + u, \quad [3.6]$$

where

β_0 is the **intercept**.
β_1 is the parameter associated with x_1.
β_2 is the parameter associated with x_2, and so on.

Since there are k independent variables and an intercept, equation (3.6) contains $k + 1$ (unknown) population parameters. For shorthand purposes, we will sometimes refer to the parameters other than the intercept as **slope parameters**, even though this is not always literally what they are. [See equation (3.4), where neither β_1 nor β_2 is itself a slope, but together they determine the slope of the relationship between consumption and income.]

The terminology for multiple regression is similar to that for simple regression and is given in Table 3.1. Just as in simple regression, the variable u is the **error term** or **disturbance**. It contains factors other than $x_1, x_2, \ldots, x_k$ that affect y. No matter how many explanatory variables we include in our model, there will always be factors we cannot include, and these are collectively contained in u.

When applying the general multiple regression model, we must know how to interpret the parameters. We will get plenty of practice now and in subsequent chapters, but it is useful at this point to be reminded of some things we already know. Suppose that CEO salary (*salary*) is related to firm sales (*sales*) and CEO tenure (*ceoten*) with the firm by

$$\log(salary) = \beta_0 + \beta_1 \log(sales) + \beta_2 ceoten + \beta_3 ceoten^2 + u. \quad [3.7]$$

TABLE 3.1 Terminology for Multiple Regression

y	$x_1, x_2, ..., x_k$
Dependent variable	Independent variables
Explained variable	Explanatory variables
Response variable	Control variables
Predicted variable	Predictor variables
Regressand	Regressors

This fits into the multiple regression model (with $k = 3$) by defining $y = \log(salary)$, $x_1 = \log(sales)$, $x_2 = ceoten$, and $x_3 = ceoten^2$. As we know from Chapter 2, the parameter β_1 is the (ceteris paribus) *elasticity* of *salary* with respect to *sales*. If $\beta_3 = 0$, then $100\beta_2$ is approximately the ceteris paribus percentage increase in *salary* when *ceoten* increases by one year. When $\beta_3 \neq 0$, the effect of *ceoten* on *salary* is more complicated. We will postpone a detailed treatment of general models with quadratics until Chapter 6.

Equation (3.7) provides an important reminder about multiple regression analysis. The term "linear" in a multiple linear regression model means that equation (3.6) is linear in the *parameters*, β_j. Equation (3.7) is an example of a multiple regression model that, while linear in the β_j, is a nonlinear relationship between *salary* and the variables *sales* and *ceoten*. Many applications of multiple linear regression involve nonlinear relationships among the underlying variables.

The key assumption for the general multiple regression model is easy to state in terms of a conditional expectation:

$$E(u|x_1, x_2, ..., x_k) = 0. \quad [3.8]$$

At a minimum, equation (3.8) requires that all factors in the unobserved error term be uncorrelated with the explanatory variables. It also means that we have correctly accounted for the functional relationships between the explained and explanatory variables. Any problem that causes u to be correlated with any of the independent variables causes (3.8) to fail. In Section 3.3, we will show that assumption (3.8) implies that OLS is unbiased and will derive the bias that arises when a key variable has been omitted from the equation. In Chapters 15 and 16, we will study other reasons that might cause (3.8) to fail and show what can be done in cases where it does fail.

3.2 Mechanics and Interpretation of Ordinary Least Squares

We now summarize some computational and algebraic features of the method of ordinary least squares as it applies to a particular set of data. We also discuss how to interpret the estimated equation.

Obtaining the OLS Estimates

We first consider estimating the model with two independent variables. The estimated OLS equation is written in a form similar to the simple regression case:

$$\hat{y} = \hat{\beta}_0 + \hat{\beta}_1 x_1 + \hat{\beta}_2 x_2, \quad [3.9]$$

where

$\hat{\beta}_0$ = the estimate of β_0.
$\hat{\beta}_1$ = the estimate of β_1.
$\hat{\beta}_2$ = the estimate of β_2.

But how do we obtain $\hat{\beta}_0$, $\hat{\beta}_1$, and $\hat{\beta}_2$? The method of **ordinary least squares** chooses the estimates to minimize the sum of squared residuals. That is, given n observations on y, x_1, and x_2, $\{(x_{i1}, x_{i2}, y_i): i = 1, 2, \ldots, n\}$, the estimates $\hat{\beta}_0$, $\hat{\beta}_1$, and $\hat{\beta}_2$ are chosen simultaneously to make

$$\sum_{i=1}^{n} (y_i - \hat{\beta}_0 - \hat{\beta}_1 x_{i1} - \hat{\beta}_2 x_{i2})^2 \qquad [3.10]$$

as small as possible.

To understand what OLS is doing, it is important to master the meaning of the indexing of the independent variables in (3.10). The independent variables have two subscripts here, i followed by either 1 or 2. The i subscript refers to the observation number. Thus, the sum in (3.10) is over all $i = 1$ to n observations. The second index is simply a method of distinguishing between different independent variables. In the example relating *wage* to *educ* and *exper*, $x_{i1} = educ_i$ is education for person i in the sample, and $x_{i2} = exper_i$ is experience for person i. The sum of squared residuals in equation (3.10) is $\sum_{i=1}^{n} (wage_i - \hat{\beta}_0 - \hat{\beta}_1 educ_i - \hat{\beta}_2 exper_i)^2$. In what follows, the i subscript is reserved for indexing the observation number. If we write x_{ij}, then this means the ith observation on the jth independent variable. (Some authors prefer to switch the order of the observation number and the variable number, so that x_{1i} is observation i on variable one. But this is just a matter of notational taste.)

In the general case with k independent variables, we seek estimates $\hat{\beta}_0, \hat{\beta}_1, \ldots, \hat{\beta}_k$ in the equation

$$\hat{y} = \hat{\beta}_0 + \hat{\beta}_1 x_1 + \hat{\beta}_2 x_2 + \ldots + \hat{\beta}_k x_k. \qquad [3.11]$$

The OLS estimates, $k + 1$ of them, are chosen to minimize the sum of squared residuals:

$$\sum_{i=1}^{n} (y_i - \hat{\beta}_0 - \hat{\beta}_1 x_{i1} - \ldots - \hat{\beta}_k x_{ik})^2. \qquad [3.12]$$

This minimization problem can be solved using multivariable calculus (see Appendix 3A). This leads to $k + 1$ linear equations in $k + 1$ unknowns $\hat{\beta}_0, \hat{\beta}_1, \ldots, \hat{\beta}_k$:

$$\begin{aligned}
&\sum_{i=1}^{n} (y_i - \hat{\beta}_0 - \hat{\beta}_1 x_{i1} - \ldots - \hat{\beta}_k x_{ik}) = 0 \\
&\sum_{i=1}^{n} x_{i1}(y_i - \hat{\beta}_0 - \hat{\beta}_1 x_{i1} - \ldots - \hat{\beta}_k x_{ik}) = 0 \\
&\sum_{i=1}^{n} x_{i2}(y_i - \hat{\beta}_0 - \hat{\beta}_1 x_{i1} - \ldots - \hat{\beta}_k x_{ik}) = 0 \qquad [3.13] \\
&\vdots \\
&\sum_{i=1}^{n} x_{ik}(y_i - \hat{\beta}_0 - \hat{\beta}_1 x_{i1} - \ldots - \hat{\beta}_k x_{ik}) = 0.
\end{aligned}$$

These are often called the OLS **first order conditions**. As with the simple regression model in Section 2.2, the OLS first order conditions can be obtained by the method of moments: under assumption (3.8), $E(u) = 0$ and $E(x_j u) = 0$, where $j = 1, 2, \ldots, k$. The equations in (3.13) are the sample counterparts of these population moments, although we have omitted the division by the sample size n.

For even moderately sized n and k, solving the equations in (3.13) by hand calculations is tedious. Nevertheless, modern computers running standard statistics and econometrics software can solve these equations with large n and k very quickly.

There is only one slight caveat: we must assume that the equations in (3.13) can be solved *uniquely* for the $\hat{\beta}_j$. For now, we just assume this, as it is usually the case in well-specified models. In Section 3.3, we state the assumption needed for unique OLS estimates to exist (see Assumption MLR.3).

As in simple regression analysis, equation (3.11) is called the **OLS regression line** or the **sample regression function (SRF)**. We will call $\hat{\beta}_0$ the **OLS intercept estimate** and $\hat{\beta}_1, \ldots, \hat{\beta}_k$ the **OLS slope estimates** (corresponding to the independent variables $x_1, x_2, \ldots, x_k$).

To indicate that an OLS regression has been run, we will either write out equation (3.11) with y and $x_1, \ldots, x_k$ replaced by their variable names (such as *wage*, *educ*, and *exper*), or we will say that "we ran an OLS regression of y on $x_1, x_2, \ldots, x_k$" or that "we regressed y on $x_1, x_2, \ldots, x_k$." These are shorthand for saying that the method of ordinary least squares was used to obtain the OLS equation (3.11). Unless explicitly stated otherwise, we always estimate an intercept along with the slopes.

Interpreting the OLS Regression Equation

More important than the details underlying the computation of the $\hat{\beta}_j$ is the *interpretation* of the estimated equation. We begin with the case of two independent variables:

$$\hat{y} = \hat{\beta}_0 + \hat{\beta}_1 x_1 + \hat{\beta}_2 x_2. \quad [3.14]$$

The intercept $\hat{\beta}_0$ in equation (3.14) is the predicted value of y when $x_1 = 0$ and $x_2 = 0$. Sometimes, setting x_1 and x_2 both equal to zero is an interesting scenario; in other cases, it will not make sense. Nevertheless, the intercept is always needed to obtain a prediction of y from the OLS regression line, as (3.14) makes clear.

The estimates $\hat{\beta}_1$ and $\hat{\beta}_2$ have **partial effect**, or **ceteris paribus**, interpretations. From equation (3.14), we have

$$\Delta\hat{y} = \hat{\beta}_1 \Delta x_1 + \hat{\beta}_2 \Delta x_2,$$

so we can obtain the predicted change in y given the changes in x_1 and x_2. (Note how the intercept has nothing to do with the changes in y.) In particular, when x_2 is held fixed, so that $\Delta x_2 = 0$, then

$$\Delta\hat{y} = \hat{\beta}_1 \Delta x_1,$$

holding x_2 fixed. The key point is that, by including x_2 in our model, we obtain a coefficient on x_1 with a ceteris paribus interpretation. This is why multiple regression analysis is so useful. Similarly,

$$\Delta\hat{y} = \hat{\beta}_2 \Delta x_2,$$

holding x_1 fixed.

EXAMPLE 3.1 DETERMINANTS OF COLLEGE GPA

The variables in GPA1.RAW include the college grade point average (*colGPA*), high school GPA (*hsGPA*), and achievement test score (*ACT*) for a sample of 141 students from a large university; both college and high school GPAs are on a four-point scale. We obtain the following OLS regression line to predict college GPA from high school GPA and achievement test score:

$$\widehat{colGPA} = 1.29 + .453\ hsGPA + .0094\ ACT$$
$$n = 141. \qquad [3.15]$$

How do we interpret this equation? First, the intercept 1.29 is the predicted college GPA if *hsGPA* and *ACT* are both set as zero. Since no one who attends college has either a zero high school GPA or a zero on the achievement test, the intercept in this equation is not, by itself, meaningful.

More interesting estimates are the slope coefficients on *hsGPA* and *ACT*. As expected, there is a positive partial relationship between *colGPA* and *hsGPA*: Holding *ACT* fixed, another point on *hsGPA* is associated with .453 of a point on the college GPA, or almost half a point. In other words, if we choose two students, A and B, and these students have the same ACT score, but the high school GPA of Student A is one point higher than the high school GPA of Student B, then we predict Student A to have a college GPA .453 higher than that of Student B. (This says nothing about any two actual people, but it is our best prediction.)

The sign on *ACT* implies that, while holding *hsGPA* fixed, a change in the ACT score of 10 points—a very large change, since the maximum ACT score is 36 and the average score in the sample is about 24 with a standard deviation less than three—affects *colGPA* by less than one-tenth of a point. This is a small effect, and it suggests that, once high school GPA is accounted for, the ACT score is not a strong predictor of college GPA. (Naturally, there are many other factors that contribute to GPA, but here we focus on statistics available for high school students.) Later, after we discuss statistical inference, we will show that not only is the coefficient on ACT practically small, it is also statistically insignificant.

If we focus on a simple regression analysis relating *colGPA* to *ACT* only, we obtain

$$\widehat{colGPA} = 2.40 + .0271\ ACT$$
$$n = 141;$$

thus, the coefficient on *ACT* is almost three times as large as the estimate in (3.15). But this equation does *not* allow us to compare two people with the same high school GPA; it corresponds to a different experiment. We say more about the differences between multiple and simple regression later.

The case with more than two independent variables is similar. The OLS regression line is

$$\hat{y} = \hat{\beta}_0 + \hat{\beta}_1 x_1 + \hat{\beta}_2 x_2 + \ldots + \hat{\beta}_k x_k. \qquad [3.16]$$

Written in terms of changes,

$$\Delta\hat{y} = \hat{\beta}_1 \Delta x_1 + \hat{\beta}_2 \Delta x_2 + \ldots + \hat{\beta}_k \Delta x_k. \qquad [3.17]$$

The coefficient on x_1 measures the change in $\hat{y}$ due to a one-unit increase in x_1, holding all other independent variables fixed. That is,

$$\Delta\hat{y} = \hat{\beta}_1 \Delta x_1, \qquad [3.18]$$

holding $x_2, x_3, \ldots, x_k$ fixed. Thus, we have *controlled for* the variables $x_2, x_3, \ldots, x_k$ when estimating the effect of x_1 on y. The other coefficients have a similar interpretation.

The following is an example with three independent variables.

EXAMPLE 3.2 HOURLY WAGE EQUATION

Using the 526 observations on workers in WAGE1.RAW, we include *educ* (years of education), *exper* (years of labor market experience), and *tenure* (years with the current employer) in an equation explaining log(*wage*). The estimated equation is

$$\begin{aligned} \widehat{\log(wage)} &= .284 + .092\ educ + .0041\ exper + .022\ tenure \\ n &= 526. \end{aligned} \qquad [3.19]$$

As in the simple regression case, the coefficients have a percentage interpretation. The only difference here is that they also have a ceteris paribus interpretation. The coefficient .092 means that, holding *exper* and *tenure* fixed, another year of education is predicted to increase log(*wage*) by .092, which translates into an approximate 9.2% [100(.092)] increase in *wage*. Alternatively, if we take two people with the same levels of experience and job tenure, the coefficient on *educ* is the proportionate difference in predicted wage when their education levels differ by one year. This measure of the return to education at least keeps two important productivity factors fixed; whether it is a good estimate of the ceteris paribus return to another year of education requires us to study the statistical properties of OLS (see Section 3.3).

On the Meaning of "Holding Other Factors Fixed" in Multiple Regression

The partial effect interpretation of slope coefficients in multiple regression analysis can cause some confusion, so we provide a further discussion now.

In Example 3.1, we observed that the coefficient on *ACT* measures the predicted difference in *colGPA*, holding *hsGPA* fixed. The power of multiple regression analysis is that it provides this ceteris paribus interpretation even though the data have *not* been collected in a ceteris paribus fashion. In giving the coefficient on *ACT* a partial effect interpretation, it may seem that we actually went out and sampled people with the same high school GPA but possibly with different ACT scores. This is not the case. The data are a random sample from a large university: there were no restrictions placed on the sample values of *hsGPA* or *ACT* in obtaining the data. Rarely do we have the luxury of holding certain variables fixed in obtaining our sample. *If* we could collect a sample of individuals with the same high school GPA, then we could perform a simple regression analysis relating *colGPA* to *ACT*. Multiple regression effectively allows us to mimic this situation without restricting the values of any independent variables.

The power of multiple regression analysis is that it allows us to do in nonexperimental environments what natural scientists are able to do in a controlled laboratory setting: keep other factors fixed.

Changing More Than One Independent Variable Simultaneously

Sometimes, we want to change more than one independent variable at the same time to find the resulting effect on the dependent variable. This is easily done using equation (3.17). For example, in equation (3.19), we can obtain the estimated effect on *wage* when an individual stays at the same firm for another year: *exper* (general workforce experience) and *tenure* both increase by one year. The total effect (holding *educ* fixed) is

$$\Delta\widehat{\log(wage)} = .0041\ \Delta exper + .022\ \Delta tenure = .0041 + .022 = .0261,$$

or about 2.6%. Since *exper* and *tenure* each increase by one year, we just add the coefficients on *exper* and *tenure* and multiply by 100 to turn the effect into a percentage.

OLS Fitted Values and Residuals

After obtaining the OLS regression line (3.11), we can obtain a *fitted* or *predicted value* for each observation. For observation i, the fitted value is simply

$$\hat{y}_i = \hat{\beta}_0 + \hat{\beta}_1 x_{i1} + \hat{\beta}_2 x_{i2} + \ldots + \hat{\beta}_k x_{ik}, \qquad [3.20]$$

which is just the predicted value obtained by plugging the values of the independent variables for observation i into equation (3.11). We should not forget about the intercept in obtaining the fitted values; otherwise, the answer can be very misleading. As an example, if in (3.15), $hsGPA_i = 3.5$ and $ACT_i = 24$, $\widehat{colGPA}_i = 1.29 + .453(3.5) + .0094(24) =$ 3.101 (rounded to three places after the decimal).

Normally, the actual value y_i for any observation i will not equal the predicted value, $\hat{y}_i$: OLS minimizes the *average* squared prediction error, which says nothing about the prediction error for any particular observation. The **residual** for observation i is defined just as in the simple regression case,

$$\hat{u}_i = y_i - \hat{y}_i. \qquad [3.21]$$

There is a residual for each observation. If $\hat{u}_i > 0$, then $\hat{y}_i$ is below y_i, which means that, for this observation, y_i is underpredicted. If $\hat{u}_i < 0$, then $y_i < \hat{y}_i$, and y_i is overpredicted.

The OLS fitted values and residuals have some important properties that are immediate extensions from the single variable case:

1. The sample average of the residuals is zero and so $\bar{y} = \bar{\hat{y}}$.
2. The sample covariance between each independent variable and the OLS residuals is zero. Consequently, the sample covariance between the OLS fitted values and the OLS residuals is zero.
3. The point $(\bar{x}_1, \bar{x}_2, \ldots, \bar{x}_k, \bar{y})$ is always on the OLS regression line: $\bar{y} = \hat{\beta}_0 + \hat{\beta}_1\bar{x}_1 + \hat{\beta}_2\bar{x}_2 + \ldots + \hat{\beta}_k\bar{x}_k$.

EXPLORING FURTHER 3.2

In Example 3.1, the OLS fitted line explaining college GPA in terms of high school GPA and ACT score is

$$\widehat{colGPA} = 1.29 + .453\ hsGPA + .0094\ ACT.$$

If the average high school GPA is about 3.4 and the average ACT score is about 24.2, what is the average college GPA in the sample?

The first two properties are immediate consequences of the set of equations used to obtain the OLS estimates. The first equation in (3.13) says that the sum of the residuals is zero. The remaining equations are of the form $\sum_{i=1}^{n} x_{ij}\hat{u}_i = 0$, which implies that each independent variable has zero sample covariance with $\hat{u}_i$. Property (3) follows immediately from property (1).

A "Partialling Out" Interpretation of Multiple Regression

When applying OLS, we do not need to know explicit formulas for the $\hat{\beta}_j$ that solve the system of equations in (3.13). Nevertheless, for certain derivations, we do need explicit formulas for the $\hat{\beta}_j$. These formulas also shed further light on the workings of OLS.

Consider again the case with $k = 2$ independent variables, $\hat{y} = \hat{\beta}_0 + \hat{\beta}_1 x_1 + \hat{\beta}_2 x_2$. For concreteness, we focus on $\hat{\beta}_1$. One way to express $\hat{\beta}_1$ is

$$\hat{\beta}_1 = \left(\sum_{i=1}^{n} \hat{r}_{i1} y_i\right) \Bigg/ \left(\sum_{i=1}^{n} \hat{r}_{i1}^2\right), \qquad [3.22]$$

where the $\hat{r}_{i1}$ are the OLS residuals from a simple regression of x_1 on x_2, using the sample at hand. We regress our first independent variable, x_1, on our second independent variable, x_2, and then obtain the residuals (y plays no role here). Equation (3.22) shows that we can then do a simple regression of y on $\hat{r}_1$ to obtain $\hat{\beta}_1$. (Note that the residuals $\hat{r}_{i1}$ have a zero sample average, and so $\hat{\beta}_1$ is the usual slope estimate from simple regression.)

The representation in equation (3.22) gives another demonstration of $\hat{\beta}_1$'s partial effect interpretation. The residuals $\hat{r}_{i1}$ are the part of x_{i1} that is uncorrelated with x_{i2}. Another way of saying this is that $\hat{r}_{i1}$ is x_{i1} after the effects of x_{i2} have been *partialled out*, or *netted out*. Thus, $\hat{\beta}_1$ measures the sample relationship between y and x_1 after x_2 has been partialled out.

In simple regression analysis, there is no partialling out of other variables because no other variables are included in the regression. Computer Exercise C5 steps you through the partialling out process using the wage data from Example 3.2. For practical purposes, the important thing is that $\hat{\beta}_1$ in the equation $\hat{y} = \hat{\beta}_0 + \hat{\beta}_1 x_1 + \hat{\beta}_2 x_2$ measures the change in y given a one-unit increase in x_1, holding x_2 fixed.

In the general model with k explanatory variables, $\hat{\beta}_1$ can still be written as in equation (3.22), but the residuals $\hat{r}_{i1}$ come from the regression of x_1 on $x_2, \ldots, x_k$. Thus, $\hat{\beta}_1$ measures the effect of x_1 on y after $x_2, \ldots, x_k$ have been partialled or netted out.

Comparison of Simple and Multiple Regression Estimates

Two special cases exist in which the simple regression of y on x_1 will produce the *same* OLS estimate on x_1 as the regression of y on x_1 and x_2. To be more precise, write the simple regression of y on x_1 as $\tilde{y} = \tilde{\beta}_0 + \tilde{\beta}_1 x_1$, and write the multiple regression as $\hat{y} = \hat{\beta}_0 + \hat{\beta}_1 x_1 + \hat{\beta}_2 x_2$. We know that the simple regression coefficient $\tilde{\beta}_1$ does not usually equal the multiple regression coefficient $\hat{\beta}_1$. It turns out there is a simple relationship between $\tilde{\beta}_1$ and $\hat{\beta}_1$, which allows for interesting comparisons between simple and multiple regression:

$$\tilde{\beta}_1 = \hat{\beta}_1 + \hat{\beta}_2\tilde{\delta}_1, \quad [3.23]$$

where $\tilde{\delta}_1$ is the slope coefficient from the simple regression of x_{i2} on x_{i1}, $i = 1, \ldots, n$. This equation shows how $\tilde{\beta}_1$ differs from the partial effect of x_1 on $\hat{y}$. The confounding term is the partial effect of x_2 on $\hat{y}$ times the slope in the sample regression of x_2 on x_1. (See Section 3A.4 in the chapter appendix for a more general verification.)

The relationship between $\tilde{\beta}_1$ and $\hat{\beta}_1$ also shows there are two distinct cases where they are equal:

1. The partial effect of x_2 on $\hat{y}$ is zero in the sample. That is, $\hat{\beta}_2 = 0$.
2. x_1 and x_2 are uncorrelated in the sample. That is, $\tilde{\delta}_1 = 0$.

Even though simple and multiple regression estimates are almost never identical, we can use the above formula to characterize why they might be either very different or quite similar. For example, if $\hat{\beta}_2$ is small, we might expect the multiple and simple regression estimates of β_1 to be similar. In Example 3.1, the sample correlation between *hsGPA* and *ACT* is about 0.346, which is a nontrivial correlation. But the coefficient on *ACT* is fairly little. It is not surprising to find that the simple regression of *colGPA* on *hsGPA* produces a slope estimate of .482, which is not much different from the estimate .453 in (3.15).

EXAMPLE 3.3 PARTICIPATION IN 401(k) PENSION PLANS

We use the data in 401K.RAW to estimate the effect of a plan's match rate (*mrate*) on the participation rate (*prate*) in its 401(k) pension plan. The match rate is the amount the firm contributes to a worker's fund for each dollar the worker contributes (up to some limit); thus, *mrate* = .75 means that the firm contributes 75¢ for each dollar contributed by the worker. The participation rate is the percentage of eligible workers having a 401(k) account. The variable *age* is the age of the 401(k) plan. There are 1,534 plans in the data set, the average *prate* is 87.36, the average *mrate* is .732, and the average *age* is 13.2.

Regressing *prate* on *mrate*, *age* gives

$$\widehat{prate} = 80.12 + 5.52\, mrate + .243\, age$$
$$n = 1{,}534.$$

Thus, both *mrate* and *age* have the expected effects. What happens if we do not control for *age*? The estimated effect of *age* is not trivial, and so we might expect a large change in the estimated effect of *mrate* if *age* is dropped from the regression. However, the simple regression of *prate* on *mrate* yields $\widehat{prate} = 83.08 + 5.86\, mrate$. The simple regression estimate of the effect of *mrate* on *prate* is clearly different from the multiple regression estimate, but the difference is not very big. (The simple regression estimate is only about 6.2% larger than the multiple regression estimate.) This can be explained by the fact that the sample correlation between *mrate* and *age* is only .12.

In the case with k independent variables, the simple regression of y on x_1 and the multiple regression of y on $x_1, x_2, \ldots, x_k$ produce an identical estimate of x_1 only if (1) the OLS coefficients on x_2 through x_k are all zero *or* (2) x_1 is uncorrelated with *each of* $x_2, \ldots, x_k$.

Neither of these is very likely in practice. But if the coefficients on x_2 through x_k are small, or the sample correlations between x_1 and the other independent variables are insubstantial, then the simple and multiple regression estimates of the effect of x_1 on y can be similar.

Goodness-of-Fit

As with simple regression, we can define the **total sum of squares (SST)**, the **explained sum of squares (SSE)**, and the **residual sum of squares** or **sum of squared residuals (SSR)** as

$$\text{SST} \equiv \sum_{i=1}^{n} (y_i - \bar{y})^2 \quad [3.24]$$

$$\text{SSE} \equiv \sum_{i=1}^{n} (\hat{y}_i - \bar{y})^2 \quad [3.25]$$

$$\text{SSR} \equiv \sum_{i=1}^{n} \hat{u}_i^2. \quad [3.26]$$

Using the same argument as in the simple regression case, we can show that

$$\text{SST} = \text{SSE} + \text{SSR}. \quad [3.27]$$

In other words, the total variation in $\{y_i\}$ is the sum of the total variations in $\{\hat{y}_i\}$ and in $\{\hat{u}_i\}$.

Assuming that the total variation in y is nonzero, as is the case unless y_i is constant in the sample, we can divide (3.27) by SST to get

$$\text{SSR/SST} + \text{SSE/SST} = 1.$$

Just as in the simple regression case, the R-squared is defined to be

$$R^2 \equiv \text{SSE/SST} = 1 - \text{SSR/SST}, \quad [3.28]$$

and it is interpreted as the proportion of the sample variation in y_i that is explained by the OLS regression line. By definition, R^2 is a number between zero and one.

R^2 can also be shown to equal the squared correlation coefficient between the actual y_i and the fitted values $\hat{y}_i$. That is,

$$R^2 = \frac{\left(\sum_{i=1}^{n} (y_i - \bar{y})(\hat{y}_i - \bar{\hat{y}})\right)^2}{\left(\sum_{i=1}^{n} (y_i - \bar{y})^2\right)\left(\sum_{i=1}^{n} (\hat{y}_i - \bar{\hat{y}})^2\right)}. \quad [3.29]$$

[We have put the average of the $\hat{y}_i$ in (3.29) to be true to the formula for a correlation coefficient; we know that this average equals $\bar{y}$ because the sample average of the residuals is zero and $y_i = \hat{y}_i + \hat{u}_i$.]

An important fact about R^2 is that it never decreases, and it usually increases when another independent variable is added to a regression. This algebraic fact follows because, by definition, the sum of squared residuals never increases when additional regressors are added to the model. For example, the last digit of one's social security number has nothing to do with one's hourly wage, but adding this digit to a wage equation will increase the R^2 (by a little, at least).

The fact that R^2 never decreases when *any* variable is added to a regression makes it a poor tool for deciding whether one variable or several variables should be added to a model. The factor that should determine whether an explanatory variable belongs in a model is whether the explanatory variable has a nonzero partial effect on y in the *population*. We will show how to test this hypothesis in Chapter 4 when we cover statistical inference. We will also see that, when used properly, R^2 allows us to *test* a group of variables to see if it is important for explaining y. For now, we use it as a goodness-of-fit measure for a given model.

EXAMPLE 3.4 DETERMINANTS OF COLLEGE GPA

From the grade point average regression that we did earlier, the equation with R^2 is

$$\widehat{colGPA} = 1.29 + .453\ hsGPA + .0094\ ACT$$

$$n = 141, R^2 = .176.$$

This means that *hsGPA* and *ACT* together explain about 17.6% of the variation in college GPA for this sample of students. This may not seem like a high percentage, but we must remember that there are many other factors—including family background, personality, quality of high school education, affinity for college—that contribute to a student's college performance. If *hsGPA* and *ACT* explained almost all of the variation in *colGPA*, then performance in college would be preordained by high school performance!

Example 3.5 deserves a final word of caution. The fact that the four explanatory variables included in the second regression explain only about 4.2% of the variation in *narr86* does not necessarily mean that the equation is useless. Even though these variables collectively do not explain much of the variation in arrests, it is still possible that the OLS estimates are reliable estimates of the ceteris paribus effects of each independent variable on *narr86*. As we will see, whether this is the case does not directly depend on the size of R^2. Generally, a low R^2 indicates that it is hard to predict individual outcomes on y with much accuracy, something we study in more detail in Chapter 6. In the arrest example, the small R^2 reflects what we already suspect in the social sciences: it is generally very difficult to predict individual behavior.

Regression through the Origin

Sometimes, an economic theory or common sense suggests that β_0 should be zero, and so we should briefly mention OLS estimation when the intercept is zero. Specifically, we now seek an equation of the form

$$\tilde{y} = \tilde{\beta}_1 x_1 + \tilde{\beta}_2 x_2 + \ldots + \tilde{\beta}_k x_k, \quad [3.30]$$

where the symbol "~" over the estimates is used to distinguish them from the OLS estimates obtained along with the intercept [as in (3.11)]. In (3.30), when $x_1 = 0$, $x_2 = 0$, …, $x_k = 0$, the predicted value is zero. In this case, $\tilde{\beta}_1$, …, $\tilde{\beta}_k$ are said to be the OLS estimates from the regression of y on x_1, x_2, …, x_k *through the origin*.

The OLS estimates in (3.30), as always, minimize the sum of squared residuals, but with the intercept set at zero. You should be warned that the properties of OLS that we derived earlier no longer hold for regression through the origin. In particular, the OLS

EXAMPLE 3.5 EXPLAINING ARREST RECORDS

CRIME1.RAW contains data on arrests during the year 1986 and other information on 2,725 men born in either 1960 or 1961 in California. Each man in the sample was arrested at least once prior to 1986. The variable *narr86* is the number of times the man was arrested during 1986: it is zero for most men in the sample (72.29%), and it varies from 0 to 12. (The percentage of men arrested once during 1986 was 20.51.) The variable *pcnv* is the proportion (not percentage) of arrests prior to 1986 that led to conviction, *avgsen* is average sentence length served for prior convictions (zero for most people), *ptime86* is months spent in prison in 1986, and *qemp86* is the number of quarters during which the man was employed in 1986 (from zero to four).

A linear model explaining arrests is

$$narr86 = \beta_0 + \beta_1 pcnv + \beta_2 avgsen + \beta_3 ptime86 + \beta_4 qemp86 + u,$$

where *pcnv* is a proxy for the likelihood for being convicted of a crime and *avgsen* is a measure of expected severity of punishment, if convicted. The variable *ptime86* captures the incarcerative effects of crime: if an individual is in prison, he cannot be arrested for a crime outside of prison. Labor market opportunities are crudely captured by *qemp86*.

First, we estimate the model without the variable *avgsen*. We obtain

$$\widehat{narr86} = .712 - .150\, pcnv - .034\, ptime86 - .104\, qemp86$$
$$n = 2{,}725,\ R^2 = .0413.$$

This equation says that, as a group, the three variables *pcnv*, *ptime86*, and *qemp86* explain about 4.1% of the variation in *narr86*.

Each of the OLS slope coefficients has the anticipated sign. An increase in the proportion of convictions lowers the predicted number of arrests. If we increase *pcnv* by .50 (a large increase in the probability of conviction), then, holding the other factors fixed, $\Delta\widehat{narr86} = -.150(.50) = -.075$. This may seem unusual because an arrest cannot change by a fraction. But we can use this value to obtain the predicted change in expected arrests for a large group of men. For example, among 100 men, the predicted fall in arrests when *pcnv* increases by .50 is -7.5.

Similarly, a longer prison term leads to a lower predicted number of arrests. In fact, if *ptime86* increases from 0 to 12, predicted arrests for a particular man fall by .034(12) = .408. Another quarter in which legal employment is reported lowers predicted arrests by .104, which would be 10.4 arrests among 100 men.

If *avgsen* is added to the model, we know that R^2 will increase. The estimated equation is

$$\widehat{narr86} = .707 - .151\, pcnv + .0074\, avgsen - .037\, ptime86 - .103\, qemp86$$
$$n = 2{,}725,\ R^2 = .0422.$$

Thus, adding the average sentence variable increases R^2 from .0413 to .0422, a practically small effect. The sign of the coefficient on *avgsen* is also unexpected: it says that a longer average sentence length increases criminal activity.

residuals no longer have a zero sample average. Further, if R^2 is defined as $1 - \text{SSR}/\text{SST}$, where SST is given in (3.24) and SSR is now $\sum_{i=1}^{n}(y_i - \tilde{\beta}_1 x_{i1} - \ldots - \tilde{\beta}_k x_{ik})^2$, then R^2 can actually be negative. This means that the sample average, $\bar{y}$, "explains" more of the variation in the y_i than the explanatory variables. Either we should include an intercept in the regression or conclude that the explanatory variables poorly explain y. To always have a nonnegative R-squared, some economists prefer to calculate R^2 as the squared correlation coefficient between the actual and fitted values of y, as in (3.29). (In this case, the average fitted value must be computed directly since it no longer equals $\bar{y}$.) However, there is no set rule on computing R-squared for regression through the origin.

One serious drawback with regression through the origin is that, if the intercept β_0 in the population model is different from zero, then the OLS estimators of the slope parameters will be biased. The bias can be severe in some cases. The cost of estimating an intercept when β_0 is truly zero is that the variances of the OLS slope estimators are larger.

3.3 The Expected Value of the OLS Estimators

We now turn to the statistical properties of OLS for estimating the parameters in an underlying population model. In this section, we derive the expected value of the OLS estimators. In particular, we state and discuss four assumptions, which are direct extensions of the simple regression model assumptions, under which the OLS estimators are unbiased for the population parameters. We also explicitly obtain the bias in OLS when an important variable has been omitted from the regression.

You should remember that statistical properties have nothing to do with a particular sample, but rather with the property of estimators when random sampling is done repeatedly. Thus, Sections 3.3, 3.4, and 3.5 are somewhat abstract. Although we give examples of deriving bias for particular models, it is not meaningful to talk about the statistical properties of a set of estimates obtained from a single sample.

The first assumption we make simply defines the multiple linear regression (MLR) model.

Assumption MLR.1 Linear in Parameters

The model in the population can be written as

$$y = \beta_0 + \beta_1 x_1 + \beta_2 x_2 + \ldots + \beta_k x_k + u, \quad [3.31]$$

where $\beta_0, \beta_1, \ldots, \beta_k$ are the unknown parameters (constants) of interest and u is an unobserved random error or disturbance term.

Equation (3.31) formally states the **population model**, sometimes called the **true model**, to allow for the possibility that we might estimate a model that differs from (3.31). The key feature is that the model is linear in the parameters $\beta_0, \beta_1, \ldots, \beta_k$. As we know, (3.31) is quite flexible because y and the independent variables can be arbitrary functions of the underlying variables of interest, such as natural logarithms and squares [see, for example, equation (3.7)].

Assumption MLR.2 Random Sampling

We have a random sample of n observations, $\{(x_{i1}, x_{i2}, ..., x_{ik}, y_i): i = 1, 2, ..., n\}$, following the population model in Assumption MLR.1.

Sometimes, we need to write the equation for a particular observation i: for a randomly drawn observation from the population, we have

$$y_i = \beta_0 + \beta_1 x_{i1} + \beta_2 x_{i2} + ... + \beta_k x_{ik} + u_i. \quad [3.32]$$

Remember that i refers to the observation, and the second subscript on x is the variable number. For example, we can write a CEO salary equation for a particular CEO i as

$$\log(salary_i) = \beta_0 + \beta_1 \log(sales_i) + \beta_2 ceoten_i + \beta_3 ceoten_i^2 + u_i. \quad [3.33]$$

The term u_i contains the unobserved factors for CEO i that affect his or her salary. For applications, it is usually easiest to write the model in population form, as in (3.31). It contains less clutter and emphasizes the fact that we are interested in estimating a population relationship.

In light of model (3.31), the OLS estimators $\hat{\beta}_0, \hat{\beta}_1, \hat{\beta}_2, \ldots, \hat{\beta}_k$ from the regression of y on $x_1, \ldots, x_k$ are now considered to be estimators of $\beta_0, \beta_1, \ldots, \beta_k$. In Section 3.2, we saw that OLS chooses the intercept and slope estimates for a particular sample so that the residuals average to zero and the sample correlation between each independent variable and the residuals is zero. Still, we did not include conditions under which the OLS estimates are well defined for a given sample. The next assumption fills that gap.

Assumption MLR.3 No Perfect Collinearity

In the sample (and therefore in the population), none of the independent variables is constant, and there are no *exact linear* relationships among the independent variables.

Assumption MLR.3 is more complicated than its counterpart for simple regression because we must now look at relationships between all independent variables. If an independent variable in (3.31) is an exact linear combination of the other independent variables, then we say the model suffers from **perfect collinearity**, and it cannot be estimated by OLS.

It is important to note that Assumption MLR.3 *does* allow the independent variables to be correlated; they just cannot be *perfectly* correlated. If we did not allow for any correlation among the independent variables, then multiple regression would be of very limited use for econometric analysis. For example, in the model relating test scores to educational expenditures and average family income,

$$avgscore = \beta_0 + \beta_1 expend + \beta_2 avginc + u,$$

we fully expect *expend* and *avginc* to be correlated: school districts with high average family incomes tend to spend more per student on education. In fact, the primary motivation for including *avginc* in the equation is that we suspect it is correlated with *expend*, and so we would like to hold it fixed in the analysis. Assumption MLR.3 only rules out *perfect* correlation between *expend* and *avginc* in our sample. We would be very unlucky to obtain a sample where per student expenditures are perfectly correlated with average family income. But some correlation, perhaps a substantial amount, is expected and certainly allowed.

The simplest way that two independent variables can be perfectly correlated is when one variable is a constant multiple of another. This can happen when a researcher inadvertently puts the same variable measured in different units into a regression equation. For example, in estimating a relationship between consumption and income, it makes no sense to include as independent variables income measured in dollars as well as income measured in thousands of dollars. One of these is redundant. What sense would it make to hold income measured in dollars fixed while changing income measured in thousands of dollars?

We already know that different nonlinear functions of the same variable *can* appear among the regressors. For example, the model $cons = \beta_0 + \beta_1 inc + \beta_2 inc^2 + u$ does not violate Assumption MLR.3: even though $x_2 = inc^2$ is an exact function of $x_1 = inc$, inc^2 is not an exact *linear* function of *inc*. Including inc^2 in the model is a useful way to generalize functional form, unlike including income measured in dollars and in thousands of dollars.

Common sense tells us not to include the same explanatory variable measured in different units in the same regression equation. There are also more subtle ways that one independent variable can be a multiple of another. Suppose we would like to estimate an extension of a constant elasticity consumption function. It might seem natural to specify a model such as

$$\log(cons) = \beta_0 + \beta_1 \log(inc) + \beta_2 \log(inc^2) + u, \quad [3.34]$$

where $x_1 = \log(inc)$ and $x_2 = \log(inc^2)$. Using the basic properties of the natural log (see Appendix A), $\log(inc^2) = 2\cdot\log(inc)$. That is, $x_2 = 2x_1$, and naturally this holds for all observations in the sample. This violates Assumption MLR.3. What we should do instead is include $[\log(inc)]^2$, not $\log(inc^2)$, along with $\log(inc)$. This is a sensible extension of the constant elasticity model, and we will see how to interpret such models in Chapter 6.

Another way that independent variables can be perfectly collinear is when one independent variable can be expressed as an exact linear function of two or more of the other independent variables. For example, suppose we want to estimate the effect of campaign spending on campaign outcomes. For simplicity, assume that each election has two candidates. Let *voteA* be the percentage of the vote for Candidate A, let *expendA* be campaign expenditures by Candidate A, let *expendB* be campaign expenditures by Candidate B, and let *totexpend* be total campaign expenditures; the latter three variables are all measured in dollars. It may seem natural to specify the model as

$$voteA = \beta_0 + \beta_1 expendA + \beta_2 expendB + \beta_3 totexpend + u, \quad [3.35]$$

in order to isolate the effects of spending by each candidate and the total amount of spending. But this model violates Assumption MLR.3 because $x_3 = x_1 + x_2$ by definition. Trying to interpret this equation in a ceteris paribus fashion reveals the problem. The parameter of β_1 in equation (3.35) is supposed to measure the effect of increasing expenditures by Candidate A by one dollar on Candidate A's vote, holding Candidate B's spending *and* total spending fixed. This is nonsense, because if *expendB* and *totexpend* are held fixed, then we cannot increase *expendA*.

The solution to the perfect collinearity in (3.35) is simple: drop any one of the three variables from the model. We would probably drop *totexpend*, and then the coefficient on *expendA* would measure the effect of increasing expenditures by A on the percentage of the vote received by A, holding the spending by B fixed.

The prior examples show that Assumption MLR.3 can fail if we are not careful in specifying our model. Assumption MLR.3 also fails if the sample size, n, is too small in relation to the number of parameters being estimated. In the general regression model in equation (3.31), there are $k + 1$ parameters, and MLR.3 fails if $n < k + 1$. Intuitively, this makes sense: to estimate $k + 1$ parameters, we need at least $k + 1$ observations. Not surprisingly, it is better to have as many observations as possible, something we will see with our variance calculations in Section 3.4.

If the model is carefully specified and $n \geq k + 1$, Assumption MLR.3 can fail in rare cases due to bad luck in collecting the sample. For example, in a wage equation with education and experience as variables, it is possible that we could obtain a random sample where each individual has exactly twice as much education as years of experience. This scenario would cause Assumption MLR.3 to fail, but it can be considered very unlikely unless we have an extremely small sample size.

EXPLORING FURTHER 3.3

In the previous example, if we use as explanatory variables *expendA*, *expendB*, and *shareA*, where *shareA* $= 100\cdot($*expendA*/*totexpend*$)$ is the percentage share of total campaign expenditures made by Candidate A, does this violate Assumption MLR.3?

The final, and most important, assumption needed for unbiasedness is a direct extension of Assumption SLR.4.

Assumption MLR.4 Zero Conditional Mean

The error u has an expected value of zero given any values of the independent variables. In other words,

$$E(u|x_1, x_2, \ldots, x_k) = 0. \quad [3.36]$$

One way that Assumption MLR.4 can fail is if the functional relationship between the explained and explanatory variables is misspecified in equation (3.31): for example, if we forget to include the quadratic term inc^2 in the consumption function $cons = \beta_0 + \beta_1 inc + \beta_2 inc^2 + u$ when we estimate the model. Another functional form misspecification occurs when we use the level of a variable when the log of the variable is what actually shows up in the population model, or vice versa. For example, if the true model has log(*wage*) as the dependent variable but we use *wage* as the dependent variable in our regression analysis, then the estimators will be biased. Intuitively, this should be pretty clear. We will discuss ways of detecting functional form misspecification in Chapter 9.

Omitting an important factor that is correlated with any of $x_1, x_2, \ldots, x_k$ causes Assumption MLR.4 to fail also. With multiple regression analysis, we are able to include many factors among the explanatory variables, and omitted variables are less likely to be a problem in multiple regression analysis than in simple regression analysis. Nevertheless, in any application, there are always factors that, due to data limitations or ignorance, we will not be able to include. If we think these factors should be controlled for and they are correlated with one or more of the independent variables, then Assumption MLR.4 will be violated. We will derive this bias later.

There are other ways that u can be correlated with an explanatory variable. In Chapters 9 and 15, we will discuss the problem of measurement error in an explanatory variable. In Chapter 16, we cover the conceptually more difficult problem in which one or more of the explanatory variables is determined jointly with y—as occurs when we view quantities and prices as being determined by the intersection of supply and demand curves. We must postpone our study of these problems until we have a firm grasp of multiple regression analysis under an ideal set of assumptions.

When Assumption MLR.4 holds, we often say that we have **exogenous explanatory variables**. If x_j is correlated with u for any reason, then x_j is said to be an **endogenous explanatory variable**. The terms "exogenous" and "endogenous" originated in simultaneous equations analysis (see Chapter 16), but the term "endogenous explanatory variable" has evolved to cover any case in which an explanatory variable may be correlated with the error term.

Before we show the unbiasedness of the OLS estimators under MLR.1 to MLR.4, a word of caution. Beginning students of econometrics sometimes confuse Assumptions MLR.3 and MLR.4, but they are quite different. Assumption MLR.3 rules out certain relationships among the independent or explanatory variables and has *nothing* to do with the error, u. You will know immediately when carrying out OLS estimation whether or not Assumption MLR.3 holds. On the other hand, Assumption MLR.4—the much more important of the two—restricts the relationship between the unobserved factors in u and the explanatory variables. Unfortunately, we will never know for sure whether the average value of the unobserved factors is unrelated to the explanatory variables. But this is the critical assumption.

We are now ready to show unbiasedness of OLS under the first four multiple regression assumptions. As in the simple regression case, the expectations are conditional on the values of the explanatory variables in the sample, something we show explicitly in Appendix 3A but not in the text.

THEOREM 3.1

UNBIASEDNESS OF OLS

Under Assumptions MLR.1 through MLR.4,

$$E(\hat{\beta}_j) = \beta_j,\ j = 0, 1, \ldots, k, \qquad [3.37]$$

for any values of the population parameter β_j. In other words, the OLS estimators are unbiased estimators of the population parameters.

In our previous empirical examples, Assumption MLR.3 has been satisfied (because we have been able to compute the OLS estimates). Furthermore, for the most part, the samples are randomly chosen from a well-defined population. If we believe that the specified models are correct under the key Assumption MLR.4, then we can conclude that OLS is unbiased in these examples.

Since we are approaching the point where we can use multiple regression in serious empirical work, it is useful to remember the meaning of unbiasedness. It is tempting, in examples such as the wage equation in (3.19), to say something like "9.2% is an unbiased estimate of the return to education." As we know, an estimate cannot be unbiased: an estimate is a fixed number, obtained from a particular sample, which usually is not equal to the population parameter. When we say that OLS is unbiased under Assumptions MLR.1 through MLR.4, we mean that the *procedure* by which the OLS estimates are obtained is unbiased when we view the procedure as being applied across all possible random samples. We hope that we have obtained a sample that gives us an estimate close to the population value, but, unfortunately, this cannot be assured. What is assured is that we have no reason to believe our estimate is more likely to be too big or more likely to be too small.

Including Irrelevant Variables in a Regression Model

One issue that we can dispense with fairly quickly is that of **inclusion of an irrelevant variable** or **overspecifying the model** in multiple regression analysis. This means that one (or more) of the independent variables is included in the model even though it has no partial effect on y in the population. (That is, its population coefficient is zero.)

To illustrate the issue, suppose we specify the model as

$$y = \beta_0 + \beta_1 x_1 + \beta_2 x_2 + \beta_3 x_3 + u, \quad [3.38]$$

and this model satisfies Assumptions MLR.1 through MLR.4. However, x_3 has no effect on y after x_1 and x_2 have been controlled for, which means that $\beta_3 = 0$. The variable x_3 may or may not be correlated with x_1 or x_2; all that matters is that, once x_1 and x_2 are controlled for, x_3 has no effect on y. In terms of conditional expectations, $\mathrm{E}(y|x_1, x_2, x_3) = \mathrm{E}(y|x_1, x_2) = \beta_0 + \beta_1 x_1 + \beta_2 x_2$.

Because we do not know that $\beta_3 = 0$, we are inclined to estimate the equation including x_3:

$$\hat{y} = \hat{\beta}_0 + \hat{\beta}_1 x_1 + \hat{\beta}_2 x_2 + \hat{\beta}_3 x_3. \quad [3.39]$$

We have included the irrelevant variable, x_3, in our regression. What is the effect of including x_3 in (3.39) when its coefficient in the population model (3.38) is zero? In terms of the unbiasedness of $\hat{\beta}_1$ and $\hat{\beta}_2$, there is *no effect*. This conclusion requires no special derivation, as it follows immediately from Theorem 3.1. Remember, unbiasedness means $\mathrm{E}(\hat{\beta}_j) = \beta_j$ for *any* value of β_j, including $\beta_j = 0$. Thus, we can conclude that $\mathrm{E}(\hat{\beta}_0) = \beta_0$, $\mathrm{E}(\hat{\beta}_1) = \beta_1$, $\mathrm{E}(\hat{\beta}_2) = \beta_2$, and $\mathrm{E}(\hat{\beta}_3) = 0$ (for any values of β_0, β_1, and β_2). Even though $\hat{\beta}_3$ itself will never be exactly zero, its average value across all random samples will be zero.

The conclusion of the preceding example is much more general: including one or more irrelevant variables in a multiple regression model, or overspecifying the model, does not affect the unbiasedness of the OLS estimators. Does this mean it is harmless to include irrelevant variables? No. As we will see in Section 3.4, including irrelevant variables can have undesirable effects on the *variances* of the OLS estimators.

Omitted Variable Bias: The Simple Case

Now suppose that, rather than including an irrelevant variable, we omit a variable that actually belongs in the true (or population) model. This is often called the problem of **excluding a relevant variable** or **underspecifying the model**. We claimed in Chapter 2 and earlier in this chapter that this problem generally causes the OLS estimators to be biased. It is time to show this explicitly and, just as importantly, to derive the direction and size of the bias.

Deriving the bias caused by omitting an important variable is an example of **misspecification analysis**. We begin with the case where the true population model has two explanatory variables and an error term:

$$y = \beta_0 + \beta_1 x_1 + \beta_2 x_2 + u, \qquad [3.40]$$

and we assume that this model satisfies Assumptions MLR.1 through MLR.4.

Suppose that our primary interest is in β_1, the partial effect of x_1 on y. For example, y is hourly wage (or log of hourly wage), x_1 is education, and x_2 is a measure of innate ability. In order to get an unbiased estimator of β_1, we *should* run a regression of y on x_1 and x_2 (which gives unbiased estimators of β_0, β_1, and β_2). However, due to our ignorance or data unavailability, we estimate the model by *excluding* x_2. In other words, we perform a simple regression of y on x_1 only, obtaining the equation

$$\tilde{y} = \tilde{\beta}_0 + \tilde{\beta}_1 x_1. \qquad [3.41]$$

We use the symbol "~" rather than "^" to emphasize that $\tilde{\beta}_1$ comes from an underspecified model.

When first learning about the omitted variable problem, it can be difficult to distinguish between the underlying true model, (3.40) in this case, and the model that we actually estimate, which is captured by the regression in (3.41). It may seem silly to omit the variable x_2 if it belongs in the model, but often we have no choice. For example, suppose that *wage* is determined by

$$wage = \beta_0 + \beta_1 educ + \beta_2 abil + u. \qquad [3.42]$$

Since ability is not observed, we instead estimate the model

$$wage = \beta_0 + \beta_1 educ + v,$$

where $v = \beta_2 abil + u$. The estimator of β_1 from the simple regression of *wage* on *educ* is what we are calling $\tilde{\beta}_1$.

We derive the expected value of $\tilde{\beta}_1$ conditional on the sample values of x_1 and x_2. Deriving this expectation is not difficult because $\tilde{\beta}_1$ is just the OLS slope estimator from a simple regression, and we have already studied this estimator extensively in Chapter 2. The difference here is that we must analyze its properties when the simple regression model is misspecified due to an omitted variable.

As it turns out, we have done almost all of the work to derive the bias in the simple regression estimator of $\tilde{\beta}_1$. From equation (3.23) we have the algebraic relationship $\tilde{\beta}_1 = \hat{\beta}_1 + \hat{\beta}_2 \tilde{\delta}_1$, where $\hat{\beta}_1$ and $\hat{\beta}_2$ are the slope estimators (if we could have them) from the multiple regression

$$y_i \text{ on } x_{i1}, x_{i2}, i = 1, \dots, n \qquad [3.43]$$

and $\tilde{\delta}_1$ is the slope from the simple regression

$$x_{i2} \text{ on } x_{i1}, i = 1, \dots, n. \qquad [3.44]$$

Because $\tilde{\delta}_1$ depends only on the independent variables in the sample, we treat it as fixed (nonrandom) when computing $E(\tilde{\beta}_1)$. Further, since the model in (3.40) satisfies

Assumptions MLR.1 to MLR.4, we know that $\hat{\beta}_1$ and $\hat{\beta}_2$ would be unbiased for β_1 and β_2, respectively. Therefore,

$$\begin{aligned} E(\tilde{\beta}_1) &= E(\hat{\beta}_1 + \hat{\beta}_2\tilde{\delta}_1) = E(\hat{\beta}_1) + E(\hat{\beta}_2)\tilde{\delta}_1 \\ &= \beta_1 + \beta_2\tilde{\delta}_1, \end{aligned} \quad [3.45]$$

which implies the bias in $\tilde{\beta}_1$ is

$$\text{Bias}(\tilde{\beta}_1) = E(\tilde{\beta}_1) - \beta_1 = \beta_2\tilde{\delta}_1. \quad [3.46]$$

Because the bias in this case arises from omitting the explanatory variable x_2, the term on the right-hand side of equation (3.46) is often called the **omitted variable bias**.

From equation (3.46), we see that there are two cases where $\tilde{\beta}_1$ is unbiased. The first is pretty obvious: if $\beta_2 = 0$—so that x_2 does not appear in the true model (3.40)—then $\tilde{\beta}_1$ is unbiased. We already know this from the simple regression analysis in Chapter 2. The second case is more interesting. If $\tilde{\delta}_1 = 0$, then $\tilde{\beta}_1$ is unbiased for β_1, even if $\beta_2 \neq 0$.

Because $\tilde{\delta}_1$ is the sample covariance between x_1 and x_2 over the sample variance of x_1, $\tilde{\delta}_1 = 0$ if, and only if, x_1 and x_2 are uncorrelated in the sample. Thus, we have the important conclusion that, if x_1 and x_2 are uncorrelated in the sample, then $\tilde{\beta}_1$ is unbiased. This is not surprising: in Section 3.2, we showed that the simple regression estimator $\tilde{\beta}_1$ and the multiple regression estimator $\hat{\beta}_1$ are the same when x_1 and x_2 are uncorrelated in the sample. [We can also show that $\tilde{\beta}_1$ is unbiased without conditioning on the x_{i2} if $E(x_2|x_1) = E(x_2)$; then, for estimating β_1, leaving x_2 in the error term does not violate the zero conditional mean assumption for the error, once we adjust the intercept.]

When x_1 and x_2 are correlated, $\tilde{\delta}_1$ has the same sign as the correlation between x_1 and x_2: $\tilde{\delta}_1 > 0$ if x_1 and x_2 are positively correlated and $\tilde{\delta}_1 < 0$ if x_1 and x_2 are negatively correlated. The sign of the bias in $\tilde{\beta}_1$ depends on the signs of both β_2 and $\tilde{\delta}_1$ and is summarized in Table 3.2 for the four possible cases when there is bias. Table 3.2 warrants careful study. For example, the bias in $\tilde{\beta}_1$ is positive if $\beta_2 > 0$ (x_2 has a positive effect on y) and x_1 and x_2 are positively correlated, the bias is negative if $\beta_2 > 0$ and x_1 and x_2 are negatively correlated, and so on.

Table 3.2 summarizes the direction of the bias, but the size of the bias is also very important. A small bias of either sign need not be a cause for concern. For example, if the return to education in the population is 8.6% and the bias in the OLS estimator is 0.1% (a tenth of one percentage point), then we would not be very concerned. On the other hand, a bias on the order of three percentage points would be much more serious. The size of the bias is determined by the sizes of β_2 and $\tilde{\delta}_1$.

In practice, since β_2 is an unknown population parameter, we cannot be certain whether β_2 is positive or negative. Nevertheless, we usually have a pretty good idea about the direction of the partial effect of x_2 on y. Further, even though the sign of the correlation between x_1 and x_2 cannot be known if x_2 is not observed, in many cases, we can make an educated guess about whether x_1 and x_2 are positively or negatively correlated.

In the wage equation (3.42), by definition, more ability leads to higher productivity and therefore higher wages: $\beta_2 > 0$. Also, there are reasons to believe that *educ* and *abil* are positively correlated: on average, individuals with more innate ability choose higher

TABLE 3.2 Summary of Bias in $\tilde{\beta}_1$ when x_2 Is Omitted in Estimating Eqution (3.40)

	$\text{Corr}(x_1, x_2) > 0$	$\text{Corr}(x_1, x_2) < 0$
$\beta_2 > 0$	Positive bias	Negative bias
$\beta_2 < 0$	Negative bias	Positive bias

levels of education. Thus, the OLS estimates from the simple regression equation $wage = \beta_0 + \beta_1 educ + v$ are *on average* too large. This does not mean that the estimate obtained from our sample is too big. We can only say that if we collect many random samples and obtain the simple regression estimates each time, then the average of these estimates will be greater than β_1.

EXAMPLE 3.6 HOURLY WAGE EQUATION

Suppose the model $\log(wage) = \beta_0 + \beta_1 educ + \beta_2 abil + u$ satisfies Assumptions MLR.1 through MLR.4. The data set in WAGE1.RAW does not contain data on ability, so we estimate β_1 from the simple regression

$$\widehat{\log(wage)} = .584 + .083\ educ$$
$$n = 526,\ R^2 = .186. \qquad [3.47]$$

This is the result from only a single sample, so we cannot say that .083 is greater than β_1; the true return to education could be lower or higher than 8.3% (and we will never know for sure). Nevertheless, we know that the average of the estimates across all random samples would be too large.

As a second example, suppose that, at the elementary school level, the average score for students on a standardized exam is determined by

$$avgscore = \beta_0 + \beta_1 expend + \beta_2 povrate + u, \qquad [3.48]$$

where *expend* is expenditure per student and *povrate* is the poverty rate of the children in the school. Using school district data, we only have observations on the percentage of students with a passing grade and per student expenditures; we do not have information on poverty rates. Thus, we estimate β_1 from the simple regression of *avgscore* on *expend*.

We can again obtain the likely bias in $\tilde{\beta}_1$. First, β_2 is probably negative: There is ample evidence that children living in poverty score lower, on average, on standardized tests. Second, the average expenditure per student is probably negatively correlated with the poverty rate: The higher the poverty rate, the lower the average per student spending, so that $\text{Corr}(x_1, x_2) < 0$. From Table 3.2, $\tilde{\beta}_1$ will have a positive bias. This observation has important implications. It could be that the true effect of spending is zero; that is, $\beta_1 = 0$. However, the simple regression estimate of β_1 will usually be greater than zero, and this could lead us to conclude that expenditures are important when they are not.

When reading and performing empirical work in economics, it is important to master the terminology associated with biased estimators. In the context of omitting a variable from model (3.40), if $\text{E}(\tilde{\beta}_1) > \beta_1$, then we say that $\tilde{\beta}_1$ has an **upward bias**. When $\text{E}(\tilde{\beta}_1) < \beta_1$, $\tilde{\beta}_1$ has a **downward bias**. These definitions are the same whether β_1 is positive or negative. The phrase **biased toward zero** refers to cases where $\text{E}(\tilde{\beta}_1)$ is closer to zero than is β_1. Therefore, if β_1 is positive, then $\tilde{\beta}_1$ is biased toward zero if it has a downward bias. On the other hand, if $\beta_1 < 0$, then $\tilde{\beta}_1$ is biased toward zero if it has an upward bias.

Omitted Variable Bias: More General Cases

Deriving the sign of omitted variable bias when there are multiple regressors in the estimated model is more difficult. We must remember that correlation between a single explanatory variable and the error generally results in *all* OLS estimators being biased. For example, suppose the population model

$$y = \beta_0 + \beta_1 x_1 + \beta_2 x_2 + \beta_3 x_3 + u \quad [3.49]$$

satisfies Assumptions MLR.1 through MLR.4. But we omit x_3 and estimate the model as

$$\tilde{y} = \tilde{\beta}_0 + \tilde{\beta}_1 x_1 + \tilde{\beta}_2 x_2. \quad [3.50]$$

Now, suppose that x_2 and x_3 are uncorrelated, but that x_1 is correlated with x_3. In other words, x_1 is correlated with the omitted variable, but x_2 is not. It is tempting to think that, while $\tilde{\beta}_1$ is probably biased based on the derivation in the previous subsection, $\tilde{\beta}_2$ is unbiased because x_2 is uncorrelated with x_3. Unfortunately, this is *not* generally the case: both $\tilde{\beta}_1$ and $\tilde{\beta}_2$ will normally be biased. The only exception to this is when x_1 and x_2 are also uncorrelated.

Even in the fairly simple model above, it can be difficult to obtain the direction of bias in $\tilde{\beta}_1$ and $\tilde{\beta}_2$. This is because x_1, x_2, and x_3 can all be pairwise correlated. Nevertheless, an approximation is often practically useful. If we assume that x_1 and x_2 are uncorrelated, then we can study the bias in $\tilde{\beta}_1$ as if x_2 were absent from both the population and the estimated models. In fact, when x_1 and x_2 are uncorrelated, it can be shown that

$$\mathrm{E}(\tilde{\beta}_1) = \beta_1 + \beta_3 \frac{\sum_{i=1}^{n}(x_{i1} - \bar{x}_1)x_{i3}}{\sum_{i=1}^{n}(x_{i1} - \bar{x}_1)^2}.$$

This is just like equation (3.45), but β_3 replaces β_2, and x_3 replaces x_2 in regression (3.44). Therefore, the bias in $\tilde{\beta}_1$ is obtained by replacing β_2 with β_3 and x_2 with x_3 in Table 3.2. If $\beta_3 > 0$ and $\mathrm{Corr}(x_1, x_3) > 0$, the bias in $\tilde{\beta}_1$ is positive, and so on.

As an example, suppose we add *exper* to the wage model:

$$wage = \beta_0 + \beta_1 educ + \beta_2 exper + \beta_3 abil + u.$$

If *abil* is omitted from the model, the estimators of both β_1 and β_2 are biased, even if we assume *exper* is uncorrelated with *abil*. We are mostly interested in the return to education, so it would be nice if we could conclude that $\tilde{\beta}_1$ has an upward or a downward bias due to omitted ability. This conclusion is not possible without further assumptions. As an *approximation*, let us suppose that, in addition to *exper* and *abil* being uncorrelated, *educ* and *exper* are also uncorrelated. (In reality, they are somewhat negatively correlated.) Since $\beta_3 > 0$ and *educ* and *abil* are positively correlated, $\tilde{\beta}_1$ would have an upward bias, just as if *exper* were not in the model.

The reasoning used in the previous example is often followed as a rough guide for obtaining the likely bias in estimators in more complicated models. Usually, the focus is on the relationship between a particular explanatory variable, say, x_1, and the key omitted factor. Strictly speaking, ignoring all other explanatory variables is a valid practice only when each one is uncorrelated with x_1, but it is still a useful guide. Appendix 3A contains a more careful analysis of omitted variable bias with multiple explanatory variables.

3.4 The Variance of the OLS Estimators

We now obtain the variance of the OLS estimators so that, in addition to knowing the central tendencies of the $\hat{\beta}_j$, we also have a measure of the spread in its sampling distribution. Before finding the variances, we add a homoskedasticity assumption, as in Chapter 2. We do this for two reasons. First, the formulas are simplified by imposing the constant error variance assumption. Second, in Section 3.5, we will see that OLS has an important efficiency property if we add the homoskedasticity assumption.

In the multiple regression framework, homoskedasticity is stated as follows:

Assumption MLR.5 Homoskedasticity

The error u has the same variance given any values of the explanatory variables. In other words, $\text{Var}(u|x_1, \ldots, x_k) = \sigma^2$.

Assumption MLR.5 means that the variance in the error term, u, conditional on the explanatory variables, is the *same* for all combinations of outcomes of the explanatory variables. If this assumption fails, then the model exhibits heteroskedasticity, just as in the two-variable case.

In the equation

$$wage = \beta_0 + \beta_1 educ + \beta_2 exper + \beta_3 tenure + u,$$

homoskedasticity requires that the variance of the unobserved error u does not depend on the levels of education, experience, or tenure. That is,

$$\text{Var}(u|educ, exper, tenure) = \sigma^2.$$

If this variance changes with any of the three explanatory variables, then heteroskedasticity is present.

Assumptions MLR.1 through MLR.5 are collectively known as the **Gauss-Markov assumptions** (for cross-sectional regression). So far, our statements of the assumptions are suitable only when applied to cross-sectional analysis with random sampling. As we will see, the Gauss-Markov assumptions for time series analysis, and for other situations such as panel data analysis, are more difficult to state, although there are many similarities.

In the discussion that follows, we will use the symbol $\mathbf{x}$ to denote the set of all independent variables, $(x_1, \ldots, x_k)$. Thus, in the wage regression with *educ*, *exper*, and *tenure* as independent variables, $\mathbf{x} = (educ, exper, tenure)$. Then we can write Assumptions MLR.1 and MLR.4 as

$$E(y|\mathbf{x}) = \beta_0 + \beta_1 x_1 + \beta_2 x_2 + \ldots + \beta_k x_k,$$

and Assumption MLR.5 is the same as $\text{Var}(y|\mathbf{x}) = \sigma^2$. Stating the assumptions in this way clearly illustrates how Assumption MLR.5 differs greatly from Assumption MLR.4. Assumption MLR.4 says that the expected value of y, given $\mathbf{x}$, is linear in the parameters, but it certainly depends on $x_1, x_2, \ldots, x_k$. Assumption MLR.5 says that the variance of y, given $\mathbf{x}$, does *not* depend on the values of the independent variables.

We can now obtain the variances of the $\hat{\beta}_j$, where we again condition on the sample values of the independent variables. The proof is in the appendix to this chapter.

THEOREM 3.2

SAMPLING VARIANCES OF THE OLS SLOPE ESTIMATORS

Under Assumptions MLR.1 through MLR.5, conditional on the sample values of the independent variables,

$$\mathrm{Var}(\hat{\beta}_j) = \frac{\sigma^2}{\mathrm{SST}_j(1 - R_j^2)}, \quad [3.51]$$

for $j = 1, 2, \ldots, k$, where $\mathrm{SST}_j = \sum_{i=1}^{n} (x_{ij} - \bar{x}_j)^2$ is the total sample variation in x_j, and R_j^2 is the R-squared from regressing x_j on all other independent variables (and including an intercept).

The careful reader may be wondering whether there is a simple formula for the variance of $\hat{\beta}_j$ where we do not condition on the sample outcomes of the explanatory variables. The answer is: None that is useful. The formula in (3.51) is a highly nonlinear function of the x_{ij}, making averaging out across the population distribution of the explanatory variables virtually impossible. Fortunately, for any practical purpose equation (3.51) is what we want. Even when we turn to approximate, large-sample properties of OLS in Chapter 5 it turns out that (3.51) estimates the quantity we need for large-sample analysis, provided Assumptions MLR.1 through MLR.5 hold.

Before we study equation (3.51) in more detail, it is important to know that all of the Gauss-Markov assumptions are used in obtaining this formula. Whereas we did not need the homoskedasticity assumption to conclude that OLS is unbiased, we do need it to validate equation (3.51).

The size of $\mathrm{Var}(\hat{\beta}_j)$ is practically important. A larger variance means a less precise estimator, and this translates into larger confidence intervals and less accurate hypotheses tests (as we will see in Chapter 4). In the next subsection, we discuss the elements comprising (3.51).

The Components of the OLS Variances: Multicollinearity

Equation (3.51) shows that the variance of $\hat{\beta}_j$ depends on three factors: σ^2, SST_j, and R_j^2. Remember that the index j simply denotes any one of the independent variables (such as education or poverty rate). We now consider each of the factors affecting $\mathrm{Var}(\hat{\beta}_j)$ in turn.

The Error Variance, σ^2. From equation (3.51), a larger σ^2 means larger variances for the OLS estimators. This is not at all surprising: more "noise" in the equation (a larger σ^2) makes it more difficult to estimate the partial effect of any of the independent variables on y, and this is reflected in higher variances for the OLS slope estimators. Because σ^2 is a feature of the population, it has nothing to do with the sample size. It is the one component of (3.51) that is unknown. We will see later how to obtain an unbiased estimator of σ^2.

For a given dependent variable y, there is really only one way to reduce the error variance, and that is to add more explanatory variables to the equation (take some factors out of the error term). Unfortunately, it is not always possible to find additional legitimate factors that affect y.

The Total Sample Variation in x_j, SST_j. From equation (3.51), we see that the larger the total variation in x_j is, the smaller is $\mathrm{Var}(\hat{\beta}_j)$. Thus, everything else being equal, for estimating β_j we prefer to have as much sample variation in x_j as possible. We already discovered this in the simple regression case in Chapter 2. Although it is rarely possible for us to choose the sample values of the independent variables, there *is* a way to increase the sample variation in each of the independent variables: increase the sample size. In fact, when one samples randomly from a population, SST_j increases without bound as the sample size gets larger and larger. This is the component of the variance that systematically depends on the sample size.

When SST_j is small, $\text{Var}(\hat{\beta}_j)$ can get very large, but a small SST_j is not a violation of Assumption MLR.3. Technically, as SST_j goes to zero, $\text{Var}(\hat{\beta}_j)$ approaches infinity. The extreme case of no sample variation in x_j, $\text{SST}_j = 0$, is not allowed by Assumption MLR.3.

The Linear Relationships among the Independent Variables, R_j^2. The term R_j^2 in equation (3.51) is the most difficult of the three components to understand. This term does not appear in simple regression analysis because there is only one independent variable in such cases. It is important to see that this R-squared is distinct from the R-squared in the regression of y on $x_1, x_2, \ldots, x_k$: R_j^2 is obtained from a regression involving only the independent variables in the original model, where x_j plays the role of a dependent variable.

Consider first the $k = 2$ case: $y = \beta_0 + \beta_1 x_1 + \beta_2 x_2 + u$. Then, $\text{Var}(\hat{\beta}_1) = \sigma^2/[\text{SST}_1(1 - R_1^2)]$, where R_1^2 is the R-squared from the simple regression of x_1 on x_2 (and an intercept, as always). Because the R-squared measures goodness-of-fit, a value of R_1^2 close to one indicates that x_2 explains much of the variation in x_1 in the sample. This means that x_1 and x_2 are highly correlated.

As R_1^2 increases to one, $\text{Var}(\hat{\beta}_1)$ gets larger and larger. Thus, a high degree of linear relationship between x_1 and x_2 can lead to large variances for the OLS slope estimators. (A similar argument applies to $\hat{\beta}_2$.) See Figure 3.1 for the relationship between $\text{Var}(\hat{\beta}_1)$ and the R-squared from the regression of x_1 on x_2.

In the general case, R_j^2 is the proportion of the total variation in x_j that can be explained by the *other* independent variables appearing in the equation. For a given σ^2 and SST_j, the smallest $\text{Var}(\hat{\beta}_j)$ is obtained when $R_j^2 = 0$, which happens if, and only if, x_j has zero sample correlation with *every other* independent variable. This is the best case for estimating β_j, but it is rarely encountered.

The other extreme case, $R_j^2 = 1$, is ruled out by Assumption MLR.3, because $R_j^2 = 1$ means that, in the sample, x_j is a *perfect* linear combination of some of the other independent variables in the regression. A more relevant case is when R_j^2 is "close" to one. From equation (3.51) and Figure 3.1, we see that this can cause $\text{Var}(\hat{\beta}_j)$ to be large: $\text{Var}(\hat{\beta}_j) \to \infty$ as $R_j^2 \to 1$. High (but not perfect) correlation between two or more independent variables is called **multicollinearity**.

Before we discuss the multicollinearity issue further, it is important to be very clear on one thing: A case where R_j^2 is close to one is *not* a violation of Assumption MLR.3.

Since multicollinearity violates none of our assumptions, the "problem" of multicollinearity is not really well defined. When we say that multicollinearity arises for estimating β_j when R_j^2 is "close" to one, we put "close" in quotation marks because there is no absolute number that we can cite to conclude that multicollinearity is a problem. For example, $R_j^2 = .9$ means that 90% of the sample variation in x_j can be explained by the other independent variables in the regression model. Unquestionably, this means that x_j has a strong linear relationship to the other independent variables. But whether this translates into a $\text{Var}(\hat{\beta}_j)$ that is too large to be useful depends on the sizes of σ^2 and SST_j. As we

FIGURE 3.1 Var($\hat{\beta}_1$) as a function of R_1^2.

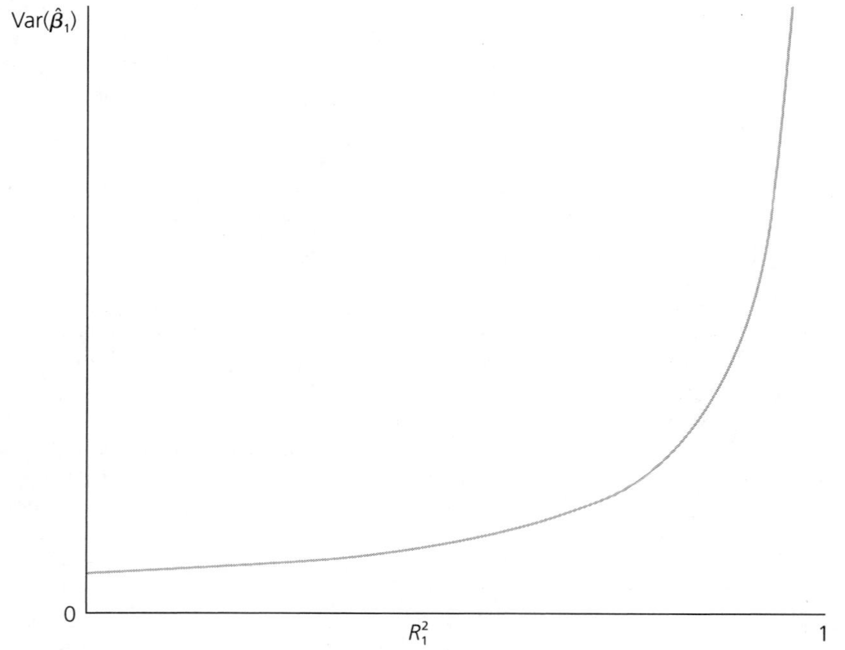

will see in Chapter 4, for statistical inference, what ultimately matters is how big $\hat{\beta}_j$ is in relation to its standard deviation.

Just as a large value of R_j^2 can cause a large Var($\hat{\beta}_j$), so can a small value of SST_j. Therefore, a small sample size can lead to large sampling variances, too. Worrying about high degrees of correlation among the independent variables in the sample is really no different from worrying about a small sample size: both work to increase Var($\hat{\beta}_j$). The famous University of Wisconsin econometrician Arthur Goldberger, reacting to econometricians' obsession with multicollinearity, has (tongue in cheek) coined the term **micronumerosity**, which he defines as the "problem of small sample size." [For an engaging discussion of multicollinearity and micronumerosity, see Goldberger (1991).]

Although the problem of multicollinearity cannot be clearly defined, one thing is clear: everything else being equal, for estimating β_j, it is better to have less correlation between x_j and the other independent variables. This observation often leads to a discussion of how to "solve" the multicollinearity problem. In the social sciences, where we are usually passive collectors of data, there is no good way to reduce variances of unbiased estimators other than to collect more data. For a given data set, we can try dropping other independent variables from the model in an effort to reduce multicollinearity. Unfortunately, dropping a variable that belongs in the population model can lead to bias, as we saw in Section 3.3.

Perhaps an example at this point will help clarify some of the issues raised concerning multicollinearity. Suppose we are interested in estimating the effect of various school expenditure categories on student performance. It is likely that expenditures on teacher salaries, instructional materials, athletics, and so on are highly correlated: Wealthier schools tend to spend more on everything, and poorer schools spend less on everything. Not surprisingly, it can be difficult to estimate the effect of any particular expenditure category on student performance when there is little variation in one category that cannot largely be explained by variations in the other expenditure categories (this leads to high R_j^2 for each of the expenditure variables). Such multicollinearity problems can be mitigated by collecting more data, but in a sense we have imposed the problem on ourselves: we are asking questions that may be too subtle for the available data to answer with any precision. We can probably do much better by changing the scope of the analysis and lumping all expenditure categories together, since we would no longer be trying to estimate the partial effect of each separate category.

Another important point is that a high degree of correlation between certain independentvariables can be irrelevant as to how well we can estimate other parameters in the model. For example, consider a model with three independent variables:

$$y = \beta_0 + \beta_1 x_1 + \beta_2 x_2 + \beta_3 x_3 + u,$$

where x_2 and x_3 are highly correlated. Then $\text{Var}(\hat{\beta}_2)$ and $\text{Var}(\hat{\beta}_3)$ may be large. But the amount of correlation between x_2 and x_3 has no direct effect on $\text{Var}(\hat{\beta}_1)$. In fact, if x_1 is uncorrelated with x_2 and x_3, then $R_1^2 = 0$ and $\text{Var}(\hat{\beta}_1) = \sigma^2/\text{SST}_1$, regardless of how much correlation there is between x_2 and x_3. If β_1 is the parameter of interest, we do not really care about the amount of correlation between x_2 and x_3.

The previous observation is important because economists often include many control variables in order to isolate the causal effect of a particular variable. For example, in looking at the relationship between loan approval rates and percentage of minorities in a neighborhood, we might include variables like average income, average housing value, measures of creditworthiness, and so on, because these factors need to be accounted for in order to draw causal conclusions about discrimination. Income, housing prices, and creditworthiness are generally highly correlated with each other. But high correlations among these controls do not make it more difficult to determine the effects of discrimination.

EXPLORING FURTHER 3.4

Suppose you postulate a model explaining final exam score in terms of class attendance. Thus, the dependent variable is final exam score, and the key explanatory variable is number of classes attended. To control for student abilities and efforts outside the classroom, you include among the explanatory variables cumulative GPA, SAT score, and measures of high school performance. Someone says, "You cannot hope to learn anything from this exercise because cumulative GPA, SAT score, and high school performance are likely to be highly collinear." What should be your response?

Some researchers find it useful to compute statistics intended to determine the severity of multicollinearity in a given application. Unfortunately, it is easy to misuse such statistics because, as we have discussed, we cannot specify how much correlation among explanatory variables is "too much." Some multicollinearity "diagnostics" are omnibus statistics in the sense that they detect a strong linear relationship among any subset of explanatory variables. For reasons that we just saw, such statistics are of questionable value because they might reveal a "problem" simply because two control variables, whose coefficients we do not care about, are highly correlated. [Probably the most common omnibus multicollinearity statistic is the so-called *condition number*, which is defined in terms of the full data matrix and is beyond the scope of this text. See, for example, Belsley, Kuh, and Welsh (1980).]

Somewhat more useful, but still prone to misuse, are statistics for individual coefficients. The most common of these is the **variance inflation factor (VIF)**, which is obtained directly from equation (3.51). The VIF for slope coefficient j is simply $\text{VIF}_j = 1/(1 - R_j^2)$, precisely the term in $\text{Var}(\hat{\beta}_j)$ that is determined by correlation between x_j and the other explanatory variables. We can write $\text{Var}(\hat{\beta}_j)$ in equation (3.51) as

$$\text{Var}(\hat{\beta}_j) = \frac{\sigma^2}{\text{SST}_j} \cdot \text{VIF}_j,$$

which shows that VIF_j is the factor by which $\text{Var}(\hat{\beta}_j)$ is higher because x_j is not uncorrelated with the other explanatory variables. Because VIF_j is a function of R_j^2—indeed, Figure 3.1 is essentially a graph of VIF_1—our previous discussion can be cast entirely in terms of the VIF. For example, if we had the choice, we would like VIF_j to be smaller (other things equal). But we rarely have the choice. If we think certain explanatory variables need to be included in a regression to infer causality of x_j, then we are hesitant to drop them, and whether we think VIF_j is "too high" cannot really affect that decision. If, say, our main interest is in the causal effect of x_1 on y, then we should ignore entirely the VIFs of other coefficients. Finally, setting a cutoff value for VIF above which we conclude multicollinearity is a "problem" is arbitrary and not especially helpful. Sometimes the value 10 is chosen: If VIF_j is above 10 (equivalently, R_j^2 is above .9), then we conclude that multicollinearity is a "problem" for estimating β_j. But a VIF_j above 10 does not mean that the standard deviation of $\hat{\beta}_j$ is too large to be useful because the standard deviation also depends on σ and SST_j, and the latter can be increased by increasing the sample size. Therefore, just as with looking at the size of R_j^2 directly, looking at the size of VIF_j is of limited use, although one might want to do so out of curiosity.

Variances in Misspecified Models

The choice of whether to include a particular variable in a regression model can be made by analyzing the tradeoff between bias and variance. In Section 3.3, we derived the bias induced by leaving out a relevant variable when the true model contains two explanatory variables. We continue the analysis of this model by comparing the variances of the OLS estimators.

Write the true population model, which satisfies the Gauss-Markov assumptions, as

$$y = \beta_0 + \beta_1 x_1 + \beta_2 x_2 + u.$$

We consider two estimators of β_1. The estimator $\hat{\beta}_1$ comes from the multiple regression

$$\hat{y} = \hat{\beta}_0 + \hat{\beta}_1 x_1 + \hat{\beta}_2 x_2. \quad [3.52]$$

In other words, we include x_2, along with x_1, in the regression model. The estimator $\tilde{\beta}_1$ is obtained by omitting x_2 from the model and running a simple regression of y on x_1:

$$\tilde{y} = \tilde{\beta}_0 + \tilde{\beta}_1 x_1. \quad [3.53]$$

When $\beta_2 \neq 0$, equation (3.53) excludes a relevant variable from the model and, as we saw in Section 3.3, this induces a bias in $\tilde{\beta}_1$ unless x_1 and x_2 are uncorrelated. On the other hand, $\hat{\beta}_1$ is unbiased for β_1 for any value of β_2, including $\beta_2 = 0$. It follows that, if bias is used as the only criterion, $\hat{\beta}_1$ is preferred to $\tilde{\beta}_1$.

The conclusion that $\hat{\beta}_1$ is always preferred to $\tilde{\beta}_1$ does not carry over when we bring variance into the picture. Conditioning on the values of x_1 and x_2 in the sample, we have, from (3.51),

$$\text{Var}(\hat{\beta}_1) = \sigma^2/[\text{SST}_1(1 - R_1^2)], \quad [3.54]$$

where SST_1 is the total variation in x_1, and R_1^2 is the R-squared from the regression of x_1 on x_2. Further, a simple modification of the proof in Chapter 2 for two-variable regression shows that

$$\text{Var}(\tilde{\beta}_1) = \sigma^2/\text{SST}_1. \quad [3.55]$$

Comparing (3.55) to (3.54) shows that $\text{Var}(\tilde{\beta}_1)$ is always *smaller* than $\text{Var}(\hat{\beta}_1)$, unless x_1 and x_2 are uncorrelated in the sample, in which case the two estimators $\tilde{\beta}_1$ and $\hat{\beta}_1$ are the same. Assuming that x_1 and x_2 are not uncorrelated, we can draw the following conclusions:

1. When $\beta_2 \neq 0$, $\tilde{\beta}_1$ is biased, $\hat{\beta}_1$ is unbiased, and $\text{Var}(\tilde{\beta}_1) < \text{Var}(\hat{\beta}_1)$.
2. When $\beta_2 = 0$, $\tilde{\beta}_1$ and $\hat{\beta}_1$ are both unbiased, and $\text{Var}(\tilde{\beta}_1) < \text{Var}(\hat{\beta}_1)$.

From the second conclusion, it is clear that $\tilde{\beta}_1$ is preferred if $\beta_2 = 0$. Intuitively, if x_2 does not have a partial effect on y, then including it in the model can only exacerbate the multicollinearity problem, which leads to a less efficient estimator of β_1. A higher variance for the estimator of β_1 is the cost of including an irrelevant variable in a model.

The case where $\beta_2 \neq 0$ is more difficult. Leaving x_2 out of the model results in a biased estimator of β_1. Traditionally, econometricians have suggested comparing the likely size of the bias due to omitting x_2 with the reduction in the variance—summarized in the size of R_1^2—to decide whether x_2 should be included. However, when $\beta_2 \neq 0$, there are two favorable reasons for including x_2 in the model. The most important of these is that any bias in $\tilde{\beta}_1$ does not shrink as the sample size grows; in fact, the bias does not necessarily follow any pattern. Therefore, we can usefully think of the bias as being roughly the same for any sample size. On the other hand, $\text{Var}(\tilde{\beta}_1)$ and $\text{Var}(\hat{\beta}_1)$ both shrink to zero as n gets large, which means that the multicollinearity induced by adding x_2 becomes less important as the sample size grows. In large samples, we would prefer $\hat{\beta}_1$.

The other reason for favoring $\hat{\beta}_1$ is more subtle. The variance formula in (3.55) is conditional on the values of x_{i1} and x_{i2} in the sample, which provides the best scenario for $\tilde{\beta}_1$. When $\beta_2 \neq 0$, the variance of $\tilde{\beta}_1$ conditional only on x_1 is larger than that presented in (3.55). Intuitively, when $\beta_2 \neq 0$ and x_2 is excluded from the model, the error variance increases because the error effectively contains part of x_2. But (3.55) ignores the error variance increase because it treats both regressors as nonrandom. A full discussion of which independent variables to condition on would lead us too far astray. It is sufficient to say that (3.55) is too generous when it comes to measuring the precision in $\tilde{\beta}_1$.

Estimating σ^2: Standard Errors of the OLS Estimators

We now show how to choose an unbiased estimator of σ^2, which then allows us to obtain unbiased estimators of $\text{Var}(\hat{\beta}_j)$.

Because $\sigma^2 = \text{E}(u^2)$, an unbiased "estimator" of σ^2 is the sample average of the squared errors: $n^{-1}\sum_{i=1}^{n} u_i^2$. Unfortunately, this is not a true estimator because we do not observe the u_i. Nevertheless, recall that the errors can be written as $u_i = y_i - \beta_0 - \beta_1 x_{i1} -$

$\beta_2 x_{i2} - \ldots - \beta_k x_{ik}$, and so the reason we do not observe the u_i is that we do not know the β_j. When we replace each β_j with its OLS estimator, we get the OLS residuals:

$$\hat{u}_i = y_i - \hat{\beta}_0 - \hat{\beta}_1 x_{i1} - \hat{\beta}_2 x_{i2} - \ldots - \hat{\beta}_k x_{ik}.$$

It seems natural to estimate σ^2 by replacing u_i with the $\hat{u}_i$. In the simple regression case, we saw that this leads to a biased estimator. The unbiased estimator of σ^2 in the general multiple regression case is

$$\hat{\sigma}^2 = \left(\sum_{i=1}^{n} \hat{u}_i^2\right) \Big/ (n - k - 1) = \text{SSR}/(n - k - 1). \quad [3.56]$$

We already encountered this estimator in the $k = 1$ case in simple regression.

The term $n - k - 1$ in (3.56) is the **degrees of freedom (df)** for the general OLS problem with n observations and k independent variables. Since there are $k + 1$ parameters in a regression model with k independent variables and an intercept, we can write

$$\begin{aligned} df &= n - (k + 1) \\ &= \text{(number of observations)} - \text{(number of estimated parameters)}. \end{aligned} \quad [3.57]$$

This is the easiest way to compute the degrees of freedom in a particular application: count the number of parameters, including the intercept, and subtract this amount from the number of observations. (In the rare case that an intercept is not estimated, the number of parameters decreases by one.)

Technically, the division by $n - k - 1$ in (3.56) comes from the fact that the expected value of the sum of squared residuals is $\text{E(SSR)} = (n - k - 1)\sigma^2$. Intuitively, we can figure out why the degrees of freedom adjustment is necessary by returning to the first order conditions for the OLS estimators. These can be written $\sum_{i=1}^{n} \hat{u}_i = 0$ and $\sum_{i=1}^{n} x_{ij} \hat{u}_i = 0$, where $j = 1, 2, \ldots, k$. Thus, in obtaining the OLS estimates, $k + 1$ restrictions are imposed on the OLS residuals. This means that, given $n - (k + 1)$ of the residuals, the remaining $k + 1$ residuals are known: there are only $n - (k + 1)$ degrees of freedom in the residuals. (This can be contrasted with the *errors* u_i, which have n degrees of freedom in the sample.)

For reference, we summarize this discussion with Theorem 3.3. We proved this theorem for the case of simple regression analysis in Chapter 2 (see Theorem 2.3). (A general proof that requires matrix algebra is provided in Appendix E.)

THEOREM 3.3 UNBIASED ESTIMATION OF σ^2

Under the Gauss-Markov assumptions MLR.1 through MLR.5, $\text{E}(\hat{\sigma}^2) = \sigma^2$.

The positive square root of $\hat{\sigma}^2$, denoted $\hat{\sigma}$, is called the **standard error of the regression (SER)**. The SER is an estimator of the standard deviation of the error term. This estimate is usually reported by regression packages, although it is called different things by different packages. (In addition to SER, $\hat{\sigma}$ is also called the *standard error of the estimate* and the *root mean squared error*.)

Note that $\hat{\sigma}$ can either decrease or increase when another independent variable is added to a regression (for a given sample). This is because, although SSR must fall when another explanatory variable is added, the degrees of freedom also falls by one. Because

SSR is in the numerator and *df* is in the denominator, we cannot tell beforehand which effect will dominate.

For constructing confidence intervals and conducting tests in Chapter 4, we will need to estimate the **standard deviation of $\hat{\beta}_j$**, which is just the square root of the variance:

$$\text{sd}(\hat{\beta}_j) = \sigma/[\text{SST}_j(1 - R_j^2)]^{1/2}.$$

Since σ is unknown, we replace it with its estimator, $\hat{\sigma}$. This gives us the **standard error of $\hat{\beta}_j$**:

$$\text{se}(\hat{\beta}_j) = \hat{\sigma}/[\text{SST}_j(1 - R_j^2)]^{1/2}. \quad [3.58]$$

Just as the OLS estimates can be obtained for any given sample, so can the standard errors. Since $\text{se}(\hat{\beta}_j)$ depends on $\hat{\sigma}$, the standard error has a sampling distribution, which will play a role in Chapter 4.

We should emphasize one thing about standard errors. Because (3.58) is obtained directly from the variance formula in (3.51), and because (3.51) relies on the homoskedasticity Assumption MLR.5, it follows that the standard error formula in (3.58) is *not* a valid estimator of $\text{sd}(\hat{\beta}_j)$ if the errors exhibit heteroskedasticity. Thus, while the presence of heteroskedasticity does not cause bias in the $\hat{\beta}_j$, it does lead to bias in the usual formula for $\text{Var}(\hat{\beta}_j)$, which then invalidates the standard errors. This is important because any regression package computes (3.58) as the default standard error for each coefficient (with a somewhat different representation for the intercept). If we suspect heteroskedasticity, then the "usual" OLS standard errors are invalid, and some corrective action should be taken. We will see in Chapter 8 what methods are available for dealing with heteroskedasticity.

For some purposes it is helpful to write

$$\text{se}(\hat{\beta}_j) = \frac{\hat{\sigma}}{\sqrt{n}\,\text{sd}(x_j)\sqrt{1 - R_j^2}}, \quad [3.59]$$

in which we take $\text{sd}(x_j) = \sqrt{n^{-1}\sum_{i=1}^{n}(x_{ij} - \bar{x}_j)^2}$ to be the sample standard deviation where the total sum of squares is divided by n rather than $n - 1$. The importance of equation (3.59) is that it shows how the sample size, n, directly affects the standard errors. The other three terms in the formula—$\hat{\sigma}$, $\text{sd}(x_j)$, and R_j^2—will change with different samples, but as n gets large they settle down to constants. Therefore, we can see from equation (3.59) that the standard errors shrink to zero at the rate $1/\sqrt{n}$. This formula demonstrates the value of getting more data: the precision of the $\hat{\beta}_j$ increases as n increases. (By contrast, recall that unbiasedness holds for any sample size subject to being able to compute the estimators.) We will talk more about large sample properties of OLS in Chapter 5.

3.5 Efficiency of OLS: The Gauss-Markov Theorem

In this section, we state and discuss the important **Gauss-Markov Theorem**, which justifies the use of the OLS method rather than using a variety of competing estimators. We know one justification for OLS already: under Assumptions MLR.1 through MLR.4, OLS is unbiased. However, there are *many* unbiased estimators of the β_j under these assumptions (for example, see Problem 13). Might there be other unbiased estimators with variances smaller than the OLS estimators?

If we limit the class of competing estimators appropriately, then we can show that OLS *is* best within this class. Specifically, we will argue that, under Assumptions MLR.1

through MLR.5, the OLS estimator $\hat{\beta}_j$ for β_j is the **best linear unbiased estimator (BLUE)**. To state the theorem, we need to understand each component of the acronym "BLUE." First, we know what an estimator is: it is a rule that can be applied to any sample of data to produce an estimate. We also know what an unbiased estimator is: in the current context, an estimator, say, $\tilde{\beta}_j$, of β_j is an unbiased estimator of β_j if $E(\tilde{\beta}_j) = \beta_j$ for any β_0, $\beta_1, \ldots, \beta_k$.

What about the meaning of the term "linear"? In the current context, an estimator $\tilde{\beta}_j$ of β_j is linear if, and only if, it can be expressed as a linear function of the data on the dependent variable:

$$\tilde{\beta}_j = \sum_{i=1}^{n} w_{ij} y_i, \qquad [3.60]$$

where each w_{ij} can be a function of the sample values of all the independent variables. The OLS estimators are linear, as can be seen from equation (3.22).

Finally, how do we define "best"? For the current theorem, best is defined as *having the smallest variance*. Given two unbiased estimators, it is logical to prefer the one with the smallest variance (see Appendix C).

Now, let $\hat{\beta}_0, \hat{\beta}_1, \ldots, \hat{\beta}_k$ denote the OLS estimators in model (3.31) under Assumptions MLR.1 through MLR.5. The Gauss-Markov Theorem says that, for any estimator $\tilde{\beta}_j$ that is *linear* and *unbiased*, $\mathrm{Var}(\hat{\beta}_j) \leq \mathrm{Var}(\tilde{\beta}_j)$, and the inequality is usually strict. In other words, in the class of linear unbiased estimators, OLS has the smallest variance (under the five Gauss-Markov assumptions). Actually, the theorem says more than this. If we want to estimate any linear function of the β_j, then the corresponding linear combination of the OLS estimators achieves the smallest variance among all linear unbiased estimators. We conclude with a theorem, which is proven in Appendix 3A.

THEOREM 3.4

GAUSS-MARKOV THEOREM

Under Assumptions MLR.1 through MLR.5, $\hat{\beta}_0, \hat{\beta}_1, \ldots, \hat{\beta}_k$ are the best linear unbiased estimators (BLUEs) of $\beta_0, \beta_1, \ldots, \beta_k$, respectively.

It is because of this theorem that Assumptions MLR.1 through MLR.5 are known as the Gauss-Markov assumptions (for cross-sectional analysis).

The importance of the Gauss-Markov Theorem is that, when the standard set of assumptions holds, we need not look for alternative unbiased estimators of the form in (3.60): none will be better than OLS. Equivalently, if we are presented with an estimator that is both linear and unbiased, then we know that the variance of this estimator is at least as large as the OLS variance; no additional calculation is needed to show this.

For our purposes, Theorem 3.4 justifies the use of OLS to estimate multiple regression models. If any of the Gauss-Markov assumptions fail, then this theorem no longer holds. We already know that failure of the zero conditional mean assumption (Assumption MLR.4) causes OLS to be biased, so Theorem 3.4 also fails. We also know that heteroskedasticity (failure of Assumption MLR.5) does not cause OLS to be biased. However, OLS no longer has the smallest variance among linear unbiased estimators in the presence of heteroskedasticity. In Chapter 8, we analyze an estimator that improves upon OLS when we know the brand of heteroskedasticity.

3.6 Some Comments on the Language of Multiple Regression Analysis

It is common for beginners, and not unheard of for experienced empirical researchers, to report that they "estimated an OLS model." While we can usually figure out what someone means by this statement, it is important to understand that it is wrong—on more than just an aesthetic level—and reflects a misunderstanding about the components of a multiple regression analysis.

The first thing to remember is that ordinary least squares (OLS) is an estimation method, not a model. A model describes an underlying population and depends on unknown parameters. The *linear model* that we have been studying in this chapter can be written—in the population—as

$$y = \beta_0 + \beta_1 x_1 + \ldots + \beta_k x_k + u, \tag{3.61}$$

where the parameters are the β_j. Importantly, we can talk about the meaning of the β_j without ever looking at data. It is true we cannot hope to learn much about the β_j without data, but the interpretation of the β_j is obtained from the linear model in equation (3.61).

Once we have a sample of data we can estimate the parameters. While it is true that we have so far only discussed OLS as a possibility, there are actually many more ways to use the data than we can even list. We have focused on OLS due to its widespread use, which is justified by using the statistical considerations we covered previously in this chapter. But the various justifications for OLS rely on the assumptions we have made (MLR.1 through MLR.5). As we will see in later chapters, under different assumptions different estimation methods are preferred—even though our model can still be represented by equation (3.61). Just a few examples include weighted least squares in Chapter 8, least absolute deviations in Chapter 9, and instrumental variables in Chapter 15.

One might argue that the discussion here is overlay pedantic, and that the phrase "estimating an OLS model" should be taken as a useful shorthand for "I estimated a linear model by OLS." This stance has some merit, but we must remember that we have studied the properties of the OLS estimators under different assumptions. For example, we know OLS is unbiased under the first four Gauss-Markov assumptions, but it has no special efficiency properties without Assumption MLR.5. We have also seen, through the study of the omitted variables problem, that OLS is biased if we do not have Assumption MLR.4. The problem with using imprecise language is that it leads to vagueness on the most important considerations: What assumptions are being made on the underlying linear model? The issue of the assumptions we are using is conceptually different from the estimator we wind up applying.

Ideally, one writes down an equation like (3.61), with variable names that are easy to decipher, such as

$$\begin{aligned} math4 = {} & \beta_0 + \beta_1 classize4 + \beta_2 math3 + \beta_3 \log(income) \\ & + \beta_4 motheduc + \beta_5 fatheduc + u \end{aligned} \tag{3.62}$$

if we are trying to explain outcomes on a fourth-grade math test. Then, in the context of equation (3.62), one includes a discussion of whether it is reasonable to maintain Assumption MLR.4, focusing on the factors that might still be in u and whether more complicated functional relationships are needed (a topic we study in detail in Chapter 6). Next, one describes the data source (which ideally is obtained via random sampling) as well as the OLS estimates obtained from the sample. A proper way to introduce a discussion of the estimates is to say "I estimated equation (3.62) by ordinary least squares. Under the assumption that no important variables have been omitted from the equation, and assuming random sampling, the OLS estimator of the class size effect, β_1, is unbiased. If the error term u has constant variance, the OLS estimator is actually best linear unbiased." As we will see in Chapters 4 and 5, we can often say even more about OLS. Of course, one might want to admit that while controlling for third-grade math score, family income, and parents' education might account for important differences across students, it might not be enough—for example, u can include motivation of the student or parents—in which case OLS might be biased.

A more subtle reason for being careful in distinguishing between an underlying population model and an estimation method used to estimate a model is that estimation methods such as OLS can be used as essentially an exercise in curve fitting or prediction, without explicitly worrying about an underlying model and the usual statistical properties of unbiasedness and efficiency. For example, we might just want to use OLS to estimate a line that allows us to predict future college GPA for a set of high school students with given characteristics.

Summary

1. The multiple regression model allows us to effectively hold other factors fixed while examining the effects of a particular independent variable on the dependent variable. It explicitly allows the independent variables to be correlated.
2. Although the model is linear in its *parameters*, it can be used to model nonlinear relationships by appropriately choosing the dependent and independent variables.
3. The method of ordinary least squares is easily applied to estimate the multiple regression model. Each slope estimate measures the partial effect of the corresponding independent variable on the dependent variable, holding all other independent variables fixed.
4. R^2 is the proportion of the sample variation in the dependent variable explained by the independent variables, and it serves as a goodness-of-fit measure. It is important not to put too much weight on the value of R^2 when evaluating econometric models.
5. Under the first four Gauss-Markov assumptions (MLR.1 through MLR.4), the OLS estimators are unbiased. This implies that including an irrelevant variable in a model has no effect on the unbiasedness of the intercept and other slope estimators. On the other hand, omitting a relevant variable causes OLS to be biased. In many circumstances, the direction of the bias can be determined.
6. Under the five Gauss-Markov assumptions, the variance of an OLS slope estimator is given by $\text{Var}(\hat{\beta}_j) = \sigma^2/[\text{SST}_j(1 - R_j^2)]$. As the error variance σ^2 increases, so does $\text{Var}(\hat{\beta}_j)$, while $\text{Var}(\hat{\beta}_j)$ decreases as the sample variation in x_j, SST_j, increases. The term R_j^2 measures the amount of collinearity between x_j and the other explanatory variables. As R_j^2 approaches one, $\text{Var}(\hat{\beta}_j)$ is unbounded.
7. Adding an irrelevant variable to an equation generally increases the variances of the remaining OLS estimators because of multicollinearity.
8. Under the Gauss-Markov assumptions (MLR.1 through MLR.5), the OLS estimators are the best linear unbiased estimators (BLUEs).

THE GAUSS-MARKOV ASSUMPTIONS

The following is a summary of the five Gauss-Markov assumptions that we used in this chapter. Remember, the first four were used to establish unbiasedness of OLS, whereas the fifth was added to derive the usual variance formulas and to conclude that OLS is best linear unbiased.

Assumption MLR.1 (Linear in Parameters)

The model in the population can be written as

$$y = \beta_0 + \beta_1 x_1 + \beta_2 x_2 + \ldots + \beta_k x_k + u,$$

where $\beta_0, \beta_1, \ldots, \beta_k$ are the unknown parameters (constants) of interest and u is an unobserved random error or disturbance term.

Assumption MLR.2 (Random Sampling)

We have a random sample of n observations, $\{(x_{i1}, x_{i2}, \ldots, x_{ik}, y_i): i = 1, 2, \ldots, n\}$, following the population model in Assumption MLR.1.

Assumption MLR.3 (No Perfect Collinearity)

In the sample (and therefore in the population), none of the independent variables is constant, and there are no *exact linear* relationships among the independent variables.

Assumption MLR.4 (Zero Conditional Mean)

The error u has an expected value of zero given any values of the independent variables. In other words,

$$\mathrm{E}(u|x_1, x_2, \ldots, x_k) = 0.$$

Assumption MLR.5 (Homoskedasticity)

The error u has the same variance given any value of the explanatory variables. In other words,

$$\mathrm{Var}(u|x_1, \ldots, x_k) = \sigma^2.$$

Key Terms

- Best Linear Unbiased Estimator (BLUE)
- Biased Toward Zero
- Ceteris Paribus
- Degrees of Freedom (*df*)
- Disturbance
- Downward Bias
- Endogenous Explanatory Variable
- Error Term
- Excluding a Relevant Variable
- Exogenous Explanatory Variable
- Explained Sum of Squares (SSE)
- First Order Conditions
- Gauss-Markov Assumptions
- Gauss-Markov Theorem
- Inclusion of an Irrelevant Variable
- Intercept
- Micronumerosity
- Misspecification Analysis
- Multicollinearity
- Multiple Linear Regression Model
- Multiple Regression Analysis
- OLS Intercept Estimate
- OLS Regression Line
- OLS Slope Estimate
- Omitted Variable Bias
- Ordinary Least Squares
- Overspecifying the Model
- Partial Effect
- Perfect Collinearity
- Population Model
- Residual
- Residual Sum of Squares
- Sample Regression Function (SRF)
- Slope Parameter

Standard Deviation of $\hat{\beta}_j$
Standard Error of $\hat{\beta}_j$
Standard Error of the Regression (SER)
Sum of Squared Residuals (SSR)
Total Sum of Squares (SST)
True Model
Underspecifying the Model
Upward Bias
Variance Inflation Factor (VIF)

Problems

1 Using the data in GPA2.RAW on 4,137 college students, the following equation was estimated by OLS:

$$\widehat{colgpa} = 1.392 - .0135\ hsperc + .00148\ sat$$
$$n = 4{,}137,\ R^2 = .273,$$

where *colgpa* is measured on a four-point scale, *hsperc* is the percentile in the high school graduating class (defined so that, for example, *hsperc* = 5 means the *top* 5% of the class), and *sat* is the combined math and verbal scores on the student achievement test.

(i) Why does it make sense for the coefficient on *hsperc* to be negative?

(ii) What is the predicted college GPA when *hsperc* = 20 and *sat* = 1,050?

(iii) Suppose that two high school graduates, A and B, graduated in the same percentile from high school, but Student A's SAT score was 140 points higher (about one standard deviation in the sample). What is the predicted difference in college GPA for these two students? Is the difference large?

(iv) Holding *hsperc* fixed, what difference in SAT scores leads to a predicted *colgpa* difference of .50, or one-half of a grade point? Comment on your answer.

2 The data in WAGE2.RAW on working men was used to estimate the following equation:

$$\widehat{educ} = 10.36 - .094\ sibs + .131\ meduc + .210\ feduc$$
$$n = 722,\ R^2 = .214,$$

where *educ* is years of schooling, *sibs* is number of siblings, *meduc* is mother's years of schooling, and *feduc* is father's years of schooling.

(i) Does *sibs* have the expected effect? Explain. Holding *meduc* and *feduc* fixed, by how much does *sibs* have to increase to reduce predicted years of education by one year? (A noninteger answer is acceptable here.)

(ii) Discuss the interpretation of the coefficient on *meduc*.

(iii) Suppose that Man A has no siblings, and his mother and father each have 12 years of education. Man B has no siblings, and his mother and father each have 16 years of education. What is the predicted difference in years of education between B and A?

3 The following model is a simplified version of the multiple regression model used by Biddle and Hamermesh (1990) to study the tradeoff between time spent sleeping and working and to look at other factors affecting sleep:

$$sleep = \beta_0 + \beta_1 totwrk + \beta_2 educ + \beta_3 age + u,$$

where *sleep* and *totwrk* (total work) are measured in minutes per week and *educ* and *age* are measured in years. (See also Computer Exercise C3 in Chapter 2.)

(i) If adults trade off sleep for work, what is the sign of β_1?

(ii) What signs do you think β_2 and β_3 will have?

(iii) Using the data in SLEEP75.RAW, the estimated equation is

$$\widehat{sleep} = 3{,}638.25 - .148\ totwrk - 11.13\ educ + 2.20\ age$$
$$n = 706,\ R^2 = .113.$$

If someone works five more hours per week, by how many minutes is *sleep* predicted to fall? Is this a large tradeoff?

(iv) Discuss the sign and magnitude of the estimated coefficient on *educ*.

(v) Would you say *totwrk*, *educ*, and *age* explain much of the variation in *sleep*? What other factors might affect the time spent sleeping? Are these likely to be correlated with *totwrk*?

4 The median starting salary for new law school graduates is determined by

$$\log(salary) = \beta_0 + \beta_1 LSAT + \beta_2 GPA + \beta_3 \log(libvol) + \beta_4 \log(cost) + \beta_5 rank + u,$$

where *LSAT* is the median LSAT score for the graduating class, *GPA* is the median college GPA for the class, *libvol* is the number of volumes in the law school library, *cost* is the annual cost of attending law school, and *rank* is a law school ranking (with $rank = 1$ being the best).

(i) Explain why we expect $\beta_5 \leq 0$.

(ii) What signs do you expect for the other slope parameters? Justify your answers.

(iii) Using the data in LAWSCH85.RAW, the estimated equation is

$$\widehat{\log(salary)} = 8.34 + .0047\ LSAT + .248\ GPA + .095\ \log(libvol) + .038\ \log(cost) - .0033\ rank$$
$$n = 136,\ R^2 = .842.$$

What is the predicted ceteris paribus difference in salary for schools with a median GPA different by one point? (Report your answer as a percentage.)

(iv) Interpret the coefficient on the variable log(*libvol*).

(v) Would you say it is better to attend a higher ranked law school? How much is a difference in ranking of 20 worth in terms of predicted starting salary?

5 In a study relating college grade point average to time spent in various activities, you distribute a survey to several students. The students are asked how many hours they spend each week in four activities: studying, sleeping, working, and leisure. Any activity is put into one of the four categories, so that for each student, the sum of hours in the four activities must be 168.

(i) In the model

$$GPA = \beta_0 + \beta_1 study + \beta_2 sleep + \beta_3 work + \beta_4 leisure + u,$$

does it make sense to hold *sleep*, *work*, and *leisure* fixed, while changing *study*?

(ii) Explain why this model violates Assumption MLR.3.

(iii) How could you reformulate the model so that its parameters have a useful interpretation and it satisfies Assumption MLR.3?

6 Consider the multiple regression model containing three independent variables, under Assumptions MLR.1 through MLR.4:

$$y = \beta_0 + \beta_1 x_1 + \beta_2 x_2 + \beta_3 x_3 + u.$$

You are interested in estimating the sum of the parameters on x_1 and x_2; call this $\theta_1 = \beta_1 + \beta_2$.

(i) Show that $\hat{\theta}_1 = \hat{\beta}_1 + \hat{\beta}_2$ is an unbiased estimator of θ_1.

(ii) Find $\text{Var}(\hat{\theta}_1)$ in terms of $\text{Var}(\hat{\beta}_1)$, $\text{Var}(\hat{\beta}_2)$, and $\text{Corr}(\hat{\beta}_1, \hat{\beta}_2)$.

7 Which of the following can cause OLS estimators to be biased?

(i) Heteroskedasticity.

(ii) Omitting an important variable.

(iii) A sample correlation coefficient of .95 between two independent variables both included in the model.

8 Suppose that average worker productivity at manufacturing firms (*avgprod*) depends on two factors, average hours of training (*avgtrain*) and average worker ability (*avgabil*):

$$avgprod = \beta_0 + \beta_1 avgtrain + \beta_2 avgabil + u.$$

Assume that this equation satisfies the Gauss-Markov assumptions. If grants have been given to firms whose workers have less than average ability, so that *avgtrain* and *avgabil* are negatively correlated, what is the likely bias in $\tilde{\beta}_1$ obtained from the simple regression of *avgprod* on *avgtrain*?

9 The following equation describes the median housing price in a community in terms of amount of pollution (*nox* for nitrous oxide) and the average number of rooms in houses in the community (*rooms*):

$$\log(price) = \beta_0 + \beta_1 \log(nox) + \beta_2 rooms + u.$$

(i) What are the probable signs of β_1 and β_2? What is the interpretation of β_1? Explain.

(ii) Why might *nox* [or more precisely, log(*nox*)] and *rooms* be negatively correlated? If this is the case, does the simple regression of log(*price*) on log(*nox*) produce an upward or a downward biased estimator of β_1?

(iii) Using the data in HPRICE2.RAW, the following equations were estimated:

$$\widehat{\log(price)} = 11.71 - 1.043 \log(nox),\ n = 506,\ R^2 = .264.$$

$$\widehat{\log(price)} = 9.23 - .718 \log(nox) + .306\, rooms,\ n = 506,\ R^2 = .514.$$

Is the relationship between the simple and multiple regression estimates of the elasticity of *price* with respect to *nox* what you would have predicted, given your answer in part? (ii) Does this mean that $-.718$ is definitely closer to the true elasticity than -1.043?

10 Suppose that you are interested in estimating the ceteris paribus relationship between y and x_1. For this purpose, you can collect data on two control variables, x_2 and x_3. (For concreteness, you might think of y as final exam score, x_1 as class attendance, x_2 as GPA up through

the previous semester, and x_3 as SAT or ACT score.) Let $\tilde{\beta}_1$ be the simple regression estimate from y on x_1 and let $\hat{\beta}_1$ be the multiple regression estimate from y on x_1, x_2, x_3.

(i) If x_1 is highly correlated with x_2 and x_3 in the sample, and x_2 and x_3 have large partial effects on y, would you expect $\tilde{\beta}_1$ and $\hat{\beta}_1$ to be similar or very different? Explain.

(ii) If x_1 is almost uncorrelated with x_2 and x_3, but x_2 and x_3 are highly correlated, will $\tilde{\beta}_1$ and $\hat{\beta}_1$ tend to be similar or very different? Explain.

(iii) If x_1 is highly correlated with x_2 and x_3, and x_2 and x_3 have small partial effects on y, would you expect $\text{se}(\tilde{\beta}_1)$ or $\text{se}(\hat{\beta}_1)$ to be smaller? Explain.

(iv) If x_1 is almost uncorrelated with x_2 and x_3, x_2 and x_3 have large partial effects on y, and x_2 and x_3 are highly correlated, would you expect $\text{se}(\tilde{\beta}_1)$ or $\text{se}(\hat{\beta}_1)$ to be smaller? Explain.

11 Suppose that the population model determining y is

$$y = \beta_0 + \beta_1 x_1 + \beta_2 x_2 + \beta_3 x_3 + u,$$

and this model satisifies Assumptions MLR.1 through MLR.4. However, we estimate the model that omits x_3. Let $\tilde{\beta}_0$, $\tilde{\beta}_1$, and $\tilde{\beta}_2$ be the OLS estimators from the regression of y on x_1 and x_2. Show that the expected value of $\tilde{\beta}_1$ (given the values of the independent variables in the sample) is

$$\text{E}(\tilde{\beta}_1) = \beta_1 + \beta_3 \frac{\sum_{i=1}^{n} \hat{r}_{i1} x_{i3}}{\sum_{i=1}^{n} \hat{r}_{i1}^2},$$

where the $\hat{r}_{i1}$ are the OLS residuals from the regression of x_1 on x_2. [*Hint:* The formula for $\tilde{\beta}_1$ comes from equation (3.22). Plug $y_i = \beta_0 + \beta_1 x_{i1} + \beta_2 x_{i2} + \beta_3 x_{i3} + u_i$ into this equation. After some algebra, take the expectation treating x_{i3} and $\hat{r}_{i1}$ as nonrandom.]

12 The following equation represents the effects of tax revenue mix on subsequent employment growth for the population of counties in the United States:

$$growth = \beta_0 + \beta_1 share_P + \beta_2 share_I + \beta_3 share_S + other\ factors,$$

where *growth* is the percentage change in employment from 1980 to 1990, $share_P$ is the share of property taxes in total tax revenue, $share_I$ is the share of income tax revenues, and $share_S$ is the share of sales tax revenues. All of these variables are measured in 1980. The omitted share, $share_F$, includes fees and miscellaneous taxes. By definition, the four shares add up to one. Other factors would include expenditures on education, infrastructure, and so on (all measured in 1980).

(i) Why must we omit one of the tax share variables from the equation?

(ii) Give a careful interpretation of β_1.

13 (i) Consider the simple regression model $y = \beta_0 + \beta_1 x + u$ under the first four Gauss-Markov assumptions. For some function $g(x)$, for example $g(x) = x^2$ or $g(x) = \log(1 + x^2)$, define $z_i = g(x_i)$. Define a slope estimator as

$$\tilde{\beta}_1 = \left(\sum_{i=1}^{n} (z_i - \bar{z}) y_i\right) \Bigg/ \left(\sum_{i=1}^{n} (z_i - \bar{z}) x_i\right).$$

Show that $\tilde{\beta}_1$ is linear and unbiased. Remember, because $\text{E}(u|x) = 0$, you can treat both x_i and z_i as nonrandom in your derivation.

(ii) Add the homoskedasticity assumption, MLR.5. Show that

$$\text{Var}(\tilde{\beta}_1) = \sigma^2\left(\sum_{i=1}^{n}(z_i - \bar{z})^2\right)\bigg/\left(\sum_{i=1}^{n}(z_i - \bar{z})x_i\right)^2.$$

(iii) Show directly that, under the Gauss-Markov assumptions, $\text{Var}(\hat{\beta}_1) \leq \text{Var}(\tilde{\beta}_1)$, where $\hat{\beta}_1$ is the OLS estimator. [*Hint:* The Cauchy-Schwartz inequality in Appendix B implies that

$$\left(n^{-1}\sum_{i=1}^{n}(z_i - \bar{z})(x_i - \bar{x})\right)^2 \leq \left(n^{-1}\sum_{i=1}^{n}(z_i - \bar{z})^2\right)\left(n^{-1}\sum_{i=1}^{n}(x_i - \bar{x})^2\right);$$

notice that we can drop $\bar{x}$ from the sample covariance.]

Computer Exercises

C1 A problem of interest to health officials (and others) is to determine the effects of smoking during pregnancy on infant health. One measure of infant health is birth weight; a birth weight that is too low can put an infant at risk for contracting various illnesses. Since factors other than cigarette smoking that affect birth weight are likely to be correlated with smoking, we should take those factors into account. For example, higher income generally results in access to better prenatal care, as well as better nutrition for the mother. An equation that recognizes this is

$$bwght = \beta_0 + \beta_1 cigs + \beta_2 \, faminc + u.$$

(i) What is the most likely sign for β_2?

(ii) Do you think *cigs* and *faminc* are likely to be correlated? Explain why the correlation might be positive or negative.

(iii) Now, estimate the equation with and without *faminc*, using the data in BWGHT .RAW. Report the results in equation form, including the sample size and *R*-squared. Discuss your results, focusing on whether adding *faminc* substantially changes the estimated effect of *cigs* on *bwght*.

C2 Use the data in HPRICE1.RAW to estimate the model

$$price = \beta_0 + \beta_1 sqrft + \beta_2 bdrms + u,$$

where *price* is the house price measured in thousands of dollars.

(i) Write out the results in equation form.

(ii) What is the estimated increase in price for a house with one more bedroom, holding square footage constant?

(iii) What is the estimated increase in price for a house with an additional bedroom that is 140 square feet in size? Compare this to your answer in part (ii).

(iv) What percentage of the variation in price is explained by square footage and number of bedrooms?

(v) The first house in the sample has $sqrft = 2{,}438$ and $bdrms = 4$. Find the predicted selling price for this house from the OLS regression line.

(vi) The actual selling price of the first house in the sample was \$300,000 (so $price = 300$). Find the residual for this house. Does it suggest that the buyer underpaid or overpaid for the house?

C3 The file CEOSAL2.RAW contains data on 177 chief executive officers and can be used to examine the effects of firm performance on CEO salary.

(i) Estimate a model relating annual salary to firm sales and market value. Make the model of the constant elasticity variety for both independent variables. Write the results out in equation form.

(ii) Add *profits* to the model from part (i). Why can this variable not be included in logarithmic form? Would you say that these firm performance variables explain most of the variation in CEO salaries?

(iii) Add the variable *ceoten* to the model in part (ii). What is the estimated percentage return for another year of CEO tenure, holding other factors fixed?

(iv) Find the sample correlation coefficient between the variables log(*mktval*) and *profits*. Are these variables highly correlated? What does this say about the OLS estimators?

C4 Use the data in ATTEND.RAW for this exercise.

(i) Obtain the minimum, maximum, and average values for the variables *atndrte*, *priGPA*, and *ACT*.

(ii) Estimate the model

$$atndrte = \beta_0 + \beta_1 priGPA + \beta_2 ACT + u,$$

and write the results in equation form. Interpret the intercept. Does it have a useful meaning?

(iii) Discuss the estimated slope coefficients. Are there any surprises?

(iv) What is the predicted *atndrte* if $priGPA = 3.65$ and $ACT = 20$? What do you make of this result? Are there any students in the sample with these values of the explanatory variables?

(v) If Student A has $priGPA = 3.1$ and $ACT = 21$ and Student B has $priGPA = 2.1$ and $ACT = 26$, what is the predicted difference in their attendance rates?

C5 Confirm the partialling out interpretation of the OLS estimates by explicitly doing the partialling out for Example 3.2. This first requires regressing *educ* on *exper* and *tenure* and saving the residuals, $\hat{r}_1$. Then, regress log(*wage*) on $\hat{r}_1$. Compare the coefficient on $\hat{r}_1$ with the coefficient on *educ* in the regression of log(*wage*) on *educ*, *exper*, and *tenure*.

C6 Use the data set in WAGE2.RAW for this problem. As usual, be sure all of the following regressions contain an intercept.

(i) Run a simple regression of *IQ* on *educ* to obtain the slope coefficient, say, $\tilde{\delta}_1$.

(ii) Run the simple regression of log(*wage*) on *educ*, and obtain the slope coefficient, $\tilde{\beta}_1$.

(iii) Run the multiple regression of log(*wage*) on *educ* and *IQ*, and obtain the slope coefficients, $\hat{\beta}_1$ and $\hat{\beta}_2$, respectively.

(iv) Verify that $\tilde{\beta}_1 = \hat{\beta}_1 + \hat{\beta}_2\tilde{\delta}_1$.

C7 Use the data in MEAP93.RAW to answer this question.

(i) Estimate the model

$$math10 = \beta_0 + \beta_1 \log(expend) + \beta_2 lnchprg + u,$$

and report the results in the usual form, including the sample size and *R*-squared. Are the signs of the slope coefficients what you expected? Explain.

(ii) What do you make of the intercept you estimated in part (i)? In particular, does it make sense to set the two explanatory variables to zero? [*Hint*: Recall that $\log(1)=0$.]

(iii) Now run the simple regression of *math10* on log(*expend*), and compare the slope coefficient with the estimate obtained in part (i). Is the estimated spending effect now larger or smaller than in part (i)?

(iv) Find the correlation between *lexpend* = log(*expend*) and *lnchprg*. Does its sign make sense to you?

(v) Use part (iv) to explain your findings in part (iii).

C8 Use the data in DISCRIM.RAW to answer this question. These are ZIP code–level data on prices for various items at fast-food restaurants, along with characteristics of the zip code population, in New Jersey and Pennsylvania. The idea is to see whether fast-food restaurants charge higher prices in areas with a larger concentration of blacks.

(i) Find the average values of *prpblck* and *income* in the sample, along with their standard deviations. What are the units of measurement of *prpblck* and *income*?

(ii) Consider a model to explain the price of soda, *psoda*, in terms of the proportion of the population that is black and median income:

$$psoda = \beta_0 + \beta_1 prpblck + \beta_2 income + u.$$

Estimate this model by OLS and report the results in equation form, including the sample size and *R*-squared. (Do not use scientific notation when reporting the estimates.) Interpret the coefficient on *prpblck*. Do you think it is economically large?

(iii) Compare the estimate from part (ii) with the simple regression estimate from *psoda* on *prpblck*. Is the discrimination effect larger or smaller when you control for income?

(iv) A model with a constant price elasticity with respect to income may be more appropriate. Report estimates of the model

$$\log(psoda) = \beta_0 + \beta_1 prpblck + \beta_2 \log(income) + u.$$

If *prpblck* increases by .20 (20 percentage points), what is the estimated percentage change in *psoda*? (*Hint*: The answer is 2.*xx*, where you fill in the "*xx*.")

(v) Now add the variable *prppov* to the regression in part (iv). What happens to $\hat{\beta}_{prpblck}$?

(vi) Find the correlation between log(*income*) and *prppov*. Is it roughly what you expected?

(vii) Evaluate the following statement: "Because log(*income*) and *prppov* are so highly correlated, they have no business being in the same regression."

C9 Use the data in CHARITY.RAW to answer the following questions:

(i) Estimate the equation

$$gift = \beta_0 + \beta_1 mailsyear + \beta_2 giftlast + \beta_3 propresp + u$$

by OLS and report the results in the usual way, including the sample size and *R*-squared. How does the *R*-squared compare with that from the simple regression that omits *giftlast* and *propresp*?

(ii) Interpret the coefficient on *mailsyear*. Is it bigger or smaller than the corresponding simple regression coefficient?

(iii) Interpret the coefficient on *propresp*. Be careful to notice the units of measurement of *propresp*.

(iv) Now add the variable *avggift* to the equation. What happens to the estimated effect of *mailsyear*?

(v) In the equation from part (iv), what has happened to the coefficient on *giftlast*? What do you think is happening?

C10 Use the data in HTV.RAW to answer this question. The data set includes information on wages, education, parents' education, and several other variables for 1,230 working men in 1991.

(i) What is the range of the *educ* variable in the sample? What percentage of men completed 12th grade but no higher grade? Do the men or their parents have, on average, higher levels of education?

(ii) Estimate the regression model

$$educ = \beta_0 + \beta_1 motheduc + \beta_2 fatheduc + u$$

by OLS and report the results in the usual form. How much sample variation in *educ* is explained by parents' education? Interpret the coefficient on *motheduc*.

(iii) Add the variable *abil* (a measure of cognitive ability) to the regression from part (ii), and report the results in equation form. Does "ability" help to explain variations in education, even after controlling for parents' education? Explain.

(iv) (Requires calculus) Now estimate an equation where *abil* appears in quadratic form:

$$educ = \beta_0 + \beta_1 motheduc + \beta_2 fatheduc + \beta_3 abil + \beta_4 abil^2 + u.$$

Using the estimates $\hat{\beta}_3$ and $\hat{\beta}_4$, use calculus to find the value of *abil*, call it $abil^*$, where *educ* is minimized. (The other coefficients and values of parents' education variables have no effect; we are holding parents' education fixed.) Notice that *abil* is measured so that negative values are permissible. You might also verify that the second derivative is positive so that you do indeed have a minimum.

(v) Argue that only a small fraction of men in the sample have "ability" less than the value calculated in part (iv). Why is this important?

(vi) If you have access to a statistical program that includes graphing capabilities, use the estimates in part (iv) to graph the relationship beween the predicted education and *abil*. Let *motheduc* and *fatheduc* have their average values in the sample, 12.18 and 12.45, respectively.

APPENDIX 3A

3A.1 Derivation of the First Order Conditions in Equation (3.13)

The analysis is very similar to the simple regression case. We must characterize the solutions to the problem

$$\min_{b_0, b_1, \ldots, b_k} \sum_{i=1}^{n} (y_i - b_0 - b_1 x_{i1} - \ldots - b_k x_{ik})^2.$$

Taking the partial derivatives with respect to each of the b_j (see Appendix A), evaluating them at the solutions, and setting them equal to zero gives

$$-2\sum_{i=1}^{n}(y_i - \hat{\beta}_0 - \hat{\beta}_1 x_{i1} - \ldots - \hat{\beta}_k x_{ik}) = 0$$

$$-2\sum_{i=1}^{n} x_{ij}(y_i - \hat{\beta}_0 - \hat{\beta}_1 x_{i1} - \ldots - \hat{\beta}_k x_{ik}) = 0, \quad \text{for all} \quad j = 1, \ldots, k.$$

Canceling the -2 gives the first order conditions in (3.13).

3A.2 Derivation of Equation (3.22)

To derive (3.22), write x_{i1} in terms of its fitted value and its residual from the regression of x_1 on $x_2, \ldots, x_k$: $x_{i1} = \hat{x}_{i1} + \hat{r}_{i1}$, for all $i = 1, \ldots, n$. Now, plug this into the second equation in (3.13):

$$\sum_{i=1}^{n}(\hat{x}_{i1} + \hat{r}_{i1})(y_i - \hat{\beta}_0 - \hat{\beta}_1 x_{i1} - \ldots - \hat{\beta}_k x_{ik}) = 0. \quad [3.63]$$

By the definition of the OLS residual $\hat{u}_i$, since $\hat{x}_{i1}$ is just a linear function of the explanatory variables $x_{i2}, \ldots, x_{ik}$, it follows that $\sum_{i=1}^{n}\hat{x}_{i1}\hat{u}_i = 0$. Therefore, equation (3.63) can be expressed as

$$\sum_{i=1}^{n}\hat{r}_{i1}(y_i - \hat{\beta}_0 - \hat{\beta}_1 x_{i1} - \ldots - \hat{\beta}_k x_{ik}) = 0. \quad [3.64]$$

Since the $\hat{r}_{i1}$ are the residuals from regressing x_1 on $x_2, \ldots, x_k$, $\sum_{i=1}^{n} x_{ij}\hat{r}_{i1} = 0$, for all $j = 2, \ldots, k$. Therefore, (3.64) is equivalent to $\sum_{i=1}^{n}\hat{r}_{i1}(y_i - \hat{\beta}_1 x_{i1}) = 0$. Finally, we use the fact that $\sum_{i=1}^{n}\hat{x}_{i1}\hat{r}_{i1} = 0$, which means that $\hat{\beta}_1$ solves

$$\sum_{i=1}^{n}\hat{r}_{i1}(y_i - \hat{\beta}_1\hat{r}_{i1}) = 0.$$

Now, straightforward algebra gives (3.22), provided, of course, that $\sum_{i=1}^{n}\hat{r}_{i1}^2 > 0$; this is ensured by Assumption MLR.3.

3A.3 Proof of Theorem 3.1

We prove Theorem 3.1 for $\hat{\beta}_1$; the proof for the other slope parameters is virtually identical. (See Appendix E for a more succinct proof using matrices.) Under Assumption MLR.3, the OLS estimators exist, and we can write $\hat{\beta}_1$ as in (3.22). Under Assumption MLR.1, we can write y_i as in (3.32); substitute this for y_i in (3.22). Then, using $\sum_{i=1}^{n}\hat{r}_{i1} = 0$, $\sum_{i=1}^{n}x_{ij}\hat{r}_{i1} = 0$, for all $j = 2, \ldots, k$, and $\sum_{i=1}^{n}x_{i1}\hat{r}_{i1} = \sum_{i=1}^{n}\hat{r}_{i1}^2$, we have

$$\hat{\beta}_1 = \beta_1 + \left(\sum_{i=1}^{n}\hat{r}_{i1}u_i\right)\Bigg/\left(\sum_{i=1}^{n}\hat{r}_{i1}^2\right). \quad [3.65]$$

Now, under Assumptions MLR.2 and MLR.4, the expected value of each u_i, given all independent variables in the sample, is zero. Since the $\hat{r}_{i1}$ are just functions of the sample independent variables, it follows that

$$\begin{aligned} E(\hat{\beta}_1|\mathbf{X}) &= \beta_1 + \left(\sum_{i=1}^{n} \hat{r}_{i1} E(u_i|\mathbf{X})\right) \Big/ \left(\sum_{i=1}^{n} \hat{r}_{i1}^2\right) \\ &= \beta_1 + \left(\sum_{i=1}^{n} \hat{r}_{i1} \cdot 0\right) \Big/ \left(\sum_{i=1}^{n} \hat{r}_{i1}^2\right) = \beta_1, \end{aligned}$$

where $\mathbf{X}$ denotes the data on all independent variables and $E(\hat{\beta}_1|\mathbf{X})$ is the expected value of $\hat{\beta}_1$, given $x_{i1}, \ldots, x_{ik}$, for all $i = 1, \ldots, n$. This completes the proof.

3A.4 General Omitted Variable Bias

We can derive the omitted variable bias in the general model in equation (3.31) under the first four Gauss-Markov assumptions. In particular, let the $\hat{\beta}_j$, $j = 0, 1, \ldots, k$ be the OLS estimators from the regression using the full set of explanatory variables. Let the $\tilde{\beta}_j$, $j = 0, 1, \ldots, k - 1$ be the OLS estimators from the regression that leaves out x_k. Let $\tilde{\delta}_j$, $j = 1, \ldots, k - 1$ be the slope coefficient on x_j in the auxiliary regression of x_{ik} on x_{i1}, $x_{i2}, \ldots x_{i,k-1}$, $i = 1, \ldots, n$. A useful fact is that

$$\tilde{\beta}_j = \hat{\beta}_j + \hat{\beta}_k \tilde{\delta}_j. \qquad [3.66]$$

This shows explicitly that, when we do not control for x_k in the regression, the estimated partial effect of x_j equals the partial effect when we include x_k plus the partial effect of x_k on $\hat{y}$ times the partial relationship between the omitted variable, x_k, and x_j, $j < k$. Conditional on the entire set of explanatory variables, $\mathbf{X}$, we know that the $\hat{\beta}_j$ are all unbiased for the corresponding β_j, $j = 1, \ldots, k$. Further, since $\tilde{\delta}_j$ is just a function of $\mathbf{X}$, we have

$$\begin{aligned} E(\tilde{\beta}_j|\mathbf{X}) &= E(\hat{\beta}_j|\mathbf{X}) + E(\hat{\beta}_k|\mathbf{X})\tilde{\delta}_j \\ &= \beta_j + \beta_k \tilde{\delta}_j. \end{aligned} \qquad [3.67]$$

Equation (3.67) shows that $\tilde{\beta}_j$ is biased for β_j unless $\beta_k = 0$—in which case x_k has no partial effect in the population—or $\tilde{\delta}_j$ equals zero, which means that x_{ik} and x_{ij} are partially uncorrelated in the sample. The key to obtaining equation (3.67) is equation (3.66). To show equation (3.66), we can use equation (3.22) a couple of times. For simplicity, we look at $j = 1$. Now, $\tilde{\beta}_1$ is the slope coefficient in the simple regression of y_i on $\tilde{r}_{i1}$, $i = 1, \ldots, n$, where the $\tilde{r}_{i1}$ are the OLS residuals from the regression of x_{i1} on $x_{i2}, x_{i3}, \ldots, x_{i,k-1}$. Consider the numerator of the expression for $\tilde{\beta}_1$: $\sum_{i=1}^{n} \tilde{r}_{i1} y_i$. But for each i, we can write $y_i = \hat{\beta}_0 + \hat{\beta}_1 x_{i1} + \ldots + \hat{\beta}_k x_{ik} + \hat{u}_i$ and plug in for y_i. Now, by properties of the OLS residuals, the $\tilde{r}_{i1}$ have zero sample average and are uncorrelated with $x_{i2}, x_{i3}, \ldots, x_{i,k-1}$ in the sample. Similarly, the $\hat{u}_i$ have zero sample average and zero sample correlation with $x_{i1}, x_{i2}, \ldots, x_{ik}$. It follows that the $\tilde{r}_{i1}$ and $\hat{u}_i$ are uncorrelated in the sample (since the $\tilde{r}_{i1}$ are just linear combinations of $x_{i1}, x_{i2}, \ldots, x_{i,k-1}$). So

$$\sum_{i=1}^{n} \tilde{r}_{i1} y_i = \hat{\beta}_1 \left(\sum_{i=1}^{n} \tilde{r}_{i1} x_{i1}\right) + \hat{\beta}_k \left(\sum_{i=1}^{n} \tilde{r}_{i1} x_{ik}\right). \qquad [3.68]$$

Now, $\sum_{i=1}^{n} \tilde{r}_{i1}x_{i1} = \sum_{i=1}^{n} \tilde{r}_{i1}^2$, which is also the denominator of $\tilde{\beta}_1$. Therefore, we have shown that

$$\tilde{\beta}_1 = \hat{\beta}_1 + \hat{\beta}_k\left(\sum_{i=1}^{n} \tilde{r}_{i1}x_{ik}\right)\Big/\left(\sum_{i=1}^{n} \tilde{r}_{i1}^2\right)$$

$$= \hat{\beta}_1 + \hat{\beta}_k\tilde{\delta}_1.$$

This is the relationship we wanted to show.

3A.5 Proof of Theorem 3.2

Again, we prove this for $j = 1$. Write $\hat{\beta}_1$ as in equation (3.65). Now, under MLR.5, $\text{Var}(u_i|\mathbf{X}) = \sigma^2$, for all $i = 1, \ldots, n$. Under random sampling, the u_i are independent, even conditional on $\mathbf{X}$, and the $\hat{r}_{i1}$ are nonrandom conditional on $\mathbf{X}$. Therefore,

$$\text{Var}(\hat{\beta}_1|\mathbf{X}) = \left(\sum_{i=1}^{n} \hat{r}_{i1}^2 \text{ Var}(u_i|\mathbf{X})\right)\Big/\left(\sum_{i=1}^{n} \hat{r}_{i1}^2\right)^2$$

$$= \left(\sum_{i=1}^{n} \hat{r}_{i1}^2\sigma^2\right)\Big/\left(\sum_{i=1}^{n} \hat{r}_{i1}^2\right)^2 = \sigma^2\Big/\left(\sum_{i=1}^{n} \hat{r}_{i1}^2\right).$$

Now, since $\sum_{i=1}^{n} \hat{r}_{i1}^2$ is the sum of squared residuals from regressing x_1 on $x_2, \ldots, x_k$, $\sum_{i=1}^{n} \hat{r}_{i1}^2 = \text{SST}_1(1 - R_1^2)$. This completes the proof.

3A.6 Proof of Theorem 3.4

We show that, for any other linear unbiased estimator $\tilde{\beta}_1$ of β_1, $\text{Var}(\tilde{\beta}_1) \geq \text{Var}(\hat{\beta}_1)$, where $\hat{\beta}_1$ is the OLS estimator. The focus on $j = 1$ is without loss of generality.

For $\tilde{\beta}_1$ as in equation (3.60), we can plug in for y_i to obtain

$$\tilde{\beta}_1 = \beta_0\sum_{i=1}^{n} w_{i1} + \beta_1\sum_{i=1}^{n} w_{i1}x_{i1} + \beta_2\sum_{i=1}^{n} w_{i1}x_{i2} + \ldots + \beta_k\sum_{i=1}^{n} w_{i1}x_{ik} + \sum_{i=1}^{n} w_{i1}u_i.$$

Now, since the w_{i1} are functions of the x_{ij},

$$\text{E}(\tilde{\beta}_1|\mathbf{X}) = \beta_0\sum_{i=1}^{n} w_{i1} + \beta_1\sum_{i=1}^{n} w_{i1}x_{i1} + \beta_2\sum_{i=1}^{n} w_{i1}x_{i2} + \ldots + \beta_k\sum_{i=1}^{n} w_{i1}x_{ik} + \sum_{i=1}^{n} w_{i1}\text{E}(u_i|\mathbf{X})$$

$$= \beta_0\sum_{i=1}^{n} w_{i1} + \beta_1\sum_{i=1}^{n} w_{i1}x_{i1} + \beta_2\sum_{i=1}^{n} w_{i1}x_{i2} + \ldots + \beta_k\sum_{i=1}^{n} w_{i1}x_{ik}$$

because $\text{E}(u_i|\mathbf{X}) = 0$, for all $i = 1, \ldots, n$ under MLR.2 and MLR.4. Therefore, for $\text{E}(\tilde{\beta}_1|\mathbf{X})$ to equal β_1 for any values of the parameters, we must have

$$\sum_{i=1}^{n} w_{i1} = 0, \sum_{i=1}^{n} w_{i1}x_{i1} = 1, \sum_{i=1}^{n} w_{i1}x_{ij} = 0, \quad j = 2, \ldots, k. \qquad [3.69]$$

Now, let $\hat{r}_{i1}$ be the residuals from the regression of x_{i1} on $x_{i2}, \ldots, x_{ik}$. Then, from (3.69), it follows that

$$\sum_{i=1}^{n} w_{i1}\hat{r}_{i1} = 1 \qquad [3.70]$$

because $x_{i1} = \hat{x}_{i1} + \hat{r}_{i1}$ and $\sum_{i=1}^{n} w_{i1}\hat{x}_{i1} = 0$. Now, consider the difference between $\text{Var}(\tilde{\beta}_1|\mathbf{X})$ and $\text{Var}(\hat{\beta}_1|\mathbf{X})$ under MLR.1 through MLR.5:

$$\sigma^2 \sum_{i=1}^{n} w_{i1}^2 - \sigma^2 \Big/ \left(\sum_{i=1}^{n} \hat{r}_{i1}^2 \right). \quad [3.71]$$

Because of (3.70), we can write the difference in (3.71), without σ^2, as

$$\sum_{i=1}^{n} w_{i1}^2 - \left(\sum_{i=1}^{n} w_{i1}\hat{r}_{i1} \right)^2 \Big/ \left(\sum_{i=1}^{n} \hat{r}_{i1}^2 \right). \quad [3.72]$$

But (3.72) is simply

$$\sum_{i=1}^{n} (w_{i1} - \hat{\gamma}_1 \hat{r}_{i1})^2, \quad [3.73]$$

where $\hat{\gamma}_1 = \left(\sum_{i=1}^{n} w_{i1}\hat{r}_{i1} \right) \Big/ \left(\sum_{i=1}^{n} \hat{r}_{i1}^2 \right)$, as can be seen by squaring each term in (3.73), summing, and then canceling terms. Because (3.73) is just the sum of squared residuals from the simple regression of w_{i1} on $\hat{r}_{i1}$—remember that the sample average of $\hat{r}_{i1}$ is zero—(3.73) must be nonnegative. This completes the proof.

CHAPTER 4

Multiple Regression Analysis: Inference

This chapter continues our treatment of multiple regression analysis. We now turn to the problem of testing hypotheses about the parameters in the population regression model. We begin by finding the distributions of the OLS estimators under the added assumption that the population error is normally distributed. Sections 4.2 and 4.3 cover hypothesis testing about individual parameters, while Section 4.4 discusses how to test a single hypothesis involving more than one parameter. We focus on testing multiple restrictions in Section 4.5 and pay particular attention to determining whether a group of independent variables can be omitted from a model.

4.1 Sampling Distributions of the OLS Estimators

Up to this point, we have formed a set of assumptions under which OLS is unbiased; we have also derived and discussed the bias caused by omitted variables. In Section 3.4, we obtained the variances of the OLS estimators under the Gauss-Markov assumptions. In Section 3.5, we showed that this variance is smallest among linear unbiased estimators.

Knowing the expected value and variance of the OLS estimators is useful for describing the precision of the OLS estimators. However, in order to perform statistical inference, we need to know more than just the first two moments of $\hat{\beta}_j$; we need to know the full sampling distribution of the $\hat{\beta}_j$. Even under the Gauss-Markov assumptions, the distribution of $\hat{\beta}_j$ can have virtually any shape.

When we condition on the values of the independent variables in our sample, it is clear that the sampling distributions of the OLS estimators depend on the underlying distribution of the errors. To make the sampling distributions of the $\hat{\beta}_j$ tractable, we now assume that the unobserved error is *normally distributed* in the population. We call this the **normality assumption**.

Assumption MLR.6 Normality

The population error u is *independent* of the explanatory variables $x_1, x_2, \ldots, x_k$ and is normally distributed with zero mean and variance σ^2: $u \sim \text{Normal}(0,\sigma^2)$.

Assumption MLR.6 is much stronger than any of our previous assumptions. In fact, since u is independent of the x_j under MLR.6, $E(u|x_1, \dots, x_k) = E(u) = 0$ and $Var(u|x_1, \dots, x_k) = Var(u) = \sigma^2$. Thus, if we make Assumption MLR.6, then we are necessarily assuming MLR.4 and MLR.5. To emphasize that we are assuming more than before, we will refer to the full set of Assumptions MLR.1 through MLR.6.

For cross-sectional regression applications, Assumptions MLR.1 through MLR.6 are called the **classical linear model (CLM) assumptions**. Thus, we will refer to the model under these six assumptions as the **classical linear model**. It is best to think of the CLM assumptions as containing all of the Gauss-Markov assumptions *plus* the assumption of a normally distributed error term.

Under the CLM assumptions, the OLS estimators $\hat{\beta}_0, \hat{\beta}_1, \dots, \hat{\beta}_k$ have a stronger efficiency property than they would under the Gauss-Markov assumptions. It can be shown that the OLS estimators are the **minimum variance unbiased estimators**, which means that OLS has the smallest variance among unbiased estimators; we no longer have to restrict our comparison to estimators that are linear in the y_i. This property of OLS under the CLM assumptions is discussed further in Appendix E.

A succinct way to summarize the population assumptions of the CLM is

$$y|\mathbf{x} \sim \text{Normal}(\beta_0 + \beta_1 x_1 + \beta_2 x_2 + \dots + \beta_k x_k, \sigma^2),$$

where $\mathbf{x}$ is again shorthand for $(x_1, \dots, x_k)$. Thus, conditional on $\mathbf{x}$, y has a normal distribution with mean linear in $x_1, \dots, x_k$ and a constant variance. For a single independent variable x, this situation is shown in Figure 4.1.

FIGURE 4.1 The homoskedastic normal distribution with a single explanatory variable.

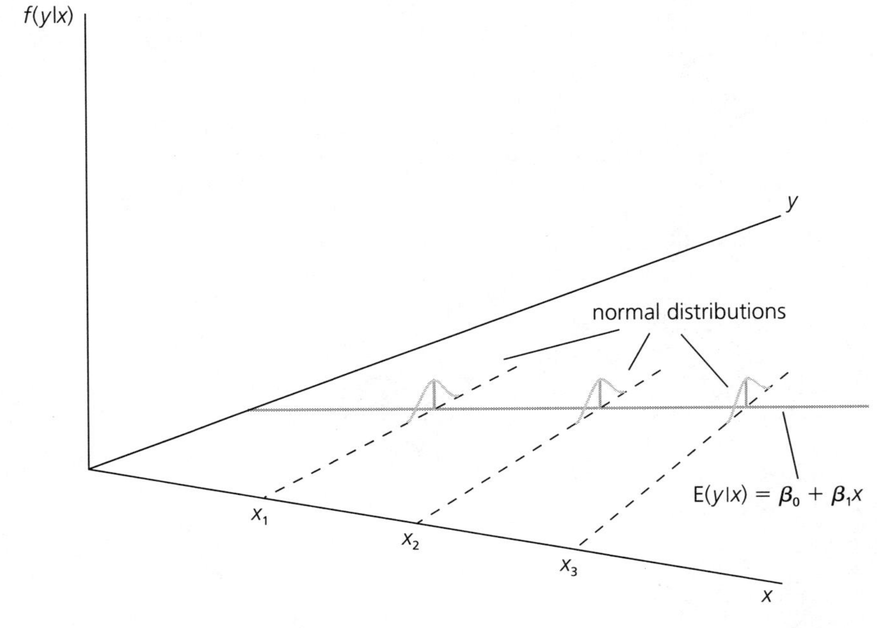

The argument justifying the normal distribution for the errors usually runs something like this: Because u is the sum of many different unobserved factors affecting y, we can invoke the central limit theorem (see Appendix C) to conclude that u has an approximate normal distribution. This argument has some merit, but it is not without weaknesses. First, the factors in u can have very different distributions in the population (for example, ability and quality of schooling in the error in a wage equation). Although the central limit theorem (CLT) can still hold in such cases, the normal approximation can be poor depending on how many factors appear in u and how different their distributions are.

A more serious problem with the CLT argument is that it assumes that all unobserved factors affect y in a separate, additive fashion. Nothing guarantees that this is so. If u is a complicated function of the unobserved factors, then the CLT argument does not really apply.

In any application, whether normality of u can be assumed is really an empirical matter. For example, there is no theorem that says *wage* conditional on *educ*, *exper*, and *tenure* is normally distributed. If anything, simple reasoning suggests that the opposite is true: Since *wage* can never be less than zero, it cannot, strictly speaking, have a normal distribution. Further, because there are minimum wage laws, some fraction of the population earns exactly the minimum wage, which also violates the normality assumption. Nevertheless, as a practical matter, we can ask whether the conditional wage distribution is "close" to being normal. Past empirical evidence suggests that normality is *not* a good assumption for wages.

Often, using a transformation, especially taking the log, yields a distribution that is closer to normal. For example, something like log(*price*) tends to have a distribution that looks more normal than the distribution of *price*. Again, this is an empirical issue. We will discuss the consequences of nonnormality for statistical inference in Chapter 5.

There are some examples where MLR.6 is clearly false. Whenever y takes on just a few values it cannot have anything close to a normal distribution. The dependent variable in Example 3.5 provides a good example. The variable *narr86*, the number of times a young man was arrested in 1986, takes on a small range of integer values and is zero for most men. Thus, *narr86* is far from being normally distributed. What can be done in these cases? As we will see in Chapter 5—and this is important—nonnormality of the errors is not a serious problem with large sample sizes. For now, we just make the normality assumption.

Normality of the error term translates into normal sampling distributions of the OLS estimators:

THEOREM 4.1

NORMAL SAMPLING DISTRIBUTIONS

Under the CLM assumptions MLR.1 through MLR.6, conditional on the sample values of the independent variables,

$$\hat{\beta}_j \sim \text{Normal}[\beta_j, \text{Var}(\hat{\beta}_j)], \quad [4.1]$$

where $\text{Var}(\hat{\beta}_j)$ was given in Chapter 3 [equation (3.51)]. Therefore,

$$(\hat{\beta}_j - \beta_j)/\text{sd}(\hat{\beta}_j) \sim \text{Normal}(0,1).$$

The proof of (4.1) is not that difficult, given the properties of normally distributed random variables in Appendix B. Each $\hat{\beta}_j$ can be written as $\hat{\beta}_j = \beta_j + \sum_{i=1}^{n} w_{ij}u_i$, where $w_{ij} = \hat{r}_{ij}/\text{SSR}_j$, $\hat{r}_{ij}$ is the ith residual from the regression of the x_j on all the other independent variables, and SSR_j is the sum of squared residuals from this regression [see equation (3.62)]. Since the w_{ij} depend only on the independent variables, they can be treated as nonrandom. Thus, $\hat{\beta}_j$ is just a linear combination of the errors in the sample, $\{u_i: i = 1, 2, ..., n\}$. Under Assumption MLR.6 (and the random sampling Assumption MLR.2), the errors are independent, identically distributed Normal$(0,\sigma^2)$ random variables. An important fact about independent normal random variables is that a linear combination of such random variables is normally distributed (see Appendix B). This basically completes the proof. In Section 3.3, we showed that $\text{E}(\hat{\beta}_j) = \beta_j$, and we derived $\text{Var}(\hat{\beta}_j)$ in Section 3.4; there is no need to re-derive these facts.

EXPLORING FURTHER 4.1

Suppose that u is independent of the explanatory variables, and it takes on the values $-2, -1, 0, 1$, and 2 with equal probability of 1/5. Does this violate the Gauss-Markov assumptions? Does this violate the CLM assumptions?

The second part of this theorem follows immediately from the fact that when we standardize a normal random variable by subtracting off its mean and dividing by its standard deviation, we end up with a standard normal random variable.

The conclusions of Theorem 4.1 can be strengthened. In addition to (4.1), any linear combination of the $\hat{\beta}_0, \hat{\beta}_1, ..., \hat{\beta}_k$ is also normally distributed, and any subset of the $\hat{\beta}_j$ has a *joint* normal distribution. These facts underlie the testing results in the remainder of this chapter. In Chapter 5, we will show that the normality of the OLS estimators is still *approximately* true in large samples even without normality of the errors.

4.2 Testing Hypotheses about a Single Population Parameter: The *t* Test

This section covers the very important topic of testing hypotheses about any single parameter in the population regression function. The population model can be written as

$$y = \beta_0 + \beta_1 x_1 + ... + \beta_k x_k + u, \qquad [4.2]$$

and we assume that it satisfies the CLM assumptions. We know that OLS produces unbiased estimators of the β_j. In this section, we study how to test hypotheses about a particular β_j. For a full understanding of hypothesis testing, one must remember that the β_j are unknown features of the population, and we will never know them with certainty. Nevertheless, we can *hypothesize* about the value of β_j and then use statistical inference to test our hypothesis.

In order to construct hypotheses tests, we need the following result:

THEOREM 4.2

***t* DISTRIBUTION FOR THE STANDARDIZED ESTIMATORS**

Under the CLM assumptions MLR.1 through MLR.6,

$$(\hat{\beta}_j - \beta_j)/\text{se}(\hat{\beta}_j) \sim t_{n-k-1} = t_{df}, \qquad [4.3]$$

where $k + 1$ is the number of unknown parameters in the population model $y = \beta_0 + \beta_1 x_1 + ... + \beta_k x_k + u$ (k slope parameters and the intercept β_0) and $n - k - 1$ is the degrees of freedom (df).

This result differs from Theorem 4.1 in some notable respects. Theorem 4.1 showed that, under the CLM assumptions, $(\hat{\beta}_j - \beta_j)/\text{sd}(\hat{\beta}_j) \sim \text{Normal}(0,1)$. The t distribution in (4.3) comes from the fact that the constant σ in $\text{sd}(\hat{\beta}_j)$ has been replaced with the random variable $\hat{\sigma}$. The proof that this leads to a t distribution with $n - k - 1$ degrees of freedom is difficult and not especially instructive. Essentially, the proof shows that (4.3) can be written as the ratio of the standard normal random variable $(\hat{\beta}_j - \beta_j)/\text{sd}(\hat{\beta}_j)$ over the square root of $\hat{\sigma}^2/\sigma^2$. These random variables can be shown to be independent, and $(n - k - 1)\hat{\sigma}^2/\sigma^2 \sim \chi^2_{n-k-1}$. The result then follows from the definition of a t random variable (see Section B.5).

Theorem 4.2 is important in that it allows us to test hypotheses involving the β_j. In most applications, our primary interest lies in testing the **null hypothesis**

$$\text{H}_0\text{: } \beta_j = 0, \qquad [4.4]$$

where j corresponds to any of the k independent variables. It is important to understand what (4.4) means and to be able to describe this hypothesis in simple language for a particular application. Since β_j measures the partial effect of x_j on (the expected value of) y, after controlling for all other independent variables, (4.4) means that, once $x_1, x_2, \ldots, x_{j-1}, x_{j+1}, \ldots, x_k$ have been accounted for, x_j has *no effect* on the expected value of y. We cannot state the null hypothesis as "x_j does have a partial effect on y" because this is true for any value of β_j other than zero. Classical testing is suited for testing *simple hypotheses* like (4.4).

As an example, consider the wage equation

$$\log(wage) = \beta_0 + \beta_1 educ + \beta_2 exper + \beta_3 tenure + u.$$

The null hypothesis $\text{H}_0\text{: } \beta_2 = 0$ means that, once education and tenure have been accounted for, the number of years in the workforce (*exper*) has no effect on hourly wage. This is an economically interesting hypothesis. If it is true, it implies that a person's work history prior to the current employment does not affect wage. If $\beta_2 > 0$, then prior work experience contributes to productivity, and hence to wage.

You probably remember from your statistics course the rudiments of hypothesis testing for the mean from a normal population. (This is reviewed in Appendix C.) The mechanics of testing (4.4) in the multiple regression context are very similar. The hard part is obtaining the coefficient estimates, the standard errors, and the critical values, but most of this work is done automatically by econometrics software. Our job is to learn how regression output can be used to test hypotheses of interest.

The statistic we use to test (4.4) (against any alternative) is called "the" ***t* statistic** or "the" ***t* ratio** of $\hat{\beta}_j$ and is defined as

$$t_{\hat{\beta}_j} \equiv \hat{\beta}_j/\text{se}(\hat{\beta}_j). \qquad [4.5]$$

We have put "the" in quotation marks because, as we will see shortly, a more general form of the t statistic is needed for testing other hypotheses about β_j. For now, it is important to know that (4.5) is suitable only for testing (4.4). For particular applications, it is helpful to index t statistics using the name of the independent variable; for example, t_{educ} would be the t statistic for $\hat{\beta}_{educ}$.

The t statistic for $\hat{\beta}_j$ is simple to compute given $\hat{\beta}_j$ and its standard error. In fact, most regression packages do the division for you and report the t statistic along with each coefficient and its standard error.

Before discussing how to use (4.5) formally to test H_0: $\beta_j = 0$, it is useful to see why $t_{\hat{\beta}_j}$ has features that make it reasonable as a test statistic to detect $\beta_j \neq 0$. First, since $se(\hat{\beta}_j)$ is always positive, $t_{\hat{\beta}_j}$ has the same sign as $\hat{\beta}_j$: if $\hat{\beta}_j$ is positive, then so is $t_{\hat{\beta}_j}$, and if $\hat{\beta}_j$ is negative, so is $t_{\hat{\beta}_j}$. Second, for a given value of $se(\hat{\beta}_j)$, a larger value of $\hat{\beta}_j$ leads to larger values of $t_{\hat{\beta}_j}$. If $\hat{\beta}_j$ becomes more negative, so does $t_{\hat{\beta}_j}$.

Since we are testing H_0: $\beta_j = 0$, it is only natural to look at our unbiased estimator of β_j, $\hat{\beta}_j$, for guidance. In any interesting application, the point estimate $\hat{\beta}_j$ will *never* exactly be zero, whether or not H_0 is true. The question is: How far is $\hat{\beta}_j$ from zero? A sample value of $\hat{\beta}_j$ very far from zero provides evidence against H_0: $\beta_j = 0$. However, we must recognize that there is a sampling error in our estimate $\hat{\beta}_j$, so the size of $\hat{\beta}_j$ must be weighed against its sampling error. Since the standard error of $\hat{\beta}_j$ is an estimate of the standard deviation of $\hat{\beta}_j$, $t_{\hat{\beta}_j}$ measures how many estimated standard deviations $\hat{\beta}_j$ is away from zero. This is precisely what we do in testing whether the mean of a population is zero, using the standard *t* statistic from introductory statistics. Values of $t_{\hat{\beta}_j}$ sufficiently far from zero will result in a rejection of H_0. The precise rejection rule depends on the alternative hypothesis and the chosen significance level of the test.

Determining a rule for rejecting (4.4) at a given significance level—that is, the probability of rejecting H_0 when it is true—requires knowing the sampling distribution of $t_{\hat{\beta}_j}$ when H_0 is true. From Theorem 4.2, we know this to be t_{n-k-1}. This is the key theoretical result needed for testing (4.4).

Before proceeding, it is important to remember that we are testing hypotheses about the *population* parameters. We are *not* testing hypotheses about the estimates from a particular sample. Thus, it never makes sense to state a null hypothesis as "H_0: $\hat{\beta}_1 = 0$" or, even worse, as "H_0: $.237 = 0$" when the estimate of a parameter is .237 in the sample. We are testing whether the unknown population value, β_1, is zero.

Some treatments of regression analysis define the *t* statistic as the *absolute value* of (4.5), so that the *t* statistic is always positive. This practice has the drawback of making testing against one-sided alternatives clumsy. Throughout this text, the *t* statistic always has the same sign as the corresponding OLS coefficient estimate.

Testing against One-Sided Alternatives

To determine a rule for rejecting H_0, we need to decide on the relevant **alternative hypothesis**. First, consider a **one-sided alternative** of the form

$$H_1: \beta_j > 0. \qquad [4.6]$$

When we state the alternative as in equation (4.6), we are really saying that the null hypothesis is H_0: $\beta_j \leq 0$. For example, if β_j is the coefficient on education in a wage regression, we only care about detecting that β_j is different from zero when β_j is actually positive. You may remember from introductory statistics that the null value that is hardest to reject in favor of (4.6) is $\beta_j = 0$. In other words, if we reject the null $\beta_j = 0$ then we automatically reject $\beta_j < 0$. Therefore, it suffices to act as if we are testing H_0: $\beta_j = 0$ against H_1: $\beta_j > 0$, effectively ignoring $\beta_j < 0$, and that is the approach we take in this book.

How should we choose a rejection rule? We must first decide on a **significance level** ("level" for short) or the probability of rejecting H_0 when it is in fact true. For concreteness, suppose we have decided on a 5% significance level, as this is the most popular choice. Thus, we are willing to mistakenly reject H_0 when it is true 5% of the time. Now, while $t_{\hat{\beta}_j}$ has a t distribution under H_0—so that it has zero mean—under the alternative $\beta_j > 0$, the expected value of $t_{\hat{\beta}_j}$ is positive. Thus, we are looking for a "sufficiently large" positive value of $t_{\hat{\beta}_j}$ in order to reject H_0: $\beta_j = 0$ in favor of H_1: $\beta_j > 0$. Negative values of $t_{\hat{\beta}_j}$ provide no evidence in favor of H_1.

The definition of "sufficiently large," with a 5% significance level, is the 95th percentile in a t distribution with $n - k - 1$ degrees of freedom; denote this by c. In other words, the **rejection rule** is that H_0 is rejected in favor of H_1 at the 5% significance level if

$$t_{\hat{\beta}_j} > c. \quad [4.7]$$

By our choice of the **critical value** c, rejection of H_0 will occur for 5% of all random samples when H_0 is true.

The rejection rule in (4.7) is an example of a **one-tailed test**. To obtain c, we only need the significance level and the degrees of freedom. For example, for a 5% level test and with $n - k - 1 = 28$ degrees of freedom, the critical value is $c = 1.701$. If $t_{\hat{\beta}_j} \leq 1.701$, then we fail to reject H_0 in favor of (4.6) at the 5% level. Note that a negative value for $t_{\hat{\beta}_j}$, no matter how large in absolute value, leads to a failure in rejecting H_0 in favor of 4.6). (See Figure 4.2.)

FIGURE 4.2 5% rejection rule for the alternative H_1: $\beta_j > 0$ with 28 *df*.

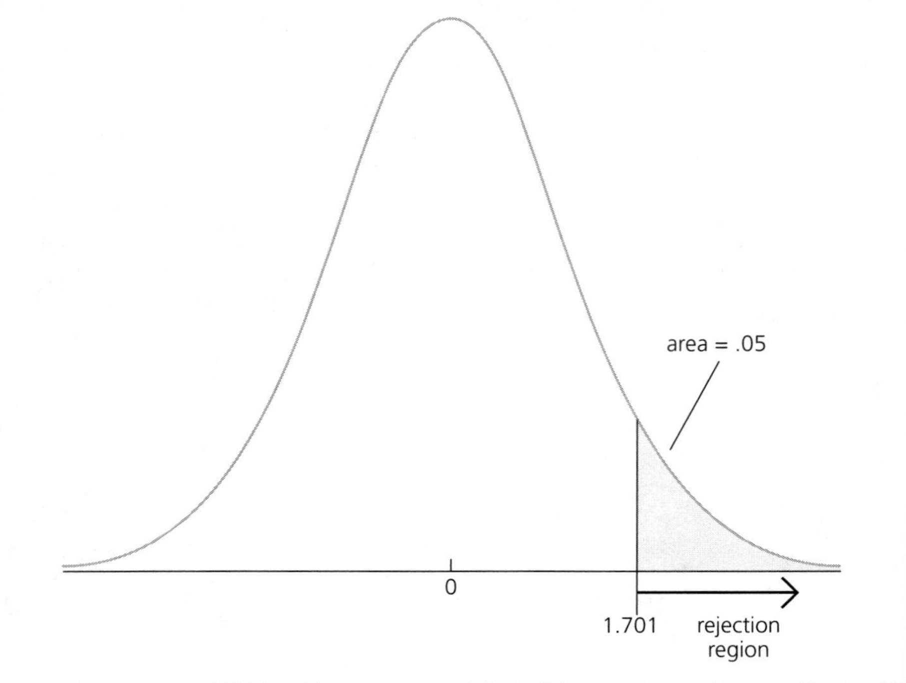

The same procedure can be used with other significance levels. For a 10% level test and if $df = 21$, the critical value is $c = 1.323$. For a 1% significance level and if $df = 21$, $c = 2.518$. All of these critical values are obtained directly from Table G.2. You should note a pattern in the critical values: As the significance level falls, the critical value increases, so that we require a larger and larger value of $t_{\hat{\beta}_j}$ in order to reject H_0. Thus, if H_0 is rejected at, say, the 5% level, then it is automatically rejected at the 10% level as well. It makes no sense to reject the null hypothesis at, say, the 5% level and then to redo the test to determine the outcome at the 10% level.

As the degrees of freedom in the t distribution get large, the t distribution approaches the standard normal distribution. For example, when $n - k - 1 = 120$, the 5% critical value for the one-sided alternative (4.7) is 1.658, compared with the standard normal value of 1.645. These are close enough for practical purposes; for degrees of freedom greater than 120, one can use the standard normal critical values.

EXAMPLE 4.1 HOURLY WAGE EQUATION

Using the data in WAGE1.RAW gives the estimated equation

$$\widehat{\log(wage)} = \underset{(.104)}{.284} + \underset{(.007)}{.092}\, educ + \underset{(.0017)}{.0041}\, exper + \underset{(.003)}{.022}\, tenure$$

$$n = 526,\ R^2 = .316,$$

where standard errors appear in parentheses below the estimated coefficients. We will follow this convention throughout the text. This equation can be used to test whether the return to *exper*, controlling for *educ* and *tenure*, is zero in the population, against the alternative that it is positive. Write this as H_0: $\beta_{exper} = 0$ versus H_1: $\beta_{exper} > 0$. (In applications, indexing a parameter by its associated variable name is a nice way to label parameters, since the numerical indices that we use in the general model are arbitrary and can cause confusion.) Remember that β_{exper} denotes the unknown population parameter. It is nonsense to write "H_0: $.0041 = 0$" or "H_0: $\hat{\beta}_{exper} = 0$."

Since we have 522 degrees of freedom, we can use the standard normal critical values. The 5% critical value is 1.645, and the 1% critical value is 2.326. The t statistic for $\hat{\beta}_{exper}$ is

$$t_{exper} = .0041/.0017 \approx 2.41,$$

and so $\hat{\beta}_{exper}$, or *exper*, is statistically significant even at the 1% level. We also say that "$\hat{\beta}_{exper}$ is statistically greater than zero at the 1% significance level."

The estimated return for another year of experience, holding tenure and education fixed, is not especially large. For example, adding three more years increases log(*wage*) by $3(.0041) = .0123$, so wage is only about 1.2% higher. Nevertheless, we have persuasively shown that the partial effect of experience *is* positive in the population.

The one-sided alternative that the parameter is less than zero,

$$H_1: \beta_j < 0, \tag{4.8}$$

also arises in applications. The rejection rule for alternative (4.8) is just the mirror image of the previous case. Now, the critical value comes from the left tail of the t distribution. In practice, it is easiest to think of the rejection rule as

$$t_{\hat{\beta}_j} < -c, \quad [4.9]$$

where c is the critical value for the alternative H_1: $\beta_j > 0$. For simplicity, we always assume c is positive, since this is how critical values are reported in t tables, and so the critical value $-c$ is a negative number.

For example, if the significance level is 5% and the degrees of freedom is 18, then $c = 1.734$, and so H_0: $\beta_j = 0$ is rejected in favor of H_1: $\beta_j < 0$ at the 5% level if $t_{\hat{\beta}_j} < -1.734$. It is important to remember that, to reject H_0 against the negative alternative (4.8), we must get a negative t statistic. A positive t ratio, no matter how large, provides no evidence in favor of (4.8). The rejection rule is illustrated in Figure 4.3.

EXPLORING FURTHER 4.2

Let community loan approval rates be determined by

$$apprate = \beta_0 + \beta_1 percmin + \beta_2 avginc + \beta_3 avgwlth + \beta_4 avgdebt + u,$$

where *percmin* is the percentage minority in the community, *avginc* is average income, *avgwlth* is average wealth, and *avgdebt* is some measure of average debt obligations. How do you state the null hypothesis that there is *no* difference in loan rates across neighborhoods due to racial and ethnic composition, when average income, average wealth, and average debt have been controlled for? How do you state the alternative that there is discrimination against minorities in loan approval rates?

FIGURE 4.3 5% rejection rule for the alternative H_1: $\beta_j < 0$ with 18 *df*.

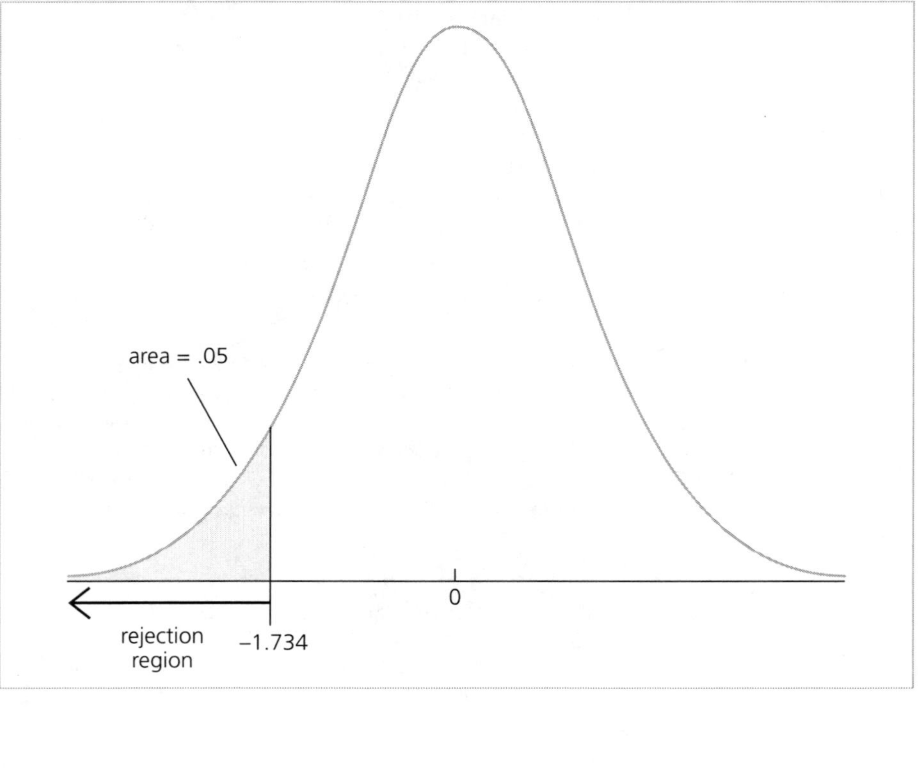

EXAMPLE 4.2 STUDENT PERFORMANCE AND SCHOOL SIZE

There is much interest in the effect of school size on student performance. (See, for example, *The New York Times Magazine*, 5/28/95.) One claim is that, everything else being equal, students at smaller schools fare better than those at larger schools. This hypothesis is assumed to be true even after accounting for differences in class sizes across schools.

The file MEAP93.RAW contains data on 408 high schools in Michigan for the year 1993. We can use these data to test the null hypothesis that school size has no effect on standardized test scores against the alternative that size has a negative effect. Performance is measured by the percentage of students receiving a passing score on the Michigan Educational Assessment Program (MEAP) standardized tenth-grade math test (*math*10). School size is measured by student enrollment (*enroll*). The null hypothesis is H_0: $\beta_{enroll} = 0$, and the alternative is H_1: $\beta_{enroll} < 0$. For now, we will control for two other factors, average annual teacher compensation (*totcomp*) and the number of staff per one thousand students (*staff*). Teacher compensation is a measure of teacher quality, and staff size is a rough measure of how much attention students receive.

The estimated equation, with standard errors in parentheses, is

$$\begin{aligned}\widehat{math10} &= \underset{(6.113)}{2.274} + \underset{(.00010)}{.00046}\ totcomp + \underset{(.040)}{.048}\ staff - \underset{(.00022)}{.00020}\ enroll \\ n &= 408,\ R^2 = .0541.\end{aligned}$$

The coefficient on *enroll*, $-.00020$, is in accordance with the conjecture that larger schools hamper performance: higher enrollment leads to a lower percentage of students with a passing tenth-grade math score. (The coefficients on *totcomp* and *staff* also have the signs we expect.) The fact that *enroll* has an estimated coefficient different from zero could just be due to sampling error; to be convinced of an effect, we need to conduct a *t* test.

Since $n - k - 1 = 408 - 4 = 404$, we use the standard normal critical value. At the 5% level, the critical value is -1.65; the *t* statistic on *enroll* must be *less* than -1.65 to reject H_0 at the 5% level.

The *t* statistic on *enroll* is $-.00020/.00022 \approx -.91$, which is larger than -1.65: we *fail* to reject H_0 in favor of H_1 at the 5% level. In fact, the 15% critical value is -1.04, and since $-.91 > -1.04$, we fail to reject H_0 even at the 15% level. We conclude that *enroll* is not statistically significant at the 15% level.

The variable *totcomp* is statistically significant even at the 1% significance level because its *t* statistic is 4.6. On the other hand, the *t* statistic for *staff* is 1.2, and so we cannot reject H_0: $\beta_{staff} = 0$ against H_1: $\beta_{staff} > 0$ even at the 10% significance level. (The critical value is $c = 1.28$ from the standard normal distribution.)

To illustrate how changing functional form can affect our conclusions, we also estimate the model with all independent variables in logarithmic form. This allows, for example, the school size effect to diminish as school size increases. The estimated equation is

$$\begin{aligned}\widehat{math10} &= \underset{(48.70)}{-207.66} + \underset{(4.06)}{21.16}\log(totcomp) + \underset{(4.19)}{3.98}\log(staff) - \underset{(0.69)}{1.29}\log(enroll) \\ n &= 408,\ R^2 = .0654.\end{aligned}$$

The *t* statistic on log(*enroll*) is about -1.87; since this is below the 5% critical value -1.65, we reject H_0: $\beta_{\log(enroll)} = 0$ in favor of H_1: $\beta_{\log(enroll)} < 0$ at the 5% level.

In Chapter 2, we encountered a model where the dependent variable appeared in its original form (called *level* form), while the independent variable appeared in log form (called *level-log* model). The interpretation of the parameters is the same in the multiple regression context, except, of course, that we can give the parameters a ceteris paribus interpretation. Holding *totcomp* and *staff* fixed, we have $\Delta\widehat{math10} = -1.29[\Delta\log(enroll)]$, so that

$$\Delta\widehat{math10} \approx -(1.29/100)(\%\Delta enroll) \approx -.013(\%\Delta enroll).$$

Once again, we have used the fact that the change in log(*enroll*), when multiplied by 100, is approximately the percentage change in *enroll*. Thus, if enrollment is 10% higher at a school, $\widehat{math10}$ is predicted to be .013(10) = 0.13 percentage points lower (*math*10 is measured as a percentage).

Which model do we prefer: the one using the level of *enroll* or the one using log(*enroll*)? In the level-level model, enrollment does not have a statistically significant effect, but in the level-log model it does. This translates into a higher *R*-squared for the level-log model, which means we explain more of the variation in *math*10 by using *enroll* in logarithmic form (6.5% to 5.4%). The level-log model is preferred because it more closely captures the relationship between *math*10 and *enroll*. We will say more about using *R*-squared to choose functional form in Chapter 6.

Two-Sided Alternatives

In applications, it is common to test the null hypothesis H_0: $\beta_j = 0$ against a **two-sided alternative**; that is,

$$H_1: \beta_j \neq 0. \quad [4.10]$$

Under this alternative, x_j has a ceteris paribus effect on y without specifying whether the effect is positive or negative. This is the relevant alternative when the sign of β_j is not well determined by theory (or common sense). Even when we know whether β_j is positive or negative under the alternative, a two-sided test is often prudent. At a minimum, using a two-sided alternative prevents us from looking at the estimated equation and then basing the alternative on whether $\hat{\beta}_j$ is positive or negative. Using the regression estimates to help us formulate the null or alternative hypotheses is not allowed because classical statistical inference presumes that we state the null and alternative about the population before looking at the data. For example, we should not first estimate the equation relating math performance to enrollment, note that the estimated effect is negative, and then decide the relevant alternative is H_1: $\beta_{enroll} < 0$.

When the alternative is two-sided, we are interested in the *absolute value* of the t statistic. The rejection rule for H_0: $\beta_j = 0$ against (4.10) is

$$|t_{\hat{\beta}_j}| > c, \quad [4.11]$$

where $|\cdot|$ denotes absolute value and c is an appropriately chosen critical value. To find c, we again specify a significance level, say 5%. For a **two-tailed test**, c is chosen to make the area in each tail of the t distribution equal 2.5%. In other words, c is the 97.5th percentile in the t distribution with $n - k - 1$ degrees of freedom. When $n - k - 1 = 25$, the 5% critical value for a two-sided test is $c = 2.060$. Figure 4.4 provides an illustration of this distribution.

FIGURE 4.4 5% rejection rule for the alternative H_1: $\beta_j \neq 0$ with 25 *df*.

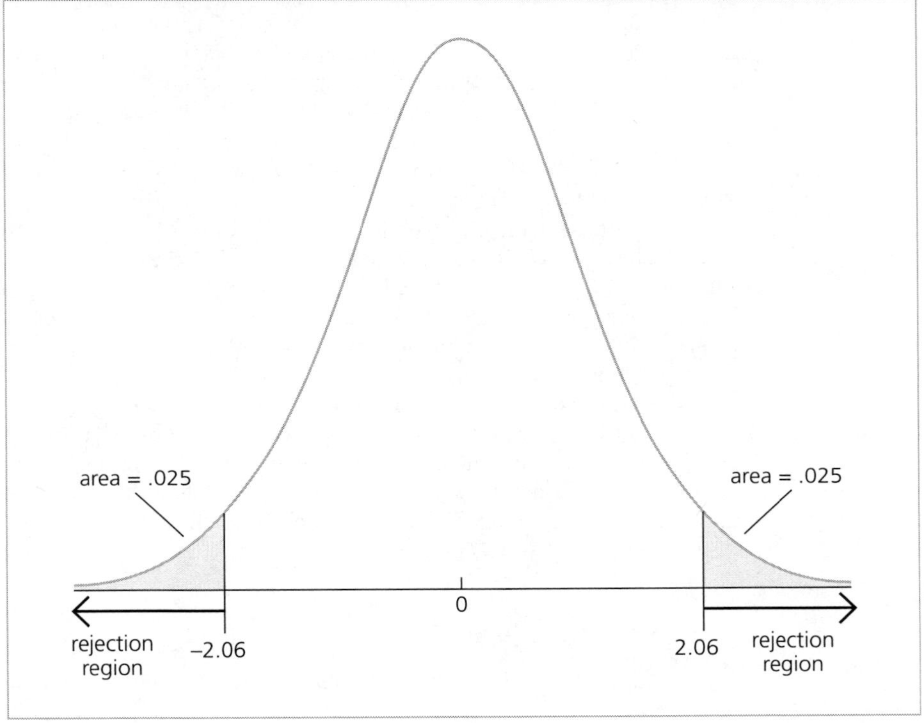

When a specific alternative is not stated, it is usually considered to be two-sided. In the remainder of this text, the default will be a two-sided alternative, and 5% will be the default significance level. When carrying out empirical econometric analysis, it is always a good idea to be explicit about the alternative and the significance level. If H_0 is rejected in favor of (4.10) at the 5% level, we usually say that "x_j is **statistically significant**, or statistically different from zero, at the 5% level." If H_0 is not rejected, we say that "x_j is **statistically insignificant** at the 5% level."

EXAMPLE 4.3 DETERMINANTS OF COLLEGE GPA

We use GPA1.RAW to estimate a model explaining college GPA (*colGPA*), with the average number of lectures missed per week (*skipped*) as an additional explanatory variable. The estimated model is

$$\widehat{colGPA} = \underset{(.33)}{1.39} + \underset{(.094)}{.412}\, hsGPA + \underset{(.011)}{.015}\, ACT - \underset{(.026)}{.083}\, skipped$$
$$n = 141,\ R^2 = .234.$$

We can easily compute t statistics to see which variables are statistically significant, using a two-sided alternative in each case. The 5% critical value is about 1.96, since the degrees of freedom (141 − 4 = 137) is large enough to use the standard normal approximation. The 1% critical value is about 2.58.

The t statistic on *hsGPA* is 4.38, which is significant at very small significance levels. Thus, we say that "*hsGPA* is statistically significant at any *conventional* significance level." The t statistic on *ACT* is 1.36, which is not statistically significant at the 10% level against a two-sided alternative. The coefficient on *ACT* is also practically small: a 10-point increase in *ACT*, which is large, is predicted to increase *colGPA* by only .15 points. Thus, the variable *ACT* is practically, as well as statistically, insignificant.

The coefficient on *skipped* has a t statistic of −.083/.026 = −3.19, so *skipped* is statistically significant at the 1% significance level (3.19 > 2.58). This coefficient means that another lecture missed per week lowers predicted *colGPA* by about .083. Thus, holding *hsGPA* and *ACT* fixed, the predicted difference in *colGPA* between a student who misses no lectures per week and a student who misses five lectures per week is about .42. Remember that this says nothing about specific students; rather, .42 is the estimated average across a subpopulation of students.

In this example, for each variable in the model, we could argue that a one-sided alternative is appropriate. The variables *hsGPA* and *skipped* are very significant using a two-tailed test and have the signs that we expect, so there is no reason to do a one-tailed test. On the other hand, against a one-sided alternative ($\beta_3 > 0$), *ACT* is significant at the 10% level but not at the 5% level. This does not change the fact that the coefficient on *ACT* is pretty small.

Testing Other Hypotheses about β_j

Although H_0: $\beta_j = 0$ is the most common hypothesis, we sometimes want to test whether β_j is equal to some other given constant. Two common examples are $\beta_j = 1$ and $\beta_j = -1$. Generally, if the null is stated as

$$H_0\colon \beta_j = a_j, \qquad [4.12]$$

where a_j is our hypothesized value of β_j, then the appropriate t statistic is

$$t = (\hat{\beta}_j - a_j)/\mathrm{se}(\hat{\beta}_j).$$

As before, t measures how many estimated standard deviations $\hat{\beta}_j$ is away from the hypothesized value of β_j. The general t statistic is usefully written as

$$t = \frac{(\textit{estimate} - \textit{hypothesized value})}{\textit{standard error}}. \qquad [4.13]$$

Under (4.12), this t statistic is distributed as t_{n-k-1} from Theorem 4.2. The usual t statistic is obtained when $a_j = 0$.

We can use the general t statistic to test against one-sided or two-sided alternatives. For example, if the null and alternative hypotheses are H_0: $\beta_j = 1$ and H_1: $\beta_j > 1$, then we find the critical value for a one-sided alternative *exactly* as before: the difference is in how we compute the t statistic, not in how we obtain the appropriate c. We reject H_0 in favor of H_1 if $t > c$. In this case, we would say that "$\hat{\beta}_j$ is statistically greater than one" at the appropriate significance level.

EXAMPLE 4.4 CAMPUS CRIME AND ENROLLMENT

Consider a simple model relating the annual number of crimes on college campuses (*crime*) to student enrollment (*enroll*):

$$\log(crime) = \beta_0 + \beta_1\log(enroll) + u.$$

This is a constant elasticity model, where β_1 is the elasticity of crime with respect to enrollment. It is not much use to test H_0: $\beta_1 = 0$, as we expect the total number of crimes to increase as the size of the campus increases. A more interesting hypothesis to test would be that the elasticity of crime with respect to enrollment is one: H_0: $\beta_1 = 1$. This means that a 1% increase in enrollment leads to, on average, a 1% increase in crime. A noteworthy alternative is H_1: $\beta_1 > 1$, which implies that a 1% increase in enrollment increases campus crime by *more* than 1%. If $\beta_1 > 1$, then, in a relative sense—not just an absolute sense—crime is more of a problem on larger campuses. One way to see this is to take the exponential of the equation:

$$crime = \exp(\beta_0)enroll^{\beta_1}\exp(u).$$

(See Appendix A for properties of the natural logarithm and exponential functions.) For $\beta_0 = 0$ and $u = 0$, this equation is graphed in Figure 4.5 for $\beta_1 < 1$, $\beta_1 = 1$, and $\beta_1 > 1$.

FIGURE 4.5 Graph of $crime = enroll^{\beta_1}$ for $\beta_1 < 1$, $\beta_1 = 1$, and $\beta_1 > 1$.

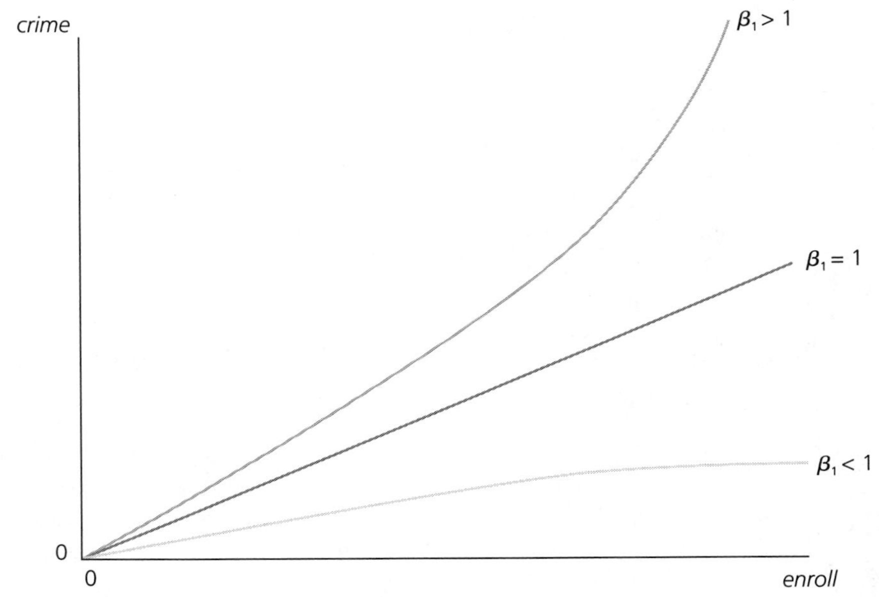

We test $\beta_1 = 1$ against $\beta_1 > 1$ using data on 97 colleges and universities in the United States for the year 1992, contained in the data file CAMPUS.RAW. The data come from the FBI's *Uniform Crime Reports*, and the average number of campus crimes in the sample is about 394, while the average enrollment is about 16,076. The estimated equation (with estimates and standard errors rounded to two decimal places) is

$$\begin{aligned} \widehat{\log(crime)} &= -6.63 + 1.27 \log(enroll) \\ &\quad\;\; (1.03) \quad (0.11) \\ n &= 97, R^2 = .585. \end{aligned} \qquad [4.14]$$

The estimated elasticity of *crime* with respect to *enroll*, 1.27, is in the direction of the alternative $\beta_1 > 1$. But is there enough evidence to conclude that $\beta_1 > 1$? We need to be careful in testing this hypothesis, especially because the statistical output of standard regression packages is much more complex than the simplified output reported in equation (4.14). Our first instinct might be to construct "the" t statistic by taking the coefficient on log(*enroll*) and dividing it by its standard error, which is the t statistic reported by a regression package. But this is the *wrong* statistic for testing $H_0: \beta_1 = 1$. The correct t statistic is obtained from (4.13): we subtract the hypothesized value, unity, from the estimate and divide the result by the standard error of $\hat{\beta}_1$: $t = (1.27 - 1)/.11 = .27/.11 \approx 2.45$. The one-sided 5% critical value for a t distribution with $97 - 2 = 95$ *df* is about 1.66 (using $df = 120$), so we clearly reject $\beta_1 = 1$ in favor of $\beta_1 > 1$ at the 5% level. In fact, the 1% critical value is about 2.37, and so we reject the null in favor of the alternative at even the 1% level.

We should keep in mind that this analysis holds no other factors constant, so the elasticity of 1.27 is not necessarily a good estimate of ceteris paribus effect. It could be that larger enrollments are correlated with other factors that cause higher crime: larger schools might be located in higher crime areas. We could control for this by collecting data on crime rates in the local city.

For a two-sided alternative, for example $H_0: \beta_j = -1$, $H_1: \beta_j \neq -1$, we still compute the t statistic as in (4.13): $t = (\hat{\beta}_j + 1)/\text{se}(\hat{\beta}_j)$ (notice how subtracting -1 means adding 1). The rejection rule is the usual one for a two-sided test: reject H_0 if $|t| > c$, where c is a two-tailed critical value. If H_0 is rejected, we say that "$\hat{\beta}_j$ is statistically different from negative one" at the appropriate significance level.

EXAMPLE 4.5 HOUSING PRICES AND AIR POLLUTION

For a sample of 506 communities in the Boston area, we estimate a model relating median housing price (*price*) in the community to various community characteristics: *nox* is the amount of nitrogen oxide in the air, in parts per million; *dist* is a weighted distance of the community from five employment centers, in miles; *rooms* is the average number of rooms in houses in the community; and *stratio* is the average student-teacher ratio of schools in the community. The population model is

$$\log(price) = \beta_0 + \beta_1 \log(nox) + \beta_2 \log(dist) + \beta_3 rooms + \beta_4 stratio + u.$$

Thus, β_1 is the elasticity of *price* with respect to *nox*. We wish to test $H_0: \beta_1 = -1$ against the alternative $H_1: \beta_1 \neq -1$. The t statistic for doing this test is $t = (\hat{\beta}_1 + 1)/\text{se}(\hat{\beta}_1)$.

Using the data in HPRICE2.RAW, the estimated model is

$$\widehat{\log(price)} = \underset{(0.32)}{11.08} - \underset{(.117)}{.954}\log(nox) - \underset{(.043)}{.134}\log(dist) + \underset{(.019)}{.255}\,rooms - \underset{(.006)}{.052}\,stratio$$

$$n = 506, R^2 = .581.$$

The slope estimates all have the anticipated signs. Each coefficient is statistically different from zero at very small significance levels, including the coefficient on log(*nox*). But we do not want to test that $\beta_1 = 0$. The null hypothesis of interest is H_0: $\beta_1 = -1$, with corresponding t statistic $(-.954 + 1)/.117 = .393$. There is little need to look in the t table for a critical value when the t statistic is this small: the estimated elasticity is not statistically different from -1 even at very large significance levels. Controlling for the factors we have included, there is little evidence that the elasticity is different from -1.

Computing *p*-Values for *t* Tests

So far, we have talked about how to test hypotheses using a classical approach: after stating the alternative hypothesis, we choose a significance level, which then determines a critical value. Once the critical value has been identified, the value of the t statistic is compared with the critical value, and the null is either rejected or not rejected at the given significance level.

Even after deciding on the appropriate alternative, there is a component of arbitrariness to the classical approach, which results from having to choose a significance level ahead of time. Different researchers prefer different significance levels, depending on the particular application. There is no "correct" significance level.

Committing to a significance level ahead of time can hide useful information about the outcome of a hypothesis test. For example, suppose that we wish to test the null hypothesis that a parameter is zero against a two-sided alternative, and with 40 degrees of freedom we obtain a t statistic equal to 1.85. The null hypothesis is not rejected at the 5% level, since the t statistic is less than the two-tailed critical value of $c = 2.021$. A researcher whose agenda is not to reject the null could simply report this outcome along with the estimate: the null hypothesis is not rejected at the 5% level. Of course, if the t statistic, or the coefficient and its standard error, are reported, then we can also determine that the null hypothesis would be rejected at the 10% level, since the 10% critical value is $c = 1.684$.

Rather than testing at different significance levels, it is more informative to answer the following question: Given the observed value of the t statistic, what is the *smallest* significance level at which the null hypothesis would be rejected? This level is known as the ***p*-value** for the test (see Appendix C). In the previous example, we know the p-value is greater than .05, since the null is not rejected at the 5% level, and we know that the p-value is less than .10, since the null is rejected at the 10% level. We obtain the actual p-value by computing the probability that a t random variable, with 40 *df*, is larger than 1.85 in absolute value. That is, the p-value is the significance level of the test when we use the value of the test statistic, 1.85 in the above example, as the critical value for the test. This p-value is shown in Figure 4.6.

Because a p-value is a probability, its value is always between zero and one. In order to compute p-values, we either need extremely detailed printed tables of the

FIGURE 4.6 Obtaining the p-value against a two-sided alternative, when $t = 1.85$ and $df = 40$.

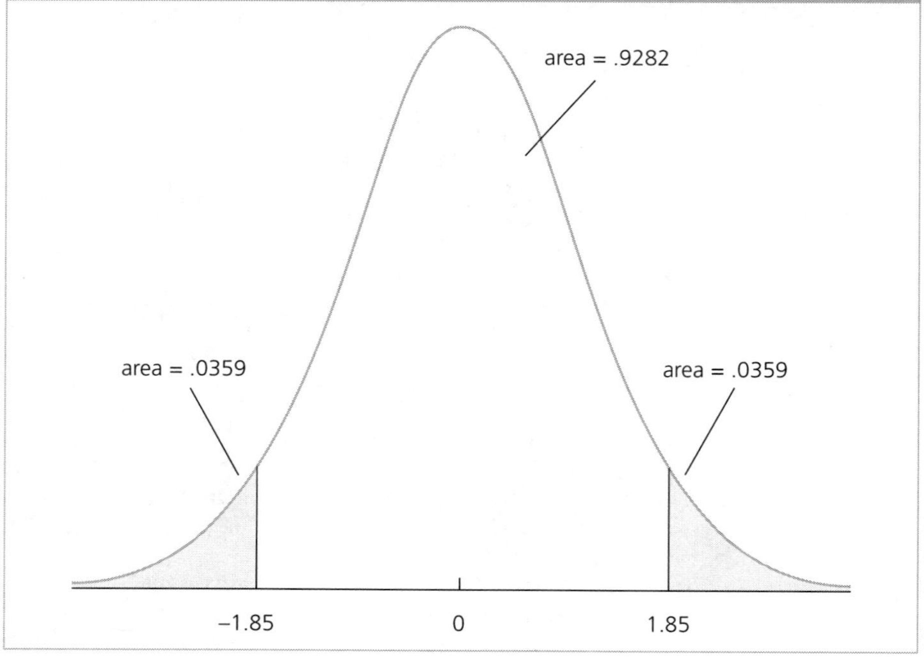

t distribution—which is not very practical—or a computer program that computes areas under the probability density function of the t distribution. Most modern regression packages have this capability. Some packages compute p-values routinely with each OLS regression, but only for certain hypotheses. If a regression package reports a p-value along with the standard OLS output, it is almost certainly the p-value for testing the null hypothesis H_0: $\beta_j = 0$ against the two-sided alternative. The p-value in this case is

$$P(|T| > |t|), \tag{4.15}$$

where, for clarity, we let T denote a t distributed random variable with $n - k - 1$ degrees of freedom and let t denote the numerical value of the test statistic.

The p-value nicely summarizes the strength or weakness of the empirical evidence against the null hypothesis. Perhaps its most useful interpretation is the following: the p-value is the probability of observing a t statistic as extreme as we did *if the null hypothesis is true*. This means that *small* p-values are evidence *against* the null; large p-values provide little evidence against H_0. For example, if the p-value $= .50$ (reported always as a decimal, not a percentage), then we would observe a value of the t statistic as extreme as we did in 50% of all random samples when the null hypothesis is true; this is pretty weak evidence against H_0.

In the example with $df = 40$ and $t = 1.85$, the p-value is computed as

$$p\text{-value} = P(|T| > 1.85) = 2P(T > 1.85) = 2(.0359) = .0718,$$

where P($T > 1.85$) is the area to the right of 1.85 in a t distribution with 40 *df*. (This value was computed using the econometrics package Stata; it is not available in Table G.2.) This means that, if the null hypothesis is true, we would observe an absolute value of the t statistic as large as 1.85 about 7.2 percent of the time. This provides some evidence against the null hypothesis, but we would not reject the null at the 5% significance level.

The previous example illustrates that once the p-value has been computed, a classical test can be carried out at any desired level. If α denotes the significance level of the test (in decimal form), then H_0 is rejected if p-value $< \alpha$; otherwise, H_0 is not rejected at the $100{\cdot}\alpha\%$ level.

Computing p-values for one-sided alternatives is also quite simple. Suppose, for example, that we test H_0: $\beta_j = 0$ against H_1: $\beta_j > 0$. If $\hat{\beta}_j < 0$, then computing a p-value is not important: we know that the p-value is greater than .50, which will never cause us to reject H_0 in favor of H_1. If $\hat{\beta}_j > 0$, then $t > 0$ and the p-value is just the probability that a t random variable with the appropriate *df* exceeds the value t. Some regression packages only compute p-values for two-sided alternatives. But it is simple to obtain the one-sided p-value: just divide the two-sided p-value by 2.

If the alternative is H_1: $\beta_j < 0$, it makes sense to compute a p-value if $\hat{\beta}_j < 0$ (and hence $t < 0$): p-value $= P(T < t) = P(T > |t|)$ because the t distribution is symmetric about zero. Again, this can be obtained as one-half of the p-value for the two-tailed test.

EXPLORING FURTHER 4.3

Suppose you estimate a regression model and obtain $\hat{\beta}_1 = .56$ and p-value $= .086$ for testing H_0: $\beta_1 = 0$ against H_1: $\beta_1 \neq 0$. What is the p-value for testing H_0: $\beta_1 = 0$ against H_1: $\beta_1 > 0$?

Because you will quickly become familiar with the magnitudes of t statistics that lead to statistical significance, especially for large sample sizes, it is not always crucial to report p-values for t statistics. But it does not hurt to report them. Further, when we discuss F testing in Section 4.5, we will see that it is important to compute p-values, because critical values for F tests are not so easily memorized.

A Reminder on the Language of Classical Hypothesis Testing

When H_0 is not rejected, we prefer to use the language "we fail to reject H_0 at the x% level," rather than "H_0 is accepted at the x% level." We can use Example 4.5 to illustrate why the former statement is preferred. In this example, the estimated elasticity of *price* with respect to *nox* is $-.954$, and the t statistic for testing H_0: $\beta_{nox} = -1$ is $t = .393$; therefore, we cannot reject H_0. But there are many other values for β_{nox} (more than we can count) that cannot be rejected. For example, the t statistic for H_0: $\beta_{nox} = -.9$ is $(-.954 + .9)/.117 = -.462$, and so this null is not rejected either. Clearly $\beta_{nox} = -1$ and $\beta_{nox} = -.9$ cannot both be true, so it makes no sense to say that we "accept" either of these hypotheses. All we can say is that the data do not allow us to reject either of these hypotheses at the 5% significance level.

Economic, or Practical, versus Statistical Significance

Because we have emphasized *statistical significance* throughout this section, now is a good time to remember that we should pay attention to the magnitude of the *coefficient* estimates in addition to the size of the t statistics. The statistical significance of a variable x_j is determined entirely by the size of $t_{\hat{\beta}_j}$, whereas the **economic significance** or **practical significance** of a variable is related to the size (and sign) of $\hat{\beta}_j$.

Recall that the t statistic for testing H_0: $\beta_j = 0$ is defined by dividing the estimate by its standard error: $t_{\hat{\beta}_j} = \hat{\beta}_j / \text{se}(\hat{\beta}_j)$. Thus, $t_{\hat{\beta}_j}$ can indicate statistical significance either because $\hat{\beta}_j$ is "large" or because $\text{se}(\hat{\beta}_j)$ is "small." It is important in practice to distinguish between these reasons for statistically significant t statistics. Too much focus on statistical significance can lead to the false conclusion that a variable is "important" for explaining y even though its estimated effect is modest.

EXAMPLE 4.6 PARTICIPATION RATES IN 401(k) PLANS

In Example 3.3, we used the data on 401(k) plans to estimate a model describing participation rates in terms of the firm's match rate and the age of the plan. We now include a measure of firm size, the total number of firm employees (*totemp*). The estimated equation is

$$\begin{aligned} \widehat{prate} &= \underset{(0.78)}{80.29} + \underset{(0.52)}{5.44}\, mrate + \underset{(.045)}{.269}\, age - \underset{(.00004)}{.00013}\, totemp \\ n &= 1{,}534,\ R^2 = .100. \end{aligned}$$

The smallest t statistic in absolute value is that on the variable *totemp*: $t = -.00013/.00004 = -3.25$, and this is statistically significant at very small significance levels. (The two-tailed p-value for this t statistic is about .001.) Thus, all of the variables are statistically significant at rather small significance levels.

How big, in a practical sense, is the coefficient on *totemp*? Holding *mrate* and *age* fixed, if a firm grows by 10,000 employees, the participation rate falls by $10{,}000(.00013) = 1.3$ percentage points. This is a huge increase in number of employees with only a modest effect on the participation rate. Thus, although firm size does affect the participation rate, the effect is not practically very large.

The previous example shows that it is especially important to interpret the magnitude of the coefficient, in addition to looking at t statistics, when working with large samples. With large sample sizes, parameters can be estimated very precisely: Standard errors are often quite small relative to the coefficient estimates, which usually results in statistical significance.

Some researchers insist on using smaller significance levels as the sample size increases, partly as a way to offset the fact that standard errors are getting smaller. For example, if we feel comfortable with a 5% level when n is a few hundred, we might use the 1% level when n is a few thousand. Using a smaller significance level means that economic and statistical significance are more likely to coincide, but there are no guarantees: In the previous example, even if we use a significance level as small as .1% (one-tenth of 1%), we would still conclude that *totemp* is statistically significant.

Most researchers are also willing to entertain larger significance levels in applications with small sample sizes, reflecting the fact that it is harder to find significance with smaller sample sizes (the critical values are larger in magnitude, and the estimators are less precise). Unfortunately, whether or not this is the case can depend on the researcher's underlying agenda.

EXAMPLE 4.7 EFFECT OF JOB TRAINING ON FIRM SCRAP RATES

The scrap rate for a manufacturing firm is the number of defective items—products that must be discarded—out of every 100 produced. Thus, for a given number of items produced, a decrease in the scrap rate reflects higher worker productivity.

We can use the scrap rate to measure the effect of worker training on productivity. Using the data in JTRAIN.RAW, but only for the year 1987 and for nonunionized firms, we obtain the following estimated equation:

$$\widehat{\log(scrap)} = \underset{(5.69)}{12.46} - \underset{(.023)}{.029}\, hrsemp - \underset{(.453)}{.962} \log(sales) + \underset{(.407)}{.761} \log(employ)$$
$$n = 29, R^2 = .262.$$

The variable *hrsemp* is annual hours of training per employee, *sales* is annual firm sales (in dollars), and *employ* is the number of firm employees. For 1987, the average scrap rate in the sample is about 4.6 and the average of *hrsemp* is about 8.9.

The main variable of interest is *hrsemp*. One more hour of training per employee lowers log(*scrap*) by .029, which means the scrap rate is about 2.9% lower. Thus, if *hrsemp* increases by 5—each employee is trained 5 more hours per year—the scrap rate is estimated to fall by 5(2.9) = 14.5%. This seems like a reasonably large effect, but whether the additional training is worthwhile to the firm depends on the cost of training and the benefits from a lower scrap rate. We do not have the numbers needed to do a cost benefit analysis, but the estimated effect seems nontrivial.

What about the *statistical significance* of the training variable? The t statistic on *hrsemp* is $-.029/.023 = -1.26$, and now you probably recognize this as not being large enough in magnitude to conclude that *hrsemp* is statistically significant at the 5% level. In fact, with $29 - 4 = 25$ degrees of freedom for the one-sided alternative, H_1: $\beta_{hrsemp} < 0$, the 5% critical value is about -1.71. Thus, using a strict 5% level test, we must conclude that *hrsemp* is not statistically significant, even using a one-sided alternative.

Because the sample size is pretty small, we might be more liberal with the significance level. The 10% critical value is -1.32, and so *hrsemp* is almost significant against the one-sided alternative at the 10% level. The p-value is easily computed as $P(T_{25} < -1.26) = .110$. This may be a low enough p-value to conclude that the estimated effect of training is not just due to sampling error, but opinions would legitimately differ on whether a one-sided p-value of .11 is sufficiently small.

Remember that large standard errors can also be a result of multicollinearity (high correlation among some of the independent variables), even if the sample size seems fairly large. As we discussed in Section 3.4, there is not much we can do about this problem other than to collect more data or change the scope of the analysis by dropping or combining certain independent variables. As in the case of a small sample size, it can be hard to precisely estimate partial effects when some of the explanatory variables are highly correlated. (Section 4.5 contains an example.)

We end this section with some guidelines for discussing the economic and statistical significance of a variable in a multiple regression model:

1. Check for statistical significance. If the variable is statistically significant, discuss the magnitude of the coefficient to get an idea of its practical or economic importance. This latter step can require some care, depending on how the independent and dependent variables appear in the equation. (In particular, what are the units of measurement? Do the variables appear in logarithmic form?)
2. If a variable is not statistically significant at the usual levels (10%, 5%, or 1%), you might still ask if the variable has the expected effect on y and whether that effect is practically large. If it is large, you should compute a p-value for the t statistic. For small sample sizes, you can sometimes make a case for p-values as large as .20 (but there are no hard rules). With large p-values, that is, small t statistics, we are treading on thin ice because the practically large estimates may be due to sampling error: A different random sample could result in a very different estimate.
3. It is common to find variables with small t statistics that have the "wrong" sign. For practical purposes, these can be ignored: we conclude that the variables are statistically insignificant. A significant variable that has the unexpected sign and a practically large effect is much more troubling and difficult to resolve. One must usually think more about the model and the nature of the data to solve such problems. Often, a counterintuitive, significant estimate results from the omission of a key variable or from one of the important problems we will discuss in Chapters 9 and 15.

4.3 Confidence Intervals

Under the classical linear model assumptions, we can easily construct a **confidence interval (CI)** for the population parameter β_j. Confidence intervals are also called *interval estimates* because they provide a range of likely values for the population parameter, and not just a point estimate.

Using the fact that $(\hat{\beta}_j - \beta_j)/\text{se}(\hat{\beta}_j)$ has a t distribution with $n - k - 1$ degrees of freedom [see (4.3)], simple manipulation leads to a CI for the unknown β_j: a *95% confidence interval*, given by

$$\hat{\beta}_j \pm c \cdot \text{se}(\hat{\beta}_j), \tag{4.16}$$

where the constant c is the 97.5th percentile in a t_{n-k-1} distribution. More precisely, the lower and upper bounds of the confidence interval are given by

$$\underline{\beta}_j \equiv \hat{\beta}_j - c \cdot \text{se}(\hat{\beta}_j)$$

and

$$\bar{\beta}_j \equiv \hat{\beta}_j + c \cdot \text{se}(\hat{\beta}_j),$$

respectively.

At this point, it is useful to review the meaning of a confidence interval. If random samples were obtained over and over again, with $\underline{\beta}_j$ and $\bar{\beta}_j$ computed each time, then the (unknown) population value β_j would lie in the interval $(\underline{\beta}_j, \bar{\beta}_j)$ for 95% of the samples. Unfortunately, for the single sample that we use to construct the CI, we do not know whether β_j is actually contained in the interval. We hope we have obtained a sample that is one of the 95% of all samples where the interval estimate contains β_j, but we have no guarantee.

Constructing a confidence interval is very simple when using current computing technology. Three quantities are needed: $\hat{\beta}_j$, se($\hat{\beta}_j$), and c. The coefficient estimate and its standard error are reported by any regression package. To obtain the value c, we must know the degrees of freedom, $n - k - 1$, and the level of confidence—95% in this case. Then, the value for c is obtained from the t_{n-k-1} distribution.

As an example, for $df = n - k - 1 = 25$, a 95% confidence interval for any β_j is given by $[\hat{\beta}_j - 2.06 \cdot \text{se}(\hat{\beta}_j), \hat{\beta}_j + 2.06 \cdot \text{se}(\hat{\beta}_j)]$.

When $n - k - 1 > 120$, the t_{n-k-1} distribution is close enough to normal to use the 97.5th percentile in a standard normal distribution for constructing a 95% CI: $\hat{\beta}_j \pm 1.96 \cdot \text{se}(\hat{\beta}_j)$. In fact, when $n - k - 1 > 50$, the value of c is so close to 2 that we can use a simple *rule of thumb* for a 95% confidence interval: $\hat{\beta}_j$ plus or minus two of its standard errors. For small degrees of freedom, the exact percentiles should be obtained from the t tables.

It is easy to construct confidence intervals for any other level of confidence. For example, a 90% CI is obtained by choosing c to be the 95th percentile in the t_{n-k-1} distribution. When $df = n - k - 1 = 25$, $c = 1.71$, and so the 90% CI is $\hat{\beta}_j \pm 1.71 \cdot \text{se}(\hat{\beta}_j)$, which is necessarily narrower than the 95% CI. For a 99% CI, c is the 99.5th percentile in the t_{25} distribution. When $df = 25$, the 99% CI is roughly $\hat{\beta}_j \pm 2.79 \cdot \text{se}(\hat{\beta}_j)$, which is inevitably wider than the 95% CI.

Many modern regression packages save us from doing any calculations by reporting a 95% CI along with each coefficient and its standard error. Once a confidence interval is constructed, it is easy to carry out two-tailed hypotheses tests. If the null hypothesis is H_0: $\beta_j = a_j$, then H_0 is rejected against H_1: $\beta_j \neq a_j$ at (say) the 5% significance level if, and only if, a_j is *not* in the 95% confidence interval.

EXAMPLE 4.8 MODEL OF R&D EXPENDITURES

Economists studying industrial organization are interested in the relationship between firm size—often measured by annual sales—and spending on research and development (R&D). Typically, a constant elasticity model is used. One might also be interested in the ceteris paribus effect of the profit margin—that is, profits as a percentage of sales—on R&D spending. Using the data in RDCHEM.RAW on 32 U.S. firms in the chemical industry, we estimate the following equation (with standard errors in parentheses below the coefficients):

$$\widehat{\log(rd)} = \underset{(.47)}{-4.38} + \underset{(.060)}{1.084}\log(sales) + \underset{(.0128)}{.0217}\,profmarg$$

$$n = 32, R^2 = .918.$$

The estimated elasticity of R&D spending with respect to firm sales is 1.084, so that, holding profit margin fixed, a 1% increase in sales is associated with a 1.084% increase in R&D spending. (Incidentally, R&D and sales are both measured in millions of dollars, but their units of measurement have no effect on the elasticity estimate.) We can construct a 95% confidence interval for the sales elasticity once we note that the estimated model has $n - k - 1 = 32 - 2 - 1 = 29$ degrees of freedom. From Table G.2, we find the

97.5th percentile in a t_{29} distribution: $c = 2.045$. Thus, the 95% confidence interval for $\beta_{\log(sales)}$ is $1.084 \pm .060(2.045)$, or about (.961,1.21) That zero is well outside this interval is hardly surprising: we expect R&D spending to increase with firm size. More interesting is that unity is included in the 95% confidence interval for $\beta_{\log(sales)}$, which means that we cannot reject H_0: $\beta_{\log(sales)} = 1$ against H_1: $\beta_{\log(sales)} \neq 1$ at the 5% significance level. In other words, the estimated R&D-sales elasticity is not statistically different from 1 at the 5% level. (The estimate is not practically different from 1, either.)

The estimated coefficient on *profmarg* is also positive, and the 95% confidence interval for the population parameter, $\beta_{profmarg}$, is $.0217 \pm .0128(2.045)$, or about $(-.0045, .0479)$. In this case, zero is included in the 95% confidence interval, so we fail to reject H_0: $\beta_{profmarg} = 0$ against H_1: $\beta_{profmarg} \neq 0$ at the 5% level. Nevertheless, the *t* statistic is about 1.70, which gives a two-sided *p*-value of about .10, and so we would conclude that *profmarg* is statistically significant at the 10% level against the two-sided alternative, or at the 5% level against the one-sided alternative H_1: $\beta_{profmarg} > 0$. Plus, the economic size of the profit margin coefficient is not trivial: holding *sales* fixed, a one percentage point increase in *profmarg* is estimated to increase R&D spending by $100(.0217) \approx 2.2\%$. A complete analysis of this example goes beyond simply stating whether a particular value, zero in this case, is or is not in the 95% confidence interval.

You should remember that a confidence interval is only as good as the underlying assumptions used to construct it. If we have omitted important factors that are correlated with the explanatory variables, then the coefficient estimates are not reliable: OLS is biased. If heteroskedasticity is present—for instance, in the previous example, if the variance of log(*rd*) depends on any of the explanatory variables—then the standard error is not valid as an estimate of $\mathrm{sd}(\hat{\beta}_j)$ (as we discussed in Section 3.4), and the confidence interval computed using these standard errors will not truly be a 95% CI. We have also used the normality assumption on the errors in obtaining these CIs, but, as we will see in Chapter 5, this is not as important for applications involving hundreds of observations.

4.4 Testing Hypotheses about a Single Linear Combination of the Parameters

The previous two sections have shown how to use classical hypothesis testing or confidence intervals to test hypotheses about a single β_j at a time. In applications, we must often test hypotheses involving more than one of the population parameters. In this section, we show how to test a single hypothesis involving more than one of the β_j. Section 4.5 shows how to test multiple hypotheses.

To illustrate the general approach, we will consider a simple model to compare the returns to education at junior colleges and four-year colleges; for simplicity, we refer to the latter as "universities." [Kane and Rouse (1995) provide a detailed analysis of the returns to two- and four-year colleges.] The population includes working people with a high school degree, and the model is

$$\log(wage) = \beta_0 + \beta_1 jc + \beta_2 univ + \beta_3 exper + u, \qquad [4.17]$$

where

jc = number of years attending a two-year college.
$univ$ = number of years at a four-year college.
$exper$ = months in the workforce.

Note that any combination of junior college and four-year college is allowed, including $jc = 0$ and $univ = 0$.

The hypothesis of interest is whether one year at a junior college is worth one year at a university: this is stated as

$$H_0: \beta_1 = \beta_2. \quad [4.18]$$

Under H_0, another year at a junior college and another year at a university lead to the same ceteris paribus percentage increase in *wage*. For the most part, the alternative of interest is one-sided: a year at a junior college is worth less than a year at a university. This is stated as

$$H_1: \beta_1 < \beta_2. \quad [4.19]$$

The hypotheses in (4.18) and (4.19) concern *two* parameters, β_1 and β_2, a situation we have not faced yet. We cannot simply use the individual t statistics for $\hat{\beta}_1$ and $\hat{\beta}_2$ to test H_0. However, conceptually, there is no difficulty in constructing a t statistic for testing (4.18). To do so, we rewrite the null and alternative as $H_0: \beta_1 - \beta_2 = 0$ and $H_1: \beta_1 - \beta_2 < 0$, respectively. The t statistic is based on whether the estimated difference $\hat{\beta}_1 - \hat{\beta}_2$ is sufficiently less than zero to warrant rejecting (4.18) in favor of (4.19). To account for the sampling error in our estimators, we standardize this difference by dividing by the standard error:

$$t = \frac{\hat{\beta}_1 - \hat{\beta}_2}{\text{se}(\hat{\beta}_1 - \hat{\beta}_2)}. \quad [4.20]$$

Once we have the t statistic in (4.20), testing proceeds as before. We choose a significance level for the test and, based on the *df*, obtain a critical value. Because the alternative is of the form in (4.19), the rejection rule is of the form $t < -c$, where c is a positive value chosen from the appropriate t distribution. Or we compute the t statistic and then compute the p-value (see Section 4.2).

The only thing that makes testing the equality of two different parameters more difficult than testing about a single β_j is obtaining the standard error in the denominator of (4.20). Obtaining the numerator is trivial once we have performed the OLS regression. Using the data in TWOYEAR.RAW, which comes from Kane and Rouse (1995), we estimate equation (4.17):

$$\begin{aligned} \widehat{\log(wage)} &= \underset{(.021)}{1.472} + \underset{(.0068)}{.0667}\, jc + \underset{(.0023)}{.0769}\, univ + \underset{(.0002)}{.0049}\, exper \\ n &= 6{,}763,\ R^2 = .222. \end{aligned} \quad [4.21]$$

It is clear from (4.21) that *jc* and *univ* have both economically and statistically significant effects on wage. This is certainly of interest, but we are more concerned about testing whether the estimated *difference* in the coefficients is statistically significant. The difference is estimated as $\hat{\beta}_1 - \hat{\beta}_2 = -.0102$, so the return to a year at a junior college is about one percentage point less than a year at a university. Economically, this is not a trivial difference. The difference of $-.0102$ is the numerator of the t statistic in (4.20).

Unfortunately, the regression results in equation (4.21) do *not* contain enough information to obtain the standard error of $\hat{\beta}_1 - \hat{\beta}_2$. It might be tempting to claim that $\text{se}(\hat{\beta}_1 - \hat{\beta}_2) = \text{se}(\hat{\beta}_1) - \text{se}(\hat{\beta}_2)$, but this is not true. In fact, if we reversed the roles of $\hat{\beta}_1$ and $\hat{\beta}_2$, we would wind up with a negative standard error of the difference using the difference in standard errors. Standard errors must *always* be positive because they are estimates of standard deviations. Although the standard error of the difference $\hat{\beta}_1 - \hat{\beta}_2$ certainly depends on $\text{se}(\hat{\beta}_1)$ and $\text{se}(\hat{\beta}_2)$, it does so in a somewhat complicated way. To find $\text{se}(\hat{\beta}_1 - \hat{\beta}_2)$, we first obtain the variance of the difference. Using the results on variances in Appendix B, we have

$$\text{Var}(\hat{\beta}_1 - \hat{\beta}_2) = \text{Var}(\hat{\beta}_1) + \text{Var}(\hat{\beta}_2) - 2\,\text{Cov}(\hat{\beta}_1,\hat{\beta}_2). \quad [4.22]$$

Observe carefully how the two variances are *added* together, and twice the covariance is then subtracted. The standard deviation of $\hat{\beta}_1 - \hat{\beta}_2$ is just the square root of (4.22), and, since $[\text{se}(\hat{\beta}_1)]^2$ is an unbiased estimator of $\text{Var}(\hat{\beta}_1)$, and similarly for $[\text{se}(\hat{\beta}_2)]^2$, we have

$$\text{se}(\hat{\beta}_1 - \hat{\beta}_2) = \left\{[\text{se}(\hat{\beta}_1)]^2 + [\text{se}(\hat{\beta}_2)]^2 - 2s_{12}\right\}^{1/2}, \quad [4.23]$$

where s_{12} denotes an estimate of $\text{Cov}(\hat{\beta}_1,\hat{\beta}_2)$. We have not displayed a formula for $\text{Cov}(\hat{\beta}_1,\hat{\beta}_2)$. Some regression packages have features that allow one to obtain s_{12}, in which case one can compute the standard error in (4.23) and then the t statistic in (4.20). Appendix E shows how to use matrix algebra to obtain s_{12}.

Some of the more sophisticated econometrics programs include special commands that can be used for testing hypotheses about linear combinations. Here, we cover an approach that is simple to compute in virtually any statistical package. Rather than trying to compute $\text{se}(\hat{\beta}_1 - \hat{\beta}_2)$ from (4.23), it is much easier to estimate a different model that directly delivers the standard error of interest. Define a new parameter as the difference between β_1 and β_2: $\theta_1 = \beta_1 - \beta_2$. Then, we want to test

$$\text{H}_0\colon \theta_1 = 0 \text{ against } \text{H}_1\colon \theta_1 < 0. \quad [4.24]$$

The t statistic in (4.20) in terms of $\hat{\theta}_1$ is just $t = \hat{\theta}_1/\text{se}(\hat{\theta}_1)$. The challenge is finding $\text{se}(\hat{\theta}_1)$.

We can do this by rewriting the model so that θ_1 appears directly on one of the independent variables. Because $\theta_1 = \beta_1 - \beta_2$, we can also write $\beta_1 = \theta_1 + \beta_2$. Plugging this into (4.17) and rearranging gives the equation

$$\begin{aligned}\log(wage) &= \beta_0 + (\theta_1 + \beta_2)jc + \beta_2 univ + \beta_3 exper + u \\ &= \beta_0 + \theta_1 jc + \beta_2(jc + univ) + \beta_3 exper + u.\end{aligned} \quad [4.25]$$

The key insight is that the parameter we are interested in testing hypotheses about, θ_1, now multiplies the variable *jc*. The intercept is still β_0, and *exper* still shows up as being multiplied by β_3. More importantly, there is a new variable multiplying β_2, namely *jc* + *univ*. Thus, if we want to directly estimate θ_1 and obtain the standard error $\hat{\theta}_1$, then we must construct the new variable *jc* + *univ* and include it in the regression model in place of *univ*. In this example, the new variable has a natural interpretation: it is *total* years of college, so define *totcoll* = *jc* + *univ* and write (4.25) as

$$\log(wage) = \beta_0 + \theta_1 jc + \beta_2 totcoll + \beta_3 exper + u. \quad [4.26]$$

The parameter β_1 has disappeared from the model, while θ_1 appears explicitly. This model is really just a different way of writing the original model. The only reason we have defined this new model is that, when we estimate it, the coefficient on *jc* is $\hat{\theta}_1$, and, more importantly, se($\hat{\theta}_1$) is reported along with the estimate. The t statistic that we want is the one reported by any regression package on the variable *jc* (*not* the variable *totcoll*).

When we do this with the 6,763 observations used earlier, the result is

$$\begin{aligned}\widehat{\log(wage)} &= 1.472 - .0102\,jc + .0769\,totcoll + .0049\,exper \\ &\quad\;\; (.021)\quad (.0069)\qquad (.0023)\qquad\quad (.0002) \\ n &= 6{,}763,\ R^2 = .222.\end{aligned} \qquad [4.27]$$

The only number in this equation that we could not get from (4.21) is the standard error for the estimate $-.0102$, which is .0069. The t statistic for testing (4.18) is $-.0102/.0069 = -1.48$. Against the one-sided alternative (4.19), the p-value is about .070, so there is some, but not strong, evidence against (4.18).

The intercept and slope estimate on *exper*, along with their standard errors, are the same as in (4.21). This fact *must* be true, and it provides one way of checking whether the transformed equation has been properly estimated. The coefficient on the new variable, *totcoll*, is the same as the coefficient on *univ* in (4.21), and the standard error is also the same. We know that this must happen by comparing (4.17) and (4.25).

It is quite simple to compute a 95% confidence interval for $\theta_1 = \beta_1 - \beta_2$. Using the standard normal approximation, the CI is obtained as usual: $\hat{\theta}_1 \pm 1.96\,\text{se}(\hat{\theta}_1)$, which in this case leads to $-.0102 \pm .0135$.

The strategy of rewriting the model so that it contains the parameter of interest works in all cases and is easy to implement. (See Computer Exercises C1 and C3 for other examples.)

4.5 Testing Multiple Linear Restrictions: The *F* Test

The t statistic associated with any OLS coefficient can be used to test whether the corresponding unknown parameter in the population is equal to any given constant (which is usually, but not always, zero). We have just shown how to test hypotheses about a single linear combination of the β_j by rearranging the equation and running a regression using transformed variables. But so far, we have only covered hypotheses involving a *single* restriction. Frequently, we wish to test *multiple* hypotheses about the underlying parameters $\beta_0, \beta_1, \ldots, \beta_k$. We begin with the leading case of testing whether a set of independent variables has no partial effect on a dependent variable.

Testing Exclusion Restrictions

We already know how to test whether a particular variable has no partial effect on the dependent variable: use the t statistic. Now, we want to test whether a *group* of variables has no effect on the dependent variable. More precisely, the null hypothesis is that a set of variables has no effect on y, once another set of variables has been controlled.

As an illustration of why testing significance of a group of variables is useful, we consider the following model that explains major league baseball players' salaries:

$$\begin{aligned}\log(salary) = \beta_0 &+ \beta_1 years + \beta_2 gamesyr + \beta_3 bavg \\ &+ \beta_4 hrunsyr + \beta_5 rbisyr + u,\end{aligned} \qquad [4.28]$$

where *salary* is the 1993 total salary, *years* is years in the league, *gamesyr* is average games played per year, *bavg* is career batting average (for example, *bavg* = 250), *hrunsyr* is home runs per year, and *rbisyr* is runs batted in per year. Suppose we want to test the null hypothesis that, once years in the league and games per year have been controlled for, the statistics measuring performance—*bavg*, *hrunsyr*, and *rbisyr*—have no effect on salary. Essentially, the null hypothesis states that productivity as measured by baseball statistics has no effect on salary.

In terms of the parameters of the model, the null hypothesis is stated as

$$H_0: \beta_3 = 0, \beta_4 = 0, \beta_5 = 0. \qquad [4.29]$$

The null (4.29) constitutes three **exclusion restrictions**: If (4.29) is true, then *bavg*, *hrunsyr*, and *rbisyr* have no effect on log(*salary*) after *years* and *gamesyr* have been controlled for and therefore should be excluded from the model. This is an example of a set of **multiple restrictions** because we are putting more than one restriction on the parameters in (4.28); we will see more general examples of multiple restrictions later. A test of multiple restrictions is called a **multiple hypotheses test** or a **joint hypotheses test**.

What should be the alternative to (4.29)? If what we have in mind is that "performance statistics matter, even after controlling for years in the league and games per year," then the appropriate alternative is simply

$$H_1: H_0 \text{ is not true.} \qquad [4.30]$$

The alternative (4.30) holds if at least one of β_3, β_4, or β_5 is different from zero. (Any or all could be different from zero.) The test we study here is constructed to detect any violation of H_0. It is also valid when the alternative is something like H_1: $\beta_3 > 0$, or $\beta_4 > 0$, or $\beta_5 > 0$, but it will not be the best possible test under such alternatives. We do not have the space or statistical background necessary to cover tests that have more power under multiple one-sided alternatives.

How should we proceed in testing (4.29) against (4.30)? It is tempting to test (4.29) by using the *t* statistics on the variables *bavg*, *hrunsyr*, and *rbisyr* to determine whether each variable is *individually* significant. This option is not appropriate. A particular *t* statistic tests a hypothesis that puts no restrictions on the other parameters. Besides, we would have three outcomes to contend with—one for each *t* statistic. What would constitute rejection of (4.29) at, say, the 5% level? Should all three or only one of the three *t* statistics be required to be significant at the 5% level? These are hard questions, and fortunately we do not have to answer them. Furthermore, using separate *t* statistics to test a multiple hypothesis like (4.29) can be very misleading. We need a way to test the exclusion restrictions *jointly*.

To illustrate these issues, we estimate equation (4.28) using the data in MLB1.RAW. This gives

$$\begin{aligned}\widehat{\log(salary)} = {} & \underset{(0.29)}{11.19} + \underset{(.0121)}{.0689}\, years + \underset{(.0026)}{.0126}\, gamesyr \\ & + \underset{(.00110)}{.00098}\, bavg + \underset{(.0161)}{.0144}\, hrunsyr + \underset{(.0072)}{.0108}\, rbisyr \qquad [4.31] \\ n = {} & 353, \text{SSR} = 183.186, R^2 = .6278,\end{aligned}$$

where SSR is the sum of squared residuals. (We will use this later.) We have left several terms after the decimal in SSR and R-squared to facilitate future comparisons. Equation (4.31) reveals that, whereas *years* and *gamesyr* are statistically significant, none of the variables *bavg*, *hrunsyr*, and *rbisyr* has a statistically significant t statistic against a two-sided alternative, at the 5% significance level. (The t statistic on *rbisyr* is the closest to being significant; its two-sided p-value is .134.) Thus, based on the three t statistics, it appears that we cannot reject H_0.

This conclusion turns out to be wrong. To see this, we must derive a test of multiple restrictions whose distribution is known and tabulated. The sum of squared residuals now turns out to provide a very convenient basis for testing multiple hypotheses. We will also show how the R-squared can be used in the special case of testing for exclusion restrictions.

Knowing the sum of squared residuals in (4.31) tells us nothing about the truth of the hypothesis in (4.29). However, the factor that will tell us something is how much the SSR increases when we drop the variables *bavg*, *hrunsyr*, and *rbisyr* from the model. Remember that, because the OLS estimates are chosen to minimize the sum of squared residuals, the SSR *always* increases when variables are dropped from the model; this is an algebraic fact. The question is whether this increase is large enough, *relative* to the SSR in the model with all of the variables, to warrant rejecting the null hypothesis.

The model without the three variables in question is simply

$$\log(salary) = \beta_0 + \beta_1 years + \beta_2 gamesyr + u. \qquad [4.32]$$

In the context of hypothesis testing, equation (4.32) is the **restricted model** for testing (4.29); model (4.28) is called the **unrestricted model**. The restricted model always has fewer parameters than the unrestricted model.

When we estimate the restricted model using the data in MLB1.RAW, we obtain

$$\begin{aligned} \widehat{\log(salary)} &= \underset{(.11)}{11.22} + \underset{(.0125)}{.0713}\, years + \underset{(.0013)}{.0202}\, gamesyr \\ n &= 353,\ \text{SSR} = 198.311,\ R^2 = .5971. \end{aligned} \qquad [4.33]$$

As we surmised, the SSR from (4.33) is greater than the SSR from (4.31), and the R-squared from the restricted model is less than the R-squared from the unrestricted model. What we need to decide is whether the increase in the SSR in going from the unrestricted model to the restricted model (183.186 to 198.311) is large enough to warrant rejection of (4.29). As with all testing, the answer depends on the significance level of the test. But we cannot carry out the test at a chosen significance level until we have a statistic whose distribution is known, and can be tabulated, under H_0. Thus, we need a way to combine the information in the two SSRs to obtain a test statistic with a known distribution under H_0.

Because it is no more difficult, we might as well derive the test for the general case. Write the *unrestricted* model with k independent variables as

$$y = \beta_0 + \beta_1 x_1 + \ldots + \beta_k x_k + u; \qquad [4.34]$$

the number of parameters in the unrestricted model is $k + 1$. (Remember to add one for the intercept.) Suppose that we have q exclusion restrictions to test: that is, the null hypothesis states that q of the variables in (4.34) have zero coefficients. For notational simplicity, assume that it is the last q variables in the list of independent variables: $x_{k-q+1}, \ldots, x_k$. (The order of the variables, of course, is arbitrary and unimportant.) The null hypothesis is stated as

$$H_0: \beta_{k-q+1} = 0, \ldots, \beta_k = 0, \qquad [4.35]$$

which puts q exclusion restrictions on the model (4.34). The alternative to (4.35) is simply that it is false; this means that at least one of the parameters listed in (4.35) is different from zero. When we impose the restrictions under H_0, we are left with the restricted model:

$$y = \beta_0 + \beta_1 x_1 + \dots + \beta_{k-q} x_{k-q} + u. \quad [4.36]$$

In this subsection, we assume that both the unrestricted and restricted models contain an intercept, since that is the case most widely encountered in practice.

Now, for the test statistic itself. Earlier, we suggested that looking at the relative increase in the SSR when moving from the unrestricted to the restricted model should be informative for testing the hypothesis (4.35). The ***F* statistic** (or *F ratio*) is defined by

$$F \equiv \frac{(\mathrm{SSR}_r - \mathrm{SSR}_{ur})/q}{\mathrm{SSR}_{ur}/(n-k-1)}, \quad [4.37]$$

where SSR_r is the sum of squared residuals from the restricted model and SSR_{ur} is the sum of squared residuals from the unrestricted model.

You should immediately notice that, since SSR_r can be no smaller than SSR_{ur}, the F statistic is *always* nonnegative (and almost always strictly positive). Thus, if you compute a negative F statistic, then something is wrong; the order of the SSRs in the numerator of F has usually been reversed. Also, the SSR in the denominator of F is the SSR from the *unrestricted* model. The easiest way to remember where the SSRs appear is to think of F as measuring the relative increase in SSR when moving from the unrestricted to the restricted model.

The difference in SSRs in the numerator of F is divided by q, which is the number of restrictions imposed in moving from the unrestricted to the restricted model (q independent variables are dropped). Therefore, we can write

$$q = \textbf{numerator degrees of freedom} = df_r - df_{ur}, \quad [4.38]$$

which also shows that q is the difference in degrees of freedom between the restricted and unrestricted models. (Recall that df = number of observations − number of estimated parameters.) Since the restricted model has fewer parameters—and each model is estimated using the same n observations—df_r is always greater than df_{ur}.

The SSR in the denominator of F is divided by the degrees of freedom in the unrestricted model:

$$n - k - 1 = \textbf{denominator degrees of freedom} = df_{ur}. \quad [4.39]$$

In fact, the denominator of F is just the unbiased estimator of $\sigma^2 = \mathrm{Var}(u)$ in the unrestricted model.

EXPLORING FURTHER 4.4

Consider relating individual performance on a standardized test, *score*, to a variety of other variables. School factors include average class size, per-student expenditures, average teacher compensation, and total school enrollment. Other variables specific to the student are family income, mother's education, father's education, and number of siblings. The model is

$$\begin{aligned} score = {} & \beta_0 + \beta_1 classize + \beta_2 expend \\ & + \beta_3 tchcomp + \beta_4 enroll \\ & + \beta_5 faminc + \beta_6 motheduc \\ & + \beta_7 fatheduc + \beta_8 siblings + u. \end{aligned}$$

State the null hypothesis that student-specific variables have no effect on standardized test performance once school-related factors have been controlled for. What are k and q for this example? Write down the restricted version of the model.

In a particular application, computing the F statistic is easier than wading through the somewhat cumbersome notation used to describe the general case. We first obtain the degrees of freedom in the unrestricted model, df_{ur}. Then, we count how many variables are excluded in the restricted model; this is q. The SSRs are reported with every OLS regression, and so forming the F statistic is simple.

In the major league baseball salary regression, $n = 353$, and the full model (4.28) contains six parameters. Thus, $n - k - 1 = df_{ur} = 353 - 6 = 347$. The restricted model (4.32) contains three fewer independent variables than (4.28), and so $q = 3$. Thus, we have all of the ingredients to compute the F statistic; we hold off doing so until we know what to do with it.

To use the F statistic, we must know its sampling distribution under the null in order to choose critical values and rejection rules. It can be shown that, under H_0 (and assuming the CLM assumptions hold), F is distributed as an F random variable with $(q,n - k - 1)$ degrees of freedom. We write this as

$$F \sim F_{q,n-k-1}.$$

The distribution of $F_{q,n-k-1}$ is readily tabulated and available in statistical tables (see Table G.3) and, even more importantly, in statistical software.

We will not derive the F distribution because the mathematics is very involved. Basically, it can be shown that equation (4.37) is actually the ratio of two independent chi-square random variables, divided by their respective degrees of freedom. The numerator chi-square random variable has q degrees of freedom, and the chi-square in the denominator has $n - k - 1$ degrees of freedom. This is the definition of an F distributed random variable (see Appendix B).

It is pretty clear from the definition of F that we will reject H_0 in favor of H_1 when F is sufficiently "large." How large depends on our chosen significance level. Suppose that we have decided on a 5% level test. Let c be the 95th percentile in the $F_{q,n-k-1}$ distribution. This critical value depends on q (the numerator *df*) and $n - k - 1$ (the denominator *df*). It is important to keep the numerator and denominator degrees of freedom straight.

The 10%, 5%, and 1% critical values for the F distribution are given in Table G.3. The rejection rule is simple. Once c has been obtained, we reject H_0 in favor of H_1 at the chosen significance level if

$$F > c. \qquad [4.40]$$

With a 5% significance level, $q = 3$, and $n - k - 1 = 60$, the critical value is $c = 2.76$. We would reject H_0 at the 5% level if the computed value of the F statistic exceeds 2.76. The 5% critical value and rejection region are shown in Figure 4.7. For the same degrees of freedom, the 1% critical value is 4.13.

In most applications, the numerator degrees of freedom (q) will be notably smaller than the denominator degrees of freedom ($n - k - 1$). Applications where $n - k - 1$ is small are unlikely to be successful because the parameters in the unrestricted model will probably not be precisely estimated. When the denominator *df* reaches about 120, the F distribution is no longer sensitive to it. (This is entirely analogous to the t distribution being well approximated by the standard normal distribution as the *df* gets large.) Thus, there is an entry in the table for the denominator $df = \infty$, and this is what we use with large samples (because $n - k - 1$ is then large). A similar statement holds for a very large numerator *df*, but this rarely occurs in applications.

FIGURE 4.7 The 5% critical value and rejection region in an $F_{3,60}$ distribution.

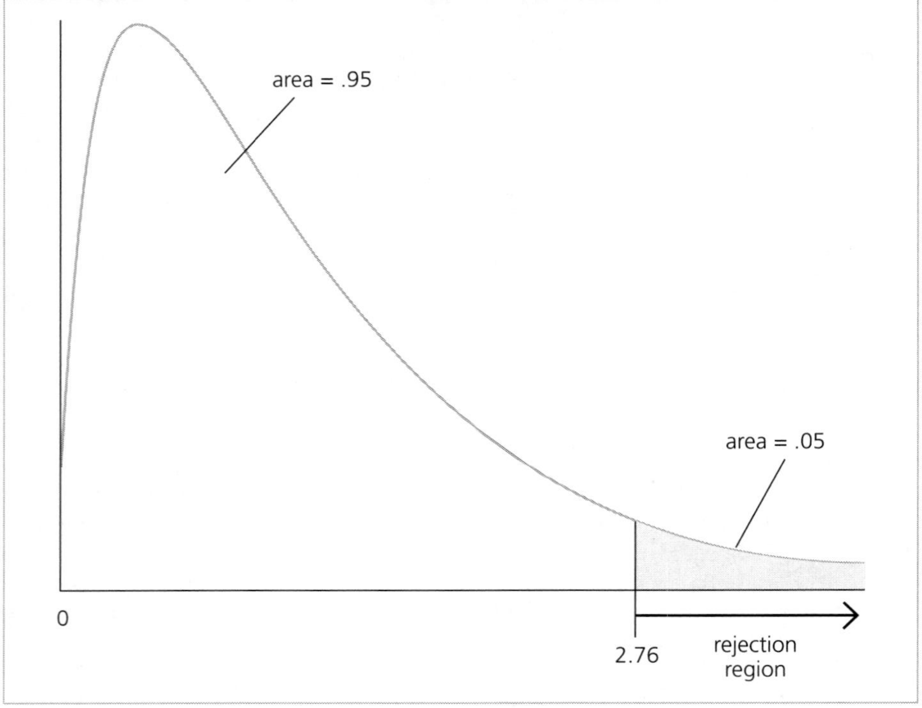

If H_0 is rejected, then we say that $x_{k-q+1}, \ldots, x_k$ are **jointly statistically significant** (or just *jointly significant*) at the appropriate significance level. This test alone does not allow us to say which of the variables has a partial effect on y; they may all affect y or maybe only one affects y. If the null is not rejected, then the variables are **jointly insignificant**, which often justifies dropping them from the model.

For the major league baseball example with three numerator degrees of freedom and 347 denominator degrees of freedom, the 5% critical value is 2.60, and the 1% critical value is 3.78. We reject H_0 at the 1% level if F is above 3.78; we reject at the 5% level if F is above 2.60.

We are now in a position to test the hypothesis that we began this section with: After controlling for *years* and *gamesyr*, the variables *bavg*, *hrunsyr*, and *rbisyr* have no effect on players' salaries. In practice, it is easiest to first compute $(\mathrm{SSR}_r - \mathrm{SSR}_{ur})/\mathrm{SSR}_{ur}$ and to multiply the result by $(n - k - 1)/q$; the reason the formula is stated as in (4.37) is that it makes it easier to keep the numerator and denominator degrees of freedom straight. Using the SSRs in (4.31) and (4.33), we have

$$F = \frac{(198.311 - 183.186)}{183.186} \cdot \frac{347}{3} \approx 9.55.$$

This number is well above the 1% critical value in the F distribution with 3 and 347 degrees of freedom, and so we soundly reject the hypothesis that *bavg*, *hrunsyr*, and *rbisyr* have no effect on salary.

The outcome of the joint test may seem surprising in light of the insignificant t statistics for the three variables. What is happening is that the two variables *hrunsyr* and *rbisyr* are highly correlated, and this multicollinearity makes it difficult to uncover the partial effect of each variable; this is reflected in the individual t statistics. The F statistic tests whether these variables (including *bavg*) are *jointly* significant, and multicollinearity between *hrunsyr* and *rbisyr* is much less relevant for testing this hypothesis. In Problem 16, you are asked to reestimate the model while dropping *rbisyr*, in which case *hrunsyr* becomes very significant. The same is true for *rbisyr* when *hrunsyr* is dropped from the model.

The F statistic is often useful for testing exclusion of a group of variables when the variables in the group are highly correlated. For example, suppose we want to test whether firm performance affects the salaries of chief executive officers. There are many ways to measure firm performance, and it probably would not be clear ahead of time which measures would be most important. Since measures of firm performance are likely to be highly correlated, hoping to find individually significant measures might be asking too much due to multicollinearity. But an F test can be used to determine whether, as a group, the firm performance variables affect salary.

Relationship between F and t Statistics

We have seen in this section how the F statistic can be used to test whether a group of variables should be included in a model. What happens if we apply the F statistic to the case of testing significance of a *single* independent variable? This case is certainly not ruled out by the previous development. For example, we can take the null to be $\text{H}_0\text{: } \beta_k = 0$ and $q = 1$ (to test the single exclusion restriction that x_k can be excluded from the model). From Section 4.2, we know that the t statistic on β_k can be used to test this hypothesis. The question, then, is: Do we have two separate ways of testing hypotheses about a single coefficient? The answer is no. It can be shown that the F statistic for testing exclusion of a single variable is equal to the *square* of the corresponding t statistic. Since t_{n-k-1}^2 has an $F_{1,n-k-1}$ distribution, the two approaches lead to exactly the same outcome, provided that the alternative is two-sided. The t statistic is more flexible for testing a single hypothesis because it can be directly used to test against one-sided alternatives. Since t statistics are also easier to obtain than F statistics, there is really no reason to use an F statistic to test hypotheses about a single parameter.

We have already seen in the salary regressions for major league baseball players that two (or more) variables that each have insignificant t statistics can be jointly very significant. It is also possible that, in a group of several explanatory variables, one variable has a significant t statistic but the group of variables is jointly insignificant at the usual significance levels. What should we make of this kind of outcome? For concreteness, suppose that in a model with many explanatory variables we cannot reject the null hypothesis that β_1, β_2, β_3, β_4, and β_5 are all equal to zero at the 5% level, yet the t statistic for $\hat{\beta}_1$ is significant at the 5% level. Logically, we cannot have $\beta_1 \neq 0$ but also have β_1, β_2, β_3, β_4, and β_5 all equal to zero! But as a matter of testing, it is possible that we can group a bunch of insignificant variables with a significant variable and conclude that the entire set of variables is jointly insignificant. (Such possible conflicts between a t test and a joint F test give another example of why we should not "accept" null hypotheses; we should only fail to reject them.) The F statistic is intended to detect whether a set of coefficients is different from zero, but it is never the best test for determining whether a single coefficient is different from zero. The t test is best suited for testing a single hypothesis. (In statistical terms, an F statistic for joint restrictions including $\beta_1 = 0$ will have less power for detecting $\beta_1 \neq 0$ than the usual t statistic. See Section C.6 in Appendix C for a discussion of the power of a test.)

Unfortunately, the fact that we can sometimes hide a statistically significant variable along with some insignificant variables could lead to abuse if regression results are not carefully reported. For example, suppose that, in a study of the determinants of loan-acceptance rates at the city level, x_1 is the fraction of black households in the city. Suppose that the variables x_2, x_3, x_4, and x_5 are the fractions of households headed by different age groups. In explaining loan rates, we would include measures of income, wealth, credit ratings, and so on. Suppose that age of household head has no effect on loan approval rates, once other variables are controlled for. Even if race has a marginally significant effect, it is possible that the race and age variables could be jointly insignificant. Someone wanting to conclude that race is not a factor could simply report something like "Race and age variables were added to the equation, but they were jointly insignificant at the 5% level." Hopefully, peer review prevents these kinds of misleading conclusions, but you should be aware that such outcomes are possible.

Often, when a variable is very statistically significant and it is tested jointly with another set of variables, the set will be jointly significant. In such cases, there is no logical inconsistency in rejecting both null hypotheses.

The *R*-Squared Form of the *F* Statistic

For testing exclusion restrictions, it is often more convenient to have a form of the F statistic that can be computed using the R-squareds from the restricted and unrestricted models. One reason for this is that the R-squared is always between zero and one, whereas the SSRs can be very large depending on the unit of measurement of y, making the calculation based on the SSRs tedious. Using the fact that $\text{SSR}_r = \text{SST}(1 - R_r^2)$ and $\text{SSR}_{ur} = \text{SST}(1 - R_{ur}^2)$, we can substitute into (4.37) to obtain

$$F = \frac{(R_{ur}^2 - R_r^2)/q}{(1 - R_{ur}^2)/(n - k - 1)} = \frac{(R_{ur}^2 - R_r^2)/q}{(1 - R_{ur}^2)/df_{ur}} \qquad [4.41]$$

(note that the SST terms cancel everywhere). This is called the ***R*-squared form of the *F* statistic**. [At this point, you should be cautioned that although equation (4.41) is very convenient for testing exclusion restrictions, it cannot be applied for testing all linear restrictions. As we will see when we discuss testing general linear restrictions, the sum of squared residuals form of the F statistic is sometimes needed.]

Because the R-squared is reported with almost all regressions (whereas the SSR is not), it is easy to use the R-squareds from the unrestricted and restricted models to test for exclusion of some variables. Particular attention should be paid to the order of the R-squareds in the numerator: the *unrestricted* R-squared comes first [contrast this with the SSRs in (4.37)]. Because $R_{ur}^2 > R_r^2$, this shows again that F will always be positive.

In using the R-squared form of the test for excluding a set of variables, it is important to *not* square the R-squared before plugging it into formula (4.41); the squaring has already been done. All regressions report R^2, and these numbers are plugged directly into (4.41). For the baseball salary example, we can use (4.41) to obtain the F statistic:

$$F = \frac{(.6278 - .5971)}{(1 - .6278)} \cdot \frac{347}{3} \approx 9.54,$$

which is very close to what we obtained before. (The difference is due to rounding error.)

EXAMPLE 4.9 PARENTS' EDUCATION IN A BIRTH WEIGHT EQUATION

As another example of computing an F statistic, consider the following model to explain child birth weight in terms of various factors:

$$bwght = \beta_0 + \beta_1 cigs + \beta_2 parity + \beta_3 faminc + \beta_4 motheduc + \beta_5 fatheduc + u, \quad [4.42]$$

where

$bwght$ = birth weight, in pounds.
$cigs$ = average number of cigarettes the mother smoked per day during pregnancy.
$parity$ = the birth order of this child.
$faminc$ = annual family income.
$motheduc$ = years of schooling for the mother.
$fatheduc$ = years of schooling for the father.

Let us test the null hypothesis that, after controlling for *cigs*, *parity*, and *faminc*, parents' education has no effect on birth weight. This is stated as H_0: $\beta_4 = 0$, $\beta_5 = 0$, and so there are $q = 2$ exclusion restrictions to be tested. There are $k + 1 = 6$ parameters in the unrestricted model (4.42); so the *df* in the unrestricted model is $n - 6$, where n is the sample size.

We will test this hypothesis using the data in BWGHT.RAW. This data set contains information on 1,388 births, but we must be careful in counting the observations used in testing the null hypothesis. It turns out that information on at least one of the variables *motheduc* and *fatheduc* is missing for 197 births in the sample; these observations cannot be included when estimating the unrestricted model. Thus, we really have $n = 1{,}191$ observations, and so there are $1{,}191 - 6 = 1{,}185$ *df* in the unrestricted model. We must be sure to use these *same* 1,191 observations when estimating the restricted model (not the full 1,388 observations that are available). Generally, when estimating the restricted model to compute an F test, we must use the same observations to estimate the unrestricted model; otherwise, the test is not valid. When there are no missing data, this will not be an issue.

The numerator *df* is 2, and the denominator *df* is 1,185; from Table G.3, the 5% critical value is $c = 3.0$. Rather than report the complete results, for brevity, we present only the R-squareds. The R-squared for the full model turns out to be $R^2_{ur} = .0387$. When *motheduc* and *fatheduc* are dropped from the regression, the R-squared falls to $R^2_r = .0364$. Thus, the F statistic is $F = [(.0387 - .0364)/(1 - .0387)](1{,}185/2) = 1.42$; since this is well below the 5% critical value, we fail to reject H_0. In other words, *motheduc* and *fatheduc* are jointly insignificant in the birth weight equation.

Computing p-Values for F Tests

For reporting the outcomes of F tests, p-values are especially useful. Since the F distribution depends on the numerator and denominator *df*, it is difficult to get a feel for how strong or weak the evidence is against the null hypothesis simply by looking at the value of the F statistic and one or two critical values.

In the F testing context, the p-value is defined as

$$p\text{-value} = \mathrm{P}(\mathcal{F} > F), \quad [4.43]$$

where, for emphasis, we let $\mathcal{F}$ denote an F random variable with $(q,n - k - 1)$ degrees of freedom, and F is the actual value of the test statistic. The p-value still has the same interpretation as it did for t statistics: it is the probability of observing a value of F at least as large as we did, *given* that the null hypothesis is true. A small p-value is evidence against H_0. For example, p-value $= .016$ means that the chance of observing a value of F as large as we did when the null hypothesis was true is only 1.6%; we usually reject H_0 in such cases. If the p-value $=.314$, then the chance of observing a value of the F statistic as large as we did under the null hypothesis is 31.4%. Most would find this to be pretty weak evidence against H_0.

EXPLORING FURTHER 4.5

The data in ATTEND.RAW were used to estimate the two equations

$$\widehat{atndrte} = \underset{(2.87)}{47.13} + \underset{(1.09)}{13.37}\, priGPA$$
$$n = 680,\ R^2 = .183$$

and

$$\widehat{atndrte} = \underset{(3.88)}{75.70} + \underset{(1.08)}{17.26}\, priGPA - \underset{(?)}{1.72}\, ACT$$
$$n = 680,\ R^2 = .291,$$

where, as always, standard errors are in parentheses; the standard error for *ACT* is missing in the second equation. What is the t statistic for the coefficient on *ACT*? (*Hint:* First compute the F statistic for significance of *ACT*.)

As with t testing, once the p-value has been computed, the F test can be carried out at any significance level. For example, if the p-value $= .024$, we reject H_0 at the 5% significance level but not at the 1% level.

The p-value for the F test in Example 4.9 is .238, and so the null hypothesis that $\beta_{motheduc}$ and $\beta_{fatheduc}$ are both zero is not rejected at even the 20% significance level.

Many econometrics packages have a built-in feature for testing multiple exclusion restrictions. These packages have several advantages over calculating the statistics by hand: we will less likely make a mistake, p-values are computed automatically, and the problem of missing data, as in Example 4.9, is handled without any additional work on our part.

The F Statistic for Overall Significance of a Regression

A special set of exclusion restrictions is routinely tested by most regression packages. These restrictions have the same interpretation, regardless of the model. In the model with k independent variables, we can write the null hypothesis as

$$H_0\text{: } x_1, x_2, \ldots, x_k \text{ do not help to explain } y.$$

This null hypothesis is, in a way, very pessimistic. It states that *none* of the explanatory variables has an effect on y. Stated in terms of the parameters, the null is that all slope parameters are zero:

$$H_0\text{: } \beta_1 = \beta_2 = \ldots = \beta_k = 0, \qquad [4.44]$$

and the alternative is that at least one of the β_j is different from zero. Another useful way of stating the null is that H_0: $E(y|x_1, x_2, \ldots, x_k) = E(y)$, so that knowing the values of x_1, $x_2, \ldots, x_k$ does not affect the expected value of y.

There are k restrictions in (4.44), and when we impose them, we get the restricted model

$$y = \beta_0 + u; \qquad [4.45]$$

all independent variables have been dropped from the equation. Now, the R-squared from estimating (4.45) is zero; none of the variation in y is being explained because there are no explanatory variables. Therefore, the F statistic for testing (4.44) can be written as

$$\frac{R^2/k}{(1 - R^2)/(n - k - 1)}, \quad [4.46]$$

where R^2 is just the usual R-squared from the regression of y on $x_1, x_2, \ldots, x_k$.

Most regression packages report the F statistic in (4.46) automatically, which makes it tempting to use this statistic to test general exclusion restrictions. You must avoid this temptation. The F statistic in (4.41) is used for general exclusion restrictions; it depends on the R-squareds from the restricted and unrestricted models. The special form of (4.46) is valid only for testing joint exclusion of *all* independent variables. This is sometimes called determining the **overall significance of the regression**.

If we fail to reject (4.44), then there is no evidence that any of the independent variables help to explain y. This usually means that we must look for other variables to explain y. For Example 4.9, the F statistic for testing (4.44) is about 9.55 with $k = 5$ and $n - k - 1 =$ 1,185 *df*. The p-value is zero to four places after the decimal point, so that (4.44) is rejected very strongly. Thus, we conclude that the variables in the *bwght* equation *do* explain some variation in *bwght*. The amount explained is not large: only 3.87%. But the seemingly small R-squared results in a highly significant F statistic. That is why we must compute the F statistic to test for joint significance and not just look at the size of the R-squared.

Occasionally, the F statistic for the hypothesis that all independent variables are jointly insignificant is the focus of a study. Problem 10 asks you to use stock return data to test whether stock returns over a four-year horizon are predictable based on information known only at the beginning of the period. Under the *efficient markets hypothesis*, the returns should not be predictable; the null hypothesis is precisely (4.44).

Testing General Linear Restrictions

Testing exclusion restrictions is by far the most important application of F statistics. Sometimes, however, the restrictions implied by a theory are more complicated than just excluding some independent variables. It is still straightforward to use the F statistic for testing.

As an example, consider the following equation:

$$\begin{aligned}\log(price) = {} & \beta_0 + \beta_1\log(assess) + \beta_2\log(lotsize) \\ & + \beta_3\log(sqrft) + \beta_4 bdrms + u,\end{aligned} \quad [4.47]$$

where

$price$ = house price.
$assess$ = the assessed housing value (before the house was sold).
$lotsize$ = size of the lot, in feet.
$sqrft$ = square footage.
$bdrms$ = number of bedrooms.

Now, suppose we would like to test whether the assessed housing price is a rational valuation. If this is the case, then a 1% change in *assess* should be associated with a 1% change in *price*; that is, $\beta_1 = 1$. In addition, *lotsize*, *sqrft*, and *bdrms* should not help to explain log(*price*), once the assessed value has been controlled for. Together, these hypotheses can be stated as

$$H_0: \beta_1 = 1, \beta_2 = 0, \beta_3 = 0, \beta_4 = 0. \quad [4.48]$$

Four restrictions have to be tested; three are exclusion restrictions, but $\beta_1 = 1$ is not. How can we test this hypothesis using the F statistic?

As in the exclusion restriction case, we estimate the unrestricted model, (4.47) in this case, and then impose the restrictions in (4.48) to obtain the restricted model. It is the second step that can be a little tricky. But all we do is plug in the restrictions. If we write (4.47) as

$$y = \beta_0 + \beta_1 x_1 + \beta_2 x_2 + \beta_3 x_3 + \beta_4 x_4 + u, \quad [4.49]$$

then the restricted model is $y = \beta_0 + x_1 + u$. Now, to impose the restriction that the coefficient on x_1 is unity, we must estimate the following model:

$$y - x_1 = \beta_0 + u. \quad [4.50]$$

This is just a model with an intercept (β_0) but with a different dependent variable than in (4.49). The procedure for computing the F statistic is the same: estimate (4.50), obtain the SSR (SSR_r), and use this with the unrestricted SSR from (4.49) in the F statistic (4.37). We are testing $q = 4$ restrictions, and there are $n - 5$ *df* in the unrestricted model. The F statistic is simply $[(\text{SSR}_r - \text{SSR}_{ur})/\text{SSR}_{ur}][(n - 5)/4]$.

Before illustrating this test using a data set, we must emphasize one point: we cannot use the R-squared form of the F statistic for this example because the dependent variable in (4.50) is different from the one in (4.49). This means the total sum of squares from the two regressions will be different, and (4.41) is no longer equivalent to (4.37). As a general rule, the SSR form of the F statistic should be used if a different dependent variable is needed in running the restricted regression.

The estimated unrestricted model using the data in HPRICE1.RAW is

$$\begin{aligned}\widehat{\log(price)} = \underset{(.570)}{.264} + \underset{(.151)}{1.043} \log(assess) + \underset{(.0386)}{.0074} \log(lotsize) \\ - \underset{(.1384)}{.1032} \log(sqrft) + \underset{(.0221)}{.0338}\, bdrms \\ n = 88, \text{SSR} = 1.822, R^2 = .773.\end{aligned}$$

If we use separate t statistics to test each hypothesis in (4.48), we fail to reject each one. But rationality of the assessment is a joint hypothesis, so we should test the restrictions jointly. The SSR from the restricted model turns out to be $\text{SSR}_r = 1.880$, and so the F statistic is $[(1.880 - 1.822)/1.822](83/4) = .661$. The 5% critical value in an F distribution with (4,83) *df* is about 2.50, and so we fail to reject H_0. There is essentially no evidence against the hypothesis that the assessed values are rational.

4.6 Reporting Regression Results

We end this chapter by providing a few guidelines on how to report multiple regression results for relatively complicated empirical projects. This should help you to read published works in the applied social sciences, while also preparing you to write your own empirical papers. We will expand on this topic in the remainder of the text by reporting results from various examples, but many of the key points can be made now.

Naturally, the estimated OLS coefficients should always be reported. For the key variables in an analysis, you should *interpret* the estimated coefficients (which often requires knowing the units of measurement of the variables). For example, is an estimate an elasticity, or does it have some other interpretation that needs explanation? The economic or practical importance of the estimates of the key variables should be discussed.

The standard errors should always be included along with the estimated coefficients. Some authors prefer to report the t statistics rather than the standard errors (and sometimes just the absolute value of the t statistics). Although nothing is really wrong with this, there is some preference for reporting standard errors. First, it forces us to think carefully about the null hypothesis being tested; the null is not always that the population parameter is zero. Second, having standard errors makes it easier to compute confidence intervals.

The R-squared from the regression should always be included. We have seen that, in addition to providing a goodness-of-fit measure, it makes calculation of F statistics for exclusion restrictions simple. Reporting the sum of squared residuals and the standard error of the regression is sometimes a good idea, but it is not crucial. The number of observations used in estimating any equation should appear near the estimated equation.

If only a couple of models are being estimated, the results can be summarized in equation form, as we have done up to this point. However, in many papers, several equations are estimated with many different sets of independent variables. We may estimate the same equation for different groups of people, or even have equations explaining different dependent variables. In such cases, it is better to summarize the results in one or more tables. The dependent variable should be indicated clearly in the table, and the independent variables should be listed in the first column. Standard errors (or t statistics) can be put in parentheses below the estimates.

EXAMPLE 4.10 SALARY-PENSION TRADEOFF FOR TEACHERS

Let *totcomp* denote average total annual compensation for a teacher, including salary and all fringe benefits (pension, health insurance, and so on). Extending the standard wage equation, total compensation should be a function of productivity and perhaps other characteristics. As is standard, we use logarithmic form:

$$\log(totcomp) = f(productivity\ characteristics, other\ factors),$$

where $f(\cdot)$ is some function (unspecified for now). Write

$$totcomp = salary + benefits = salary\left(1 + \frac{benefits}{salary}\right).$$

This equation shows that total compensation is the product of two terms: *salary* and $1 + b/s$, where b/s is shorthand for the "benefits to salary ratio." Taking the log of this equation gives log(*totcomp*) = log(*salary*) + log(1 + *b/s*). Now, for "small" *b/s*, log(1 + *b/s*) ≈ *b/s*; we will use this approximation. This leads to the econometric model

$$\log(salary) = \beta_0 + \beta_1(b/s) + other\ factors.$$

Testing the salary-benefits tradeoff then is the same as a test of H_0: $\beta_1 = -1$ against H_1: $\beta_1 \neq -1$.

We use the data in MEAP93.RAW to test this hypothesis. These data are averaged at the school level, and we do not observe very many other factors that could affect total compensation. We will include controls for size of the school (*enroll*), staff per thousand students (*staff*), and measures such as the school dropout and graduation rates. The average *b/s* in the sample is about .205, and the largest value is .450.

The estimated equations are given in Table 4.1, where standard errors are given in parentheses below the coefficient estimates. The key variable is *b/s*, the benefits-salary ratio.

From the first column in Table 4.1, we see that, without controlling for any other factors, the OLS coefficient for *b/s* is −.825. The *t* statistic for testing the null hypothesis H_0: $\beta_1 = -1$ is $t = (-.825 + 1)/.200 = .875$, and so the simple regression fails to reject H_0. After adding controls for school size and staff size (which roughly captures the number of students taught by each teacher), the estimate of the *b/s* coefficient becomes −.605. Now, the test of $\beta_1 = -1$ gives a *t* statistic of about 2.39; thus, H_0 is rejected at the 5% level against a two-sided alternative. The variables log(*enroll*) and log(*staff*) are very statistically significant.

EXPLORING FURTHER 4.6

How does adding *droprate* and *gradrate* affect the estimate of the salary-benefits tradeoff? Are these variables jointly significant at the 5% level? What about the 10% level?

TABLE 4.1 Testing the Salary-Benefits Tradeoff

	Dependent Variable: log(*salary*)		
Independent Variables	**(1)**	**(2)**	**(3)**
b/s	−.825 (.200)	−.605 (.165)	−.589 (.165)
log(*enroll*)	—	.0874 (.0073)	.0881 (.0073)
log(*staff*)	—	−.222 (.050)	−.218 (.050)
droprate	—	—	−.00028 (.00161)
gradrate	—	—	.00097 .00066)
intercept	10.523 (0.042)	10.884 (0.252)	10.738 (0.258)
Observations	408	408	408
R-squared	.040	.353	.361

Summary

In this chapter, we have covered the very important topic of statistical inference, which allows us to infer something about the population model from a random sample. We summarize the main points:

1. Under the classical linear model assumptions MLR.1 through MLR.6, the OLS estimators are normally distributed.
2. Under the CLM assumptions, the t statistics have t distributions under the null hypothesis.
3. We use t statistics to test hypotheses about a single parameter against one- or two-sided alternatives, using one- or two-tailed tests, respectively. The most common null hypothesis is H_0: $\beta_j = 0$, but we sometimes want to test other values of β_j under H_0.
4. In classical hypothesis testing, we first choose a significance level, which, along with the *df* and alternative hypothesis, determines the critical value against which we compare the t statistic. It is more informative to compute the p-value for a t test—the smallest significance level for which the null hypothesis is rejected—so that the hypothesis can be tested at any significance level.
5. Under the CLM assumptions, confidence intervals can be constructed for each β_j. These CIs can be used to test any null hypothesis concerning β_j against a two-sided alternative.
6. Single hypothesis tests concerning more than one β_j can always be tested by rewriting the model to contain the parameter of interest. Then, a standard t statistic can be used.
7. The F statistic is used to test multiple exclusion restrictions, and there are two equivalent forms of the test. One is based on the SSRs from the restricted and unrestricted models. A more convenient form is based on the R-squareds from the two models.
8. When computing an F statistic, the numerator *df* is the number of restrictions being tested, while the denominator *df* is the degrees of freedom in the unrestricted model.
9. The alternative for F testing is two-sided. In the classical approach, we specify a significance level which, along with the numerator *df* and the denominator *df*, determines the critical value. The null hypothesis is rejected when the statistic, F, exceeds the critical value, c. Alternatively, we can compute a p-value to summarize the evidence against H_0.
10. General multiple linear restrictions can be tested using the sum of squared residuals form of the F statistic.
11. The F statistic for the overall significance of a regression tests the null hypothesis that *all* slope parameters are zero, with the intercept unrestricted. Under H_0, the explanatory variables have no effect on the expected value of y.

THE CLASSICAL LINEAR MODEL ASSUMPTIONS

Now is a good time to review the full set of classical linear model (CLM) assumptions for cross-sectional regression. Following each assumption is a comment about its role in multiple regression analysis.

Assumption MLR.1 (Linear in Parameters)

The model in the population can be written as

$$y = \beta_0 + \beta_1 x_1 + \beta_2 x_2 + \ldots + \beta_k x_k + u,$$

where $\beta_0, \beta_1, \ldots, \beta_k$ are the unknown parameters (constants) of interest and u is an unobserved random error or disturbance term.

Assumption MLR.1 describes the population relationship we hope to estimate, and explicitly sets out the β_j—the ceteris paribus population effects of the x_j on y—as the parameters of interest.

Assumption MLR.2 (Random Sampling)

We have a random sample of n observations, $\{(x_{i1}, x_{i2}, \ldots, x_{ik}, y_i): i = 1, \ldots, n\}$, following the population model in Assumption MLR.1.

This random sampling assumption means that we have data that can be used to estimate the β_j, and that the data have been chosen to be representative of the population described in Assumption MLR.1.

Assumption MLR.3 (No Perfect Collinearity)

In the sample (and therefore in the population), none of the independent variables is constant, and there are no exact *linear* relationships among the independent variables.

Once we have a sample of data, we need to know that we can use the data to compute the OLS estimates, the $\hat{\beta}_j$. This is the role of Assumption MLR.3: if we have sample variation in each independent variable and no exact linear relationships among the independent variables, we can compute the $\hat{\beta}_j$.

Assumption MLR.4 (Zero Conditional Mean)

The error u has an expected value of zero given any values of the explanatory variables. In other words, $E(u|x_1, x_2, \ldots, x_k) = 0$.

As we discussed in the text, assuming that the unobserved factors are, on average, unrelated to the explanatory variables is key to deriving the first statistical property of each OLS estimator: its unbiasedness for the corresponding population parameter. Of course, all of the previous assumptions are used to show unbiasedness.

Assumption MLR.5 (Homoskedasticity)

The error u has the same variance given any values of the explanatory variables. In other words,

$$\text{Var}(u|x_1, x_2, \ldots, x_k) = \sigma^2.$$

Compared with Assumption MLR.4, the homoskedasticity assumption is of secondary importance; in particular, Assumption MLR.5 has no bearing on the unbiasedness of the $\hat{\beta}_j$. Still, homoskedasticity has two important implications: (1) We can derive formulas for the sampling variances whose components are easy to characterize; (2) We can conclude, under the Gauss-Markov assumptions MLR.1 to MLR.5, that the OLS estimators have smallest variance among *all* linear, unbiased estimators.

Assumption MLR.6 (Normality)

The population error u is *independent* of the explanatory variables $x_1, x_2, \ldots, x_k$ and is normally distributed with zero mean and variance σ^2: $u \sim \text{Normal}(0, \sigma^2)$.

In this chapter, we added Assumption MLR.6 to obtain the exact sampling distributions of t statistics and F statistics, so that we can carry out exact hypotheses tests. In the next chapter, we will see that MLR.6 can be dropped if we have a reasonably large sample size. Assumption MLR.6 does imply a stronger efficiency property of OLS: the OLS estimators have smallest variance among *all* unbiased estimators; the comparison group is no longer restricted to estimators linear in the $\{y_i: i = 1, 2, \ldots, n\}$.

Key Terms

Alternative Hypothesis
Classical Linear Model
Classical Linear Model (CLM) Assumptions
Confidence Interval (CI)
Critical Value
Denominator Degrees of Freedom
Economic Significance
Exclusion Restrictions
F Statistic
Joint Hypotheses Test
Jointly Insignificant
Jointly Statistically Significant
Minimum Variance Unbiased Estimators
Multiple Hypotheses Test
Multiple Restrictions
Normality Assumption
Null Hypothesis
Numerator Degrees of Freedom
One-Sided Alternative
One-Tailed Test
Overall Significance of the Regression
p-Value
Practical Significance
R-squared Form of the F Statistic
Rejection Rule
Restricted Model
Significance Level
Statistically Insignificant
Statistically Significant
t Ratio
t Statistic
Two-Sided Alternative
Two-Tailed Test
Unrestricted Model

Problems

1 Which of the following can cause the usual OLS t statistics to be invalid (that is, not to have t distributions under H_0)?
(i) Heteroskedasticity.
(ii) A sample correlation coefficient of .95 between two independent variables that are in the model.
(iii) Omitting an important explanatory variable.

2 Consider an equation to explain salaries of CEOs in terms of annual firm sales, return on equity (*roe*, in percentage form), and return on the firm's stock (*ros*, in percentage form):

$$\log(salary) = \beta_0 + \beta_1 \log(sales) + \beta_2 roe + \beta_3 ros + u.$$

(i) In terms of the model parameters, state the null hypothesis that, after controlling for *sales* and *roe*, *ros* has no effect on CEO salary. State the alternative that better stock market performance increases a CEO's salary.
(ii) Using the data in CEOSAL1.RAW, the following equation was obtained by OLS:

$$\widehat{\log(salary)} = \underset{(.32)}{4.32} + \underset{(.035)}{.280} \log(sales) + \underset{(.0041)}{.0174}\, roe + \underset{(.00054)}{.00024}\, ros$$
$$n = 209, R^2 = .283.$$

By what percentage is *salary* predicted to increase if *ros* increases by 50 points? Does *ros* have a practically large effect on *salary*?
(iii) Test the null hypothesis that *ros* has no effect on *salary* against the alternative that *ros* has a positive effect. Carry out the test at the 10% significance level.
(iv) Would you include *ros* in a final model explaining CEO compensation in terms of firm performance? Explain.

3 The variable *rdintens* is expenditures on research and development (R&D) as a percentage of sales. Sales are measured in millions of dollars. The variable *profmarg* is profits as a percentage of sales.

Using the data in RDCHEM.RAW for 32 firms in the chemical industry, the following equation is estimated:

$$\widehat{rdintens} = \underset{(1.369)}{.472} + \underset{(.216)}{.321}\log(sales) + \underset{(.046)}{.050}\,profmarg$$
$$n = 32, R^2 = .099.$$

(i) Interpret the coefficient on log(*sales*). In particular, if *sales* increases by 10%, what is the estimated percentage point change in *rdintens*? Is this an economically large effect?
(ii) Test the hypothesis that R&D intensity does not change with *sales* against the alternative that it does increase with sales. Do the test at the 5% and 10% levels.
(iii) Interpret the coefficient on *profmarg*. Is it economically large?
(iv) Does *profmarg* have a statistically significant effect on *rdintens*?

4 Are rent rates influenced by the student population in a college town? Let *rent* be the average monthly rent paid on rental units in a college town in the United States. Let *pop* denote the total city population, *avginc* the average city income, and *pctstu* the student population as a percentage of the total population. One model to test for a relationship is

$$\log(rent) = \beta_0 + \beta_1\log(pop) + \beta_2\log(avginc) + \beta_3 pctstu + u.$$

(i) State the null hypothesis that size of the student body relative to the population has no ceteris paribus effect on monthly rents. State the alternative that there is an effect.
(ii) What signs do you expect for β_1 and β_2?
(iii) The equation estimated using 1990 data from RENTAL.RAW for 64 college towns is

$$\widehat{\log(rent)} = \underset{(.844)}{.043} + \underset{(.039)}{.066}\log(pop) + \underset{(.081)}{.507}\log(avginc) + \underset{(.0017)}{.0056}\,pctstu$$
$$n = 64, R^2 = .458.$$

What is wrong with the statement: "A 10% increase in population is associated with about a 6.6% increase in rent"?
(iv) Test the hypothesis stated in part (i) at the 1% level.

5 Consider the estimated equation from Example 4.3, which can be used to study the effects of skipping class on college GPA:

$$\widehat{colGPA} = \underset{(.33)}{1.39} + \underset{(.094)}{.412}\,hsGPA + \underset{(.011)}{.015}\,ACT - \underset{(.026)}{.083}\,skipped$$
$$n = 141, R^2 = .234.$$

(i) Using the standard normal approximation, find the 95% confidence interval for β_{hsGPA}.
(ii) Can you reject the hypothesis H_0: $\beta_{hsGPA} = .4$ against the two-sided alternative at the 5% level?
(iii) Can you reject the hypothesis H_0: $\beta_{hsGPA} = 1$ against the two-sided alternative at the 5% level?

6 In Section 4.5, we used as an example testing the rationality of assessments of housing prices. There, we used a log-log model in *price* and *assess* [see equation (4.47)]. Here, we use a level-level formulation.
(i) In the simple regression model

$$price = \beta_0 + \beta_1 assess + u,$$

the assessment is rational if $\beta_1 = 1$ and $\beta_0 = 0$. The estimated equation is

$$\widehat{price} = \underset{(16.27)}{-14.47} + \underset{(.049)}{.976}\ assess$$

$$n = 88,\ \text{SSR} = 165{,}644.51,\ R^2 = .820.$$

First, test the hypothesis that H_0: $\beta_0 = 0$ against the two-sided alternative. Then, test H_0: $\beta_1 = 1$ against the two-sided alternative. What do you conclude?

(ii) To test the joint hypothesis that $\beta_0 = 0$ and $\beta_1 = 1$, we need the SSR in the restricted model. This amounts to computing $\sum_{i=1}^{n}(price_i - assess_i)^2$, where $n = 88$, since the residuals in the restricted model are just $price_i - assess_i$. (No estimation is needed for the restricted model because both parameters are specified under H_0.) This turns out to yield SSR = 209,448.99. Carry out the F test for the joint hypothesis.

(iii) Now, test H_0: $\beta_2 = 0$, $\beta_3 = 0$, and $\beta_4 = 0$ in the model

$$price = \beta_0 + \beta_1 assess + \beta_2 lotsize + \beta_3 sqrft + \beta_4 bdrms + u.$$

The R-squared from estimating this model using the same 88 houses is .829.

(iv) If the variance of *price* changes with *assess*, *lotsize*, *sqrft*, or *bdrms*, what can you say about the F test from part (iii)?

7 In Example 4.7, we used data on nonunionized manufacturing firms to estimate the relationship between the scrap rate and other firm characteristics. We now look at this example more closely and use all available firms.

(i) The population model estimated in Example 4.7 can be written as

$$\log(scrap) = \beta_0 + \beta_1 hrsemp + \beta_2 \log(sales) + \beta_3 \log(employ) + u.$$

Using the 43 observations available for 1987, the estimated equation is

$$\widehat{\log(scrap)} = \underset{(4.57)}{11.74} - \underset{(.019)}{.042}\ hrsemp - \underset{(.370)}{.951}\ \log(sales) + \underset{(.360)}{.992}\ \log(employ)$$

$$n = 43,\ R^2 = .310.$$

Compare this equation to that estimated using only the 29 nonunionized firms in the sample.

(ii) Show that the population model can also be written as

$$\log(scrap) = \beta_0 + \beta_1 hrsemp + \beta_2 \log(sales/employ) + \theta_3 \log(employ) + u,$$

where $\theta_3 = \beta_2 + \beta_3$. [*Hint:* Recall that $\log(x_2/x_3) = \log(x_2) - \log(x_3)$.] Interpret the hypothesis H_0: $\theta_3 = 0$.

(iii) When the equation from part (ii) is estimated, we obtain

$$\widehat{\log(scrap)} = \underset{(4.57)}{11.74} - \underset{(.019)}{.042}\ hrsemp - \underset{(.370)}{.951}\ \log(sales/employ) + \underset{(.205)}{.041}\ \log(employ)$$

$$n = 43,\ R^2 = .310.$$

Controlling for worker training and for the sales-to-employee ratio, do bigger firms have larger statistically significant scrap rates?

(iv) Test the hypothesis that a 1% increase in *sales/employ* is associated with a 1% drop in the scrap rate.

8 Consider the multiple regression model with three independent variables, under the classical linear model assumptions MLR.1 through MLR.6:

$$y = \beta_0 + \beta_1 x_1 + \beta_2 x_2 + \beta_3 x_3 + u.$$

You would like to test the null hypothesis H_0: $\beta_1 - 3\beta_2 = 1$.

(i) Let $\hat{\beta}_1$ and $\hat{\beta}_2$ denote the OLS estimators of β_1 and β_2. Find $\text{Var}(\hat{\beta}_1 - 3\hat{\beta}_2)$ in terms of the variances of $\hat{\beta}_1$ and $\hat{\beta}_2$ and the covariance between them. What is the standard error of $\hat{\beta}_1 - 3\hat{\beta}_2$?

(ii) Write the t statistic for testing H_0: $\beta_1 - 3\beta_2 = 1$.

(iii) Define $\theta_1 = \beta_1 - 3\beta_2$ and $\hat{\theta}_1 = \hat{\beta}_1 - 3\hat{\beta}_2$. Write a regression equation involving β_0, θ_1, β_2, and β_3 that allows you to directly obtain $\hat{\theta}_1$ and its standard error.

9 In Problem 3 in Chapter 3, we estimated the equation

$$\begin{aligned}\widehat{sleep} = \underset{(112.28)}{3{,}638.25} - \underset{(.017)}{.148}\ totwrk - \underset{(5.88)}{11.13}\ educ + \underset{(1.45)}{2.20}\ age\end{aligned}$$

$$n = 706,\ R^2 = .113,$$

where we now report standard errors along with the estimates.

(i) Is either *educ* or *age* individually significant at the 5% level against a two-sided alternative? Show your work.

(ii) Dropping *educ* and *age* from the equation gives

$$\widehat{sleep} = \underset{(38.91)}{3{,}586.38} - \underset{(.017)}{.151}\ totwrk$$

$$n = 706,\ R^2 = .103.$$

Are *educ* and *age* jointly significant in the original equation at the 5% level? Justify your answer.

(iii) Does including *educ* and *age* in the model greatly affect the estimated tradeoff between sleeping and working?

(iv) Suppose that the sleep equation contains heteroskedasticity. What does this mean about the tests computed in parts (i) and (ii)?

10 Regression analysis can be used to test whether the market efficiently uses information in valuing stocks. For concreteness, let *return* be the total return from holding a firm's stock over the four-year period from the end of 1990 to the end of 1994. The *efficient markets hypothesis* says that these returns should not be systematically related to information known in 1990. If firm characteristics known at the beginning of the period help to predict stock returns, then we could use this information in choosing stocks.

For 1990, let *dkr* be a firm's debt to capital ratio, let *eps* denote the earnings per share, let *netinc* denote net income, and let *salary* denote total compensation for the CEO.

(i) Using the data in RETURN.RAW, the following equation was estimated:

$$\widehat{return} = \underset{(6.89)}{-14.37} + \underset{(.201)}{.321}\ dkr + \underset{(.078)}{.043}\ eps - \underset{(.0047)}{.0051}\ netinc + \underset{(.0022)}{.0035}\ salary$$

$$n = 142,\ R^2 = .0395.$$

Test whether the explanatory variables are jointly significant at the 5% level. Is any explanatory variable individually significant?

(ii) Now, reestimate the model using the log form for *netinc* and *salary*:

$$\widehat{return} = \underset{(39.37)}{-36.30} + \underset{(.203)}{.327}\ dkr + \underset{(.080)}{.069}\ eps - \underset{(3.39)}{4.74}\ \log(netinc) + \underset{(6.31)}{7.24}\ \log(salary)$$

$$n = 142,\ R^2 = .0330.$$

Do any of your conclusions from part (i) change?

(iii) In this sample, some firms have zero debt and others have negative earnings. Should we try to use log(*dkr*) or log(*eps*) in the model to see if these improve the fit? Explain.

(iv) Overall, is the evidence for predictability of stock returns strong or weak?

11 The following table was created using the data in CEOSAL2.RAW, where standard errors are in parentheses below the coefficients:

	Dependent Variable: log(*salary*)		
Independent Variables	**(1)**	**(2)**	**(3)**
log(*sales*)	.224 (.027)	.158 (.040)	.188 (.040)
log(*mktval*)	——	.112 (.050)	.100 (.049)
profmarg	——	−.0023 (.0022)	−.0022 (.0021)
ceoten	——	——	.0171 (.0055)
comten	——	——	−.0092 (.0033)
intercept	4.94 (0.20)	4.62 (0.25)	4.57 (0.25)
Observations	177	177	177
R-squared	.281	.304	.353

The variable *mktval* is market value of the firm, *profmarg* is profit as a percentage of sales, *ceoten* is years as CEO with the current company, and *comten* is total years with the company.

(i) Comment on the effect of *profmarg* on CEO salary.

(ii) Does market value have a significant effect? Explain.

(iii) Interpret the coefficients on *ceoten* and *comten*. Are these explanatory variables statistically significant?

(iv) What do you make of the fact that longer tenure with the company, holding the other factors fixed, is associated with a lower salary?

12 The following analysis was obtained using data in MEAP93.RAW, which contains school-level pass rates (as a percent) on a 10th grade math test.

(i) The variable *expend* is expenditures per student, in dollars, and *math*10 is the pass rate on the exam. The following simple regression relates *math*10 to *lexpend* = log(*expend*):

$$\widehat{math10} = \underset{(25.53)}{-69.34} + \underset{(3.17)}{11.16}\ lexpend$$

$$n = 408,\ R^2 = .0297$$

Interpret the coefficient on *lexpend*. In particular, if *expend* increases by 10%, what is the estimated percentage point change in *math*10? What do you make of the large negative intercept estimate? (The minimum value of *lexpend* is 8.11 and its average value is 8.37.)

(ii) Does the small *R*-squared in part (i) imply that spending is correlated with other factors affecting *math*10? Explain. Would you expect the *R*-squared to be much higher if expenditures were randomly assigned to schools—that is, independent of other school and student characteristics—rather than having the school districts determine spending?

(iii) When log of enrollment and the percent of students eligible for the federal free lunch program are included, the estimated equation becomes

$$\widehat{math10} = \underset{(24.99)}{-23.14} + \underset{(3.04)}{7.75}\ lexpend - \underset{(0.58)}{1.26}\ lenroll - \underset{(0.36)}{.324}\ lnchprg$$
$$n = 408,\ R^2 = .1893$$

Comment on what happens to the coefficient on *lexpend*. Is the spending coefficient still statistically different from zero?

(iv) What do you make of the *R*-squared in part (iii)? What are some other factors that could be used to explain *math*10 (at the school level)?

Computer Exercises

C1 The following model can be used to study whether campaign expenditures affect election outcomes:

$$voteA = \beta_0 + \beta_1\log(expendA) + \beta_2\log(expendB) + \beta_3\, prtystrA + u,$$

where *voteA* is the percentage of the vote received by Candidate A, *expendA* and *expendB* are campaign expenditures by Candidates A and B, and *prtystrA* is a measure of party strength for Candidate A (the percentage of the most recent presidential vote that went to A's party).

(i) What is the interpretation of β_1?

(ii) In terms of the parameters, state the null hypothesis that a 1% increase in A's expenditures is offset by a 1% increase in B's expenditures.

(iii) Estimate the given model using the data in VOTE1.RAW and report the results in usual form. Do A's expenditures affect the outcome? What about B's expenditures? Can you use these results to test the hypothesis in part (ii)?

(iv) Estimate a model that directly gives the *t* statistic for testing the hypothesis in part (ii). What do you conclude? (Use a two-sided alternative.)

C2 Use the data in LAWSCH85.RAW for this exercise.

(i) Using the same model as in Problem 4 in Chapter 3, state and test the null hypothesis that the rank of law schools has no ceteris paribus effect on median starting salary.

(ii) Are features of the incoming class of students—namely, *LSAT* and *GPA*—individually or jointly significant for explaining *salary*? (Be sure to account for missing data on *LSAT* and *GPA*.)

(iii) Test whether the size of the entering class (*clsize*) or the size of the faculty (*faculty*) needs to be added to this equation; carry out a single test. (Be careful to account for missing data on *clsize* and *faculty*.)

(iv) What factors might influence the rank of the law school that are not included in the salary regression?

C3 Refer to Computer Exercise C2 in Chapter 3. Now, use the log of the housing price as the dependent variable:

$$\log(price) = \beta_0 + \beta_1 sqrft + \beta_2 bdrms + u.$$

(i) You are interested in estimating and obtaining a confidence interval for the percentage change in *price* when a 150-square-foot bedroom is added to a house. In decimal form, this is $\theta_1 = 150\beta_1 + \beta_2$. Use the data in HPRICE1.RAW to estimate θ_1.
(ii) Write β_2 in terms of θ_1 and β_1 and plug this into the log(*price*) equation.
(iii) Use part (ii) to obtain a standard error for $\hat{\theta}_1$ and use this standard error to construct a 95% confidence interval.

C4 In Example 4.9, the restricted version of the model can be estimated using all 1,388 observations in the sample. Compute the *R*-squared from the regression of *bwght* on *cigs*, *parity*, and *faminc* using all observations. Compare this to the *R*-squared reported for the restricted model in Example 4.9.

C5 Use the data in MLB1.RAW for this exercise.
(i) Use the model estimated in equation (4.31) and drop the variable *rbisyr*. What happens to the statistical significance of *hrunsyr*? What about the size of the coefficient on *hrunsyr*?
(ii) Add the variables *runsyr* (runs per year), *fldperc* (fielding percentage), and *sbasesyr* (stolen bases per year) to the model from part (i). Which of these factors are individually significant?
(iii) In the model from part (ii), test the joint significance of *bavg*, *fldperc*, and *sbasesyr*.

C6 Use the data in WAGE2.RAW for this exercise.
(i) Consider the standard wage equation

$$\log(wage) = \beta_0 + \beta_1 educ + \beta_2 exper + \beta_3 tenure + u.$$

State the null hypothesis that another year of general workforce experience has the same effect on log(*wage*) as another year of tenure with the current employer.
(ii) Test the null hypothesis in part (i) against a two-sided alternative, at the 5% significance level, by constructing a 95% confidence interval. What do you conclude?

C7 Refer to the example used in Section 4.4. You will use the data set TWOYEAR.RAW.
(i) The variable *phsrank* is the person's high school percentile. (A higher number is better. For example, 90 means you are ranked better than 90 percent of your graduating class.) Find the smallest, largest, and average *phsrank* in the sample.
(ii) Add *phsrank* to equation (4.26) and report the OLS estimates in the usual form. Is *phsrank* statistically significant? How much is 10 percentage points of high school rank worth in terms of wage?
(iii) Does adding *phsrank* to (4.26) substantively change the conclusions on the returns to two- and four-year colleges? Explain.
(iv) The data set contains a variable called *id*. Explain why if you add *id* to equation (4.17) or (4.26) you expect it to be statistically insignificant. What is the two-sided *p*-value?

C8 The data set 401KSUBS.RAW contains information on net financial wealth (*nettfa*), age of the survey respondent (*age*), annual family income (*inc*), family size (*fsize*), and participation in certain pension plans for people in the United States. The wealth and income variables are both recorded in thousands of dollars. For this question, use only the data for single-person households (so $fsize = 1$).

(i) How many single-person households are there in the data set?

(ii) Use OLS to estimate the model

$$nettfa = \beta_0 + \beta_1 inc + \beta_2 age + u,$$

and report the results using the usual format. Be sure to use only the single-person households in the sample. Interpret the slope coefficients. Are there any surprises in the slope estimates?

(iii) Does the intercept from the regression in part (ii) have an interesting meaning? Explain.

(iv) Find the p-value for the test H_0: $\beta_2 = 1$ against H_1: $\beta_2 < 1$. Do you reject H_0 at the 1% significance level?

(v) If you do a simple regression of *nettfa* on *inc*, is the estimated coefficient on *inc* much different from the estimate in part (ii)? Why or why not?

C9 Use the data in DISCRIM.RAW to answer this question. (See also Computer Exercise C8 in Chapter 3.)

(i) Use OLS to estimate the model

$$\log(psoda) = \beta_0 + \beta_1 prpblck + \beta_2 \log(income) + \beta_3 prppov + u,$$

and report the results in the usual form. Is $\hat{\beta}_1$ statistically different from zero at the 5% level against a two-sided alternative? What about at the 1% level?

(ii) What is the correlation between log(*income*) and *prppov*? Is each variable statistically significant in any case? Report the two-sided p-values.

(iii) To the regression in part (i), add the variable log(*hseval*). Interpret its coefficient and report the two-sided p-value for H_0: $\beta_{\log(hseval)} = 0$.

(iv) In the regression in part (iii), what happens to the individual statistical significance of log(*income*) and *prppov*? Are these variables jointly significant? (Compute a p-value.) What do you make of your answers?

(v) Given the results of the previous regressions, which one would you report as most reliable in determining whether the racial makeup of a zip code influences local fast-food prices?

C10 Use the data in ELEM94_95 to answer this question. The findings can be compared with those in Table 4.1. The dependent variable *lavgsal* is the log of average teacher salary and *bs* is the ratio of average benefits to average salary (by school).

(i) Run the simple regression of *lavgsal* on *bs*. Is the estimated slope statistically different from zero? Is it statistically different from -1?

(ii) Add the variables *lenrol* and *lstaff* to the regression from part (i). What happens to the coefficient on *bs*? How does the situation compare with that in Table 4.1?

(iii) How come the standard error on the *bs* coefficient is smaller in part (ii) than in part (i)? (*Hint:* What happens to the error variance versus multicollinearity when *lenrol* and *lstaff* are added?)

(iv) How come the coefficient on *lstaff* is negative? Is it large in magnitude?

(v) Now add the variable *lunch* to the regression. Holding other factors fixed, are teachers being compensated for teaching students from disadvantaged backgrounds? Explain.

(vi) Overall, is the pattern of results that you find with ELEM94_95.RAW consistent with the pattern in Table 4.1?

C11 Use the data in HTV.RAW to answer this question. See also Computer Exercise C10 in Chapter 3.

(i) Estimate the regression model

$$educ = \beta_0 + \beta_1 motheduc + \beta_2 fatheduc + \beta_3 abil + \beta_4 abil^2 + u$$

by OLS and report the results in the usual form. Test the null hypothesis that *educ* is linearly related to *abil* against the alternative that the relationship is quadratic.

(ii) Using the equation in part (i), test H_0: $\beta_1 = \beta_2$ against a two-sided alternative. What is the *p*-value of the test?

(iii) Add the two college tuition variables to the regression from part (i) and determine whether they are jointly statistically significant.

(iv) What is the correlation between *tuit*17 and *tuit*18? Explain why using the average of the tuition over the two years might be preferred to adding each separately. What happens when you do use the average?

(v) Do the findings for the average tuition variable in part (iv) make sense when interpreted causally? What might be going on?

CHAPTER 5

Multiple Regression Analysis: OLS Asymptotics

In Chapters 3 and 4, we covered what are called *finite sample*, *small sample*, or *exact* properties of the OLS estimators in the population model

$$y = \beta_0 + \beta_1 x_1 + \beta_2 x_2 + \dots + \beta_k x_k + u. \qquad [5.1]$$

For example, the unbiasedness of OLS (derived in Chapter 3) under the first four Gauss-Markov assumptions is a finite sample property because it holds for *any* sample size n (subject to the mild restriction that n must be at least as large as the total number of parameters in the regression model, $k + 1$). Similarly, the fact that OLS is the best linear unbiased estimator under the full set of Gauss-Markov assumptions (MLR.1 through MLR.5) is a finite sample property.

In Chapter 4, we added the classical linear model Assumption MLR.6, which states that the error term u is normally distributed and independent of the explanatory variables. This allowed us to derive the *exact* sampling distributions of the OLS estimators (conditional on the explanatory variables in the sample). In particular, Theorem 4.1 showed that the OLS estimators have normal sampling distributions, which led directly to the t and F distributions for t and F statistics. If the error is not normally distributed, the distribution of a t statistic is not exactly t, and an F statistic does not have an exact F distribution for any sample size.

In addition to finite sample properties, it is important to know the **asymptotic properties** or **large sample properties** of estimators and test statistics. These properties are not defined for a particular sample size; rather, they are defined as the sample size grows without bound. Fortunately, under the assumptions we have made, OLS has satisfactory large sample properties. One practically important finding is that even without the normality assumption (Assumption MLR.6), t and F statistics have *approximately* t and F distributions, at least in large sample sizes. We discuss this in more detail in Section 5.2, after we cover the consistency of OLS in Section 5.1.

Because the material in this chapter is more difficult to understand, and because one can conduct empirical work without a deep understanding of its contents, this chapter may be skipped. However, we will necessarily refer to large sample properties of OLS when we relax the homoskedasticity assumption in Chapter 8 and when we delve into estimation using time series data in Part 2. Furthermore, virtually all advanced econometric methods derive their justification using large-sample analysis, so readers who will continue into Part 3 should be familiar with the contents of this chapter.

5.1 Consistency

Unbiasedness of estimators, although important, cannot always be achieved. For example, as we discussed in Chapter 3, the standard error of the regression, $\hat{\sigma}$, is not an unbiased estimator for σ, the standard deviation of the error u in a multiple regression model. Although the OLS estimators are unbiased under MLR.1 through MLR.4, in Chapter 11 we will find that there are time series regressions where the OLS estimators are not unbiased. Further, in Part 3 of the text, we encounter several other estimators that are biased yet useful.

Although not all useful estimators are unbiased, virtually all economists agree that **consistency** is a minimal requirement for an estimator. The Nobel Prize–winning econometrician Clive W. J. Granger once remarked, "If you can't get it right as n goes to infinity,you shouldn't be in this business." The implication is that, if your estimator of a particular population parameter is not consistent, then you are wasting your time.

There are a few different ways to describe consistency. Formal definitions and results are given in Appendix C; here, we focus on an intuitive understanding. For concreteness, let $\hat{\beta}_j$ be the OLS estimator of β_j for some j. For each n, $\hat{\beta}_j$ has a probability distribution (representing its possible values in different random samples of size n). Because $\hat{\beta}_j$ is unbiased under Assumptions MLR.1 through MLR.4, this distribution has mean value β_j. If this estimator is consistent, then the distribution of $\hat{\beta}_j$ becomes more and more tightly distributed around β_j as the sample size grows. As n tends to infinity, the distribution of $\hat{\beta}_j$ collapses to the single point β_j. In effect, this means that we can make our estimator arbitrarily close to β_j if we can collect as much data as we want. This convergence is illustrated in Figure 5.1.

Naturally, for any application, we have a fixed sample size, which is a major reason an asymptotic property such as consistency can be difficult to grasp. Consistency involves a thought experiment about what would happen as the sample size gets large (while, at the same time, we obtain numerous random samples for each sample size). If obtaining more and more data does not generally get us closer to the parameter value of interest, then we are using a poor estimation procedure.

Conveniently, the same set of assumptions implies both unbiasedness and consistency of OLS. We summarize with a theorem.

THEOREM 5.1 CONSISTENCY OF OLS

Under Assumptions MLR.1 through MLR.4, the OLS estimator $\hat{\beta}_j$ is consistent for β_j, for all $j = 0,1, ..., k$.

FIGURE 5.1 Sampling distributions of $\hat{\beta}_1$ for sample sizes $n_1 < n_2 < n_3$.

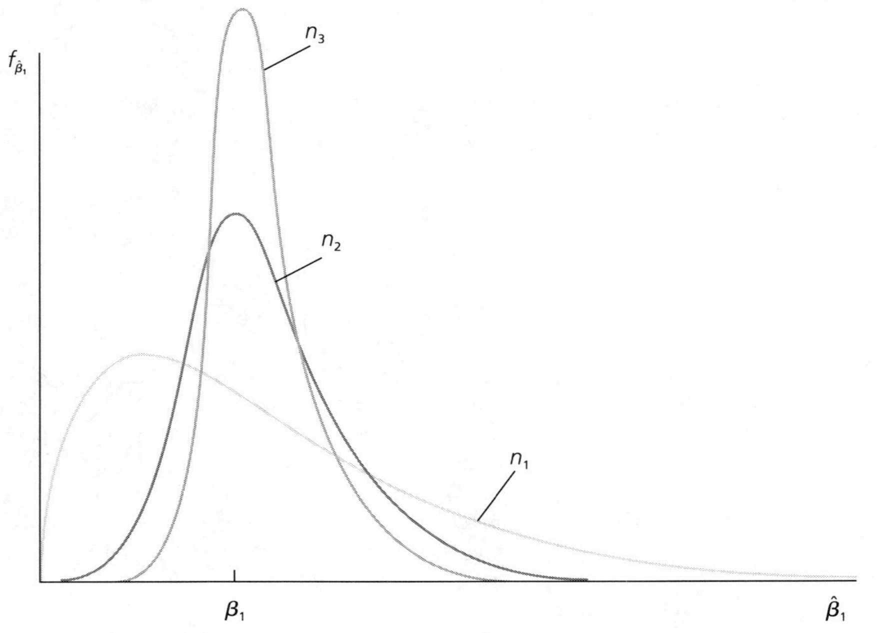

A general proof of this result is most easily developed using the matrix algebra methods described in Appendices D and E. But we can prove Theorem 5.1 without difficulty in the case of the simple regression model. We focus on the slope estimator, $\hat{\beta}_1$.

The proof starts out the same as the proof of unbiasedness: we write down the formula for $\hat{\beta}_1$, and then plug in $y_i = \beta_0 + \beta_1 x_{i1} + u_i$:

$$\begin{aligned}\hat{\beta}_1 &= \left(\sum_{i=1}^{n}(x_{i1} - \bar{x}_1)y_i\right) \bigg/ \left(\sum_{i=1}^{n}(x_{i1} - \bar{x}_1)^2\right) \\ &= \beta_1 + \left(n^{-1}\sum_{i=1}^{n}(x_{i1} - \bar{x}_1)u_i\right) \bigg/ \left(n^{-1}\sum_{i=1}^{n}(x_{i1} - \bar{x}_1)^2\right),\end{aligned} \quad [5.2]$$

where dividing both the numerator and denominator by n does not change the expression but allows us to directly apply the law of large numbers. When we apply the law of large numbers to the averages in the second part of equation (5.2), we conclude that the numerator and denominator converge in probability to the population quantities, $\text{Cov}(x_1,u)$ and $\text{Var}(x_1)$, respectively. Provided that $\text{Var}(x_1) \neq 0$—which is assumed in MLR.3—we can use the properties of *probability limits* (see Appendix C) to get

$$\begin{aligned}\text{plim}\,\hat{\beta}_1 &= \beta_1 + \text{Cov}(x_1,u)/\text{Var}(x_1) \\ &= \beta_1 \text{ because } \text{Cov}(x_1,u) = 0.\end{aligned} \quad [5.3]$$

We have used the fact, discussed in Chapters 2 and 3, that $\mathrm{E}(u|x_1) = 0$ (Assumption MLR.4) implies that x_1 and u are uncorrelated (have zero covariance).

As a technical matter, to ensure that the probability limits exist, we should assume that $\mathrm{Var}(x_1) < \infty$ and $\mathrm{Var}(u) < \infty$ (which means that their probability distributions are not too spread out), but we will not worry about cases where these assumptions might fail.

The previous arguments, and equation (5.3) in particular, show that OLS is consistent in the simple regression case if we assume only zero correlation. This is also true in the general case. We now state this as an assumption.

Assumption MLR.4′ Zero Mean and Zero Correlation

$\mathrm{E}(u) = 0$ and $\mathrm{Cov}(x_j, u) = 0$, for $j = 1, 2, ..., k$.

Assumption MLR.4′ is weaker than Assumption MLR.4 in the sense that the latter implies the former. One way to characterize the zero conditional mean assumption, $\mathrm{E}(u|x_1, ..., x_k) = 0$, is that *any* function of the explanatory variables is uncorrelated with u. Assumption MLR.4′ requires only that each x_j is uncorrelated with u (and that u has a zero mean in the population). In Chapter 2 we actually motivated the OLS estimator for simple regression using Assumption MLR.4′, and the first order conditions for OLS in the multiple regression case, given in equations (3.13), are simply the sample analogs of the population zero correlation assumptions (and zero mean assumption). Therefore, in some ways, Assumption MLR.4′ is more natural an assumption because it leads directly to the OLS estimates. Further, when we think about violations of Assumption MLR.4, we usually think in terms of $\mathrm{Cov}(x_j, u) \neq 0$ for some j. So how come we have used Assumption MLR.4 until now? There are two reasons, both of which we have touched on earlier. First, OLS turns out to be biased (but consistent) under Assumption MLR.4′ if $\mathrm{E}(u|x_1, ..., x_k)$ depends on any of the x_j. Because we have previously focused on finite sample, or exact, sampling properties of the OLS estimators, we have needed the stronger zero conditional mean assumption.

Second, and probably more important, is that the zero conditional mean assumption means that we have properly modeled the population regression function (PRF). That is, under Assumption MLR.4 we can write

$$\mathrm{E}(y|x_1, ..., x_k) = \beta_0 + \beta_1 x_1 + ... + \beta_k x_k,$$

and so we can obtain partial effects of the explanatory variables on the average or expected value of y. If we instead only assume Assumption MLR.4′, $\beta_0 + \beta_1 x_1 + ... + \beta_k x_k$ need not represent the population regression function, and we face the possibility that some nonlinear functions of the x_j, such as x_j^2, could be correlated with the error u. A situation like this means that we have neglected nonlinearities in the model that could help us better explain y; if we knew that, we would usually include such nonlinear functions. In other words, most of the time we hope to get a good estimate of the PRF, and so the zero conditional mean assumption is natural. Nevertheless, the weaker zero correlation assumption turns out to be useful in interpreting OLS estimation of a linear model as providing the best linear approximation to the PRF. It is also used in more advanced settings, such as in Chapter 15, where we have no interest in modeling a PRF. For further discussion of this somewhat subtle point, see Wooldridge (2010, Chapter 4).

Deriving the Inconsistency in OLS

Just as failure of $E(u|x_1, ..., x_k) = 0$ causes bias in the OLS estimators, correlation between u and *any* of $x_1, x_2, ..., x_k$ generally causes *all* of the OLS estimators to be inconsistent. This simple but important observation is often summarized as: *if the error is correlated with any of the independent variables, then OLS is biased and inconsistent.* This is very unfortunate because it means that any bias persists as the sample size grows.

In the simple regression case, we can obtain the inconsistency from the first part of equation (5.3), which holds whether or not u and x_1 are uncorrelated. The **inconsistency** in $\hat{\beta}_1$ (sometimes loosely called the **asymptotic bias**) is

$$\text{plim}\,\hat{\beta}_1 - \beta_1 = \text{Cov}(x_1, u)/\text{Var}(x_1). \qquad [5.4]$$

Because $\text{Var}(x_1) > 0$, the inconsistency in $\hat{\beta}_1$ is positive if x_1 and u are positively correlated, and the inconsistency is negative if x_1 and u are negatively correlated. If the covariance between x_1 and u is small relative to the variance in x_1, the inconsistency can be negligible; unfortunately, we cannot even estimate how big the covariance is because u is unobserved.

We can use (5.4) to derive the asymptotic analog of the omitted variable bias (see Table 3.2 in Chapter 3). Suppose the true model,

$$y = \beta_0 + \beta_1 x_1 + \beta_2 x_2 + v,$$

satisfies the first four Gauss-Markov assumptions. Then v has a zero mean and is uncorrelated with x_1 and x_2. If $\hat{\beta}_0$, $\hat{\beta}_1$, and $\hat{\beta}_2$ denote the OLS estimators from the regression of y on x_1 and x_2, then Theorem 5.1 implies that these estimators are consistent. If we omit x_2 from the regression and do the simple regression of y on x_1, then $u = \beta_2 x_2 + v$. Let $\tilde{\beta}_1$ denote the simple regression slope estimator. Then

$$\text{plim}\,\tilde{\beta}_1 = \beta_1 + \beta_2 \delta_1, \qquad [5.5]$$

where

$$\delta_1 = \text{Cov}(x_1, x_2)/\text{Var}(x_1). \qquad [5.6]$$

Thus, for practical purposes, we can view the inconsistency as being the same as the bias. The difference is that the inconsistency is expressed in terms of the population variance of x_1 and the population covariance between x_1 and x_2, while the bias is based on their sample counterparts (because we condition on the values of x_1 and x_2 in the sample).

If x_1 and x_2 are uncorrelated (in the population), then $\delta_1 = 0$, and $\tilde{\beta}_1$ is a consistent estimator of β_1 (although not necessarily unbiased). If x_2 has a positive partial effect on y, so that $\beta_2 > 0$, and x_1 and x_2 are positively correlated, so that $\delta_1 > 0$, then the inconsistency in $\tilde{\beta}_1$ is positive. And so on. We can obtain the direction of the inconsistency or asymptotic bias from Table 3.2. If the covariance between x_1 and x_2 is small relative to the variance of x_1, the inconsistency can be small.

EXAMPLE 5.1

HOUSING PRICES AND DISTANCE FROM AN INCINERATOR

Let y denote the price of a house (*price*), let x_1 denote the distance from the house to a new trash incinerator (*distance*), and let x_2 denote the "quality" of the house (*quality*). The variable *quality* is left vague so that it can include things like size of the house and lot, number of bedrooms and bathrooms, and intangibles such as attractiveness of the neighborhood. If the incinerator depresses house prices, then β_1 should be positive: everything else being equal, a house that is farther away from the incinerator is worth more. By definition, β_2 is positive since higher quality houses sell for more, other factors being equal. If the incinerator was built farther away, on average, from better homes, then *distance* and *quality* are positively correlated, and so $\delta_1 > 0$. A simple regression of *price* on *distance* [or log(*price*) on log(*distance*)] will tend to overestimate the effect of the incinerator: $\beta_1 + \beta_2\delta_1 > \beta_1$.

EXPLORING FURTHER 5.1

Suppose that the model

$$score = \beta_0 + \beta_1 skipped + \beta_2 priGPA + u$$

satisfies the first four Gauss-Markov assumptions, where *score* is score on a final exam, *skipped* is number of classes skipped, and *priGPA* is GPA prior to the current semester. If $\tilde{\beta}_1$ is from the simple regression of *score* on *skipped*, what is the direction of the asymptotic bias in $\tilde{\beta}_1$?

An important point about inconsistency in OLS estimators is that, by definition, the problem does not go away by adding more observations to the sample. If anything, the problem gets worse with more data: the OLS estimator gets closer and closer to $\beta_1 + \beta_2\delta_1$ as the sample size grows.

Deriving the sign and magnitude of the inconsistency in the general k regressor case is harder, just as deriving the bias is more difficult. We need to remember that if we have the model in equation (5.1) where, say, x_1 is correlated with u but the other independent variables are uncorrelated with u, *all* of the OLS estimators are generally inconsistent. For example, in the $k = 2$ case,

$$y = \beta_0 + \beta_1 x_1 + \beta_2 x_2 + u,$$

suppose that x_2 and u are uncorrelated but x_1 and u are correlated. Then the OLS estimators $\hat{\beta}_1$ and $\hat{\beta}_2$ will generally both be inconsistent. (The intercept will also be inconsistent.) The inconsistency in $\hat{\beta}_2$ arises when x_1 and x_2 are correlated, as is usually the case. If x_1 and x_2 are uncorrelated, then any correlation between x_1 and u does *not* result in the inconsistency of $\hat{\beta}_2$: $\text{plim}\,\hat{\beta}_2 = \beta_2$. Further, the inconsistency in $\hat{\beta}_1$ is the same as in (5.4). The same statement holds in the general case: if x_1 is correlated with u, but x_1 and u are uncorrelated with the other independent variables, then only $\hat{\beta}_1$ is inconsistent, and the inconsistency is given by (5.4). The general case is very similar to the omitted variable case in Section 3A.4 of Appendix 3A.

5.2 Asymptotic Normality and Large Sample Inference

Consistency of an estimator is an important property, but it alone does not allow us to perform statistical inference. Simply knowing that the estimator is getting closer to the population value as the sample size grows does not allow us to test hypotheses about the parameters. For testing, we need the sampling distribution of the OLS estimators. Under the classical linear model assumptions MLR.1 through MLR.6, Theorem 4.1 shows that the sampling distributions are normal. This result is the basis for deriving the t and F distributions that we use so often in applied econometrics.

The exact normality of the OLS estimators hinges crucially on the normality of the distribution of the error, u, in the population. If the errors $u_1, u_2, ..., u_n$ are random draws from some distribution other than the normal, the $\hat{\beta}_j$ will not be normally distributed, which means that the t statistics will not have t distributions and the F statistics will not have F distributions. This is a potentially serious problem because our inference hinges on being able to obtain critical values or p-values from the t or F distributions.

Recall that Assumption MLR.6 is equivalent to saying that the distribution of y given $x_1, x_2, ..., x_k$ is normal. Because y is observed and u is not, in a particular application, it is much easier to think about whether the distribution of y is likely to be normal. In fact, we have already seen a few examples where y definitely cannot have a conditional normal distribution. A normally distributed random variable is symmetrically distributed about its mean, it can take on any positive or negative value (but with zero probability), and more than 95% of the area under the distribution is within two standard deviations.

In Example 3.5, we estimated a model explaining the number of arrests of young men during a particular year (*narr86*). In the population, most men are not arrested during the year, and the vast majority are arrested one time at the most. (In the sample of 2,725 men in the data set CRIME1.RAW, fewer than 8% were arrested more than once during 1986.) Because *narr86* takes on only two values for 92% of the sample, it cannot be close to being normally distributed in the population.

In Example 4.6, we estimated a model explaining participation percentages (*prate*) in 401(k) pension plans. The frequency distribution (also called a *histogram*) in Figure 5.2 shows

FIGURE 5.2 Histogram of *prate* using the data in 401K.RAW.

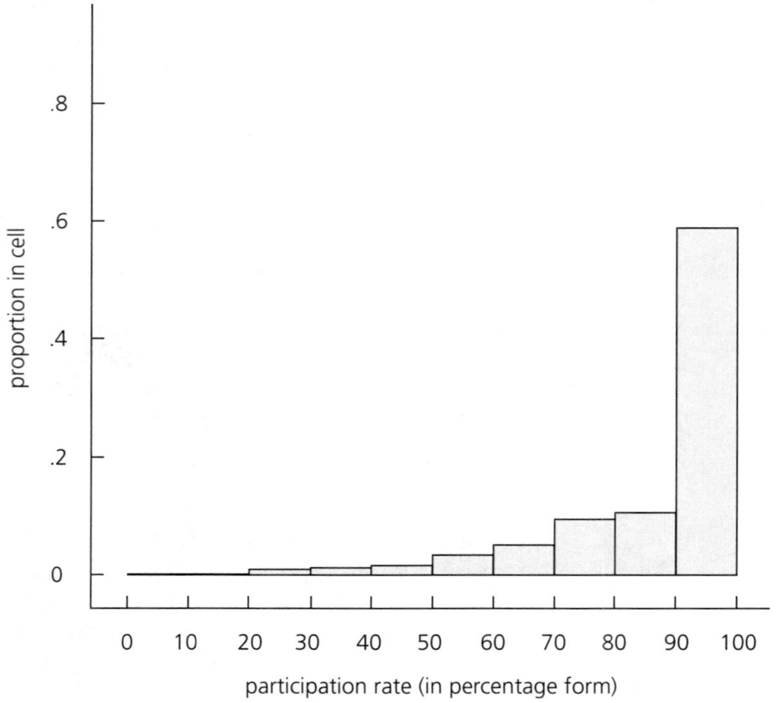

that the distribution of *prate* is heavily skewed to the right, rather than being normally distributed. In fact, over 40% of the observations on *prate* are at the value 100, indicating 100% participation. This violates the normality assumption even conditional on the explanatory variables.

We know that normality plays no role in the unbiasedness of OLS, nor does it affect the conclusion that OLS is the best linear unbiased estimator under the Gauss-Markov assumptions. But exact inference based on t and F statistics requires MLR.6. Does this mean that, in our analysis of *prate* in Example 4.6, we must abandon the t statistics for determining which variables are statistically significant? Fortunately, the answer to this question is *no*. Even though the y_i are not from a normal distribution, we can use the central limit theorem from Appendix C to conclude that the OLS estimators satisfy **asymptotic normality**, which means they are approximately normally distributed in large enough sample sizes.

THEOREM 5.2

ASYMPTOTIC NORMALITY OF OLS

Under the Gauss-Markov Assumptions MLR.1 through MLR.5,

(i) $\sqrt{n}(\hat{\beta}_j - \beta_j) \stackrel{a}{\sim} \text{Normal}(0, \sigma^2/a_j^2)$, where $\sigma^2/a_j^2 > 0$ is the **asymptotic variance** of $\sqrt{n}(\hat{\beta}_j - \beta_j)$; for the slope coefficients, $a_j^2 = \text{plim}\left(n^{-1}\sum_{i=1}^{n}\hat{r}_{ij}^2\right)$, where the $\hat{r}_{ij}$ are the residuals from regressing x_j on the other independent variables. We say that $\hat{\beta}_j$ is *asymptotically normally distributed* (see Appendix C);

(ii) $\hat{\sigma}^2$ is a consistent estimator of $\sigma^2 = \text{Var}(u)$;

(iii) For each j,

$$(\hat{\beta}_j - \beta_j)/\text{sd}(\hat{\beta}_j) \stackrel{a}{\sim} \text{Normal}(0,1)$$

and

$$(\hat{\beta}_j - \beta_j)/\text{se}(\hat{\beta}_j) \stackrel{a}{\sim} \text{Normal}(0,1), \qquad [5.7]$$

where $\text{se}(\hat{\beta}_j)$ is the usual OLS standard error.

The proof of asymptotic normality is somewhat complicated and is sketched in the appendix for the simple regression case. Part (ii) follows from the law of large numbers, and part (iii) follows from parts (i) and (ii) and the asymptotic properties discussed in Appendix C.

Theorem 5.2 is useful because the normality assumption MLR.6 has been dropped; the only restriction on the distribution of the error is that it has finite variance, something we will always assume. We have also assumed zero conditional mean (MLR.4) and homoskedasticity of u (MLR.5).

In trying to understand the meaning of Theorem 5.2, it is important to keep separate the notions of the population distribution of the error term, u, and the sampling distributions of the $\hat{\beta}_j$ as the sample size grows. A common mistake is to think that something is happening to the distribution of u—namely, that it is getting "closer" to normal—as the sample size grows. But remember that the population distribution is immutable and has nothing to do with the sample size. For example, we previously discussed *narr*86, the number of times a young man is arrested during the year 1986. The nature of this variable—it takes on small, nonnegative integer values—is fixed in the population. Whether we sample 10 men or 1,000 men from this population obviously has no effect on the population distribution.

What Theorem 5.2 says is that, regardless of the population distribution of u, the OLS estimators, when properly standardized, have approximate standard normal distributions. This approximation comes about by the central limit theorem because the OLS estimators involve—in a complicated way—the use of sample averages. Effectively, the sequence of distributions of averages of the underlying errors is approaching normality for virtually any population distribution.

Notice how the standardized $\hat{\beta}_j$ has an asymptotic standard normal distribution whether we divide the difference $\hat{\beta}_j - \beta_j$ by sd $(\hat{\beta}_j)$ (which we do not observe because it depends on σ) or by se$(\hat{\beta}_j)$ (which we can compute from our data because it depends on $\hat{\sigma}$). In other words, from an asymptotic point of view it does not matter that we have to replace σ with $\hat{\sigma}$. Of course, replacing σ with $\hat{\sigma}$ affects the exact distribution of the standardized $\hat{\beta}_j$. We just saw in Chapter 4 that under the classical linear model assumptions, $(\hat{\beta}_j - \beta_j)/\text{sd}(\hat{\beta}_j)$ has an exact Normal(0,1) distribution and $(\hat{\beta}_j - \beta_j)/\text{se}(\hat{\beta}_j)$ has an exact t_{n-k-1} distribution.

How should we use the result in equaton (5.7)? It may seem one consequence is that, if we are going to appeal to large-sample analysis, we should now use the standard normal distribution for inference rather than the t distribution. But from a practical perspective it is just as legitimate to write

$$(\hat{\beta}_j - \beta_j)/\text{se}(\hat{\beta}_j) \overset{a}{\sim} t_{n-k-1} = t_{df}, \qquad [5.8]$$

because t_{df} approaches the Normal(0,1), distribution as df gets large. Because we know under the CLM the t_{n-k-1} holds exactly, it makes sense to treat $(\hat{\beta}_j - \beta_j)/\text{se}(\hat{\beta}_j)$ as a t_{n-k-1} random variable generally, even when MLR.6 does not hold.

Equation (5.8) tells us that t testing and the construction of confidence intervals are carried out *exactly* as under the classical linear model assumptions. This means that our analysis of dependent variables like *prate* and *narr86* does not have to change at all if the Gauss-Markov assumptions hold: in both cases, we have at least 1,500 observations, which is certainly enough to justify the approximation of the central limit theorem.

If the sample size is not very large, then the t distribution can be a poor approximation to the distribution of the t statistics when u is not normally distributed. Unfortunately, there are no general prescriptions on how big the sample size must be before the approximation is good enough. Some econometricians think that $n = 30$ is satisfactory, but this cannot be sufficient for all possible distributions of u. Depending on the distribution of u, more observations may be necessary before the central limit theorem delivers a useful approximation. Further, the quality of the approximation depends not just on n, but on the df, $n - k - 1$: With more independent variables in the model, a larger sample size is usually needed to use the t approximation. Methods for inference with small degrees of freedom and nonnormal errors are outside the scope of this text. We will simply use the t statistics as we always have without worrying about the normality assumption.

It is very important to see that Theorem 5.2 *does* require the homoskedasticity assumption (along with the zero conditional mean assumption). If $\text{Var}(y|\mathbf{x})$ is not constant, the usual t statistics and confidence intervals are invalid no matter how large the sample size is; the central limit theorem does not bail us out when it comes to heteroskedasticity. For this reason, we devote all of Chapter 8 to discussing what can be done in the presence of heteroskedasticity.

One conclusion of Theorem 5.2 is that $\hat{\sigma}^2$ is a consistent estimator of σ^2; we already know from Theorem 3.3 that $\hat{\sigma}^2$ is unbiased for σ^2 under the Gauss-Markov assumptions. The consistency implies that $\hat{\sigma}$ is a consistent estimator of σ, which is important in establishing the asymptotic normality result in equation (5.7).

Remember that $\hat{\sigma}$ appears in the standard error for each $\hat{\beta}_j$. In fact, the estimated variance of $\hat{\beta}_j$ is

$$\widehat{\mathrm{Var}(\hat{\beta}_j)} = \frac{\hat{\sigma}^2}{\mathrm{SST}_j(1 - R_j^2)}, \quad [5.9]$$

where SST_j is the total sum of squares of x_j in the sample, and R_j^2 is the R-squared from regressing x_j on all of the other independent variables. In Section 3.4, we studied each component of (5.9), which we will now expound on in the context of asymptotic analysis. As the sample size grows, $\hat{\sigma}^2$ converges in probability to the constant σ^2. Further, R_j^2 approaches a number strictly between zero and unity (so that $1 - R_j^2$ converges to some number between zero and one). The sample variance of x_j is SST_j/n, and so SST_j/n converges to $\mathrm{Var}(x_j)$ as the sample size grows. This means that SST_j grows at approximately the same rate as the sample size: $\mathrm{SST}_j \approx n\sigma_j^2$, where σ_j^2 is the population variance of x_j. When we combine these facts, we find that $\widehat{\mathrm{Var}(\hat{\beta}_j)}$ shrinks to zero at the rate of $1/n$; this is why larger sample sizes are better.

EXPLORING FURTHER 5.2

In a regression model with a large sample size, what is an approximate 95% confidence interval for $\hat{\beta}_j$ under MLR.1 through MLR.5? We call this an **asymptotic confidence interval**.

When u is not normally distributed, the square root of (5.9) is sometimes called the **asymptotic standard error**, and t statistics are called **asymptotic t statistics**. Because these are the same quantities we dealt with in Chapter 4, we will just call them standard errors and t statistics, with the understanding that sometimes they have only large-sample justification. A similar comment holds for an **asymptotic confidence interval** constructed from the asymptotic standard error.

Using the preceding argument about the estimated variance, we can write

$$\mathrm{se}(\hat{\beta}_j) \approx c_j/\sqrt{n}, \quad [5.10]$$

where c_j is a positive constant that does *not* depend on the sample size. In fact, the constant c_j can be shown to be

$$c_j = \frac{\sigma}{\sigma_j\sqrt{1-\rho_j^2}}$$

where $\sigma = \mathrm{sd}(u)$, $\sigma_j = \mathrm{sd}(x_j)$, and ρ_j^2 is the population R-squared from regressing x_j on the other explanatory variables. Just like studying equation (5.9) to see which variables affect $\mathrm{Var}(\hat{\beta}_j)$ under the Gauss-Markov assumptions, we can use this expression for c_j to study the impact of larger error standard deviation (σ), more population variation in x_j (σ_j), and multicollinearity in the population (ρ_j^2).

Equation (5.10) is only an approximation, but it is a useful rule of thumb: standard errors can be expected to shrink at a rate that is the inverse of the *square root* of the sample size.

EXAMPLE 5.2 STANDARD ERRORS IN A BIRTH WEIGHT EQUATION

We use the data in BWGHT.RAW to estimate a relationship where log of birth weight is the dependent variable, and cigarettes smoked per day (*cigs*) and log of family income are independent variables. The total number of observations is 1,388. Using the first half of the observations (694), the standard error for $\hat{\beta}_{cigs}$ is about .0013. The standard error using all of the observations is about .00086. The ratio of the latter standard error to the former is .00086/.0013 $\approx$ .662. This is pretty close to $\sqrt{694/1,388} \approx .707$, the ratio obtained from the approximation in (5.10). In other words, equation (5.10) implies that the standard error using the larger sample size should be about 70.7% of the standard error using the smaller sample. This percentage is pretty close to the 66.2% we actually compute from the ratio of the standard errors.

The asymptotic normality of the OLS estimators also implies that the F statistics have approximate F distributions in large sample sizes. Thus, for testing exclusion restrictions or other multiple hypotheses, nothing changes from what we have done before.

Other Large Sample Tests: The Lagrange Multiplier Statistic

Once we enter the realm of asymptotic analysis, other test statistics can be used for hypothesis testing. For most purposes, there is little reason to go beyond the usual t and F statistics: as we just saw, these statistics have large sample justification without the normality assumption. Nevertheless, sometimes it is useful to have other ways to test multiple exclusion restrictions, and we now cover the **Lagrange multiplier (*LM*) statistic**, which has achieved some popularity in modern econometrics.

The name "Lagrange multiplier statistic" comes from constrained optimization, a topic beyond the scope of this text. [See Davidson and MacKinnon (1993).] The name **score statistic**—which also comes from optimization using calculus—is used as well. Fortunately, in the linear regression framework, it is simple to motivate the *LM* statistic without delving into complicated mathematics.

The form of the *LM* statistic we derive here relies on the Gauss-Markov assumptions, the same assumptions that justify the F statistic in large samples. We do not need the normality assumption.

To derive the *LM* statistic, consider the usual multiple regression model with k independent variables:

$$y = \beta_0 + \beta_1 x_1 + \ldots + \beta_k x_k + u. \qquad [5.11]$$

We would like to test whether, say, the last q of these variables all have zero population parameters: the null hypothesis is

$$\text{H}_0\text{: } \beta_{k-q+1} = 0, \ldots, \beta_k = 0, \qquad [5.12]$$

which puts q exclusion restrictions on the model (5.11). As with F testing, the alternative to (5.12) is that at least one of the parameters is different from zero.

The *LM* statistic requires estimation of the *restricted* model only. Thus, assume that we have run the regression

$$y = \tilde{\beta}_0 + \tilde{\beta}_1 x_1 + ... + \tilde{\beta}_{k-q} x_{k-q} + \tilde{u}, \quad [5.13]$$

where "~" indicates that the estimates are from the restricted model. In particular, $\tilde{u}$ indicates the residuals from the restricted model. (As always, this is just shorthand to indicate that we obtain the restricted residual for each observation in the sample.)

If the omitted variables x_{k-q+1} through x_k truly have zero population coefficients, then, at least approximately, $\tilde{u}$ should be uncorrelated with each of these variables in the sample. This suggests running a regression of these residuals on those independent variables excluded under H_0, which is almost what the *LM* test does. However, it turns out that, to get a usable test statistic, we must include *all* of the independent variables in the regression. (We must include all regressors because, in general, the omitted regressors in the restricted model are correlated with the regressors that appear in the restricted model.) Thus, we run the regression of

$$\tilde{u} \text{ on } x_1, x_2, ..., x_k. \quad [5.14]$$

This is an example of an **auxiliary regression**, a regression that is used to compute a test statistic but whose coefficients are not of direct interest.

How can we use the regression output from (5.14) to test (5.12)? If (5.12) is true, the *R*-squared from (5.14) should be "close" to zero, subject to sampling error, because $\tilde{u}$ will be approximately uncorrelated with all the independent variables. The question, as always with hypothesis testing, is how to determine when the statistic is large enough to reject the null hypothesis at a chosen significance level. It turns out that, under the null hypothesis, the sample size multiplied by the usual *R*-squared from the auxiliary regression (5.14) is distributed asymptotically as a chi-square random variable with q degrees of freedom. This leads to a simple procedure for testing the joint significance of a set of q independent variables.

The Lagrange Multiplier Statistic for q Exclusion Restrictions:

(i) Regress y on the *restricted* set of independent variables and save the residuals, $\tilde{u}$.

(ii) Regress $\tilde{u}$ on *all* of the independent variables and obtain the *R*-squared, say, R_u^2 (to distinguish it from the *R*-squareds obtained with y as the dependent variable).

(iii) Compute $LM = nR_u^2$ [the sample size times the *R*-squared obtained from step (ii)].

(iv) Compare *LM* to the appropriate critical value, c, in a χ_q^2 distribution; if $LM > c$, the null hypothesis is rejected. Even better, obtain the p-value as the probability that a χ_q^2 random variable exceeds the value of the test statistic. If the p-value is less than the desired significance level, then H_0 is rejected. If not, we fail to reject H_0. The rejection rule is essentially the same as for *F* testing.

Because of its form, the *LM* statistic is sometimes referred to as the ***n-R*-squared statistic**. Unlike with the *F* statistic, the degrees of freedom in the unrestricted model plays no role in carrying out the *LM* test. All that matters is the number of restrictions being tested (q), the size of the auxiliary *R*-squared (R_u^2), and the sample size (n). The *df* in the unrestricted model plays no role because of the asymptotic nature of the *LM* statistic. But we must be sure to multiply R_u^2 by the sample size to obtain *LM*; a seemingly low value of the *R*-squared can still lead to joint significance if n is large.

Before giving an example, a word of caution is in order. If in step (i), we mistakenly regress y on all of the independent variables and obtain the residuals from this unrestricted regression to be used in step (ii), we do not get an interesting statistic: the resulting R-squared will be exactly zero! This is because OLS chooses the estimates so that the residuals are uncorrelated in samples with all included independent variables [see equations in (3.13)]. Thus, we can only test (5.12) by regressing the restricted residuals on *all* of the independent variables. (Regressing the restricted residuals on the restricted set of independent variables will also produce $R^2 = 0$.)

EXAMPLE 5.3 ECONOMIC MODEL OF CRIME

We illustrate the *LM* test by using a slight extension of the crime model from Example 3.5:

$$narr86 = \beta_0 + \beta_1 pcnv + \beta_2 avgsen + \beta_3 tottime + \beta_4 ptime86 + \beta_5 qemp86 + u,$$

where

narr86 = the number of times a man was arrested.
pcnv = the proportion of prior arrests leading to conviction.
avgsen = average sentence served from past convictions.
tottime = total time the man has spent in prison prior to 1986 since reaching the age of 18.
ptime86 = months spent in prison in 1986.
qemp86 = number of quarters in 1986 during which the man was legally employed.

We use the *LM* statistic to test the null hypothesis that *avgsen* and *tottime* have no effect on *narr86* once the other factors have been controlled for.

In step (i), we estimate the restricted model by regressing *narr86* on *pcnv*, *ptime86*, and *qemp86*; the variables *avgsen* and *tottime* are excluded from this regression. We obtain the residuals $\tilde{u}$ from this regression, 2,725 of them. Next, we run the regression of

$$\tilde{u} \text{ on } pcnv, ptime86, qemp86, avgsen, \text{ and } tottime; \quad [5.15]$$

as always, the order in which we list the independent variables is irrelevant. This second regression produces R_u^2, which turns out to be about .0015. This may seem small, but we must multiply it by n to get the *LM* statistic: $LM = 2{,}725(.0015) \approx 4.09$. The 10% critical value in a chi-square distribution with two degrees of freedom is about 4.61 (rounded to two decimal places; see Table G.4). Thus, we fail to reject the null hypothesis that $\beta_{avgsen} = 0$ and $\beta_{tottime} = 0$ at the 10% level. The p-value is $P(\chi_2^2 > 4.09) \approx .129$, so we would reject H_0 at the 15% level.

As a comparison, the F test for joint significance of *avgsen* and *tottime* yields a p-value of about .131, which is pretty close to that obtained using the *LM* statistic. This is not surprising since, asymptotically, the two statistics have the same probability of Type I error. (That is, they reject the null hypothesis with the same frequency when the null is true.)

As the previous example suggests, with a large sample, we rarely see important discrepancies between the outcomes of *LM* and F tests. We will use the F statistic for the most part because it is computed routinely by most regression packages. But you should be aware of the *LM* statistic as it is used in applied work.

One final comment on the *LM* statistic. As with the *F* statistic, we must be sure to use the same observations in steps (i) and (ii). If data are missing for some of the independent variables that are excluded under the null hypothesis, the residuals from step (i) should be obtained from a regression on the reduced data set.

5.3 Asymptotic Efficiency of OLS

We know that, under the Gauss-Markov assumptions, the OLS estimators are best linear unbiased. OLS is also **asymptotically efficient** among a certain class of estimators under the Gauss-Markov assumptions. A general treatment requires matrix algebra and advanced asymptotic analysis. First, we describe the result in the simple regression case.

In the model

$$y = \beta_0 + \beta_1 x + u, \qquad [5.16]$$

u has a zero conditional mean under MLR.4: $\mathrm{E}(u|x) = 0$. This opens up a variety of consistent estimators for β_0 and β_1; as usual, we focus on the slope parameter, β_1. Let $g(x)$ be any function of x; for example, $g(x) = x^2$ or $g(x) = 1/(1 + |x|)$. Then u is uncorrelated with $g(x)$ (see Property CE.5 in Appendix B). Let $z_i = g(x_i)$ for all observations i. Then the estimator

$$\tilde{\beta}_1 = \left(\sum_{i=1}^{n} (z_i - \bar{z})y_i\right) \Big/ \left(\sum_{i=1}^{n} (z_i - \bar{z})x_i\right) \qquad [5.17]$$

is consistent for β_1, provided $g(x)$ and x are correlated. [Remember, it is possible that $g(x)$ and x are uncorrelated because correlation measures *linear* dependence.] To see this, we can plug in $y_i = \beta_0 + \beta_1 x_i + u_i$ and write $\tilde{\beta}_1$ as

$$\tilde{\beta}_1 = \beta_1 + \left(n^{-1}\sum_{i=1}^{n} (z_i - \bar{z})u_i\right) \Big/ \left(n^{-1}\sum_{i=1}^{n} (z_i - \bar{z})x_i\right). \qquad [5.18]$$

Now, we can apply the law of large numbers to the numerator and denominator, which converge in probability to $\mathrm{Cov}(z,u)$ and $\mathrm{Cov}(z,x)$, respectively. Provided that $\mathrm{Cov}(z,x) \neq 0$—so that z and x are correlated—we have

$$\mathrm{plim}\ \tilde{\beta}_1 = \beta_1 + \mathrm{Cov}(z,u)/\mathrm{Cov}(z,x) = \beta_1,$$

because $\mathrm{Cov}(z,u) = 0$ under MLR.4.

It is more difficult to show that $\tilde{\beta}_1$ is asymptotically normal. Nevertheless, using arguments similar to those in the appendix, it can be shown that $\sqrt{n}(\tilde{\beta}_1 - \beta_1)$ is asymptotically normal with mean zero and asymptotic variance $\sigma^2\mathrm{Var}(z)/[\mathrm{Cov}(z,x)]^2$. The asymptotic variance of the OLS estimator is obtained when $z = x$, in which case, $\mathrm{Cov}(z,x) = \mathrm{Cov}(x,x) = \mathrm{Var}(x)$. Therefore, the asymptotic variance of $\sqrt{n}(\hat{\beta}_1 - \beta_1)$, where $\hat{\beta}_1$ is the OLS estimator, is $\sigma^2\mathrm{Var}(x)/[\mathrm{Var}(x)]^2 = \sigma^2/\mathrm{Var}(x)$. Now, the Cauchy-Schwartz inequality (see Appendix B.4) implies that $[\mathrm{Cov}(z,x)]^2 \leq \mathrm{Var}(z)\mathrm{Var}(x)$, which implies that the asymptotic variance of $\sqrt{n}(\hat{\beta}_1 - \beta_1)$ is no larger than that of $\sqrt{n}(\tilde{\beta}_1 - \beta_1)$. We have shown in the simple regression case that, under the Gauss-Markov assumptions, the OLS estimator has a smaller asymptotic variance than any estimator of the form (5.17). [The estimator in (5.17) is an example of an *instrumental variables estimator*, which we will study extensively in Chapter 15.] If the homoskedasticity assumption fails, then there are estimators of the form (5.17) that have a smaller asymptotic variance than OLS. We will see this in Chapter 8.

The general case is similar but much more difficult mathematically. In the k regressor case, the class of consistent estimators is obtained by generalizing the OLS first order conditions:

$$\sum_{i=1}^{n} g_j(\boldsymbol{x}_i)(y_i - \tilde{\beta}_0 - \tilde{\beta}_1 x_{i1} - \ldots - \tilde{\beta}_k x_{ik}) = 0, j = 0, 1, \ldots, k, \qquad [5.19]$$

where $g_j(\boldsymbol{x}_i)$ denotes any function of all explanatory variables for observation i. As can be seen by comparing (5.19) with the OLS first order conditions in (3.13), we obtain the OLS estimators when $g_0(\boldsymbol{x}_i) = 1$ and $g_j(\boldsymbol{x}_i) = x_{ij}$ for $j = 1, 2, \ldots, k$. The class of estimators in (5.19) is infinite, because we can use any functions of the x_{ij} that we want.

THEOREM 5.3

ASYMPTOTIC EFFICIENCY OF OLS

Under the Gauss-Markov assumptions, let $\tilde{\beta}_j$ denote estimators that solve equations of the form (5.19) and let $\hat{\beta}_j$ denote the OLS estimators. Then for $j = 0, 1, 2, \ldots, k$, the OLS estimators have the smallest asymptotic variances: $\text{Avar}\ \sqrt{n}(\hat{\beta}_j - \beta_j) \leq \text{Avar}\ \sqrt{n}(\tilde{\beta}_j - \beta_j)$.

Proving consistency of the estimators in (5.19), let alone showing they are asymptotically normal, is mathematically difficult. See Wooldridge (2010, Chapter 5).

Summary

The claims underlying the material in this chapter are fairly technical, but their practical implications are straightforward. We have shown that the first four Gauss-Markov assumptions imply that OLS is consistent. Furthermore, all of the methods of testing and constructing confidence intervals that we learned in Chapter 4 are approximately valid without assuming that the errors are drawn from a normal distribution (equivalently, the distribution of y given the explanatory variables is not normal). This means that we can apply OLS and use previous methods for an array of applications where the dependent variable is not even approximately normally distributed. We also showed that the *LM* statistic can be used instead of the *F* statistic for testing exclusion restrictions.

Before leaving this chapter, we should note that examples such as Example 5.3 may very well have problems that *do* require special attention. For a variable such as *narr86*, which is zero or one for most men in the population, a linear model may not be able to adequately capture the functional relationship between *narr86* and the explanatory variables. Moreover, even if a linear model does describe the expected value of arrests, heteroskedasticity might be a problem. Problems such as these are not mitigated as the sample size grows, and we will return to them in later chapters.

Key Terms

Asymptotic Bias
Asymptotic Confidence Interval
Asymptotic Normality
Asymptotic Properties
Asymptotic Standard Error
Asymptotic t Statistics
Asymptotic Variance
Asymptotically Efficient
Auxiliary Regression
Consistency
Inconsistency
Lagrange Multiplier (*LM*) Statistic
Large Sample Properties
n-R-Squared Statistic
Score Statistic

Problems

1 In the simple regression model under MLR.1 through MLR.4, we argued that the slope estimator, $\hat{\beta}_1$, is consistent for β_1. Using $\hat{\beta}_0 = \bar{y} - \hat{\beta}_1 \bar{x}_1$, show that plim $\hat{\beta}_0 = \beta_0$. [You need to use the consistency of $\hat{\beta}_1$ and the law of large numbers, along with the fact that $\beta_0 = \mathrm{E}(y) = \beta_1 \mathrm{E}(x_1)$.]

2 Suppose that the model

$$pctstck = \beta_0 + \beta_1 funds + \beta_2 risktol + u$$

satisfies the first four Gauss-Markov assumptions, where *pctstck* is the percentage of a worker's pension invested in the stock market, *funds* is the number of mutual funds that the worker can choose from, and *risktol* is some measure of risk tolerance (larger *risktol* means the person has a higher tolerance for risk). If *funds* and *risktol* are positively correlated, what is the inconsistency in $\tilde{\beta}_1$, the slope coefficient in the simple regression of *pctstck* on *funds*?

3 The data set SMOKE.RAW contains information on smoking behavior and other variables for a random sample of single adults from the United States. The variable *cigs* is the (average) number of cigarettes smoked per day. Do you think *cigs* has a normal distribution in the U.S. adult population? Explain.

4 In the simple regression model (5.16), under the first four Gauss-Markov assumptions, we showed that estimators of the form (5.17) are consistent for the slope, β_1. Given such an estimator, define an estimator of β_0 by $\tilde{\beta}_0 = \bar{y} - \tilde{\beta}_1 \bar{x}$. Show that plim $\tilde{\beta}_0 = \beta_0$.

Computer Exercises

C1 Use the data in WAGE1.RAW for this exercise.

(i) Estimate the equation

$$wage = \beta_0 + \beta_1 educ + \beta_2 exper + \beta_3 tenure + u.$$

Save the residuals and plot a histogram.

(ii) Repeat part (i), but with log(*wage*) as the dependent variable.

(iii) Would you say that Assumption MLR.6 is closer to being satisfied for the level-level model or the log-level model?

C2 Use the data in GPA2.RAW for this exercise.

(i) Using all 4,137 observations, estimate the equation

$$colgpa = \beta_0 + \beta_1 hsperc + \beta_2 sat + u$$

and report the results in standard form.

(ii) Reestimate the equation in part (i), using the first 2,070 observations.

(iii) Find the ratio of the standard errors on *hsperc* from parts (i) and (ii). Compare this with the result from (5.10).

C3 In equation (4.42) of Chapter 4, using the data set BWGHT.RAW, compute the *LM* statistic for testing whether *motheduc* and *fatheduc* are jointly significant. In obtaining the residuals for the restricted model, be sure that the restricted model is estimated using only those observations for which all variables in the unrestricted model are available (see Example 4.9).

C4 Several statistics are commonly used to detect nonnormality in underlying population distributions. Here we will study one that measures the amount of skewness in a distribution. Recall that any normally distributed random variable is symmetric about its mean; therefore, if we standardize a symmetrically distributed random variable, say $z = (y - \mu_y)/\sigma_y$, where $\mu_y = \mathrm{E}(y)$ and $\sigma_y = \mathrm{sd}(y)$, then z has mean zero, variance one, and $\mathrm{E}(z^3) = 0$. Given a sample of data $\{y_i : i = 1, ..., n\}$, we can standardize y_i in the sample by using $z_i = (y_i - \hat{\mu}_y)/\hat{\sigma}_y$, where $\hat{\mu}_y$ is the sample mean and $\hat{\sigma}_y$ is the sample standard deviation. (We ignore the fact that these are estimates based on the sample.) A sample statistic that measures skewness is $n^{-1}\sum_{i=1}^{n} z_i^3$, or where n is replaced with $(n - 1)$ as a degrees-of-freedom adjustment. If y has a normal distribution in the population, the skewness measure in the sample for the standardized values should not differ significantly from zero.

(i) First use the data set 401KSUBS.RAW, keeping only observations with $fsize = 1$. Find the skewness measure for *inc*. Do the same for log(*inc*). Which variable has more skewness and therefore seems less likely to be normally distributed?

(ii) Next use BWGHT2.RAW. Find the skewness measures for *bwght* and log(*bwght*). What do you conclude?

(iii) Evaluate the following statement: "The logarithmic transformation always makes a positive variable look more normally distributed."

(iv) If we are interested in the normality assumption in the context of regression, should we be evaluating the unconditional distributions of y and $\log(y)$? Explain.

C5 Consider the analysis in Computer Exercise C11 in Chapter 4 using the data in HTV.RAW, where *educ* is the dependent variable in a regression.

(i) How many different values are taken on by *educ* in the sample? Does *educ* have a continuous distribution?

(ii) Plot a histogram of *educ* with a normal distribution overlay. Does the distribution of *educ* appear anything close to normal?

(iii) Which of the CLM assumptions seems clearly violated in the model

$$educ = \beta_0 + \beta_1 motheduc + \beta_2 fatheduc + \beta_3 abil + \beta_4 abil^2 + u?$$

How does this violation change the statistical inference procedures carried out in Computer Exercise C11 in Chapter 4?

APPENDIX 5A

Asymptotic Normality of OLS

We sketch a proof of the asymptotic normality of OLS [Theorem 5.2(i)] in the simple regression case. Write the simple regression model as in equation (5.16). Then, by the usual algebra of simple regression, we can write

$$\sqrt{n}(\hat{\beta}_1 - \beta_1) = (1/s_x^2)\left[n^{-1/2}\sum_{i=1}^{n}(x_i - \bar{x})u_i\right],$$

where we use s_x^2 to denote the sample variance of $\{x_i: i = 1, 2, ..., n\}$. By the law of large numbers (see Appendix C), $s_x^2 \xrightarrow{p} \sigma_x^2 = \text{Var}(x)$. Assumption MLR.3 rules out no perfect collinearity, which means that $\text{Var}(x) > 0$ (x_i varies in the sample, and therefore x is not constant in the population). Next, $n^{-1/2}\sum_{i=1}^{n}(x_i - \bar{x})u_i = n^{-1/2}\sum_{i=1}^{n}(x_i - \mu)u_i + (\mu - \bar{x})[n^{-1/2}\sum_{i=1}^{n}u_i]$, where $\mu = \text{E}(x)$ is the population mean of x. Now $\{u_i\}$ is a sequence of i.i.d. random variables with mean zero and variance σ^2, and so $n^{-1/2}\sum_{i=1}^{n}u_i$ converges to the Normal$(0,\sigma^2)$ distribution as $n \to \infty$; this is just the central limit theorem from Appendix C. By the law of large numbers, $\text{plim}(\mu - \bar{x}) = 0$. A standard result in asymptotic theory is that if $\text{plim}(w_n) = 0$ and z_n has an asymptotic normal distribution, then $\text{plim}(w_n z_n) = 0$. [See Wooldridge (2010, Chapter 3) for more discussion.] This implies that $(\mu - \bar{x})[n^{-1/2}\sum_{i=1}^{n}u_i]$ has zero plim. Next, $\{(x_i - \mu)u_i: i = 1, 2, ...\}$ is an indefinite sequence of i.i.d. random variables with mean zero—because u and x are uncorrelated under Assumption MLR.4—and variance $\sigma^2\sigma_x^2$ by the homoskedasticity Assumption MLR.5. Therefore, $n^{-1/2}\sum_{i=1}^{n}(x_i - \mu)u_i$ has an asymptotic Normal$(0,\sigma^2\sigma_x^2)$ distribution. We just showed that the difference between $n^{-1/2}\sum_{i=1}^{n}(x_i - \bar{x})u_i$ and $n^{-1/2}\sum_{i=1}^{n}(x_i - \mu)u_i$ has zero plim. A result in asymptotic theory is that if z_n has an asymptotic normal distribution and $\text{plim}(v_n - z_n) = 0$, then v_n has the same asymptotic normal distribution as z_n. It follows that $n^{-1/2}\sum_{i=1}^{n}(x_i - \bar{x})u_i$ also has an asymptotic Normal$(0,\sigma^2\sigma_x^2)$ distribution. Putting all of the pieces together gives

$$\sqrt{n}(\hat{\beta}_1 - \beta_1) = (1/\sigma_x^2)\left[n^{-1/2}\sum_{i=1}^{n}(x_i - \bar{x})u_i\right]$$

$$+ [(1/s_x^2) - (1/\sigma_x^2)]\left[n^{-1/2}\sum_{i=1}^{n}(x_i - \bar{x})u_i\right],$$

and since $\text{plim}(1/s_x^2) = 1/\sigma_x^2$, the second term has zero plim. Therefore, the asymptotic distribution of $\sqrt{n}(\hat{\beta}_1 - \beta_1)$ is Normal$(0,\{\sigma^2\sigma_x^2\}/\{\sigma_x^2\}^2) = $ Normal$(0,\sigma^2/\sigma_x^2)$. This completes the proof in the simple regression case, as $a_1^2 = \sigma_x^2$ in this case. See Wooldridge (2010, Chapter 4) for the general case.

CHAPTER

6

Multiple Regression Analysis: Further Issues

This chapter brings together several issues in multiple regression analysis that we could not conveniently cover in earlier chapters. These topics are not as fundamental as the material in Chapters 3 and 4, but they are important for applying multiple regression to a broad range of empirical problems.

6.1 Effects of Data Scaling on OLS Statistics

In Chapter 2 on bivariate regression, we briefly discussed the effects of changing the units of measurement on the OLS intercept and slope estimates. We also showed that changing the units of measurement did not affect *R*-squared. We now return to the issue of data scaling and examine the effects of rescaling the dependent or independent variables on standard errors, *t* statistics, *F* statistics, and confidence intervals.

We will discover that everything we expect to happen, does happen. When variables are rescaled, the coefficients, standard errors, confidence intervals, *t* statistics, and *F* statistics change in ways that preserve all measured effects and testing outcomes. Although this is no great surprise—in fact, we would be very worried if it were not the case—it is useful to see what occurs explicitly. Often, data scaling is used for cosmetic purposes, such as to reduce the number of zeros after a decimal point in an estimated coefficient. By judiciously choosing units of measurement, we can improve the appearance of an estimated equation while changing nothing that is essential.

We could treat this problem in a general way, but it is much better illustrated with examples. Likewise, there is little value here in introducing an abstract notation.

We begin with an equation relating infant birth weight to cigarette smoking and family income:

$$\widehat{bwght} = \hat{\beta}_0 + \hat{\beta}_1 cigs + \hat{\beta}_2 faminc, \tag{6.1}$$

where

bwght = child birth weight, in ounces.
cigs = number of cigarettes smoked by the mother while pregnant, per day.
faminc = annual family income, in thousands of dollars.

TABLE 6.1 Effects of Data Scaling

Dependent Variable	**(1)** ***bwght***	**(2)** ***bwghtlbs***	**(3)** ***bwght***
Independent Variables			
cigs	−.4634 (.0916)	−.0289 (.0057)	—
packs	—	—	−9.268 (1.832)
faminc	.0927 (.0292)	.0058 (.0018)	.0927 (.0292)
intercept	116.974 (1.049)	7.3109 (.0656)	116.974 (1.049)
Observations	1,388	1,388	1,388
R-Squared	.0298	.0298	.0298
SSR	557,485.51	2,177.6778	557,485.51
SER	20.063	1.2539	20.063

The estimates of this equation, obtained using the data in BWGHT.RAW, are given in the first column of Table 6.1. Standard errors are listed in parentheses. The estimate on *cigs* says that if a woman smoked 5 more cigarettes per day, birth weight is predicted to be about .4634(5) = 2.317 ounces less. The *t* statistic on *cigs* is −5.06, so the variable is very statistically significant.

Now, suppose that we decide to measure birth weight in pounds, rather than in ounces. Let *bwghtlbs* = *bwght*/16 be birth weight in pounds. What happens to our OLS statistics if we use this as the dependent variable in our equation? It is easy to find the effect on the coefficient estimates by simple manipulation of equation (6.1). Divide this entire equation by 16:

$$\widehat{bwght}/16 = \hat{\beta}_0/16 + (\hat{\beta}_1/16)cigs + (\hat{\beta}_2/16)faminc.$$

Since the left-hand side is birth weight in pounds, it follows that each new coefficient will be the corresponding old coefficient divided by 16. To verify this, the regression of *bwghtlbs* on *cigs*, and *faminc* is reported in column (2) of Table 6.1. Up to four digits, the intercept and slopes in column (2) are just those in column (1) divided by 16. For example, the coefficient on *cigs* is now −.0289; this means that if *cigs* were higher by five, birth weight would be .0289(5) = .1445 *pounds* lower. In terms of ounces, we have .1445(16) = 2.312, which is slightly different from the 2.317 we obtained earlier due to rounding error. The point is, once the effects are transformed into the same units, we get exactly the same answer, regardless of how the dependent variable is measured.

What about statistical significance? As we expect, changing the dependent variable from ounces to pounds has no effect on how statistically important the independent variables are. The standard errors in column (2) are 16 times smaller than those in column (1). A few quick calculations show that the *t* statistics in column (2) are indeed identical to the *t* statistics in column (1). The endpoints for the confidence intervals in column (2) are just the endpoints in column (1) divided by 16. This is because the CIs change by the same factor as the standard errors. [Remember that the 95% CI here is $\hat{\beta}_j \pm 1.96\ \text{se}(\hat{\beta}_j)$.]

In terms of goodness-of-fit, the R-squareds from the two regressions are identical, as should be the case. Notice that the sum of squared residuals, SSR, and the standard error of the regression, SER, do differ across equations. These differences are easily explained. Let $\hat{u}_i$ denote the residual for observation i in the original equation (6.1). Then the residual when *bwghtlbs* is the dependent variable is simply $\hat{u}_i/16$. Thus, the *squared* residual in the second equation is $(\hat{u}_i/16)^2 = \hat{u}_i^2/256$. This is why the sum of squared residuals in column (2) is equal to the SSR in column (1) divided by 256.

Since SER $= \hat{\sigma} = \sqrt{\text{SSR}/(n - k - 1)} = \sqrt{\text{SSR}/1{,}385}$, the SER in column (2) is 16 times smaller than that in column (1). Another way to think about this is that the error in the equation with *bwghtlbs* as the dependent variable has a standard deviation 16 times smaller than the standard deviation of the original error. This does not mean that we have reduced the error by changing how birth weight is measured; the smaller SER simply reflects a difference in units of measurement.

Next, let us return the dependent variable to its original units: *bwght* is measured in ounces. Instead, let us change the unit of measurement of one of the independent variables, *cigs*. Define *packs* to be the number of packs of cigarettes smoked per day. Thus, *packs* = *cigs*/20. What happens to the coefficients and other OLS statistics now? Well, we can write

$$\widehat{bwght} = \hat{\beta}_0 + (20\hat{\beta}_1)(cigs/20) + \hat{\beta}_2 faminc = \hat{\beta}_0 + (20\hat{\beta}_1)packs + \hat{\beta}_2 faminc.$$

Thus, the intercept and slope coefficient on *faminc* are unchanged, but the coefficient on *packs* is 20 times that on *cigs*. This is intuitively appealing. The results from the regression of *bwght* on *packs* and *faminc* are in column (3) of Table 6.1. Incidentally, remember that it would make no sense to include both *cigs* and *packs* in the same equation; this would induce perfect multicollinearity and would have no interesting meaning.

Other than the coefficient on *packs*, there is one other statistic in column (3) that differs from that in column (1): the standard error on *packs* is 20 times larger than that on *cigs* in column (1). This means that the t statistic for testing the significance of cigarette smoking is the same whether we measure smoking in terms of cigarettes or packs. This is only natural.

EXPLORING FURTHER 6.1

In the original birth weight equation (6.1), suppose that *faminc* is measured in dollars rather than in thousands of dollars. Thus, define the variable *fincdol* = 1,000·*faminc*. How will the OLS statistics change when *fincdol* is substituted for *faminc*? For the purpose of presenting the regression results, do you think it is better to measure income in dollars or in thousands of dollars?

The previous example spells out most of the possibilities that arise when the dependent and independent variables are rescaled. Rescaling is often done with dollar amounts in economics, especially when the dollar amounts are very large.

In Chapter 2, we argued that, if the dependent variable appears in logarithmic form, changing the unit of measurement does not affect the slope coefficient. The same is true here: changing the unit of measurement of the dependent variable, when it appears in logarithmic form, does not affect any of the slope estimates. This follows from the simple fact that $\log(c_1 y_i) = \log(c_1) + \log(y_i)$ for any constant $c_1 > 0$. The new intercept will be $\log(c_1) + \hat{\beta}_0$. Similarly, changing the unit of measurement of any x_j, where $\log(x_j)$ appears in the regression, only affects the intercept. This corresponds to what we know about percentage changes and, in particular, elasticities: they are invariant to the units of measurement of either y or the x_j. For example, if we had specified the dependent variable in (6.1) to be log(*bwght*), estimated the equation, and then reestimated it with log(*bwghtlbs*) as the dependent variable, the coefficients on *cigs* and *faminc* would be the same in both regressions; only the intercept would be different.

Beta Coefficients

Sometimes, in econometric applications, a key variable is measured on a scale that is difficult to interpret. Labor economists often include test scores in wage equations, and the scale on which these tests are scored is often arbitrary and not easy to interpret (at least for economists!). In almost all cases, we are interested in how a particular individual's score compares with the population. Thus, instead of asking about the effect on hourly wage if, say, a test score is 10 points higher, it makes more sense to ask what happens when the test score is one *standard deviation* higher.

Nothing prevents us from seeing what happens to the dependent variable when an independent variable in an estimated model increases by a certain number of standard deviations, assuming that we have obtained the sample standard deviation (which is easy in most regression packages). This is often a good idea. So, for example, when we look at the effect of a standardized test score, such as the SAT score, on college GPA, we can find the standard deviation of SAT and see what happens when the SAT score increases by one or two standard deviations.

Sometimes, it is useful to obtain regression results when *all* variables involved, the dependent as well as all the independent variables, have been *standardized*. A variable is standardized in the sample by subtracting off its mean and dividing by its standard deviation (see Appendix C). This means that we compute the *z-score* for every variable in the sample. Then, we run a regression using the *z*-scores.

Why is standardization useful? It is easiest to start with the original OLS equation, with the variables in their original forms:

$$y_i = \hat{\beta}_0 + \hat{\beta}_1 x_{i1} + \hat{\beta}_2 x_{i2} + \dots + \hat{\beta}_k x_{ik} + \hat{u}_i. \qquad [6.2]$$

We have included the observation subscript i to emphasize that our standardization is applied to all sample values. Now, if we average (6.2), use the fact that the $\hat{u}_i$ have a zero sample average, and subtract the result from (6.2), we get

$$y_i - \bar{y} = \hat{\beta}_1(x_{i1} - \bar{x}_1) + \hat{\beta}_2(x_{i2} - \bar{x}_2) + \dots + \hat{\beta}_k(x_{ik} - \bar{x}_k) + \hat{u}_i.$$

Now, let $\hat{\sigma}_y$ be the sample standard deviation for the dependent variable, let $\hat{\sigma}_1$ be the sample *sd* for x_1, let $\hat{\sigma}_2$ be the sample *sd* for x_2, and so on. Then, simple algebra gives the equation

$$(y_i - \bar{y})/\hat{\sigma}_y = (\hat{\sigma}_1/\hat{\sigma}_y)\hat{\beta}_1[(x_{i1} - \bar{x}_1)/\hat{\sigma}_1] + \dots$$
$$+ (\hat{\sigma}_k/\hat{\sigma}_y)\hat{\beta}_k[(x_{ik} - \bar{x}_k)/\hat{\sigma}_k] + (\hat{u}_i/\hat{\sigma}_y). \qquad [6.3]$$

Each variable in (6.3) has been standardized by replacing it with its *z*-score, and this has resulted in new slope coefficients. For example, the slope coefficient on $(x_{i1} - \bar{x}_1)/\hat{\sigma}_1$ is $(\hat{\sigma}_1/\hat{\sigma}_y)\hat{\beta}_1$. This is simply the original coefficient, $\hat{\beta}_1$, multiplied by the ratio of the standard deviation of x_1 to the standard deviation of y. The intercept has dropped out altogether.

It is useful to rewrite (6.3), dropping the i subscript, as

$$z_y = \hat{b}_1 z_1 + \hat{b}_2 z_2 + \dots + \hat{b}_k z_k + error, \qquad [6.4]$$

where z_y denotes the z-score of y, z_1 is the z-score of x_1, and so on. The new coefficients are

$$\hat{b}_j = (\hat{\sigma}_j/\hat{\sigma}_y)\hat{\beta}_j \text{ for } j = 1, ..., k. \quad [6.5]$$

These $\hat{b}_j$ are traditionally called **standardized coefficients** or **beta coefficients**. (The latter name is more common, which is unfortunate because we have been using beta hat to denote the *usual* OLS estimates.)

Beta coefficients receive their interesting meaning from equation (6.4): If x_1 increases by one standard deviation, then $\hat{y}$ changes by $\hat{b}_1$ standard deviations. Thus, we are measuring effects not in terms of the original units of y or the x_j, but in standard deviation units. Because it makes the scale of the regressors irrelevant, this equation puts the explanatory variables on equal footing. In a standard OLS equation, it is not possible to simply look at the size of different coefficients and conclude that the explanatory variable with the largest coefficient is "the most important." We just saw that the magnitudes of coefficients can be changed at will by changing the units of measurement of the x_j. But, when each x_j has been standardized, comparing the magnitudes of the resulting beta coefficients is more compelling. When the regression equation has only a single explanatory variable, x_1, its standardized coefficient is simply the sample correlation coefficient between y and x_1, which means it must lie in the range -1 to 1.

Even in situations where the coefficients are easily interpretable—say, the dependent variable and independent variables of interest are in logarithmic form, so the OLS coefficients of interest are estimated elasticities—there is still room for computing beta coefficients. Although elasticities are free of units of measurement, a change in a particular explanatory variable by, say, 10% may represent a larger or smaller change over a variable's range than changing another explanatory variable by 10%. For example, in a state with wide income variation but relatively little variation in spending per student, it might not make much sense to compare performance elasticities with respect to the income and spending. Comparing beta coefficient magnitudes can be helpful.

To obtain the beta coefficients, we can always standardize $y, x_1, \dots, x_k$ and then run the OLS regression of the z-score of y on the z-scores of $x_1, ..., x_k$—where it is not necessary to include an intercept, as it will be zero. This can be tedious with many independent variables. Some regression packages provide beta coefficients via a simple command. The following example illustrates the use of beta coefficients.

EXAMPLE 6.1 EFFECTS OF POLLUTION ON HOUSING PRICES

We use the data from Example 4.5 (in the file HPRICE2.RAW) to illustrate the use of beta coefficients. Recall that the key independent variable is *nox*, a measure of the nitrogen oxide in the air over each community. One way to understand the size of the pollution effect—without getting into the science underlying nitrogen oxide's effect on air quality—is to compute beta coefficients. (An alternative approach is contained in Example 4.5: we obtained a price elasticity with respect to *nox* by using *price* and *nox* in logarithmic form.)

The population equation is the level-level model

$$price = \beta_0 + \beta_1 nox + \beta_2 crime + \beta_3 rooms + \beta_4 dist + \beta_5 stratio + u,$$

where all the variables except *crime* were defined in Example 4.5; *crime* is the number of reported crimes per capita. The beta coefficients are reported in the following equation (so each variable has been converted to its *z*-score):

$$\widehat{zprice} = -.340\ znox - .143\ zcrime + .514\ zrooms - .235\ zdist - .270\ zstratio.$$

This equation shows that a one standard deviation increase in *nox* decreases price by .34 standard deviation; a one standard deviation increase in *crime* reduces price by .14 standard deviation. Thus, the same relative movement of pollution in the population has a larger effect on housing prices than crime does. Size of the house, as measured by number of rooms (*rooms*), has the largest standardized effect. If we want to know the effects of each independent variable on the dollar value of median house price, we should use the unstandardized variables.

Whether we use standardized or unstandardized variables does not affect statistical significance: the *t* statistics are the same in both cases.

6.2 More on Functional Form

In several previous examples, we have encountered the most popular device in econometrics for allowing nonlinear relationships between the explained and explanatory variables: using logarithms for the dependent or independent variables. We have also seen models containing quadratics in some explanatory variables, but we have yet to provide a systematic treatment of them. In this section, we cover some variations and extensions on functional forms that often arise in applied work.

More on Using Logarithmic Functional Forms

We begin by reviewing how to interpret the parameters in the model

$$\log(price) = \beta_0 + \beta_1 \log(nox) + \beta_2 rooms + u, \quad [6.6]$$

where these variables are taken from Example 4.5. Recall that throughout the text log(x) is the *natural* log of x. The coefficient β_1 is the elasticity of *price* with respect to *nox* (pollution). The coefficient β_2 is the change in log(*price*), when $\Delta rooms = 1$; as we have seen many times, when multiplied by 100, this is the approximate percentage change in *price*. Recall that $100 \cdot \beta_2$ is sometimes called the semi-elasticity of *price* with respect to *rooms*.

When estimated using the data in HPRICE2.RAW, we obtain

$$\begin{aligned}\widehat{\log(price)} &= \underset{(0.19)}{9.23} - \underset{(.066)}{.718} \log(nox) + \underset{(.019)}{.306}\ rooms \\ n &= 506,\ R^2 = .514.\end{aligned} \quad [6.7]$$

Thus, when *nox* increases by 1%, *price* falls by .718%, holding only *rooms* fixed. When *rooms* increases by one, *price* increases by approximately 100(.306) = 30.6%.

The estimate that one more room increases price by about 30.6% turns out to be somewhat inaccurate for this application. The approximation error occurs because, as the change in log(y) becomes larger and larger, the approximation $\%\Delta y \approx 100 \cdot \Delta \log(y)$

becomes more and more inaccurate. Fortunately, a simple calculation is available to compute the exact percentage change.

To describe the procedure, we consider the general estimated model

$$\widehat{\log(y)} = \hat{\beta}_0 + \hat{\beta}_1\log(x_1) + \hat{\beta}_2 x_2.$$

(Adding additional independent variables does not change the procedure.) Now, fixing x_1, we have $\Delta\widehat{\log(y)} = \hat{\beta}_2\Delta x_2$. Using simple algebraic properties of the exponential and logarithmic functions gives the *exact* percentage change in the predicted y as

$$\%\Delta\hat{y} = 100\cdot[\exp(\hat{\beta}_2\Delta x_2) - 1], \qquad [6.8]$$

where the multiplication by 100 turns the proportionate change into a percentage change. When $\Delta x_2 = 1$,

$$\%\Delta\hat{y} = 100\cdot[\exp(\hat{\beta}_2) - 1]. \qquad [6.9]$$

Applied to the housing price example with x_2 = rooms and $\hat{\beta}_2 = .306$, $\%\Delta\widehat{price} = 100[\exp(.306) - 1] = 35.8\%$, which is notably larger than the approximate percentage change, 30.6%, obtained directly from (6.7). {Incidentally, this is not an unbiased estimator because $\exp(\cdot)$ is a nonlinear function; it is, however, a consistent estimator of $100[\exp(\beta_2) - 1]$. This is because the probability limit passes through continuous functions, while the expected value operator does not. See Appendix C.}

The adjustment in equation (6.8) is not as crucial for small percentage changes. For example, when we include the student-teacher ratio in equation (6.7), its estimated coefficient is $-.052$, which means that if *stratio* increases by one, *price* decreases by approximately 5.2%. The exact proportionate change is $\exp(-.052) - 1 \approx -.051$, or -5.1%. On the other hand, if we increase *stratio* by five, then the approximate percentage change in price is -26%, while the exact change obtained from equation (6.8) is $100[\exp(-.26) - 1] \approx -22.9\%$.

The logarithmic approximation to percentage changes has an advantage that justifies its reporting even when the percentage change is large. To describe this advantage, consider again the effect on price of changing the number of rooms by one. The logarithmic approximation is just the coefficient on rooms in equation (6.7) multiplied by 100, namely, 30.6%. We also computed an estimate of the exact percentage change for *increasing* the number of rooms by one as 35.8%. But what if we want to estimate the percentage change for *decreasing* the number of rooms by one? In equation (6.8) we take $\Delta x_2 = -1$ and $\hat{\beta}_2 = .306$, and so $\%\Delta\widehat{price} = 100[\exp(-.306) - 1] = -26.4$, or a drop of 26.4%. Notice that the approximation based on using the coefficient on *rooms* is between 26.4 and 35.8—an outcome that always occurs. In other words, simply using the coefficient (multiplied by 100) gives us an estimate that is always between the absolute value of the estimates for an increase and a decrease. If we are specifically interested in an increase or a decrease, we can use the calculation based on equation (6.8).

The point just made about computing percentage changes is essentially the one made in introductory economics when it comes to computing, say, price elasticities of demand based on large price changes: the result depends on whether we use the beginning or ending price and quantity in computing the percentage changes. Using the logarithmic approximation is similar in spirit to calculating an arc elasticity of demand, where the average of prices and quantities is used in the denominators in computing the percentage changes.

We have seen that using natural logs leads to coefficients with appealing interpretations, and we can be ignorant about the units of measurement of variables appearing in logarithmic form because the slope coefficients are invariant to rescalings. There are several other reasons logs are used so much in applied work. First, when $y > 0$, models using $\log(y)$ as the dependent variable often satisfy the CLM assumptions more closely than models using the level of y. Strictly positive variables often have conditional distributions that are heteroskedastic or skewed; taking the log can mitigate, if not eliminate, both problems.

Another potential benefit of using logs is that taking the log of a variable often narrows its range. This is particularly true of variables that can be large monetary values, such as firms' annual sales or baseball players' salaries. Population variables also tend to vary widely. Narrowing the range of the dependent and independent variables can make OLS estimates less sensitive to outlying (or extreme values); we take up the issue of outlying observations in Chapter 9.

However, one must not indiscriminantly use the logarithmic transformation because in some cases it can actually create extreme values. An example is when a variable y is between zero and one (such as a proportion) and takes on values close to zero. In this case, $\log(y)$ (which is necessarily negative) can be very large in magnitude whereas the original variable, y, is bounded between zero and one.

There are some standard rules of thumb for taking logs, although none is written in stone. When a variable is a positive dollar amount, the log is often taken. We have seen this for variables such as wages, salaries, firm sales, and firm market value. Variables such as population, total number of employees, and school enrollment often appear in logarithmic form; these have the common feature of being large integer values.

Variables that are measured in years—such as education, experience, tenure, age, and so on—usually appear in their original form. A variable that is a proportion or a percent—such as the unemployment rate, the participation rate in a pension plan, the percentage of students passing a standardized exam, and the arrest rate on reported crimes—can appear in either original or logarithmic form, although there is a tendency to use them in level forms. This is because any regression coefficients involving the *original* variable—whether it is the dependent or independent variable—will have a *percentage point* change interpretation. (See Appendix A for a review of the distinction between a percentage change and a percentage point change.) If we use, say, log(*unem*) in a regression, where *unem* is the percentage of unemployed individuals, we must be very careful to distinguish between a percentage point change and a percentage change. Remember, if *unem* goes from 8 to 9, this is an increase of one percentage point, but a 12.5% increase from the initial unemployment level. Using the log means that we are looking at the percentage change in the unemployment rate: $\log(9) - \log(8) \approx .118$ or 11.8%, which is the logarithmic approximation to the actual 12.5% increase.

One limitation of the log is that it cannot be used if a variable takes on zero or negative values. In cases where a variable y is nonnegative but can take on the value 0, $\log(1+y)$ is sometimes used. The percentage change interpretations are often closely preserved, except for changes beginning at $y = 0$ (where the percentage change is not even defined). Generally, using $\log(1+y)$ and then interpreting the estimates as if the variable were $\log(y)$ is acceptable when the data on y contain relatively few zeros. An example might be where y is hours of training per employee for the population of manufacturing firms,

EXPLORING FURTHER 6.2

Suppose that the annual number of drunk driving arrests is determined by

$$\log(arrests) = \beta_0 + \beta_1\log(pop) + \beta_2 age16\_25 + \text{other factors},$$

where *age16_25* is the proportion of the population between 16 and 25 years of age. Show that β_2 has the following (ceteris paribus) interpretation: it is the percentage change in *arrests* when the percentage of the people aged 16 to 25 increases by one percentage point.

if a large fraction of firms provides training to at least one worker. Technically, however, $\log(1 + y)$ cannot be normally distributed (although it might be less heteroskedastic than y). Useful, albeit more advanced, alternatives are the Tobit and Poisson models in Chapter 17.

One drawback to using a dependent variable in logarithmic form is that it is more difficult to predict the original variable. The original model allows us to predict $\log(y)$, not y. Nevertheless, it is fairly easy to turn a prediction for $\log(y)$ into a prediction for y (see Section 6.4). A related point is that it is *not* legitimate to compare R-squareds from models where y is the dependent variable in one case and $\log(y)$ is the dependent variable in the other. These measures explain variations in different variables. We discuss how to compute comparable goodness-of-fit measures in Section 6.4.

Models with Quadratics

Quadratic functions are also used quite often in applied economics to capture decreasing or increasing marginal effects. You may want to review properties of quadratic functions in Appendix A.

In the simplest case, y depends on a single observed factor x, but it does so in a quadratic fashion:

$$y = \beta_0 + \beta_1 x + \beta_2 x^2 + u.$$

For example, take $y = wage$ and $x = exper$. As we discussed in Chapter 3, this model falls outside of simple regression analysis but is easily handled with multiple regression.

It is important to remember that β_1 does not measure the change in y with respect to x; it makes no sense to hold x^2 fixed while changing x. If we write the estimated equation as

$$\hat{y} = \hat{\beta}_0 + \hat{\beta}_1 x + \hat{\beta}_2 x^2, \quad [6.10]$$

then we have the approximation

$$\Delta\hat{y} \approx (\hat{\beta}_1 + 2\hat{\beta}_2 x)\Delta x, \text{ so } \Delta\hat{y}/\Delta x \approx \hat{\beta}_1 + 2\hat{\beta}_2 x. \quad [6.11]$$

This says that the slope of the relationship between x and y depends on the value of x; the estimated slope is $\hat{\beta}_1 + 2\hat{\beta}_2 x$. If we plug in $x = 0$, we see that $\hat{\beta}_1$ can be interpreted as the approximate slope in going from $x = 0$ to $x = 1$. After that, the second term, $2\hat{\beta}_2 x$, must be accounted for.

If we are only interested in computing the predicted change in y given a starting value for x and a change in x, we could use (6.10) directly: there is no reason to use the calculus approximation at all. However, we are usually more interested in quickly summarizing the effect of x on y, and the interpretation of $\hat{\beta}_1$ and $\hat{\beta}_2$ in equation (6.11) provides that summary. Typically, we might plug in the average value of x in the sample, or some other interesting values, such as the median or the lower and upper quartile values.

In many applications, $\hat{\beta}_1$ is positive and $\hat{\beta}_2$ is negative. For example, using the wage data in WAGE1.RAW, we obtain

$$\begin{aligned}\widehat{wage} &= \underset{(.35)}{3.73} + \underset{(.041)}{.298}\, exper - \underset{(.0009)}{.0061}\, exper^2 \\ n &= 526, R^2 = .093.\end{aligned} \quad [6.12]$$

This estimated equation implies that *exper* has a diminishing effect on *wage*. The first year of experience is worth roughly 30¢ per hour ($.298). The second year of experience is worth less [about $.298 - 2(.0061)(1) \approx .286$, or 28.6¢, according to the approximation in (6.11) with $x = 1$]. In going from 10 to 11 years of experience, *wage* is predicted to increase by about $.298 - 2(.0061)(10) = .176$, or 17.6¢. And so on.

When the coefficient on x is positive and the coefficient on x^2 is negative, the quadratic has a parabolic shape. There is always a positive value of x where the effect of x on y is zero; before this point, x has a positive effect on y; after this point, x has a negative effect on y. In practice, it can be important to know where this turning point is.

In the estimated equation (6.10) with $\hat{\beta}_1 > 0$ and $\hat{\beta}_2 < 0$, the turning point (or maximum of the function) is always achieved at the coefficient on x over *twice* the absolute value of the coefficient on x^2:

$$x^* = |\hat{\beta}_1/(2\hat{\beta}_2)|. \quad [6.13]$$

In the wage example, $x^* = exper^*$ is $.298/[2(.0061)] \approx 24.4$. (Note how we just drop the minus sign on $-.0061$ in doing this calculation.) This quadratic relationship is illustrated in Figure 6.1.

In the wage equation (6.12), the return to experience becomes zero at about 24.4 years. What should we make of this? There are at least three possible explanations. First, it may be that few people in the sample have more than 24 years of experience, and so the part of the curve to the right of 24 can be ignored. The cost of using a quadratic to capture diminishing effects is that the quadratic must eventually turn around. If this point is beyond all but a small percentage of the people in the sample, then this is not of much concern.

FIGURE 6.1 Quadratic relationship between $\widehat{wage}$ and *exper*.

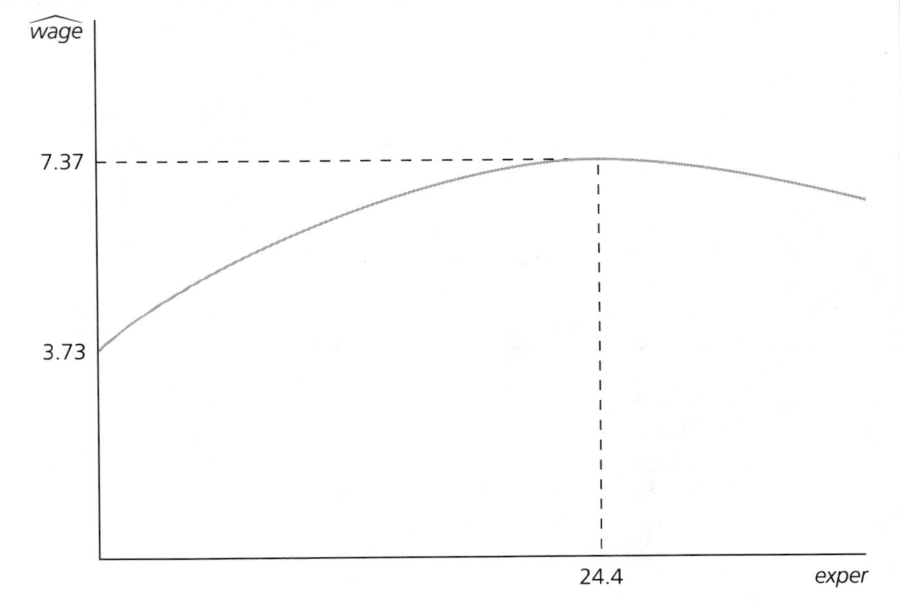

But in the data set WAGE1.RAW, about 28% of the people in the sample have more than 24 years of experience; this is too high a percentage to ignore.

It is possible that the return to *exper* really becomes negative at some point, but it is hard to believe that this happens at 24 years of experience. A more likely possibility is that the estimated effect of *exper* on *wage* is biased because we have controlled for no other factors, or because the functional relationship between *wage* and *exper* in equation (6.12) is not entirely correct. Computer Exercise C2 asks you to explore this possibility by controlling for education, in addition to using log(*wage*) as the dependent variable.

When a model has a dependent variable in logarthmic form and an explanatory variable entering as a quadratic, some care is needed in reporting the partial effects. The following example also shows that the quadratic can have a U-shape, rather than a parabolic shape. A U-shape arises in equation (6.10) when $\hat{\beta}_1$ is negative and $\hat{\beta}_2$ is positive; this captures an increasing effect of x on y.

EXAMPLE 6.2 EFFECTS OF POLLUTION ON HOUSING PRICES

We modify the housing price model from Example 4.5 to include a quadratic term in *rooms*:

$$\log(price) = \beta_0 + \beta_1 \log(nox) + \beta_2 \log(dist) + \beta_3 rooms + \beta_4 rooms^2 + \beta_5 stratio + u. \quad [6.14]$$

The model estimated using the data in HPRICE2.RAW is

$$\begin{aligned}\widehat{\log(price)} &= \underset{(.57)}{13.39} - \underset{(.115)}{.902}\log(nox) - \underset{(.043)}{.087}\log(dist) \\ &\quad - \underset{(.165)}{.545}\, rooms + \underset{(.013)}{.062}\, rooms^2 - \underset{(.006)}{.048}\, stratio \\ n &= 506, R^2 = .603.\end{aligned}$$

The quadratic term $rooms^2$ has a t statistic of about 4.77, and so it is very statistically significant. But what about interpreting the effect of *rooms* on log(*price*)? Initially, the effect appears to be strange. Because the coefficient on *rooms* is negative and the coefficient on $rooms^2$ is positive, this equation literally implies that, at low values of *rooms*, an additional room has a *negative* effect on log(*price*). At some point, the effect becomes positive, and the quadratic shape means that the semi-elasticity of *price* with respect to *rooms* is increasing as *rooms* increases. This situation is shown in Figure 6.2.

We obtain the turnaround value of *rooms* using equation (6.13) (even though $\hat{\beta}_1$ is negative and $\hat{\beta}_2$ is positive). The absolute value of the coefficient on *rooms*, .545, divided by twice the coefficient on $rooms^2$, .062, gives $rooms^* = .545/[2(.062)] \approx 4.4$; this point is labeled in Figure 6.2.

Do we really believe that starting at three rooms and increasing to four rooms actually reduces a house's expected value? Probably not. It turns out that only five of the 506 communities in the sample have houses averaging 4.4 rooms or less, about 1% of the sample. This is so small that the quadratic to the left of 4.4 can, for practical purposes, be ignored. To the right of 4.4, we see that adding another room has an increasing effect on the percentage change in price:

$$\Delta\widehat{\log(price)} \approx \{[-.545 + 2(.062)]rooms\}\Delta rooms$$

FIGURE 6.2 $\widehat{\log(price)}$ as a quadratic function of *rooms*.

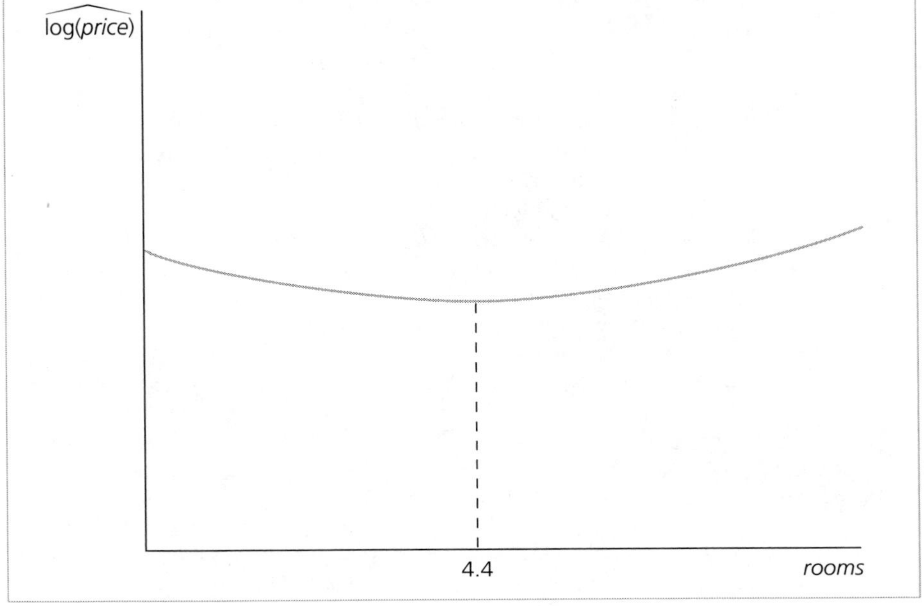

and so

$$\%\Delta\widehat{price} \approx 100\{[-.545 + 2(.062)]rooms\}\Delta rooms$$
$$= (-54.5 + 12.4\ rooms)\Delta rooms.$$

Thus, an increase in *rooms* from, say, five to six increases price by about $-54.5 + 12.4(5) = 7.5\%$; the increase from six to seven increases price by roughly $-54.5 + 12.4(6) = 19.9\%$. This is a very strong increasing effect.

The strong increasing effect of rooms on log(*price*) in this example illustrates an important lesson: one cannot simply look at the coefficient on the quadratic term—in this case, .062—and declare that it is too small to bother with based only on its magnitude. In many applications with quadratics the coefficient on the squared variable has one or more zeros after the decimal point: after all, this coefficient measures how the slope is changing as x (*rooms*) changes. A seemingly small coefficient can have practically important consequences, as we just saw. As a general rule, one must compute the partial effect and see how it varies with x to determine if the quadratic term is practically important. In doing so, it is useful to compare the changing slope implied by the quadratic model with the constant slope obtained from the model with only a linear term. If we drop $rooms^2$ from the equation, the coefficient on *rooms* becomes about .255, which implies that each additional room—starting from any number of rooms—increases median price by about 25.5%. This is very different from the quadratic model, where the effect becomes 25.5% at $rooms = 6.45$ but changes rapidly as *rooms* gets smaller or larger. For example, at $rooms = 7$, the return to the next room is about 32.3%.

What happens generally if the coefficients on the level and squared terms have the *same* sign (either both positive or both negative) and the explanatory variable is necessarily nonnegative (as in the case of *rooms* or *exper*)? In either case, there is no turning point for values $x > 0$. For example, if β_1 and β_2 are both positive, the smallest expected value of y is at $x = 0$, and increases in x always have a positive and increasing effect on y. (This is also true if $\beta_1 = 0$ and $\beta_2 > 0$, which means that the partial effect is zero at $x = 0$ and increasing as x increases.) Similarly, if β_1 and β_2 are both negative, the largest expected value of y is at $x = 0$, and increases in x have a negative effect on y, with the magnitude of the effect increasing as x gets larger.

The general formula for the turning point of any quadratic is $x^* = -\hat{\beta}_1/(2\hat{\beta}_2)$, which leads to a positive value if $\hat{\beta}_1$ and $\hat{\beta}_2$ have opposite signs and a negative value when $\hat{\beta}_1$ and $\hat{\beta}_2$ have the same sign. Knowing this simple formula is useful in cases where x may take on both positive and negative values; one can compute the turning point and see if it makes sense, taking into account the range of x in the sample.

There are many other possibilities for using quadratics along with logarithms. For example, an extension of (6.14) that allows a nonconstant elasticity between *price* and *nox* is

$$\log(price) = \beta_0 + \beta_1\log(nox) + \beta_2[\log(nox)]^2 + \beta_3 crime + \beta_4 rooms + \beta_5 rooms^2 + \beta_6 stratio + u. \quad [6.15]$$

If $\beta_2 = 0$, then β_1 is the elasticity of *price* with respect to *nox*. Otherwise, this elasticity depends on the level of *nox*. To see this, we can combine the arguments for the partial effects in the quadratic and logarithmic models to show that

$$\%\Delta price \approx [\beta_1 + 2\beta_2\log(nox)]\%\Delta nox; \quad [6.16]$$

therefore, the elasticity of *price* with respect to *nox* is $\beta_1 + 2\beta_2\log(nox)$, so that it depends on $\log(nox)$.

Finally, other polynomial terms can be included in regression models. Certainly, the quadratic is seen most often, but a cubic and even a quartic term appear now and then. An often reasonable functional form for a total cost function is

$$cost = \beta_0 + \beta_1 quantity + \beta_2 quantity^2 + \beta_3 quantity^3 + u.$$

Estimating such a model causes no complications. Interpreting the parameters is more involved (though straightforward using calculus); we do not study these models further.

Models with Interaction Terms

Sometimes, it is natural for the partial effect, elasticity, or semi-elasticity of the dependent variable with respect to an explanatory variable to depend on the magnitude of yet *another* explanatory variable. For example, in the model

$$price = \beta_0 + \beta_1 sqrft + \beta_2 bdrms + \beta_3 sqrft \cdot bdrms + \beta_4 bthrms + u,$$

the partial effect of *bdrms* on *price* (holding all other variables fixed) is

$$\frac{\Delta price}{\Delta bdrms} = \beta_2 + \beta_3 sqrft. \quad [6.17]$$

If $\beta_3 > 0$, then (6.17) implies that an additional bedroom yields a higher increase in housing price for larger houses. In other words, there is an **interaction effect** between square footage and number of bedrooms. In summarizing the effect of *bdrms* on *price*, we must evaluate (6.17) at interesting values of *sqrft*, such as the mean value, or the lower and upper quartiles in the sample. Whether or not β_3 is zero is something we can easily test.

The parameters on the original variables can be tricky to interpret when we include an interaction term. For example, in the previous housing price equation, equation (6.17) shows that β_2 is the effect of *bdrms* on *price* for a home with zero square feet! This effect is clearly not of much interest. Instead, we must be careful to put interesting values of *sqrft*, such as the mean or median values in the sample, into the estimated version of equation (6.17).

Often, it is useful to reparameterize a model so that the coefficients on the original variables have an interesting meaning. Consider a model with two explanatory variables and an interaction:

$$y = \beta_0 + \beta_1 x_1 + \beta_2 x_2 + \beta_3 x_1 x_2 + u.$$

As just mentioned, β_2 is the partial effect of x_2 on y when $x_1 = 0$. Often, this is not of interest. Instead, we can reparameterize the model as

$$y = \alpha_0 + \delta_1 x_1 + \delta_2 x_2 + \beta_3(x_1 - \mu_1)(x_2 - \mu_2) + u,$$

where μ_1 is the population mean of x_1 and μ_2 is the population mean of x_2. We can easily see that now the coefficient on x_2, δ_2, is the partial effect of x_2 on y at the mean value of x_1. (By multiplying out the interaction in the second equation and comparing the coefficients, we can easily show that $\delta_2 = \beta_2 + \beta_3\mu_1$. The parameter δ_1 has a similar interpretation.) Therefore, if we subtract the means of the variables—in practice, these would typically be the sample means—before creating the interaction term, the coefficients on the original variables have a useful interpretation. Plus, we immediately obtain standard errors for the partial effects at the mean values. Nothing prevents us from replacing μ_1 or μ_2 with other values of the explanatory variables that may be of interest. The following example illustrates how we can use interaction terms.

EXAMPLE 6.3 EFFECTS OF ATTENDANCE ON FINAL EXAM PERFORMANCE

A model to explain the standardized outcome on a final exam (*stndfnl*) in terms of percentage of classes attended, prior college grade point average, and ACT score is

$$\begin{aligned} stndfnl = {} & \beta_0 + \beta_1 atndrte + \beta_2 priGPA + \beta_3 ACT + \beta_4 priGPA^2 \\ & + \beta_5 ACT^2 + \beta_6 priGPA \cdot atndrte + u. \end{aligned} \quad [6.18]$$

(We use the standardized exam score for the reasons discussed in Section 6.1: it is easier to interpret a student's performance relative to the rest of the class.) In addition to quadratics in *priGPA* and *ACT*, this model includes an interaction between *priGPA* and the attendance rate. The idea is that class attendance might have a different effect for students who have performed differently in the past, as measured by *priGPA*. We are interested in the effects of attendance on final exam score: $\Delta stndfnl/\Delta atndrte = \beta_1 + \beta_6 priGPA$.

Using the 680 observations in ATTEND.RAW, for students in a course on microeconomic principles, the estimated equation is

$$\begin{aligned}\widehat{stndfnl} &= \underset{(1.36)}{2.05} - \underset{(.0102)}{.0067}\, atndrte - \underset{(.48)}{1.63}\, priGPA - \underset{(.098)}{.128}\, ACT \\ &+ \underset{(.101)}{.296}\, priGPA^2 + \underset{(.0022)}{.0045}\, ACT^2 + \underset{(.0043)}{.0056}\, priGPA \cdot atndrte \\ n &= 680,\ R^2 = .229,\ \bar{R}^2 = .222.\end{aligned} \tag{6.19}$$

We must interpret this equation with extreme care. If we simply look at the coefficient on *atndrte*, we will incorrectly conclude that attendance has a *negative* effect on final exam score. But this coefficient supposedly measures the effect when $priGPA = 0$, which is not interesting (in this sample, the smallest prior GPA is about .86). We must also take care not to look separately at the estimates of β_1 and β_6 and conclude that, because each t statistic is insignificant, we cannot reject H_0: $\beta_1 = 0, \beta_6 = 0$. In fact, the p-value for the F test of this joint hypothesis is .014, so we certainly reject H_0 at the 5% level. This is a good example of where looking at separate t statistics when testing a joint hypothesis can lead one far astray.

How should we estimate the partial effect of *atndrte* on *stndfnl*? We must plug in interesting values of *priGPA* to obtain the partial effect. The mean value of *priGPA* in the sample is 2.59, so at the mean *priGPA*, the effect of *atndrte* on *stndfnl* is $-.0067 + .0056(2.59) \approx .0078$. What does this mean? Because *atndrte* is measured as a percentage, it means that a 10 percentage point increase in *atndrte* increases $\widehat{stndfnl}$ by .078 standard deviations from the mean final exam score.

EXPLORING FURTHER 6.3

If we add the term $\beta_7 ACT \cdot atndrte$ to equation (6.18), what is the partial effect of *atndrte* on *stndfnl*?

How can we tell whether the estimate .0078 is statistically different from zero? We need to rerun the regression, where we replace *priGPA·atndrte* with $(priGPA - 2.59) \cdot atndrte$. This gives, as the new coefficient on *atndrte*, the estimated effect at $priGPA = 2.59$, along with its standard error; nothing else in the regression changes. (We described this device in Section 4.4.) Running this new regression gives the standard error of $\hat{\beta}_1 + \hat{\beta}_6(2.59) = .0078$ as .0026, which yields $t = .0078/.0026 = 3$. Therefore, at the average *priGPA*, we conclude that attendance has a statistically significant positive effect on final exam score.

Things are even more complicated for finding the effect of *priGPA* on *stndfnl* because of the quadratic term $priGPA^2$. To find the effect at the mean value of *priGPA* and the mean attendance rate, 82, we would replace $priGPA^2$ with $(priGPA - 2.59)^2$ and *priGPA·atndrte* with $priGPA \cdot (atndrte - 82)$. The coefficient on *priGPA* becomes the partial effect at the mean values, and we would have its standard error. (See Computer Exercise C7.)

6.3 More on Goodness-of-Fit and Selection of Regressors

Until now, we have not focused much on the size of R^2 in evaluating our regression models, because beginning students tend to put too much weight on R-squared. As we will see shortly, choosing a set of explanatory variables based on the size of the R-squared can lead to nonsensical models. In Chapter 10, we will discover that R-squareds obtained from time series regressions can be artificially high and can result in misleading conclusions.

Nothing about the classical linear model assumptions requires that R^2 be above any particular value; R^2 is simply an estimate of how much variation in y is explained by x_1, x_2, …, x_k in the population. We have seen several regressions that have had pretty small R-squareds. Although this means that we have not accounted for several factors that affect y, this does not mean that the factors in u are correlated with the independent variables. The zero conditional mean assumption MLR.4 is what determines whether we get unbiased estimators of the ceteris paribus effects of the independent variables, and the size of the R-squared has no direct bearing on this.

A small R-squared does imply that the error variance is large relative to the variance of y, which means we may have a hard time precisely estimating the β_j. But remember, we saw in Section 3.4 that a large error variance can be offset by a large sample size: if we have enough data, we may be able to precisely estimate the partial effects even though we have not controlled for many unobserved factors. Whether or not we can get precise enough estimates depends on the application. For example, suppose that some incoming students at a large university are randomly given grants to buy computer equipment. If the amount of the grant is truly randomly determined, we can estimate the ceteris paribus effect of the grant amount on subsequent college grade point average by using simple regression analysis. (Because of random assignment, all of the other factors that affect GPA would be uncorrelated with the amount of the grant.) It seems likely that the grant amount would explain little of the variation in GPA, so the R-squared from such a regression would probably be very small. But, if we have a large sample size, we still might get a reasonably precise estimate of the effect of the grant.

Another good illustration of where poor explanatory power has nothing to do with unbiased estimation of the β_j is given by analyzing the data set APPLE.RAW. Unlike the other data sets we have used, the key explanatory variables in APPLE.RAW were set experimentally—that is, without regard to other factors that might affect the dependent variable. The variable we would like to explain, *ecolbs*, is the (hypothetical) pounds of "ecologically friendly" ("ecolabeled") apples a family would demand. Each family (actually, family head) was presented with a description of ecolabeled apples, along with prices of regular apples (*regprc*) and prices of the hypothetical ecolabeled apples (*ecoprc*). Because the price pairs were randomly assigned to each family, they are unrelated to other observed factors (such as family income) and unobserved factors (such as desire for a clean environment). Therefore, the regression of *ecolbs* on *ecoprc*, *regprc* (across all samples generated in this way) produces unbiased estimators of the price effects. Nevertheless, the R-squared from the regression is only .0364: the price variables explain only about 3.6% of the total variation in *ecolbs*. So, here is a case where we explain very little of the variation in y, yet we are in the rare situation of knowing that the data have been generated so that unbiased estimation of the β_j is possible. (Incidentally, adding observed family characteristics has a very small effect on explanatory power. See Computer Exercise C11.)

Remember, though, that the relative *change* in the R-squared when variables are added to an equation is very useful: the F statistic in (4.41) for testing the joint significance crucially depends on the difference in R-squareds between the unrestricted and restricted models.

As we will see in Section 6.4, an important consequence of a low R-squared is that prediction is difficult. Because most of the variation in y is explained by unobserved factors (or at least factors we do not include in our model), we will generally have a hard time using the OLS equation to predict future outcomes on y given a set of values for the explanatory variables.

Adjusted *R*-Squared

Most regression packages will report, along with the *R*-squared, a statistic called the **adjusted *R*-squared**. Because the adjusted *R*-squared is reported in much applied work, and because it has some useful features, we cover it in this subsection.

To see how the usual *R*-squared might be adjusted, it is usefully written as

$$R^2 = 1 - (\text{SSR}/n)/(\text{SST}/n), \tag{6.20}$$

where SSR is the sum of squared residuals and SST is the total sum of squares; compared with equation (3.28), all we have done is divide both SSR and SST by n. This expression reveals what R^2 is actually estimating. Define σ_y^2 as the population variance of y and let σ_u^2 denote the population variance of the error term, u. (Until now, we have used σ^2 to denote σ_u^2, but it is helpful to be more specific here.) The **population *R*-squared** is defined as $\rho^2 = 1 - \sigma_u^2/\sigma_y^2$; this is the proportion of the variation in y in the population explained by the independent variables. This is what R^2 is supposed to be estimating.

R^2 estimates σ_u^2 by SSR/n, which we know to be biased. So why not replace SSR/n with SSR/$(n - k - 1)$? Also, we can use SST/$(n - 1)$ in place of SST/n, as the former is the unbiased estimator of σ_y^2. Using these estimators, we arrive at the adjusted *R*-squared:

$$\begin{aligned} \bar{R}^2 &= 1 - [\text{SSR}/(n - k - 1)]/[\text{SST}/(n - 1)] \\ &= 1 - \hat{\sigma}^2/[\text{SST}/(n - 1)], \end{aligned} \tag{6.21}$$

because $\hat{\sigma}^2 = \text{SSR}/(n - k - 1)$. Because of the notation used to denote the adjusted *R*-squared, it is sometimes called *R-bar squared.*

The adjusted *R*-squared is sometimes called the *corrected R-squared*, but this is not a good name because it implies that $\bar{R}^2$ is somehow better than R^2 as an estimator of the population *R*-squared. Unfortunately, $\bar{R}^2$ is *not* generally known to be a better estimator. It is tempting to think that $\bar{R}^2$ corrects the bias in R^2 for estimating the population *R*-squared, ρ^2, but it does not: the ratio of two unbiased estimators is not an unbiased estimator.

The primary attractiveness of $\bar{R}^2$ is that it imposes a penalty for adding additional independent variables to a model. We know that R^2 can never fall when a new independent variable is added to a regression equation: this is because SSR never goes up (and usually falls) as more independent variables are added. But the formula for $\bar{R}^2$ shows that it depends explicitly on k, the number of independent variables. If an independent variable is added to a regression, SSR falls, but so does the *df* in the regression, $n - k - 1$. SSR/$(n - k - 1)$ can go up or down when a new independent variable is added to a regression.

An interesting algebraic fact is the following: If we add a new independent variable to a regression equation, $\bar{R}^2$ increases if, and only if, the t statistic on the new variable is greater than one in absolute value. (An extension of this is that $\bar{R}^2$ increases when a group of variables is added to a regression if, and only if, the F statistic for joint significance of the new variables is greater than unity.) Thus, we see immediately that using $\bar{R}^2$ to decide whether a certain independent variable (or set of variables) belongs in a model gives us a different answer than standard t or F testing (because a t or F statistic of unity is not statistically significant at traditional significance levels).

It is sometimes useful to have a formula for $\bar{R}^2$ in terms of R^2. Simple algebra gives

$$\bar{R}^2 = 1 - (1 - R^2)(n - 1)/(n - k - 1). \tag{6.22}$$

For example, if $R^2 = .30$, $n = 51$, and $k = 10$, then $\bar{R}^2 = 1 - .70(50)/40 = .125$. Thus, for small n and large k, $\bar{R}^2$ can be substantially below R^2. In fact, if the usual R-squared is small, and $n - k - 1$ is small, $\bar{R}^2$ can actually be negative! For example, you can plug in $R^2 = .10$, $n = 51$, and $k = 10$ to verify that $\bar{R}^2 = -.125$. A negative $\bar{R}^2$ indicates a very poor model fit relative to the number of degrees of freedom.

The adjusted R-squared is sometimes reported along with the usual R-squared in regressions, and sometimes $\bar{R}^2$ is reported in place of R^2. It is important to remember that it is R^2, not $\bar{R}^2$, that appears in the F statistic in (4.41). The same formula with $\bar{R}_r^2$ and $\bar{R}_{ur}^2$ is *not* valid.

Using Adjusted *R*-Squared to Choose between Nonnested Models

In Section 4.5, we learned how to compute an F statistic for testing the joint significance of a group of variables; this allows us to decide, at a particular significance level, whether at least one variable in the group affects the dependent variable. This test does not allow us to decide *which* of the variables has an effect. In some cases, we want to choose a model without redundant independent variables, and the adjusted R-squared can help with this.

In the major league baseball salary example in Section 4.5, we saw that neither *hrunsyr* nor *rbisyr* was individually significant. These two variables are highly correlated, so we might want to choose between the models

$$\log(salary) = \beta_0 + \beta_1 years + \beta_2 gamesyr + \beta_3 bavg + \beta_4 hrunsyr + u$$

and

$$\log(salary) = \beta_0 + \beta_1 years + \beta_2 gamesyr + \beta_3 bavg + \beta_4 rbisyr + u.$$

These two equations are **nonnested models** because neither equation is a special case of the other. The F statistics we studied in Chapter 4 only allow us to test *nested* models: one model (the restricted model) is a special case of the other model (the unrestricted model). See equations (4.32) and (4.28) for examples of restricted and unrestricted models. One possibility is to create a composite model that contains *all* explanatory variables from the original models and then to test each model against the general model using the F test. The problem with this process is that either both models might be rejected or neither model might be rejected (as happens with the major league baseball salary example in Section 4.5). Thus, it does not always provide a way to distinguish between models with nonnested regressors.

In the baseball player salary regression, $\bar{R}^2$ for the regression containing *hrunsyr* is .6211, and $\bar{R}^2$ for the regression containing *rbisyr* is .6226. Thus, based on the adjusted R-squared, there is a very slight preference for the model with *rbisyr*. But the difference is practically very small, and we might obtain a different answer by controlling for some of the variables in Computer Exercise C5 in Chapter 4. (Because both nonnested models contain five parameters, the usual R-squared can be used to draw the same conclusion.)

Comparing $\bar{R}^2$ to choose among different nonnested sets of independent variables can be valuable when these variables represent different functional forms. Consider two models relating R&D intensity to firm sales:

$$rdintens = \beta_0 + \beta_1 \log(sales) + u. \qquad [6.23]$$

$$rdintens = \beta_0 + \beta_1 sales + \beta_2 sales^2 + u. \qquad [6.24]$$

The first model captures a diminishing return by including *sales* in logarithmic form; the second model does this by using a quadratic. Thus, the second model contains one more parameter than the first.

When equation (6.23) is estimated using the 32 observations on chemical firms in RDCHEM.RAW, R^2 is .061, and R^2 for equation (6.24) is .148. Therefore, it appears that the quadratic fits much better. But a comparison of the usual *R*-squareds is unfair to the first model because it contains one fewer parameter than (6.24). That is, (6.23) is a more parsimonious model than (6.24).

Everything else being equal, simpler models are better. Since the usual *R*-squared does not penalize more complicated models, it is better to use $\bar{R}^2$. $\bar{R}^2$ for (6.23) is .030, while $\bar{R}^2$ for (6.24) is .090. Thus, even after adjusting for the difference in degrees of freedom, the quadratic model wins out. The quadratic model is also preferred when profit margin is added to each regression.

There is an important limitation in using $\bar{R}^2$ to choose between nonnested models: we cannot use it to choose between different functional forms for the dependent variable. This is unfortunate, because we often want to decide on whether y or $\log(y)$ (or maybe some other transformation) should be used as the dependent variable based on goodness-of-fit. But neither R^2 nor $\bar{R}^2$ can be used for this purpose. The reason is simple: these *R*-squareds measure the explained proportion of the total variation in whatever dependent variable we are using in the regression, and different functions of the dependent variable will have different amounts of variation to explain. For example, the total variations in y and $\log(y)$ are not the same, and are often very different. Comparing the adjusted *R*-squareds from regressions with these different forms of the dependent variables does not tell us anything about which model fits better; they are fitting two separate dependent variables.

EXPLORING FURTHER 6.4

Explain why choosing a model by maximizing $\bar{R}^2$ or minimizing $\hat{\sigma}$ (the standard error of the regression) is the same thing.

EXAMPLE 6.4 CEO COMPENSATION AND FIRM PERFORMANCE

Consider two estimated models relating CEO compensation to firm performance:

$$\begin{aligned} \widehat{salary} &= \underset{(223.90)}{830.63} + \underset{(.0089)}{.0163}\, sales + \underset{(11.08)}{19.63}\, roe \\ n &= 209,\ R^2 = .029,\ \bar{R}^2 = .020 \end{aligned} \qquad [6.25]$$

and

$$\begin{aligned} \widehat{lsalary} &= \underset{(0.29)}{4.36} + \underset{(.033)}{.275}\, lsales + \underset{(.0040)}{.0179}\, roe \\ n &= 209,\ R^2 = .282,\ \bar{R}^2 = .275, \end{aligned} \qquad [6.26]$$

where *roe* is the return on equity discussed in Chapter 2. For simplicity, *lsalary* and *lsales* denote the natural logs of *salary* and *sales*. We already know how to interpret these different estimated equations. But can we say that one model fits better than the other?

The *R*-squared for equation (6.25) shows that *sales* and *roe* explain only about 2.9% of the variation in CEO salary in the sample. Both *sales* and *roe* have marginal statistical significance.

Equation (6.26) shows that log(*sales*) and *roe* explain about 28.2% of the variation in log(*salary*). In terms of goodness-of-fit, this much higher *R*-squared would seem to imply that model (6.26) is much better, but this is not necessarily the case. The total sum of squares for *salary* in the sample is 391,732,982, while the total sum of squares for log(*salary*) is only 66.72. Thus, there is much less variation in log(*salary*) that needs to be explained.

At this point, we can use features other than R^2 or $\bar{R}^2$ to decide between these models. For example, log(*sales*) and *roe* are much more statistically significant in (6.26) than are *sales* and *roe* in (6.25), and the coefficients in (6.26) are probably of more interest. To be sure, however, we will need to make a valid goodness-of-fit comparison.

In Section 6.4, we will offer a goodness-of-fit measure that does allow us to compare models where *y* appears in both level and log form.

Controlling for Too Many Factors in Regression Analysis

In many of the examples we have covered, and certainly in our discussion of omitted variables bias in Chapter 3, we have worried about omitting important factors from a model that might be correlated with the independent variables. It is also possible to control for too *many* variables in a regression analysis.

If we overemphasize goodness-of-fit, we open ourselves to controlling for factors in a regression model that should not be controlled for. To avoid this mistake, we need to remember the ceteris paribus interpretation of multiple regression models.

To illustrate this issue, suppose we are doing a study to assess the impact of state beer taxes on traffic fatalities. The idea is that a higher tax on beer will reduce alcohol consumption, and likewise drunk driving, resulting in fewer traffic fatalities. To measure the ceteris paribus effect of taxes on fatalities, we can model *fatalities* as a function of several factors, including the beer *tax*:

$$fatalities = \beta_0 + \beta_1 tax + \beta_2 miles + \beta_3 percmale + \beta_4 perc16\_21 + \ldots,$$

where

$$\begin{aligned} miles &= \text{total miles driven.} \\ percmale &= \text{percentage of the state population that is male.} \\ perc16\_21 &= \text{percentage of the population between ages 16 and 21, and so on.} \end{aligned}$$

Notice how we have not included a variable measuring per capita beer consumption. Are we committing an omitted variables error? The answer is no. If we control for beer consumption in this equation, then how would beer taxes affect traffic fatalities? In the equation

$$fatalities = \beta_0 + \beta_1 tax + \beta_2 beercons + \ldots,$$

β_1 measures the difference in fatalities due to a one percentage point increase in *tax*, holding *beercons* fixed. It is difficult to understand why this would be interesting. We should not be controlling for differences in *beercons* across states, unless we want to test for some sort of indirect effect of beer taxes. Other factors, such as gender and age distribution, should be controlled for.

As a second example, suppose that, for a developing country, we want to estimate the effects of pesticide usage among farmers on family health expenditures. In addition to pesticide usage amounts, should we include the number of doctor visits as an explanatory variable? No. Health expenditures include doctor visits, and we would like to pick up all effects of pesticide use on health expenditures. If we include the number of doctor visits as an explanatory variable, then we are only measuring the effects of pesticide use on health expenditures other than doctor visits. It makes more sense to use number of doctor visits as a dependent variable in a separate regression on pesticide amounts.

The previous examples are what can be called **over controlling** for factors in multiple regression. Often this results from nervousness about potential biases that might arise by leaving out an important explanatory variable. But it is important to remember the ceteris paribus nature of multiple regression. In some cases, it makes no sense to hold some factors fixed precisely because they should be allowed to change when a policy variable changes.

Unfortunately, the issue of whether or not to control for certain factors is not always clear-cut. For example, Betts (1995) studies the effect of high school quality on subsequent earnings. He points out that, if better school quality results in more education, then controlling for education in the regression along with measures of quality will underestimate the return to quality. Betts does the analysis with and without years of education in the equation to get a range of estimated effects for quality of schooling.

To see explicitly how pursuing high R-squareds can lead to trouble, consider the housing price example from Section 4.5 that illustrates the testing of multiple hypotheses. In that case, we wanted to test the rationality of housing price assessments. We regressed log(*price*) on log(*assess*), log(*lotsize*), log(*sqrft*), and *bdrms* and tested whether the latter three variables had zero population coefficients while log(*assess*) had a coefficient of unity. But what if we change the purpose of the analysis and estimate a *hedonic price model*, which allows us to obtain the marginal values of various housing attributes? Should we include log(*assess*) in the equation? The adjusted R-squared from the regression with log(*assess*) is .762, while the adjusted R-squared without it is .630. Based on goodness-of-fit only, we should include log(*assess*). But this is incorrect if our goal is to determine the effects of lot size, square footage, and number of bedrooms on housing values. Including log(*assess*) in the equation amounts to holding one measure of value fixed and then asking how much an additional bedroom would change another measure of value. This makes no sense for valuing housing attributes.

If we remember that different models serve different purposes, and we focus on the ceteris paribus interpretation of regression, then we will not include the wrong factors in a regression model.

Adding Regressors to Reduce the Error Variance

We have just seen some examples of where certain independent variables should not be included in a regression model, even though they are correlated with the dependent variable. From Chapter 3, we know that adding a new independent variable to a regression can exacerbate the multicollinearity problem. On the other hand, since we are taking something out of the error term, adding a variable generally reduces the error variance. Generally, we cannot know which effect will dominate.

However, there is one case that is clear: we should always include independent variables that affect y and are *uncorrelated* with all of the independent variables of interest. Why?

Because adding such a variable does not induce multicollinearity in the population (and therefore multicollinearity in the sample should be negligible), but it will reduce the error variance. In large sample sizes, the standard errors of all OLS estimators will be reduced.

As an example, consider estimating the individual demand for beer as a function of the average county beer price. It may be reasonable to assume that individual characteristics are uncorrelated with county-level prices, and so a simple regression of beer consumption on county price would suffice for estimating the effect of price on individual demand. But it is possible to get a more precise estimate of the price elasticity of beer demand by including individual characteristics, such as age and amount of education. If these factors affect demand and are uncorrelated with price, then the standard error of the price coefficient will be smaller, at least in large samples.

As a second example, consider the grants for computer equipment given at the beginning of Section 6.3. If, in addition to the grant variable, we control for other factors that can explain college GPA, we can probably get a more precise estimate of the effect of the grant. Measures of high school grade point average and rank, SAT and ACT scores, and family background variables are good candidates. Because the grant amounts are randomly assigned, all additional control variables are uncorrelated with the grant amount; in the sample, multicollinearity between the grant amount and other independent variables should be minimal. But adding the extra controls might significantly reduce the error variance, leading to a more precise estimate of the grant effect. Remember, the issue is not unbiasedness here: we obtain an unbiased and consistent estimator whether or not we add the high school performance and family background variables. The issue is getting an estimator with a smaller sampling variance.

Unfortunately, cases where we have information on additional explanatory variables that are uncorrelated with the explanatory variables of interest are somewhat rare in the social sciences. But it is worth remembering that when these variables are available, they can be included in a model to reduce the error variance without inducing multicollinearity.

6.4 Prediction and Residual Analysis

In Chapter 3, we defined the OLS predicted or fitted values and the OLS residuals. **Predictions** are certainly useful, but they are subject to sampling variation, because they are obtained using the OLS estimators. Thus, in this section, we show how to obtain confidence intervals for a prediction from the OLS regression line.

From Chapters 3 and 4, we know that the residuals are used to obtain the sum of squared residuals and the *R*-squared, so they are important for goodness-of-fit and testing. Sometimes, economists study the residuals for particular observations to learn about individuals (or firms, houses, etc.) in the sample.

Confidence Intervals for Predictions

Suppose we have estimated the equation

$$\hat{y} = \hat{\beta}_0 + \hat{\beta}_1 x_1 + \hat{\beta}_2 x_2 + \ldots + \hat{\beta}_k x_k. \quad [6.27]$$

When we plug in particular values of the independent variables, we obtain a prediction for y, which is an estimate of the *expected value* of y given the particular values for the explanatory variables. For emphasis, let $c_1, c_2, \ldots, c_k$ denote particular values for each of the k independent variables; these may or may not correspond to an actual data point in our sample. The parameter we would like to estimate is

$$\begin{aligned}\theta_0 &= \beta_0 + \beta_1 c_1 + \beta_2 c_2 + \ldots + \beta_k c_k \\ &= \mathrm{E}(y|x_1 = c_1, x_2 = c_2, \ldots, x_k = c_k).\end{aligned} \quad [6.28]$$

The estimator of θ_0 is

$$\hat{\theta}_0 = \hat{\beta}_0 + \hat{\beta}_1 c_1 + \hat{\beta}_2 c_2 + \ldots + \hat{\beta}_k c_k. \quad [6.29]$$

In practice, this is easy to compute. But what if we want some measure of the uncertainty in this predicted value? It is natural to construct a confidence interval for θ_0, which is centered at $\hat{\theta}_0$.

To obtain a confidence interval for θ_0, we need a standard error for $\hat{\theta}_0$. Then, with a large *df*, we can construct a 95% confidence interval using the rule of thumb $\hat{\theta}_0 \pm 2 \cdot \mathrm{se}(\hat{\theta}_0)$. (As always, we can use the exact percentiles in a t distribution.)

How do we obtain the standard error of $\hat{\theta}_0$? This is the same problem we encountered in Section 4.4: we need to obtain a standard error for a linear combination of the OLS estimators. Here, the problem is even more complicated, because all of the OLS estimators generally appear in $\hat{\theta}_0$ (unless some c_j are zero). Nevertheless, the same trick that we used in Section 4.4 will work here. Write $\beta_0 = \theta_0 - \beta_1 c_1 - \ldots - \beta_k c_k$ and plug this into the equation

$$y = \beta_0 + \beta_1 x_1 + \ldots + \beta_k x_k + u$$

to obtain

$$y = \theta_0 + \beta_1(x_1 - c_1) + \beta_2(x_2 - c_2) + \ldots + \beta_k(x_k - c_k) + u. \quad [6.30]$$

In other words, we subtract the value c_j from each observation on x_j, and then we run the regression of

$$y_i \text{ on } (x_{i1} - c_1), \ldots, (x_{ik} - c_k), i = 1, 2, \ldots, n. \quad [6.31]$$

The predicted value in (6.29) and, more importantly, its standard error, are obtained from the *intercept* (or constant) in regression (6.31).

As an example, we obtain a confidence interval for a prediction from a college GPA regression, where we use high school information.

EXAMPLE 6.5 CONFIDENCE INTERVAL FOR PREDICTED COLLEGE GPA

Using the data in GPA2.RAW, we obtain the following equation for predicting college GPA:

$$\begin{aligned}\widehat{colgpa} &= \underset{(0.075)}{1.493} + \underset{(.00007)}{.00149}\, sat - \underset{(.00056)}{.01386}\, hsperc \\ &\quad - \underset{(.01650)}{.06088}\, hsize + \underset{(.00227)}{.00546}\, hsize^2 \\ n &= 4{,}137, R^2 = .278, \bar{R}^2 = .277, \hat{\sigma} = .560,\end{aligned} \quad [6.32]$$

where we have reported estimates to several digits to reduce round-off error. What is predicted college GPA, when $sat = 1{,}200$, $hsperc = 30$, and $hsize = 5$ (which means 500)? This is easy to get by plugging these values into equation (6.32): $\widehat{colgpa} = 2.70$ (rounded to two digits). Unfortunately, we cannot use equation (6.32) directly to get a confidence interval for the expected *colgpa* at the given values of the independent variables. One simple way to obtain a confidence interval is to define a new set of independent variables: $sat0 = sat - 1{,}200$, $hsperc0 = hsperc - 30$, $hsize0 = hsize - 5$, and $hsizesq0 = hsize^2 - 25$. When we regress *colgpa* on these new independent variables, we get

$$\begin{aligned}\widehat{colgpa} &= \underset{(0.020)}{2.700} + \underset{(.00007)}{.00149}\, sat0 - \underset{(.00056)}{.01386}\, hsperc0 \\ &\quad - \underset{(.01650)}{.06088}\, hsize0 + \underset{(.00227)}{.00546}\, hsizesq0 \\ n &= 4{,}137,\ R^2 = .278,\ \bar{R}^2 = .277,\ \hat{\sigma} = .560.\end{aligned}$$

The only difference between this regression and that in (6.32) is the intercept, which is the prediction we want, along with its standard error, .020. It is not an accident that the slope coefficents, their standard errors, *R*-squared, and so on are the same as before; this provides a way to check that the proper transformations were done. We can easily construct a 95% confidence interval for the expected college GPA: $2.70 \pm 1.96(.020)$ or about 2.66 to 2.74. This confidence interval is rather narrow due to the very large sample size.

Because the variance of the intercept estimator is smallest when each explanatory variable has zero sample mean (see Question 2.5 for the simple regression case), it follows from the regression in (6.31) that the variance of the prediction is smallest at the mean values of the x_j. (That is, $c_j = \bar{x}_j$ for all j.) This result is not too surprising, since we have the most faith in our regression line near the middle of the data. As the values of the c_j get farther away from the $\bar{x}_j$, $\mathrm{Var}(\hat{y})$ gets larger and larger.

The previous method allows us to put a confidence interval around the OLS estimate of $\mathrm{E}(y|x_1, \ldots, x_k)$ for any values of the explanatory variables. In other words, we obtain a confidence interval for the *average* value of y for the subpopulation with a given set of covariates. But a confidence interval for the average person in the subpopulation is not the same as a confidence interval for a particular unit (individual, family, firm, and so on) from the population. In forming a confidence interval for an unknown outcome on y, we must account for another very important source of variation: the variance in the unobserved error, which measures our ignorance of the unobserved factors that affect y.

Let y^0 denote the value for which we would like to construct a confidence interval, which we sometimes call a **prediction interval**. For example, y^0 could represent a person or firm not in our original sample. Let $x_1^0, \ldots, x_k^0$ be the new values of the independent variables, which we assume we observe, and let u^0 be the unobserved error. Therefore, we have

$$y^0 = \beta_0 + \beta_1 x_1^0 + \beta_2 x_2^0 + \ldots + \beta_k x_k^0 + u^0. \tag{6.33}$$

As before, our best prediction of y^0 is the expected value of y^0 given the explanatory variables, which we estimate from the OLS regression line: $\hat{y}^0 = \hat{\beta}_0 + \hat{\beta}_1 x_1^0 + \hat{\beta}_2 x_2^0 + \ldots + \hat{\beta}_k x_k^0$. The **prediction error** in using $\hat{y}^0$ to predict y^0 is

$$\hat{e}^0 = y^0 - \hat{y}^0 = (\beta_0 + \beta_1 x_1^0 + \ldots + \beta_k x_k^0) + u^0 - \hat{y}^0. \tag{6.34}$$

Now, $\mathrm{E}(\hat{y}^0) = \mathrm{E}(\hat{\beta}_0) + \mathrm{E}(\hat{\beta}_1)x_1^0 + \mathrm{E}(\hat{\beta}_2)x_2^0 + \ldots + \mathrm{E}(\hat{\beta}_k)x_k^0 = \beta_0 + \beta_1 x_1^0 + \ldots + \beta_k x_k^0$, because the $\hat{\beta}_j$ are unbiased. (As before, these expectations are all conditional on the sample values of the independent variables.) Because u^0 has zero mean, $\mathrm{E}(\hat{e}^0) = 0$. We have shown that the expected prediction error is zero.

In finding the variance of $\hat{e}^0$, note that u^0 is uncorrelated with each $\hat{\beta}_j$, because u^0 is uncorrelated with the errors in the sample used to obtain the $\hat{\beta}_j$. By basic properties of covariance (see Appendix B), u^0 and $\hat{y}^0$ are uncorrelated. Therefore, the **variance of the prediction error** (conditional on all in-sample values of the independent variables) is the sum of the variances:

$$\mathrm{Var}(\hat{e}^0) = \mathrm{Var}(\hat{y}^0) + \mathrm{Var}(u^0) = \mathrm{Var}(\hat{y}^0) + \sigma^2, \quad [6.35]$$

where $\sigma^2 = \mathrm{Var}(u^0)$ is the error variance. There are two sources of variation in $\hat{e}^0$. The first is the sampling error in $\hat{y}^0$, which arises because we have estimated the β_j. Because each $\hat{\beta}_j$ has a variance proportional to $1/n$, where n is the sample size, $\mathrm{Var}(\hat{y}^0)$ is proportional to $1/n$. This means that, for large samples, $\mathrm{Var}(\hat{y}^0)$ can be very small. By contrast, σ^2 is the variance of the error in the population; it does not change with the sample size. In many examples, σ^2 will be the dominant term in (6.35).

Under the classical linear model assumptions, the $\hat{\beta}_j$ and u^0 are normally distributed, and so $\hat{e}^0$ is also normally distributed (conditional on all sample values of the explanatory variables). Earlier, we described how to obtain an unbiased estimator of $\mathrm{Var}(\hat{y}^0)$, and we obtained our unbiased estimator of σ^2 in Chapter 3. By using these estimators, we can define the standard error of $\hat{e}^0$ as

$$\mathrm{se}(\hat{e}^0) = \{[\mathrm{se}(\hat{y}^0)]^2 + \hat{\sigma}^2\}^{1/2}. \quad [6.36]$$

Using the same reasoning for the t statistics of the $\hat{\beta}_j$, $\hat{e}^0/\mathrm{se}(\hat{e}^0)$ has a t distribution with $n - (k + 1)$ degrees of freedom. Therefore,

$$\mathrm{P}[-t_{.025} \leq \hat{e}^0/\mathrm{se}(\hat{e}^0) \leq t_{.025}] = .95,$$

where $t_{.025}$ is the 97.5th percentile in the t_{n-k-1} distribution. For large $n - k - 1$, remember that $t_{.025} \approx 1.96$. Plugging in $\hat{e}^0 = y^0 - \hat{y}^0$ and rearranging gives a 95% prediction interval for y^0:

$$\hat{y}^0 \pm t_{.025} \cdot \mathrm{se}(\hat{e}^0); \quad [6.37]$$

as usual, except for small *df*, a good rule of thumb is $\hat{y}^0 \pm 2\mathrm{se}(\hat{e}^0)$. This is wider than the confidence interval for $\hat{y}^0$ itself because of $\hat{\sigma}^2$ in (6.36); it often is much wider to reflect the factors in u^0 that we have not accounted for.

EXAMPLE 6.6 CONFIDENCE INTERVAL FOR FUTURE COLLEGE GPA

Suppose we want a 95% CI for the future college GPA of a high school student with *sat* = 1,200, *hsperc* = 30, and *hsize* = 5. In Example 6.5, we obtained a 95% confidence interval for the *average* college GPA among all students with the particular characteristics *sat* = 1,200, *hsperc* = 30, and *hsize* = 5. Now, we want a 95% confidence interval for any *particular* student with these characteristics. The 95% prediction interval must account for the variation in the individual, unobserved characteristics that affect college performance. We have everything we need to obtain a CI for *colgpa*. $\mathrm{se}(\hat{y}^0) = .020$ and

$\hat{\sigma} = .560$ and so, from (6.36), $\text{se}(\hat{e}^0) = [(.020)^2 + (.560)^2]^{1/2} \approx .560$. Notice how small $\text{se}(\hat{y}^0)$ is relative to $\hat{\sigma}$: virtually all of the variation in $\hat{e}^0$ comes from the variation in u^0. The 95% CI is 2.70 ± 1.96(.560) or about 1.60 to 3.80. This is a wide confidence interval and shows that, based on the factors we included in the regression, we cannot accurately pin down an individual's future college grade point average. (In one sense, this is good news, as it means that high school rank and performance on the SAT do not preordain one's performance in college.) Evidently, the unobserved characteristics that affect college GPA vary widely among individuals with the same observed SAT score and high school rank.

Residual Analysis

Sometimes, it is useful to examine individual observations to see whether the actual value of the dependent variable is above or below the predicted value; that is, to examine the residuals for the individual observations. This process is called **residual analysis**. Economists have been known to examine the residuals from a regression in order to aid in the purchase of a home. The following housing price example illustrates residual analysis. Housing price is related to various observable characteristics of the house. We can list all of the characteristics that we find important, such as size, number of bedrooms, number of bathrooms, and so on. We can use a sample of houses to estimate a relationship between price and attributes, where we end up with a predicted value and an actual value for each house. Then, we can construct the residuals, $\hat{u}_i = y_i - \hat{y}_i$. The house with the most negative residual is, at least based on the factors we have controlled for, the most underpriced one relative to its *observed* characteristics. Of course, a selling price substantially below its predicted price could indicate some undesirable feature of the house that we have failed to account for, and which is therefore contained in the unobserved error. In addition to obtaining the prediction and residual, it also makes sense to compute a confidence interval for what the future selling price of the home could be, using the method described in equation (6.37).

Using the data in HPRICE1.RAW, we run a regression of *price* on *lotsize*, *sqrft*, and *bdrms*. In the sample of 88 homes, the most negative residual is −120.206, for the 81st house. Therefore, the asking price for this house is $120,206 below its predicted price.

There are many other uses of residual analysis. One way to rank law schools is to regress median starting salary on a variety of student characteristics (such as median LSAT scores of entering class, median college GPA of entering class, and so on) and to obtain a predicted value and residual for each law school. The law school with the largest residual has the highest predicted value added. (Of course, there is still much uncertainty about how an individual's starting salary would compare with the median for a law school overall.) These residuals can be used along with the costs of attending each law school to determine the best value; this would require an appropriate discounting of future earnings.

Residual analysis also plays a role in legal decisions. A *New York Times* article entitled "Judge Says Pupil's Poverty, Not Segregation, Hurts Scores" (6/28/95) describes an important legal case. The issue was whether the poor performance on standardized tests in the Hartford School District, relative to performance in surrounding suburbs, was due to poor school quality at the highly segregated schools. The judge concluded that "the disparity in test scores does not indicate that Hartford is doing an inadequate or poor job in educating its students or that its schools are failing, because the predicted scores based upon the relevant socioeconomic factors are about at the levels that one would expect." This conclusion is based on a regression analysis of average or median scores on

EXPLORING FURTHER 6.5

How would you use residual analysis to determine which professional athletes are overpaid or underpaid relative to their performance?

socioeconomic characteristics of various school districts in Connecticut. The judge's conclusion suggests that, given the poverty levels of students at Hartford schools, the actual test scores were similar to those predicted from a regression analysis: the residual for Hartford was not sufficiently negative to conclude that the schools themselves were the cause of low test scores.

Predicting y When $\log(y)$ Is the Dependent Variable

Because the natural log transformation is used so often for the dependent variable in empirical economics, we devote this subsection to the issue of predicting y when $\log(y)$ is the dependent variable. As a byproduct, we will obtain a goodness-of-fit measure for the log model that can be compared with the R-squared from the level model.

To obtain a prediction, it is useful to define $logy = \log(y)$; this emphasizes that it is the log of y that is predicted in the model

$$logy = \beta_0 + \beta_1 x_1 + \beta_2 x_2 + \dots + \beta_k x_k + u. \qquad [6.38]$$

In this equation, the x_j might be transformations of other variables; for example, we could have $x_1 = \log(sales)$, $x_2 = \log(mktval)$, $x_3 = ceoten$ in the CEO salary example.

Given the OLS estimators, we know how to predict $logy$ for any value of the independent variables:

$$\widehat{logy} = \hat{\beta}_0 + \hat{\beta}_1 x_1 + \hat{\beta}_2 x_2 + \dots + \hat{\beta}_k x_k. \qquad [6.39]$$

Now, since the exponential undoes the log, our first guess for predicting y is to simply exponentiate the predicted value for $\log(y)$: $\hat{y} = \exp(\widehat{logy})$. This does not work; in fact, it will systematically *underestimate* the expected value of y. In fact, if model (6.38) follows the CLM assumptions MLR.1 through MLR.6, it can be shown that

$$E(y|\mathbf{x}) = \exp(\sigma^2/2)\cdot\exp(\beta_0 + \beta_1 x_1 + \beta_2 x_2 + \dots + \beta_k x_k),$$

where $\mathbf{x}$ denotes the independent variables and σ^2 is the variance of u. [If $u \sim \text{Normal}(0,\sigma^2)$, then the expected value of $\exp(u)$ is $\exp(\sigma^2/2)$.] This equation shows that a simple adjustment is needed to predict y:

$$\hat{y} = \exp(\hat{\sigma}^2/2)\exp(\widehat{logy}), \qquad [6.40]$$

where $\hat{\sigma}^2$ is simply the unbiased estimator of σ^2. Because $\hat{\sigma}$, the standard error of the regression, is always reported, obtaining predicted values for y is easy. Because $\hat{\sigma}^2 > 0$, $\exp(\hat{\sigma}^2/2) > 1$. For large $\hat{\sigma}^2$, this adjustment factor can be substantially larger than unity.

The prediction in (6.40) is not unbiased, but it is consistent. There are no unbiased predictions of y, and in many cases, (6.40) works well. However, it does rely on the normality of the error term, u. In Chapter 5, we showed that OLS has desirable properties, even when u is not normally distributed. Therefore, it is useful to have a prediction that does not rely on normality. If we just assume that u is independent of the explanatory variables, then we have

$$E(y|\mathbf{x}) = \alpha_0 \exp(\beta_0 + \beta_1 x_1 + \beta_2 x_2 + \dots + \beta_k x_k), \qquad [6.41]$$

where α_0 is the expected value of $\exp(u)$, which must be greater than unity.

Given an estimate $\hat{\alpha}_0$, we can predict y as

$$\hat{y} = \hat{\alpha}_0 \exp(\widehat{logy}), \tag{6.42}$$

which again simply requires exponentiating the predicted value from the log model and multiplying the result by $\hat{\alpha}_0$.

Two approaches suggest themselves for estimating α_0 without the normality assumption. The first is based on $\alpha_0 = \mathrm{E}[\exp(u)]$. To estimate α_0 we replace the population expectation with a sample average and then we replace the unobserved errors, u_i, with the OLS residuals, $\hat{u}_i = \log(y_i) - \hat{\beta}_0 - \hat{\beta}_1 x_{i1} - \ldots - \hat{\beta}_k x_{ik}$. This leads to the method of moments estimator (see Appendix C)

$$\hat{\alpha}_0 = n^{-1}\sum_{i=1}^{n}\exp(\hat{u}_i). \tag{6.43}$$

Not surprisingly, $\hat{\alpha}_0$ is a consistent estimator of α_0, but it is not unbiased because we have replaced u_i with $\hat{u}_i$ inside a nonlinear function. This version of $\hat{\alpha}_0$ is a special case of what Duan (1983) called a **smearing estimate**. Because the OLS residuals have a zero sample average, it can be shown that, for any data set, $\hat{\alpha}_0 > 1$. (Technically, $\hat{\alpha}_0$ would equal one if all the OLS residuals were zero, but this never happens in any interesting application.) That $\hat{\alpha}_0$ is necessarily greater than one is convenient because it must be that $\alpha_0 > 1$.

A different estimate of α_0 is based on a simple regression through the origin. To see how it works, define $m_i = \exp(\beta_0 + \beta_1 x_{i1} + \ldots + \beta_k x_{ik})$, so that, from equation (6.41), $\mathrm{E}(y_i|m_i) = \alpha_0 m_i$. If we could observe the m_i, we could obtain an unbiased estimator of α_0 from the regression y_i on m_i without an intercept. Instead, we replace the β_j with their OLS estimates and obtain $\hat{m}_i = \exp(\widehat{logy}_i)$, where, of course, the $\widehat{logy}_i$ are the fitted values from the regression $logy_i$ on $x_{i1}, \ldots, x_{ik}$ (with an intercept). Then $\check{\alpha}_0$ [to distinguish it from $\hat{\alpha}_0$ in equation (6.43)] is the OLS slope estimate from the simple regression y_i on $\hat{m}_i$ (no intercept):

$$\check{\alpha}_0 = \left(\sum_{i=1}^{n}\hat{m}_i^2\right)^{-1}\left(\sum_{i=1}^{n}\hat{m}_i y_i\right). \tag{6.44}$$

We will call $\check{\alpha}_0$ the regression estimate of α_0. Like $\hat{\alpha}_0$, $\check{\alpha}_0$ is consistent but not unbiased. Interestingly, $\check{\alpha}_0$ is not guaranteed to be greater than one, although it will be in most applications. If $\check{\alpha}_0$ is less than one, and especially if it is much less than one, it is likely that the assumption of independence between u and the x_j is violated. If $\check{\alpha}_0 < 1$, one possibility is to just use the estimate in (6.43), although this may simply be masking a problem with the linear model for log(y). We summarize the steps:

Predicting y When the Dependent Variable Is log(y):

1. Obtain the fitted values, $\widehat{logy}_i$, and residuals, $\hat{u}_i$, from the regression $logy$ on $x_1, \ldots, x_k$.
2. Obtain $\hat{\alpha}_0$ as in equation (6.43) or $\check{\alpha}_0$ in equation (6.44).
3. For given values of $x_1, \ldots, x_k$, obtain $\widehat{logy}$ from (6.42).
4. Obtain the prediction $\hat{y}$ from (6.42) (with $\hat{\alpha}_0$ or $\check{\alpha}_0$).

We now show how to predict CEO salaries using this procedure.

EXAMPLE 6.7 PREDICTING CEO SALARIES

The model of interest is

$$\log(salary) = \beta_0 + \beta_1 \log(sales) + \beta_2 \log(mktval) + \beta_3 ceoten + u,$$

so that β_1 and β_2 are elasticities and $100 \cdot \beta_3$ is a semi-elasticity. The estimated equation using CEOSAL2.RAW is

$$\begin{aligned} \widehat{lsalary} &= \underset{(.257)}{4.504} + \underset{(.039)}{.163}\, lsales + \underset{(.050)}{.109}\, lmktval + \underset{(.0053)}{.0117}\, ceoten \\ n &= 177,\ R^2 = .318, \end{aligned} \qquad [6.45]$$

where, for clarity, we let *lsalary* denote the log of *salary*, and similarly for *lsales* and *lmktval*. Next, we obtain $\hat{m}_i = \exp(\widehat{lsalary}_i)$ for each observation in the sample.

The Duan smearing estimate from (6.43) is about $\hat{\alpha}_0 = 1.136$, and the regression estimate from (6.44) is $\check{\alpha}_0 = 1.117$. We can use either estimate to predict *salary* for any values of *sales*, *mktval*, and *ceoten*. Let us find the prediction for *sales* = 5,000 (which means \$5 billion because *sales* is in millions), *mktval* = 10,000 (or \$10 billion), and *ceoten* = 10. From (6.45), the prediction for *lsalary* is $4.504 + .163 \cdot \log(5{,}000) + .109 \cdot \log(10{,}000) + .0117(10) \approx 7.013$, and $\exp(7.013) \approx 1{,}110.983$. Using the estimate of α_0 from (6.43), the predicted salary is about 1,262.077, or \$1,262,077. Using the estimate from (6.44) gives an estimated salary of about \$1,240,968. These differ from each other by much less than each differs from the naive prediction of \$1,110,983.

We can use the previous method of obtaining predictions to determine how well the model with $\log(y)$ as the dependent variable explains y. We already have measures for models when y is the dependent variable: the R-squared and the adjusted R-squared. The goal is to find a goodness-of-fit measure in the $\log(y)$ model that can be compared with an R-squared from a model where y is the dependent variable.

There are different ways to define a goodness-of-fit measure after retransforming a model for $\log(y)$ to predict y. Here we present an approach that is easy to implement and that gives the same value whether we estimate α_0 as in (6.40), (6.43), or (6.44). To motivate the measure, recall that in the linear regression equation estimated by OLS,

$$\hat{y} = \hat{\beta}_0 + \hat{\beta}_1 x_1 + \ldots + \hat{\beta}_k x_k, \qquad [6.46]$$

the usual R-squared is simply the square of the correlation between y_i and $\hat{y}_i$ (see Section 3.2). Now, if instead we compute fitted values from (6.42)—that is, $\hat{y}_i = \hat{\alpha}_0 m_i$ for all observations i—then it makes sense to use the square of the correlation between y_i and these fitted values as an R-squared. Because correlation is unaffected if we multiply by a constant, it does not matter which estimate of α_0 we use. In fact, this R-squared measure for y [not $\log(y)$] is just the squared correlation between y_i and $\hat{m}_i$. We can compare this directly with the R-squared from equation (6.46). [Because the R-squared calculation does not depend on the estimate of α_0, it does not allow us to choose among (6.40), (6.43), and (6.44). But we know that (6.44) minimizes the sum of squared residuals between y_i and $\hat{m}_i$, without a constant. In other words, given the $\hat{m}_i$, $\check{\alpha}_0$ is chosen to produce the best fit based on sum of squared residuals. We are interested here in choosing between the linear model for y and $\log(y)$, and so an R-squared measure that does not depend on how we estimate α_0 is suitable.]

EXAMPLE 6.8 PREDICTING CEO SALARIES

After we obtain the $\hat{m}_i$, we just obtain the correlation between $salary_i$ and $\hat{m}_i$; it is .493. The square of it is about .243, and this is a measure of how well the log model explains the variation in *salary*, not log(*salary*). [The R^2 from (6.45), .318, tells us that the log model explains about 31.8% of the variation in log(*salary*).]

As a competing linear model, suppose we estimate a model with all variables in levels:

$$salary = \beta_0 + \beta_1 sales + \beta_2 mktval + \beta_3 ceoten + u. \quad [6.47]$$

The key is that the dependent variable is *salary*. We could use logs of *sales* or *mktval* on the right-hand side, but it makes more sense to have all dollar values in levels if one (*salary*) appears as a level. The *R*-squared from estimating this equation using the same 177 observations is .201. Thus, the log model explains more of the variation in *salary*, and so we prefer it to (6.47) on goodness-of-fit grounds. The log model is also preferred because it seems more realistic and its parameters are easier to interpret.

If we maintain the full set of classical linear model assumptions in the model (6.38), we can easily obtain prediction intervals for $y^0 = \exp(\beta_0 + \beta_1 x_1^0 + \ldots + \beta_k x_k^0 + u^0)$ when we have estimated a linear model for log(*y*). Recall that $x_1^0, x_2^0, \ldots, x_k^0$ are known values and u^0 is the unobserved error that partly determines y^0. From equation (6.37), a 95% prediction interval for $logy^0 = \log(y^0)$ is simply $\widehat{logy}^0 \pm t_{.025} \cdot \text{se}(\hat{e}^0)$, where $\text{se}(\hat{e}^0)$ is obtained from the regression of log(*y*) on $x_1, \ldots, x_k$ using the original *n* observations. Let $c_l = -t_{.025} \cdot \text{se}(\hat{e}^0)$ and $c_u = t_{.025} \cdot \text{se}(\hat{e}^0)$ be the lower and upper bounds of the prediction interval for $logy^0$. That is, $\text{P}(c_l \leq logy^0 \leq c_u) = .95$. Because the exponential function is strictly increasing, it is also true that $\text{P}[\exp(c_l) \leq \exp(logy^0) \leq \exp(c_u)] = .95$,that is, $\text{P}[\exp(c_l) \leq y^0 \leq \exp(c_u)] = .95$. Therefore, we can take $\exp(c_l)$ and $\exp(c_u)$ as the lower and upper bounds, respectively, for a 95% prediction interval for y^0. For large *n*, $t_{.025} = 1.96$, and so a 95% prediction interval for y^0 is $\exp[-1.96 \cdot \text{se}(\hat{e}^0)] \exp(\hat{\beta}_0 + \mathbf{x}^0\hat{\boldsymbol{\beta}})$ to $\exp[-1.96 \cdot \text{se}(\hat{e}^0)] \exp(\hat{\beta}_0 + \mathbf{x}^0\hat{\boldsymbol{\beta}})$, where $\mathbf{x}^0\hat{\boldsymbol{\beta}}$ is shorthand for $\hat{\beta}_1 x_1^0 + \ldots + \hat{\beta}_k x_k^0$. Remember, the $\hat{\beta}_j$ and $\text{se}(\hat{e}^0)$ are obtained from the regression with log(*y*) as the dependent variable. Because we assume normality of *u* in (6.38), we probably would use (6.40) to obtain a point prediction for y^0. Unlike in equation (6.37), this point prediction will not lie halfway between the upper and lower bounds $\exp(c_l)$ and $\exp(c_u)$. One can obtain different 95% prediction intervalues by choosing different quantiles in the t_{n-k-1} distribution. If $q_{\alpha1}$ and $q_{\alpha2}$ are quantiles with $\alpha_2 - \alpha_1 = .95$, then we can choose $c_l = q_{\alpha1}\text{se}(\hat{e}^0)$ and $c_u = q_{\alpha2}\text{se}(\hat{e}^0)$.

As an example, consider the CEO salary regression, where we make the prediction at the same values of *sales*, *mktval*, and *ceoten* as in Example 6.7. The standard error of the regression for (6.43) is about .505, and the standard error of $\widehat{logy}^0$ is about .075. Therefore, using equation (6.36), $\text{se}(\hat{e}^0) \approx .511$; as in the GPA example, the error variance swamps the estimation error in the parameters, even though here the sample size is only 177. A 95% prediction interval for $salary^0$ is $\exp[-1.96 \cdot (.511)] \exp(7.013)$ to $\exp[1.96 \cdot (.511)] \exp(7.013)$, or about 408.071 to 3,024.678, that is, \$408,071 to \$3,024,678. This very wide 95% prediction interval for CEO salary at the given sales, market value, and tenure values shows that there is much else that we have not included in the regression that determines salary. Incidentally, the point prediction for salary, using (6.40), is about \$1,262,075—higher than the predictions using the other estimates of α_0 and closer to the lower bound than the upper bound of the 95% prediction interval.

Summary

In this chapter, we have covered some important multiple regression analysis topics.

Section 6.1 showed that a change in the units of measurement of an independent variable changes the OLS coefficient in the expected manner: if x_j is multiplied by c, its coefficient is divided by c. If the dependent variable is multiplied by c, *all* OLS coefficients are multiplied by c. Neither t nor F statistics are affected by changing the units of measurement of any variables.

We discussed beta coefficients, which measure the effects of the independent variables on the dependent variable in standard deviation units. The beta coefficients are obtained from a standard OLS regression after the dependent and independent variables have been transformed into z-scores.

We provided a detailed discussion of functional form, including the logarithmic transformation, quadratics, and interaction terms. It is helpful to summarize some of our conclusions.

CONSIDERATIONS WHEN USING LOGARITHIMS

1. The coefficients have percentage change interpretations. We can be ignorant of the units of measurement of any variable that appears in logarithmic form, and changing units from, say, dollars to thousands of dollars has no effect on a variable's coefficient when that variable appears in logarithmic form.
2. Logs are often used for dollar amounts that are always positive, as well as for variables such as population, especially when there is a lot of variation. They are used less often for variables measured in years, such as schooling, age, and experience. Logs are used infrequently for variables that are already percents or proportions, such as an unemployment rate or a pass rate on a test.
3. Models with $\log(y)$ as the dependent variable often more closely satisfy the classical linear model assumptions. For example, the model has a better chance of being linear, homoskedasticity is more likely to hold, and normality is often more plausible.
4. In many cases, taking the log greatly reduces the variation of a variable, making OLS estimates less prone to outlier influence. However, in cases where y is a fraction and close to zero for many observations, $\log(y_i)$ can have much more variability than y_i. For values y_i very close to zero, $\log(y_i)$ is a negative number very large in magnitude.
5. If $y \geq 0$ but $y = 0$ is possible, we cannot use $\log(y)$. Sometimes $\log(1 + y)$ is used, but interpretation of the coefficients is difficult.
6. For large changes in an explanatory variable, we can compute a more accurate estimate of the percentage change effect.
7. It is harder (but possible) to predict y when we have estimated a model for $\log(y)$.

CONSIDERATIONS WHEN USING QUADRATICS

1. A quadratic function in an explanatory variable allows for an increasing or decreasing effect.
2. The turning point of a quadratic is easily calculated, and it should be calculated to see if it makes sense.
3. Quadratic functions where the coefficients have the opposite sign have a strictly positive turning point; if the signs of the coefficients are the same, the turning point is at a negative value of x.
4. A seemingly small coefficient on the square of a variable can be practically important in what it implies about a changing slope. One can use a t test to see if the quadratic is statistically significant, and compute the slope at various values of x to see if it is practically important.

5. For a model quadratic in a variable x, the coefficient on x measures the partial effect starting from $x = 0$, as can be seen in equation (6.11). If zero is not a possible or interesting value of x, one can center x about a more interesting value, such as the average in the sample, before computing the square. Computing Exercise 6.12 provides an example.

CONSIDERATIONS WHEN USING INTERACTIONS

1. Interaction terms allow the partial effect of an explanatory variable, say x_1, to depend on the level of another variable, say x_2—and vice versa.
2. Interpreting models with interactions can be tricky. The coefficient on x_1, say β_1, measures the partial effect of x_1 on y when $x_2 = 0$, which may be impossible or uninteresting. Centering x_1 and x_2 around interesting values before constructing the interaction term typically leads to an equation that is visually more appealing.
3. A standard t test can be used to determine if an interaction term is statistically significant. Computing the partial effects at different values of the explanatory variables can be used to determine the practical importance of interactions.

We introduced the adjusted R-squared, $\bar{R}^2$, as an alternative to the usual R-squared for measuring goodness-of-fit. Whereas R^2 can never fall when another variable is added to a regression, $\bar{R}^2$ penalizes the number of regressors and can drop when an independent variable is added. This makes $\bar{R}^2$ preferable for choosing between nonnested models with different numbers of explanatory variables. Neither R^2 nor $\bar{R}^2$ can be used to compare models with different dependent variables. Nevertheless, it is fairly easy to obtain goodness-of-fit measures for choosing between y and $\log(y)$ as the dependent variable, as shown in Section 6.4.

In Section 6.3, we discussed the somewhat subtle problem of relying too much on R^2 or $\bar{R}^2$ in arriving at a final model: it is possible to control for too many factors in a regression model. For this reason, it is important to think ahead about model specification, particularly the ceteris paribus nature of the multiple regression equation. Explanatory variables that affect y and are uncorrelated with all the other explanatory variables can be used to reduce the error variance without inducing multicollinearity.

In Section 6.4, we demonstrated how to obtain a confidence interval for a prediction made from an OLS regression line. We also showed how a confidence interval can be constructed for a future, unknown value of y.

Occasionally, we want to predict y when $\log(y)$ is used as the dependent variable in a regression model. Section 6.4 explains this simple method. Finally, we are sometimes interested in knowing about the sign and magnitude of the residuals for particular observations. Residual analysis can be used to determine whether particular members of the sample have predicted values that are well above or well below the actual outcomes.

Key Terms

Adjusted R-Squared
Beta Coefficients
Bootstrap
Bootstrap Standard Error
Interaction Effect
Nonnested Models
Over Controlling
Population R-Squared
Prediction Error
Prediction Interval
Predictions
Quadratic Functions
Resampling Method
Residual Analysis
Smearing Estimate
Standardized Coefficients
Variance of the Prediction Error

Problems

1 The following equation was estimated using the data in CEOSAL1.RAW:

$$\widehat{\log(salary)} = \underset{(.324)}{4.322} + \underset{(.033)}{.276} \log(sales) + \underset{(.0129)}{.0215}\, roe - \underset{(.00026)}{.00008}\, roe^2$$
$$n = 209,\ R^2 = .282.$$

This equation allows *roe* to have a diminishing effect on log(*salary*). Is this generality necessary? Explain why or why not.

2 Let $\hat{\beta}_0, \hat{\beta}_1, \ldots, \hat{\beta}_k$ be the OLS estimates from the regression of y_i on $x_{i1}, \ldots, x_{ik}$, $i=1, 2, \ldots, n$. For nonzero constants $c_1, \ldots, c_k$, argue that the OLS intercept and slopes from the regression of $c_0 y_i$ on $c_1 x_{i1}, \ldots, c_k x_{ik}$, $i = 1, 2, \ldots, n$, are given by $\tilde{\beta}_0 = c_0\hat{\beta}_0$, $\tilde{\beta}_1 = (c_0/c_1)\hat{\beta}_1, \ldots, \tilde{\beta}_k = (c_0/c_k)\hat{\beta}_k$. [*Hint*: Use the fact that the $\hat{\beta}_j$ solve the first order conditions in (3.13), and the $\tilde{\beta}_j$ must solve the first order conditions involving the rescaled dependent and independent variables.]

3 Using the data in RDCHEM.RAW, the following equation was obtained by OLS:

$$\widehat{rdintens} = \underset{(.429)}{2.613} + \underset{(.00014)}{.00030}\, sales - \underset{(.0000000037)}{.0000000070}\, sales^2$$
$$n = 32,\ R^2 = .1484.$$

(i) At what point does the marginal effect of *sales* on *rdintens* become negative?
(ii) Would you keep the quadratic term in the model? Explain.
(iii) Define *salesbil* as sales measured in billions of dollars: $salesbil = sales/1{,}000$. Rewrite the estimated equation with *salesbil* and $salesbil^2$ as the independent variables. Be sure to report standard errors and the *R*-squared. [*Hint*: Note that $salesbil^2 = sales^2/(1{,}000)^2$.]
(iv) For the purpose of reporting the results, which equation do you prefer?

4 The following model allows the return to education to depend upon the total amount of both parents' education, called *pareduc*:

$$\log(wage) = \beta_0 + \beta_1 educ + \beta_2 educ{\cdot}pareduc + \beta_3 exper + \beta_4 tenure + u.$$

(i) Show that, in decimal form, the return to another year of education in this model is

$$\Delta\log(wage)/\Delta educ = \beta_1 + \beta_2 pareduc.$$

What sign do you expect for β_2? Why?
(ii) Using the data in WAGE2.RAW, the estimated equation is

$$\widehat{\log(wage)} = \underset{(.13)}{5.65} + \underset{(.010)}{.047}\, educ + \underset{(.00021)}{.00078}\, educ{\cdot}pareduc +$$
$$\underset{(.004)}{.019}\, exper + \underset{(.003)}{.010}\, tenure$$
$$n = 722,\ R^2 = .169.$$

(Only 722 observations contain full information on parents' education.) Interpret the coefficient on the interaction term. It might help to choose two specific values for *pareduc*—for example, $pareduc = 32$ if both parents have a college education, or $pareduc = 24$ if both parents have a high school education—and to compare the estimated return to *educ*.

(iii) When *pareduc* is added as a separate variable to the equation, we get:

$$\widehat{\log(wage)} = \underset{(.38)}{4.94} + \underset{(.027)}{.097}\ educ + \underset{(.017)}{.033}\ pareduc - \underset{(.0012)}{.0016}\ educ \cdot pareduc$$
$$+ \underset{(.004)}{.020}\ exper + \underset{(.003)}{.010}\ tenure$$
$$n = 722,\ R^2 = .174.$$

Does the estimated return to education now depend positively on parent education? Test the null hypothesis that the return to education does not depend on parent education.

5 In Example 4.2, where the percentage of students receiving a passing score on a tenth-grade math exam (*math*10) is the dependent variable, does it make sense to include *sci11*—the percentage of eleventh graders passing a science exam—as an additional explanatory variable?

6 When $atndrte^2$ and $ACT \cdot atndrte$ are added to the equation estimated in (6.19), the *R*-squared becomes .232. Are these additional terms jointly significant at the 10% level? Would you include them in the model?

7 The following three equations were estimated using the 1,534 observations in 401K.RAW:

$$\widehat{prate} = \underset{(.78)}{80.29} + \underset{(.52)}{5.44}\ mrate + \underset{(.045)}{.269}\ age - \underset{(.00004)}{.00013}\ totemp$$
$$R^2 = .100,\ \bar{R}^2 = .098.$$

$$\widehat{prate} = \underset{(1.95)}{97.32} + \underset{(0.51)}{5.02}\ mrate + \underset{(.044)}{.314}\ age - \underset{(.28)}{2.66}\ \log(totemp)$$
$$R^2 = .144,\ \bar{R}^2 = .142.$$

$$\widehat{prate} = \underset{(.78)}{80.62} + \underset{(.52)}{5.34}\ mrate + \underset{(.045)}{.290}\ age - \underset{(.00009)}{.00043}\ totemp$$
$$+ \underset{(.0000000010)}{.0000000039}\ totemp^2$$
$$R^2 = .108,\ \bar{R}^2 = .106.$$

Which of these three models do you prefer? Why?

8 Suppose we want to estimate the effects of alcohol consumption (*alcohol*) on college grade point average (*colGPA*). In addition to collecting information on grade point averages and alcohol usage, we also obtain attendance information (say, percentage of lectures attended, called *attend*). A standardized test score (say, *SAT*) and high school GPA (*hsGPA*) are also available.

(i) Should we include *attend* along with *alcohol* as explanatory variables in a multiple regression model? (Think about how you would interpret $\beta_{alcohol}$.)

(ii) Should *SAT* and *hsGPA* be included as explanatory variables? Explain.

9 If we start with (6.38) under the CLM assumptions, assume large n, and ignore the estimation error in the $\hat{\beta}_j$, a 95% prediction interval for y^0 is $[\exp(-1.96\hat{\sigma})\exp(\widehat{logy^0}),$ $\exp(1.96\hat{\sigma})\exp(\widehat{logy^0})]$. The point prediction for y^0 is $\hat{y}^0 = \exp(\hat{\sigma}^2/2)\exp(\widehat{logy^0})$.
   (i) For what values of $\hat{\sigma}$ will the point prediction be in the 95% prediction interval? Does this condition seem likely to hold in most applications?
   (ii) Verify that the condition from part (i) is satisfied in the CEO salary example.

Computer Exercises

C1 Use the data in KIELMC.RAW, only for the year 1981, to answer the following questions. The data are for houses that sold during 1981 in North Andover, Massachusetts; 1981 was the year construction began on a local garbage incinerator.
   (i) To study the effects of the incinerator location on housing price, consider the simple regression model

$$\log(price) = \beta_0 + \beta_1\log(dist) + u,$$

   where *price* is housing price in dollars and *dist* is distance from the house to the incinerator measured in feet. Interpreting this equation causally, what sign do you expect for β_1 if the presence of the incinerator depresses housing prices? Estimate this equation and interpret the results.
   (ii) To the simple regression model in part (i), add the variables log(*intst*), log(*area*), log(*land*), *rooms*, *baths*, and *age*, where *intst* is distance from the home to the interstate, *area* is square footage of the house, *land* is the lot size in square feet, *rooms* is total number of rooms, *baths* is number of bathrooms, and *age* is age of the house in years. Now, what do you conclude about the effects of the incinerator? Explain why (i) and (ii) give conflicting results.
   (iii) Add $[\log(intst)]^2$ to the model from part (ii). Now what happens? What do you conclude about the importance of functional form?
   (iv) Is the square of log(*dist*) significant when you add it to the model from part (iii)?

C2 Use the data in WAGE1.RAW for this exercise.
   (i) Use OLS to estimate the equation

$$\log(wage) = \beta_0 + \beta_1 educ + \beta_2 exper + \beta_3 exper^2 + u$$

   and report the results using the usual format.
   (ii) Is $exper^2$ statistically significant at the 1% level?
   (iii) Using the approximation

$$\%\Delta\widehat{wage} \approx 100(\hat{\beta}_2 + 2\hat{\beta}_3 exper)\Delta exper,$$

   find the approximate return to the fifth year of experience. What is the approximate return to the twentieth year of experience?
   (iv) At what value of *exper* does additional experience actually lower predicted log(*wage*)? How many people have more experience in this sample?

C3 Consider a model where the return to education depends upon the amount of work experience (and vice versa):

$$\log(wage) = \beta_0 + \beta_1 educ + \beta_2 exper + \beta_3 educ\cdot exper + u.$$

(i) Show that the return to another year of education (in decimal form), holding *exper* fixed, is $\beta_1 + \beta_3 exper$.

(ii) State the null hypothesis that the return to education does not depend on the level of *exper*. What do you think is the appropriate alternative?

(iii) Use the data in WAGE2.RAW to test the null hypothesis in (ii) against your stated alternative.

(iv) Let θ_1 denote the return to education (in decimal form), when $exper = 10$: $\theta_1 = \beta_1 + 10\beta_3$. Obtain $\hat{\theta}_1$ and a 95% confidence interval for θ_1. (*Hint:* Write $\beta_1 = \theta_1 - 10\beta_3$ and plug this into the equation; then rearrange. This gives the regression for obtaining the confidence interval for θ_1.)

C4 Use the data in GPA2.RAW for this exercise.

(i) Estimate the model

$$sat = \beta_0 + \beta_1 hsize + \beta_2 hsize^2 + u,$$

where *hsize* is the size of the graduating class (in hundreds), and write the results in the usual form. Is the quadratic term statistically significant?

(ii) Using the estimated equation from part (i), what is the "optimal" high school size? Justify your answer.

(iii) Is this analysis representative of the academic performance of *all* high school seniors? Explain.

(iv) Find the estimated optimal high school size, using log(*sat*) as the dependent variable. Is it much different from what you obtained in part (ii)?

C5 Use the housing price data in HPRICE1.RAW for this exercise.

(i) Estimate the model

$$\log(price) = \beta_0 + \beta_1 \log(lotsize) + \beta_2 \log(sqrft) + \beta_3 bdrms + u$$

and report the results in the usual OLS format.

(ii) Find the predicted value of log(*price*), when $lotsize = 20{,}000$, $sqrft = 2{,}500$, and $bdrms = 4$. Using the methods in Section 6.4, find the predicted value of *price* at the same values of the explanatory variables.

(iii) For explaining variation in *price*, decide whether you prefer the model from part (i) or the model

$$price = \beta_0 + \beta_1 lotsize + \beta_2 sqrft + \beta_3 bdrms + u.$$

C6 Use the data in VOTE1.RAW for this exercise.

(i) Consider a model with an interaction between expenditures:

$$voteA = \beta_0 + \beta_1 prtystrA + \beta_2 expendA + \beta_3 expendB + \beta_4 expendA \cdot expendB + u.$$

What is the partial effect of *expendB* on *voteA*, holding *prtystrA* and *expendA* fixed? What is the partial effect of *expendA* on *voteA*? Is the expected sign for β_4 obvious?

(ii) Estimate the equation in part (i) and report the results in the usual form. Is the interaction term statistically significant?

(iii) Find the average of *expendA* in the sample. Fix *expendA* at 300 (for $300,000). What is the estimated effect of another $100,000 spent by Candidate B on *voteA*? Is this a large effect?

(iv) Now fix *expendB* at 100. What is the estimated effect of $\Delta expendA = 100$ on *voteA*? Does this make sense?

(v) Now, estimate a model that replaces the interaction with *shareA*, Candidate A's percentage share of total campaign expenditures. Does it make sense to hold both *expendA* and *expendB* fixed, while changing *shareA*?

(vi) (Requires calculus) In the model from part (v), find the partial effect of *expendB* on *voteA*, holding *prtystrA* and *expendA* fixed. Evaluate this at $expendA = 300$ and $expendB = 0$ and comment on the results.

C7 Use the data in ATTEND.RAW for this exercise.

(i) In the model of Example 6.3, argue that

$$\Delta stndfnl/\Delta priGPA \approx \beta_2 + 2\beta_4 priGPA + \beta_6 atndrte.$$

Use equation (6.19) to estimate the partial effect when $priGPA = 2.59$ and $atndrte = 82$. Interpret your estimate.

(ii) Show that the equation can be written as

$$stndfnl = \theta_0 + \beta_1 atndrte + \theta_2 priGPA + \beta_3 ACT + \beta_4(priGPA - 2.59)^2 + \beta_5 ACT^2 + \beta_6 priGPA(atndrte - 82) + u,$$

where $\theta_2 = \beta_2 + 2\beta_4(2.59) + \beta_6(82)$. (Note that the intercept has changed, but this is unimportant.) Use this to obtain the standard error of $\hat{\theta}_2$ from part (i).

(iii) Suppose that, in place of $priGPA(atndrte - 82)$, you put $(priGPA - 2.59)\cdot(atndrte - 82)$. Now how do you interpret the coefficients on *atndrte* and *priGPA*?

C8 Use the data in HPRICE1.RAW for this exercise.

(i) Estimate the model

$$price = \beta_0 + \beta_1 lotsize + \beta_2 sqrft + \beta_3 bdrms + u$$

and report the results in the usual form, including the standard error of the regression. Obtain predicted price, when we plug in $lotsize = 10{,}000$, $sqrft = 2{,}300$, and $bdrms = 4$; round this price to the nearest dollar.

(ii) Run a regression that allows you to put a 95% confidence interval around the predicted value in part (i). Note that your prediction will differ somewhat due to rounding error.

(iii) Let $price^0$ be the unknown future selling price of the house with the characteristics used in parts (i) and (ii). Find a 95% CI for $price^0$ and comment on the width of this confidence interval.

C9 The data set NBASAL.RAW contains salary information and career statistics for 269 players in the National Basketball Association (NBA).

(i) Estimate a model relating points-per-game (*points*) to years in the league (*exper*), *age*, and years played in college (*coll*). Include a quadratic in *exper*; the other variables should appear in level form. Report the results in the usual way.

(ii) Holding college years and age fixed, at what value of experience does the next year of experience actually reduce points-per-game? Does this make sense?

(iii) Why do you think *coll* has a negative and statistically significant coefficient? (*Hint:* NBA players can be drafted before finishing their college careers and even directly out of high school.)

(iv) Add a quadratic in *age* to the equation. Is it needed? What does this appear to imply about the effects of age, once experience and education are controlled for?

(v) Now regress log(*wage*) on *points*, *exper*, $exper^2$, *age*, and *coll*. Report the results in the usual format.

(vi) Test whether *age* and *coll* are jointly significant in the regression from part (v). What does this imply about whether age and education have separate effects on wage, once productivity and seniority are accounted for?

C10 Use the data in BWGHT2.RAW for this exercise.

(i) Estimate the equation

$$\log(bwght) = \beta_0 + \beta_1 npvis + \beta_2 npvis^2 + u$$

by OLS, and report the results in the usual way. Is the quadratic term significant?

(ii) Show that, based on the equation from part (i), the number of prenatal visits that maximizes log(*bwght*) is estimated to be about 22. How many women had at least 22 prenatal visits in the sample?

(iii) Does it make sense that birth weight is actually predicted to decline after 22 prenatal visits? Explain.

(iv) Add mother's age to the equation, using a quadratic functional form. Holding *npvis* fixed, at what mother's age is the birth weight of the child maximized? What fraction of women in the sample are older than the "optimal" age?

(v) Would you say that mother's age and number of prenatal visits explain a lot of the variation in log(*bwght*)?

(vi) Using quadratics for both *npvis* and *age*, decide whether using the natural log or the level of *bwght* is better for predicting *bwght*.

C11 Use APPLE.RAW to verify some of the claims made in Section 6.3.

(i) Run the regression *ecolbs* on *ecoprc*, *regprc* and report the results in the usual form, including the *R*-squared and adjusted *R*-squared. Interpret the coefficients on the price variables and comment on their signs and magnitudes.

(ii) Are the price variables statistically significant? Report the *p*-values for the individual *t* tests.

(iii) What is the range of fitted values for *ecolbs*? What fraction of the sample reports $ecolbs = 0$? Comment.

(iv) Do you think the price variables together do a good job of explaining variation in *ecolbs*? Explain.

(v) Add the variables *faminc*, *hhsize* (household size), *educ*, and *age* to the regression from part (i). Find the *p*-value for their joint significance. What do you conclude?

(vi) Run separate simple regressions of *ecolbs* on *ecoprc* and then *ecolbs* on *regprc*. How do the simple regression coefficients compare with the multiple regression from part (i)? Find the correlation coefficient between *ecoprc* and *regprc* to help explain your findings.

C12 Use the subset of 401KSUBS.RAW with $fsize = 1$; this restricts the analysis to single-person households; see also Computer Exercise C8 in Chapter 4.

(i) What is the youngest age of people in this sample? How many people are at that age?

(ii) In the model

$$nettfa = \beta_0 + \beta_1 inc + \beta_2 age + \beta_3 age^2 + u,$$

what is the literal interpretation of β_2? By itself, is it of much interest?

(iii) Estimate the model from part (ii) and report the results in standard form. Are you concerned that the coefficient on *age* is negative? Explain.

(iv) Because the youngest people in the sample are 25, it makes sense to think that, for a given level of income, the lowest average amount of net total financial assets is at age 25. Recall that the partial effect of *age* on *nettfa* is $\beta_2 + 2\beta_3 age$, so the partial effect at age 25 is $\beta_2 + 2\beta_3(25) = \beta_2 + 50\beta_3$; call this θ_2. Find $\hat{\theta}_2$ and obtain the two-sided *p*-value for testing H_0: $\theta_2 = 0$. You should conclude that $\hat{\theta}_2$ is small and very statistically insignificant. [*Hint:* One way to do this is to estimate the model $nettfa = \alpha_0 + \beta_1 inc + \theta_2 age + \beta_3(age - 25)^2 + u$, where the intercept, α_0, is different from β_0. There are other ways, too.]

(v) Because the evidence against H_0: $\theta_2 = 0$ is very weak, set it to zero and estimate the model

$$nettfa = \alpha_0 + \beta_1 inc + \beta_3(age - 25)^2 + u.$$

In terms of goodness-of-fit, does this model fit better than that in part (ii)?

(vi) For the estimated equation in part (v), set $inc = 30$ (roughly, the average value) and graph the relationship between *nettfa* and *age*, but only for $age \geq 25$. Describe what you see.

(vii) Check to see whether including a quadratic in *inc* is necessary.

C13 Use the data in MEAP00.RAW to answer this question.

(i) Estimate the model

$$math4 = \beta_0 + \beta_2 lexppp + \beta_2 lenroll + \beta_3 lunch + u$$

by OLS, and report the results in the usual form. Is each explanatory variable statistically significant at the 5% level?

(ii) Obtain the fitted values from the regression in part (i). What is the range of fitted values? How does it compare with the range of the actual data on *math*4?

(iii) Obtain the residuals from the regression in part (i). What is the building code of the school that has the largest (positive) residual? Provide an interpretation of this residual.

(iv) Add quadratics of all explanatory variables to the equation, and test them for joint significance. Would you leave them in the model?

(v) Returning to the model in part (i), divide the dependent variable and each explanatory variable by its sample standard deviation, and rerun the regression. (Include an intercept unless you also first subtract the mean from each variable.) In terms of standard deviation units, which explanatory variable has the largest effect on the math pass rate?

C14 Use the data in BENEFITS.RAW to answer this question. It is a school-level data set at the K–5 level on average teacher salary and benefits. See Example 4.10 for background.

(i) Regress *lavgsal* on *bs* and report the results in the usual form. Can you reject H_0: $\beta_{bs} = 0$ against a two-sided alternative? Can you reject H_0: $\beta_{bs} = -1$ against H_1: $\beta_{bs} > -1$? Report the *p*-values for both tests.

(ii) Define *lbs* = log(*bs*). Find the range of values for *lbs* and find its standard deviation. How do these compare to the range and standard deviation for *bs*?

(iii) Regress *lavgsal* on *lbs*. Does this fit better than the regression from part (i)?

(iv) Estimate the equation

$$lavgsal = \beta_0 + \beta_1 bs + \beta_2 lenroll + \beta_3 lstaff + \beta_4 lunch + u$$

and report the results in the usual form. What happens to the coefficient on *bs*? Is it now statistically different from zero?

(v) Interpret the coefficient on *lstaff*. Why do you think it is negative?

(vi) Add $lunch^2$ to the equation from part (iv). Is it statistically significant? Compute the turning point (minimum value) in the quadratic, and show that it is within the range of the observed data on *lunch*. How many values of *lunch* are higher than the calculated turning point?

(vii) Based on the findings from part (vi), describe how teacher salaries relate to school poverty rates. In terms of teacher salary, and holding other factors fixed, is it better to teach at a school with *lunch* = 0 (no poverty), *lunch* = 50, or *lunch* = 100 (all kids eligible for the free lunch program)?

APPENDIX 6A

6A. A Brief Introduction to Bootstrapping

In many cases where formulas for standard errors are hard to obtain mathematically, or where they are thought not to be very good approximations to the true sampling variation of an estimator, we can rely on a **resampling method**. The general idea is to treat the observed data as a population that we can draw samples from. The most common resampling method is the **bootstrap**. (There are actually several versions of the bootstrap, but the most general, and most easily applied, is called the *nonparametric bootstrap*, and that is what we describe here.)

Suppose we have an estimate, $\hat{\theta}$, of a population parameter, θ. We obtained this estimate, which could be a function of OLS estimates (or estimates that we cover in later chapters), from a random sample of size n. We would like to obtain a standard error for $\hat{\theta}$ that can be used for constructing t statistics or confidence intervals. Remarkably, we can obtain a valid standard error by computing the estimate from different random samples drawn from the original data.

Implementation is easy. If we list our observations from 1 through n, we draw n numbers randomly, with replacement, from this list. This produces a new data set (of size n) that consists of the original data, but with many observations appearing multiple times (except in the rather unusual case that we resample the original data). Each time we randomly sample from the original data, we can estimate θ using the same procedure that we used on the original data. Let $\hat{\theta}^{(b)}$ denote the estimate from bootstrap sample b. Now, if we repeat the resampling and estimation m times, we have m new estimates, $\{\hat{\theta}^{(b)}: b = 1, 2, \ldots, m\}$. The **bootstrap standard error** of $\hat{\theta}$ is just the sample standard deviation of the $\hat{\theta}^{(b)}$, namely,

$$\text{bse}(\hat{\theta}) = \left[(m-1)^{-1}\sum_{b=1}^{m}(\hat{\theta}^{(b)} - \bar{\hat{\theta}})^2\right]^{1/2}, \quad [6.48]$$

where $\bar{\hat{\theta}}$ is the average of the bootstrap estimates.

If obtaining an estimate of θ on a sample of size n requires little computational time, as in the case of OLS and all the other estimators we encounter in this text, we can afford to choose m—the number of bootstrap replications—to be large. A typical value is m = 1,000, but even m = 500 or a somewhat smaller value can produce a reliable standard error. Note that the size of m—the number of times we resample the original data—has nothing to do with the sample size, n. (For certain estimation problems beyond the scope of this text, a large n can force one to do fewer bootstrap replications.) Many statistics and econometrics packages have built-in bootstrap commands, and this makes the calculation of bootstrap standard errors simple, especially compared with the work often required to obtain an analytical formula for an asymptotic standard error.

One can actually do better in most cases by using the bootstrap sample to compute p-values for t statistics (and F statistics), or for obtaining confidence intervals, rather than obtaining a bootstrap standard error to be used in the construction of t statistics or confidence intervals. See Horowitz (2001) for a comprehensive treatment.

CHAPTER 7

Multiple Regression Analysis with Qualitative Information: Binary (or Dummy) Variables

In previous chapters, the dependent and independent variables in our multiple regression models have had *quantitative* meaning. Just a few examples include hourly wage rate, years of education, college grade point average, amount of air pollution, level of firm sales, and number of arrests. In each case, the magnitude of the variable conveys useful information. In empirical work, we must also incorporate *qualitative* factors into regression models. The gender or race of an individual, the industry of a firm (manufacturing, retail, and so on), and the region in the United States where a city is located (South, North, West, and so on) are all considered to be qualitative factors.

Most of this chapter is dedicated to qualitative *independent* variables. After we discuss the appropriate ways to describe qualitative information in Section 7.1, we show how qualitative explanatory variables can be easily incorporated into multiple regression models in Sections 7.2, 7.3, and 7.4. These sections cover almost all of the popular ways that qualitative independent variables are used in cross-sectional regression analysis.

In Section 7.5, we discuss a binary dependent variable, which is a particular kind of qualitative dependent variable. The multiple regression model has an interesting interpretation in this case and is called the linear probability model. While much maligned by some econometricians, the simplicity of the linear probability model makes it useful in many empirical contexts. We will describe its drawbacks in Section 7.5, but they are often secondary in empirical work.

7.1 Describing Qualitative Information

Qualitative factors often come in the form of binary information: a person is female or male; a person does or does not own a personal computer; a firm offers a certain kind of employee pension plan or it does not; a state administers capital punishment or it does not. In all of these examples, the relevant information can be captured by defining a **binary variable** or a **zero-one variable**. In econometrics, binary variables are most commonly called **dummy variables**, although this name is not especially descriptive.

TABLE 7.1 A Partial Listing of the Data in WAGE1.RAW

person	*wage*	*educ*	*exper*	*female*	*married*
1	3.10	11	2	1	0
2	3.24	12	22	1	1
3	3.00	11	2	0	0
4	6.00	8	44	0	1
5	5.30	12	7	0	1
.	.	.	.	.	.
.	.	.	.	.	.
.	.	.	.	.	.
525	11.56	16	5	0	1
526	3.50	14	5	1	0

In defining a dummy variable, we must decide which event is assigned the value one and which is assigned the value zero. For example, in a study of individual wage determination, we might define *female* to be a binary variable taking on the value one for females and the value zero for males. The name in this case indicates the event with the value one. The same information is captured by defining *male* to be one if the person is male and zero if the person is female. Either of these is better than using *gender* because this name does not make it clear when the dummy variable is one: does *gender* = 1 correspond to male or female? What we call our variables is unimportant for getting regression results, but it always helps to choose names that clarify equations and expositions.

EXPLORING FURTHER 7.1

Suppose that, in a study comparing election outcomes between Democratic and Republican candidates, you wish to indicate the party of each candidate. Is a name such as *party* a wise choice for a binary variable in this case? What would be a better name?

Suppose in the wage example that we have chosen the name *female* to indicate gender. Further, we define a binary variable *married* to equal one if a person is married and zero if otherwise. Table 7.1 gives a partial listing of a wage data set that might result. We see that Person 1 is female and not married, Person 2 is female and married, Person 3 is male and not married, and so on.

Why do we use the values zero and one to describe qualitative information? In a sense, these values are arbitrary: any two different values would do. The real benefit of capturing qualitative information using zero-one variables is that it leads to regression models where the parameters have very natural interpretations, as we will see now.

7.2 A Single Dummy Independent Variable

How do we incorporate binary information into regression models? In the simplest case, with only a single dummy explanatory variable, we just add it as an independent variable in the equation. For example, consider the following simple model of hourly wage determination:

$$wage = \beta_0 + \delta_0 female + \beta_1 educ + u. \qquad [7.1]$$

We use δ_0 as the parameter on *female* in order to highlight the interpretation of the parameters multiplying dummy variables; later, we will use whatever notation is most convenient.

In model (7.1), only two observed factors affect wage: gender and education. Because $female = 1$ when the person is female, and $female = 0$ when the person is male, the parameter δ_0 has the following interpretation: δ_0 is the difference in hourly wage between females and males, *given* the same amount of education (and the same error term u). Thus, the coefficient δ_0 determines whether there is discrimination against women: if $\delta_0 < 0$, then, for the same level of other factors, women earn less than men on average.

In terms of expectations, if we assume the zero conditional mean assumption $E(u|female,educ) = 0$, then

$$\delta_0 = E(wage|female = 1,educ) - E(wage|female = 0,educ).$$

Because $female = 1$ corresponds to females and $female = 0$ corresponds to males, we can write this more simply as

$$\delta_0 = E(wage|female,educ) - E(wage|male,educ). \quad [7.2]$$

The key here is that the level of education is the same in both expectations; the difference, δ_0, is due to gender only.

The situation can be depicted graphically as an **intercept shift** between males and females. In Figure 7.1, the case $\delta_0 < 0$ is shown, so that men earn a fixed amount more per

FIGURE 7.1 Graph of $wage = \beta_0 + \delta_0\,female + \beta_1\,educ$ for $\delta_0 < 0$.

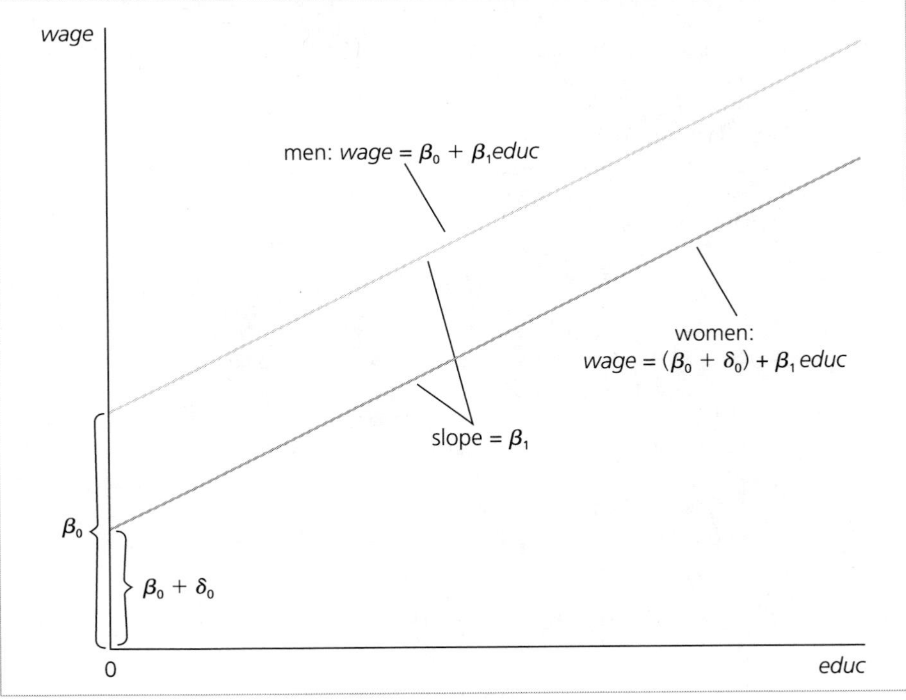

hour than women. The difference does not depend on the amount of education, and this explains why the wage-education profiles for women and men are parallel.

At this point, you may wonder why we do not also include in (7.1) a dummy variable, say *male*, which is one for males and zero for females. This would be redundant. In (7.1), the intercept for males is β_0, and the intercept for females is $\beta_0 + \delta_0$. Because there are just two groups, we only need two different intercepts. This means that, in addition to β_0, we need to use only *one* dummy variable; we have chosen to include the dummy variable for females. Using two dummy variables would introduce perfect collinearity because $female + male = 1$, which means that *male* is a perfect linear function of *female*. Including dummy variables for both genders is the simplest example of the so-called **dummy variable trap**, which arises when too many dummy variables describe a given number of groups. We will discuss this problem later.

In (7.1), we have chosen males to be the **base group** or **benchmark group**, that is, the group against which comparisons are made. This is why β_0 is the intercept for males, and δ_0 is the *difference* in intercepts between females and males. We could choose females as the base group by writing the model as

$$wage = \alpha_0 + \gamma_0 male + \beta_1 educ + u,$$

where the intercept for females is α_0 and the intercept for males is $\alpha_0 + \gamma_0$; this implies that $\alpha_0 = \beta_0 + \delta_0$ and $\alpha_0 + \gamma_0 = \beta_0$. In any application, it does not matter how we choose the base group, but it is important to keep track of which group is the base group.

Some researchers prefer to drop the overall intercept in the model and to include dummy variables for each group. The equation would then be $wage = \beta_0 male + \alpha_0 female + \beta_1 educ + u$, where the intercept for men is β_0 and the intercept for women is α_0. There is no dummy variable trap in this case because we do not have an overall intercept. However, this formulation has little to offer, since testing for a difference in the intercepts is more difficult, and there is no generally agreed upon way to compute R-squared in regressions without an intercept. Therefore, we will always include an overall intercept for the base group.

Nothing much changes when more explanatory variables are involved. Taking males as the base group, a model that controls for experience and tenure in addition to education is

$$wage = \beta_0 + \delta_0 female + \beta_1 educ + \beta_2 exper + \beta_3 tenure + u. \quad [7.3]$$

If *educ*, *exper*, and *tenure* are all relevant productivity characteristics, the null hypothesis of *no* difference between men and women is H_0: $\delta_0 = 0$. The alternative that there is discrimination against women is H_1: $\delta_0 < 0$.

How can we actually test for wage discrimination? The answer is simple: just estimate the model by OLS, *exactly* as before, and use the usual t statistic. Nothing changes about the mechanics of OLS or the statistical theory when some of the independent variables are defined as dummy variables. The only difference with what we have done up until now is in the interpretation of the coefficient on the dummy variable.

EXAMPLE 7.1 HOURLY WAGE EQUATION

Using the data in WAGE1.RAW, we estimate model (7.3). For now, we use *wage*, rather than log(*wage*), as the dependent variable:

$$\begin{aligned}\widehat{wage} &= \underset{(.72)}{-1.57} - \underset{(.26)}{1.81}\, female + \underset{(.049)}{.572}\, educ \\ &\quad + \underset{(.012)}{.025}\, exper + \underset{(.021)}{.141}\, tenure \\ n &= 526,\ R^2 = .364.\end{aligned} \qquad [7.4]$$

The negative intercept—the intercept for men, in this case—is not very meaningful because no one has zero values for all of *educ*, *exper*, and *tenure* in the sample. The coefficient on *female* is interesting because it measures the average difference in hourly wage between a man and a woman who have the *same* levels of *educ*, *exper*, and *tenure*. If we take a woman and a man with the same levels of education, experience, and tenure, the woman earns, on average, \$1.81 less per hour than the man. (Recall that these are 1976 wages.)

It is important to remember that, because we have performed multiple regression and controlled for *educ*, *exper*, and *tenure*, the \$1.81 wage differential cannot be explained by different average levels of education, experience, or tenure between men and women. We can conclude that the differential of \$1.81 is due to gender or factors associated with gender that we have not controlled for in the regression. [In 2003 dollars, the wage differential is about $3.23(1.81) \approx 5.85$.]

It is informative to compare the coefficient on *female* in equation (7.4) to the estimate we get when all other explanatory variables are dropped from the equation:

$$\begin{aligned}\widehat{wage} &= \underset{(.21)}{7.10} - \underset{(.30)}{2.51}\, female \\ n &= 526,\ R^2 = .116.\end{aligned} \qquad [7.5]$$

The coefficients in (7.5) have a simple interpretation. The intercept is the average wage for men in the sample (let *female* = 0), so men earn \$7.10 per hour on average. The coefficient on *female* is the difference in the average wage between women and men. Thus, the average wage for women in the sample is $7.10 - 2.51 = 4.59$, or \$4.59 per hour. (Incidentally, there are 274 men and 252 women in the sample.)

Equation (7.5) provides a simple way to carry out a *comparison-of-means test* between the two groups, which in this case are men and women. The estimated difference, -2.51, has a *t* statistic of -8.37, which is very statistically significant (and, of course, \$2.51 is economically large as well). Generally, simple regression on a constant and a dummy variable is a straightforward way to compare the means of two groups. For the usual *t* test to be valid, we must assume that the homoskedasticity assumption holds, which means that the population variance in wages for men is the same as that for women.

The estimated wage differential between men and women is larger in (7.5) than in (7.4) because (7.5) does not control for differences in education, experience, and tenure, and these are lower, on average, for women than for men in this sample. Equation (7.4) gives a more reliable estimate of the ceteris paribus gender wage gap; it still indicates a very large differential.

In many cases, dummy independent variables reflect choices of individuals or other economic units (as opposed to something predetermined, such as gender). In such situations, the matter of causality is again a central issue. In the following example, we would like to know whether personal computer ownership *causes* a higher college grade point average.

EXAMPLE 7.2 EFFECTS OF COMPUTER OWNERSHIP ON COLLEGE GPA

In order to determine the effects of computer ownership on college grade point average, we estimate the model

$$colGPA = \beta_0 + \delta_0 PC + \beta_1 hsGPA + \beta_2 ACT + u,$$

where the dummy variable *PC* equals one if a student owns a personal computer and zero otherwise. There are various reasons PC ownership might have an effect on *colGPA*. A student's work might be of higher quality if it is done on a computer, and time can be saved by not having to wait at a computer lab. Of course, a student might be more inclined to play computer games or surf the Internet if he or she owns a PC, so it is not obvious that δ_0 is positive. The variables *hsGPA* (high school GPA) and *ACT* (achievement test score) are used as controls: it could be that stronger students, as measured by high school *GPA* and *ACT* scores, are more likely to own computers. We control for these factors because we would like to know the average effect on *colGPA* if a student is picked at random and given a personal computer.

Using the data in GPA1.RAW, we obtain

$$\begin{aligned}\widehat{colGPA} &= \underset{(.33)}{1.26} + \underset{(.057)}{.157}\,PC + \underset{(.094)}{.447}\,hsGPA + \underset{(.0105)}{.0087}\,ACT \\ n &= 141,\ R^2 = .219.\end{aligned} \quad [7.6]$$

This equation implies that a student who owns a PC has a predicted GPA about .16 points higher than a comparable student without a PC (remember, both *colGPA* and *hsGPA* are on a four-point scale). The effect is also very statistically significant, with $t_{PC} = .157/.057 \approx 2.75$.

What happens if we drop *hsGPA* and *ACT* from the equation? Clearly, dropping the latter variable should have very little effect, as its coefficient and t statistic are very small. But *hsGPA* is very significant, and so dropping it could affect the estimate of β_{PC}. Regressing *colGPA* on *PC* gives an estimate on *PC* equal to about .170, with a standard error of .063; in this case, $\hat{\beta}_{PC}$ and its t statistic do not change by much.

In the exercises at the end of the chapter, you will be asked to control for other factors in the equation to see if the computer ownership effect disappears, or if it at least gets notably smaller.

Each of the previous examples can be viewed as having relevance for **policy analysis**. In the first example, we were interested in gender discrimination in the workforce. In the second example, we were concerned with the effect of computer ownership on college performance. A special case of policy analysis is **program evaluation**, where we would like to know the effect of economic or social programs on individuals, firms, neighborhoods, cities, and so on.

In the simplest case, there are two groups of subjects. The **control group** does not participate in the program. The **experimental group** or **treatment group** does take part in the program. These names come from literature in the experimental sciences, and they should not be taken literally. Except in rare cases, the choice of the control and treatment groups is not random. However, in some cases, multiple regression analysis can be used to control for enough other factors in order to estimate the causal effect of the program.

EXAMPLE 7.3 EFFECTS OF TRAINING GRANTS ON HOURS OF TRAINING

Using the 1988 data for Michigan manufacturing firms in JTRAIN.RAW, we obtain the following estimated equation:

$$\begin{aligned}\widehat{hrsemp} &= \underset{(43.41)}{46.67} + \underset{(5.59)}{26.25}\, grant - \underset{(3.54)}{.98}\log(sales)\\ &\quad - \underset{(3.88)}{6.07}\log(employ)\\ n &= 105,\ R^2 = .237.\end{aligned} \quad [7.7]$$

The dependent variable is hours of training per employee, at the firm level. The variable *grant* is a dummy variable equal to one if the firm received a job training grant for 1988 and zero otherwise. The variables *sales* and *employ* represent annual sales and number of employees, respectively. We cannot enter *hrsemp* in logarithmic form because *hrsemp* is zero for 29 of the 105 firms used in the regression.

The variable *grant* is very statistically significant, with $t_{grant} = 4.70$. Controlling for sales and employment, firms that received a grant trained each worker, on average, 26.25 hours more. Because the average number of hours of per worker training in the sample is about 17, with a maximum value of 164, *grant* has a large effect on training, as is expected.

The coefficient on log(*sales*) is small and very insignificant. The coefficient on log(*employ*) means that, if a firm is 10% larger, it trains its workers about .61 hour less. Its *t* statistic is -1.56, which is only marginally statistically significant.

As with any other independent variable, we should ask whether the measured effect of a qualitative variable is causal. In equation (7.7), is the difference in training between firms that receive grants and those that do not due to the grant, or is grant receipt simply an indicator of something else? It might be that the firms receiving grants would have, on average, trained their workers more even in the absence of a grant. Nothing in this analysis tells us whether we have estimated a causal effect; we must know how the firms receiving grants were determined. We can only hope we have controlled for as many factors as possible that might be related to whether a firm received a grant and to its levels of training.

We will return to policy analysis with dummy variables in Section 7.6, as well as in later chapters.

Interpreting Coefficients on Dummy Explanatory Variables When the Dependent Variable Is log(*y*)

A common specification in applied work has the dependent variable appearing in logarithmic form, with one or more dummy variables appearing as independent variables. How do we interpret the dummy variable coefficients in this case? Not surprisingly, the coefficients have a *percentage* interpretation.

EXAMPLE 7.4 HOUSING PRICE REGRESSION

Using the data in HPRICE1.RAW, we obtain the equation

$$\begin{aligned}\widehat{\log(price)} &= \underset{(.65)}{-1.35} + \underset{(.038)}{.168}\log(lotsize) + \underset{(.093)}{.707}\log(sqrft) \\ &\quad + \underset{(.029)}{.027}\,bdrms + \underset{(.045)}{.054}\,colonial \\ n &= 88,\ R^2 = .649.\end{aligned} \tag{7.8}$$

All the variables are self-explanatory except *colonial*, which is a binary variable equal to one if the house is of the colonial style. What does the coefficient on *colonial* mean? For given levels of *lotsize*, *sqrft*, and *bdrms*, the difference in $\widehat{\log(price)}$ between a house of colonial style and that of another style is .054. This means that a colonial-style house is predicted to sell for about 5.4% more, holding other factors fixed.

This example shows that, when $\log(y)$ is the dependent variable in a model, the coefficient on a dummy variable, when multiplied by 100, is interpreted as the percentage difference in y, holding all other factors fixed. When the coefficient on a dummy variable suggests a large proportionate change in y, the exact percentage difference can be obtained exactly as with the semi-elasticity calculation in Section 6.2.

EXAMPLE 7.5 LOG HOURLY WAGE EQUATION

Let us reestimate the wage equation from Example 7.1, using log(*wage*) as the dependent variable and adding quadratics in *exper* and *tenure*:

$$\begin{aligned}\widehat{\log(wage)} &= \underset{(.099)}{.417} - \underset{(.036)}{.297}\,female + \underset{(.007)}{.080}\,educ + \underset{(.005)}{.029}\,exper \\ &\quad - \underset{(.00010)}{.00058}\,exper^2 + \underset{(.007)}{.032}\,tenure - \underset{(.00023)}{.00059}\,tenure^2 \\ n &= 526,\ R^2 = .441.\end{aligned} \tag{7.9}$$

Using the same approximation as in Example 7.4, the coefficient on *female* implies that, for the same levels of *educ*, *exper*, and *tenure*, women earn about 100(.297) = 29.7% less than men. We can do better than this by computing the exact percentage difference in predicted wages. What we want is the proportionate difference in wages between females and males, holding other factors fixed: $(\widehat{wage}_F - \widehat{wage}_M)/\widehat{wage}_M$. What we have from (7.9) is

$$\widehat{\log(wage_F)} - \widehat{\log(wage_M)} = -.297.$$

Exponentiating and subtracting one gives

$$(\widehat{wage}_F - \widehat{wage}_M)/\widehat{wage}_M = \exp(-.297) - 1 \approx -.257.$$

This more accurate estimate implies that a woman's wage is, on average, 25.7% below a comparable man's wage.

If we had made the same correction in Example 7.4, we would have obtained $\exp(.054) - 1 \approx .0555$, or about 5.6%. The correction has a smaller effect in Example 7.4 than in the wage example because the magnitude of the coefficient on the dummy variable is much smaller in (7.8) than in (7.9).

Generally, if $\hat{\beta}_1$ is the coefficient on a dummy variable, say x_1, when $\log(y)$ is the dependent variable, the exact percentage difference in the predicted y when $x_1 = 1$ versus when $x_1 = 0$ is

$$100 \cdot [\exp(\hat{\beta}_1) - 1]. \quad [7.10]$$

The estimate $\hat{\beta}_1$ can be positive or negative, and it is important to preserve its sign in computing (7.10).

The logarithmic approximation has the advantage of providing an estimate between the magnitudes obtained by using each group as the base group. In particular, although equation (7.10) gives us a better estimate than $100 \cdot \hat{\beta}_1$ of the percentage by which y for $x_1 = 1$ is greater than y for $x_1 = 0$, (7.10) is not a good estimate if we switch the base group. In Example 7.5, we can estimate the percentage by which a man's wage exceeds a comparable woman's wage, and this estimate is $100 \cdot [\exp(-\hat{\beta}_1) - 1] = 100 \cdot [\exp(.297) - 1] \approx 34.6$. The approximation, based on $100 \cdot \hat{\beta}_1$, 29.7, is between 25.7 and 34.6 (and close to the middle). Therefore, it makes sense to report that "the difference in predicted wages between men and women is about 29.7%," without having to take a stand on which is the base group.

7.3 Using Dummy Variables for Multiple Categories

We can use several dummy independent variables in the same equation. For example, we could add the dummy variable *married* to equation (7.9). The coefficient on *married* gives the (approximate) proportional differential in wages between those who are and are not married, holding gender, *educ*, *exper*, and *tenure* fixed. When we estimate this model, the coefficient on *married* (with standard error in parentheses) is .053 (.041), and the coefficient on *female* becomes −.290 (.036). Thus, the "marriage premium" is estimated to be about 5.3%, but it is not statistically different from zero ($t = 1.29$). An important limitation of this model is that the marriage premium is assumed to be the same for men and women; this is relaxed in the following example.

EXAMPLE 7.6 LOG HOURLY WAGE EQUATION

Let us estimate a model that allows for wage differences among four groups: married men, married women, single men, and single women. To do this, we must select a base group; we choose single men. Then, we must define dummy variables for each of the remaining groups. Call these *marrmale*, *marrfem*, and *singfem*. Putting these three variables into (7.9) (and, of course, dropping *female*, since it is now redundant) gives

$$\begin{aligned}
\widehat{\log(wage)} = &\ \underset{(.100)}{.321} + \underset{(.055)}{.213}\ marrmale - \underset{(.058)}{.198}\ marrfem \\
&- \underset{(.056)}{.110}\ singfem + \underset{(.007)}{.079}\ educ + \underset{(.005)}{.027}\ exper - \underset{(.00011)}{.00054}\ exper^2 \\
&+ \underset{(.007)}{.029}\ tenure - \underset{(.00023)}{.00053}\ tenure^2 \\
n = &\ 526,\ R^2 = .461.
\end{aligned} \quad [7.11]$$

All of the coefficients, with the exception of *singfem*, have t statistics well above two in absolute value. The t statistic for *singfem* is about -1.96, which is just significant at the 5% level against a two-sided alternative.

To interpret the coefficients on the dummy variables, we must remember that the base group is single males. Thus, the estimates on the three dummy variables measure the proportionate difference in wage *relative* to single males. For example, married men are estimated to earn about 21.3% more than single men, holding levels of education, experience, and tenure fixed. [The more precise estimate from (7.10) is about 23.7%.] A married woman, on the other hand, earns a predicted 19.8% less than a single man with the same levels of the other variables.

Because the base group is represented by the intercept in (7.11), we have included dummy variables for only three of the four groups. If we were to add a dummy variable for single males to (7.11), we would fall into the dummy variable trap by introducing perfect collinearity. Some regression packages will automatically correct this mistake for you, while others will just tell you there is perfect collinearity. It is best to carefully specify the dummy variables because then we are forced to properly interpret the final model.

Even though single men is the base group in (7.11), we can use this equation to obtain the estimated difference between any two groups. Because the overall intercept is common to all groups, we can ignore that in finding differences. Thus, the estimated proportionate difference between single and married women is $-.110 - (-.198) = .088$, which means that single women earn about 8.8% more than married women. Unfortunately, we cannot use equation (7.11) for testing whether the estimated difference between single and married women is statistically significant. Knowing the standard errors on *marrfem* and *singfem* is not enough to carry out the test (see Section 4.4). The easiest thing to do is to choose one of these groups to be the base group and to reestimate the equation. Nothing substantive changes, but we get the needed estimate and its standard error directly. When we use married women as the base group, we obtain

$$\widehat{\log(wage)} = \underset{(.106)}{.123} + \underset{(.056)}{.411}\, marrmale + \underset{(.058)}{.198}\, singmale + \underset{(.052)}{.088}\, singfem + \ldots,$$

where, of course, none of the unreported coefficients or standard errors have changed. The estimate on *singfem* is, as expected, .088. Now, we have a standard error to go along with this estimate. The t statistic for the null that there is no difference in the population between married and single women is $t_{singfem} = .088/.052 \approx 1.69$. This is marginal evidence against the null hypothesis. We also see that the estimated difference between married men and married women is very statistically significant ($t_{marrmale} = 7.34$).

The previous example illustrates a general principle for including dummy variables to indicate different groups: if the regression model is to have different intercepts for, say, g groups or categories, we need to include $g - 1$ dummy variables in the model along with an intercept. The intercept for the base group is the overall intercept in the model, and the dummy variable coefficient for a particular group represents the estimated difference in intercepts between that group and the base group. Including g dummy variables along with an intercept will result in the dummy variable trap. An alternative is to include g dummy variables and to exclude an overall intercept. Including g dummies without an overall intercept is sometimes useful, but it has two practical drawbacks. First, it makes it more cumbersome to test for differences relative to a base group. Second, regression packages usually change the way R-squared is computed when an overall intercept is not included. In particular, in the formula $R^2 = 1 - \text{SSR/SST}$, the total sum of squares, SST, is replaced with a total sum of squares that does not center y_i about its mean, say, $\text{SST}_0 = \sum_{i=1}^{n} y_i^2$. The resulting R-squared, say $R_0^2 = 1 - \text{SSR}/\text{SST}_0$, is sometimes called the **uncentered *R*-squared**. Unfortunately, R_0^2 is rarely suitable as a goodness of fit measure. It is always true that $\text{SST}_0 \geq \text{SST}$ with equality only if $\bar{y} = 0$. Often, SST_0 is much larger that SST, which means that R_0^2 is much larger than R^2. For example, if in the previous example we regress log(*wage*) on *marrmale*, *singmale*, *marrfem*, *singfem*, and the other explanatory variables—without an intercept—the reported R-squared from Stata, which is R_0^2, is .948. This high R-squared is an artifact of not centering the total sum of squares in the calculation. The correct R-squared is given in equation (7.11) as .461. Some regression packages, including Stata, have an option to force calculation of the centered R-squared even though an overall intercept has not been included, and using this option is generally a good idea. In the vast majority of cases, any R-squared based on comparing an SSR and SST should have SST computed by centering the y_i about $\bar{y}$. We can think of this SST as the sum of squared residuals obtained if we just use the sample average, $\bar{y}$, to predict each y_i. Surely we are setting the bar pretty low for any model if all we measure is its fit relative to using a constant predictor. For a model without an intercept that fits poorly, it is possible that SSR > SST, which means R^2 would be negative. The uncentered R-squared will always be between zero and one, which likely explains why it is usually the default when an intercept is not estimated in regression models.

EXPLORING FURTHER 7.2

In the baseball salary data found in MLB1.RAW, players are given one of six positions: *frstbase, scndbase, thrdbase, shrtstop, outfield,* or *catcher*. To allow for salary differentials across position, with outfielders as the base group, which dummy variables would you include as independent variables?

Incorporating Ordinal Information by Using Dummy Variables

Suppose that we would like to estimate the effect of city credit ratings on the municipal bond interest rate (*MBR*). Several financial companies, such as Moody's Investors Service and Standard and Poor's, rate the quality of debt for local governments, where the ratings depend on things like probability of default. (Local governments prefer lower interest rates in order to reduce their costs of borrowing.) For simplicity, suppose that rankings range from zero to four, with zero being the worst credit rating and four being the best. This is an example of an **ordinal variable**. Call this variable *CR* for concreteness. The question we need to address is: How do we incorporate the variable *CR* into a model to explain *MBR*?

One possibility is to just include *CR* as we would include any other explanatory variable:

$$MBR = \beta_0 + \beta_1 CR + \textit{other factors},$$

where we do not explicitly show what other factors are in the model. Then β_1 is the percentage point change in *MBR* when *CR* increases by one unit, holding other factors fixed. Unfortunately, it is rather hard to interpret a one-unit increase in *CR*. We know the quantitative meaning of another year of education, or another dollar spent per student, but things like credit ratings typically have only ordinal meaning. We know that a *CR* of four is better than a *CR* of three, but is the difference between four and three the same as the difference between one and zero? If not, then it might not make sense to assume that a one-unit increase in *CR* has a constant effect on *MBR*.

A better approach, which we can implement because *CR* takes on relatively few values, is to define dummy variables for each value of *CR*. Thus, let $CR_1 = 1$ if $CR = 1$, and $CR_1 = 0$ otherwise; $CR_2 = 1$ if $CR = 2$, and $CR_2 = 0$ otherwise; and so on. Effectively, we take the single credit rating and turn it into five categories. Then, we can estimate the model

$$MBR = \beta_0 + \delta_1 CR_1 + \delta_2 CR_2 + \delta_3 CR_3 + \delta_4 CR_4 + other\ factors. \qquad [7.12]$$

Following our rule for including dummy variables in a model, we include four dummy variables because we have five categories. The omitted category here is a credit rating of zero, and so it is the base group. (This is why we do not need to define a dummy variable for this category.) The coefficients are easy to interpret: δ_1 is the difference in *MBR* (other factors fixed) between a municipality with a credit rating of one and a municipality with a credit rating of zero; δ_2 is the difference in *MBR* between a municipality with a credit rating of two and a municipality with a credit rating of zero; and so on. The movement between each credit rating is allowed to have a different effect, so using (7.12) is much more flexible than simply putting *CR* in as a single variable. Once the dummy variables are defined, estimating (7.12) is straightforward.

EXPLORING FURTHER 7.3

In model (7.12), how would you test the null hypothesis that credit rating has no effect on *MBR*?

Equation (7.12) contains the model with a constant partial effect as a special case. One way to write the three restrictions that imply a constant partial effect is $\delta_2 = 2\delta_1$, $\delta_3 = 3\delta_1$, and $\delta_4 = 4\delta_1$. When we plug these into equation (7.12) and rearrange, we get $MBR = \beta_0 + \delta_1(CR_1 + 2CR_2 + 3CR_3 + 4CR_4) + other\ factors$. Now, the term multiplying δ_1 is simply the original credit rating variable, *CR*. To obtain the *F* statistic for testing the constant partial effect restrictions, we obtain the unrestricted *R*-squared from (7.12) and the restricted *R*-squared from the regression of *MBR* on *CR* and the other factors we have controlled for. The *F* statistic is obtained as in equation (4.41) with $q = 3$.

EXAMPLE 7.7 EFFECTS OF PHYSICAL ATTRACTIVENESS ON WAGE

Hamermesh and Biddle (1994) used measures of physical attractiveness in a wage equation. (The file BEAUTY.RAW contains fewer variables but more observations than used by Hamermesh and Biddle. See Computer Exercise C12.) Each person in the sample was ranked by an interviewer for physical attractiveness, using five categories (homely, quite plain, average, good looking, and strikingly beautiful or handsome). Because there are so few people at the two extremes, the authors put people into one of three groups for the regression analysis: average, below average, and above average, where the base group is *average*. Using data from the 1977 Quality of Employment Survey, after controlling for the usual productivity characteristics, Hamermesh and Biddle estimated an equation for men:

$$\widehat{\log(wage)} = \hat{\beta}_0 - \underset{(.046)}{.164}\ belavg + \underset{(.033)}{.016}\ abvavg + other\ factors$$

$$n = 700, \bar{R}^2 = .403$$

and an equation for women:

$$\widehat{\log(wage)} = \hat{\beta}_0 - \underset{(.066)}{.124}\, belavg + \underset{(.049)}{.035}\, abvavg + other\ factors$$
$$n = 409, \bar{R}^2 = .330.$$

The other factors controlled for in the regressions include education, experience, tenure, marital status, and race; see Table 3 in Hamermesh and Biddle's paper for a more complete list. In order to save space, the coefficients on the other variables are not reported in the paper and neither is the intercept.

For men, those with below average looks are estimated to earn about 16.4% less than an average-looking man who is the same in other respects (including education, experience, tenure, marital status, and race). The effect is statistically different from zero, with $t = -3.57$. Similarly, men with above average looks earn an estimated 1.6% more, although the effect is not statistically significant ($t < .5$).

A woman with below average looks earns about 12.4% less than an otherwise comparable average-looking woman, with $t = -1.88$. As was the case for men, the estimate on *abvavg* is not statistically different from zero.

In related work, Biddle and Hamermesh (1998) revisit the effects of looks on earnings using a more homogeneous group: graduates of a particular law school. The authors continue to find that physical appearance has an effect on annual earnings, something that is perhaps not too surprising among people practicing law.

In some cases, the ordinal variable takes on too many values so that a dummy variable cannot be included for each value. For example, the file LAWSCH85.RAW contains data on median starting salaries for law school graduates. One of the key explanatory variables is the rank of the law school. Because each law school has a different rank, we clearly cannot include a dummy variable for each rank. If we do not wish to put the rank directly in the equation, we can break it down into categories. The following example shows how this is done.

EXAMPLE 7.8 EFFECTS OF LAW SCHOOL RANKINGS ON STARTING SALARIES

Define the dummy variables *top10*, *r11_25*, *r26_40*, *r41_60*, *r61_100* to take on the value unity when the variable *rank* falls into the appropriate range. We let schools ranked below 100 be the base group. The estimated equation is

$$\begin{aligned}\widehat{\log(salary)} = {} & \underset{(.41)}{9.17} + \underset{(.053)}{.700}\, top10 + \underset{(.039)}{.594}\, r11\_25 + \underset{(.034)}{.375}\, r26\_40 \\ & + \underset{(.028)}{.263}\, r41\_60 + \underset{(.021)}{.132}\, r61\_100 + \underset{(.0031)}{.0057}\, LSAT \\ & + \underset{(.074)}{.014}\, GPA + \underset{(.026)}{.036} \log(libvol) + \underset{(.0251)}{.0008} \log(cost) \\ n = {} & 136, R^2 = .911, \bar{R}^2 = .905.\end{aligned} \qquad [7.13]$$

We see immediately that all of the dummy variables defining the different ranks are very statistically significant. The estimate on *r61_100* means that, holding *LSAT*, *GPA*, *libvol*, and *cost* fixed, the median salary at a law school ranked between 61 and 100 is about 13.2% higher than that at a law school ranked below 100. The difference between a top 10 school and a below 100 school is quite large. Using the exact calculation given in equation (7.10) gives exp(.700) − 1 ≈ 1.014, and so the predicted median salary is more than 100% higher at a top 10 school than it is at a below 100 school.

As an indication of whether breaking the rank into different groups is an improvement, we can compare the adjusted *R*-squared in (7.13) with the adjusted *R*-squared from including *rank* as a single variable: the former is .905 and the latter is .836, so the additional flexibility of (7.13) is warranted.

Interestingly, once the rank is put into the (admittedly somewhat arbitrary) given categories, all of the other variables become insignificant. In fact, a test for joint significance of *LSAT, GPA*, log(*libvol*), and log(*cost*) gives a *p*-value of .055, which is borderline significant. When *rank* is included in its original form, the *p*-value for joint significance is zero to four decimal places.

One final comment about this example: In deriving the properties of ordinary least squares, we assumed that we had a random sample. The current application violates that assumption because of the way *rank* is defined: a school's rank necessarily depends on the rank of the other schools in the sample, and so the data cannot represent independent draws from the population of all law schools. This does not cause any serious problems provided the error term is uncorrelated with the explanatory variables.

7.4 Interactions Involving Dummy Variables

Interactions among Dummy Variables

Just as variables with quantitative meaning can be interacted in regression models, so can dummy variables. We have effectively seen an example of this in Example 7.6, where we defined four categories based on marital status and gender. In fact, we can recast that model by adding an **interaction term** between *female* and *married* to the model where *female* and *married* appear separately. This allows the marriage premium to depend on gender, just as it did in equation (7.11). For purposes of comparison, the estimated model with the *female-married* interaction term is

$$\begin{aligned}\widehat{\log(wage)} = {} & \underset{(.100)}{.321} - \underset{(.056)}{.110}\, female + \underset{(.055)}{.213}\, married \\ & - \underset{(.072)}{.301}\, female \cdot married + \ldots,\end{aligned} \quad [7.14]$$

where the rest of the regression is necessarily identical to (7.11). Equation (7.14) shows explicitly that there is a statistically significant interaction between gender and marital status. This model also allows us to obtain the estimated wage differential among all four groups, but here we must be careful to plug in the correct combination of zeros and ones.

Setting *female* = 0 and *married* = 0 corresponds to the group single men, which is the base group, since this eliminates *female*, *married*, and *female·married*. We can find the intercept for married men by setting *female* = 0 and *married* = 1 in (7.14); this gives an intercept of .321 + .213 = .534, and so on.

Equation (7.14) is just a different way of finding wage differentials across all gender–marital status combinations. It allows us to easily test the null hypothesis that the gender differential does not depend on marital status (equivalently, that the marriage differential does not depend on gender). Equation (7.11) is more convenient for testing for wage differentials between any group and the base group of single men.

EXAMPLE 7.9 EFFECTS OF COMPUTER USAGE ON WAGES

Krueger (1993) estimates the effects of computer usage on wages. He defines a dummy variable, which we call *compwork*, equal to one if an individual uses a computer at work. Another dummy variable, *comphome*, equals one if the person uses a computer at home. Using 13,379 people from the 1989 Current Population Survey, Krueger (1993, Table 4) obtains

$$\begin{aligned}\widehat{\log(wage)} &= \hat{\beta}_0 + \underset{(.009)}{.177}\, compwork + \underset{(.019)}{.070}\, comphome \\ &\quad + \underset{(.023)}{.017}\, compwork \cdot comphome + other\ factors.\end{aligned} \quad [7.15]$$

(The other factors are the standard ones for wage regressions, including education, experience, gender, and marital status; see Krueger's paper for the exact list.) Krueger does not report the intercept because it is not of any importance; all we need to know is that the base group consists of people who do not use a computer at home or at work. It is worth noticing that the estimated return to using a computer at work (but not at home) is about 17.7%. (The more precise estimate is 19.4%.) Similarly, people who use computers at home but not at work have about a 7% wage premium over those who do not use a computer at all. The differential between those who use a computer at both places, relative to those who use a computer in neither place, is about 26.4% (obtained by adding all three coefficients and multiplying by 100), or the more precise estimate 30.2% obtained from equation (7.10).

The interaction term in (7.15) is not statistically significant, nor is it very big economically. But it is causing little harm by being in the equation.

Allowing for Different Slopes

We have now seen several examples of how to allow different intercepts for any number of groups in a multiple regression model. There are also occasions for interacting dummy variables with explanatory variables that are not dummy variables to allow for a **difference in slopes**. Continuing with the wage example, suppose that we wish to test whether the return to education is the same for men and women, allowing for a constant wage differential between men and women (a differential for which we have already found evidence). For simplicity, we include only education and gender in the model. What kind of model allows for different returns to education? Consider the model

$$\log(wage) = (\beta_0 + \delta_0 female) + (\beta_1 + \delta_1 female)educ + u. \quad [7.16]$$

FIGURE 7.2 Graphs of equation (7.16): (a) $\delta_0 < 0$, $\delta_1 < 0$; (b) $\delta_0 < 0$, $\delta_1 > 0$.

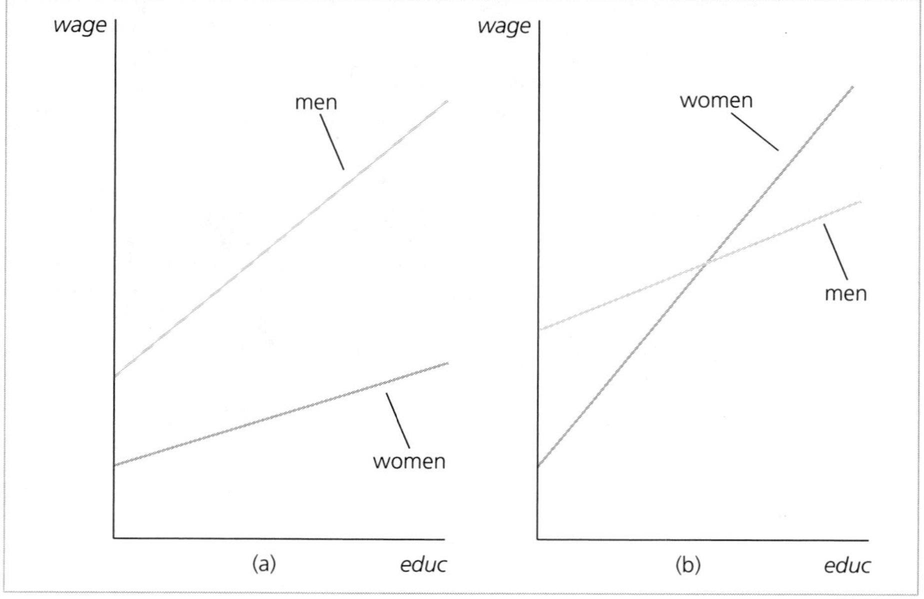

If we plug *female* = 0 into (7.16), then we find that the intercept for males is β_0, and the slope on education for males is β_1. For females, we plug in *female* = 1; thus, the intercept for females is $\beta_0 + \delta_0$, and the slope is $\beta_1 + \delta_1$. Therefore, δ_0 measures the difference in intercepts between women and men, and δ_1 measures the difference in the return to education between women and men. Two of the four cases for the signs of δ_0 and δ_1 are presented in Figure 7.2.

Graph (a) shows the case where the intercept for women is below that for men, and the slope of the line is smaller for women than for men. This means that women earn less than men at all levels of education, and the gap increases as *educ* gets larger. In graph (b), the intercept for women is below that for men, but the slope on education is larger for women. This means that women earn less than men at low levels of education, but the gap narrows as education increases. At some point, a woman earns more than a man, given the same levels of education (and this point is easily found given the estimated equation).

How can we estimate model (7.16)? To apply OLS, we must write the model with an interaction between *female* and *educ*:

$$\log(wage) = \beta_0 + \delta_0 female + \beta_1 educ + \delta_1 female \cdot educ + u. \qquad [7.17]$$

The parameters can now be estimated from the regression of log(*wage*) on *female*, *educ*, and *female·educ*. Obtaining the interaction term is easy in any regression package. Do not be daunted by the odd nature of *female·educ*, which is zero for any man in the sample and equal to the level of education for any woman in the sample.

An important hypothesis is that the return to education is the same for women and men. In terms of model (7.17), this is stated as H_0: $\delta_1 = 0$, which means that the slope of log(*wage*) with respect to *educ* is the same for men and women. Note that this hypothesis puts no restrictions on the difference in intercepts, δ_0. A wage differential between men and women is allowed under this null, but it must be the same at all levels of education. This situation is described by Figure 7.1.

We are also interested in the hypothesis that average wages are identical for men and women who have the same levels of education. This means that δ_0 and δ_1 must *both* be zero under the null hypothesis. In equation (7.17), we must use an F test to test H_0: $\delta_0 = 0$, $\delta_1 = 0$. In the model with just an intercept difference, we reject this hypothesis because H_0: $\delta_0 = 0$ is soundly rejected against H_1: $\delta_0 < 0$.

EXAMPLE 7.10 LOG HOURLY WAGE EQUATION

We add quadratics in experience and tenure to (7.17):

$$\begin{aligned}
\widehat{\log(wage)} &= \underset{(.119)}{.389} - \underset{(.168)}{.227}\, female + \underset{(.008)}{.082}\, educ \\
&\quad - \underset{(.0131)}{.0056}\, female \cdot educ + \underset{(.005)}{.029}\, exper - \underset{(.00011)}{.00058}\, exper^2 \\
&\quad + \underset{(.007)}{.032}\, tenure - \underset{(.00024)}{.00059}\, tenure^2 \\
n &= 526,\ R^2 = .441.
\end{aligned} \tag{7.18}$$

The estimated return to education for men in this equation is .082, or 8.2%. For women, it is .082 − .0056 = .0764, or about 7.6%. The difference, −.56%, or just over one-half a percentage point less for women, is not economically large nor statistically significant: the t statistic is $-.0056/.0131 \approx -.43$. Thus, we conclude that there is no evidence against the hypothesis that the return to education is the same for men and women.

The coefficient on *female*, while remaining economically large, is no longer significant at conventional levels ($t = -1.35$). Its coefficient and t statistic in the equation without the interaction were −.297 and −8.25, respectively [see equation (7.9)]. Should we now conclude that there is no statistically significant evidence of lower pay for women at the same levels of *educ*, *exper*, and *tenure*? This would be a serious error. Because we have added the interaction *female·educ* to the equation, the coefficient on *female* is now estimated much less precisely than it was in equation (7.9): the standard error has increased by almost fivefold ($.168/.036 \approx 4.67$). This occurs because *female* and *female·educ* are highly correlated in the sample. In this example, there is a useful way to think about the multicollinearity: in equation (7.17) and the more general equation estimated in (7.18), δ_0 measures the wage differential between women and men when $educ = 0$. Very few people in the sample have very low levels of education, so it is not surprising that we have a difficult time estimating the differential at $educ = 0$ (nor is the differential at zero years of education very informative). More interesting would be to estimate the gender differential at, say, the average education level in the sample (about 12.5). To do this, we would replace *female·educ* with *female·(educ* − 12.5) and rerun the regression; this only changes the coefficient on *female* and its standard error. (See Computer Exercise C7.)

If we compute the F statistic for H_0: $\delta_0 = 0, \delta_1 = 0$, we obtain $F = 34.33$, which is a huge value for an F random variable with numerator $df = 2$ and denominator $df = 518$: the p-value is zero to four decimal places. In the end, we prefer model (7.9), which allows for a constant wage differential between women and men.

EXPLORING FURTHER 7.4

How would you augment the model estimated in (7.18) to allow the return to *tenure* to differ by gender?

As a more complicated example involving interactions, we now look at the effects of race and city racial composition on major league baseball player salaries.

EXAMPLE 7.11 EFFECTS OF RACE ON BASEBALL PLAYER SALARIES

Using MLB1.RAW, the following equation is estimated for the 330 major league baseball players for which city racial composition statistics are available. The variables *black* and *hispan* are binary indicators for the individual players. (The base group is white players.) The variable *percblck* is the percentage of the team's city that is black, and *perchisp* is the percentage of Hispanics. The other variables measure aspects of player productivity and longevity. Here, we are interested in race effects after controlling for these other factors.

In addition to including *black* and *hispan* in the equation, we add the interactions *black·percblck* and *hispan·perchisp*. The estimated equation is

$$
\begin{aligned}
\widehat{\log(salary)} = {} & \underset{(2.18)}{10.34} + \underset{(.0129)}{.0673}\, years + \underset{(.0034)}{.0089}\, gamesyr \\
& + \underset{(.00151)}{.00095}\, bavg + \underset{(.0164)}{.0146}\, hrunsyr + \underset{(.0076)}{.0045}\, rbisyr \\
& + \underset{(.0046)}{.0072}\, runsyr + \underset{(.0021)}{.0011}\, fldperc + \underset{(.0029)}{.0075}\, allstar \\
& - \underset{(.125)}{.198}\, black - \underset{(.153)}{.190}\, hispan + \underset{(.0050)}{.0125}\, black{\cdot}percblck \\
& + \underset{(.0098)}{.0201}\, hispan{\cdot}perchisp \\
n = {} & 330,\ R^2 = .638.
\end{aligned}
\tag{7.19}
$$

First, we should test whether the four race variables, *black*, *hispan*, *black·percblck*, and *hispan·perchisp*, are jointly significant. Using the same 330 players, the R-squared when the four race variables are dropped is .626. Since there are four restrictions and $df = 330 - 13$ in the unrestricted model, the F statistic is about 2.63, which yields a p-value of .034. Thus, these variables are jointly significant at the 5% level (though not at the 1% level).

How do we interpret the coefficients on the race variables? In the following discussion, all productivity factors are held fixed. First, consider what happens for black players, holding *perchisp* fixed. The coefficient $-.198$ on *black* literally means that, if a black player is in a city with no blacks ($percblck = 0$), then the black player earns about 19.8%

less than a comparable white player. As *percblck* increases—which means the white population decreases, since *perchisp* is held fixed—the salary of blacks increases relative to that for whites. In a city with 10% blacks, log(*salary*) for blacks compared to that for whites is $-.198 + .0125(10) = -.073$, so salary is about 7.3% less for blacks than for whites in such a city. When $percblck = 20$, blacks earn about 5.2% more than whites. The largest percentage of blacks in a city is about 74% (Detroit).

Similarly, Hispanics earn less than whites in cities with a low percentage of Hispanics. But we can easily find the value of *perchisp* that makes the differential between whites and Hispanics equal zero: it must make $-.190 + .0201\ perchisp = 0$, which gives $perchisp \approx 9.45$. For cities in which the percentage of Hispanics is less than 9.45%, Hispanics are predicted to earn less than whites (for a given black population), and the opposite is true if the percentage of Hispanics is above 9.45%. Twelve of the 22 cities represented in the sample have Hispanic populations that are less than 9.45% of the total population. The largest percentage of Hispanics is about 31%.

How do we interpret these findings? We cannot simply claim discrimination exists against blacks and Hispanics, because the estimates imply that whites earn less than blacks and Hispanics in cities heavily populated by minorities. The importance of city composition on salaries might be due to player preferences: perhaps the best black players live disproportionately in cities with more blacks and the best Hispanic players tend to be in cities with more Hispanics. The estimates in (7.19) allow us to determine that some relationship is present, but we cannot distinguish between these two hypotheses.

Testing for Differences in Regression Functions across Groups

The previous examples illustrate that interacting dummy variables with other independent variables can be a powerful tool. Sometimes, we wish to test the null hypothesis that two populations or groups follow the same regression function, against the alternative that one or more of the slopes differ across the groups. We will also see examples of this in Chapter 13, when we discuss pooling different cross sections over time.

Suppose we want to test whether the same regression model describes college grade point averages for male and female college athletes. The equation is

$$cumgpa = \beta_0 + \beta_1 sat + \beta_2 hsperc + \beta_3 tothrs + u,$$

where *sat* is SAT score, *hsperc* is high school rank percentile, and *tothrs* is total hours of college courses. We know that, to allow for an intercept difference, we can include a dummy variable for either males or females. If we want any of the slopes to depend on gender, we simply interact the appropriate variable with, say, *female*, and include it in the equation.

If we are interested in testing whether there is *any* difference between men and women, then we must allow a model where the intercept and all slopes can be different across the two groups:

$$\begin{aligned} cumgpa = {} & \beta_0 + \delta_0 female + \beta_1 sat + \delta_1 female \cdot sat + \beta_2 hsperc \\ & + \delta_2 female \cdot hsperc + \beta_3 tothrs + \delta_3 female \cdot tothrs + u. \end{aligned} \qquad [7.20]$$

The parameter δ_0 is the difference in the intercept between women and men, δ_1 is the slope difference with respect to *sat* between women and men, and so on. The null hypothesis that *cumgpa* follows the same model for males and females is stated as

$$H_0: \delta_0 = 0, \delta_1 = 0, \delta_2 = 0, \delta_3 = 0. \quad [7.21]$$

If one of the δ_j is different from zero, then the model is different for men and women.

Using the spring semester data from the file GPA3.RAW, the full model is estimated as

$$\begin{aligned}
\widehat{cumgpa} = {} & \underset{(0.21)}{1.48} - \underset{(.411)}{.353}\, female + \underset{(.0002)}{.0011}\, sat + \underset{(.00039)}{.00075}\, female \cdot sat \\
& - \underset{(.0014)}{.0085}\, hsperc - \underset{(.00316)}{.00055}\, female \cdot hsperc + \underset{(.0009)}{.0023}\, tothrs \\
& - \underset{(.00163)}{.00012}\, female \cdot tothrs \\
n = {} & 366,\ R^2 = .406,\ \bar{R}^2 = .394.
\end{aligned} \quad [7.22]$$

None of the four terms involving the female dummy variable is very statistically significant; only the *female·sat* interaction has a *t* statistic close to two. But we know better than to rely on the individual *t* statistics for testing a joint hypothesis such as (7.21). To compute the *F* statistic, we must estimate the restricted model, which results from dropping *female* and all of the interactions; this gives an R^2 (the restricted R^2) of about .352, so the *F* statistic is about 8.14; the *p*-value is zero to five decimal places, which causes us to soundly reject (7.21). Thus, men and women athletes do follow different GPA models, even though each term in (7.22) that allows women and men to be different is individually insignificant at the 5% level.

The large standard errors on *female* and the interaction terms make it difficult to tell exactly how men and women differ. We must be very careful in interpreting equation (7.22) because, in obtaining differences between women and men, the interaction terms must be taken into account. If we look only at the *female* variable, we would wrongly conclude that *cumgpa* is about .353 less for women than for men, holding other factors fixed. This is the estimated difference only when *sat*, *hsperc*, and *tothrs* are all set to zero, which is not close to being a possible scenario. At $sat = 1{,}100$, $hsperc = 10$, and $tothrs = 50$, the predicted *difference* between a woman and a man is $-.353 + .00075(1{,}100) - .00055(10) - .00012(50) \approx .461$. That is, the female athlete is predicted to have a GPA that is almost one-half a point higher than the comparable male athlete.

In a model with three variables, *sat*, *hsperc*, and *tothrs*, it is pretty simple to add all of the interactions to test for group differences. In some cases, many more explanatory variables are involved, and then it is convenient to have a different way to compute the statistic. It turns out that the sum of squared residuals form of the *F* statistic can be computed easily even when many independent variables are involved.

In the general model with *k* explanatory variables and an intercept, suppose we have two groups; call them $g = 1$ and $g = 2$. We would like to test whether the intercept and all slopes are the same across the two groups. Write the model as

$$y = \beta_{g,0} + \beta_{g,1}x_1 + \beta_{g,2}x_2 + \ldots + \beta_{g,k}x_k + u, \quad [7.23]$$

for $g = 1$ and $g = 2$. The hypothesis that each beta in (7.23) is the same across the two groups involves $k + 1$ restrictions (in the GPA example, $k + 1 = 4$). The unrestricted model, which we can think of as having a group dummy variable and k interaction terms in addition to the intercept and variables themselves, has $n - 2(k + 1)$ degrees of freedom. [In the GPA example, $n - 2(k + 1) = 366 - 2(4) = 358$.] So far, there is nothing new. The key insight is that the sum of squared residuals from the unrestricted model can be obtained from two *separate* regressions, one for each group. Let SSR_1 be the sum of squared residuals obtained estimating (7.23) for the first group; this involves n_1 observations. Let SSR_2 be the sum of squared residuals obtained from estimating the model using the second group (n_2 observations). In the previous example, if group 1 is females, then $n_1 = 90$ and $n_2 = 276$. Now, the sum of squared residuals for the unrestricted model is simply $SSR_{ur} = SSR_1 + SSR_2$. The restricted sum of squared residuals is just the SSR from pooling the groups and estimating a single equation, say SSR_P. Once we have these, we compute the F statistic as usual:

$$F = \frac{[SSR_P - (SSR_1 + SSR_2)]}{SSR_1 + SSR_2} \cdot \frac{[n - 2(k + 1)]}{k + 1}, \qquad [7.24]$$

where n is the *total* number of observations. This particular F statistic is usually called the **Chow statistic** in econometrics. Because the Chow test is just an F test, it is only valid under homoskedasticity. In particular, under the null hypothesis, the error variances for the two groups must be equal. As usual, normality is not needed for asymptotic analysis.

To apply the Chow statistic to the GPA example, we need the SSR from the regression that pooled the groups together: this is $SSR_P = 85.515$. The SSR for the 90 women in the sample is $SSR_1 = 19.603$, and the SSR for the men is $SSR_2 = 58.752$. Thus, $SSR_{ur} = 19.603 + 58.752 = 78.355$. The F statistic is $[(85.515 - 78.355)/78.355](358/4) \approx 8.18]$; of course, subject to rounding error, this is what we get using the R-squared form of the test in the models with and without the interaction terms. (A word of caution: there is no simple R-squared form of the test if separate regressions have been estimated for each group; the R-squared form of the test can be used only if interactions have been included to create the unrestricted model.)

One important limitation of the traditional Chow test, regardless of the method used to implement it, is that the null hypothesis allows for no differences at all between the groups. In many cases, it is more interesting to allow for an intercept difference between the groups and then to test for slope differences; we saw one example of this in the wage equation in Example 7.10. There are two ways to allow the intercepts to differ under the null hypothesis. One is to include the group dummy and all interaction terms, as in equation (7.22), but then test joint significance of the interaction terms only. The second approach, which produces an identical statistic, is to form a sum-of-squared-residuals F statistic, as in equation (7.24), but where the restricted SSR, called "SSR_P" in equation (7.24), is obtained using a regression that contains only an intercept shift. Because we are testing k restrictions, rather than $k + 1$, the F statistic becomes

$$F = \frac{[SSR_P - (SSR_1 + SSR_2)]}{SSR_1 + SSR_2} \cdot \frac{[n - 2(k + 1)]}{k}.$$

Using this approach in the GPA example, SSR_P is obtained from the regression *cumgpa* on *female*, *sat*, *hsperc*, and *tothrs* using the data for both male and female student-athletes.

Because there are relatively few explanatory variables in the GPA example, it is easy to estimate (7.20) and test $H_0: \delta_1 = 0, \delta_2 = 0, \delta_3 = 0$ (with δ_0 unrestricted under the null).

The F statistic for the three exclusion restrictions gives a p-value equal to .205, and so we do not reject the null hypothesis at even the 20% significance level.

Failure to reject the hypothesis that the parameters multiplying the interaction terms are all zero suggests that the best model allows for an intercept difference only:

$$\begin{aligned}\widehat{cumgpa} &= \underset{(.18)}{1.39} + \underset{(.059)}{.310}\, female + \underset{(.0002)}{.0012}\, sat - \underset{(.0012)}{.0084}\, hsperc \\ &\quad + \underset{(.0007)}{.0025}\, tothrs \\ n &= 366,\ R^2 = .398,\ \bar{R}^2 = .392.\end{aligned} \qquad [7.25]$$

The slope coefficients in (7.25) are close to those for the base group (males) in (7.22); dropping the interactions changes very little. However, *female* in (7.25) is highly significant: its t statistic is over 5, and the estimate implies that, at given levels of *sat*, *hsperc*, and *tothrs*, a female athlete has a predicted GPA that is .31 point higher than that of a male athlete. This is a practically important difference.

7.5 A Binary Dependent Variable: The Linear Probability Model

By now, we have learned much about the properties and applicability of the multiple linear regression model. In the last several sections, we studied how, through the use of binary independent variables, we can incorporate qualitative information as explanatory variables in a multiple regression model. In all of the models up until now, the dependent variable y has had *quantitative* meaning (for example, y is a dollar amount, a test score, a percentage, or the logs of these). What happens if we want to use multiple regression to *explain* a qualitative event?

In the simplest case, and one that often arises in practice, the event we would like to explain is a binary outcome. In other words, our dependent variable, y, takes on only two values: zero and one. For example, y can be defined to indicate whether an adult has a high school education; y can indicate whether a college student used illegal drugs during a given school year; or y can indicate whether a firm was taken over by another firm during a given year. In each of these examples, we can let $y = 1$ denote one of the outcomes and $y = 0$ the other outcome.

What does it mean to write down a multiple regression model, such as

$$y = \beta_0 + \beta_1 x_1 + \ldots + \beta_k x_k + u, \qquad [7.26]$$

when y is a binary variable? Because y can take on only two values, β_j cannot be interpreted as the change in y given a one-unit increase in x_j, holding all other factors fixed: y either changes from zero to one or from one to zero (or does not change). Nevertheless, the β_j still have useful interpretations. If we assume that the zero conditional mean assumption MLR.4 holds, that is, $E(u|x_1, \ldots, x_k) = 0$, then we have, as always,

$$E(y|\mathbf{x}) = \beta_0 + \beta_1 x_1 + \ldots + \beta_k x_k,$$

where $\mathbf{x}$ is shorthand for all of the explanatory variables.

The key point is that when y is a binary variable taking on the values zero and one, it is always true that $P(y = 1|\mathbf{x}) = E(y|\mathbf{x})$: the probability of "success"—that is, the probability that $y = 1$—is the same as the expected value of y. Thus, we have the important equation

$$P(y = 1|\mathbf{x}) = \beta_0 + \beta_1 x_1 + \ldots + \beta_k x_k, \quad [7.27]$$

which says that the probability of success, say, $p(\mathbf{x}) = P(y = 1|\mathbf{x})$, is a linear function of the x_j. Equation (7.27) is an example of a binary response model, and $P(y = 1|\mathbf{x})$ is also called the **response probability**. (We will cover other binary response models in Chapter 17.) Because probabilities must sum to one, $P(y = 0|\mathbf{x}) = 1 - P(y = 1|\mathbf{x})$ is also a linear function of the x_j.

The multiple linear regression model with a binary dependent variable is called the **linear probability model (LPM)** because the response probability is linear in the parameters β_j. In the LPM, β_j measures the change in the probability of success when x_j changes, holding other factors fixed:

$$\Delta P(y = 1|\mathbf{x}) = \beta_j \Delta x_j. \quad [7.28]$$

With this in mind, the multiple regression model can allow us to estimate the effect of various explanatory variables on qualitative events. The mechanics of OLS are the same as before.

If we write the estimated equation as

$$\hat{y} = \hat{\beta}_0 + \hat{\beta}_1 x_1 + \ldots + \hat{\beta}_k x_k,$$

we must now remember that $\hat{y}$ is the predicted probability of success. Therefore, $\hat{\beta}_0$ is the predicted probability of success when each x_j is set to zero, which may or may not be interesting. The slope coefficient $\hat{\beta}_1$ measures the predicted change in the probability of success when x_1 increases by one unit.

To correctly interpret a linear probability model, we must know what constitutes a "success." Thus, it is a good idea to give the dependent variable a name that describes the event $y = 1$. As an example, let *inlf* ("in the labor force") be a binary variable indicating labor force participation by a married woman during 1975: $inlf = 1$ if the woman reports working for a wage outside the home at some point during the year, and zero otherwise. We assume that labor force participation depends on other sources of income, including husband's earnings (*nwifeinc*, measured in thousands of dollars), years of education (*educ*), past years of labor market experience (*exper*), *age*, number of children less than six years old (*kidslt6*), and number of kids between 6 and 18 years of age (*kidsge6*). Using the data in MROZ.RAW from Mroz (1987), we estimate the following linear probability model, where 428 of the 753 women in the sample report being in the labor force at some point during 1975:

$$\begin{aligned}
\widehat{inlf} = {} & \underset{(.154)}{.586} - \underset{(.0014)}{.0034}\, nwifeinc + \underset{(.007)}{.038}\, educ + \underset{(.006)}{.039}\, exper \\
& - \underset{(.00018)}{.00060}\, exper^2 - \underset{(.002)}{.016}\, age - \underset{(.034)}{.262}\, kidslt6 + \underset{(.013)}{.013}\, kidsge6 \qquad [7.29] \\
n = {} & 753,\ R^2 = .264.
\end{aligned}$$

Using the usual t statistics, all variables in (7.29) except *kidsge6* are statistically significant, and all of the significant variables have the effects we would expect based on economic theory (or common sense).

To interpret the estimates, we must remember that a change in the independent variable changes the probability that $inlf = 1$. For example, the coefficient on *educ* means that, everything else in (7.29) held fixed, another year of education increases the probability of labor force participation by .038. If we take this equation literally, 10 more years of education increases the probability of being in the labor force by .038(10) = .38, which is a pretty large increase in a probability. The relationship between the probability of labor force participation and *educ* is plotted in Figure 7.3. The other independent variables are fixed at the values $nwifeinc = 50$, $exper = 5$, $age = 30$, $kidslt6 = 1$, and $kidsge6 = 0$ for illustration purposes. The predicted probability is negative until education equals 3.84 years. This should not cause too much concern because, in this sample, no woman has less than five years of education. The largest reported education is 17 years, and this leads to a predicted probability of .5. If we set the other independent variables at different values, the range of predicted probabilities would change. But the marginal effect of another year of education on the probability of labor force participation is always .038.

The coefficient on *nwifeinc* implies that, if $\Delta nwifeinc = 10$ (which means an increase of \$10,000), the probability that a woman is in the labor force falls by .034. This is not an especially large effect given that an increase in income of \$10,000 is substantial in terms of 1975 dollars. Experience has been entered as a quadratic to allow the effect of past experience to have a diminishing effect on the labor force participation probability. Holding other factors fixed, the estimated change in the probability is approximated as $.039 - 2(.0006)exper = .039 - .0012\, exper$. The point at which past experience has no

FIGURE 7.3 Estimated relationship between the probability of being in the labor force and years of education, with other explanatory variables fixed.

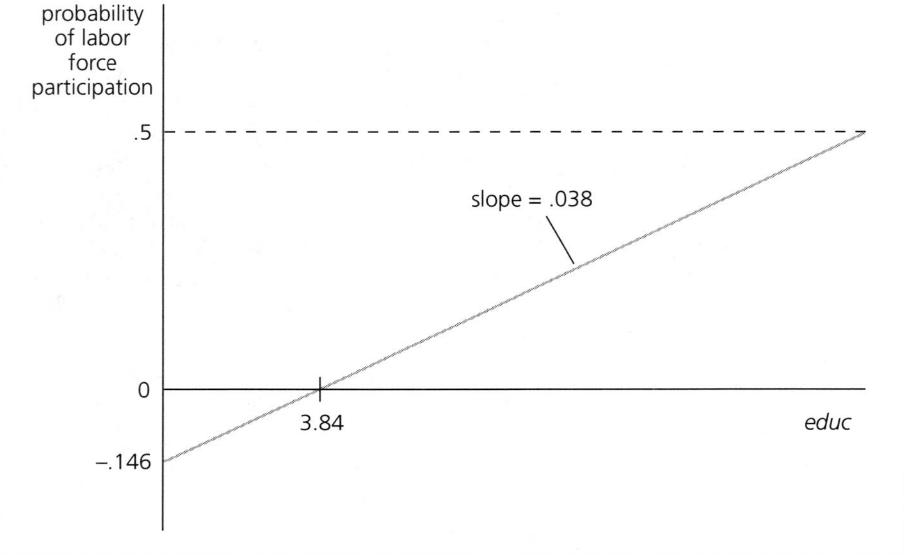

effect on the probability of labor force participation is .039/.0012 = 32.5, which is a high level of experience: only 13 of the 753 women in the sample have more than 32 years of experience.

Unlike the number of older children, the number of young children has a huge impact on labor force participation. Having one additional child less than six years old reduces the probability of participation by −.262, at given levels of the other variables. In the sample, just under 20% of the women have at least one young child.

This example illustrates how easy linear probability models are to estimate and interpret, but it also highlights some shortcomings of the LPM. First, it is easy to see that, if we plug certain combinations of values for the independent variables into (7.29), we can get predictions either less than zero or greater than one. Since these are predicted probabilities, and probabilities must be between zero and one, this can be a little embarassing. For example, what would it mean to predict that a woman is in the labor force with a probability of −.10? In fact, of the 753 women in the sample, 16 of the fitted values from (7.29) are less than zero, and 17 of the fitted values are greater than one.

A related problem is that a probability cannot be linearly related to the independent variables for all their possible values. For example, (7.29) predicts that the effect of going from zero children to one young child reduces the probability of working by .262. This is also the predicted drop if the woman goes from having one young child to two. It seems more realistic that the first small child would reduce the probability by a large amount, but subsequent children would have a smaller marginal effect. In fact, when taken to the extreme, (7.29) implies that going from zero to four young children reduces the probability of working by $\Delta\widehat{inlf} = .262(\Delta kidslt6) = .262(4) = 1.048$, which is impossible.

Even with these problems, the linear probability model is useful and often applied in economics. It usually works well for values of the independent variables that are near the averages in the sample. In the labor force participation example, no women in the sample have four young children; in fact, only three women have three young children. Over 96% of the women have either no young children or one small child, and so we should probably restrict attention to this case when interpreting the estimated equation.

Predicted probabilities outside the unit interval are a little troubling when we want to make predictions. Still, there are ways to use the estimated probabilities (even if some are negative or greater than one) to predict a zero-one outcome. As before, let $\hat{y}_i$ denote the fitted values—which may not be bounded between zero and one. Define a predicted value as $\tilde{y}_i = 1$ if $\hat{y}_i \geq .5$ and $\tilde{y}_i = 0$ if $\hat{y}_i < .5$. Now we have a set of predicted values, $\tilde{y}_i$, $i = 1, \ldots, n$, that, like the y_i, are either zero or one. We can use the data on y_I and $\tilde{y}_i$ to obtain the frequencies with which we correctly predict $y_i = 1$ and $y_i = 0$, as well as the proportion of overall correct predictions. The latter measure, when turned into a percentage, is a widely used goodness-of-fit measure for binary dependent variables: the **percent correctly predicted**. An example is given in Computer Exercise C9(v), and further discussion, in the context of more advanced models, can be found in Section 17.1.

Due to the binary nature of y, the linear probability model does violate one of the Gauss-Markov assumptions. When y is a binary variable, its variance, conditional on $\mathbf{x}$, is

$$\mathrm{Var}(y|\mathbf{x}) = p(\mathbf{x})[1 - p(\mathbf{x})], \quad [7.30]$$

where $p(\mathbf{x})$ is shorthand for the probability of success: $p(\mathbf{x}) = \beta_0 + \beta_1 x_1 + \ldots + \beta_k x_k$. This means that, except in the case where the probability does not depend on any of the independent variables, there *must* be heteroskedasticity in a linear probability model. We know from Chapter 3 that this does not cause bias in the OLS estimators of the β_j. But we also know from Chapters 4 and 5 that homoskedasticity is crucial for justifying the usual t and F statistics, even in large samples. Because the standard errors in (7.29) are not generally valid, we should use them with caution. We will show how to correct the standard errors for heteroskedasticity in Chapter 8. It turns out that, in many applications, the usual OLS statistics are not far off, and it is still acceptable in applied work to present a standard OLS analysis of a linear probability model.

EXAMPLE 7.12 A LINEAR PROBABILITY MODEL OF ARRESTS

Let *arr86* be a binary variable equal to unity if a man was arrested during 1986, and zero otherwise. The population is a group of young men in California born in 1960 or 1961 who have at least one arrest prior to 1986. A linear probability model for describing *arr86* is

$$arr86 = \beta_0 + \beta_1 pcnv + \beta_2 avgsen + \beta_3 tottime + \beta_4 ptime86 + \beta_5 qemp86 + u,$$

where

$pcnv$ = the proportion of prior arrests that led to a conviction.
$avgsen$ = the average sentence served from prior convictions (in months).
$tottime$ = months spent in prison since age 18 prior to 1986.
$ptime86$ = months spent in prison in 1986.
$qemp86$ = the number of quarters (0 to 4) that the man was legally employed in 1986.

The data we use are in CRIME1.RAW, the same data set used for Example 3.5. Here, we use a binary dependent variable because only 7.2% of the men in the sample were arrested more than once. About 27.7% of the men were arrested at least once during 1986. The estimated equation is

$$\begin{aligned}\widehat{arr86} = {} & \underset{(.017)}{.441} - \underset{(.021)}{.162}\, pcnv + \underset{(.0065)}{.0061}\, avgsen - \underset{(.0050)}{.0023}\, tottime \\ & - \underset{(.005)}{.022}\, ptime86 - \underset{(.005)}{.043}\, qemp86 \\ n = {} & 2{,}725,\ R^2 = .0474.\end{aligned} \quad [7.31]$$

The intercept, .441, is the predicted probability of arrest for someone who has not been convicted (and so *pcnv* and *avgsen* are both zero), has spent no time in prison since age 18, spent no time in prison in 1986, and was unemployed during the entire year. The variables *avgsen* and *tottime* are insignificant both individually and jointly (the F test gives p-value = .347), and *avgsen* has a counterintuitive sign if longer sentences are supposed to deter crime. Grogger (1991), using a superset of these data and different econometric methods, found that *tottime* has a statistically significant *positive* effect on arrests and concluded that *tottime* is a measure of human capital built up in criminal activity.

Increasing the probability of conviction does lower the probability of arrest, but we must be careful when interpreting the magnitude of the coefficient. The variable *pcnv* is a proportion between zero and one; thus, changing *pcnv* from zero to one essentially means a change from no chance of being convicted to being convicted with certainty. Even this large change reduces the probability of arrest only by .162; increasing *pcnv* by .5 decreases the probability of arrest by .081.

The incarcerative effect is given by the coefficient on *ptime86*. If a man is in prison, he cannot be arrested. Since *ptime86* is measured in months, six more months in prison reduces the probability of arrest by .022(6) = .132. Equation (7.31) gives another example of where the linear probability model cannot be true over all ranges of the independent variables. If a man is in prison all 12 months of 1986, he cannot be arrested in 1986. Setting all other variables equal to zero, the predicted probability of arrest when *ptime86* = 12 is .441 − .022(12) = .177, which is not zero. Nevertheless, if we start from the unconditional probability of arrest, .277, 12 months in prison reduces the probability to essentially zero: .277 − .022(12) = .013.

Finally, employment reduces the probability of arrest in a significant way. All other factors fixed, a man employed in all four quarters is .172 less likely to be arrested than a man who is not employed at all.

We can also include dummy independent variables in models with dummy dependent variables. The coefficient measures the predicted difference in probability relative to the base group. For example, if we add two race dummies, *black* and *hispan*, to the arrest equation, we obtain

$$\begin{aligned}\widehat{arr86} = \underset{(.019)}{.380} &- \underset{(.021)}{.152}\, pcnv + \underset{(.0064)}{.0046}\, avgsen - \underset{(.0049)}{.0026}\, tottime \\ &- \underset{(.005)}{.024}\, ptime86 - \underset{(.005)}{.038}\, qemp86 + \underset{(.024)}{.170}\, black + \underset{(.021)}{.096}\, hispan \\ n = 2{,}725&,\ R^2 = .0682.\end{aligned} \tag{7.32}$$

EXPLORING FURTHER 7.5

What is the predicted probability of arrest for a black man with no prior convictions—so that *pcnv, avgsen, tottime,* and *ptime86* are all zero—who was employed all four quarters in 1986? Does this seem reasonable?

The coefficient on *black* means that, all other factors being equal, a black man has a .17 higher chance of being arrested than a white man (the base group). Another way to say this is that the probability of arrest is 17 percentage points higher for blacks than for whites. The difference is statistically significant as well. Similarly, Hispanic men have a .096 higher chance of being arrested than white men.

7.6 More on Policy Analysis and Program Evaluation

We have seen some examples of models containing dummy variables that can be useful for evaluating policy. Example 7.3 gave an example of program evaluation, where some firms received job training grants and others did not.

As we mentioned earlier, we must be careful when evaluating programs because in most examples in the social sciences the control and treatment groups are not randomly assigned. Consider again the Holzer et al. (1993) study, where we are now interested in the effect of the job training grants on worker productivity (as opposed to amount of job training). The equation of interest is

$$\log(scrap) = \beta_0 + \beta_1 grant + \beta_2 \log(sales) + \beta_3 \log(employ) + u,$$

where *scrap* is the firm's scrap rate, and the latter two variables are included as controls. The binary variable *grant* indicates whether the firm received a grant in 1988 for job training.

Before we look at the estimates, we might be worried that the unobserved factors affecting worker productivity—such as average levels of education, ability, experience, and tenure—might be correlated with whether the firm receives a grant. Holzer et al. point out that grants were given on a first-come, first-served basis. But this is not the same as giving out grants randomly. It might be that firms with less productive workers saw an opportunity to improve productivity and therefore were more diligent in applying for the grants.

Using the data in JTRAIN.RAW for 1988—when firms actually were eligible to receive the grants—we obtain

$$\begin{aligned} \widehat{\log(scrap)} = {} & \underset{(4.66)}{4.99} - \underset{(.431)}{.052}\, grant - \underset{(.373)}{.455} \log(sales) \\ & + \underset{(.365)}{.639} \log(employ) \\ n = {} & 50, R^2 = .072. \end{aligned} \qquad [7.33]$$

(Seventeen out of the 50 firms received a training grant, and the average scrap rate is 3.47 across all firms.) The point estimate of $-.052$ on *grant* means that, for given *sales* and *employ*, firms receiving a grant have scrap rates about 5.2% lower than firms without grants. This is the direction of the expected effect if the training grants are effective, but the *t* statistic is very small. Thus, from this cross-sectional analysis, we must conclude that the grants had no effect on firm productivity. We will return to this example in Chapter 9 and show how adding information from a prior year leads to a much different conclusion.

Even in cases where the policy analysis does not involve assigning units to a control group and a treatment group, we must be careful to include factors that might be systematically related to the binary independent variable of interest. A good example of this is testing for racial discrimination. Race is something that is not determined by an individual or by government administrators. In fact, race would appear to be the perfect example of an exogenous explanatory variable, given that it is determined at birth. However, for historical reasons, race is often related to other relevant factors: there are systematic differences in backgrounds across race, and these differences can be important in testing for *current* discrimination.

As an example, consider testing for discrimination in loan approvals. If we can collect data on, say, individual mortgage applications, then we can define the dummy dependent variable *approved* as equal to one if a mortgage application was approved, and zero otherwise. A systematic difference in approval rates across races is an indication of discrimination. However, since approval depends on many other factors, including income, wealth, credit ratings, and a general ability to pay back the loan, we must control for them *if* there are systematic differences in these factors across race. A linear probability model to test for discrimination might look like the following:

$$approved = \beta_0 + \beta_1 nonwhite + \beta_2 income + \beta_3 wealth + \beta_4 credrate + other\ factors.$$

Discrimination against minorities is indicated by a rejection of H_0: $\beta_1 = 0$ in favor of H_0: $\beta_1 < 0$, because β_1 is the amount by which the probability of a nonwhite getting an approval differs from the probability of a white getting an approval, given the same levels of other variables in the equation. If *income*, *wealth*, and so on are systematically different across races, then it is important to control for these factors in a multiple regression analysis.

Another problem that often arises in policy and program evaluation is that individuals (or firms or cities) choose whether or not to participate in certain behaviors or programs. For example, individuals choose to use illegal drugs or drink alcohol. If we want to examine the effects of such behaviors on unemployment status, earnings, or criminal behavior, we should be concerned that drug usage might be correlated with other factors that can affect employment and criminal outcomes. Children eligible for programs such as Head Start participate based on parental decisions. Since family background plays a role in Head Start decisions and affects student outcomes, we should control for these factors when examining the effects of Head Start [see, for example, Currie and Thomas (1995)]. Individuals selected by employers or government agencies to participate in job training programs can participate or not, and this decision is unlikely to be random [see, for example, Lynch (1992)]. Cities and states choose whether to implement certain gun control laws, and it is likely that this decision is systematically related to other factors that affect violent crime [see, for example, Kleck and Patterson (1993)].

The previous paragraph gives examples of what are generally known as **self-selection** problems in economics. Literally, the term comes from the fact that individuals self-select into certain behaviors or programs: participation is not randomly determined. The term is used generally when a binary indicator of participation might be systematically related to unobserved factors. Thus, if we write the simple model

$$y = \beta_0 + \beta_1 partic + u, \tag{7.34}$$

where y is an outcome variable and *partic* is a binary variable equal to unity if the individual, firm, or city participates in a behavior or a program or has a certain kind of law, then we are worried that the average value of u depends on participation: $\mathrm{E}(u|partic = 1) \neq \mathrm{E}(u|partic = 0)$. As we know, this causes the simple regression estimator of β_1 to be biased, and so we will not uncover the true effect of participation. Thus, the self-selection problem is another way that an explanatory variable (*partic* in this case) can be endogenous.

By now, we know that multiple regression analysis can, to some degree, alleviate the self-selection problem. Factors in the error term in (7.34) that are correlated with *partic* can be included in a multiple regression equation, assuming, of course, that we can collect data on these factors. Unfortunately, in many cases, we are worried that unobserved factors are related to participation, in which case multiple regression produces biased estimators.

With standard multiple regression analysis using cross-sectional data, we must be aware of finding spurious effects of programs on outcome variables due to the self-selection problem. A good example of this is contained in Currie and Cole (1993). These authors examine the effect of AFDC (Aid to Families with Dependent Children) participation on the birth weight of a child. Even after controlling for a variety of family and background characteristics, the authors obtain OLS estimates that imply participation in AFDC *lowers* birth weight. As the authors point out, it is hard to believe that AFDC participation itself *causes* lower birth weight. [See Currie (1995) for additional examples.] Using a different econometric method that we will discuss in Chapter 15, Currie and Cole find evidence for either no effect or a *positive* effect of AFDC participation on birth weight.

When the self-selection problem causes standard multiple regression analysis to be biased due to a lack of sufficient control variables, the more advanced methods covered in Chapters 13, 14, and 15 can be used instead.

7.7 Interpreting Regression Results with Discrete Dependent Variables

A binary response is the most extreme form of a discrete random variable: it takes on only two values, zero and one. As we discussed in Section 7.5, the parameters in a linear probability model can be interpreted as measuring the change in the *probability* that $y = 1$ due to a one-unit increase in an explanatory variable. We also discussed that, because y is a zero-one outcome, $P(y = 1) = E(y)$, and this equality continues to hold when we condition on explanatory variables.

Other discrete dependent variables arise in practice, and we have already seen some examples, such as the number of times someone is arrested in a given year (Example 3.5). Studies on factors affecting fertility often use the number of living children as the dependent variable in a regression analysis. As with number of arrests, the number of living children takes on a small set of integer values, and zero is a common value. The data in FERTIL2.RAW, which contains information on a large sample of women in Botswana is one such example. Often demographers are interested in the effects of education on fertility, with special attention to trying to determine whether education has a causal effect on fertility. Such examples raise a question about how one interprets regression coefficients: after all, one cannot have a fraction of a child.

To illustrate the issues, the regression below uses the data in FERTIL2.RAW:

$$\widehat{children} = -1.997 + .175\ age - .090\ educ \quad [7.35]$$
$$(.094)\quad (.003)\quad (.006)$$
$$n = 4{,}361,\ R^2 = .560.$$

At this time, we ignore the issue of whether this regression adequately controls for all factors that affect fertility. Instead we focus on interpreting the regression coefficients.

Consider the main coefficient of interest, $\hat{\beta}_{educ} = -.090$. If we take this estimate literally, it says that each additional year of education reduces the estimated number of children by .090—something obviously impossible for any particular woman. A similar problem arises when trying to interpret $\hat{\beta}_{age} = .175$. How can we make sense of these coefficients?

To interpret regression results generally, even in cases where y is discrete and takes on a small number of values, it is useful to remember the interpretation of OLS as estimating the effects of the x_j on the *expected* (or *average*) value of y. Generally, under Assumptions MLR.1 and MLR.4,

$$E(y|x_1, x_2, \ldots, x_k) = \beta_0 + \beta_1 x_1 + \ldots + \beta_k x_k. \quad [7.36]$$

Therefore, β_j is the effect of a ceteris paribus increase of x_j on the expected value of y. As we discussed in Section 6.4, for a given set of x_j values we interpret the predicted value, $\hat{\beta}_0 + \hat{\beta}_1 x_1 + \ldots + \hat{\beta}_k x_k$, as an estimate of $E(y|x_1, x_2, \ldots, x_k)$. Therefore, $\hat{\beta}_j$ is our estimate of how the *average* of y changes when $\Delta x_j = 1$ (keeping other factors fixed).

Seen in this light, we can now provide meaning to regression results as in equation (7.35). The coefficient $\hat{\beta}_{educ} = -.090$ means that we estimate that *average* fertility falls by .09 children given one more year of education. A nice way to summarize this interpretation is that if each woman in a group of 100 obtains another year of education, we estimate there will be nine fewer children among them.

Adding dummy variables to regressions when y is itself discrete causes no problems when we intepret the estimated effect in terms of average values. Using the data in FERTIL2.RAW we get

$$\widehat{children} = \underset{(.095)}{-2.071} + \underset{(.003)}{.177}\, age - \underset{(.006)}{.079}\, educ - \underset{(.068)}{.362}\, electric \qquad [7.37]$$

$$n = 4{,}358,\ R^2 = .562,$$

where *electric* is a dummy variable equal to one if the woman lives in a home with electricity. Of course it cannot be true that a particular woman who has electricity has .362 less children than an otherwise comparable woman who does not. But we can say that when comparing 100 women with electricity to 100 women without—at the same age and level of education—we estimate the former group to have about 36 fewer children.

Incidentally, when y is discrete the linear model does not always provide the best estimates of partial effects on $\mathrm{E}(y|x_1, x_2, \ldots, x_k)$. Chapter 17 contains more advanced models and estimation methods that tend to fit the data better when the range of y is limited in some substantive way. Nevertheless, a linear model estimated by OLS often provides a good approximation to the true partial effects, at least on average.

Summary

In this chapter, we have learned how to use qualitative information in regression analysis. In the simplest case, a dummy variable is defined to distinguish between two groups, and the coefficient estimate on the dummy variable estimates the ceteris paribus difference between the two groups. Allowing for more than two groups is accomplished by defining a set of dummy variables: if there are g groups, then $g - 1$ dummy variables are included in the model. All estimates on the dummy variables are interpreted relative to the base or benchmark group (the group for which no dummy variable is included in the model).

Dummy variables are also useful for incorporating ordinal information, such as a credit or a beauty rating, in regression models. We simply define a set of dummy variables representing different outcomes of the ordinal variable, allowing one of the categories to be the base group.

Dummy variables can be interacted with quantitative variables to allow slope differences across different groups. In the extreme case, we can allow each group to have its own slope on every variable, as well as its own intercept. The Chow test can be used to detect whether there are any differences across groups. In many cases, it is more interesting to test whether, after allowing for an intercept difference, the slopes for two different groups are the same. A standard F test can be used for this purpose in an unrestricted model that includes interactions between the group dummy and all variables.

The linear probability model, which is simply estimated by OLS, allows us to explain a binary response using regression analysis. The OLS estimates are now interpreted as changes in the probability of "success" ($y = 1$), given a one-unit increase in the corresponding explanatory variable. The LPM does have some drawbacks: it can produce predicted probabilities that are less than zero or greater than one, it implies a constant marginal effect of each explanatory variable that appears in its original form, and it contains heteroskedasticity. The first two problems are often not serious when we are obtaining estimates of the partial effects of the explanatory variables for the middle ranges of the data. Heteroskedasticity does invalidate the usual OLS standard errors and test statistics, but, as we will see in the next chapter, this is easily fixed in large enough samples.

Section 7.6 provides a discussion of how binary variables are used to evaluate policies and programs. As in all regression analysis, we must remember that program participation, or some other binary regressor with policy implications, might be correlated with unobserved factors that affect the dependent variable, resulting in the usual omitted variables bias.

We ended this chapter with a general discussion of how to interpret regression equations when the dependent variable is discrete. The key is to remember that the coefficients can be interpreted as the effects on the expected value of the dependent variable.

Key Terms

Base Group
Benchmark Group
Binary Variable
Chow Statistic
Control Group
Difference in Slopes
Dummy Variable Trap
Dummy Variables
Experimental Group
Interaction Term
Intercept Shift
Linear Probability Model (LPM)
Ordinal Variable
Percent Correctly Predicted
Policy Analysis
Program Evaluation
Response Probability
Self-Selection
Treatment Group
Uncentered *R*-Squared
Zero-One Variable

Problems

1 Using the data in SLEEP75.RAW (see also Problem 3 in Chapter 3), we obtain the estimated equation

$$\begin{aligned}\widehat{sleep} = {} & \underset{(235.11)}{3{,}840.83} - \underset{(.018)}{.163}\, totwrk - \underset{(5.86)}{11.71}\, educ - \underset{(11.21)}{8.70}\, age \\ & + \underset{(.134)}{.128}\, age^2 + \underset{(34.33)}{87.75}\, male \\ & n = 706,\ R^2 = .123,\ \bar{R}^2 = .117.\end{aligned}$$

The variable *sleep* is total minutes per week spent sleeping at night, *totwrk* is total weekly minutes spent working, *educ* and *age* are measured in years, and *male* is a gender dummy.

(i) All other factors being equal, is there evidence that men sleep more than women? How strong is the evidence?

(ii) Is there a statistically significant tradeoff between working and sleeping? What is the estimated tradeoff?

(iii) What other regression do you need to run to test the null hypothesis that, holding other factors fixed, age has no effect on sleeping?

2 The following equations were estimated using the data in BWGHT.RAW:

$$\begin{aligned}\widehat{\log(bwght)} = {} & \underset{(.22)}{4.66} - \underset{(.0009)}{.0044}\, cigs + \underset{(.0059)}{.0093}\, \log(faminc) + \underset{(.006)}{.016}\, parity \\ & + \underset{(.010)}{.027}\, male + \underset{(.013)}{.055}\, white \\ & n = 1{,}388,\ R^2 = .0472\end{aligned}$$

and

$$\widehat{\log(bwght)} = \underset{(.38)}{4.65} - \underset{(.0010)}{.0052}\ cigs + \underset{(.0085)}{.0110} \log(faminc) + \underset{(.006)}{.017}\ parity$$
$$+ \underset{(.011)}{.034}\ male + \underset{(.015)}{.045}\ white - \underset{(.0030)}{.0030}\ motheduc + \underset{(.0026)}{.0032}\ fatheduc$$
$$n = 1{,}191,\ R^2 = .0493.$$

The variables are defined as in Example 4.9, but we have added a dummy variable for whether the child is male and a dummy variable indicating whether the child is classified as white.

(i) In the first equation, interpret the coefficient on the variable *cigs*. In particular, what is the effect on birth weight from smoking 10 more cigarettes per day?

(ii) How much more is a white child predicted to weigh than a nonwhite child, holding the other factors in the first equation fixed? Is the difference statistically significant?

(iii) Comment on the estimated effect and statistical significance of *motheduc*.

(iv) From the given information, why are you unable to compute the F statistic for joint significance of *motheduc* and *fatheduc*? What would you have to do to compute the F statistic?

3 Using the data in GPA2.RAW, the following equation was estimated:

$$\widehat{sat} = \underset{(6.29)}{1{,}028.10} + \underset{(3.83)}{19.30}\ hsize - \underset{(.53)}{2.19}\ hsize^2 - \underset{(4.29)}{45.09}\ female$$
$$- \underset{(12.71)}{169.81}\ black + \underset{(18.15)}{62.31}\ female \cdot black$$
$$n = 4{,}137,\ R^2 = .0858.$$

The variable *sat* is the combined SAT score, *hsize* is size of the student's high school graduating class, in hundreds, *female* is a gender dummy variable, and *black* is a race dummy variable equal to one for blacks and zero otherwise.

(i) Is there strong evidence that $hsize^2$ should be included in the model? From this equation, what is the optimal high school size?

(ii) Holding *hsize* fixed, what is the estimated difference in SAT score between nonblack females and nonblack males? How statistically significant is this estimated difference?

(iii) What is the estimated difference in SAT score between nonblack males and black males? Test the null hypothesis that there is no difference between their scores, against the alternative that there is a difference.

(iv) What is the estimated difference in SAT score between black females and nonblack females? What would you need to do to test whether the difference is statistically significant?

4 An equation explaining chief executive officer salary is

$$\widehat{\log(salary)} = \underset{(.30)}{4.59} + \underset{(.032)}{.257} \log(sales) + \underset{(.004)}{.011}\ roe + \underset{(.089)}{.158}\ finance$$
$$+ \underset{(.085)}{.181}\ consprod - \underset{(.099)}{.283}\ utility$$
$$n = 209,\ R^2 = .357.$$

The data used are in CEOSAL1.RAW, where *finance*, *consprod*, and *utility* are binary variables indicating the financial, consumer products, and utilities industries. The omitted industry is transportation.

(i) Compute the approximate percentage difference in estimated salary between the utility and transportation industries, holding *sales* and *roe* fixed. Is the difference statistically significant at the 1% level?

(ii) Use equation (7.10) to obtain the exact percentage difference in estimated salary between the utility and transportation industries and compare this with the answer obtained in part (i).

(iii) What is the approximate percentage difference in estimated salary between the consumer products and finance industries? Write an equation that would allow you to test whether the difference is statistically significant.

5 In Example 7.2, let *noPC* be a dummy variable equal to one if the student does not own a PC, and zero otherwise.

(i) If *noPC* is used in place of *PC* in equation (7.6), what happens to the intercept in the estimated equation? What will be the coefficient on *noPC*? (*Hint:* Write $PC = 1 - noPC$ and plug this into the equation $\widehat{colGPA} = \hat{\beta}_0 + \hat{\delta}_0 PC + \hat{\beta}_1 hsGPA + \hat{\beta}_2 ACT$.)

(ii) What will happen to the *R*-squared if *noPC* is used in place of *PC*?

(iii) Should *PC* and *noPC* both be included as independent variables in the model? Explain.

6 To test the effectiveness of a job training program on the subsequent wages of workers, we specify the model

$$\log(wage) = \beta_0 + \beta_1 train + \beta_2 educ + \beta_3 exper + u,$$

where *train* is a binary variable equal to unity if a worker participated in the program. Think of the error term *u* as containing unobserved worker ability. If less able workers have a greater chance of being selected for the program, and you use an OLS analysis, what can you say about the likely bias in the OLS estimator of β_1? (*Hint:* Refer back to Chapter 3.)

7 In the example in equation (7.29), suppose that we define *outlf* to be one if the woman is out of the labor force, and zero otherwise.

(i) If we regress *outlf* on all of the independent variables in equation (7.29), what will happen to the intercept and slope estimates? (*Hint:* $inlf = 1 - outlf$. Plug this into the population equation $inlf = \beta_0 + \beta_1 nwifeinc + \beta_2 educ + \dots$ and rearrange.)

(ii) What will happen to the standard errors on the intercept and slope estimates?

(iii) What will happen to the *R*-squared?

8 Suppose you collect data from a survey on wages, education, experience, and gender. In addition, you ask for information about marijuana usage. The original question is: "On how many separate occasions last month did you smoke marijuana?"

(i) Write an equation that would allow you to estimate the effects of marijuana usage on wage, while controlling for other factors. You should be able to make statements such as, "Smoking marijuana five more times per month is estimated to change wage by *x*%."

(ii) Write a model that would allow you to test whether drug usage has different effects on wages for men and women. How would you test that there are no differences in the effects of drug usage for men and women?

(iii) Suppose you think it is better to measure marijuana usage by putting people into one of four categories: nonuser, light user (1 to 5 times per month), moderate user (6 to 10 times per month), and heavy user (more than 10 times per month). Now, write a model that allows you to estimate the effects of marijuana usage on wage.

(iv) Using the model in part (iii), explain in detail how to test the null hypothesis that marijuana usage has no effect on wage. Be very specific and include a careful listing of degrees of freedom.

(v) What are some potential problems with drawing causal inference using the survey data that you collected?

9 Let d be a dummy (binary) variable and let z be a quantitative variable. Consider the model

$$y = \beta_0 + \delta_0 d + \beta_1 z + \delta_1 d \cdot z + u;$$

this is a general version of a model with an interaction between a dummy variable and a quantitative variable. [An example is in equation (7.17).]

(i) Since it changes nothing important, set the error to zero, $u = 0$. Then, when $d = 0$ we can write the relationship between y and z as the function $f_0(z) = \beta_0 + \beta_1 z$. Write the same relationship when $d = 1$, where you should use $f_1(z)$ on the left-hand side to denote the linear function of z.

(ii) Assuming that $\delta_1 \neq 0$ (which means the two lines are not parallel), show that the value of z^* such that $f_0(z^*) = f_1(z^*)$ is $z^* = -\delta_0/\delta_1$. This is the point at which the two lines intersect [as in Figure 7.2(b)]. Argue that z^* is positive if and only if δ_0 and δ_1 have opposite signs.

(iii) Using the data in TWOYEAR.RAW, the following equation can be estimated:

$$\widehat{\log(wage)} = \underset{(0.011)}{2.289} - \underset{(.015)}{.357}\, female + \underset{(.003)}{.50}\, totcoll + \underset{(.005)}{.030}\, female \cdot totcoll$$
$$n = 6{,}763,\ R^2 = .202,$$

where all coefficients and standard errors have been rounded to three decimal places. Using this equation, find the value of *totcoll* such that the predicted values of $\log(wage)$ are the same for men and women.

(iv) Based on the equation in part (iii), can women realistically get enough years of college so that their earnings catch up to those of men? Explain.

10 For a child i living in a particular school district, let $voucher_i$ be a dummy variable equal to one if a child is selected to participate in a school voucher program, and let $score_i$ be that child's score on a subsequent standardized exam. Suppose that the participation variable, $voucher_i$, is completely randomized in the sense that it is independent of both observed and unobserved factors that can affect the test score.

(i) If you run a simple regression $score_i$ on $voucher_i$ using a random sample of size n, does the OLS estimator provide an unbiased estimator of the effect of the voucher program?

(ii) Suppose you can collect additional background information, such as family income, family structure (e.g., whether the child lives with both parents), and parents' education levels. Do you need to control for these factors to obtain an unbiased estimator of the effects of the voucher program? Explain.

(iii) Why should you include the family background variables in the regression? Is there a situation in which you would not include the background variables?

Computer Exercises

C1 Use the data in GPA1.RAW for this exercise.

(i) Add the variables *mothcoll* and *fathcoll* to the equation estimated in (7.6) and report the results in the usual form. What happens to the estimated effect of PC ownership? Is *PC* still statistically significant?

(ii) Test for joint significance of *mothcoll* and *fathcoll* in the equation from part (i) and be sure to report the *p*-value.

(iii) Add $hsGPA^2$ to the model from part (i) and decide whether this generalization is needed.

C2 Use the data in WAGE2.RAW for this exercise.

(i) Estimate the model

$$\log(wage) = \beta_0 + \beta_1 educ + \beta_2 exper + \beta_3 tenure + \beta_4 married + \beta_5 black + \beta_6 south + \beta_7 urban + u$$

and report the results in the usual form. Holding other factors fixed, what is the approximate difference in monthly salary between blacks and nonblacks? Is this difference statistically significant?

(ii) Add the variables $exper^2$ and $tenure^2$ to the equation and show that they are jointly insignificant at even the 20% level.

(iii) Extend the original model to allow the return to education to depend on race and test whether the return to education does depend on race.

(iv) Again, start with the original model, but now allow wages to differ across four groups of people: married and black, married and nonblack, single and black, and single and nonblack. What is the estimated wage differential between married blacks and married nonblacks?

C3 A model that allows major league baseball player salary to differ by position is

$$\log(salary) = \beta_0 + \beta_1 years + \beta_2 gamesyr + \beta_3 bavg + \beta_4 hrunsyr + \beta_5 rbisyr + \beta_6 runsyr + \beta_7 fldperc + \beta_8 allstar + \beta_9 frstbase + \beta_{10} scndbase + \beta_{11} thrdbase + \beta_{12} shrtstop + \beta_{13} catcher + u,$$

where outfield is the base group.

(i) State the null hypothesis that, controlling for other factors, catchers and outfielders earn, on average, the same amount. Test this hypothesis using the data in MLB1.RAW and comment on the size of the estimated salary differential.

(ii) State and test the null hypothesis that there is no difference in average salary across positions, once other factors have been controlled for.

(iii) Are the results from parts (i) and (ii) consistent? If not, explain what is happening.

C4 Use the data in GPA2.RAW for this exercise.

(i) Consider the equation

$$colgpa = \beta_0 + \beta_1 hsize + \beta_2 hsize^2 + \beta_3 hsperc + \beta_4 sat + \beta_5 female + \beta_6 athlete + u,$$

where *colgpa* is cumulative college grade point average, *hsize* is size of high school graduating class, in hundreds, *hsperc* is academic percentile in graduating class, *sat* is combined SAT score, *female* is a binary gender variable, and *athlete* is a binary variable, which is one for student-athletes. What are your expectations for the coefficients in this equation? Which ones are you unsure about?

(ii) Estimate the equation in part (i) and report the results in the usual form. What is the estimated GPA differential between athletes and nonathletes? Is it statistically significant?

(iii) Drop *sat* from the model and reestimate the equation. Now, what is the estimated effect of being an athlete? Discuss why the estimate is different than that obtained in part (ii).

(iv) In the model from part (i), allow the effect of being an athlete to differ by gender and test the null hypothesis that there is no ceteris paribus difference between women athletes and women nonathletes.

(v) Does the effect of *sat* on *colgpa* differ by gender? Justify your answer.

C5 In Problem 2 in Chapter 4, we added the return on the firm's stock, *ros*, to a model explaining CEO salary; *ros* turned out to be insignificant. Now, define a dummy variable, *rosneg*, which is equal to one if $ros < 0$ and equal to zero if $ros \geq 0$. Use CEOSAL1.RAW to estimate the model

$$\log(salary) = \beta_0 + \beta_1 \log(sales) + \beta_2 roe + \beta_3 rosneg + u.$$

Discuss the interpretation and statistical significance of $\hat{\beta}_3$.

C6 Use the data in SLEEP75.RAW for this exercise. The equation of interest is

$$sleep = \beta_0 + \beta_1 totwrk + \beta_2 educ + \beta_3 age + \beta_4 age^2 + \beta_5 yngkid + u.$$

(i) Estimate this equation separately for men and women and report the results in the usual form. Are there notable differences in the two estimated equations?

(ii) Compute the Chow test for equality of the parameters in the sleep equation for men and women. Use the form of the test that adds *male* and the interaction terms *male·totwrk*, ..., *male·yngkid* and uses the full set of observations. What are the relevant *df* for the test? Should you reject the null at the 5% level?

(iii) Now, allow for a different intercept for males and females and determine whether the interaction terms involving *male* are jointly significant.

(iv) Given the results from parts (ii) and (iii), what would be your final model?

C7 Use the data in WAGE1.RAW for this exercise.

(i) Use equation (7.18) to estimate the gender differential when $educ = 12.5$. Compare this with the estimated differential when $educ = 0$.

(ii) Run the regression used to obtain (7.18), but with $female \cdot (educ - 12.5)$ replacing $female \cdot educ$. How do you interpret the coefficient on *female* now?

(iii) Is the coefficient on *female* in part (ii) statistically significant? Compare this with (7.18) and comment.

C8 Use the data in LOANAPP.RAW for this exercise. The binary variable to be explained is *approve*, which is equal to one if a mortgage loan to an individual was approved. The key explanatory variable is *white*, a dummy variable equal to one if the applicant was white. The other applicants in the data set are black and Hispanic.

To test for discrimination in the mortgage loan market, a linear probability model can be used:

$$approve = \beta_0 + \beta_1 white + other\, factors.$$

(i) If there is discrimination against minorities, and the appropriate factors have been controlled for, what is the sign of β_1?

(ii) Regress *approve* on *white* and report the results in the usual form. Interpret the coefficient on *white*. Is it statistically significant? Is it practically large?

(iii) As controls, add the variables *hrat*, *obrat*, *loanprc*, *unem*, *male*, *married*, *dep*, *sch*, *cosign*, *chist*, *pubrec*, *mortlat1*, *mortlat2*, and *vr*. What happens to the coefficient on *white*? Is there still evidence of discrimination against nonwhites?

(iv) Now, allow the effect of race to interact with the variable measuring other obligations as a percentage of income (*obrat*). Is the interaction term significant?

(v) Using the model from part (iv), what is the effect of being white on the probability of approval when *obrat* = 32, which is roughly the mean value in the sample? Obtain a 95% confidence interval for this effect.

C9 There has been much interest in whether the presence of 401(k) pension plans, available to many U.S. workers, increases net savings. The data set 401KSUBS.RAW contains information on net financial assets (*nettfa*), family income (*inc*), a binary variable for eligibility in a 401(k) plan (*e401k*), and several other variables.

(i) What fraction of the families in the sample are eligible for participation in a 401(k) plan?

(ii) Estimate a linear probability model explaining 401(k) eligibility in terms of income, age, and gender. Include income and age in quadratic form, and report the results in the usual form.

(iii) Would you say that 401(k) eligibility is independent of income and age? What about gender? Explain.

(iv) Obtain the fitted values from the linear probability model estimated in part (ii). Are any fitted values negative or greater than one?

(v) Using the fitted values $\widehat{e401k}_i$ from part (iv), define $\widetilde{e401k}_i = 1$ if $\widehat{e401k} \geq .5$ and $\widetilde{401k} = 0$ if $\widehat{e401k} < .5$. Out of 9,275 families, how many are predicted to be eligible for a 401(k) plan?

(vi) For the 5,638 families not eligible for a 401(k), what percentage of these are predicted not to have a 401(k), using the predictor $\widetilde{e401k}_i$? For the 3,637 families eligible for a 401(k) plan, what percentage are predicted to have one? (It is helpful if your econometrics package has a "tabulate" command.)

(vii) The overall percent correctly predicted is about 64.9%. Do you think this is a complete description of how well the model does, given your answers in part (vi)?

(viii) Add the variable *pira* as an explanatory variable to the linear probability model. Other things equal, if a family has someone with an individual retirement account, how much higher is the estimated probability that the family is eligible for a 401(k) plan? Is it statistically different from zero at the 10% level?

C10 Use the data in NBASAL.RAW for this exercise.

(i) Estimate a linear regression model relating points per game to experience in the league and position (guard, forward, or center). Include experience in quadratic form and use centers as the base group. Report the results in the usual form.

(ii) Why do you not include all three position dummy variables in part (i)?

(iii) Holding experience fixed, does a guard score more than a center? How much more? Is the difference statistically significant?

(iv) Now, add marital status to the equation. Holding position and experience fixed, are married players more productive (based on points per game)?

(v) Add interactions of marital status with both experience variables. In this expanded model, is there strong evidence that marital status affects points per game?

(vi) Estimate the model from part (iv) but use assists per game as the dependent variable. Are there any notable differences from part (iv)? Discuss.

C11 Use the data in 401KSUBS.RAW for this exercise.

(i) Compute the average, standard deviation, minimum, and maximum values of *nettfa* in the sample.

(ii) Test the hypothesis that average *nettfa* does not differ by 401(k) eligibility status; use a two-sided alternative. What is the dollar amount of the estimated difference?

(iii) From part (ii) of Computer Exercise C9, it is clear that *e401k* is not exogenous in a simple regression model; at a minimum, it changes by income and age. Estimate a multiple linear regression model for *nettfa* that includes income, age, and *e401k* as explanatory variables. The income and age variables should appear as quadratics. Now, what is the estimated dollar effect of 401(k) eligibility?

(iv) To the model estimated in part (iii), add the interactions $e401k \cdot (age - 41)$ and $e401k \cdot (age - 41)^2$. Note that the average age in the sample is about 41, so that in the new model, the coefficient on *e401k* is the estimated effect of 401(k) eligibility at the average age. Which interaction term is significant?

(v) Comparing the estimates from parts (iii) and (iv), do the estimated effects of 401(k) eligibility at age 41 differ much? Explain.

(vi) Now, drop the interaction terms from the model, but define five family size dummy variables: *fsize1, fsize2, fsize3, fsize4,* and *fsize5*. The variable *fsize5* is unity for families with five or more members. Include the family size dummies in the model estimated from part (iii); be sure to choose a base group. Are the family dummies significant at the 1% level?

(vii) Now, do a Chow test for the model

$$nettfa = \beta_0 + \beta_1 inc + \beta_2 inc^2 + \beta_3 age + \beta_4 age^2 + \beta_5 e401k + u$$

across the five family size categories, allowing for intercept differences. The restricted sum of squared residuals, SSR_r, is obtained from part (vi) because that regression assumes all slopes are the same. The unrestricted sum of squared residuals is $SSR_{ur} = SSR_1 + SSR_2 + ... + SSR_5$, where SSR_f is the sum of squared residuals for the equation estimated using only family size *f*. You should convince yourself that there are 30 parameters in the unrestricted model (5 intercepts plus 25 slopes) and 10 parameters in the restricted model (5 intercepts plus 5 slopes). Therefore, the number of restrictions being tested is $q = 20$, and the *df* for the unrestricted model is $9{,}275 - 30 = 9{,}245$.

C12 Use the data set in BEAUTY.RAW, which contains a subset of the variables (but more usable observations than in the regressions) reported by Hamermesh and Biddle (1994).

(i) Find the separate fractions of men and women that are classified as having above average looks. Are more people rated as having above average or below average looks?

(ii) Test the null hypothesis that the population fractions of above-average-looking women and men are the same. Report the one-sided p-value that the fraction is higher for women. (*Hint:* Estimating a simple linear probability model is easiest.)

(iii) Now estimate the model

$$\log(wage) = \beta_0 + \beta_1 belavg + \beta_2 abvavg + u$$

separately for men and women, and report the results in the usual form. In both cases, interpret the coefficient on *belavg*. Explain in words what the hypothesis H_0: $\beta_1 = 0$ against H_1: $\beta_1 < 0$ means, and find the p-values for men and women.

(iv) Is there convincing evidence that women with above average looks earn more than women with average looks? Explain.

(v) For both men and women, add the explanatory variables *educ*, *exper*, $exper^2$, *union*, *goodhlth*, *black*, *married*, *south*, *bigcity*, *smllcity*, and *service*. Do the effects of the "looks" variables change in important ways?

(vi) Use the SSR form of the Chow F statistic to test whether the slopes of the regression functions in part (v) differ across men and women. Be sure to allow for an intercept shift under the null.

C13 Use the data in APPLE.RAW to answer this question.

(i) Define a binary variable as $ecobuy = 1$ if $ecolbs > 0$ and $ecobuy = 0$ if $ecolbs = 0$. In other words, *ecobuy* indicates whether, at the prices given, a family would buy any ecologically friendly apples. What fraction of families claim they would buy ecolabeled apples?

(ii) Estimate the linear probability model

$$ecobuy = \beta_0 + \beta_1 ecoprc + \beta_2 regprc + \beta_3 faminc + \beta_4 hhsize + \beta_5 educ + \beta_6 age + u,$$

and report the results in the usual form. Carefully interpret the coefficients on the price variables.

(iii) Are the nonprice variables jointly significant in the LPM? (Use the usual F statistic, even though it is not valid when there is heteroskedasticity.) Which explanatory variable other than the price variables seems to have the most important effect on the decision to buy ecolabeled apples? Does this make sense to you?

(iv) In the model from part (ii), replace *faminc* with log(*faminc*). Which model fits the data better, using *faminc* or log(*faminc*)? Interpret the coefficient on log(*faminc*).

(v) In the estimation in part (iv), how many estimated probabilities are negative? How many are bigger than one? Should you be concerned?

(vi) For the estimation in part (iv), compute the percent correctly predicted for each outcome, $ecobuy = 0$ and $ecobuy = 1$. Which outcome is best predicted by the model?

C14 Use the data in CHARITY.RAW to answer this question. The variable *respond* is a dummy variable equal to one if a person responded with a contribution on the most recent mailing sent by a charitable organization. The variable *resplast* is a dummy variable equal to one if the person responded to the previous mailing, *avggift* is the average of past gifts (in Dutch guilders), and *propresp* is the proportion of times the person has responded to past mailings.

(i) Estimate a linear probability model relating *respond* to *resplast* and *avggift*. Report the results in the usual form, and interpret the coefficient on *resplast*.
(ii) Does the average value of past gifts seem to affect the probability of responding?
(iii) Add the variable *propresp* to the model, and interpret its coefficient. (Be careful here: an increase of one in *propresp* is the largest possible change.)
(iv) What happened to the coefficient on *resplast* when *propresp* was added to the regression? Does this make sense?
(v) Add *mailsyear*, the number of mailings per year, to the model. How big is its estimated effect? Why might this not be a good estimate of the causal effect of mailings on responding?

C15 Use the data in FERTIL2.RAW to answer this question.
(i) Find the smallest and largest values of *children* in the sample. What is the average of *children*? Does any woman have exactly the average number of children?
(ii) What percentage of women have electricity in the home?
(iii) Compute the average of *children* for those without electricity and do the same for those with electricity. Comment on what you find. Test whether the population means are the same using a simple regression.
(iv) From part (iii), can you infer that having electricity "causes" women to have fewer children? Explain.
(v) Estimate a multiple regression model of the kind reported in equation (7.37), but add age^2, *urban*, and the three religious affiliation dummies. How does the estimated effect of having electricity compare with that in part (iii)? Is it still statistically significant?
(vi) To the equation in part (v), add an interaction between *electric* and *educ*. Is its coefficient statistically significant? What happens to the coefficient on *electric*?
(vii) The median and mode value for *educ* is 7. In the equation from part (vi), use the centered interaction term *electric* • (*educ* – 7) in place of *electric* • *educ*. What happens to the coefficient on *electric* compared with part (vi)? Why? How does the coefficient on *electric* compare with that in part (v)?

CHAPTER 8

Heteroskedasticity

The homoskedasticity assumption, introduced in Chapter 3 for multiple regression, states that the variance of the unobserved error, u, conditional on the explanatory variables, is constant. Homoskedasticity fails whenever the variance of the unobserved factors changes across different segments of the population, where the segments are determined by the different values of the explanatory variables. For example, in a savings equation, heteroskedasticity is present if the variance of the unobserved factors affecting savings increases with income.

In Chapters 4 and 5, we saw that homoskedasticity is needed to justify the usual t tests, F tests, and confidence intervals for OLS estimation of the linear regression model, even with large sample sizes. In this chapter, we discuss the available remedies when heteroskedasticity occurs, and we also show how to test for its presence. We begin by briefly reviewing the consequences of heteroskedasticity for ordinary least squares estimation.

8.1 Consequences of Heteroskedasticity for OLS

Consider again the multiple linear regression model:

$$y = \beta_0 + \beta_1 x_1 + \beta_2 x_2 + \ldots + \beta_k x_k + u. \quad [8.1]$$

In Chapter 3, we proved unbiasedness of the OLS estimators $\hat{\beta}_0, \hat{\beta}_1, \hat{\beta}_2, \ldots, \hat{\beta}_k$ under the first four Gauss-Markov assumptions, MLR.1 through MLR.4. In Chapter 5, we showed that the same four assumptions imply consistency of OLS. The homoskedasticity assumption MLR.5, stated in terms of the error variance as $\text{Var}(u|x_1, x_2, \ldots, x_k) = \sigma^2$, played no role in showing whether OLS was unbiased or consistent. It is important to remember that heteroskedasticity does not cause bias or inconsistency in the OLS estimators of the β_j, whereas something like omitting an important variable would have this effect.

The interpretation of our goodness-of-fit measures, R^2 and $\bar{R}^2$, is also unaffected by the presence of heteroskedasticity. Why? Recall from Section 6.3 that the usual R-squared and the adjusted R-squared are different ways of estimating the population R-squared, which is simply $1 - \sigma_u^2/\sigma_y^2$, where σ_u^2 is the population error variance and σ_y^2 is the population variance of y. The key point is that because both variances in the population R-squared are unconditional variances, the population R-squared is unaffected by the presence of heteroskedasticity in $\text{Var}(u|x_1, \ldots, x_k)$. Further, SSR/$n$ consistently estimates σ_u^2, and SST/n consistently estimates σ_y^2, whether or not $\text{Var}(u|x_1, \ldots, x_k)$ is constant. The same is true when we use the degrees of freedom adjustments. Therefore, R^2 and $\bar{R}^2$ are both consistent estimators of the population R-squared whether or not the homoskedasticity assumption holds.

If heteroskedasticity does not cause bias or inconsistency in the OLS estimators, why did we introduce it as one of the Gauss-Markov assumptions? Recall from Chapter 3 that the estimators of the *variances*, $\text{Var}(\hat{\beta}_j)$, are biased without the homoskedasticity assumption. Since the OLS standard errors are based directly on these variances, they are no longer valid for constructing confidence intervals and t statistics. The usual OLS t statistics do not have t distributions in the presence of heteroskedasticity, and the problem is not resolved by using large sample sizes. We will see this explicitly for the simple regression case in the next section, where we derive the variance of the OLS slope estimator under heteroskedasticity and propose a valid estimator in the presence of heteroskedasticity. Similarly, F statistics are no longer F distributed, and the LM statistic no longer has an asymptotic chi-square distribution. In summary, the statistics we used to test hypotheses under the Gauss-Markov assumptions are not valid in the presence of heteroskedasticity.

We also know that the Gauss-Markov Theorem, which says that OLS is best linear unbiased, relies crucially on the homoskedasticity assumption. If $\text{Var}(u|\mathbf{x})$ is not constant, OLS is no longer BLUE. In addition, OLS is no longer asymptotically efficient in the class of estimators described in Theorem 5.3. As we will see in Section 8.4, it is possible to find estimators that are more efficient than OLS in the presence of heteroskedasticity (although it requires knowing the form of the heteroskedasticity). With relatively large sample sizes, it might not be so important to obtain an efficient estimator. In the next section, we show how the usual OLS test statistics can be modified so that they are valid, at least asymptotically.

8.2 Heteroskedasticity-Robust Inference after OLS Estimation

Because testing hypotheses is such an important component of any econometric analysis and the usual OLS inference is generally faulty in the presence of heteroskedasticity, we must decide if we should entirely abandon OLS. Fortunately, OLS is still useful. In the last two decades, econometricians have learned how to adjust standard errors and t, F, and LM statistics so that they are valid in the presence of **heteroskedasticity of unknown form**. This is very convenient because it means we can report new statistics that work regardless of the kind of heteroskedasticity present in the population. The methods in this section are known as *heteroskedasticity-robust* procedures because they are valid—at least in large samples—whether or not the errors have constant variance, and we do not need to know which is the case.

We begin by sketching how the variances, $\text{Var}(\hat{\beta}_j)$, can be estimated in the presence of heteroskedasticity. A careful derivation of the theory is well beyond the scope of this text, but the application of heteroskedasticity-robust methods is very easy now because many statistics and econometrics packages compute these statistics as an option.

First, consider the model with a single independent variable, where we include an i subscript for emphasis:

$$y_i = \beta_0 + \beta_1 x_i + u_i.$$

We assume throughout that the first four Gauss-Markov assumptions hold. If the errors contain heteroskedasticity, then

$$\text{Var}(u_i|x_i) = \sigma_i^2,$$

where we put an i subscript on σ^2 to indicate that the variance of the error depends upon the particular value of x_i.

Write the OLS estimator as

$$\hat{\beta}_1 = \beta_1 + \frac{\sum_{i=1}^{n}(x_i - \bar{x})u_i}{\sum_{i=1}^{n}(x_i - \bar{x})^2}.$$

Under Assumptions MLR.1 through MLR.4 (that is, without the homoskedasticity assumption), and conditioning on the values x_i in the sample, we can use the same arguments from Chapter 2 to show that

$$\text{Var}(\hat{\beta}_1) = \frac{\sum_{i=1}^{n}(x_i - \bar{x})^2\sigma_i^2}{\text{SST}_x^2}, \qquad [8.2]$$

where $\text{SST}_x = \sum_{i=1}^{n}(x_i - \bar{x})^2$ is the total sum of squares of the x_i. When $\sigma_i^2 = \sigma^2$ for all i, this formula reduces to the usual form, σ^2/SST_x. Equation (8.2) explicitly shows that, for the simple regression case, the variance formula derived under homoskedasticity is no longer valid when heteroskedasticity is present.

Since the standard error of $\hat{\beta}_1$ is based directly on estimating $\text{Var}(\hat{\beta}_1)$, we need a way to estimate equation (8.2) when heteroskedasticity is present. White (1980) showed how this can be done. Let $\hat{u}_i$ denote the OLS residuals from the initial regression of y on x. Then, a valid estimator of $\text{Var}(\hat{\beta}_1)$, for heteroskedasticity of *any* form (including homoskedasticity), is

$$\frac{\sum_{i=1}^{n}(x_i - \bar{x})^2\hat{u}_i^2}{\text{SST}_x^2}, \qquad [8.3]$$

which is easily computed from the data after the OLS regression.

In what sense is (8.3) a valid estimator of $\text{Var}(\hat{\beta}_1)$? This is pretty subtle. Briefly, it can be shown that when equation (8.3) is multiplied by the sample size n, it converges in probability to $\text{E}[(x_i - \mu_x)^2u_i^2]/(\sigma_x^2)^2$, which is the probability limit of n times (8.2). Ultimately, this is what is necessary for justifying the use of standard errors to construct confidence intervals and t statistics. The law of large numbers and the central limit theorem play key roles in establishing these convergences. You can refer to White's original paper for details, but that paper is quite technical. See also Wooldridge (2010, Chapter 4).

A similar formula works in the general multiple regression model

$$y = \beta_0 + \beta_1 x_1 + \dots + \beta_k x_k + u.$$

It can be shown that a valid estimator of Var($\hat{\beta}_j$), under Assumptions MLR.1 through MLR.4, is

$$\widehat{\text{Var}}(\hat{\beta}_j) = \frac{\sum_{i=1}^{n} \hat{r}_{ij}^2 \hat{u}_i^2}{\text{SSR}_j^2}, \qquad [8.4]$$

where $\hat{r}_{ij}$ denotes the ith residual from regressing x_j on all other independent variables, and SSR_j is the sum of squared residuals from this regression (see Section 3.2 for the partialling out representation of the OLS estimates). The square root of the quantity in (8.4) is called the **heteroskedasticity-robust standard error** for $\hat{\beta}_j$. In econometrics, these robust standard errors are usually attributed to White (1980). Earlier works in statistics, notably those by Eicker (1967) and Huber (1967), pointed to the possibility of obtaining such robust standard errors. In applied work, these are sometimes called *White, Huber*, or *Eicker standard errors* (or some hyphenated combination of these names). We will just refer to them as *heteroskedasticity-robust standard errors*, or even just *robust standard errors* when the context is clear.

Sometimes, as a degrees of freedom correction, (8.4) is multiplied by $n/(n - k - 1)$ before taking the square root. The reasoning for this adjustment is that, if the squared OLS residuals $\hat{u}_i^2$ were the same for all observations i—the strongest possible form of homoskedasticity in a sample—we would get the usual OLS standard errors. Other modifications of (8.4) are studied in MacKinnon and White (1985). Since all forms have only asymptotic justification and they are asymptotically equivalent, no form is uniformly preferred above all others. Typically, we use whatever form is computed by the regression package at hand.

Once heteroskedasticity-robust standard errors are obtained, it is simple to construct a **heteroskedasticity-robust *t* statistic**. Recall that the general form of the t statistic is

$$t = \frac{\textit{estimate} - \textit{hypothesized value}}{\textit{standard error}}. \qquad [8.5]$$

Because we are still using the OLS estimates and we have chosen the hypothesized value ahead of time, the only difference between the usual OLS t statistic and the heteroskedasticity-robust t statistic is in how the standard error in the denominator is computed.

The term SSRj in equation (8.4) can be replaced with SST$j$$(1 - R_j^2)$, where SST$j$ is the total sum of squares of x_j and R_j^2 is the usual R-squared from regressing x_j on all other explanatory variables. [We implicitly used this equivalance in deriving equation (3.51).] Consequently, little sample variation in x_j, or a strong linear relationship between x_j and the other explanatory variables—that is, multicollinearity—can cause the heteroskedasticity-robust standard errrors to be large. We discussed these issues with the usual OLS standard errors in Section 3.4.

EXAMPLE 8.1 LOG WAGE EQUATION WITH HETEROSKEDASTICITY-ROBUST STANDARD ERRORS

We estimate the model in Example 7.6, but we report the heteroskedasticity-robust standard errors along with the usual OLS standard errors. Some of the estimates are reported to more digits so that we can compare the usual standard errors with the heteroskedasticity-robust standard errors:

$$
\begin{aligned}
\widehat{\log(wage)} = {} & \underset{\substack{(.100)\\ [.109]}}{.321} + \underset{\substack{(.055)\\ [.057]}}{.213}\ marrmale - \underset{\substack{(.058)\\ [.058]}}{.198}\ marrfem - \underset{\substack{(.056)\\ [.057]}}{.110}\ singfem \\
& + \underset{\substack{(.0067)\\ [.0074]}}{.0789}\ educ + \underset{\substack{(.0055)\\ [.0051]}}{.0268}\ exper - \underset{\substack{(.00011)\\ [.00011]}}{.00054}\ exper^2 \\
& + \underset{\substack{(.0068)\\ [.0069]}}{.0291}\ tenure - \underset{\substack{(.00023)\\ [.00024]}}{.00053}\ tenure^2 \\
n = {} & 526,\ R^2 = .461.
\end{aligned}
\tag{8.6}
$$

The usual OLS standard errors are in parentheses, ( ), below the corresponding OLS estimate, and the heteroskedasticity-robust standard errors are in brackets, [ ]. The numbers in brackets are the only new things, since the equation is still estimated by OLS.

Several things are apparent from equation (8.6). First, in this particular application, any variable that was statistically significant using the usual *t* statistic is still statistically significant using the heteroskedasticity-robust *t* statistic. This occurs because the two sets of standard errors are not very different. (The associated *p*-values will differ slightly because the robust *t* statistics are not identical to the usual, nonrobust *t* statistics.) The largest relative change in standard errors is for the coefficient on *educ:* the usual standard error is .0067, and the robust standard error is .0074. Still, the robust standard error implies a robust *t* statistic above 10.

Equation (8.6) also shows that the robust standard errors can be either larger or smaller than the usual standard errors. For example, the robust standard error on *exper* is .0051, whereas the usual standard error is .0055. We do not know which will be larger ahead of time. As an empirical matter, the robust standard errors are often found to be larger than the usual standard errors.

Before leaving this example, we must emphasize that we do not know, at this point, whether heteroskedasticity is even present in the population model underlying equation (8.6). All we have done is report, along with the usual standard errors, those that are valid (asymptotically) whether or not heteroskedasticity is present. We can see that no important conclusions are overturned by using the robust standard errors in this example. This often happens in applied work, but in other cases, the differences between the usual and robust standard errors are much larger. As an example of where the differences are substantial, see Computer Exercise C2.

At this point, you may be asking the following question: If the heteroskedasticity-robust standard errors are valid more often than the usual OLS standard errors, why do we bother with the usual standard errors at all? This is a sensible question. One reason the usual standard errors are still used in cross-sectional work is that, if the homoskedasticity assumption holds and the errors are normally distributed, then the usual t statistics have *exact t* distributions, regardless of the sample size (see Chapter 4). The robust standard errors and robust t statistics are justified only as the sample size becomes large, even if the CLM assumptions are true. With small sample sizes, the robust t statistics can have distributions that are not very close to the t distribution, and that could throw off our inference.

In large sample sizes, we can make a case for always reporting only the heteroskedasticity-robust standard errors in cross-sectional applications, and this practice is being followed more and more in applied work. It is also common to report both standard errors, as in equation (8.6), so that a reader can determine whether any conclusions are sensitive to the standard error in use.

It is also possible to obtain F and LM statistics that are robust to heteroskedasticity of an unknown, arbitrary form. The **heteroskedasticity-robust F statistic** (or a simple transformation of it) is also called a *heteroskedasticity-robust Wald statistic*. A general treatment of the Wald statistic requires matrix algebra and is sketched in Appendix E; see Wooldridge (2010, Chapter 4) for a more detailed treatment. Nevertheless, using heteroskedasticity-robust statistics for multiple exclusion restrictions is straightforward because many econometrics packages now compute such statistics routinely.

EXAMPLE 8.2 HETEROSKEDASTICITY-ROBUST *F* STATISTIC

Using the data for the spring semester in GPA3.RAW, we estimate the following equation:

$$\begin{aligned}\widehat{cumgpa} = {} & \underset{\substack{(.23)\\ [.22]}}{1.47} + \underset{\substack{(.00018)\\ [.00019]}}{.00114}\, sat - \underset{\substack{(.00124)\\ [.00140]}}{.00857}\, hsperc + \underset{\substack{(.00073)\\ [.00073]}}{.00250}\, tothrs \\ & + \underset{\substack{(.059)\\ [.059]}}{.303}\, female - \underset{\substack{(.147)\\ [.118]}}{.128}\, black - \underset{\substack{(.141)\\ [.110]}}{.059}\, white \\ & n = 366,\ R^2 = .4006,\ \bar{R}^2 = .3905.\end{aligned} \tag{8.7}$$

Again, the differences between the usual standard errors and the heteroskedasticity-robust standard errors are not very big, and use of the robust t statistics does not change the statistical significance of any independent variable. Joint significance tests are not much affected either. Suppose we wish to test the null hypothesis that, after the other factors are controlled for, there are no differences in *cumgpa* by race. This is stated as H_0: $\beta_{black} = 0$, $\beta_{white} = 0$. The usual F statistic is easily obtained, once we have the R-squared from the restricted model; this turns out to be .3983. The F statistic is then $[(.4006 - .3983)/(1 - .4006)](359/2) \approx .69$. If heteroskedasticity is present, this version of the test is invalid. The heteroskedasticity-robust version has no simple form, but it can be computed using certain statistical packages. The value of the heteroskedasticity-robust F statistic turns out to be .75, which differs only slightly from the nonrobust version. The p-value for the robust test is .474, which is not close to standard significance levels. We fail to reject the null hypothesis using either test.

Because the usual sum-of-squared residuals form of the F statistic is not valid under heteroskedasticity, it can be important when computing a Chow test to use the form that includes a full set of interactions between the group dummy variable and the other explanatory variables. This can be tedious but is necessary for obtaining heteroskedasticity-robust F statistics using popular regression packages. See Computer Exercise C14 for an example.

Computing Heteroskedasticity-Robust *LM* Tests

> **EXPLORING FURTHER 8.1**
>
> Evaluate the following statement: The heteroskedasticity-robust standard errors are always bigger than the usual standard errors.

Not all regression packages compute F statistics that are robust to heteroskedasticity. Therefore, it is sometimes convenient to have a way of obtaining a test of multiple exclusion restrictions that is robust to heteroskedasticity and does not require a particular kind of econometric software. It turns out that a **heteroskedasticity-robust *LM* statistic** is easily obtained using virtually any regression package.

To illustrate computation of the robust LM statistic, consider the model

$$y = \beta_0 + \beta_1 x_1 + \beta_2 x_2 + \beta_3 x_3 + \beta_4 x_4 + \beta_5 x_5 + u,$$

and suppose we would like to test H_0: $\beta_4 = 0$, $\beta_5 = 0$. To obtain the usual LM statistic, we would first estimate the restricted model (that is, the model without x_4 and x_5) to obtain the residuals, $\tilde{u}$. Then, we would regress $\tilde{u}$ on all of the independent variables and the $LM = n \cdot R^2_{\tilde{u}}$ where $R^2_{\tilde{u}}$ is the usual R-squared from this regression.

Obtaining a version that is robust to heteroskedasticity requires more work. One way to compute the statistic requires only OLS regressions. We need the residuals, say, $\tilde{r}_1$, from the regression of x_4 on x_1, x_2, x_3. Also, we need the residuals, say, $\tilde{r}_2$, from the regression of x_5 on x_1, x_2, x_3. Thus, we regress each of the independent variables excluded under the null on all of the included independent variables. We keep the residuals each time. The final step appears odd, but it is, after all, just a computational device. Run the regression of

$$1 \text{ on } \tilde{r}_1\tilde{u}, \tilde{r}_2\tilde{u}, \qquad [8.8]$$

without an intercept. Yes, we actually define a dependent variable equal to the value one for all observations. We regress this onto the products $\tilde{r}_1\tilde{u}$ and $\tilde{r}_2\tilde{u}$. The robust LM statistic turns out to be $n - \text{SSR}_1$, where SSR_1 is just the usual sum of squared residuals from regression (8.8).

The reason this works is somewhat technical. Basically, this is doing for the LM test what the robust standard errors do for the t test. [See Wooldridge (1991b) or Davidson and MacKinnon (1993) for a more detailed discussion.]

We now summarize the computation of the heteroskedasticity-robust LM statistic in the general case.

A Heteroskedasticity-Robust *LM* Statistic:

1. Obtain the residuals $\tilde{u}$ from the restricted model.
2. Regress each of the independent variables excluded under the null on all of the included independent variables; if there are q excluded variables, this leads to q sets of residuals $(\tilde{r}_1, \tilde{r}_2, \ldots, \tilde{r}_q)$.
3. Find the products between each $\tilde{r}_j$ and $\tilde{u}$ (for all observations).

4. Run the regression of 1 on $\tilde{r}_1\tilde{u}, \tilde{r}_2\tilde{u}, \ldots, \tilde{r}_q\tilde{u}$, without an intercept. The heteroskedasticity-robust *LM* statistic is $n - SSR_1$, where SSR_1 is just the usual sum of squared residuals from this final regression. Under H_0, *LM* is distributed approximately as χ^2_q.

Once the robust *LM* statistic is obtained, the rejection rule and computation of *p*-values are the same as for the usual *LM* statistic in Section 5.2.

EXAMPLE 8.3 HETEROSKEDASTICITY-ROBUST *LM* STATISTIC

We use the data in CRIME1.RAW to test whether the average sentence length served for past convictions affects the number of arrests in the current year (1986). The estimated model is

$$\begin{aligned}\widehat{narr86} = {} & \underset{\substack{(.036)\\ [.040]}}{.567} - \underset{\substack{(.040)\\ [.034]}}{.136}\, pcnv + \underset{\substack{(.0097)\\ [.0101]}}{.0178}\, avgsen - \underset{\substack{(.00030)\\ [.00021]}}{.00052}\, avgsen^2 \\ & - \underset{\substack{(.0087)\\ [.0062]}}{.0394}\, ptime86 - \underset{\substack{(.0144)\\ [.0142]}}{.0505}\, qemp86 - \underset{\substack{(.00034)\\ [.00023]}}{.00148}\, inc86 \\ & + \underset{\substack{(.045)\\ [.058]}}{.325}\, black + \underset{\substack{(.040)\\ [.040]}}{.193}\, hispan \\ n = {} & 2{,}725,\ R^2 = .0728.\end{aligned} \tag{8.9}$$

In this example, there are more substantial differences between some of the usual standard errors and the robust standard errors. For example, the usual *t* statistic on $avgsen^2$ is about −1.73, while the robust *t* statistic is about −2.48. Thus, $avgsen^2$ is more significant using the robust standard error.

The effect of *avgsen* on *narr86* is somewhat difficult to reconcile. Because the relationship is quadratic, we can figure out where *avgsen* has a positive effect on *narr86* and where the effect becomes negative. The turning point is $.0178/[2(.00052)] \approx 17.12$; recall that this is measured in months. Literally, this means that *narr86* is positively related to *avgsen* when *avgsen* is less than 17 months; then *avgsen* has the expected deterrent effect after 17 months.

To see whether average sentence length has a statistically significant effect on *narr86*, we must test the joint hypothesis H_0: $\beta_{avgsen} = 0, \beta_{avgsen^2} = 0$. Using the usual *LM* statistic (see Section 5.2), we obtain $LM = 3.54$; in a chi-square distribution with two *df*, this yields a *p*-value = .170. Thus, we do not reject H_0 at even the 15% level. The heteroskedasticity-robust *LM* statistic is $LM = 4.00$ (rounded to two decimal places), with a *p*-value = .135. This is still not very strong evidence against H_0; *avgsen* does not appear to have a strong effect on *narr86*. [Incidentally, when *avgsen* appears alone in (8.9), that is, without the quadratic term, its usual *t* statistic is .658, and its robust *t* statistic is .592.]

8.3 Testing for Heteroskedasticity

The heteroskedasticity-robust standard errors provide a simple method for computing *t* statistics that are asymptotically *t* distributed whether or not heteroskedasticity is present. We have also seen that heteroskedasticity-robust *F* and *LM* statistics are available.

Implementing these tests does not require knowing whether or not heteroskedasticity is present. Nevertheless, there are still some good reasons for having simple tests that can detect its presence. First, as we mentioned in the previous section, the usual t statistics have exact t distributions under the classical linear model assumptions. For this reason, many economists still prefer to see the usual OLS standard errors and test statistics reported, unless there is evidence of heteroskedasticity. Second, if heteroskedasticity is present, the OLS estimator is no longer the best linear unbiased estimator. As we will see in Section 8.4, it is possible to obtain a better estimator than OLS when the form of heteroskedasticity is known.

Many tests for heteroskedasticity have been suggested over the years. Some of them, while having the ability to detect heteroskedasticity, do not directly test the assumption that the variance of the error does not depend upon the independent variables. We will restrict ourselves to more modern tests, which detect the kind of heteroskedasticity that invalidates the usual OLS statistics. This also has the benefit of putting all tests in the same framework.

As usual, we start with the linear model

$$y = \beta_0 + \beta_1 x_1 + \beta_2 x_2 + \ldots + \beta_k x_k + u, \quad [8.10]$$

where Assumptions MLR.1 through MLR.4 are maintained in this section. In particular, we assume that $\mathrm{E}(u|x_1, x_2, \ldots, x_k) = 0$, so that OLS is unbiased and consistent.

We take the null hypothesis to be that Assumption MLR.5 is true:

$$\mathrm{H}_0\text{: Var}(u|x_1, x_2, \ldots, x_k) = \sigma^2. \quad [8.11]$$

That is, we assume that the ideal assumption of homoskedasticity holds, and we require the data to tell us otherwise. If we cannot reject (8.11) at a sufficiently small significance level, we usually conclude that heteroskedasticity is not a problem. However, remember that we never accept H_0; we simply fail to reject it.

Because we are assuming that u has a zero conditional expectation, $\mathrm{Var}(u|\mathbf{x}) = \mathrm{E}(u^2|\mathbf{x})$, and so the null hypothesis of homoskedasticity is equivalent to

$$\mathrm{H}_0\text{: E}(u^2|x_1, x_2, \ldots, x_k) = \mathrm{E}(u^2) = \sigma^2.$$

This shows that, in order to test for violation of the homoskedasticity assumption, we want to test whether u^2 is related (in expected value) to one or more of the explanatory variables. If H_0 is false, the expected value of u^2, given the independent variables, can be virtually any function of the x_j. A simple approach is to assume a linear function:

$$u^2 = \delta_0 + \delta_1 x_1 + \delta_2 x_2 + \ldots + \delta_k x_k + v, \quad [8.12]$$

where v is an error term with mean zero given the x_j. Pay close attention to the dependent variable in this equation: it is the *square* of the error in the original regression equation, (8.10). The null hypothesis of homoskedasticity is

$$\mathrm{H}_0\text{: } \delta_1 = \delta_2 = \ldots = \delta_k = 0. \quad [8.13]$$

Under the null hypothesis, it is often reasonable to assume that the error in (8.12), v, is independent of $x_1, x_2, \ldots, x_k$. Then, we know from Section 5.2 that either the F or LM statistics for the overall significance of the independent variables in explaining u^2 can be used to test (8.13). Both statistics would have asymptotic justification, even though u^2 cannot be normally distributed. (For example, if u is normally distributed, then u^2/σ^2 is distributed as χ_1^2.) If we could observe the u^2 in the sample, then we could easily compute this statistic by running the OLS regression of u^2 on $x_1, x_2, \ldots, x_k$, using all n observations.

As we have emphasized before, we never know the actual errors in the population model, but we do have estimates of them: the OLS residual, $\hat{u}_i$, is an estimate of the error u_i for observation i. Thus, we can estimate the equation

$$\hat{u}^2 = \delta_0 + \delta_1 x_1 + \delta_2 x_2 + \ldots + \delta_k x_k + error \qquad [8.14]$$

and compute the F or LM statistics for the joint significance of $x_1, \ldots, x_k$. It turns out that using the OLS residuals in place of the errors does not affect the large sample distribution of the F or LM statistics, although showing this is pretty complicated.

The F and LM statistics both depend on the R-squared from regression (8.14); call this $R^2_{\hat{u}^2}$ to distinguish it from the R-squared in estimating equation (8.10). Then, the F statistic is

$$F = \frac{R^2_{\hat{u}^2}/k}{(1 - R^2_{\hat{u}^2})/(n - k - 1)}, \qquad [8.15]$$

where k is the number of regressors in (8.14); this is the same number of independent variables in (8.10). Computing (8.15) by hand is rarely necessary, because most regression packages automatically compute the F statistic for overall significance of a regression. This F statistic has (approximately) an $F_{k,n-k-1}$ distribution under the null hypothesis of homoskedasticity.

The LM statistic for heteroskedasticity is just the sample size times the R-squared from (8.14):

$$LM = n \cdot R^2_{\hat{u}^2}. \qquad [8.16]$$

Under the null hypothesis, LM is distributed asymptotically as χ_k^2. This is also very easy to obtain after running regression (8.14).

The LM version of the test is typically called the **Breusch-Pagan test for heteroskedasticity (BP test)**. Breusch and Pagan (1979) suggested a different form of the test that assumes the errors are normally distributed. Koenker (1981) suggested the form of the LM statistic in (8.16), and it is generally preferred due to its greater applicability.

We summarize the steps for testing for heteroskedasticity using the BP test:

The Breusch-Pagan Test for Heteroskedasticity:

1. Estimate the model (8.10) by OLS, as usual. Obtain the squared OLS residuals, $\hat{u}^2$ (one for each observation).
2. Run the regression in (8.14). Keep the R-squared from this regression, $R^2_{\hat{u}^2}$.
3. Form either the F statistic or the LM statistic and compute the p-value (using the $F_{k,n-k-1}$ distribution in the former case and the χ_k^2 distribution in the latter case). If the p-value is sufficiently small, that is, below the chosen significance level, then we reject the null hypothesis of homoskedasticity.

If the BP test results in a small enough p-value, some corrective measure should be taken. One possibility is to just use the heteroskedasticity-robust standard errors and test statistics discussed in the previous section. Another possibility is discussed in Section 8.4.

EXAMPLE 8.4 HETEROSKEDASTICITY IN HOUSING PRICE EQUATIONS

We use the data in HPRICE1.RAW to test for heteroskedasticity in a simple housing price equation. The estimated equation using the levels of all variables is

$$\widehat{price} = \underset{(29.48)}{-21.77} + \underset{(.00064)}{.00207}\, lotsize + \underset{(.013)}{.123}\, sqrft + \underset{(9.01)}{13.85}\, bdrms$$
$$n = 88,\ R^2 = .672. \qquad [8.17]$$

This equation tells us *nothing* about whether the error in the population model is heteroskedastic. We need to regress the squared OLS residuals on the independent variables. The R-squared from the regression of $\hat{u}^2$ on *lotsize*, *sqrft*, and *bdrms* is $R^2_{\hat{u}^2} = .1601$. With $n = 88$ and $k = 3$, this produces an F statistic for significance of the independent variables of $F = [.1601/(1 - .1601)](84/3) \approx 5.34$. The associated p-value is .002, which is strong evidence against the null. The LM statistic is $88(.1601) \approx 14.09$; this gives a p-value $\approx$ .0028 (using the χ^2_3 distribution), giving essentially the same conclusion as the F statistic. This means that the usual standard errors reported in (8.17) are not reliable.

In Chapter 6, we mentioned that one benefit of using the logarithmic functional form for the dependent variable is that heteroskedasticity is often reduced. In the current application, let us put *price*, *lotsize*, and *sqrft* in logarithmic form, so that the elasticities of *price*, with respect to *lotsize* and *sqrft*, are constant. The estimated equation is

$$\widehat{\log(price)} = \underset{(.65)}{-1.30} + \underset{(.038)}{.168}\log(lotsize) + \underset{(.093)}{.700}\log(sqrft) + \underset{(.028)}{.037}\, bdrms$$
$$n = 88,\ R^2 = .643. \qquad [8.18]$$

Regressing the squared OLS residuals from this regression on log(*lotsize*), log(*sqrft*), and *bdrms* gives $R^2_{\hat{u}^2} = .0480$. Thus, $F = 1.41$ (p-value = .245), and $LM = 4.22$ (p-value = .239). Therefore, we fail to reject the null hypothesis of homoskedasticity in the model with the logarithmic functional forms. The occurrence of less heteroskedasticity with the dependent variable in logarithmic form has been noticed in many empirical applications.

If we suspect that heteroskedasticity depends only upon certain independent variables, we can easily modify the Breusch-Pagan test: we simply regress $\hat{u}^2$ on whatever independent variables we choose and carry out the appropriate F or LM test. Remember that the appropriate degrees of freedom depends upon the number of independent variables in the regression with $\hat{u}^2$ as the dependent variable; the number of independent variables showing up in equation (8.10) is irrelevant.

If the squared residuals are regressed on only a single independent variable, the test for heteroskedasticity is just the usual t statistic on the variable. A significant t statistic suggests that heteroskedasticity is a problem.

EXPLORING FURTHER 8.2

Consider wage equation (7.11), where you think that the conditional variance of log(*wage*) does not depend on *educ*, *exper*, or *tenure*. However, you are worried that the variance of log(*wage*) differs across the four demographic groups of married males, married females, single males, and single females. What regression would you run to test for heteroskedasticity? What are the degrees of freedom in the F test?

The White Test for Heteroskedasticity

In Chapter 5, we showed that the usual OLS standard errors and test statistics are asymptotically valid, provided all of the Gauss-Markov assumptions hold. It turns out that the homoskedasticity assumption, $\text{Var}(u_1|x_1, \ldots, x_k) = \sigma^2$, can be replaced with the weaker assumption that the squared error, u^2, is *uncorrelated* with all the independent variables (x_j), the squares of the independent variables (x_j^2), and all the cross products ($x_j x_h$ for $j \neq h$). This observation motivated White (1980) to propose a test for heteroskedasticity that adds the squares and cross products of all the independent variables to equation (8.14). The test is explicitly intended to test for forms of heteroskedasticity that invalidate the usual OLS standard errors and test statistics.

When the model contains $k = 3$ independent variables, the White test is based on an estimation of

$$\hat{u}^2 = \delta_0 + \delta_1 x_1 + \delta_2 x_2 + \delta_3 x_3 + \delta_4 x_1^2 + \delta_5 x_2^2 + \delta_6 x_3^2 \\ + \delta_7 x_1 x_2 + \delta_8 x_1 x_3 + \delta_9 x_2 x_3 + error. \quad [8.19]$$

Compared with the Breusch-Pagan test, this equation has six more regressors. The **White test for heteroskedasticity** is the *LM* statistic for testing that all of the δ_j in equation (8.19) are zero, except for the intercept. Thus, nine restrictions are being tested in this case. We can also use an *F* test of this hypothesis; both tests have asymptotic justification.

With only three independent variables in the original model, equation (8.19) has nine independent variables. With six independent variables in the original model, the White regression would generally involve 27 regressors (unless some are redundant). This abundance of regressors is a weakness in the pure form of the White test: it uses many degrees of freedom for models with just a moderate number of independent variables.

It is possible to obtain a test that is easier to implement than the White test and more conserving on degrees of freedom. To create the test, recall that the difference between the White and Breusch-Pagan tests is that the former includes the squares and cross products of the independent variables. We can preserve the spirit of the White test while conserving on degrees of freedom by using the OLS fitted values in a test for heteroskedasticity. Remember that the fitted values are defined, for each observation i, by

$$\hat{y}_i = \hat{\beta}_0 + \hat{\beta}_1 x_{i1} + \hat{\beta}_2 x_{i2} + \ldots + \hat{\beta}_k x_{ik}.$$

These are just linear functions of the independent variables. If we square the fitted values, we get a particular function of all the squares and cross products of the independent variables. This suggests testing for heteroskedasticity by estimating the equation

$$\hat{u}^2 = \delta_0 + \delta_1 \hat{y} + \delta_2 \hat{y}^2 + error, \quad [8.20]$$

where $\hat{y}$ stands for the fitted values. It is important not to confuse $\hat{y}$ and y in this equation. We use the fitted values because they are functions of the independent variables (and the estimated parameters); using y in (8.20) does not produce a valid test for heteroskedasticity.

We can use the *F* or *LM* statistic for the null hypothesis H_0: $\delta_1 = 0$, $\delta_2 = 0$ in equation (8.20). This results in two restrictions in testing the null of homoskedasticity, regardless of the number of independent variables in the original model. Conserving on degrees of freedom in this way is often a good idea, and it also makes the test easy to implement.

Since $\hat{y}$ is an estimate of the expected value of y, given the x_j, using (8.20) to test for heteroskedasticity is useful in cases where the variance is thought to change with the level of the expected value, $E(y|\mathbf{x})$. The test from (8.20) can be viewed as a special case of the White test, since equation (8.20) can be shown to impose restrictions on the parameters in equation (8.19).

A Special Case of the White Test for Heteroskedasticity:

1. Estimate the model (8.10) by OLS, as usual. Obtain the OLS residuals $\hat{u}$ and the fitted values $\hat{y}$. Compute the squared OLS residuals $\hat{u}^2$ and the squared fitted values $\hat{y}^2$.
2. Run the regression in equation (8.20). Keep the R-squared from this regression, $R^2_{\hat{u}^2}$.
3. Form either the F or LM statistic and compute the p-value (using the $F_{2,n-3}$ distribution in the former case and the χ^2_2 distribution in the latter case).

EXAMPLE 8.5 SPECIAL FORM OF THE WHITE TEST IN THE LOG HOUSING PRICE EQUATION

We apply the special case of the White test to equation (8.18), where we use the LM form of the statistic. The important thing to remember is that the chi-square distribution always has two df. The regression of $\hat{u}^2$ on $\widehat{lprice}$, $(\widehat{lprice})^2$, where $\widehat{lprice}$ denotes the fitted values from (8.18), produces $R^2_{\hat{u}^2} = .0392$; thus, $LM = 88(.0392) \approx 3.45$, and the p-value $= .178$. This is stronger evidence of heteroskedasticity than is provided by the Breusch-Pagan test, but we still fail to reject homoskedasticity at even the 15% level.

Before leaving this section, we should discuss one important caveat. We have interpreted a rejection using one of the heteroskedasticity tests as evidence of heteroskedasticity. This is appropriate provided we maintain Assumptions MLR.1 through MLR.4. But, if MLR.4 is violated—in particular, if the functional form of $E(y|\mathbf{x})$ is misspecified—then a test for heteroskedasticity can reject H_0, even if $Var(y|\mathbf{x})$ is constant. For example, if we omit one or more quadratic terms in a regression model or use the level model when we should use the log, a test for heteroskedasticity can be significant. This has led some economists to view tests for heteroskedasticity as general misspecification tests. However, there are better, more direct tests for functional form misspecification, and we will cover some of them in Section 9.1. It is better to use explicit tests for functional form first, since functional form misspecification is more important than heteroskedasticity. Then, once we are satisfied with the functional form, we can test for heteroskedasticity.

8.4 Weighted Least Squares Estimation

If heteroskedasticity is detected using one of the tests in Section 8.3, we know from Section 8.2 that one possible response is to use heteroskedasticity-robust statistics after estimation by OLS. Before the development of heteroskedasticity-robust statistics, the response to a finding of heteroskedasticity was to specify its form and use a *weighted least squares* method, which we develop in this section. As we will argue, if we have correctly specified the form of the variance (as a function of explanatory variables), then weighted least squares (WLS) is more efficient than OLS, and WLS leads to new t and F statistics that have t and F distributions. We will also discuss the implications of using the wrong form of the variance in the WLS procedure.

The Heteroskedasticity Is Known up to a Multiplicative Constant

Let $\mathbf{x}$ denote all the explanatory variables in equation (8.10) and assume that

$$\text{Var}(u|\mathbf{x}) = \sigma^2 h(\mathbf{x}), \quad [8.21]$$

where $h(\mathbf{x})$ is some function of the explanatory variables that determines the heteroskedasticity. Since variances must be positive, $h(\mathbf{x}) > 0$ for all possible values of the independent variables. For now, we assume that the function $h(\mathbf{x})$ is known. The population parameter σ^2 is unknown, but we will be able to estimate it from a data sample.

For a random drawing from the population, we can write $\sigma_i^2 = \text{Var}(u_i|\mathbf{x}_i) = \sigma^2 h(\mathbf{x}_i) = \sigma^2 h_i$, where we again use the notation $\mathbf{x}_i$ to denote all independent variables for observation i, and h_i changes with each observation because the independent variables change across observations. For example, consider the simple savings function

$$sav_i = \beta_0 + \beta_1 inc_i + u_i \quad [8.22]$$

$$\text{Var}(u_i|inc_i) = \sigma^2 inc_i. \quad [8.23]$$

Here, $h(x) = h(inc) = inc$: the variance of the error is proportional to the level of income. This means that, as income increases, the variability in savings increases. (If $\beta_1 > 0$, the expected value of savings also increases with income.) Because inc is always positive, the variance in equation (8.23) is always guaranteed to be positive. The standard deviation of u_i, conditional on inc_i, is $\sigma\sqrt{inc_i}$.

How can we use the information in equation (8.21) to estimate the β_j? Essentially, we take the original equation,

$$y_i = \beta_0 + \beta_1 x_{i1} + \beta_2 x_{i2} + \ldots + \beta_k x_{ik} + u_i, \quad [8.24]$$

which contains heteroskedastic errors, and transform it into an equation that has homoskedastic errors (and satisfies the other Gauss-Markov assumptions). Since h_i is just a function of $\mathbf{x}_i$, $u_i/\sqrt{h_i}$ has a zero expected value conditional on $\mathbf{x}_i$. Further, since $\text{Var}(u_i|\mathbf{x}_i) = \text{E}(u_i^2|\mathbf{x}_i) = \sigma^2 h_i$, the variance of $u_i/\sqrt{h_i}$ (conditional on $\mathbf{x}_i$) is σ^2:

$$\text{E}\left((u_i/\sqrt{h_i})^2\right) = \text{E}(u_i^2)/h_i = (\sigma^2 h_i)/h_i = \sigma^2,$$

where we have suppressed the conditioning on $\mathbf{x}_i$ for simplicity. We can divide equation (8.24) by $\sqrt{h_i}$ to get

$$\begin{aligned} y_i/\sqrt{h_i} &= \beta_0/\sqrt{h_i} + \beta_1(x_{i1}/\sqrt{h_i}) + \beta_2(x_{i2}/\sqrt{h_i}) + \ldots \\ &\quad + \beta_k(x_{ik}/\sqrt{h_i}) + (u_i/\sqrt{h_i}) \end{aligned} \quad [8.25]$$

or

$$y_i^* = \beta_0 x_{i0}^* + \beta_1 x_{i1}^* + \ldots + \beta_k x_{ik}^* + u_i^*, \qquad [8.26]$$

where $x_{i0}^* = 1/\sqrt{h_i}$ and the other starred variables denote the corresponding original variables divided by $\sqrt{h_i}$.

Equation (8.26) looks a little peculiar, but the important thing to remember is that we derived it so we could obtain estimators of the β_j that have better efficiency properties than OLS. The intercept β_0 in the original equation (8.24) is now multiplying the variable $x_{i0}^* = 1/\sqrt{h_i}$. Each slope parameter in β_j multiplies a new variable that rarely has a useful interpretation. This should not cause problems if we recall that, for interpreting the parameters and the model, we always want to return to the original equation (8.24).

In the preceding savings example, the transformed equation looks like

$$sav_i/\sqrt{inc_i} = \beta_0(1/\sqrt{inc_i}) + \beta_1\sqrt{inc_i} + u_i^*,$$

where we use the fact that $inc_i/\sqrt{inc_i} = \sqrt{inc_i}$. Nevertheless, β_1 is the marginal propensity to save out of income, an interpretation we obtain from equation (8.22).

Equation (8.26) is linear in its parameters (so it satisfies MLR.1), and the random sampling assumption has not changed. Further, u_i^* has a zero mean and a constant variance (σ^2), conditional on $\mathbf{x}_i^*$. This means that if the original equation satisfies the first four Gauss-Markov assumptions, then the transformed equation (8.26) satisfies all five Gauss-Markov assumptions. Also, if u_i has a normal distribution, then u_i^* has a normal distribution with variance σ^2. Therefore, the transformed equation satisfies the classical linear model assumptions (MLR.1 through MLR.6) if the original model does so except for the homoskedasticity assumption.

Since we know that OLS has appealing properties (is BLUE, for example) under the Gauss-Markov assumptions, the discussion in the previous paragraph suggests estimating the parameters in equation (8.26) by ordinary least squares. These estimators, β_0^*, β_1^*, ..., β_k^*,will be different from the OLS estimators in the original equation. The β_j^* are examples of **generalized least squares (GLS) estimators**. In this case, the GLS estimators are used to account for heteroskedasticity in the errors. We will encounter other GLS estimators in Chapter 12.

Because equation (8.26) satisfies all of the ideal assumptions, standard errors, t statistics, and F statistics can all be obtained from regressions using the transformed variables. The sum of squared residuals from (8.26) divided by the degrees of freedom is an unbiased estimator of σ^2. Further, the GLS estimators, because they are the best linear unbiased estimators of the β_j, are necessarily more efficient than the OLS estimators $\hat{\beta}_j$ obtained from the untransformed equation. Essentially, after we have transformed the variables, we simply use standard OLS analysis. But we must remember to interpret the estimates in light of the original equation.

The R-squared that is obtained from estimating (8.26), while useful for computing F statistics, is not especially informative as a goodness-of-fit measure: it tells us how much variation in y^* is explained by the x_j^*, and this is seldom very meaningful.

The GLS estimators for correcting heteroskedasticity are called **weighted least squares (WLS) estimators**. This name comes from the fact that the β_j^* minimize the *weighted* sum of squared residuals, where each squared residual is weighted by $1/h_i$. The idea is that less weight is given to observations with a higher error variance; OLS gives each observation the same weight because it is best when the error variance is identical for all partitions of the population. Mathematically, the WLS estimators are the values of the b_j that make

$$\sum_{i=1}^{n}(y_i - b_0 - b_1x_{i1} - b_2x_{i2} - \ldots - b_kx_{ik})^2/h_i \qquad [8.27]$$

as small as possible. Bringing the square root of $1/h_i$ inside the squared residual shows that the weighted sum of squared residuals is identical to the sum of squared residuals in the transformed variables:

$$\sum_{i=1}^{n}(y_i^* - b_0x_{i0}^* - b_1x_{i1}^* - b_2x_{i2}^* - \ldots - b_kx_{ik}^*)^2.$$

Since OLS minimizes the sum of squared residuals (regardless of the definitions of the dependent variable and independent variable), it follows that the WLS estimators that minimize (8.27) are simply the OLS estimators from (8.26). Note carefully that the squared residuals in (8.27) are weighted by $1/h_i$, whereas the transformed variables in (8.26) are weighted by $1/\sqrt{h_i}$.

A weighted least squares estimator can be defined for any set of positive weights. OLS is the special case that gives equal weight to all observations. The efficient procedure, GLS, weights each squared residual by the *inverse* of the conditional variance of u_i given $\mathbf{x}_i$.

Obtaining the transformed variables in equation (8.25) in order to manually perform weighted least squares can be tedious, and the chance of making mistakes is nontrivial. Fortunately, most modern regression packages have a feature for computing weighted least squares. Typically, along with the dependent and independent variables in the original model, we just specify the weighting function, $1/h_i$, appearing in (8.27). That is, we specify weights proportional to the inverse of the variance. In addition to making mistakes less likely, this forces us to interpret weighted least squares estimates in the original model. In fact, we can write out the estimated equation in the usual way. The estimates and standard errors will be different from OLS, but the way we *interpret* those estimates, standard errors, and test statistics is the same.

EXAMPLE 8.6 FINANCIAL WEALTH EQUATION

We now estimate equations that explain net total financial wealth (*nettfa*, measured in \$1,000s) in terms of income (*inc*, also measured in \$1,000s) and some other variables, including age, gender, and an indicator for whether the person is eligible for a 401(k) pension plan. We use the data on single people ($fsize = 1$) in 401KSUBS.RAW. In Computer Exercise C12 in Chapter 6, it was found that a specific quadratic function in *age*, namely $(age - 25)^2$, fit the data just as well as an unrestricted quadratic. Plus, the restricted form gives a simplified intepretation because the minimum age in the sample is 25: *nettfa* is an increasing function of *age* after $age = 25$.

The results are reported in Table 8.1. Because we suspect heteroskedasticity, we report the heteroskedasticity-robust standard errors for OLS. The weighted least squares estimates, and their standard errors, are obtained under the assumption $\text{Var}(u|inc) = \sigma^2 inc$.

TABLE 8.1 Dependent Variable: *nettfa*

Independent Variables	(1) OLS	(2) WLS	(3) OLS	(4) WLS
inc	.821 (.104)	.787 (.063)	.771 (.100)	.740 (.064)
$(age - 25)^2$	—	—	.0251 (.0043)	.0175 (.0019)
male	—	—	2.48 (2.06)	1.84 (1.56)
e401k	—	—	6.89 (2.29)	5.19 (1.70)
intercept	−10.57 (2.53)	−9.58 (1.65)	−20.98 (3.50)	−16.70 (1.96)
Observations	2,017	2,017	2,017	2,017
R-squared	.0827	.0709	.1279	.1115

Without controlling for other factors, another dollar of income is estimated to increase *nettfa* by about 82¢ when OLS is used; the WLS estimate is smaller, about 79¢. The difference is not large; we certainly do not expect them to be identical. The WLS coefficient does have a smaller standard error than OLS, almost 40% smaller, provided we assume the model $\text{Var}(nettfa|inc) = \sigma^2 inc$ is correct.

Adding the other controls reduced the *inc* coefficient somewhat, with the OLS estimate still larger than the WLS estimate. Again, the WLS estimate of β_{inc} is more precise. Age has an increasing effect starting at $age = 25$, with the OLS estimate showing a larger effect. The WLS estimate of β_{age} is more precise in this case. Gender does not have a statistically significant effect on *nettfa*, but being eligible for a 401(k) plan does: the OLS estimate is that those eligible, holding fixed income, age, and gender, have net total financial assets about $6,890 higher. The WLS estimate is substantially below the OLS estimate and suggests a misspecification of the functional form in the mean equation. (One possibility is to interact *e401k* and *inc*; see Computer Exercise C11.)

Using WLS, the F statistic for joint significance of $(age - 25)^2$, *male*, and *e401k* is about 30.8 if we use the R-squareds reported in Table 8.1. With 2 and 2,012 degrees of freedom, the p-value is zero to more than 15 decimal places; of course, this is not surprising given the very large t statistics for the age and 401(k) variables.

EXPLORING FURTHER 8.3

Using the OLS residuals obtained from the OLS regression reported in column (1) of Table 8.1, the regression of $\hat{u}^2$ on *inc* yields a t statistic of 2.96. Does it appear we should worry about heteroskedasticity in the financial wealth equation?

Assuming that the error variance in the financial wealth equation has a variance proportional to income is essentially arbitrary. In fact, in most cases, our choice of weights in WLS has a degree of arbitrariness. However, there is one case where the weights needed for WLS arise naturally from an underlying econometric model. This happens when, instead of using individual-level data, we only have averages of data across some group or geographic region. For example, suppose we are interested in determining the relationship between the amount a worker contributes to his or her 401(k) pension plan as a function of the plan generosity. Let i denote a particular firm and let e denote an employee within the firm. A simple model is

$$contrib_{i,e} = \beta_0 + \beta_1 earns_{i,e} + \beta_2 age_{i,e} + \beta_3 mrate_i + u_{i,e}, \quad [8.28]$$

where $contrib_{i,e}$ is the annual contribution by employee e who works for firm i, $earns_{i,e}$ is annual earnings for this person, and $age_{i,e}$ is the person's age. The variable $mrate_i$ is the amount the firm puts into an employee's account for every dollar the employee contributes.

If (8.28) satisfies the Gauss-Markov assumptions, then we could estimate it, given a sample on individuals across various employers. Suppose, however, that we only have *average* values of contributions, earnings, and age by employer. In other words, individual-level data are not available. Thus, let $\overline{contrib}_i$ denote average contribution for people at firm i, and similarly for $\overline{earns}_i$ and $\overline{age}_i$. Let m_i denote the number of employees at firm i; we assume that this is a known quantity. Then, if we average equation (8.28) across all employees at firm i, we obtain the firm-level equation

$$\overline{contrib}_i = \beta_0 + \beta_1 \overline{earns}_i + \beta_2 \overline{age}_i + \beta_3 mrate_i + \bar{u}_i, \quad [8.29]$$

where $\bar{u}_i = m_i^{-1} \sum_{e=1}^{mi} u_{i,e}$ is the average error across all employees in firm i. If we have n firms in our sample, then (8.29) is just a standard multiple linear regression model that can be estimated by OLS. The estimators are unbiased if the original model (8.28) satisfies the Gauss-Markov assumptions and the individual errors $u_{i,e}$ are independent of the firm's size, m_i [because then the expected value of $\bar{u}_i$, given the explanatory variables in (8.29), is zero].

If the individual-level equation (8.28) satisfies the homoskedasticity assumption, and the errors within firm i are uncorrelated across employees, then we can show that the firm-level equation (8.29) has a particular kind of heteroskedasticity. Specifically, if $\text{Var}(u_{i,e}) = \sigma^2$ for all i and e, and $\text{Cov}(u_{i,e}, u_{i,g}) = 0$ for every pair of employees $e \neq g$ within firm i, then $\text{Var}(\bar{u}_i) = \sigma^2/m_i$; this is just the usual formula for the variance of an average of uncorrelated random variables with common variance. In other words, the variance of the error term $\bar{u}_i$ decreases with firm size. In this case, $h_i = 1/m_i$, and so the most efficient procedure is weighted least squares, with weights equal to the number of employees at the firm ($1/h_i = m_i$). This ensures that larger firms receive more weight. This gives us an efficient way of estimating the parameters in the individual-level model when we only have averages at the firm level.

A similar weighting arises when we are using per capita data at the city, county, state, or country level. If the individual-level equation satisfies the Gauss-Markov assumptions, then the error in the per capita equation has a variance proportional to one over the size of the population. Therefore, weighted least squares with weights equal to the population is appropriate. For example, suppose we have city-level data on per capita beer consumption (in ounces), the percentage of people in the population over 21 years old, average adult education levels, average income levels, and the city price of beer. Then, the city-level model

$$beerpc = \beta_0 + \beta_1 perc21 + \beta_2 avgeduc + \beta_3 incpc + \beta_4 price + u$$

can be estimated by weighted least squares, with the weights being the city population.

The advantage of weighting by firm size, city population, and so on relies on the underlying individual equation being homoskedastic. If heteroskedasticity exists at the individual level, then the proper weighting depends on the form of heteroskedasticity. Further, if there is correlation across errors within a group (say, firm), then $\text{Var}(\bar{u}_i) \neq \sigma^2/m_i$; see Problem 7. Uncertainty about the form of $\text{Var}(\bar{u}_i)$ in equations such as (8.29) is why more and more researchers simply use OLS and compute robust standard errors and test statistics when estimating models using per capita data. An alternative is to weight by group size but to report the heteroskedasticity-robust statistics in the WLS estimation. This ensures that, while the estimation is efficient if the individual-level model satisfies the Gauss-Markov assumptions, heteroskedasticity at the individual level or within-group correlation are accounted for through robust inference.

The Heteroskedasticity Function Must Be Estimated: Feasible GLS

In the previous subsection, we saw some examples of where the heteroskedasticity is known up to a multiplicative form. In most cases, the exact form of heteroskedasticity is not obvious. In other words, it is difficult to find the function $h(\mathbf{x}_i)$ of the previous section. Nevertheless, in many cases we can model the function h and use the data to estimate the unknown parameters in this model. This results in an estimate of each h_i, denoted as $\hat{h}_i$. Using $\hat{h}_i$ instead of h_i in the GLS transformation yields an estimator called the **feasible GLS (FGLS) estimator**. Feasible GLS is sometimes called *estimated GLS*, or EGLS.

There are many ways to model heteroskedasticity, but we will study one particular, fairly flexible approach. Assume that

$$\text{Var}(u|\mathbf{x}) = \sigma^2\exp(\delta_0 + \delta_1x_1 + \delta_2x_2 + \ldots + \delta_kx_k), \qquad [8.30]$$

where $x_1, x_2, \ldots, x_k$ are the independent variables appearing in the regression model [see equation (8.1)], and the δ_j are unknown parameters. Other functions of the x_j can appear, but we will focus primarily on (8.30). In the notation of the previous subsection, $h(\mathbf{x}) = \exp(\delta_0 + \delta_1x_1 + \delta_2x_2 + \ldots + \delta_kx_k)$.

You may wonder why we have used the exponential function in (8.30). After all, when *testing* for heteroskedasticity using the Breusch-Pagan test, we assumed that heteroskedasticity was a linear function of the x_j. Linear alternatives such as (8.12) are fine when testing for heteroskedasticity, but they can be problematic when correcting for heteroskedasticity using weighted least squares. We have encountered the reason for this problem before: linear models do not ensure that predicted values are positive, and our estimated variances must be positive in order to perform WLS.

If the parameters δ_j were known, then we would just apply WLS, as in the previous subsection. This is not very realistic. It is better to use the data to estimate these parameters, and then to use these estimates to construct weights. How can we estimate the δ_j? Essentially, we will transform this equation into a linear form that, with slight modification, can be estimated by OLS.

Under assumption (8.30), we can write

$$u^2 = \sigma^2\exp(\delta_0 + \delta_1x_1 + \delta_2x_2 + \ldots + \delta_kx_k)v,$$

where v has a mean equal to unity, conditional on $\mathbf{x} = (x_1, x_2, \ldots, x_k)$. If we assume that v is actually independent of $\mathbf{x}$, we can write

$$\log(u^2) = a_0 + \delta_1 x_1 + \delta_2 x_2 + \ldots + \delta_k x_k + e, \qquad [8.31]$$

where e has a zero mean and is independent of $\mathbf{x}$; the intercept in this equation is different from δ_0, but this is not important in implementing WLS. The dependent variable is the log of the squared error. Since (8.31) satisfies the Gauss-Markov assumptions, we can get unbiased estimators of the δ_j by using OLS.

As usual, we must replace the unobserved u with the OLS residuals. Therefore, we run the regression of

$$\log(\hat{u}^2) \text{ on } x_1, x_2, \ldots, x_k. \qquad [8.32]$$

Actually, what we need from this regression are the fitted values; call these $\hat{g}_i$. Then, the estimates of h_i are simply

$$\hat{h}_i = \exp(\hat{g}_i). \qquad [8.33]$$

We now use WLS with weights $1/\hat{h}_i$ in place of $1/h_i$ in equation (8.27). We summarize the steps.

A Feasible GLS Procedure to Correct for Heteroskedasticity:

1. Run the regression of y on $x_1, x_2, \ldots, x_k$ and obtain the residuals, $\hat{u}$.
2. Create $\log(\hat{u}^2)$ by first squaring the OLS residuals and then taking the natural log.
3. Run the regression in equation (8.32) and obtain the fitted values, $\hat{g}$.
4. Exponentiate the fitted values from (8.32): $\hat{h} = \exp(\hat{g})$.
5. Estimate the equation

$$y = \beta_0 + \beta_1 x_1 + \ldots + \beta_k x_k + u$$

by WLS, using weights $1/\hat{h}$. In other words, we replace h_i with $\hat{h}_i$ in equation (8.27). Remember, the *squared* residual for observation i gets weighted by $1/\hat{h}_i$. If instead we first transform all variables and run OLS, each variable gets multiplied by $1/\sqrt{\hat{h}_i}$, including the intercept.

If we could use h_i rather than $\hat{h}_i$ in the WLS procedure, we know that our estimators would be unbiased; in fact, they would be the best linear unbiased estimators, assuming that we have properly modeled the heteroskedasticity. Having to estimate h_i using the same data means that the FGLS estimator is no longer unbiased (so it cannot be BLUE, either). Nevertheless, the FGLS estimator is consistent and *asymptotically* more efficient than OLS. This is difficult to show because of estimation of the variance parameters. But if we ignore this—as it turns out we may—the proof is similar to showing that OLS is efficient in the class of estimators in Theorem 5.3. At any rate, for large sample sizes, FGLS is an attractive alternative to OLS when there is evidence of heteroskedasticity that inflates the standard errors of the OLS estimates.

We must remember that the FGLS estimators are estimators of the parameters in the usual population model

$$y = \beta_0 + \beta_1 x_1 + \ldots + \beta_k x_k + u.$$

Just as the OLS estimates measure the marginal impact of each x_j on y, so do the FGLS estimates. We use the FGLS estimates in place of the OLS estimates because the FGLS estimators are more efficient and have associated test statistics with the usual t and F distributions, at least in large samples. If we have some doubt about the variance specified in equation (8.30), we can use heteroskedasticity-robust standard errors and test statistics in the transformed equation.

Another useful alternative for estimating h_i is to replace the independent variables in regression (8.32) with the OLS fitted values and their squares. In other words, obtain the $\hat{g}_i$ as the fitted values from the regression of

$$\log(\hat{u}^2) \text{ on } \hat{y}, \hat{y}^2 \tag{8.34}$$

and then obtain the $\hat{h}_i$ exactly as in equation (8.33). This changes only step (3) in the previous procedure.

If we use regression (8.32) to estimate the variance function, you may be wondering if we can simply test for heteroskedasticity using this same regression (an F or LM test can be used). In fact, Park (1966) suggested this. Unfortunately, when compared with the tests discussed in Section 8.3, the Park test has some problems. First, the null hypothesis must be something stronger than homoskedasticity: effectively, u and $\mathbf{x}$ must be independent. This is not required in the Breusch-Pagan or White tests. Second, using the OLS residuals $\hat{u}$ in place of u in (8.32) can cause the F statistic to deviate from the F distribution, even in large sample sizes. This is not an issue in the other tests we have covered. For these reasons, the Park test is not recommended when testing for heteroskedasticity. Regression (8.32) works well for weighted least squares because we only need consistent estimators of the δ_j, and regression (8.32) certainly delivers those.

EXAMPLE 8.7 DEMAND FOR CIGARETTES

We use the data in SMOKE.RAW to estimate a demand function for daily cigarette consumption. Since most people do not smoke, the dependent variable, *cigs*, is zero for most observations. A linear model is not ideal because it can result in negative predicted values. Nevertheless, we can still learn something about the determinants of cigarette smoking by using a linear model.

The equation estimated by ordinary least squares, with the usual OLS standard errors in parentheses, is

$$\begin{aligned} \widehat{cigs} = &-3.64 + .880 \log(income) - .751 \log(cigpric) \\ &(24.08) \quad (.728) \qquad\qquad (5.773) \\ &- .501\, educ + .771\, age - .0090\, age^2 - 2.83\, restaurn \\ &\quad (.167) \qquad (.160) \qquad (.0017) \qquad (1.11) \\ n = &\ 807, R^2 = .0526, \end{aligned} \tag{8.35}$$

where

cigs = number of cigarettes smoked per day.
income = annual income.
cigpric = the per-pack price of cigarettes (in cents).
educ = years of schooling.
age = measured in years.

restaurn = a binary indicator equal to unity if the person resides in a state with restaurant smoking restrictions.

Since we are also going to do weighted least squares, we do not report the heteroskedasticity-robust standard errors for OLS. (Incidentally, 13 out of the 807 fitted values are less than zero; this is less than 2% of the sample and is not a major cause for concern.)

Neither income nor cigarette price is statistically significant in (8.35), and their effects are not practically large. For example, if income increases by 10%, *cigs* is predicted to increase by $(.880/100)(10) = .088$, or less than one-tenth of a cigarette per day. The magnitude of the price effect is similar.

Each year of education reduces the average cigarettes smoked per day by one-half of a cigarette, and the effect is statistically significant. Cigarette smoking is also related to age, in a quadratic fashion. Smoking increases with age up until $age = .771/[2(.009)] \approx 42.83$, and then smoking decreases with age. Both terms in the quadratic are statistically significant. The presence of a restriction on smoking in restaurants decreases cigarette smoking by almost three cigarettes per day, on average.

Do the errors underlying equation (8.35) contain heteroskedasticity? The Breusch-Pagan regression of the squared OLS residuals on the independent variables in (8.35) [see equation (8.14)] produces $R^2_{\hat{u}^2} = .040$. This small *R*-squared may seem to indicate no heteroskedasticity, but we must remember to compute either the *F* or *LM* statistic. If the sample size is large, a seemingly small $R^2_{\hat{u}^2}$ can result in a very strong rejection of homoskedasticity. The *LM* statistic is $LM = 807(.040) = 32.28$, and this is the outcome of a χ^2_6 random variable. The *p*-value is less than .000015, which is very strong evidence of heteroskedasticity.

Therefore, we estimate the equation using the feasible GLS procedure based on equation (8.32). The weighted least squares estimates are

$$
\begin{aligned}
\widehat{cigs} = {} & \underset{(17.80)}{5.64} + \underset{(.44)}{1.30}\log(income) - \underset{(4.46)}{2.94}\log(cigpric) \\
& - \underset{(.120)}{.463}\,educ + \underset{(.097)}{.482}\,age - \underset{(.0009)}{.0056}\,age^2 - \underset{(.80)}{3.46}\,restaurn \\
n = {} & 807,\ R^2 = .1134.
\end{aligned}
\tag{8.36}
$$

The income effect is now statistically significant and larger in magnitude. The price effect is also notably bigger, but it is still statistically insignificant. [One reason for this is that *cigpric* varies only across states in the sample, and so there is much less variation in log(*cigpric*) than in log(*income*), *educ*, and *age*.]

The estimates on the other variables have, naturally, changed somewhat, but the basic story is still the same. Cigarette smoking is negatively related to schooling, has a quadratic relationship with *age*, and is negatively affected by restaurant smoking restrictions.

We must be a little careful in computing *F* statistics for testing multiple hypotheses after estimation by WLS. (This is true whether the sum of squared residuals or *R*-squared form of the *F* statistic is used.) It is important that the same weights be used to estimate the unrestricted and restricted models. We should first estimate the unrestricted model by OLS. Once we have obtained the weights, we can use them to estimate the restricted model as well. The F statistic can be computed as usual. Fortunately, many regression packages have a simple command for testing joint restrictions after WLS estimation, so we need not perform the restricted regression ourselves.

Example 8.7 hints at an issue that sometimes arises in applications of weighted least squares: the OLS and WLS estimates can be substantially different. This is not such a big problem in the demand for cigarettes equation because all the coefficients maintain the same signs, and the biggest changes are on variables that were statistically insignificant when the equation was estimated by OLS. The OLS and WLS estimates will always differ due to sampling error. The issue is whether their difference is enough to change important conclusions.

> **EXPLORING FURTHER 8.4**
>
> Let $\hat{u}_i$ be the WLS residuals from (8.36), which are not weighted, and let $\widehat{cigs}_i$ be the fitted values. (These are obtained using the same formulas as OLS; they differ because of different estimates of the β_j.) One way to determine whether heteroskedasticity has been eliminated is to use the $\hat{u}_i^2/\hat{h}_i = (\hat{u}_i/\sqrt{\hat{h}_i})^2$ in a test for heteroskedasticity. [If $h_i = \text{Var}(u_i|\mathbf{x}_i)$, then the transformed residuals should have little evidence of heteroskedasticity.] There are many possibilities, but one—based on White's test in the transformed equation—is to regress $\hat{u}_i^2/\hat{h}_i$ on $\widehat{cigs}_i/\sqrt{\hat{h}_i}$ and $\widehat{cigs}_i^2/\hat{h}_i$ (including an intercept). The joint F statistic when we use SMOKE.RAW is 11.15. Does it appear that our correction for heteroskedasticity has actually eliminated the heteroskedasticity?

If OLS and WLS produce statistically significant estimates that differ in sign—for example, the OLS price elasticity is positive and significant, while the WLS price elasticity is negative and significant—or the difference in magnitudes of the estimates is practically large, we should be suspicious. Typically, this indicates that one of the *other* Gauss-Markov assumptions is false, particularly the zero conditional mean assumption on the error (MLR.4). If $E(y|\mathbf{x}) \neq \beta_0 + \beta_1 x_1 + \ldots + \beta_k x_k$, then OLS and WLS have different expected values and probability limits. For WLS to be consistent for the β_j, it is not enough for u to be uncorrelated with each x_j; we need the stronger assumption MLR.4 in the linear model MLR.1. Therefore, a significant difference between OLS and WLS can indicate a functional form misspecification in $E(y|\mathbf{x})$. The *Hausman test* [Hausman (1978)] can be used to formally compare the OLS and WLS estimates to see if they differ by more than sampling error suggests they should, but this test is beyond the scope of this text. In many cases, an informal "eyeballing" of the estimates is sufficient to detect a problem.

What If the Assumed Heteroskedasticity Function Is Wrong?

We just noted that if OLS and WLS produce very different estimates, it is likely that the conditional mean $E(y|\mathbf{x})$ is misspecified. What are the properties of WLS if the variance function we use is misspecified in the sense that $\text{Var}(y|\mathbf{x}) \neq \sigma^2 h(\mathbf{x})$ for our chosen function $h(\mathbf{x})$? The most important issue is whether misspecification of $h(\mathbf{x})$ causes bias or inconsistency in the WLS estimator. Fortunately, the answer is no, at least under MLR.4. Recall that, if $E(u|\mathbf{x}) = 0$, then any function of $\mathbf{x}$ is uncorrelated with u, and so the weighted error, $u/\sqrt{h(\mathbf{x})}$, is uncorrelated with the weighted regressors, $x_j/\sqrt{h(\mathbf{x})}$, for *any* function $h(\mathbf{x})$ that is always positive. This is why, as we just discussed, we can take large differences between the OLS and WLS estimators as indicative of functional form misspecification. If we estimate parameters in the function, say $h(\mathbf{x}, \hat{\delta})$, then we can no longer claim that WLS is unbiased, but it will generally be consistent (whether or not the variance function is correctly specified).

If WLS is at least consistent under MLR.1 to MLR.4, what are the consequences of using WLS with a misspecified variance function? There are two. The first, which is very important, is that the usual WLS standard errors and test statistics, computed under the assumption that $\text{Var}(y|\mathbf{x}) = \sigma^2 h(\mathbf{x})$, are no longer valid, even in large samples. For example, the WLS estimates and standard errors in column (4) of Table 8.1 assume that $\text{Var}(nettfa|inc, age, male, e401k) = \text{Var}(nettfa|inc) = \sigma^2 inc$; so we are assuming not only that the variance depends just on income, but also that it is a linear function of income. If this assumption is false, the standard errors (and any statistics we obtain using those standard errors) are not valid. Fortunately, there is an easy fix: just as we can obtain standard errors for the OLS estimates that are robust to arbitrary heteroskedasticity, we can obtain standard errors for WLS that allow the variance function to be arbitrarily misspecified. It is easy to see why this works. Write the transformed equation as

$$y_i/\sqrt{h_i} = \beta_0\left(1/\sqrt{h_i}\right) + \beta_1\left(x_{i1}/\sqrt{h_i}\right) + \ldots + \beta_k\left(x_{ik}/\sqrt{h_i}\right) + u_i/\sqrt{h_i}.$$

Now, if $\text{Var}(u_i|\mathbf{x}_i) \neq \sigma^2 h_i$, then the weighted error $u_i/\sqrt{h_i}$ is heteroskedastic. So we can just apply the usual heteroskedasticity-robust standard errors after estimating this equation by OLS—which, remember, is identical to WLS.

To see how robust inference with WLS works in practice, column (1) of Table 8.2 reproduces the last column of Table 8.1, and column (2) contains standard errors robust to $\text{Var}(u_i|\mathbf{x}_i) \neq \sigma^2 inc_i$.

The standard errors in column (2) allow the variance function to be misspecified. We see that, for the income and age variables, the robust standard errors are somewhat above the usual WLS standard errors—certainly by enough to stretch the confidence intervals. On the other hand, the robust standard errors for *male* and *e401k* are actually smaller than those that assume a correct variance function. We saw this could happen with the heteroskedasticity-robust standard errors for OLS, too.

Even if we use flexible forms of variance functions, such as that in (8.30), there is no guarantee that we have the correct model. While exponential heteroskedasticity is

TABLE 8.2 WLS Estimation of the *nettfa* Equation

Independent Variables	With Nonrobust Standard Errors	With Robust Standard Errors
inc	.740 (.064)	.740 (.075)
$(age - 25)^2$	.0175 (.0019)	.0175 (.0026)
male	1.84 (1.56)	1.84 (1.31)
e401k	5.19 (1.70)	5.19 (1.57)
intercept	−16.70 (1.96)	−16.70 (2.24)
Observations	2,017	2,017
R-squared	.1115	.1115

appealing and reasonably flexible, it is, after all, just a model. Therefore, it is always a good idea to compute fully robust standard errors and test statistics after WLS estimation.

A modern criticism of WLS is that if the variance function is misspecified, it is not guaranteed to be more efficient than OLS. In fact, that is the case: if $\text{Var}(y|\mathbf{x})$ is neither constant nor equal to $\sigma^2 h(\mathbf{x})$, where $h(\mathbf{x})$ is the proposed model of heteroskedasticity, then we cannot rank OLS and WLS in terms of variances (or asymptotic variances when the variance parameters must be estimated). However, this theoretically correct criticism misses an important practical point. Namely, in cases of strong heteroskedasticity, it is often better to use a wrong form of heteroskedasticity and apply WLS than to ignore heteroskedasticity altogether in estimation and use OLS. Models such as (8.30) can well approximate a variety of heteroskedasticity functions and may produce estimators with smaller (asymptotic) variances. Even in Example 8.6, where the form of heteroskedasticity was assumed to have the simple form $\text{Var}(nettfa|\mathbf{x}) = \sigma^2 inc$, the fully robust standard errors for WLS are well below the fully robust standard errors for OLS. (Comparing robust standard errors for the two estimators puts them on equal footing: we assume neither homoskedasticity nor that the variance has the form $\sigma^2 inc$.) For example, the robust standard error for the WLS estimator of β_{inc} is about .075, which is 25% lower than the robust standard error for OLS (about .100). For the coefficient on $(age - 25)^2$, the robust standard error of WLS is about .0026, almost 40% below the robust standard error for OLS (about .0043).

Prediction and Prediction Intervals with Heteroskedasticity

If we start with the standard linear model under MLR.1 to MLR.4, but allow for heteroskedasticity of the form $\text{Var}(y|\mathbf{x}) = \sigma^2 h(\mathbf{x})$ [see equation (8.21)], the presence of heteroskedasticity affects the point prediction of y only insofar as it affects estimation of the β_j. Of course, it is natural to use WLS on a sample of size n to obtain the $\hat{\beta}_j$. Our prediction of an unobserved outcome, y^0, given known values of the explanatory variables $\mathbf{x}^0$, has the same form as in Section 6.4: $\hat{y}^0 = \hat{\beta}_0 + \mathbf{x}^0\hat{\boldsymbol{\beta}}$. This makes sense: once we know $\text{E}(y|\mathbf{x})$, we base our prediction on it; the structure of $\text{Var}(y|\mathbf{x})$ plays no direct role.

On the other hand, prediction *intervals* do depend directly on the nature of $\text{Var}(y|\mathbf{x})$. Recall in Section 6.4 that we constructed a prediction interval under the classical linear model assumptions. Suppose now that all the CLM assumptions hold except that (8.21) replaces the homoskedasticity assumption, MLR.5. We know that the WLS estimators are BLUE and, because of normality, have (conditional) normal distributions. We can obtain $\text{se}(\hat{y}^0)$ using the same method in Section 6.4, except that now we use WLS. [A simple approach is to write $y_i = \theta_0 + \beta_1(x_{i1} - x_1^0) + \ldots + \beta_k(x_{ik} - x_k^0) + u_i$, where the x_j^0 are the values of the explanatory variables for which we want a predicted value of y. We can estimate this equation by WLS and then obtain $\hat{y}^0 = \hat{\theta}_0$ and $\text{se}(\hat{y}^0) = \text{se}(\hat{\theta}_0)$.] We also need to estimate the standard deviation of u^0, the unobserved part of y^0. But $\text{Var}(u^0|\mathbf{x} = \mathbf{x}^0) = \sigma^2 h(\mathbf{x}^0)$, and so $\text{se}(u^0) = \hat{\sigma}\sqrt{h(\mathbf{x}^0)}$, where $\hat{\sigma}$ is the standard error of the regression from the WLS estimation. Therefore, a 95% prediction interval is

$$\hat{y}^0 \pm t_{.025} \cdot \text{se}(\hat{e}^0) \tag{8.37}$$

where $\text{se}(\hat{e}^0) = \{[\text{se}(\hat{y}^0)]^2 + \hat{\sigma}^2 h(\mathbf{x}^0)\}^{1/2}$.

This interval is exact only if we do not have to estimate the variance function. If we estimate parameters, as in model (8.30), then we cannot obtain an exact interval. In fact, accounting for the estimation error in the $\hat{\beta}_j$ and the $\hat{\delta}_j$ (the variance parameters) becomes very difficult. We saw two examples in Section 6.4 where the estimation error in the parameters was swamped by the variation in the unobservables, u^0. Therefore, we might still use equation (8.37) with $h(\mathbf{x}^0)$ simply replaced by $\hat{h}(\mathbf{x}^0)$. In fact, if we are to ignore the parameter estimation error entirely, we can drop $\text{se}(\hat{y}^0)$ from $\text{se}(\hat{e}^0)$. [Remember, $\text{se}(\hat{y}^0)$ converges to zero at the rate $1/\sqrt{n}$, while $\text{se}(\hat{u}^0)$ is roughly constant.]

We can also obtain a prediction for y in the model

$$\log(y) = \beta_0 + \beta_1 x_1 + \ldots + \beta_k x_k + u, \tag{8.38}$$

where u is heteroskedastic. We assume that u has a conditional normal distribution with a specific form of heteroskedasticity. We assume the exponential form in equation (8.30), but add the normality assumption:

$$u|x_1, x_2, \ldots, x_k \sim \text{Normal}[0, \exp(\delta_0 + \delta_1 x_1 + \ldots + \delta_k x_k)]. \tag{8.39}$$

As a notational shorthand, write the variance function as $\exp(\delta_0 + \mathbf{x}\boldsymbol{\delta})$. Then, because $\log(y)$ given $\mathbf{x}$ has a normal distribution with mean $\beta_0 + \mathbf{x}\boldsymbol{\beta}$ and variance $\exp(\delta_0 + \mathbf{x}\boldsymbol{\delta})$, it follows that

$$\text{E}(y|\mathbf{x}) = \exp(\beta_0 + \mathbf{x}\boldsymbol{\beta} + \sigma^2 \exp(\delta_0 + \mathbf{x}\boldsymbol{\delta})/2). \tag{8.40}$$

Now we estimate the β_j and d_j using WLS estimation of (8.38). That is, after OLS to obtain the residuals, run the regression in (8.32) to obtain fitted values,

$$\hat{g}_i = \hat{\alpha}_0 + \hat{\delta}_1 x_{i1} + \ldots + \hat{\delta}_k x_{ik}, \tag{8.41}$$

and then the $\hat{h}_i$ as in (8.33). Using these $\hat{h}_i$, obtain the WLS estimates, $\hat{\beta}_j$ and also $\hat{\sigma}^2$. Then, for each i, we can obtain a fitted value

$$\hat{y}_i = \exp(\widehat{logy}_i + \hat{\sigma}^2\hat{h}_i/2). \tag{8.42}$$

We can use these fitted values to obtain an R-squared measure, as described in Section 6.4: use the squared correlation coefficient between y_i and $\hat{y}_i$.

For any values of the explanatory variables $\mathbf{x}^0$, we can estimate $\text{E}(y|\mathbf{x} = \mathbf{x}^0)$ as

$$\hat{\text{E}}(y|\mathbf{x} = \mathbf{x}^0) = \exp(\hat{\beta}_0 + \mathbf{x}^0\hat{\boldsymbol{\beta}} + \hat{\sigma}^2 \exp(\hat{\alpha}_0 + \mathbf{x}^0\hat{\boldsymbol{\delta}})/2), \tag{8.43}$$

where

$\hat{\beta}_j$ = the WLS estimates.
$\hat{\alpha}_0$ = the intercept in (8.41).
$\hat{\delta}_j$ = the slopes from the same regression.

Obtaining a proper standard error for the prediction in (8.42) is very complicated analytically, but, as in Section 6.4, it would be fairly easy to obtain a standard error using a resampling method such as the bootstrap described in Appendix 6A.

Obtaining a prediction interval is more of a challenge when we estimate a model for heteroskedasticity, and a full treatment is complicated. Nevertheless, we saw in Section 6.4 two examples where the error variance swamps the estimation error, and we would make only a small mistake by ignoring the estimation error in all parameters. Using arguments similar to those in Section 6.4, an approximate 95% prediction interval (for large sample sizes) is $\exp[-1.96 \cdot \hat{\sigma}\sqrt{\hat{h}(\mathbf{x}^0)}]\exp(\hat{\beta}_0 + \mathbf{x}^0\hat{\boldsymbol{\beta}})$ to $\exp[1.96 \cdot \hat{\sigma}\sqrt{\hat{h}(\mathbf{x}^0)}]\exp(\hat{\beta}_0 + \mathbf{x}^0\hat{\boldsymbol{\beta}})$, where $\hat{h}(\mathbf{x}^0)$ is the estimated variance function evaluated at $\mathbf{x}^0$, $\hat{h}(\mathbf{x}^0) = \exp(\hat{\alpha}_0 + \hat{\delta}_1 x_1^0 + \ldots + \hat{\delta}_k x_k^0)$. As in Section 6.4, we obtain this approximate interval by simply exponentiating the endpoints.

8.5 The Linear Probability Model Revisited

As we saw in Section 7.5, when the dependent variable y is a binary variable, the model must contain heteroskedasticity, unless all of the slope parameters are zero. We are now in a position to deal with this problem.

The simplest way to deal with heteroskedasticity in the linear probability model is to continue to use OLS estimation, but to also compute robust standard errors in test statistics. This ignores the fact that we actually know the form of heteroskedasticity for the LPM. Nevertheless, OLS estimation of the LPM is simple and often produces satisfactory results.

EXAMPLE 8.8 LABOR FORCE PARTICIPATION OF MARRIED WOMEN

In the labor force participation example in Section 7.5 [see equation (7.29)], we reported the usual OLS standard errors. Now, we compute the heteroskedasticity-robust standard errors as well. These are reported in brackets below the usual standard errors:

$$
\begin{aligned}
\widehat{inlf} = {} & \underset{\substack{(.154)\\ [.151]}}{.586} - \underset{\substack{(.0014)\\ [.0015]}}{.0034}\, nwifeinc + \underset{\substack{(.007)\\ [.007]}}{.038}\, educ + \underset{\substack{(.006)\\ [.006]}}{.039}\, exper \\
& - \underset{\substack{(.00018)\\ [.00019]}}{.00060}\, exper^2 - \underset{\substack{(.002)\\ [.002]}}{.016}\, age - \underset{\substack{(.034)\\ [.032]}}{.262}\, kidslt6 + \underset{\substack{(.0132)\\ [.0135]}}{.0130}\, kidsge6 \\
n = {} & 753,\ R^2 = .264.
\end{aligned}
\qquad [8.44]
$$

Several of the robust and OLS standard errors are the same to the reported degree of precision; in all cases, the differences are practically very small. Therefore, while heteroskedasticity is a problem in theory, it is not in practice, at least not for this example. It often turns out that the usual OLS standard errors and test statistics are similar to their heteroskedasticity-robust counterparts. Furthermore, it requires a minimal effort to compute both.

Generally, the OLS estimators are inefficient in the LPM. Recall that the conditional variance of y in the LPM is

$$\mathrm{Var}(y|\mathbf{x}) = p(\mathbf{x})[1 - p(\mathbf{x})], \qquad [8.45]$$

where

$$p(\mathbf{x}) = \beta_0 + \beta_1 x_1 + \ldots + \beta_k x_k \qquad [8.46]$$

is the response probability (probability of success, $y = 1$). It seems natural to use weighted least squares, but there are a couple of hitches. The probability $p(\mathbf{x})$ clearly depends on the unknown population parameters, β_j. Nevertheless, we do have unbiased estimators of these parameters, namely the OLS estimators. When the OLS estimators are plugged into equation (8.46), we obtain the OLS fitted values. Thus, for each observation i, $\mathrm{Var}(y_i|\mathbf{x}_i)$ is estimated by

$$\hat{h}_i = \hat{y}_i(1 - \hat{y}_i), \qquad [8.47]$$

where $\hat{y}_i$ is the OLS fitted value for observation i. Now, we apply feasible GLS, just as in Section 8.4.

Unfortunately, being able to estimate h_i for each i does not mean that we can proceed directly with WLS estimation. The problem is one that we briefly discussed in Section 7.5: the fitted values $\hat{y}_i$ need not fall in the unit interval. If either $\hat{y}_i < 0$ or $\hat{y}_i > 1$, equation (8.47) shows that $\hat{h}_i$ will be negative. Since WLS proceeds by multiplying observation i by $1/\sqrt{\hat{h}_i}$, the method will fail if $\hat{h}_i$ is negative (or zero) for any observation. In other words, all of the weights for WLS must be positive.

In some cases, $0 < \hat{y}_i < 1$ for all i, in which case WLS can be used to estimate the LPM. In cases with many observations and small probabilities of success or failure, it is very common to find some fitted values outside the unit interval. If this happens, as it does in the labor force participation example in equation (8.44), it is easiest to abandon WLS and to report the heteroskedasticity-robust statistics. An alternative is to adjust those fitted values that are less than zero or greater than unity, and then to apply WLS. One suggestion is to set $\hat{y}_i = .01$ if $\hat{y}_i < 0$ and $\hat{y}_i = .99$ if $\hat{y}_i > 1$. Unfortunately, this requires an arbitrary choice on the part of the researcher—for example, why not use .001 and .999 as the adjusted values? If many fitted values are outside the unit interval, the adjustment to the fitted values can affect the results; in this situation, it is probably best to just use OLS.

Estimating the Linear Probability Model by Weighted Least Squares:

1. Estimate the model by OLS and obtain the fitted values, $\hat{y}$.
2. Determine whether all of the fitted values are inside the unit interval. If so, proceed to step (3). If not, some adjustment is needed to bring all fitted values into the unit interval.
3. Construct the estimated variances in equation (8.47).
4. Estimate the equation

$$y = \beta_0 + \beta_1 x_1 + \ldots + \beta_k x_k + u$$

by WLS, using weights $1/\hat{h}$.

EXAMPLE 8.9 DETERMINANTS OF PERSONAL COMPUTER OWNERSHIP

We use the data in GPA1.RAW to estimate the probability of owning a computer. Let *PC* denote a binary indicator equal to unity if the student owns a computer, and zero otherwise. The variable *hsGPA* is high school GPA, *ACT* is achievement test score, and *parcoll* is a binary indicator equal to unity if at least one parent attended college. (Separate college indicators for the mother and the father do not yield individually significant results, as these are pretty highly correlated.)

The equation estimated by OLS is

$$
\begin{aligned}
\widehat{PC} &= -.0004 + .065\, hsGPA + .0006\, ACT + .221\, parcoll \\
&\quad\;\; (.4905) \quad (.137) \qquad\quad (.0155) \qquad\; (.093) \\
&\quad\;\; [.4888] \quad [.139] \qquad\quad [.0158] \qquad\; [.087] \\
n &= 141,\ R^2 = .0415.
\end{aligned}
\tag{8.48}
$$

Just as with Example 8.8, there are no striking differences between the usual and robust standard errors. Nevertheless, we also estimate the model by WLS. Because all of the OLS fitted values are inside the unit interval, no adjustments are needed:

$$
\begin{aligned}
\widehat{PC} &= .026 + .033\, hsGPA + .0043\, ACT + .215\, parcoll \\
&\quad\;\; (.477) \quad (.130) \qquad\quad (.0155) \qquad\; (.086) \\
n &= 141,\ R^2 = .0464.
\end{aligned}
\tag{8.49}
$$

There are no important differences in the OLS and WLS estimates. The only significant explanatory variable is *parcoll*, and in both cases we estimate that the probability of PC ownership is about .22 higher if at least one parent attended college.

Summary

We began by reviewing the properties of ordinary least squares in the presence of heteroskedasticity. Heteroskedasticity does not cause bias or inconsistency in the OLS estimators, but the usual standard errors and test statistics are no longer valid. We showed how to compute heteroskedasticity-robust standard errors and t statistics, something that is routinely done by many regression packages. Most regression packages also compute a heteroskedasticity-robust F-type statistic.

We discussed two common ways to test for heteroskedasticity: the Breusch-Pagan test and a special case of the White test. Both of these statistics involve regressing the *squared* OLS residuals on either the independent variables (BP) or the fitted and squared fitted values (White). A simple F test is asymptotically valid; there are also Lagrange multiplier versions of the tests.

OLS is no longer the best linear unbiased estimator in the presence of heteroskedasticity. When the form of heteroskedasticity is known, generalized least squares (GLS) estimation can be used. This leads to weighted least squares as a means of obtaining the BLUE estimator. The test statistics from the WLS estimation are either exactly valid when the error term is normally distributed or asymptotically valid under nonnormality. This assumes, of course, that we have the proper model of heteroskedasticity.

More commonly, we must estimate a model for the heteroskedasticity before applying WLS. The resulting *feasible* GLS estimator is no longer unbiased, but it is consistent and asymptotically efficient. The usual statistics from the WLS regression are asymptotically valid. We discussed a method to ensure that the estimated variances are strictly positive for all observations, something needed to apply WLS.

As we discussed in Chapter 7, the linear probability model for a binary dependent variable necessarily has a heteroskedastic error term. A simple way to deal with this problem is to compute heteroskedasticity-robust statistics. Alternatively, if all the fitted values (that is, the estimated probabilities) are strictly between zero and one, weighted least squares can be used to obtain asymptotically efficient estimators.

Key Terms

Breusch-Pagan Test for Heteroskedasticity (BP Test)
Feasible GLS (FGLS) Estimator
Generalized Least Squares (GLS) Estimators
Heteroskedasticity of Unknown Form
Heteroskedasticity-Robust *F* Statistic
Heteroskedasticity-Robust *LM* Statistic
Heteroskedasticity-Robust Standard Error
Heteroskedasticity-Robust *t* Statistic
Weighted Least Squares (WLS) Estimators
White Test for Heteroskedasticity

Problems

1 Which of the following are consequences of heteroskedasticity?
   (i) The OLS estimators, $\hat{\beta}_j$, are inconsistent.
   (ii) The usual F statistic no longer has an F distribution.
   (iii) The OLS estimators are no longer BLUE.

2 Consider a linear model to explain monthly beer consumption:

$$beer = \beta_0 + \beta_1 inc + \beta_2 price + \beta_3 educ + \beta_4 female + u$$

$$\mathrm{E}(u|inc, price, educ, female) = 0$$

$$\mathrm{Var}(u|inc, price, educ, female) = \sigma^2 inc^2.$$

Write the transformed equation that has a homoskedastic error term.

3 True or False: WLS is preferred to OLS when an important variable has been omitted from the model.

4 Using the data in GPA3.RAW, the following equation was estimated for the fall and second semester students:

$$\begin{aligned}\widehat{trmgpa} = &-2.12 + .900\ crsgpa + .193\ cumgpa + .0014\ tothrs \\ &(.55)\ \ (.175)\qquad\quad (.064)\qquad\quad (.0012) \\ &[.55]\ \ [.166]\qquad\quad [.074]\qquad\quad [.0012] \\ &+ .0018\ sat - .0039\ hsperc + .351\ female - .157\ season \\ &(.0002)\qquad (.0018)\qquad\quad (.085)\qquad\quad (.098) \\ &[.0002]\qquad [.0019]\qquad\quad [.079]\qquad\quad [.080] \\ n = &\ 269,\ R^2 = .465.\end{aligned}$$

Here, *trmgpa* is term GPA, *crsgpa* is a weighted average of overall GPA in courses taken, *cumgpa* is GPA prior to the current semester, *tothrs* is total credit hours prior to the semester, *sat* is SAT score, *hsperc* is graduating percentile in high school class, *female* is a gender dummy, and *season* is a dummy variable equal to unity if the student's sport is in season during the fall. The usual and heteroskedasticity-robust standard errors are reported in parentheses and brackets, respectively.

(i) Do the variables *crsgpa*, *cumgpa*, and *tothrs* have the expected estimated effects? Which of these variables are statistically significant at the 5% level? Does it matter which standard errors are used?

(ii) Why does the hypothesis H_0: $\beta_{crsgpa} = 1$ make sense? Test this hypothesis against the two-sided alternative at the 5% level, using both standard errors. Describe your conclusions.

(iii) Test whether there is an in-season effect on term GPA, using both standard errors. Does the significance level at which the null can be rejected depend on the standard error used?

5 The variable *smokes* is a binary variable equal to one if a person smokes, and zero otherwise. Using the data in SMOKE.RAW, we estimate a linear probability model for *smokes*:

$$\begin{aligned}\widehat{smokes} = &\ \underset{[.856]}{\underset{(.855)}{.656}} - \underset{[.207]}{\underset{(.204)}{.069}} \log(cigpric) + \underset{[.026]}{\underset{(.026)}{.012}} \log(income) - \underset{[.006]}{\underset{(.006)}{.029}}\, educ \\ &+ \underset{[.005]}{\underset{(.006)}{.020}}\, age - \underset{[.00006]}{\underset{(.00006)}{.00026}}\, age^2 - \underset{[.038]}{\underset{(.039)}{.101}}\, restaurn - \underset{[.050]}{\underset{(.052)}{.026}}\, white \\ n = &\ 807,\ R^2 = .062.\end{aligned}$$

The variable *white* equals one if the respondent is white, and zero otherwise; the other independent variables are defined in Example 8.7. Both the usual and heteroskedasticity-robust standard errors are reported.

(i) Are there any important differences between the two sets of standard errors?

(ii) Holding other factors fixed, if education increases by four years, what happens to the estimated probability of smoking?

(iii) At what point does another year of age reduce the probability of smoking?

(iv) Interpret the coefficient on the binary variable *restaurn* (a dummy variable equal to one if the person lives in a state with restaurant smoking restrictions).

(v) Person number 206 in the data set has the following characteristics: $cigpric = 67.44$, $income = 6{,}500$, $educ = 16$, $age = 77$, $restaurn = 0$, $white = 0$, and $smokes = 0$. Compute the predicted probability of smoking for this person and comment on the result.

6 There are different ways to combine features of the Breusch-Pagan and White tests for heteroskedasticity. One possibility not covered in the text is to run the regression

$$\hat{u}_i^2 \text{ on } x_{i1}, x_{i2}, \ldots, x_{ik}, \hat{y}_i^2,\ i = 1, \ldots, n,$$

where the $\hat{u}_i$ are the OLS residuals and the $\hat{y}_i$ are the OLS fitted values. Then, we would test joint significance of $x_{i1}, x_{i2}, \ldots, x_{ik}$ and $\hat{y}_i^2$. (Of course, we always include an intercept in this regression.)

(i) What are the *df* associated with the proposed *F* test for heteroskedasticity?

(ii) Explain why the *R*-squared from the regression above will always be at least as large as the *R*-squareds for the BP regression and the special case of the White test.

(iii) Does part (ii) imply that the new test always delivers a smaller *p*-value than either the BP or special case of the White statistic? Explain.

(iv) Suppose someone suggests also adding $\hat{y}_i$ to the newly proposed test. What do you think of this idea?

7 Consider a model at the employee level,

$$y_{i,e} = \beta_0 + \beta_1 x_{i,e,1} + \beta_2 x_{i,e,2} + \ldots + \beta_k x_{i,e,k} + f_i + v_{i,e},$$

where the unobserved variable f_i is a "firm effect" to each employee at a given firm i. The error term $v_{i,e}$ is specific to employee e at firm i. The *composite error* is $u_{i,e} = f_i + v_{i,e}$, such as in equation (8.28).

(i) Assume that $\text{Var}(f_i) = \sigma_f^2$, $\text{Var}(v_{i,e}) = \sigma_v^2$, and f_i and $v_{i,e}$ are uncorrelated. Show that $\text{Var}(u_{i,e}) = \sigma_f^2 + \sigma_v^2$; call this σ^2.

(ii) Now suppose that for $e \neq g$, $v_{i,e}$ and $v_{i,g}$ are uncorrelated. Show that $\text{Cov}(u_{i,e}, u_{i,g}) = \sigma_f^2$

(iii) Let $\bar{u}_i = m_i^{-1}\sum_{\hat{e}=1}^{mi} u_{i,e}$ be the average of the composite errors within a firm. Show that $\text{Var}(\bar{u}_i) = \sigma_f^2 + \sigma_v^2/m_i$.

(iv) Discuss the relevance of part (iii) for WLS estimation using data averaged at the firm level, where the weight used for observation i is the usual firm size.

Computer Exercises

C1 Consider the following model to explain sleeping behavior:

$$sleep = \beta_0 + \beta_1 totwrk + \beta_2 educ + \beta_3 age + \beta_4 age^2 + \beta_5 yngkid + \beta_6 male + u.$$

(i) Write down a model that allows the variance of u to differ between men and women. The variance should not depend on other factors.

(ii) Use the data in SLEEP75.RAW to estimate the parameters of the model for heteroskedasticity. (You have to estimate the *sleep* equation by OLS, first, to obtain the OLS residuals.) Is the estimated variance of u higher for men or for women?

(iii) Is the variance of u statistically different for men and for women?

C2 (i) Use the data in HPRICE1.RAW to obtain the heteroskedasticity-robust standard errors for equation (8.17). Discuss any important differences with the usual standard errors.

(ii) Repeat part (i) for equation (8.18).

(iii) What does this example suggest about heteroskedasticity and the transformation used for the dependent variable?

C3 Apply the full White test for heteroskedasticity [see equation (8.19)] to equation (8.18). Using the chi-square form of the statistic, obtain the p-value. What do you conclude?

C4 Use VOTE1.RAW for this exercise.

(i) Estimate a model with *voteA* as the dependent variable and *prtystrA*, *democA*, log(*expendA*), and log(*expendB*) as independent variables. Obtain the OLS residuals, $\hat{u}_i$, and regress these on all of the independent variables. Explain why you obtain $R^2 = 0$.

(ii) Now, compute the Breusch-Pagan test for heteroskedasticity. Use the F statistic version and report the p-value.

(iii) Compute the special case of the White test for heteroskedasticity, again using the F statistic form. How strong is the evidence for heteroskedasticity now?

C5 Use the data in PNTSPRD.RAW for this exercise.

(i) The variable *sprdcvr* is a binary variable equal to one if the Las Vegas point spread for a college basketball game was covered. The expected value of *sprdcvr*, say μ, is the probability that the spread is covered in a randomly selected game. Test H_0: $\mu = .5$ against H_1: $\mu \neq .5$ at the 10% significance level and discuss your findings. (*Hint:* This is easily done using a *t* test by regressing *sprdcvr* on an intercept only.)

(ii) How many games in the sample of 553 were played on a neutral court?

(iii) Estimate the linear probability model

$$sprdcvr = \beta_0 + \beta_1 favhome + \beta_2 neutral + \beta_3 fav25 + \beta_4 und25 + u$$

and report the results in the usual form. (Report the usual OLS standard errors and the heteroskedasticity-robust standard errors.) Which variable is most significant, both practically and statistically?

(iv) Explain why, under the null hypothesis H_0: $\beta_1 = \beta_2 = \beta_3 = \beta_4 = 0$, there is no heteroskedasticity in the model.

(v) Use the usual *F* statistic to test the hypothesis in part (iv). What do you conclude?

(vi) Given the previous analysis, would you say that it is possible to systematically predict whether the Las Vegas spread will be covered using information available prior to the game?

C6 In Example 7.12, we estimated a linear probability model for whether a young man was arrested during 1986:

$$arr86 = \beta_0 + \beta_1 pcnv + \beta_2 avgsen + \beta_3 tottime + \beta_4 ptime86 + \beta_5 qemp86 + u.$$

(i) Using the data in CRIME1.RAW, estimate this model by OLS and verify that all fitted values are strictly between zero and one. What are the smallest and largest fitted values?

(ii) Estimate the equation by weighted least squares, as discussed in Section 8.5.

(iii) Use the WLS estimates to determine whether *avgsen* and *tottime* are jointly significant at the 5% level.

C7 Use the data in LOANAPP.RAW for this exercise.

(i) Estimate the equation in part (iii) of Computer Exercise C8 in Chapter 7, computing the heteroskedasticity-robust standard errors. Compare the 95% confidence interval on β_{white} with the nonrobust confidence interval.

(ii) Obtain the fitted values from the regression in part (i). Are any of them less than zero? Are any of them greater than one? What does this mean about applying weighted least squares?

C8 Use the data set GPA1.RAW for this exercise.

(i) Use OLS to estimate a model relating *colGPA* to *hsGPA*, *ACT*, *skipped*, and *PC*. Obtain the OLS residuals.

(ii) Compute the special case of the White test for heteroskedasticity. In the regression of $\hat{u}_i^2$ on $\widehat{colGPA}_i$, $\widehat{colGPA}_i^2$, obtain the fitted values, say $\hat{h}_i$.

(iii) Verify that the fitted values from part (ii) are all strictly positive. Then, obtain the weighted least squares estimates using weights $1/\hat{h}_i$. Compare the weighted least squares estimates for the effect of skipping lectures and the effect of PC ownership with the corresponding OLS estimates. What about their statistical significance?

(iv) In the WLS estimation from part (iii), obtain heteroskedasticity-robust standard errors. In other words, allow for the fact that the variance function estimated in part (ii) might be misspecified. (See Question 8.4.) Do the standard errors change much from part (iii)?

C9 In Example 8.7, we computed the OLS and a set of WLS estimates in a cigarette demand equation.

(i) Obtain the OLS estimates in equation (8.35).

(ii) Obtain the $\hat{h}_i$ used in the WLS estimation of equation (8.36) and reproduce equation (8.36). From this equation, obtain the *unweighted* residuals and fitted values; call these $\hat{u}_i$ and $\hat{y}_i$, respectively. (For example, in Stata, the unweighted residuals and fitted values are given by default.)

(iii) Let $\breve{u}_i = \hat{u}_i/\sqrt{\hat{h}_i}$ and $\breve{y}_i = \hat{y}_i/\sqrt{\hat{h}_i}$ be the weighted quantities. Carry out the special case of the White test for heteroskedasticity by regressing $\breve{u}_i^2$ on $\breve{y}_i$, $\breve{y}_i^2$, being sure to include an intercept, as always. Do you find heteroskedasticity in the weighted residuals?

(iv) What does the finding from part (iii) imply about the proposed form of heteroskedasticity used in obtaining (8.36)?

(v) Obtain valid standard errors for the WLS estimates that allow the variance function to be misspecified.

C10 Use the data set 401KSUBS.RAW for this exercise.

(i) Using OLS, estimate a linear probability model for *e401k*, using as explanatory variables *inc, inc*^{2}, *age, age*^{2}, and *male*. Obtain both the usual OLS standard errors and the heteroskedasticity-robust versions. Are there any important differences?

(ii) In the special case of the White test for heteroskedasticity, where we regress the squared OLS residuals on a quadratic in the OLS fitted values, $\hat{u}_i^2$ on $\hat{y}_i, \hat{y}_i^2$, $i = 1, \ldots, n$, argue that the probability limit of the coefficient on $\hat{y}_i$ should be one, the probability limit of the coefficient on $\hat{y}_i^2$ should be -1, and the probability limit of the intercept should be zero. {*Hint:* Remember that $\text{Var}(y|x_1, \ldots, x_k) = p(\mathbf{x})[1 - p(\mathbf{x})]$, where $p(\mathbf{x}) = \beta_0 + \beta_1 x_1 + \ldots + \beta_k x_k$.}

(iii) For the model estimated from part (i), obtain the White test and see if the coefficient estimates roughly correspond to the theoretical values described in part (ii).

(iv) After verifying that the fitted values from part (i) are all between zero and one, obtain the weighted least squares estimates of the linear probability model. Do they differ in important ways from the OLS estimates?

C11 Use the data in 401KSUBS.RAW for this question, restricting the sample to *fsize* = 1.

(i) To the model estimated in Table 8.1, add the interaction term, *e401k* · *inc*. Estimate the equation by OLS and obtain the usual and robust standard errors. What do you conclude about the statistical significance of the interaction term?

(ii) Now estimate the more general model by WLS using the same weights, $1/inc_i$, as in Table 8.1. Compute the usual and robust standard error for the WLS estimator. Is the interaction term statistically significant using the robust standard error?

(iii) Discuss the WLS coefficient on *e401k* in the more general model. Is it of much interest by itself? Explain.

(iv) Reestimate the model by WLS but use the interaction term $e401k \cdot (inc - 30)$; the average income in the sample is about 29.44. Now interpret the coefficient on *e401k*.

C12 Use the data in MEAP00.RAW to answer this question.

(i) Estimate the model

$$math4 = \beta_0 + \beta_1 lunch + \beta_2 \log(enroll) + \beta_3 \log(exppp) + u$$

by OLS and obtain the usual standard errors and the fully robust standard errors. How do they generally compare?

(ii) Apply the special case of the White test for heteroskedasticity. What is the value of the *F* test? What do you conclude?

(iii) Obtain $\hat{g}_i$ as the fitted values from the regression $\log(\hat{u}_i^2)$ on $\widehat{math4}_i$, $\widehat{math4}_i^2$, where $\widehat{math4}_i$ are the OLS fitted values and the $\hat{u}_i$ are the OLS residuals. Let $\hat{h}_i = \exp(\hat{g}_i)$. Use the $\hat{h}_i$ to obtain WLS estimates. Are there big differences with the OLS coefficients?

(iv) Obtain the standard errors for WLS that allow misspecification of the variance function. Do these differ much from the usual WLS standard errors?

(v) For estimating the effect of spending on *math4*, does OLS or WLS appear to be more precise?

C13 Use the data in FERTIL2.RAW to answer this question.

(i) Estimate the model

$$children = \beta_0 + \beta_1 age + \beta_2 age^2 + \beta_3 educ + \beta_4 electric + \beta_5 urban + u$$

and report the usual and heteroskedasticity-robust standard errors. Are the robust standard errors always bigger than the nonrobust ones?

(ii) Add the three religious dummy variables and test whether they are jointly significant. What are the *p*-values for the nonrobust and robust tests?

(iii) From the regresion in part (ii), obtain the fitted values $\hat{y}$ and the residuals, $\hat{u}$. Regress $\hat{u}^2$ on $\hat{y}$, $\hat{y}_2$ and test the joint significance of the two regressors. Conclude that heteroskedasticity is present in the equation for *children*.

(iv) Would you say the heteroskedasticity you found in part (iii) is practically important?

C14 Use the data in BEAUTY.RAW for this question.

(i) Using the data pooled for men and women, estimate the equation

$$lwage = \beta_0 + \beta_1 belavg + \beta_2 abvavg + \beta_3 female + \beta_4 educ + \beta_5 exper + \beta_5 exper^2 + u,$$

and report the results using heteroskedasticity-robust standard errors below coefficients. Are any of the coefficients surprising in either their signs or magnitudes? Is the coefficient on *female* practically large and statistically significant?

(ii) Add interactions of *female* with all other explanatory variables in the equation from part (i) (five interactions in all). Compute the usual *F* test of joint significance of the five interactions and a heteroskedasticity-robust version. Does using the heteroskedasticity-robust version change the outcome in any important way?

(iii) In the full model with interactions, determine whether those involving the looks variables—female • *belavg* and *female* • *abvavg*—are jointly significant. Are their coefficients practically small?

CHAPTER

9

More on Specification and Data Issues

In Chapter 8, we dealt with one failure of the Gauss-Markov assumptions. While heteroskedasticity in the errors can be viewed as a problem with a model, it is a relatively minor one. The presence of heteroskedasticity does not cause bias or inconsistency in the OLS estimators. Also, it is fairly easy to adjust confidence intervals and t and F statistics to obtain valid inference after OLS estimation, or even to get more efficient estimators by using weighted least squares.

In this chapter, we return to the much more serious problem of correlation between the error, u, and one or more of the explanatory variables. Remember from Chapter 3 that if u is, for whatever reason, correlated with the explanatory variable x_j, then we say that x_j is an **endogenous explanatory variable**. We also provide a more detailed discussion on three reasons why an explanatory variable can be endogenous; in some cases, we discuss possible remedies.

We have already seen in Chapters 3 and 5 that omitting a key variable can cause correlation between the error and some of the explanatory variables, which generally leads to bias and inconsistency in *all* of the OLS estimators. In the special case that the omitted variable is a function of an explanatory variable in the model, the model suffers from **functional form misspecification**.

We begin in the first section by discussing the consequences of functional form misspecification and how to test for it. In Section 9.2, we show how the use of proxy variables can solve, or at least mitigate, omitted variables bias. In Section 9.3, we derive and explain the bias in OLS that can arise under certain forms of **measurement error**. Additional data problems are discussed in Section 9.4.

All of the procedures in this chapter are based on OLS estimation. As we will see, certain problems that cause correlation between the error and some explanatory variables cannot be solved by using OLS on a single cross section. We postpone a treatment of alternative estimation methods until Part 3.

9.1 Functional Form Misspecification

A multiple regression model suffers from functional form misspecification when it does not properly account for the relationship between the dependent and the observed explanatory variables. For example, if hourly wage is determined by $\log(wage) = \beta_0 + \beta_1 educ + \beta_2 exper + \beta_3 exper^2 + u$, but we omit the squared experience term, $exper^2$, then we are committing a functional form misspecification. We already know from Chapter 3 that this generally leads to biased estimators of β_0, β_1, and β_2. (We do not estimate β_3 because $exper^2$ is excluded from the model.) Thus, misspecifying how *exper* affects log(*wage*) generally results in a biased estimator of the return to education, β_1. The amount of this bias depends on the size of β_3 and the correlation among *educ*, *exper*, and $exper^2$.

Things are worse for estimating the return to experience: even if we could get an unbiased estimator of β_2, we would not be able to estimate the return to experience because it equals $\beta_2 + 2\beta_3 exper$ (in decimal form). Just using the biased estimator of β_2 can be misleading, especially at extreme values of *exper*.

As another example, suppose the log(*wage*) equation is

$$\log(wage) = \beta_0 + \beta_1 educ + \beta_2 exper + \beta_3 exper^2 + \beta_4 female + \beta_5 female \cdot educ + u, \quad [9.1]$$

where *female* is a binary variable. If we omit the interaction term, *female·educ*, then we are misspecifying the functional form. In general, we will not get unbiased estimators of any of the other parameters, and since the return to education depends on gender, it is not clear what return we would be estimating by omitting the interaction term.

Omitting functions of independent variables is not the only way that a model can suffer from misspecified functional form. For example, if (9.1) is the true model satisfying the first four Gauss-Markov assumptions, but we use *wage* rather than log(*wage*) as the dependent variable, then we will not obtain unbiased or consistent estimators of the partial effects. The tests that follow have some ability to detect this kind of functional form problem, but there are better tests that we will mention in the subsection on testing against nonnested alternatives.

Misspecifying the functional form of a model can certainly have serious consequences. Nevertheless, in one important respect, the problem is minor: by definition, we have data on all the necessary variables for obtaining a functional relationship that fits the data well. This can be contrasted with the problem addressed in the next section, where a key variable is omitted on which we cannot collect data.

We already have a very powerful tool for detecting misspecified functional form: the F test for joint exclusion restrictions. It often makes sense to add quadratic terms of any significant variables to a model and to perform a joint test of significance. If the additional quadratics are significant, they can be added to the model (at the cost of complicating the interpretation of the model). However, significant quadratic terms can be symptomatic of other functional form problems, such as using the level of a variable when the logarithm is more appropriate, or vice versa. It can be difficult to pinpoint the precise reason that a functional form is misspecified. Fortunately, in many cases, using logarithms of certain variables and adding quadratics are sufficient for detecting many important nonlinear relationships in economics.

EXAMPLE 9.1 ECONOMIC MODEL OF CRIME

Table 9.1 contains OLS estimates of the economic model of crime (see Example 8.3). We first estimate the model without any quadratic terms; those results are in column (1).

In column (2), the squares of *pcnv*, *ptime86*, and *inc86* are added; we chose to include the squares of these variables because each level term is significant in column (1). The variable *qemp86* is a discrete variable taking on only five values, so we do not include its square in column (2).

Each of the squared terms is significant, and together they are jointly very significant ($F = 31.37$, with $df = 3$ and 2,713; the p-value is essentially zero). Thus, it appears that the initial model overlooked some potentially important nonlinearities.

EXPLORING FURTHER 9.1

Why do we not include the squares of *black* and *hispan* in column (2) of Table 9.1?

The presence of the quadratics makes interpreting the model somewhat difficult. For example, *pcnv* no longer has a strict deterrent effect: the relationship between *narr86* and *pcnv* is positive

TABLE 9.1 Dependent Variable: *narr86*

Independent Variables	(1)	(2)
pcnv	−.133 (.040)	.533 (.154)
$pcnv^2$	—	−.730 (.156)
avgsen	−.011 (.012)	−.017 (.012)
tottime	.012 (.009)	.012 (.009)
ptime86	−.041 (.009)	.287 (.004)
$ptime86^2$	—	−.0296 (.0039)
qemp86	−.051 (.014)	−.014 (.017)
inc86	−.0015 (.0003)	−.0034 (.0008)
$inc86^2$	—	−.000007 (.000003)
black	.327 (.045)	.292 (.045)
hispan	.194 (.040)	.164 (.039)
intercept	.596 (.036)	.505 (.037)
Observations	2,725	2,725
R-squared	.0723	.1035

up until *pcnv* = .365, and then the relationship is negative. We might conclude that there is little or no deterrent effect at lower values of *pcnv*; the effect only kicks in at higher prior conviction rates. We would have to use more sophisticated functional forms than the quadratic to verify this conclusion. It may be that *pcnv* is not entirely exogenous. For example, men who have not been convicted in the past (so that *pcnv* = 0) are perhaps casual criminals, and so they are less likely to be arrested in 1986. This could be biasing the estimates.

Similarly, the relationship between *narr86* and *ptime86* is positive up until *ptime86* = 4.85 (almost five months in prison), and then the relationship is negative. The vast majority of men in the sample spent no time in prison in 1986, so again we must be careful in interpreting the results.

Legal income has a negative effect on *narr86* until *inc86* = 242.85; since income is measured in hundreds of dollars, this means an annual income of $24,285. Only 46 of the men in the sample have incomes above this level. Thus, we can conclude that *narr86* and *inc86* are negatively related with a diminishing effect.

Example 9.1 is a tricky functional form problem due to the nature of the dependent variable. Other models are theoretically better suited for handling dependent variables taking on a small number of integer values. We will briefly cover these models in Chapter 17.

RESET as a General Test for Functional Form Misspecification

Some tests have been proposed to detect general functional form misspecification. Ramsey's (1969) **regression specification error test (RESET)** has proven to be useful in this regard.

The idea behind RESET is fairly simple. If the original model

$$y = \beta_0 + \beta_1 x_1 + \dots + \beta_k x_k + u \tag{9.2}$$

satisfies MLR.4, then no nonlinear functions of the independent variables should be significant when added to equation (9.2). In Example 9.1, we added quadratics in the significant explanatory variables. Although this often detects functional form problems, it has the drawback of using up many degrees of freedom if there are many explanatory variables in the original model (much as the straight form of the White test for heteroskedasticity consumes degrees of freedom). Further, certain kinds of neglected nonlinearities will not be picked up by adding quadratic terms. RESET adds polynomials in the OLS fitted values to equation (9.2) to detect general kinds of functional form misspecification.

To implement RESET, we must decide how many functions of the fitted values to include in an expanded regression. There is no right answer to this question, but the squared and cubed terms have proven to be useful in most applications.

Let $\hat{y}$ denote the OLS fitted values from estimating (9.2). Consider the expanded equation

$$y = \beta_0 + \beta_1 x_1 + \dots + \beta_k x_k + \delta_1 \hat{y}^2 + \delta_2 \hat{y}^3 + error. \tag{9.3}$$

This equation seems a little odd, because functions of the fitted values from the initial estimation now appear as explanatory variables. In fact, we will not be interested in the estimated parameters from (9.3); we only use this equation to test whether (9.2) has missed important nonlinearities. The thing to remember is that $\hat{y}^2$ and $\hat{y}^3$ are just nonlinear functions of the x_j.

The null hypothesis is that (9.2) is correctly specified. Thus, RESET is the F statistic for testing H_0: $\delta_1 = 0, \delta_2 = 0$ in the expanded model (9.3). A significant F statistic suggests some sort of functional form problem. The distribution of the F statistic is approximately $F_{2,n-k-3}$ in large samples under the null hypothesis (and the Gauss-Markov assumptions). The df in the expanded equation (9.3) is $n - k - 1 - 2 = n - k - 3$. An LM version is also available (and the chi-square distribution will have two df). Further, the test can be made robust to heteroskedasticity using the methods discussed in Section 8.2.

EXAMPLE 9.2 HOUSING PRICE EQUATION

We estimate two models for housing prices. The first one has all variables in level form:

$$price = \beta_0 + \beta_1 lotsize + \beta_2 sqrft + \beta_3 bdrms + u. \quad [9.4]$$

The second one uses the logarithms of all variables except *bdrms*:

$$lprice = \beta_0 + \beta_1 llotsize + \beta_2 lsqrft + \beta_3 bdrms + u. \quad [9.5]$$

Using $n = 88$ houses in HPRICE1.RAW, the RESET statistic for equation (9.4) turns out to be 4.67; this is the value of an $F_{2,82}$ random variable ($n = 88$, $k = 3$), and the associated p-value is .012. This is evidence of functional form misspecification in (9.4).

The RESET statistic in (9.5) is 2.56, with p-value $= .084$. Thus, we do not reject (9.5) at the 5% significance level (although we would at the 10% level). On the basis of RESET, the log-log model in (9.5) is preferred.

In the previous example, we tried two models for explaining housing prices. One was rejected by RESET, while the other was not (at least at the 5% level). Often, things are not so simple. A drawback with RESET is that it provides no real direction on how to proceed if the model is rejected. Rejecting (9.4) by using RESET does not immediately suggest that (9.5) is the next step. Equation (9.5) was estimated because constant elasticity models are easy to interpret and can have nice statistical properties. In this example, it so happens that it passes the functional form test as well.

Some have argued that RESET is a very general test for model misspecification, including unobserved omitted variables and heteroskedasticity. Unfortunately, such use of RESET is largely misguided. It can be shown that RESET has no power for detecting omitted variables whenever they have expectations that are linear in the included independent variables in the model [see Wooldridge (1995) for a precise statement]. Further, if the functional form is properly specified, RESET has no power for detecting heteroskedasticity. The bottom line is that RESET is a functional form test, and nothing more.

Tests against Nonnested Alternatives

Obtaining tests for other kinds of functional form misspecification—for example, trying to decide whether an independent variable should appear in level or logarithmic form—takes us outside the realm of classical hypothesis testing. It is possible to test the model

$$y = \beta_0 + \beta_1 x_1 + \beta_2 x_2 + u \quad [9.6]$$

against the model

$$y = \beta_0 + \beta_1\log(x_1) + \beta_2\log(x_2) + u, \qquad [9.7]$$

and vice versa. However, these are **nonnested models** (see Chapter 6), and so we cannot simply use a standard F test. Two different approaches have been suggested. The first is to construct a comprehensive model that contains each model as a special case and then to test the restrictions that led to each of the models. In the current example, the comprehensive model is

$$y = \gamma_0 + \gamma_1x_1 + \gamma_2x_2 + \gamma_3\log(x_1) + \gamma_4\log(x_2) + u. \qquad [9.8]$$

We can first test H_0: $\gamma_3 = 0, \gamma_4 = 0$ as a test of (9.6). We can also test H_0: $\gamma_1 = 0, \gamma_2 = 0$ as a test of (9.7). This approach was suggested by Mizon and Richard (1986).

Another approach has been suggested by Davidson and MacKinnon (1981). They point out that if (9.6) is true, then the fitted values from the other model, (9.7), should be insignificant in (9.6). Thus, to test (9.6), we first estimate model (9.7) by OLS to obtain the fitted values. Call these $\hat{\hat{y}}$. Then, the **Davidson-MacKinnon test** is based on the t statistic on $\hat{\hat{y}}$ in the equation

$$y = \beta_0 + \beta_1x_1 + \beta_2x_2 + \theta_1\hat{\hat{y}} + error.$$

A significant t statistic (against a two-sided alternative) is a rejection of (9.6).

Similarly, if $\hat{y}$ denotes the fitted values from estimating (9.6), the test of (9.7) is the t statistic on $\hat{y}$ in the model

$$y = \beta_0 + \beta_1\log(x_1) + \beta_2\log(x_2) + \theta_1\hat{y} + error;$$

a significant t statistic is evidence against (9.7). The same two tests can be used for testing any two nonnested models with the same dependent variable.

There are a few problems with nonnested testing. First, a clear winner need not emerge. Both models could be rejected or neither model could be rejected. In the latter case, we can use the adjusted R-squared to choose between them. If both models are rejected, more work needs to be done. However, it is important to know the practical consequences from using one form or the other: if the effects of key independent variables on y are not very different, then it does not really matter which model is used.

A second problem is that rejecting (9.6) using, say, the Davidson-MacKinnon test does not mean that (9.7) is the correct model. Model (9.6) can be rejected for a variety of functional form misspecifications.

An even more difficult problem is obtaining nonnested tests when the competing models have different dependent variables. The leading case is y versus $\log(y)$. We saw in Chapter 6 that just obtaining goodness-of-fit measures that can be compared requires some care. Tests have been proposed to solve this problem, but they are beyond the scope of this text. [See Wooldridge (1994a) for a test that has a simple interpretation and is easy to implement.]

9.2 Using Proxy Variables for Unobserved Explanatory Variables

A more difficult problem arises when a model excludes a key variable, usually because of data unavailability. Consider a wage equation that explicitly recognizes that ability (*abil*) affects log(*wage*):

$$\log(wage) = \beta_0 + \beta_1educ + \beta_2exper + \beta_3abil + u. \qquad [9.9]$$

This model shows explicitly that we want to hold ability fixed when measuring the return to *educ* and *exper*. If, say, *educ* is correlated with *abil*, then putting *abil* in the error term causes the OLS estimator of β_1 (and β_2) to be biased, a theme that has appeared repeatedly.

Our primary interest in equation (9.9) is in the slope parameters β_1 and β_2. We do not really care whether we get an unbiased or consistent estimator of the intercept β_0; as we will see shortly, this is not usually possible. Also, we can never hope to estimate β_3 because *abil* is not observed; in fact, we would not know how to interpret β_3 anyway, since ability is at best a vague concept.

How can we solve, or at least mitigate, the omitted variables bias in an equation like (9.9)? One possibility is to obtain a **proxy variable** for the omitted variable. Loosely speaking, a proxy variable is something that is related to the unobserved variable that we would like to control for in our analysis. In the wage equation, one possibility is to use the intelligence quotient, or IQ, as a proxy for ability. This *does not* require IQ to be the same thing as ability; what we need is for IQ to be correlated with ability, something we clarify in the following discussion.

All of the key ideas can be illustrated in a model with three independent variables, two of which are observed:

$$y = \beta_0 + \beta_1 x_1 + \beta_2 x_2 + \beta_3 x_3^* + u. \qquad [9.10]$$

We assume that data are available on y, x_1, and x_2—in the wage example, these are log(*wage*), *educ*, and *exper*, respectively. The explanatory variable x_3^* is unobserved, but we have a proxy variable for x_3^*. Call the proxy variable x_3.

What do we require of x_3? At a minimum, it should have some relationship to x_3^*. This is captured by the simple regression equation

$$x_3^* = \delta_0 + \delta_3 x_3 + v_3, \qquad [9.11]$$

where v_3 is an error due to the fact that x_3^* and x_3 are not exactly related. The parameter δ_3 measures the relationship between x_3^* and x_3; typically, we think of x_3^* and x_3 as being positively related, so that $\delta_3 > 0$. If $\delta_3 = 0$, then x_3 is not a suitable proxy for x_3^*. The intercept δ_0 in (9.11), which can be positive or negative, simply allows x_3^* and x_3 to be measured on different scales. (For example, unobserved ability is certainly not required to have the same average value as IQ in the U.S. population.)

How can we use x_3 to get unbiased (or at least consistent) estimators of β_1 and β_2? The proposal is to pretend that x_3 and x_3^* are the same, so that we run the regression of

$$y \text{ on } x_1, x_2, x_3. \qquad [9.12]$$

We call this the **plug-in solution to the omitted variables problem** because x_3 is just plugged in for x_3^* before we run OLS. If x_3 is truly related to x_3^*, this seems like a sensible thing. However, since x_3 and x_3^* are not the same, we should determine when this procedure does in fact give consistent estimators of β_1 and β_2.

The assumptions needed for the plug-in solution to provide consistent estimators of β_1 and β_2 can be broken down into assumptions about u and v_3:

(1) The error u is uncorrelated with x_1, x_2, and x_3^*, which is just the standard assumption in model (9.10). In addition, u is uncorrelated with x_3. This latter assumption just means that x_3 is irrelevant in the population model, once x_1, x_2, and x_3^* have been included.

This is essentially true by definition, since x_3 is a proxy variable for x_3^*: it is x_3^* that directly affects y, not x_3. Thus, the assumption that u is uncorrelated with x_1, x_2, x_3^*, and x_3 is not very controversial. (Another way to state this assumption is that the expected value of u, given all these variables, is zero.)

(2) The error v_3 is uncorrelated with x_1, x_2, and x_3. Assuming that v_3 is uncorrelated with x_1 and x_2 requires x_3 to be a "good" proxy for x_3^*. This is easiest to see by writing the analog of these assumptions in terms of conditional expectations:

$$E(x_3^*|x_1,x_2,x_3) = E(x_3^*|x_3) = \delta_0 + \delta_3 x_3. \quad [9.13]$$

The first equality, which is the most important one, says that, once x_3 is controlled for, the expected value of x_3^* does not depend on x_1 or x_2. Alternatively, x_3^* has zero correlation with x_1 and x_2 once x_3 is partialled out.

In the wage equation (9.9), where IQ is the proxy for ability, condition (9.13) becomes

$$E(abil|educ,exper,IQ) = E(abil|IQ) = \delta_0 + \delta_3 IQ.$$

Thus, the average level of ability only changes with IQ, not with *educ* and *exper*. Is this reasonable? Maybe it is not exactly true, but it may be close to being true. It is certainly worth including IQ in the wage equation to see what happens to the estimated return to education.

We can easily see why the previous assumptions are enough for the plug-in solution to work. If we plug equation (9.11) into equation (9.10) and do simple algebra, we get

$$y = (\beta_0 + \beta_3\delta_0) + \beta_1 x_1 + \beta_2 x_2 + \beta_3\delta_3 x_3 + u + \beta_3 v_3.$$

Call the composite error in this equation $e = u + \beta_3 v_3$; it depends on the error in the model of interest, (9.10), and the error in the proxy variable equation, v_3. Since u and v_3 both have zero mean and each is uncorrelated with x_1, x_2, and x_3, e also has zero mean and is uncorrelated with x_1, x_2, and x_3. Write this equation as

$$y = \alpha_0 + \beta_1 x_1 + \beta_2 x_2 + \alpha_3 x_3 + e,$$

where $\alpha_0 = (\beta_0 + \beta_3\delta_0)$ is the new intercept and $\alpha_3 = \beta_3\delta_3$ is the slope parameter on the proxy variable x_3. As we alluded to earlier, when we run the regression in (9.12), we will not get unbiased estimators of β_0 and β_3; instead, we will get unbiased (or at least consistent) estimators of α_0, β_1, β_2, and α_3. The important thing is that we get good estimates of the parameters β_1 and β_2.

In most cases, the estimate of α_3 is actually more interesting than an estimate of β_3 anyway. For example, in the wage equation, α_3 measures the return to wage given one more point on IQ score.

EXAMPLE 9.3 IQ AS A PROXY FOR ABILITY

The file WAGE2.RAW, from Blackburn and Neumark (1992), contains information on monthly earnings, education, several demographic variables, and IQ scores for 935 men in 1980. As a method to account for omitted ability bias, we add IQ to a standard log wage equation. The results are shown in Table 9.2.

TABLE 9.2 Dependent Variable: log(*wage*)

Independent Variables	(1)	(2)	(3)
educ	.065 (.006)	.054 (.007)	.018 (.041)
exper	.014 (.003)	.014 (.003)	.014 (.003)
tenure	.012 (.002)	.011 (.002)	.011 (.002)
married	.199 (.039)	.200 (.039)	.201 (.039)
south	−.091 (.026)	−.080 (.026)	−.080 (.026)
urban	.184 (.027)	.182 (.027)	.184 (.027)
black	−.188 (.038)	−.143 (.039)	−.147 (.040)
IQ	—	.0036 (.0010)	−.0009 (.0052)
educ·IQ	—	—	.00034 (.00038)
intercept	5.395 (.113)	5.176 (.128)	5.648 (.546)
Observations	935	935	935
R-squared	.253	.263	.263

Our primary interest is in what happens to the estimated return to education. Column (1) contains the estimates without using *IQ* as a proxy variable. The estimated return to education is 6.5%. If we think omitted ability is positively correlated with *educ*, then we assume that this estimate is too high. (More precisely, the average estimate across all random samples would be too high.) When *IQ* is added to the equation, the return to education falls to 5.4%, which corresponds with our prior beliefs about omitted ability bias.

The effect of IQ on socioeconomic outcomes has been documented in the controversial book *The Bell Curve*, by Herrnstein and Murray (1994). Column (2) shows that IQ does have a statistically significant, positive effect on earnings, after controlling for several other factors. Everything else being equal, an increase of 10 IQ points is predicted to raise monthly earnings by 3.6%. The standard deviation of IQ in the U.S. population is 15, so a one standard deviation increase in IQ is associated with higher earnings of 5.4%. This is identical to the predicted increase in wage due to another year of education. It is clear from column (2) that education still has an important role in increasing earnings, even though the effect is not as large as originally estimated.

Some other interesting observations emerge from columns (1) and (2). Adding *IQ* to the equation only increases the *R*-squared from .253 to .263. Most of the variation in log(*wage*) is not explained by the factors in column (2). Also, adding *IQ* to the equation does not eliminate the estimated earnings difference between black and white men: a black man with the same IQ, education, experience, and so on, as a white man is predicted to earn about 14.3% less, and the difference is very statistically significant.

Column (3) in Table 9.2 includes the interaction term *educ·IQ*. This allows for the possibility that *educ* and *abil* interact in determining log(*wage*). We might think that the return to education is higher for people with more ability, but this turns out not to be the case: the interaction term is not significant, and its addition makes *educ* and *IQ* individually insignificant while complicating the model. Therefore, the estimates in column (2) are preferred.

EXPLORING FURTHER 9.2

What do you make of the small and statistically insignificant coefficient on *educ* in column (3) of Table 9.2? (*Hint:* When *educ·IQ* is in the equation, what is the interpretation of the coefficient on *educ*?)

There is no reason to stop at a single proxy variable for ability in this example. The data set WAGE2.RAW also contains a score for each man on the *Knowledge of the World of Work* (KWW) test. This provides a different measure of ability, which can be used in place of IQ or along with IQ, to estimate the return to education (see Computer Exercise C2).

It is easy to see how using a proxy variable can still lead to bias if the proxy variable does not satisfy the preceding assumptions. Suppose that, instead of (9.11), the unobserved variable, x_3^*, is related to all of the observed variables by

$$x_3^* = \delta_0 + \delta_1 x_1 + \delta_2 x_2 + \delta_3 x_3 + v_3, \quad [9.14]$$

where v_3 has a zero mean and is uncorrelated with x_1, x_2, and x_3. Equation (9.11) assumes that δ_1 and δ_2 are both zero. By plugging equation (9.14) into (9.10), we get

$$\begin{aligned} y = (\beta_0 + \beta_3\delta_0) + (\beta_1 + \beta_3\delta_1)x_1 + (\beta_2 + \beta_3\delta_2)x_2 \\ + \beta_3\delta_3 x_3 + u + \beta_3 v_3, \end{aligned} \quad [9.15]$$

from which it follows that $\text{plim}(\hat{\beta}_1) = \beta_1 + \beta_3\delta_1$ and $\text{plim}(\hat{\beta}_2) = \beta_2 + \beta_3\delta_2$. [This follows because the error in (9.15), $u + \beta_3 v_3$, has zero mean and is uncorrelated with x_1, x_2, and x_3.] In the previous example where $x_1 = educ$ and $x_3^* = abil$, $\beta_3 > 0$, so there is a positive bias (inconsistency) if *abil* has a positive partial correlation with *educ* ($\delta_1 > 0$). Thus, we could still be getting an upward bias in the return to education by using *IQ* as a proxy for *abil* if *IQ* is not a good proxy. But we can reasonably hope that this bias is smaller than if we ignored the problem of omitted ability entirely.

A complaint that is sometimes aired about including variables such as *IQ* in a regression that includes *educ* is that it exacerbates the problem of multicollinearity, likely leading to a less precise estimate of β_{educ}. But this complaint misses two important points. First, the inclusion of *IQ* reduces the error variance because the part of ability explained by *IQ* has been removed from the error. Typically, this will be reflected in a smaller standard error of the regression (although it need not get smaller because of its degrees-of-freedom adjustment). Second, and most importantly, the added multicollinearity is a necessary evil if we want to get an estimator of β_{educ} with less bias: the reason *educ* and *IQ* are correlated is that *educ* and *abil* are thought to be correlated, and *IQ* is a proxy for *abil*. If we could observe *abil* we would include it in the regression, and of course there would be unavoidable multicollinearity caused by correlation between *educ* and *abil*.

Proxy variables can come in the form of binary information as well. In Example 7.9 [see equation (7.15)], we discussed Krueger's (1993) estimates of the return to using a computer on the job. Krueger also included a binary variable indicating whether the worker uses a computer at home (as well as an interaction term between computer usage at work and at home). His primary reason for including computer usage at home in the equation was to proxy for unobserved "technical ability" that could affect wage directly and be related to computer usage at work.

Using Lagged Dependent Variables as Proxy Variables

In some applications, like the earlier wage example, we have at least a vague idea about which unobserved factor we would like to control for. This facilitates choosing proxy variables. In other applications, we suspect that one or more of the independent variables is correlated with an omitted variable, but we have no idea how to obtain a proxy for that omitted variable. In such cases, we can include, as a control, the value of the dependent variable from an earlier time period. This is especially useful for policy analysis.

Using a **lagged dependent variable** in a cross-sectional equation increases the data requirements, but it also provides a simple way to account for historical factors that cause *current* differences in the dependent variable that are difficult to account for in other ways. For example, some cities have had high crime rates in the past. Many of the same unobserved factors contribute to both high current and past crime rates. Likewise, some universities are traditionally better in academics than other universities. Inertial effects are also captured by putting in lags of y.

Consider a simple equation to explain city crime rates:

$$crime = \beta_0 + \beta_1 unem + \beta_2 expend + \beta_3 crime_{-1} + u, \quad [9.16]$$

where $crime$ is a measure of per capita crime, $unem$ is the city unemployment rate, $expend$ is per capita spending on law enforcement, and $crime_{-1}$ indicates the crime rate measured in some earlier year (this could be the past year or several years ago). We are interested in the effects of $unem$ on $crime$, as well as of law enforcement expenditures on crime.

What is the purpose of including $crime_{-1}$ in the equation? Certainly, we expect that $\beta_3 > 0$ because crime has inertia. But the main reason for putting this in the equation is that cities with high historical crime rates may spend more on crime prevention. Thus, factors unobserved to us (the econometricians) that affect $crime$ are likely to be correlated with $expend$ (and $unem$). If we use a pure cross-sectional analysis, we are unlikely to get an unbiased estimator of the causal effect of law enforcement expenditures on crime. But, by including $crime_{-1}$ in the equation, we can at least do the following experiment: if two cities have the same previous crime rate and current unemployment rate, then β_2 measures the effect of another dollar of law enforcement on crime.

EXAMPLE 9.4 CITY CRIME RATES

We estimate a constant elasticity version of the crime model in equation (9.16) ($unem$, because it is a percentage, is left in level form). The data in CRIME2.RAW are from 46 cities for the year 1987. The crime rate is also available for 1982, and we use that as an additional independent variable in trying to control for city unobservables that affect crime and may be correlated with current law enforcement expenditures. Table 9.3 contains the results.

Without the lagged crime rate in the equation, the effects of the unemployment rate and expenditures on law enforcement are counterintuitive; neither is statistically significant, although the t statistic on $\log(lawexpc_{87})$ is 1.17. One possibility is that increased law enforcement expenditures improve reporting conventions, and so more crimes are *reported*. But it is also likely that cities with high recent crime rates spend more on law enforcement.

TABLE 9.3 Dependent Variable: log($crmrte_{87}$)

Independent Variables	(1)	(2)
$unem_{87}$	−.029 (.032)	.009 (.020)
log($lawexpc_{87}$)	.203 (.173)	−.140 (.109)
log($crmrte_{82}$)	—	1.194 (.132)
intercept	3.34 (1.25)	.076 (.821)
Observations	46	46
R-squared	.057	.680

Adding the log of the crime rate from five years earlier has a large effect on the expenditures coefficient. The elasticity of the crime rate with respect to expenditures becomes −.14, with $t = -1.28$. This is not strongly significant, but it suggests that a more sophisticated model with more cities in the sample could produce significant results.

Not surprisingly, the current crime rate is strongly related to the past crime rate. The estimate indicates that if the crime rate in 1982 was 1% higher, then the crime rate in 1987 is predicted to be about 1.19% higher. We cannot reject the hypothesis that the elasticity of current crime with respect to past crime is unity [$t = (1.194 - 1)/.132 \approx 1.47$]. Adding the past crime rate increases the explanatory power of the regression markedly, but this is no surprise. The primary reason for including the lagged crime rate is to obtain a better estimate of the ceteris paribus effect of log($lawexpc_{87}$) on log($crmrte_{87}$).

The practice of putting in a lagged y as a general way of controlling for unobserved variables is hardly perfect. But it can aid in getting a better estimate of the effects of policy variables on various outcomes.

Adding a lagged value of y is not the only way to use two years of data to control for omitted factors. When we discuss panel data methods in Chapters 13 and 14, we will cover other ways to use repeated data on the same cross-sectional units at different points in time.

A Different Slant on Multiple Regression

The discussion of proxy variables in this section suggests an alternative way of interpreting a multiple regression analysis when we do not necessarily observe all relevant explanatory variables. Until now, we have specified the population model of interest with an additive error, as in equation (9.9). Our discussion of that example hinged upon whether we have a suitable proxy variable (IQ score in this case, other test scores more generally) for the unobserved explanatory variable, which we called "ability."

A less structured, more general approach to multiple regression is to forego specifying models with unobservables. Rather, we begin with the premise that we have access to a set of observable explanatory variables—which includes the variable of primary interest, such as years of schooling, and controls, such as observable test scores. We then model the mean of y conditional on the observed explanatory variables. For example, in the wage example with *lwage* denoting log(*wage*), we can estimate E(*lwage*|*educ*,*exper*,*tenure*, *south,urban,black,IQ*)—exactly what is reported in Table 9.2. The difference now is that we set our goals more modestly. Namely, rather than introduce the nebulous concept of "ability" in equation (9.9), we state from the outset that we will estimate the ceteris paribus effect of education holding *IQ* (and the other observed factors) fixed. There is no need to discuss whether *IQ* is a suitable proxy for ability. Consequently, while we may not be answering the question underlying equation (9.9), we are answering a question of interest: if two people have the same *IQ* levels (and same values of experience, tenure, and so on), yet they differ in education levels by a year, what is the expected difference in their log wages?

As another example, if we include as an explanatory variable the poverty rate in a school-level regression to assess the effects of spending on standardized test scores, we should recognize that the poverty rate only crudely captures the relevant differences in children and parents across schools. But often it is all we have, and it is better to control for the poverty rate than to do nothing because we cannot find suitable proxies for student "ability," parental "involvement," and so on. Almost certainly controlling for the poverty rate gets us closer to the ceteris paribus effects of spending than if we leave the poverty rate out of the analysis.

In some applications of regression analysis, we are interested simply in predicting the outcome, y, given a set of explanatory variables, $(x_1, ..., x_k)$. In such cases, it makes little sense to think in terms of "bias" in estimated coefficients due to omitted variables. Instead, we should focus on obtaining a model that predicts as well as possible, and make sure we do not include as regressors variables that cannot be observed at the time of prediction. For example, an admissions officer for a college or university might be interested in predicting success in college, as measured by grade point average, in terms of variables that can be measured at application time. Those variables would include high school performance (maybe just grade point average, but perhaps performance in specific kinds of courses), standardized test scores, participation in various activities (such as debate or math club), and even family background variables. We would not include a variable measuring college class attendance because we do not observe attendance in college at application time. Nor would we wring our hands about potential "biases" caused by omitting an attendance variable: we have no interest in, say, measuring the effect of high school GPA holding attendance in college fixed. Likewise, we would not worry about biases in coefficients because we cannot observe factors such as motivation. Naturally, for predictive purposes it would probably help substantially if we had a measure of motivation, but in its absence we fit the best model we can with observed explanatory variables.

9.3 Models with Random Slopes

In our treatment of regression so far, we have assumed that the slope coefficients are the same across individuals in the population, or that, if the slopes differ, they differ by measurable characteristics, in which case we are led to regression models containing interaction terms. For example, as we saw in Section 7.4, we can allow the return to education to differ by men and women by interacting education with a gender dummy in a log wage equation.

Here we are interested in a related but different question: What if the partial effect of a variable depends on unobserved factors that vary by population unit? If we have only one explanatory variable, x, we can write a general model (for a random draw, i, from the population, for emphasis) as

$$y_i = a_i + b_i x_i, \qquad [9.17]$$

where a_i is the intercept for unit i and b_i is the slope. In the simple regression model from Chapter 2 we assumed $b_i = \beta$ and labeled a_i as the error, u_i. The model in (9.17) is sometimes called a **random coefficient model** or **random slope model** because the unobserved slope coefficient, b_i, is viewed as a random draw from the population along with the observed data, (x_i, y_i), and the unobserved intercept, a_i. As an example, if $y_i = \log(wage_i)$ and $x_i = educ_i$, then (9.17) allows the return to education, b_i, to vary by person. If, say, b_i contains unmeasured ability (just as a_i would), the partial effect of another year of schooling can depend on ability.

With a random sample of size n, we (implicitly) draw n values of b_i along with n values of a_i (and the observed data on x and y). Naturally, we cannot estimate a slope—or, for that matter, an intercept—for each i. But we can hope to estimate the average slope (and average intercept), where the average is across the population. Therefore, define $\alpha = \mathrm{E}(a_i)$ and $\beta = \mathrm{E}(b_i)$. Then β is the average of the partial effect of x on y, and so we call β the **average partial effect (APE)**, or the **average marginal effect (AME)**. In the context of a log wage equation, β is the average return to a year of schooling in the population.

If we write $a_i = \alpha + c_i$ and $b_i = \beta + d_i$, then d_i is the individual-specific deviation from the APE. By construction, $\mathrm{E}(c_i) = 0$ and $\mathrm{E}(d_i) = 0$. Substituting into (9.17) gives

$$y_i = \alpha + \beta x_i + c_i + d_i x_i \equiv \alpha + \beta x_i + u_i, \qquad [9.18]$$

where $u_i = c_i + d_i x_i$. (To make the notation easier to follow, we now use α, the mean value of a_i, as the intercept, and β, the mean of b_i, as the slope.) In other words, we can write the random coefficient as a constant coefficient model but where the error term contains an interaction between an unobservable, d_i, and the observed explanatory variable, x_i.

When would a simple regression of y_i on x_i provide an unbiased estimate of β (and α)? We can apply the result for unbiasedness from Chapter 2. If $\mathrm{E}(u_i|x_i) = 0$, then OLS is generally unbiased. When $u_i = c_i + d_i x_i$, sufficient is $\mathrm{E}(c_i|x_i) = \mathrm{E}(c_i) = 0$ and $\mathrm{E}(d_i|x_i) = \mathrm{E}(d_i) = 0$. We can write these in terms of the unit-specific intercept and slope as

$$\mathrm{E}(a_i|x_i) = \mathrm{E}(a_i) \quad \text{and} \quad \mathrm{E}(b_i|x_i) = \mathrm{E}(b_i); \qquad [9.19]$$

that is, a_i and b_i are both mean independent of x_i. This is a useful finding: if we allow for unit-specific slopes, OLS consistently estimates the population average of those slopes when they are mean independent of the explanatory variable. (See Problem 6 for a weaker set of conditions that imply consistency of OLS.)

The error term in (9.18) almost certainly contains heteroskedasticity. In fact, if $\mathrm{Var}(c_i|x_i) = \sigma_c^2$, $\mathrm{Var}(d_i|x_i) = \sigma_d^2$, and $\mathrm{Cov}(c_i, d_i|x_i) = 0$, then

$$\mathrm{Var}(u_i|x_i) = \sigma_c^2 + \sigma_d^2 x_i^2, \qquad [9.20]$$

and so there must be heteroskedasticity in u_i unless $\sigma_d^2 = 0$, which means $b_i = \beta$ for all i. We know how to account for heteroskedasticity of this kind. We can use OLS and compute heteroskedasticity-robust standard errors and test statistics, or we can estimate the variance function in (9.20) and apply weighted least squares. Of course the latter strategy imposes homoskedasticity on the random intercept and slope, and so we would want to make a WLS analysis fully robust to violations of (9.20).

Because of equation (9.20), some authors like to view heteroskedasticity in regression models generally as arising from random slope coefficients. But we should remember that the form of (9.20) is special, and it does not allow for heteroskedasticity in a_i or b_i.

We cannot convincingly distinguish between a random slope model, where the intercept and slope are independent of x_i, and a constant slope model with heteroskedasticity in a_i.

The treatment for multiple regression is similar. Generally, write

$$y_i = a_i + b_{i1}x_{i1} + b_{i2}x_{i2} \dots + b_{ik}x_{ik}. \quad [9.21]$$

Then, by writing $a_i = \alpha + c_i$ and $b_{ij} = \beta_j + d_{ij}$, we have

$$y_i = \alpha + \beta_1 x_{i1} + \dots + \beta_k x_{ik} + u_i, \quad [9.22]$$

where $u_i = c_i + d_{i1}x_{i1} + \dots + d_{ik}x_{ik}$. If we maintain the mean independence assumptions $E(a_i|\mathbf{x}_i) = E(a_i)$ and $E(b_{ij}|\mathbf{x}_i) = E(b_{ij}), j = 1, \dots, k$, then $E(y_i|\mathbf{x}_i) = \alpha + \beta_1 x_{i1} + \dots + \beta_k x_{ik}$, and so OLS using a random sample produces unbiases estimators of α and the β_j. As in the simple regression case, $\text{Var}(u_i|\mathbf{x}_i)$ is almost certainly heteroskedastic.

We can allow the b_{ij} to depend on observable explanatory variables as well as unobservables. For example, suppose with $k = 2$ the effect of x_{i2} depends on x_{i1}, and we write $b_{i2} = \beta_2 + \delta_1(x_{i1} - \mu_1) + d_{i2}$, where $\mu_1 = E(x_{i1})$. If we assume $E(d_{i2}|\mathbf{x}_i) = 0$ (and similarly for c_i and d_{i1}), then $E(y_i|x_{i1}, x_{i2}) = \alpha + \beta_1 x_{i1} + \beta_2 x_{i2} + \delta_1(x_{i1} - \mu_1)x_{i2}$, which means we have an interaction between x_{i1} and x_{i2}. Because we have subtracted the mean μ_1 from x_{i1}, β_2 is the average partial effect of x_{i2}.

The bottom line of this section is that allowing for random slopes is fairly straightforward if the slopes are independent, or at least mean independent, of the explanatory variables. In addition, we can easily model the slopes as functions of the exogenous variables, which leads to models with squares and interactions. Of course, in Chapter 6 we discussed how such models can be useful without ever introducing the notion of a random slope. The random slopes specification provides a separate justification for such models. Estimation becomes considerably more difficult if the random intercept as well as some slopes are correlated with some of the regressors. We cover the problem of endogenous explanatory variables in Chapter 15.

9.4 Properties of OLS under Measurement Error

Sometimes, in economic applications, we cannot collect data on the variable that truly affects economic behavior. A good example is the marginal income tax rate facing a family that is trying to choose how much to contribute to charity in a given year. The marginal rate may be hard to obtain or summarize as a single number for all income levels. Instead, we might compute the average tax rate based on total income and tax payments.

When we use an imprecise measure of an economic variable in a regression model, then our model contains measurement error. In this section, we derive the consequences of measurement error for ordinary least squares estimation. OLS will be consistent under certain assumptions, but there are others under which it is inconsistent. In some of these cases, we can derive the size of the asymptotic bias.

As we will see, the measurement error problem has a similar statistical structure to the omitted variable–proxy variable problem discussed in the previous section, but they are conceptually different. In the proxy variable case, we are looking for a variable that is somehow associated with the unobserved variable. In the measurement error case, the variable that we do not observe has a well-defined, quantitative meaning (such as a marginal tax rate or annual income), but our recorded measures of it may contain error. For example, reported annual income is a measure of actual annual income, whereas IQ score is a proxy for ability.

Another important difference between the proxy variable and measurement error problems is that, in the latter case, often the mismeasured independent variable is the one of primary interest. In the proxy variable case, the partial effect of the omitted variable is rarely of central interest: we are usually concerned with the effects of the other independent variables.

Before we consider details, we should remember that measurement error is an issue only when the variables for which the econometrician can collect data differ from the variables that influence decisions by individuals, families, firms, and so on.

Measurement Error in the Dependent Variable

We begin with the case where only the dependent variable is measured with error. Let y^* denote the variable (in the population, as always) that we would like to explain. For example, y^* could be annual family savings. The regression model has the usual form

$$y^* = \beta_0 + \beta_1 x_1 + \ldots + \beta_k x_k + u, \quad [9.23]$$

and we assume it satisfies the Gauss-Markov assumptions. We let y represent the observable measure of y^*. In the savings case, y is reported annual savings. Unfortunately, families are not perfect in their reporting of annual family savings; it is easy to leave out categories or to overestimate the amount contributed to a fund. Generally, we can expect y and y^* to differ, at least for some subset of families in the population.

The **measurement error** (in the population) is defined as the difference between the observed value and the actual value:

$$e_0 = y - y^*. \quad [9.24]$$

For a random draw i from the population, we can write $e_{i0} = y_i - y_i^*$, but the important thing is how the measurement error in the population is related to other factors. To obtain an estimable model, we write $y^* = y - e_0$, plug this into equation (9.23), and rearrange:

$$y = \beta_0 + \beta_1 x_1 + \ldots + \beta_k x_k + u + e_0. \quad [9.25]$$

The error term in equation (9.25) is $u + e_0$. Because $y, x_1, x_2, \ldots, x_k$ are observed, we can estimate this model by OLS. In effect, we just ignore the fact that y is an imperfect measure of y^* and proceed as usual.

When does OLS with y in place of y^* produce consistent estimators of the β_j? Since the original model (9.23) satisfies the Gauss-Markov assumptions, u has zero mean and is uncorrelated with each x_j. It is only natural to assume that the measurement error has zero mean; if it does not, then we simply get a biased estimator of the intercept, β_0, which is rarely a cause for concern. Of much more importance is our assumption about the relationship between the measurement error, e_0, and the explanatory variables, x_j. The usual assumption is that the measurement error in y is statistically independent of each explanatory variable. If this is true, then the OLS estimators from (9.25) are unbiased and consistent. Further, the usual OLS inference procedures (t, F, and LM statistics) are valid.

If e_0 and u are uncorrelated, as is usually assumed, then $\text{Var}(u + e_0) = \sigma_u^2 + \sigma_0^2 > \sigma_u^2$. This means that measurement error in the dependent variable results in a larger error variance than when no error occurs; this, of course, results in larger variances of the OLS estimators. This is to be expected, and there is nothing we can do about it (except collect better data). The bottom line is that, if the measurement error is uncorrelated with the independent variables, then OLS estimation has good properties.

EXAMPLE 9.5 SAVINGS FUNCTION WITH MEASUREMENT ERROR

Consider a savings function

$$sav^* = \beta_0 + \beta_1 inc + \beta_2 size + \beta_3 educ + \beta_4 age + u,$$

but where actual savings (sav^*) may deviate from reported savings (sav). The question is whether the size of the measurement error in *sav* is systematically related to the other variables. It might be reasonable to assume that the measurement error is not correlated with *inc*, *size*, *educ*, and *age*. On the other hand, we might think that families with higher incomes, or more education, report their savings more accurately. We can never know whether the measurement error is correlated with *inc* or *educ*, unless we can collect data on sav^*; then, the measurement error can be computed for each observation as $e_{i0} = sav_i - sav_i^*$.

When the dependent variable is in logarithmic form, so that $\log(y^*)$ is the dependent variable, it is natural for the measurement error equation to be of the form

$$\log(y) = \log(y^*) + e_0. \quad [9.26]$$

This follows from a **multiplicative measurement error** for y: $y = y^* a_0$, where $a_0 > 0$ and $e_0 = \log(a_0)$.

EXAMPLE 9.6 MEASUREMENT ERROR IN SCRAP RATES

In Section 7.6, we discussed an example where we wanted to determine whether job training grants reduce the scrap rate in manufacturing firms. We certainly might think the scrap rate reported by firms is measured with error. (In fact, most firms in the sample do not even report a scrap rate.) In a simple regression framework, this is captured by

$$\log(scrap^*) = \beta_0 + \beta_1 grant + u,$$

where $scrap^*$ is the true scrap rate and *grant* is the dummy variable indicating whether a firm received a grant. The measurement error equation is

$$\log(scrap) = \log(scrap^*) + e_0.$$

Is the measurement error, e_0, independent of whether the firm receives a grant? A cynical person might think that a firm receiving a grant is more likely to underreport its scrap rate in order to make the grant look effective. If this happens, then, in the estimable equation,

$$\log(scrap) = \beta_0 + \beta_1 grant + u + e_0,$$

the error $u + e_0$ is negatively correlated with *grant*. This would produce a downward bias in β_1, which would tend to make the training program look more effective than it actually was. (Remember, a more negative β_1 means the program was more effective, since increased worker productivity is associated with a lower scrap rate.)

The bottom line of this subsection is that measurement error in the dependent variable *can* cause biases in OLS if it is systematically related to one or more of the explanatory variables. If the measurement error is just a random reporting error that is independent of the explanatory variables, as is often assumed, then OLS is perfectly appropriate.

Measurement Error in an Explanatory Variable

Traditionally, measurement error in an explanatory variable has been considered a much more important problem than measurement error in the dependent variable. In this subsection, we will see why this is the case.

We begin with the simple regression model

$$y = \beta_0 + \beta_1 x_1^* + u, \quad [9.27]$$

and we assume that this satisfies at least the first four Gauss-Markov assumptions. This means that estimation of (9.27) by OLS would produce unbiased and consistent estimators of β_0 and β_1. The problem is that x_1^* is not observed. Instead, we have a measure of x_1^*; call it x_1. For example, x_1^* could be actual income, and x_1 could be reported income.

The measurement error in the population is simply

$$e_1 = x_1 - x_1^*, \quad [9.28]$$

and this can be positive, negative, or zero. We assume that the *average* measurement error in the population is zero: $\mathrm{E}(e_1) = 0$. This is natural, and, in any case, it does not affect the important conclusions that follow. A maintained assumption in what follows is that u is uncorrelated with x_1^* *and* x_1. In conditional expectation terms, we can write this as $\mathrm{E}(y|x_1^*, x_1) = \mathrm{E}(y|x_1^*)$, which just says that x_1 does not affect y after x_1^* has been controlled for. We used the same assumption in the proxy variable case, and it is not controversial; it holds almost by definition.

We want to know the properties of OLS if we simply replace x_1^* with x_1 and run the regression of y on x_1. They depend crucially on the assumptions we make about the measurement error. Two assumptions have been the focus in econometrics literature, and they both represent polar extremes. The first assumption is that e_1 is uncorrelated with the *observed* measure, x_1:

$$\mathrm{Cov}(x_1, e_1) = 0. \quad [9.29]$$

From the relationship in (9.28), if assumption (9.29) is true, then e_1 must be correlated with the unobserved variable x_1^*. To determine the properties of OLS in this case, we write $x_1^* = x_1 - e_1$ and plug this into equation (9.27):

$$y = \beta_0 + \beta_1 x_1 + (u - \beta_1 e_1). \quad [9.30]$$

Because we have assumed that u and e_1 both have zero mean and are uncorrelated with x_1, $u - \beta_1 e_1$ has zero mean and is uncorrelated with x_1. It follows that OLS estimation with x_1 in place of x_1^* produces a consistent estimator of β_1 (and also β_0). Since u is uncorrelated with e_1, the variance of the error in (9.30) is $\mathrm{Var}(u - \beta_1 e_1) = \sigma_u^2 + \beta_1^2 \sigma_{e_1}^2$. Thus, except when $\beta_1 = 0$, measurement error increases the error variance. But this does not affect any of the OLS properties (except that the variances of the $\hat{\beta}_j$ will be larger than if we observe x_1^* directly).

The assumption that e_1 is uncorrelated with x_1 is analogous to the proxy variable assumption we made in Section 9.2. Since this assumption implies that OLS has all of its nice properties, this is not usually what econometricians have in mind when they refer to measurement error in an explanatory variable. The **classical errors-in-variables (CEV)** assumption is that the measurement error is uncorrelated with the *unobserved* explanatory variable:

$$\mathrm{Cov}(x_1^*, e_1) = 0. \qquad [9.31]$$

This assumption comes from writing the observed measure as the sum of the true explanatory variable and the measurement error,

$$x_1 = x_1^* + e_1,$$

and then assuming the two components of x_1 are uncorrelated. (This has nothing to do with assumptions about u; we always maintain that u is uncorrelated with x_1^* and x_1, and therefore with e_1.)

If assumption (9.31) holds, then x_1 and e_1 *must* be correlated:

$$\mathrm{Cov}(x_1, e_1) = \mathrm{E}(x_1 e_1) = \mathrm{E}(x_1^* e_1) + \mathrm{E}(e_1^2) = 0 + \sigma_{e_1}^2 = \sigma_{e_1}^2. \qquad [9.32]$$

Thus, the covariance between x_1 and e_1 is equal to the variance of the measurement error under the CEV assumption.

Referring to equation (9.30), we can see that correlation between x_1 and e_1 is going to cause problems. Because u and x_1 are uncorrelated, the covariance between x_1 and the composite error $u - \beta_1 e_1$ is

$$\mathrm{Cov}(x_1, u - \beta_1 e_1) = -\beta_1 \mathrm{Cov}(x_1, e_1) = -\beta_1 \sigma_{e_1}^2.$$

Thus, in the CEV case, the OLS regression of y on x_1 gives a biased and inconsistent estimator.

Using the asymptotic results in Chapter 5, we can determine the amount of inconsistency in OLS. The probability limit of $\hat{\beta}_1$ is β_1 plus the ratio of the covariance between x_1 and $u - \beta_1 e_1$ and the variance of x_1:

$$\begin{aligned} \mathrm{plim}(\hat{\beta}_1) &= \beta_1 + \frac{\mathrm{Cov}(x_1, u - \beta_1 e_1)}{\mathrm{Var}(x_1)} \\ &= \beta_1 - \frac{\beta_1 \sigma_{e_1}^2}{\sigma_{x_1^*}^2 + \sigma_{e_1}^2} \\ &= \beta_1 \left(1 - \frac{\sigma_{e_1}^2}{\sigma_{x_1^*}^2 + \sigma_{e_1}^2}\right) \\ &= \beta_1 \left(\frac{\sigma_{x_1^*}^2}{\sigma_{x_1^*}^2 + \sigma_{e_1}^2}\right), \end{aligned} \qquad [9.33]$$

where we have used the fact that $\mathrm{Var}(x_1) = \mathrm{Var}(x_1^*) + \mathrm{Var}(e_1)$.

Equation (9.33) is very interesting. The term multiplying β_1, which is the ratio $\mathrm{Var}(x_1^*)/\mathrm{Var}(x_1)$, is always less than one [an implication of the CEV assumption (9.31)]. Thus,

$\text{plim}(\hat{\beta}_1)$ is always closer to zero than is β_1. This is called the **attenuation bias** in OLS due to classical errors-in-variables: on average (or in large samples), the estimated OLS effect will be *attenuated*. In particular, if β_1 is positive, $\hat{\beta}_1$ will tend to underestimate β_1. This is an important conclusion, but it relies on the CEV setup.

If the variance of x_1^* is large relative to the variance in the measurement error, then the inconsistency in OLS will be small. This is because $\text{Var}(x_1^*)/\text{Var}(x_1)$ will be close to unity when $\sigma_{x_1^*}^2/\sigma_{e_1}^2$ is large. Therefore, depending on how much variation there is in x_1^* relative to e_1, measurement error need not cause large biases.

Things are more complicated when we add more explanatory variables. For illustration, consider the model

$$y = \beta_0 + \beta_1 x_1^* + \beta_2 x_2 + \beta_3 x_3 + u, \quad [9.34]$$

where the first of the three explanatory variables is measured with error. We make the natural assumption that u is uncorrelated with x_1^*, x_2, x_3, and x_1. Again, the crucial assumption concerns the measurement error e_1. In almost all cases, e_1 is assumed to be uncorrelated with x_2 and x_3—the explanatory variables not measured with error. The key issue is whether e_1 is uncorrelated with x_1. If it is, then the OLS regression of y on x_1, x_2, and x_3 produces consistent estimators. This is easily seen by writing

$$y = \beta_0 + \beta_1 x_1 + \beta_2 x_2 + \beta_3 x_3 + u - \beta_1 e_1, \quad [9.35]$$

where u and e_1 are both uncorrelated with all the explanatory variables.

Under the CEV assumption in (9.31), OLS will be biased and inconsistent, because e_1 is correlated with x_1 in equation (9.35). Remember, this means that, in general, *all* OLS estimators will be biased, not just $\hat{\beta}_1$. What about the attenuation bias derived in equation (9.33)? It turns out that there is still an attenuation bias for estimating β_1: it can be shown that

$$\text{plim}(\hat{\beta}_1) = \beta_1 \left(\frac{\sigma_{r_1^*}^2}{\sigma_{r_1^*}^2 + \sigma_{e_1}^2} \right), \quad [9.36]$$

where r_1^* is the population error in the equation $x_1^* = \alpha_0 + \alpha_1 x_2 + \alpha_2 x_3 + r_1^*$. Formula (9.36) also works in the general k variable case when x_1 is the only mismeasured variable.

Things are less clear-cut for estimating the β_j on the variables not measured with error. In the special case that x_1^* is uncorrelated with x_2 and x_3, $\hat{\beta}_2$ and $\hat{\beta}_3$ are consistent. But this is rare in practice. Generally, measurement error in a single variable causes inconsistency in all estimators. Unfortunately, the sizes, and even the directions of the biases, are not easily derived.

EXAMPLE 9.7 GPA EQUATION WITH MEASUREMENT ERROR

Consider the problem of estimating the effect of family income on college grade point average, after controlling for *hsGPA* (high school grade point average) and *SAT* (scholastic aptitude test). It could be that, though family income is important for performance before college, it has no direct effect on college performance. To test this, we might postulate the model

$$colGPA = \beta_0 + \beta_1 faminc^* + \beta_2 hsGPA + \beta_3 SAT + u,$$

where *faminc** is actual annual family income. (This might appear in logarithmic form, but for the sake of illustration we leave it in level form.) Precise data on *colGPA*, *hsGPA*, and *SAT* are relatively easy to obtain. But family income, especially as reported by students, could be easily mismeasured. If $faminc = faminc^* + e_1$ and the CEV assumptions hold, then using reported family income in place of actual family income will bias the OLS estimator of β_1 toward zero. One consequence of the downward bias is that a test of $H_0: \beta_1 = 0$ will have less chance of detecting $\beta_1 > 0$.

Of course, measurement error can be present in more than one explanatory variable, or in some explanatory variables and the dependent variable. As we discussed earlier, any measurement error in the dependent variable is usually assumed to be uncorrelated with all the explanatory variables, whether it is observed or not. Deriving the bias in the OLS estimators under extensions of the CEV assumptions is complicated and does not lead to clear results.

In some cases, it is clear that the CEV assumption in (9.31) cannot be true. Consider a variant on Example 9.7:

$$colGPA = \beta_0 + \beta_1 smoked^* + \beta_2 hsGPA + \beta_3 SAT + u,$$

where *smoked** is the actual number of times a student smoked marijuana in the last 30 days. The variable *smoked* is the answer to this question: On how many separate occasions did you smoke marijuana in the last 30 days? Suppose we postulate the standard measurement error model

$$smoked = smoked^* + e_1.$$

Even if we assume that students try to report the truth, the CEV assumption is unlikely to hold. People who do not smoke marijuana at all—so that $smoked^* = 0$—are likely to report $smoked = 0$, so the measurement error is probably zero for students who never smoke marijuana. When $smoked^* > 0$, it is much more likely that the student miscounts how many times he or she smoked marijuana in the last 30 days. This means that the measurement error e_1 and the *actual* number of times smoked, *smoked**, are correlated, which violates the CEV assumption in (9.31). Unfortunately, deriving the implications of measurement error that do not satisfy (9.29) or (9.31) is difficult and beyond the scope of this text.

Before leaving this section, we emphasize that the CEV assumption (9.31), while more believable than assumption (9.29), is still a strong assumption. The truth is probably somewhere in between, and if e_1 is correlated with both x_1^* and x_1, OLS is inconsistent. This raises an important question: Must we live with inconsistent estimators under classical errors-in-variables, or other kinds of measurement error that are correlated with x_1? Fortunately, the answer is no. Chapter 15 shows how, under certain assumptions, the parameters can be consistently estimated in the presence of general measurement error. We postpone this discussion until later because it requires us to leave the realm of OLS estimation. (See Problem 7 for how multiple measures can be used to reduce the attenuation bias.)

EXPLORING FURTHER 9.3

Let *educ** be actual amount of schooling, measured in years (which can be a noninteger), and let *educ* be reported highest grade completed. Do you think *educ* and *educ** are related by the classical errors-in-variables model?

9.5 Missing Data, Nonrandom Samples, and Outlying Observations

The measurement error problem discussed in the previous section can be viewed as a data problem: we cannot obtain data on the variables of interest. Further, under the classical errors-in-variables model, the composite error term is correlated with the mismeasured independent variable, violating the Gauss-Markov assumptions.

Another data problem we discussed frequently in earlier chapters is multicollinearity among the explanatory variables. Remember that correlation among the explanatory variables does not violate any assumptions. When two independent variables are highly correlated, it can be difficult to estimate the partial effect of each. But this is properly reflected in the usual OLS statistics.

In this section, we provide an introduction to data problems that can violate the random sampling assumption, MLR.2. We can isolate cases in which nonrandom sampling has no practical effect on OLS. In other cases, nonrandom sampling causes the OLS estimators to be biased and inconsistent. A more complete treatment that establishes several of the claims made here is given in Chapter 17.

Missing Data

The **missing data** problem can arise in a variety of forms. Often, we collect a random sample of people, schools, cities, and so on, and then discover later that information is missing on some key variables for several units in the sample. For example, in the data set BWGHT.RAW, 197 of the 1,388 observations have no information on either mother's education, father's education, or both. In the data set on median starting law school salaries, LAWSCH85.RAW, six of the 156 schools have no reported information on median LSAT scores for the entering class; other variables are also missing for some of the law schools.

If data are missing for an observation on either the dependent variable or one of the independent variables, then the observation cannot be used in a standard multiple regression analysis. In fact, provided missing data have been properly indicated, all modern regression packages keep track of missing data and simply ignore observations when computing a regression. We saw this explicitly in the birth weight scenario in Example 4.9, when 197 observations were dropped due to missing information on parents' education.

Other than reducing the sample size available for a regression, are there any *statistical* consequences of missing data? It depends on why the data are missing. If the data are missing at random, then the size of the random sample available from the population is simply reduced. Although this makes the estimators less precise, it does not introduce any bias: the random sampling assumption, MLR.2, still holds. There are ways to use the information on observations where only some variables are missing, but this is not often done in practice. The improvement in the estimators is usually slight, while the methods are somewhat complicated. In most cases, we just ignore the observations that have missing information.

Nonrandom Samples

Missing data are more problematic when it results in a **nonrandom sample** from the population. For example, in the birth weight data set, what if the probability that education is missing is higher for those people with lower than average levels of education? Or, in

Section 9.2, we used a wage data set that included IQ scores. This data set was constructed by omitting several people from the sample for whom IQ scores were not available. If obtaining an IQ score is easier for those with higher IQs, the sample is not representative of the population. The random sampling assumption MLR.2 is violated, and we must worry about these consequences for OLS estimation.

Fortunately, certain types of nonrandom sampling do *not* cause bias or inconsistency in OLS. Under the Gauss-Markov assumptions (but without MLR.2), it turns out that the sample can be chosen on the basis of the *independent* variables without causing any statistical problems. This is called *sample selection based on the independent variables*, and it is an example of **exogenous sample selection**. To illustrate, suppose that we are estimating a saving function, where annual saving depends on income, age, family size, and perhaps some other factors. A simple model is

$$saving = \beta_0 + \beta_1 income + \beta_2 age + \beta_3 size + u. \qquad [9.37]$$

Suppose that our data set was based on a survey of people over 35 years of age, thereby leaving us with a nonrandom sample of all adults. While this is not ideal, we can still get unbiased and consistent estimators of the parameters in the population model (9.37), using the nonrandom sample. We will not show this formally here, but the reason OLS on the nonrandom sample is unbiased is that the regression function $E(saving|income,age,size)$ is the same for any subset of the population described by *income*, *age*, or *size*. Provided there is enough variation in the independent variables in the subpopulation, selection on the basis of the independent variables is not a serious problem, other than that it results in smaller sample sizes.

In the IQ example just mentioned, things are not so clear-cut, because no fixed rule based on IQ is used to include someone in the sample. Rather, the *probability* of being in the sample increases with IQ. If the other factors determining selection into the sample are independent of the error term in the wage equation, then we have another case of exogenous sample selection, and OLS using the selected sample will have all of its desirable properties under the other Gauss-Markov assumptions.

The situation is much different when selection is based on the dependent variable, y, which is called *sample selection based on the dependent variable* and is an example of **endogenous sample selection**. If the sample is based on whether the dependent variable is above or below a given value, bias always occurs in OLS in estimating the population model. For example, suppose we wish to estimate the relationship between individual wealth and several other factors in the population of all adults:

$$wealth = \beta_0 + \beta_1 educ + \beta_2 exper + \beta_3 age + u. \qquad [9.38]$$

Suppose that only people with wealth below $250,000 are included in the sample. This is a nonrandom sample from the population of interest, and it is based on the value of the dependent variable. Using a sample on people with wealth below $250,000 will result in biased and inconsistent estimators of the parameters in (9.32). Briefly, this occurs because the population regression $E(wealth|educ,exper,age)$ is not the same as the expected value conditional on *wealth* being less than $250,000.

Other sampling schemes lead to nonrandom samples from the population, usually intentionally. A common method of data collection is **stratified sampling**, in which the population is divided into nonoverlapping, exhaustive groups, or strata. Then, some groups are sampled more frequently than is dictated by their population representation, and some groups are sampled less frequently. For example, some surveys purposely oversample minority groups or low-income groups. Whether special methods are needed again hinges on whether the stratification is exogenous (based on exogenous explanatory variables) or endogenous (based on the dependent variable). Suppose that a survey of military personnel oversampled women because the initial interest was in studying the factors that determine pay for women in the military. (Oversampling a group that is relatively small in the population is common in collecting stratified samples.) Provided men were sampled as well, we can use OLS on the stratified sample to estimate any gender differential, along with the returns to education and experience for all military personnel. (We might be willing to assume that the returns to education and experience are not gender specific.) OLS is unbiased and consistent because the stratification is with respect to an explanatory variable, namely, gender.

If, instead, the survey oversampled lower-paid military personnel, then OLS using the stratified sample does not consistently estimate the parameters of the military wage equation because the stratification is endogenous. In such cases, special econometric methods are needed [see Wooldridge (2010, Chapter 19)].

Stratified sampling is a fairly obvious form of nonrandom sampling. Other sample selection issues are more subtle. For instance, in several previous examples, we have estimated the effects of various variables, particularly education and experience, on hourly wage. The data set WAGE1.RAW that we have used throughout is essentially a random sample of *working* individuals. Labor economists are often interested in estimating the effect of, say, education on the wage *offer*. The idea is this: every person of working age faces an hourly wage offer, and he or she can either work at that wage or not work. For someone who does work, the wage offer is just the wage earned. For people who do not work, we usually cannot observe the wage offer. Now, since the wage offer equation

$$\log(wage^{o}) = \beta_0 + \beta_1 educ + \beta_2 exper + u \qquad [9.39]$$

represents the population of all working-age people, we cannot estimate it using a random sample from this population; instead, we have data on the wage offer only for working people (although we can get data on *educ* and *exper* for nonworking people). If we use a random sample on working people to estimate (9.39), will we get unbiased estimators? This case is not clear-cut. Since the sample is selected based on someone's decision to work (as opposed to the size of the wage offer), this is not like the previous case. However, since the decision to work might be related to unobserved factors that affect the wage offer, selection might be endogenous, and this can result in a sample selection bias in the OLS estimators. We will cover methods that can be used to test and correct for sample selection bias in Chapter 17.

EXPLORING FURTHER 9.4

Suppose we are interested in the effects of campaign expenditures by incumbents on voter support. Some incumbents choose not to run for reelection. If we can only collect voting and spending outcomes on incumbents that actually do run, is there likely to be endogenous sample selection?

Outliers and Influential Observations

In some applications, especially, but not only, with small data sets, the OLS estimates are sensitive to the inclusion of one or several observations. A complete treatment of **outliers** and **influential observations** is beyond the scope of this book, because a formal development requires matrix algebra. Loosely speaking, an observation is an influential observation if dropping it from the analysis changes the key OLS estimates by a practically "large" amount. The notion of an outlier is also a bit vague, because it requires comparing values of the variables for one observation with those for the remaining sample. Nevertheless, one wants to be on the lookout for "unusual" observations because they can greatly affect the OLS estimates.

OLS is susceptible to outlying observations because it minimizes the sum of squared residuals: large residuals (positive or negative) receive a lot of weight in the least squares minimization problem. If the estimates change by a practically large amount when we slightly modify our sample, we should be concerned.

When statisticians and econometricians study the problem of outliers theoretically, sometimes the data are viewed as being from a random sample from a given population—albeit with an unusual distribution that can result in extreme values—and sometimes the outliers are assumed to come from a different population. From a practical perspective, outlying observations can occur for two reasons. The easiest case to deal with is when a mistake has been made in entering the data. Adding extra zeros to a number or misplacing a decimal point can throw off the OLS estimates, especially in small sample sizes. It is always a good idea to compute summary statistics, especially minimums and maximums, in order to catch mistakes in data entry. Unfortunately, incorrect entries are not always obvious.

Outliers can also arise when sampling from a small population if one or several members of the population are very different in some relevant aspect from the rest of the population. The decision to keep or drop such observations in a regression analysis can be a difficult one, and the statistical properties of the resulting estimators are complicated. Outlying observations can provide important information by increasing the variation in the explanatory variables (which reduces standard errors). But OLS results should probably be reported with and without outlying observations in cases where one or several data points substantially change the results.

EXAMPLE 9.8 R&D INTENSITY AND FIRM SIZE

Suppose that R&D expenditures as a percentage of sales (*rdintens*) are related to *sales* (in millions) and profits as a percentage of sales (*profmarg*):

$$rdintens = \beta_0 + \beta_1 sales + \beta_2 profmarg + u. \qquad [9.40]$$

The OLS equation using data on 32 chemical companies in RDCHEM.RAW is

$$\begin{aligned}\widehat{rdintens} &= \underset{(0.586)}{2.625} + \underset{(.000044)}{.000053}\, sales + \underset{(.0462)}{.0446}\, profmarg \\ n &= 32,\ R^2 = .0761,\ \bar{R}^2 = .0124.\end{aligned}$$

Neither *sales* nor *profmarg* is statistically significant at even the 10% level in this regression.

Of the 32 firms, 31 have annual sales less than \$20 billion. One firm has annual sales of almost \$40 billion. Figure 9.1 shows how far this firm is from the rest of the sample. In terms of sales, this firm is over twice as large as every other firm, so it might be a good idea to estimate the model without it. When we do this, we obtain

$$\begin{aligned}\widehat{rdintens} &= \underset{(0.592)}{2.297} + \underset{(.000084)}{.000186}\, sales + \underset{(.0445)}{.0478}\, profmarg \\ n &= 31,\ R^2 = .1728,\ \bar{R}^2 = .1137.\end{aligned}$$

FIGURE 9.1 Scatterplot of R&D intensity against firm sales.

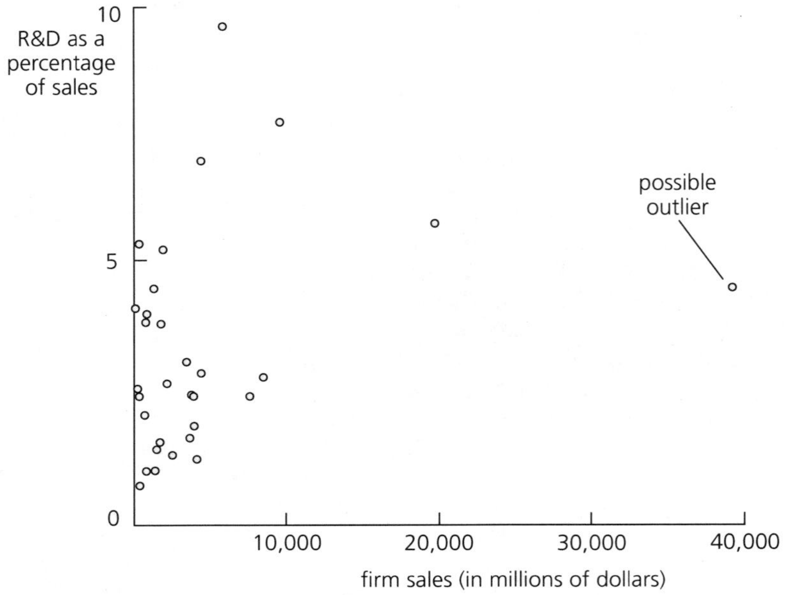

When the largest firm is dropped from the regression, the coefficient on *sales* more than triples, and it now has a *t* statistic over two. Using the sample of smaller firms, we would conclude that there is a statistically significant positive effect between R&D intensity and firm size. The profit margin is still not significant, and its coefficient has not changed by much.

Sometimes, outliers are defined by the size of the residual in an OLS regression, where all of the observations are used. Generally, this is *not* a good idea because the OLS estimates adjust to make the sum of squared residuals as small as possible. In the previous example, including the largest firm flattened the OLS regression line considerably, which made the residual for that estimation not especially large. In fact, the residual for the largest firm is -1.62 when all 32 observations are used. This value of the residual is not even one estimated standard deviation, $\hat{\sigma} = 1.82$, from the mean of the residuals, which is zero by construction.

Studentized residuals are obtained from the original OLS residuals by dividing them by an estimate of their standard deviation (conditional on the explanatory variables in the sample). The formula for the studentized residuals relies on matrix algebra, but it turns out there is a simple trick to compute a studentized residual for any observation. Namely, define a dummy variable equal to one for that observation—say, observation *h*—and then include the dummy variable in the regression (using all observations) along with the other explanatory variables. The coefficient on the dummy variable has a useful interpretation: it is the residual for observation *h* computed from the regression line using only the *other* observations.

Therefore, the dummy's coefficient can be used to see how far off the observation is from the regression line obtained without using that observation. Even better, the t statistic on the dummy variable is equal to the studentized residual for observation h. Under the classical linear model assumptions, this t statistic has a t_{n-k-2} distribution. Therefore, a large value of the t statistic (in absolute value) implies a large residual relative to its estimated standard deviation.

For Example 9.8, if we define a dummy variable for the largest firm (observation 10 in the data file), and include it as an additional regressor, its coefficient is -6.57, verifying that the observation for the largest firm is very far from the regression line obtained using the other observations. However, when studentized, the residual is only -1.82. While this is a marginally significant t statistic (two-sided p-value $= .08$), it is not close to being the largest studentized residual in the sample. If we use the same method for the observation with the highest value of *rdintens*—the first observation, with *rdintens* $\approx$ 9.42—the coefficient on the dummy variable is 6.72 with a t statistic of 4.56. Therefore, by this measure, the first observation is more of an outlier than the tenth. Yet dropping the first observation changes the coefficient on *sales* by only a small amount (to about .000051 from .000053), although the coefficient on *profmarg* becomes larger and statistically significant. So, is the first observation an "outlier" too? These calculations show the conundrum one can enter when trying to determine observations that should be excluded from a regression analysis, even when the data set is small. Unfortunately, the size of the studentized residual need not correspond to how influential an observation is for the OLS slope estimates, and certainly not for all of them at once.

A general problem with using studentized residuals is that, in effect, all other observations are used to estimate the regression line to compute the residual for a particular observation. In other words, when the studentized residual is obtained for the first observation, the tenth observation has been used in estimating the intercept and slope. Given how flat the regression line is with the largest firm (tenth observation) included, it is not too surprising that the first observation, with its high value of *rdintens*, is far off the regression line.

Of course, we can add two dummy variables at the same time—one for the first observation and one for the tenth—which has the effect of using only the remaining 30 observations to estimate the regression line. If we estimate the equation without the first and tenth observations, the results are

$$\widehat{rdintens} = \underset{(0.459)}{1.939} + \underset{(.00065)}{.000160}\, sales + \underset{(.0343)}{.0701}\, profmarg$$
$$n = 30,\ R^2 = .2711,\ \bar{R}^2 = .2171$$

The coefficient on the dummy for the first observation is 6.47 ($t = 4.58$), and for the tenth observation it is -5.41 ($t = -1.95$). Notice that the coefficients on the *sales* and *profmarg* are both statistically significant, the latter at just about the 5% level against a two-sided alternative (p-value $= .051$). Even in this regression there are still two observations with studentized residuals greater than two (corresponding to the two remaining observations with R&D intensities above six).

Certain functional forms are less sensitive to outlying observations. In Section 6.2 we mentioned that, for most economic variables, the logarithmic transformation significantly narrows the range of the data and also yields functional forms—such as constant elasticity models—that can explain a broader range of data.

EXAMPLE 9.9 R&D INTENSITY

We can test whether R&D intensity increases with firm size by starting with the model

$$rd = sales^{\beta_1}\exp(\beta_0 + \beta_2 profmarg + u). \quad [9.41]$$

Then, holding other factors fixed, R&D intensity increases with *sales* if and only if $\beta_1 > 1$. Taking the log of (9.41) gives

$$\log(rd) = \beta_0 + \beta_1\log(sales) + \beta_2 profmarg + u. \quad [9.42]$$

When we use all 32 firms, the regression equation is

$$\begin{aligned}\widehat{\log(rd)} &= \underset{(.468)}{-4.378} + \underset{(.060)}{1.084}\log(sales) + \underset{(.0128)}{.0217}\, profmarg,\\ n &= 32, R^2 = .9180, \bar{R}^2 = .9123,\end{aligned}$$

while dropping the largest firm gives

$$\begin{aligned}\widehat{\log(rd)} &= \underset{(.511)}{-4.404} + \underset{(.067)}{1.088}\log(sales) + \underset{(.0130)}{.0218}\, profmarg,\\ n &= 31, R^2 = .9037, \bar{R}^2 = .8968.\end{aligned}$$

Practically, these results are the same. In neither case do we reject the null H_0: $\beta_1 = 1$ against H_1: $\beta_1 > 1$. (Why?)

In some cases, certain observations are suspected at the outset of being fundamentally different from the rest of the sample. This often happens when we use data at very aggregated levels, such as the city, county, or state level. The following is an example.

EXAMPLE 9.10 STATE INFANT MORTALITY RATES

Data on infant mortality, per capita income, and measures of health care can be obtained at the state level from the *Statistical Abstract of the United States*. We will provide a fairly simple analysis here just to illustrate the effect of outliers. The data are for the year 1990, and we have all 50 states in the United States, plus the District of Columbia (D.C.). The variable *infmort* is number of deaths within the first year per 1,000 live births, *pcinc* is per capita income, *physic* is physicians per 100,000 members of the civilian population, and *popul* is the population (in thousands). The data are contained in INFMRT.RAW. We include all independent variables in logarithmic form:

$$\begin{aligned}\widehat{infmort} &= \underset{(20.43)}{33.86} - \underset{(2.60)}{4.68}\log(pcinc) + \underset{(1.51)}{4.15}\log(physic)\\ &\quad - \underset{(.287)}{.088}\log(popul) \quad [9.43]\\ n &= 51, R^2 = .139, \bar{R}^2 = .084.\end{aligned}$$

Higher per capita income is estimated to lower infant mortality, an expected result. But more physicians per capita is associated with *higher* infant mortality rates, something that is counterintuitive. Infant mortality rates do not appear to be related to population size.

The District of Columbia is unusual in that it has pockets of extreme poverty and great wealth in a small area. In fact, the infant mortality rate for D.C. in 1990 was 20.7, compared with 12.4 for the highest state. It also has 615 physicians per 100,000 of the civilian population, compared with 337 for the highest state. The high number of physicians coupled with the high infant mortality rate in D.C. could certainly influence the results. If we drop D.C. from the regression, we obtain

$$\begin{aligned} \widehat{infmort} &= \underset{(12.42)}{23.95} - \underset{(1.64)}{.57}\log(pcinc) - \underset{(1.19)}{2.74}\log(physic) \\ &\quad + \underset{(.191)}{.629}\log(popul) \\ n &= 50,\ R^2 = .273,\ \bar{R}^2 = .226. \end{aligned} \quad [9.44]$$

We now find that more physicians per capita lowers infant mortality, and the estimate is statistically different from zero at the 5% level. The effect of per capita income has fallen sharply and is no longer statistically significant. In equation (9.44), infant mortality rates are higher in more populous states, and the relationship is very statistically significant. Also, much more variation in *infmort* is explained when D.C. is dropped from the regression. Clearly, D.C. had substantial influence on the initial estimates, and we would probably leave it out of any further analysis.

As Example 9.8 demonstrates, inspecting observations in trying to determine which are outliers, and even which ones have substantial influence on the OLS estimates, is a difficult endeavor. More advanced treatments allow more formal approaches to determine which observations are likely to be influential observations. Using matrix algebra, Belsley, Kuh, and Welsh (1980) define the *leverage* of an observation, which formalizes the notion that an observation has a large or small influence on the OLS estimates. These authors also provide a more in-depth discussion of standardized and studentized residuals.

9.6 Least Absolute Deviations Estimation

Rather than trying to determine which observations, if any, have undue influence on the OLS estimates, a different approach to guarding against outliers is to use an estimation method that is less sensitive to outliers than OLS. One such method, which has become popular among applied econometricians, is called **least absolute deviations (LAD)**. The LAD estimators of the β_j in a linear model minimize the sum of the absolute values of the residuals,

$$\min_{b_0, b_1, \ldots, b_k} \sum_{i=1}^{n} |y_i - b_0 - b_1x_{i1} - \ldots - b_kx_{ik}|. \quad [9.45]$$

Unlike OLS, which minimizes the sum of squared residuals, the LAD estimates are not available in closed form—that is, we cannot write down formulas for them. In fact, historically, solving the problem in equation (9.45) was computationally difficult, especially

FIGURE 9.2 The OLS and LAD objective functions.

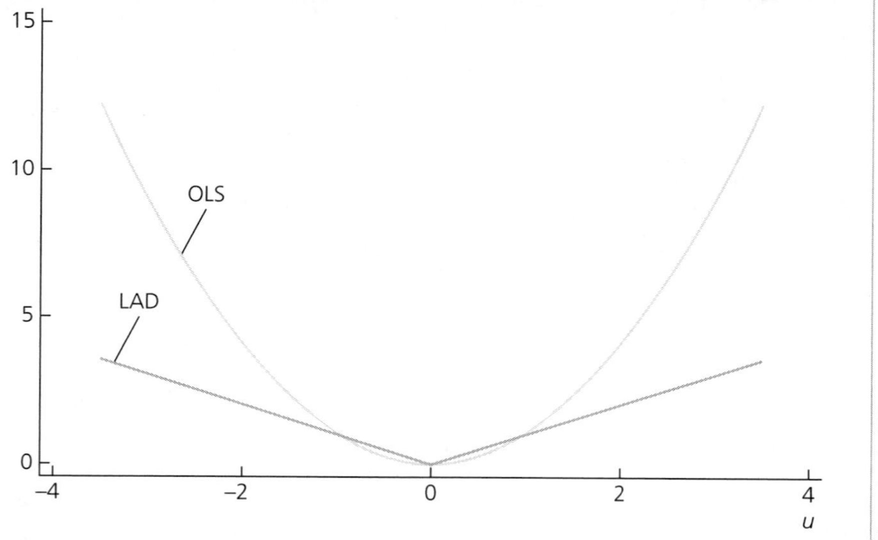

with large sample sizes and many explanatory variables. But with the vast improvements in computational speed over the past two decades, LAD estimates are fairly easy to obtain even for large data sets.

Figure 9.2 shows the OLS and LAD objective functions. The LAD objective function is linear on either side of zero, so that if, say, a positive residual increases by one unit, the LAD objective function increases by one unit. By contrast, the OLS objective function gives increasing importance to large residuals, and this makes OLS more sensitive to outlying observations.

Because LAD does not give increasing weight to larger residuals, it is much less sensitive to changes in the extreme values of the data than OLS. In fact, it is known that LAD is designed to estimate the parameters of the **conditional median** of y given $x_1, x_2, ..., x_k$ rather than the conditional mean. Because the median is not affected by large changes in the extreme observations, it follows that the LAD parameter estimates are more resilient to outlying observations. (See Section A.1 for a brief discussion of the sample median.) In choosing the estimates, OLS squares each residual, and so the OLS estimates can be very sensitive to outlying observations, as we saw in Examples 9.8 and 9.10.

In addition to LAD being more computationally intensive than OLS, a second drawback of LAD is that all statistical inference involving the LAD estimators is justified only as the sample size grows. [The formulas are somewhat complicated and require matrix algebra, and we do not need them here. Koenker (2005) provides a comprehensive treatment.] Recall that, under the classical linear model assumptions, the OLS t statistics have exact t distributions, and F statistics have exact F distributions. While asymptotic versions of these statistics are available for LAD—and reported routinely by software packages that compute LAD estimates—these are justified only in large samples. Like the additional computational burden involved in computing LAD estimates, the lack of exact inference for LAD is only of minor concern, because most applications of LAD involve several hundred, if not several thousand, observations. Of course, we might be pushing it if we apply large-sample approximations in an example such as Example 9.8, with $n = 32$. In a sense, this is not very different from OLS because, more often than not, we must appeal to large sample approximations to justify OLS inference whenever any of the CLM assumptions fail.

A more subtle but important drawback to LAD is that it does not always consistently estimate the parameters appearing in the conditional mean function, $E(y|x_1, ..., x_k)$. As mentioned earlier, LAD is intended to estimate the effects on the conditional median. Generally, the mean and median are the same only when the distribution of y given the covariates $x_1, ..., x_k$ is symmetric about $\beta_0 + \beta_1 x_1 + ... + \beta_k x_k$. (Equivalently, the population error term, u, is symmetric about zero.) Recall that OLS produces unbiased and consistent estimators of the parameters in the conditional mean whether or not the error distribution is symmetric; symmetry does not appear among the Gauss-Markov assumptions. When LAD and OLS are applied to cases with asymmetric distributions, the estimated partial effect of, say, x_1, obtained from LAD can be very different from the partial effect obtained from OLS. But such a difference could just reflect the difference between the median and the mean and might not have anything to do with outliers. See Computer Exercise C9 for an example.

If we assume that the population error u in model (9.2) is *independent* of $(x_1, ..., x_k)$, then the OLS and LAD slope estimates should differ only by sampling error whether or not the distribution of u is symmetric. The intercept estimates generally will be different to reflect the fact that, if the mean of u is zero, then its median is different from zero under asymmetry. Unfortunately, independence between the error and the explanatory variables is often unrealistically strong when LAD is applied. In particular, independence rules out heteroskedasticity, a problem that often arises in applications with asymmetric distributions.

An advantage that LAD has over OLS is that, because LAD estimates the median, it is easy to obtain partial effects—and predictions—using monotonic transformations. Here we consider the most common transformation, taking the natural log. Suppose that $\log(y)$ follows a linear model where the error has a zero conditional median:

$$\log(y) = \beta_0 + \mathbf{x}\boldsymbol{\beta} + u \qquad [9.46]$$

$$\text{Med}(u|\mathbf{x}) = 0, \qquad [9.47]$$

which implies that

$$\text{Med}[\log(y)|\mathbf{x}] = \beta_0 + \mathbf{x}\boldsymbol{\beta}$$

A well-known feature of the conditional median—see, for example, Wooldridge (2010, Chapter 12)—is that it passes through increasing functions. Therefore,

$$\text{Med}(y|\mathbf{x}) = \exp(\beta_0 + \mathbf{x}\boldsymbol{\beta}). \qquad [9.48]$$

It follows that β_j is the semi-elasticity of $\text{Med}(y|\mathbf{x})$ with respect to x_j. In other words, the partial effect of x_j in the linear equation (9.46) can be used to uncover the partial effect in the nonlinear model (9.48). It is important to understand that this holds for any distribution of u such that (9.47) holds, and we need not assume u and $\mathbf{x}$ are independent. By contrast, if we specify a linear model for $E[\log(y)|\mathbf{x}]$ then, in general, there is no way to uncover $E(y|\mathbf{x})$. If we make a full distributional assumption for u given $\mathbf{x}$ then, in principle, we can recover $E(y|\mathbf{x})$. We covered the special case in equation (6.40) under the assumption that $\log(y)$ follows a classical linear model. However, in general there is no way to find $E(y|\mathbf{x})$ from a model for $E[\log(y)|\mathbf{x}]$, even though we can always obtain $\text{Med}(y|\mathbf{x})$ from

Med[log(y)|$\mathbf{x}$]. Problem 9 investigates how heteroskedasticity in a linear model for log(y) confounds our ability to find E(y|$\mathbf{x}$).

Least absolute deviations is a special case of what is often called *robust regression*. Unfortunately, the way "robust" is used here can be confusing. In the statistics literature, a robust regression estimator is relatively insensitive to extreme observations. Effectively, observations with large residuals are given less weight than in least squares. [Berk (1990) contains an introductory treatment of estimators that are robust to outlying observations.] Based on our earlier discussion, in econometric parlance, LAD is not a robust estimator of the conditional mean because it requires extra assumptions in order to consistently estimate the conditional mean parameters. In equation (9.2), either the distribution of u given $(x_1, ..., x_k)$ has to be symmetric about zero, or u must be independent of $(x_1, ..., x_k)$. Neither of these is required for OLS.

LAD is also a special case of *quantile regression*, which is used to estimate the effect of the x_j on different parts of the distribution—not just the median (or mean). For example, in a study to see how having access to a particular pension plan affects wealth, it could be that access affects high-wealth people differently from low-wealth people, and these effects both differ from the median person. Wooldridge (2010, Chapter 12) contains a treatment and examples of quantile regression.

Summary

We have further investigated some important specification and data issues that often arise in empirical cross-sectional analysis. Misspecified functional form makes the estimated equation difficult to interpret. Nevertheless, incorrect functional form can be detected by adding quadratics, computing RESET, or testing against a nonnested alternative model using the Davidson-MacKinnon test. No additional data collection is needed.

Solving the omitted variables problem is more difficult. In Section 9.2, we discussed a possible solution based on using a proxy variable for the omitted variable. Under reasonable assumptions, including the proxy variable in an OLS regression eliminates, or at least reduces, bias. The hurdle in applying this method is that proxy variables can be difficult to find. A general possibility is to use data on a dependent variable from a prior year.

Applied economists are often concerned with measurement error. Under the classical errors-in-variables (CEV) assumptions, measurement error in the dependent variable has no effect on the statistical properties of OLS. In contrast, under the CEV assumptions for an independent variable, the OLS estimator for the coefficient on the mismeasured variable is biased toward zero. The bias in coefficients on the other variables can go either way and is difficult to determine.

Nonrandom samples from an underlying population can lead to biases in OLS. When sample selection is correlated with the error term u, OLS is generally biased and inconsistent. On the other hand, exogenous sample selection—which is either based on the explanatory variables or is otherwise independent of u—does not cause problems for OLS. Outliers in data sets can have large impacts on the OLS estimates, especially in small samples. It is important to at least informally identify outliers and to reestimate models with the suspected outliers excluded.

Least absolute deviations estimation is an alternative to OLS that is less sensitive to outliers and that delivers consistent estimates of conditional median parameters. In the past 20 years, with computational advances and improved understanding of the pros and cons of LAD and OLS, LAD is used more and more in empirical research–often as a supplement to OLS.

Key Terms

Attenuation Bias
Average Marginal Effect
Average Partial Effect (APE)
Classical Errors-in-Variables (CEV)
Conditional Median
Davidson-MacKinnon Test
Endogenous Explanatory Variable
Endogenous Sample Selection
Exogenous Sample Selection
Functional Form Misspecification
Influential Observations
Lagged Dependent Variable
Least Absolute Deviations (LAD)
Measurement Error
Missing Data
Multiplicative Measurement Error
Nonnested Models
Nonrandom Sample
Outliers
Plug-In Solution to the Omitted Variables Problem
Proxy Variable
Random Coefficient (Slope) Model
Regression Specification Error Test (RESET)
Stratified Sampling
Studentized Residuals

Problems

1 In Problem 11 in Chapter 4, the *R*-squared from estimating the model

$$\log(salary) = \beta_0 + \beta_1\log(sales) + \beta_2\log(mktval) + \beta_3 profmarg + \beta_4 ceoten + \beta_5 comten + u,$$

using the data in CEOSAL2.RAW, was $R^2 = .353$ ($n = 177$). When $ceoten^2$ and $comten^2$ are added, $R^2 = .375$. Is there evidence of functional form misspecification in this model?

2 Let us modify Computer Exercise C4 in Chapter 8 by using voting outcomes in 1990 for incumbents who were elected in 1988. Candidate A was elected in 1988 and was seeking reelection in 1990; *voteA90* is Candidate A's share of the two-party vote in 1990. The 1988 voting share of Candidate A is used as a proxy variable for quality of the candidate. All other variables are for the 1990 election. The following equations were estimated, using the data in VOTE2.RAW:

$$\begin{aligned}\widehat{voteA90} = {} & \underset{(9.25)}{75.71} + \underset{(.046)}{.312}\, prtystrA + \underset{(1.01)}{4.93}\, democA \\ & - \underset{(.684)}{.929}\log(expendA) - \underset{(.281)}{1.950}\log(expendB) \\ & n = 186, R^2 = .495, \bar{R}^2 = .483,\end{aligned}$$

and

$$\begin{aligned}\widehat{voteA90} = {} & \underset{(10.01)}{70.81} + \underset{(.052)}{.282}\, prtystrA + \underset{(1.06)}{4.52}\, democA \\ & - \underset{(.687)}{.839}\log(expendA) - \underset{(.292)}{1.846}\log(expendB) + \underset{(.053)}{.067}\, voteA88 \\ & n = 186, R^2 = .499, \bar{R}^2 = .485.\end{aligned}$$

(i) Interpret the coefficient on *voteA88* and discuss its statistical significance.
(ii) Does adding *voteA88* have much effect on the other coefficients?

3 Let *math10* denote the percentage of students at a Michigan high school receiving a passing score on a standardized math test (see also Example 4.2). We are interested in estimating the effect of per student spending on math performance. A simple model is

$$math10 = \beta_0 + \beta_1 \log(expend) + \beta_2 \log(enroll) + \beta_3 poverty + u,$$

where *poverty* is the percentage of students living in poverty.
(i) The variable *lnchprg* is the percentage of students eligible for the federally funded school lunch program. Why is this a sensible proxy variable for *poverty*?
(ii) The table that follows contains OLS estimates, with and without *lnchprg* as an explanatory variable.

Dependent Variable: *math10*		
Independent Variables	**(1)**	**(2)**
log(*expend*)	11.13 (3.30)	7.75 (3.04)
log(*enroll*)	.022 (.615)	−1.26 (.58)
lnchprg	—	−.324 (.036)
intercept	−69.24 (26.72)	−23.14 (24.99)
Observations	428	428
R-squared	.0297	.1893

Explain why the effect of expenditures on *math10* is lower in column (2) than in column (1). Is the effect in column (2) still statistically greater than zero?
(iii) Does it appear that pass rates are lower at larger schools, other factors being equal? Explain.
(iv) Interpret the coefficient on *lnchprg* in column (2).
(v) What do you make of the substantial increase in R^2 from column (1) to column (2)?

4 The following equation explains weekly hours of television viewing by a child in terms of the child's age, mother's education, father's education, and number of siblings:

$$tvhours^* = \beta_0 + \beta_1 age + \beta_2 age^2 + \beta_3 motheduc + \beta_4 fatheduc + \beta_5 sibs + u.$$

We are worried that $tvhours^*$ is measured with error in our survey. Let *tvhours* denote the reported hours of television viewing per week.
(i) What do the classical errors-in-variables (CEV) assumptions require in this application?
(ii) Do you think the CEV assumptions are likely to hold? Explain.

5 In Example 4.4, we estimated a model relating number of campus crimes to student enrollment for a sample of colleges. The sample we used was not a random sample of colleges in the United States, because many schools in 1992 did not report campus crimes. Do you think that college failure to report crimes can be viewed as exogenous sample selection? Explain.

6 In the model (9.17), show that OLS consistently estimates α and β if a_i is uncorrelated with x_i and b_i is uncorrelated with x_i and x_i^2, which are weaker assumptions than (9.19). [*Hint*: Write the equation as in (9.18) and recall from Chapter 5 that sufficient for consistency of OLS for the intercept and slope is $E(u_i) = 0$ and $Cov(x_i, u_i) = 0$.]

7 Consider the simple regression model with classical measurement error, $y = \beta_0 + \beta_1 x^* + u$, where we have m measures on x^*. Write these as $z_h = x^* + e_h$, $h = 1, \dots, m$. Assume that x^* is uncorrelated with $u, e_1, \dots, e_m$, that the measurement errors are pairwise uncorrelated, and have the same variance, σ_e^2. Let $w = (z_1 + \dots + z_m)/m$ be the average of the measures on x^*, so that, for each observation i, $w_i = (z_{i1} + \dots + z_{im})/m$ is the average of the m measures. Let $\bar{\beta}_1$ be the OLS estimator from the simple regression y_i on $1, w_i$, $i = 1, \dots, n$, using a random sample of data.

(i) Show that

$$\text{plim}(\bar{\beta}_1) = \beta_1\left\{\frac{\sigma_x^{2*}}{[\sigma_x^{2*} + (\sigma_e^2/m)]}\right\}.$$

[*Hint:* The plim of $\bar{\beta}_1$ is $Cov(w, y)/Var(w)$.]

(ii) How does the inconsistency in $\bar{\beta}_1$ compare with that when only a single measure is available (that is, $m = 1$)? What happens as m grows? Comment.

8 The point of this exercise is to show that tests for functional form cannot be relied on as a general test for omitted variables. Suppose that, conditional on the explanatory variables x_1 and x_2, a linear model relating y to x_1 and x_2 satisfies the Gauss-Markov assumptions:

$$y = \beta_0 + \beta_1 x_1 + \beta_2 x_2 + u$$
$$E(u|x_1, x_2) = 0$$
$$Var(u|x_1, x_2) = \sigma^2.$$

To make the question interesting, assume $\beta_2 \neq 0$.

Suppose further that x_2 has a simple linear relationship with x_1:

$$x_2 = \delta_0 + \delta_1 x_1 + r$$
$$E(r|x_1) = 0$$
$$Var(r|x_1) = \tau^2$$

(i) Show that

$$E(y|x_1) = (\beta_0 + \beta_2\delta_0) + (\beta_1 + \beta_2\delta_1)\, x_1.$$

Under random sampling, what is the probability limit of the OLS estimator from the simple regression of y on x_1? Is the simple regression estimator generally consistent for β_1?

(ii) If you run the regression of y on x_1, x_1^2, what will be the probability limit of the OLS estimator of the coefficient on x_1^2? Explain.

(iii) Using substitution, show that we can write

$$y = (\beta_0 + \beta_2\delta_0) + (\beta_1 + \beta_2\delta_1)x_1 + u + \beta_2 r$$

It can be shown that, if we define $v = u + \beta_2 r$ then $E(v|x_1) = 0$, $Var(v|x_1) = \sigma^2 + \beta_2^2\tau^2$. What consequences does this have for the t statistic on x_1^2 from the regression in part (ii)?

(iv) What do you conclude about adding a nonlinear function of x_1—in particular, x_1^2—in an attempt to detect omission of x_2?

9 Suppose that log(y) follows a linear model with a linear form of heteroskedasticity. We write this as

$$\log(y) = \beta_0 + \mathbf{x}\boldsymbol{\beta} + u$$
$$u|\mathbf{x} \sim \text{Normal}(0,h(\mathbf{x})),$$

so that, conditional on $\mathbf{x}$, u has a normal distribution with mean (and median) zero but with variance $h(\mathbf{x})$ that depends on $\mathbf{x}$. Because $\text{Med}(u|\mathbf{x}) = 0$, equation (9.48) holds: $\text{Med}(y|\mathbf{x}) = \exp(\beta_0 + \mathbf{x}\boldsymbol{\beta})$. Further, using an extension of the result from Chapter 6, it can be shown that

$$E(y|\mathbf{x}) = \exp[\beta_0 + \mathbf{x}\boldsymbol{\beta} + h(\mathbf{x})/2].$$

(i) Given that $h(\mathbf{x})$ can be any positive function, is it possible to conclude $\partial E(y|\mathbf{x})/\partial x_j$ is the same sign as β_j?

(ii) Suppose $h(\mathbf{x}) = \delta_0 + \mathbf{x}\boldsymbol{\delta}$ (and ignore the problem that linear functions are not necessarily always positive). Show that a particular variable, say x_1, can have a negative effect on $\text{Med}(y|\mathbf{x})$ but a positive effect on $E(y|\mathbf{x})$.

(iii) Consider the case covered in Section 6.4, where $h(\mathbf{x}) = \sigma^2$. How would you predict y using an estimate of $E(y|\mathbf{x})$? How would you predict y using an estimate of $\text{Med}(y|\mathbf{x})$? Which prediction is always larger?

Computer Exercises

C1 (i) Apply RESET from equation (9.3) to the model estimated in Computer Exercise C5 in Chapter 7. Is there evidence of functional form misspecification in the equation?

(ii) Compute a heteroskedasticity-robust form of RESET. Does your conclusion from part (i) change?

C2 Use the data set WAGE2.RAW for this exercise.

(i) Use the variable *KWW* (the "knowledge of the world of work" test score) as a proxy for ability in place of *IQ* in Example 9.3. What is the estimated return to education in this case?

(ii) Now, use *IQ* and *KWW* together as proxy variables. What happens to the estimated return to education?

(iii) In part (ii), are *IQ* and *KWW* individually significant? Are they jointly significant?

C3 Use the data from JTRAIN.RAW for this exercise.

(i) Consider the simple regression model

$$\log(scrap) = \beta_0 + \beta_1 grant + u,$$

where *scrap* is the firm scrap rate and *grant* is a dummy variable indicating whether a firm received a job training grant. Can you think of some reasons why the unobserved factors in *u* might be correlated with *grant*?

(ii) Estimate the simple regression model using the data for 1988. (You should have 54 observations.) Does receiving a job training grant significantly lower a firm's scrap rate?

(iii) Now, add as an explanatory variable $\log(scrap_{87})$. How does this change the estimated effect of *grant*? Interpret the coefficient on *grant*. Is it statistically significant at the 5% level against the one-sided alternative $H_1: \beta_{grant} < 0$?

(iv) Test the null hypothesis that the parameter on $\log(scrap_{87})$ is one against the two-sided alternative. Report the *p*-value for the test.

(v) Repeat parts (iii) and (iv), using heteroskedasticity-robust standard errors, and briefly discuss any notable differences.

C4 Use the data for the year 1990 in INFMRT.RAW for this exercise.

(i) Reestimate equation (9.43), but now include a dummy variable for the observation on the District of Columbia (called *DC*). Interpret the coefficient on *DC* and comment on its size and significance.

(ii) Compare the estimates and standard errors from part (i) with those from equation (9.44). What do you conclude about including a dummy variable for a single observation?

C5 Use the data in RDCHEM.RAW to further examine the effects of outliers on OLS estimates and to see how LAD is less sensitive to outliers. The model is

$$rdintens = \beta_0 + \beta_1 sales + \beta_2 sales^2 + \beta_3 profmarg + u,$$

where you should first change *sales* to be in billions of dollars to make the estimates easier to interpret.

(i) Estimate the above equation by OLS, both with and without the firm having annual sales of almost $40 billion. Discuss any notable differences in the estimated coefficients.

(ii) Estimate the same equation by LAD, again with and without the largest firm. Discuss any important differences in estimated coefficients.

(iii) Based on your findings in (i) and (ii), would you say OLS or LAD is more resilient to outliers?

C6 Redo Example 4.10 by dropping schools where teacher benefits are less than 1% of salary.

(i) How many observations are lost?

(ii) Does dropping these observations have any important effects on the estimated tradeoff?

C7 Use the data in LOANAPP.RAW for this exercise.

(i) How many observations have $obrat > 40$, that is, other debt obligations more than 40% of total income?

(ii) Reestimate the model in part (iii) of Computer Exercise C8, excluding observations with *obrat* > 40. What happens to the estimate and *t* statistic on *white*?

(iii) Does it appear that the estimate of β_{white} is overly sensitive to the sample used?

C8 Use the data in TWOYEAR.RAW for this exercise.

(i) The variable *stotal* is a standardized test variable, which can act as a proxy variable for unobserved ability. Find the sample mean and standard deviation of *stotal*.

(ii) Run simple regressions of *jc* and *univ* on *stotal*. Are both college education variables statistically related to *stotal*? Explain.

(iii) Add *stotal* to equation (4.17) and test the hypothesis that the returns to two- and four-year colleges are the same against the alternative that the return to four-year colleges is greater. How do your findings compare with those from Section 4.4?

(iv) Add $stotal^2$ to the equation estimated in part (iii). Does a quadratic in the test score variable seem necessary?

(v) Add the interaction terms *stotal·jc* and *stotal·univ* to the equation from part (iii). Are these terms jointly significant?

(vi) What would be your final model that controls for ability through the use of *stotal*? Justify your answer.

C9 In this exercise, you are to compare OLS and LAD estimates of the effects of 401(k) plan eligibility on net financial assets. The model is

$$nettfa = \beta_0 + \beta_1 inc + \beta_2 inc^2 + \beta_3 age + \beta_4 age^2 + \beta_5 male + \beta_6 e401k + u.$$

(i) Use the data in 401KSUBS.RAW to estimate the equation by OLS and report the results in the usual form. Interpret the coefficient on *e401k*.

(ii) Use the OLS residuals to test for heteroskedasticity using the Breusch-Pagan test. Is *u* independent of the explanatory variables?

(iii) Estimate the equation by LAD and report the results in the same form as for OLS. Interpret the LAD estimate of β_6.

(iv) Reconcile your findings from parts (i) and (iii).

C10 You need to use two data sets for this exercise, JTRAIN2.RAW and JTRAIN3.RAW. The former is the outcome of a job training experiment. The file JTRAIN3.RAW contains observational data, where individuals themselves largely determine whether they participate in job training. The data sets cover the same time period.

(i) In the data set JTRAIN2.RAW, what fraction of the men received job training? What is the fraction in JTRAIN3.RAW? Why do you think there is such a big difference?

(ii) Using JTRAIN2.RAW, run a simple regression of *re78* on *train*. What is the estimated effect of participating in job training on real earnings?

(iii) Now add as controls to the regression in part (ii) the variables *re74*, *re75*, *educ*, *age*, *black*, and *hisp*. Does the estimated effect of job training on *re78* change much? How come? (*Hint:* Remember that these are experimental data.)

(iv) Do the regressions in parts (ii) and (iii) using the data in JTRAIN3.RAW, reporting only the estimated coefficients on *train*, along with their *t* statistics. What is the effect now of controlling for the extra factors, and why?

(v) Define $avgre = (re74 + re75)/2$. Find the sample averages, standard deviations, and minimum and maximum values in the two data sets. Are these data sets representative of the same populations in 1978?

(vi) Almost 96% of men in the data set JTRAIN2.RAW have *avgre* less than \$10,000. Using only these men, run the regression

$$re78 \text{ on } train, re74, re75, educ, age, black, hisp$$

and report the training estimate and its t statistic. Run the same regression for JTRAIN3.RAW, using only men with $avgre \leq 10$. For the subsample of low-income men, how do the estimated training effects compare across the experimental and nonexperimental data sets?

(vii) Now use each data set to run the simple regression *re78* on *train*, but only for men who were unemployed in 1974 and 1975. How do the training estimates compare now?

(viii) Using your findings from the previous regressions, discuss the potential importance of having comparable populations underlying comparisons of experimental and nonexperimental estimates.

C11 Use the data in MURDER.RAW only for the year 1993 for this question, although you will need to first obtain the lagged murder rate, say $mrdrte_{-1}$.

(i) Run the regression of *mrdrte* on *exec*, *unem*. What are the coefficient and t statistic on *exec*? Does this regression provide any evidence for a deterrent effect of capital punishment?

(ii) How many executions are reported for Texas during 1993? (Actually, this is the sum of executions for the current and past two years.) How does this compare with the other states? Add a dummy variable for Texas to the regression in part (i). Is its t statistic unusually large? From this, does it appear Texas is an "outlier"?

(iii) To the regression in part (i) add the lagged murder rate. What happens to $\hat{\beta}_{exec}$ and its statistical significance?

(iv) For the regression in part (iii), does it appear Texas is an outlier? What is the effect on $\hat{\beta}_{exec}$ from dropping Texas from the regression?

C12 Use the data in ELEM94_95 to answer this question. See also Computer Exercise C10 in Chapter 4.

(i) Using all of the data, run the regression *lavgsal* on *bs*, *lenrol*, *lstaff*, and *lunch*. Report the coefficient on *bs* along with its usual and heteroskedasticity-robust standard errors. What do you conclude about the economic and statistical significance of $\hat{\beta}_{bs}$?

(ii) Now drop the four observations with $bs > .5$, that is, where average benefits are (supposedly) more than 50% of average salary. What is the coefficient on *bs*? Is it statistically significant using the heteroskedasticity-robust standard error?

(iii) Verify that the four observations with $bs > .5$ are 68, 1,127, 1,508, and 1,670. Define four dummy variables for each of these observations. (You might call them $d68$, $d1127$, $d1508$, and $d1670$.) Add these to the regression from part (i), .and verify that the OLS coefficients and standard errors on the other variables are identical to those in part (ii). Which of the four dummies has a t statistic statistically different from zero at the 5% level?

(iv) Verify that, in this data set, the data point with the largest studentized residual (largest t statistic on the dummy variable) in part (iii) has a large influence on the OLS estimates. (That is, run OLS using all observations except the one with the large studentized residual.) Does dropping, in turn, each of the other observations with $bs > .5$ have important effects?

(v) What do you conclude about the sensitivity of OLS to a single observation, even with a large sample size?

(vi) Verify that the LAD estimator is not sensitive to the inclusion of the observation identified in part (iii).

C13 Use the data in CEOSAL2.RAW to answer this question.

(i) Estimate the model

$$lsalary = \beta_0 + \beta_1 lsales + \beta_2 lmktval + \beta_3 ceoten + \beta_4 ceoten^2 + u$$

by OLS using all of the observations, where *lsalary*, *lsales*, and *lmktvale* are all natural logarithms. Report the results in the usual form with the usual OLS standard errors. (You may verify that the heteroskedasticity-robust standard errors are similar.)

(ii) In the regression from part (i) obtain the studentized residuals; call these str_i. How many studentized residuals are above 1.96 in absolute value? If the studentized residuals were independent draws from a standard normal distribution, about how many would you expect to be above two in absolute value with 177 draws?

(iii) Reestimate the equation in part (i) by OLS using only the observations with $|str_i| \leq 1.96$. How do the coefficients compare with those in part (i)?

(iv) Estimate the equation in part (i) by LAD, using all of the data. Is the estimate of β_1 closer to the OLS estimate using the full sample or the restricted sample? What about for β_3?

(v) Evaluate the following statement: "Dropping outliers based on extreme values of studentized residuals makes the resulting OLS estimates closer to the LAD estimates on the full sample."

APPENDIX

A

Basic Mathematical Tools

This appendix covers some basic mathematics that are used in econometric analysis. We summarize various properties of the summation operator, study properties of linear and certain nonlinear equations, and review proportions and percentages. We also present some special functions that often arise in applied econometrics, including quadratic functions and the natural logarithm. The first four sections require only basic algebra skills. Section A.5 contains a brief review of differential calculus; although a knowledge of calculus is not necessary to understand most of the text, it is used in some end-of-chapter appendices and in several of the more advanced chapters in Part 3.

A.1 The Summation Operator and Descriptive Statistics

The **summation operator** is a useful shorthand for manipulating expressions involving the sums of many numbers, and it plays a key role in statistics and econometric analysis. If $\{x_i: i = 1, \ldots, n\}$ denotes a sequence of n numbers, then we write the sum of these numbers as

$$\sum_{i=1}^{n} x_i \equiv x_1 + x_2 + \ldots + x_n. \quad [A.1]$$

With this definition, the summation operator is easily shown to have the following properties:

Property Sum.1: For any constant c,

$$\sum_{i=1}^{n} c = nc. \quad [A.2]$$

Property Sum.2: For any constant c,

$$\sum_{i=1}^{n} cx_i = c\sum_{i=1}^{n} x_i. \quad [A.3]$$

Property Sum.3: If $\{(x_i, y_i): i = 1, 2, \ldots, n\}$ is a set of n pairs of numbers, and a and b are constants, then

$$\sum_{i=1}^{n}(ax_i + by_i) = a\sum_{i=1}^{n}x_i + b\sum_{i=1}^{n}y_i. \quad \text{[A.4]}$$

It is also important to be aware of some things that *cannot* be done with the summation operator. Let $\{(x_i, y_i): i = 1, 2, \ldots, n\}$ again be a set of n pairs of numbers with $y_i \neq 0$ for each i. Then,

$$\sum_{i=1}^{n}(x_i/y_i) \neq \left(\sum_{i=1}^{n}x_i\right)\bigg/\left(\sum_{i=1}^{n}y_i\right).$$

In other words, the sum of the ratios is not the ratio of the sums. In the $n = 2$ case, the application of familiar elementary algebra also reveals this lack of equality: $x_1/y_1 + x_2/y_2 \neq (x_1 + x_2)/(y_1 + y_2)$. Similarly, the sum of the squares is not the square of the sum: $\sum_{i=1}^{n}x_i^2 \neq \left(\sum_{i=1}^{n}x_i\right)^2$, except in special cases. That these two quantities are not generally equal is easiest to see when $n = 2$: $x_1^2 + x_2^2 \neq (x_1 + x_2)^2 = x_1^2 + 2x_1x_2 + x_2^2$.

Given n numbers $\{x_i: i = 1, \ldots, n\}$, we compute their **average** or *mean* by adding them up and dividing by n:

$$\bar{x} = (1/n)\sum_{i=1}^{n}x_i. \quad \text{[A.5]}$$

When the x_i are a sample of data on a particular variable (such as years of education), we often call this the *sample average* (or *sample mean*) to emphasize that it is computed from a particular set of data. The sample average is an example of a **descriptive statistic**; in this case, the statistic describes the central tendency of the set of points x_i.

There are some basic properties about averages that are important to understand. First, suppose we take each observation on x and subtract off the average: $d_i \equiv x_i - \bar{x}$ (the "d" here stands for *deviation* from the average). Then, the sum of these deviations is always zero:

$$\sum_{i=1}^{n}d_i = \sum_{i=1}^{n}(x_i - \bar{x}) = \sum_{i=1}^{n}x_i - \sum_{i=1}^{n}\bar{x} = \sum_{i=1}^{n}x_i - n\bar{x} = n\bar{x} - n\bar{x} = 0.$$

We summarize this as

$$\sum_{i=1}^{n}(x_i - \bar{x}) = 0. \quad \text{[A.6]}$$

A simple numerical example shows how this works. Suppose $n = 5$ and $x_1 = 6$, $x_2 = 1$, $x_3 = -2$, $x_4 = 0$, and $x_5 = 5$. Then, $\bar{x} = 2$, and the demeaned sample is $\{4, -1, -4, -2, 3\}$. Adding these gives zero, which is just what equation (A.6) says.

In our treatment of regression analysis in Chapter 2, we need to know some additional algebraic facts involving deviations from sample averages. An important one is that the sum of squared deviations is the sum of the squared *xi* minus n times the square of $\bar{x}$:

$$\sum_{i=1}^{n}(x_i - \bar{x})^2 = \sum_{i=1}^{n}x_i^2 - n(\bar{x})^2. \quad \text{[A.7]}$$

This can be shown using basic properties of the summation operator:

$$\begin{aligned}\sum_{i=1}^{n}(x_i-\bar{x})^2 &= \sum_{i=1}^{n}(x_i^2-2x_i\bar{x}+\bar{x}^2)\\ &= \sum_{i=1}^{n}x_i^2-2\bar{x}\sum_{i=1}^{n}x_i+n(\bar{x})^2\\ &= \sum_{i=1}^{n}x_i^2-2n(\bar{x})^2+n(\bar{x})^2=\sum_{i=1}^{n}x_i^2-n(\bar{x})^2.\end{aligned}$$

Given a data set on two variables, $\{(x_i,y_i): i = 1, 2, \ldots, n\}$, it can also be shown that

$$\begin{aligned}\sum_{i=1}^{n}(x_i-\bar{x})(y_i-\bar{y}) &= \sum_{i=1}^{n}x_i(y_i-\bar{y})\\ &= \sum_{i=1}^{n}(x_i-\bar{x})y_i=\sum_{i=1}^{n}x_iy_i-n(\bar{x}\cdot\bar{y});\end{aligned} \quad \text{[A.8]}$$

this is a generalization of equation (A.7). (There, $y_i = x_i$ for all i.)

The average is the measure of central tendency that we will focus on in most of this text. However, it is sometimes informative to use the **median** (or *sample median*) to describe the central value. To obtain the median of the n numbers $\{x_1, \ldots, x_n\}$, we first order the values of the x_i from smallest to largest. Then, if n is odd, the sample median is the middle number of the ordered observations. For example, given the numbers $\{-4,8,2,0,21,-10,18\}$, the median value is 2 (because the ordered sequence is $\{-10,-4,0,2,8,18,21\}$). If we change the largest number in this list, 21, to twice its value, 42, the median is still 2. By contrast, the sample average would increase from 5 to 8, a sizable change. Generally, the median is less sensitive than the average to changes in the extreme values (large or small) in a list of numbers. This is why "median incomes" or "median housing values" are often reported, rather than averages, when summarizing income or housing values in a city or county.

If n is even, there is no unique way to define the median because there are two numbers at the center. Usually, the median is defined to be the average of the two middle values (again, after ordering the numbers from smallest to largest). Using this rule, the median for the set of numbers $\{4,12,2,6\}$ would be $(4 + 6)/2 = 5$.

A.2 Properties of Linear Functions

Linear functions play an important role in econometrics because they are simple to interpret and manipulate. If x and y are two variables related by

$$y = \beta_0 + \beta_1 x, \quad \text{[A.9]}$$

then we say that y is a **linear function** of x, and β_0 and β_1 are two parameters (numbers) describing this relationship. The **intercept** is β_0, and the **slope** is β_1.

The defining feature of a linear function is that the change in y is always β_1 times the change in x:

$$\Delta y = \beta_1 \Delta x, \quad \text{[A.10]}$$

where Δ denotes "change." In other words, the **marginal effect** of x on y is constant and equal to β_1.

EXAMPLE A.1 LINEAR HOUSING EXPENDITURE FUNCTION

Suppose that the relationship between monthly housing expenditure and monthly income is

$$housing = 164 + .27\ income. \qquad [A.11]$$

Then, for each additional dollar of income, 27 cents is spent on housing. If family income increases by \$200, then housing expenditure increases by (.27)200 = \$54. This function is graphed in Figure A.1.

According to equation (A.11), a family with no income spends \$164 on housing, which of course cannot be literally true. For low levels of income, this linear function would not describe the relationship between *housing* and *income* very well, which is why we will eventually have to use other types of functions to describe such relationships.

In (A.11), the *marginal propensity to consume* (MPC) housing out of income is .27. This is different from the *average propensity to consume* (APC), which is

$$\frac{housing}{income} = 164/income + .27.$$

The APC is not constant, it is always larger than the MPC, and it gets closer to the MPC as income increases.

Linear functions are easily defined for more than two variables. Suppose that y is related to two variables, x_1 and x_2, in the general form

$$y = \beta_0 + \beta_1 x_1 + \beta_2 x_2. \qquad [A.12]$$

FIGURE A.1 Graph of *housing* = 164 + .27 *income*.

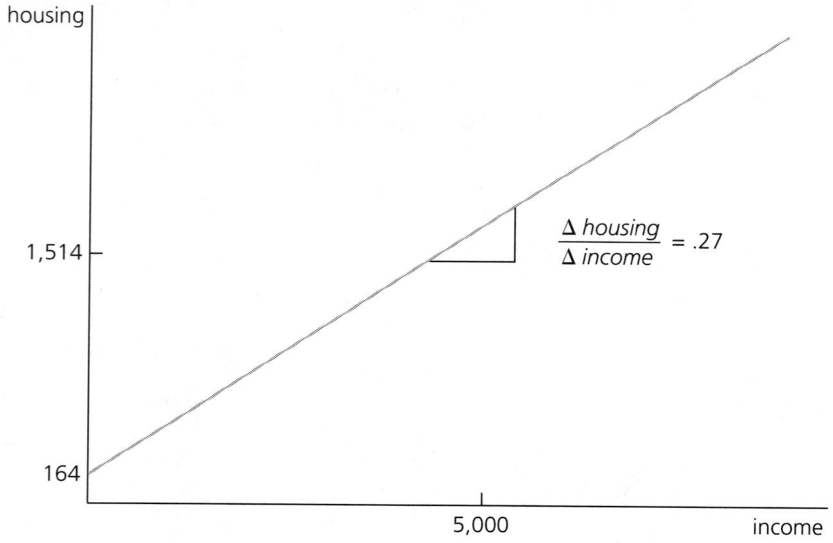

It is rather difficult to envision this function because its graph is three-dimensional. Nevertheless, β_0 is still the intercept (the value of y when $x_1 = 0$ and $x_2 = 0$), and β_1 and β_2 measure particular slopes. From (A.12), the change in y, for given changes in x_1 and x_2, is

$$\Delta y = \beta_1 \Delta x_1 + \beta_2 \Delta x_2. \quad \text{[A.13]}$$

If x_2 does not change, that is, $\Delta x_2 = 0$, then we have

$$\Delta y = \beta_1 \Delta x_1 \text{ if } \Delta x_2 = 0,$$

so that β_1 is the slope of the relationship in the direction of x_1:

$$\beta_1 = \frac{\Delta y}{\Delta x_1} \text{ if } \Delta x_2 = 0.$$

Because it measures how y changes with x_1, holding x_2 fixed, β_1 is often called the **partial effect** of x_1 on y. Because the partial effect involves holding other factors fixed, it is closely linked to the notion of **ceteris paribus**. The parameter β_2 has a similar interpretation: $\beta_2 = \Delta y / \Delta x_2$ if $\Delta x_1 = 0$, so that β_2 is the partial effect of x_2 on y.

EXAMPLE A.2 DEMAND FOR COMPACT DISCS

For college students, suppose that the monthly quantity demanded of compact discs is related to the price of compact discs and monthly discretionary income by

$$quantity = 120 - 9.8\, price + .03\, income,$$

where *price* is dollars per disc and *income* is measured in dollars. The *demand curve* is the relationship between *quantity* and *price*, holding *income* (and other factors) fixed. This is graphed in two dimensions in Figure A.2 at an income level of \$900. The slope of the demand curve, −9.8, is the *partial effect* of price on quantity: holding income fixed, if the price of compact discs increases by one dollar, then the quantity demanded falls by 9.8. (We abstract from the fact that CDs can only be purchased in discrete units.) An increase in income simply shifts the demand curve up (changes the intercept), but the slope remains the same.

A.3 Proportions and Percentages

Proportions and percentages play such an important role in applied economics that it is necessary to become very comfortable in working with them. Many quantities reported in the popular press are in the form of percentages; a few examples are interest rates, unemployment rates, and high school graduation rates.

An important skill is being able to convert proportions to percentages and vice versa. A percentage is easily obtained by multiplying a proportion by 100. For example, if the proportion of adults in a county with a high school degree is .82, then we say that 82% (82 percent) of adults have a high school degree. Another way to think of percentages and proportions is that a proportion is the decimal form of a percentage. For example, if

FIGURE A.2 Graph of *quantity* = 120 − 9.8 *price* + .03 *income*, with income fixed at $900.

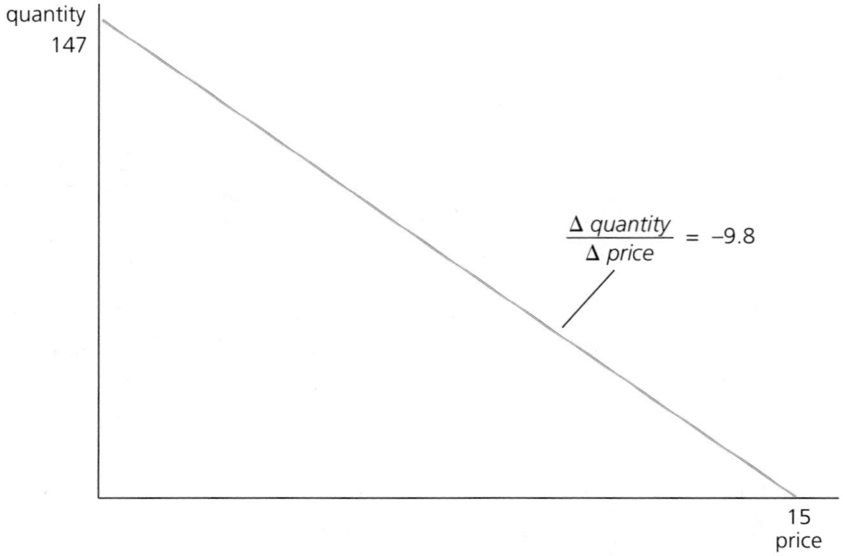

the marginal tax rate for a family earning $30,000 per year is reported as 28%, then the proportion of the next dollar of income that is paid in income taxes is .28 (or 28¢).

When using percentages, we often need to convert them to decimal form. For example, if a state sales tax is 6% and $200 is spent on a taxable item, then the sales tax paid is 200(.06) = $12. If the annual return on a certificate of deposit (CD) is 7.6% and we invest $3,000 in such a CD at the beginning of the year, then our interest income is 3,000(.076) = $228. As much as we would like it, the interest income is not obtained by multiplying 3,000 by 7.6.

We must be wary of proportions that are sometimes incorrectly reported as percentages in the popular media. If we read, "The percentage of high school students who drink alcohol is .57," we know that this really means 57% (not just over one-half of a percent, as the statement literally implies). College volleyball fans are probably familiar with press clips containing statements such as "Her hitting percentage was .372." This really means that her hitting percentage was 37.2%.

In econometrics, we are often interested in measuring the *changes* in various quantities. Let x denote some variable, such as an individual's income, the number of crimes committed in a community, or the profits of a firm. Let x_0 and x_1 denote two values for x: x_0 is the initial value, and x_1 is the subsequent value. For example, x_0 could be the annual income of an individual in 1994 and x_1 the income of the same individual in 1995. The **proportionate change** in x in moving from x_0 to x_1, sometimes called the **relative change,** is simply

$$(x_1 - x_0)/x_0 = \Delta x/x_0, \quad [A.14]$$

assuming, of course, that $x_0 \neq 0$. In other words, to get the proportionate change, we simply divide the change in x by its initial value. This is a way of standardizing the change so that it is free of units. For example, if an individual's income goes from \$30,000 per year to \$36,000 per year, then the proportionate change is $6{,}000/30{,}000 = .20$.

It is more common to state changes in terms of percentages. The **percentage change** in x in going from x_0 to x_1 is simply 100 times the proportionate change:

$$\%\Delta x = 100(\Delta x/x_0); \qquad \text{[A.15]}$$

the notation "$\%\Delta x$" is read as "the percentage change in x." For example, when income goes from \$30,000 to \$33,750, income has increased by 12.5%; to get this, we simply multiply the proportionate change, .125, by 100.

Again, we must be on guard for proportionate changes that are reported as percentage changes. In the previous example, for instance, reporting the percentage change in income as .125 is incorrect and could lead to confusion.

When we look at changes in things like dollar amounts or population, there is no ambiguity about what is meant by a percentage change. By contrast, interpreting percentage change calculations can be tricky when the variable of interest is itself a percentage, something that happens often in economics and other social sciences. To illustrate, let x denote the percentage of adults in a particular city having a college education. Suppose the initial value is $x_0 = 24$ (24% have a college education), and the new value is $x_1 = 30$. We can compute two quantities to describe how the percentage of college-educated people has changed. The first is the change in x, Δx. In this case, $\Delta x = x_1 - x_0 = 6$: the percentage of people with a college education has increased by six *percentage points*. On the other hand, we can compute the percentage change in x using equation (A.15): $\%\Delta x = 100[(30 - 24)/24] = 25$.

In this example, the percentage point change and the percentage change are very different. The **percentage point change** is just the change in the percentages. The percentage change is the change relative to the initial value. Generally, we must pay close attention to which number is being computed. The careful researcher makes this distinction perfectly clear; unfortunately, in the popular press as well as in academic research, the type of reported change is often unclear.

EXAMPLE A.3 MICHIGAN SALES TAX INCREASE

In March 1994, Michigan voters approved a sales tax increase from 4% to 6%. In political advertisements, supporters of the measure referred to this as a two percentage point increase, or an increase of two cents on the dollar. Opponents of the tax increase called it a 50% increase in the sales tax rate. Both claims are correct; they are simply different ways of measuring the increase in the sales tax. Naturally, each group reported the measure that made its position most favorable.

For a variable such as salary, it makes no sense to talk of a "percentage point change in salary" because salary is not measured as a percentage. We can describe a change in salary either in dollar or percentage terms.

A.4 Some Special Functions and Their Properties

In Section A.2, we reviewed the basic properties of linear functions. We already indicated one important feature of functions like $y = \beta_0 + \beta_1 x$: a one-unit change in x results in the *same* change in y, regardless of the initial value of x. As we noted earlier, this is the same as saying the marginal effect of x on y is constant, something that is not realistic for many economic relationships. For example, the important economic notion of *diminishing marginal returns* is not consistent with a linear relationship.

In order to model a variety of economic phenomena, we need to study several nonlinear functions. A **nonlinear function** is characterized by the fact that the change in y for a given change in x depends on the starting value of x. Certain nonlinear functions appear frequently in empirical economics, so it is important to know how to interpret them. A complete understanding of nonlinear functions takes us into the realm of calculus. Here, we simply summarize the most significant aspects of the functions, leaving the details of some derivations for Section A.5.

Quadratic Functions

One simple way to capture diminishing returns is to add a quadratic term to a linear relationship. Consider the equation

$$y = \beta_0 + \beta_1 x + \beta_2 x^2, \quad \text{[A.16]}$$

where β_0, β_1, and β_2 are parameters. When $\beta_1 > 0$ and $\beta_2 < 0$, the relationship between y and x has the parabolic shape given in Figure A.3, where $\beta_0 = 6$, $\beta_1 = 8$, and $\beta_2 = -2$.

When $\beta_1 > 0$ and $\beta_2 < 0$, it can be shown (using calculus in the next section) that the *maximum* of the function occurs at the point

$$x^* = \beta_1/(-2\beta_2). \quad \text{[A.17]}$$

For example, if $y = 6 + 8x - 2x^2$ (so $\beta_1 = 8$ and $\beta_2 = -2$), then the largest value of y occurs at $x^* = 8/4 = 2$, and this value is $6 + 8(2) - 2(2)^2 = 14$ (see Figure A.3).

The fact that equation (A.16) implies a **diminishing marginal effect** of x on y is easily seen from its graph. Suppose we start at a low value of x and then increase x by some amount, say, c. This has a larger effect on y than if we start at a higher value of x and increase x by the same amount c. In fact, once $x > x^*$, an increase in x actually decreases y.

The statement that x has a diminishing marginal effect on y is the same as saying that the slope of the function in Figure A.3 decreases as x increases. Although this is clear from looking at the graph, we usually want to quantify how quickly the slope is changing. An application of calculus gives the approximate slope of the quadratic function as

$$slope = \frac{\Delta y}{\Delta x} \approx \beta_1 + 2\beta_2 x, \quad \text{[A.18]}$$

for "small" changes in x. [The right-hand side of equation (A.18) is the **derivative** of the function in equation (A.16) with respect to x.] Another way to write this is

$$\Delta y \approx (\beta_1 + 2\beta_2 x)\Delta x \text{ for "small" } \Delta x. \quad \text{[A.19]}$$

FIGURE A.3 Graph of $y = 6 + 8x - 2x^2$.

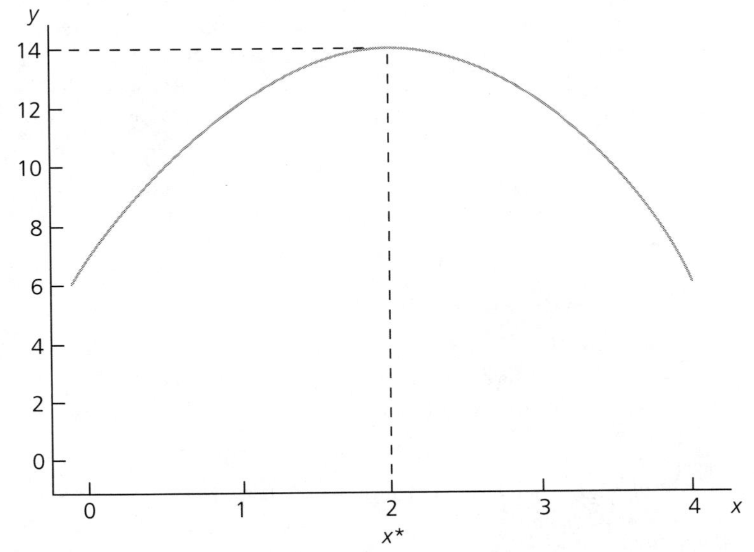

To see how well this approximation works, consider again the function $y = 6 + 8x - 2x^2$. Then, according to equation (A.19), $\Delta y \approx (8 - 4x)\Delta x$. Now, suppose we start at $x = 1$ and change x by $\Delta x = .1$. Using (A.19), $\Delta y \approx (8 - 4)(.1) = .4$. Of course, we can compute the change exactly by finding the values of y when $x = 1$ and $x = 1.1$: $y_0 = 6 + 8(1) - 2(1)^2 = 12$ and $y_1 = 6 + 8(1.1) - 2(1.1)^2 = 12.38$, so the exact change in y is .38. The approximation is pretty close in this case.

Now, suppose we start at $x = 1$ but change x by a larger amount: $\Delta x = .5$. Then, the approximation gives $\Delta y \approx 4(.5) = 2$. The exact change is determined by finding the difference in y when $x = 1$ and $x = 1.5$. The former value of y was 12, and the latter value is $6 + 8(1.5) - 2(1.5)^2 = 13.5$, so the actual change is 1.5 (not 2). The approximation is worse in this case because the change in x is larger.

For many applications, equation (A.19) can be used to compute the approximate marginal effect of x on y for any initial value of x and small changes. And, we can always compute the exact change if necessary.

EXAMPLE A.4 A QUADRATIC WAGE FUNCTION

Suppose the relationship between hourly wages and years in the workforce (*exper*) is given by

$$wage = 5.25 + .48\, exper - .008\, exper^2. \quad \text{[A.20]}$$

This function has the same general shape as the one in Figure A.3. Using equation (A.17), *exper* has a positive effect on wage up to the turning point, $exper^* = .48/[2(.008)] = 30$.

The first year of experience is worth approximately .48, or 48 cents [see (A.19) with $x = 0$, $\Delta x = 1$]. Each additional year of experience increases wage by less than the previous year—reflecting a diminishing marginal return to experience. At 30 years, an additional year of experience would actually lower the wage. This is not very realistic, but it is one of the consequences of using a quadratic function to capture a diminishing marginal effect: at some point, the function must reach a maximum and curve downward. For practical purposes, the point at which this happens is often large enough to be inconsequential, but not always.

The graph of the quadratic function in (A.16) has a U-shape if $\beta_1 < 0$ and $\beta_2 > 0$, in which case there is an increasing marginal return. The minimum of the function is at the point $-\beta_1/(2\beta_2)$.

The Natural Logarithm

The nonlinear function that plays the most important role in econometric analysis is the **natural logarithm**. In this text, we denote the natural logarithm, which we often refer to simply as the **log function**, as

$$y = \log(x). \quad \text{[A.21]}$$

You might remember learning different symbols for the natural log; $\ln(x)$ or $\log_e(x)$ are the most common. These different notations are useful when logarithms with several different bases are being used. For our purposes, only the natural logarithm is important, and so $\log(x)$ denotes the natural logarithm throughout this text. This corresponds to the notational usage in many statistical packages, although some use $\ln(x)$ [and most calculators use $\ln(x)$]. Economists use both $\log(x)$ and $\ln(x)$, which is useful to know when you are reading papers in applied economics.

The function $y = \log(x)$ is defined only for $x > 0$, and it is plotted in Figure A.4. It is not very important to know how the values of $\log(x)$ are obtained. For our purposes, the function can be thought of as a black box: we can plug in any $x > 0$ and obtain $\log(x)$ from a calculator or a computer.

Several things are apparent from Figure A.4. First, when $y = \log(x)$, the relationship between y and x displays diminishing marginal returns. One important difference between the log and the quadratic function in Figure A.3 is that when $y = \log(x)$, the effect of x on y never becomes negative: the slope of the function gets closer and closer to zero as x gets large, but the slope never quite reaches zero and certainly never becomes negative.

The following are also apparent from Figure A.4:

$$\begin{aligned} &\log(x) < 0 \text{ for } 0 < x < 1 \\ &\log(1) = 0 \\ &\log(x) > 0 \text{ for } x > 1. \end{aligned}$$

In particular, $\log(x)$ can be positive or negative. Some useful algebraic facts about the log function are

$$\begin{aligned} \log(x_1 \cdot x_2) &= \log(x_1) + \log(x_2),\ x_1, x_2 > 0 \\ \log(x_1/x_2) &= \log(x_1) - \log(x_2),\ x_1, x_2 > 0 \\ \log(x^c) &= c\log(x),\ x > 0,\ c \text{ any number.} \end{aligned}$$

Occasionally, we will need to rely on these properties.

FIGURE A.4 Graph of $y = \log(x)$.

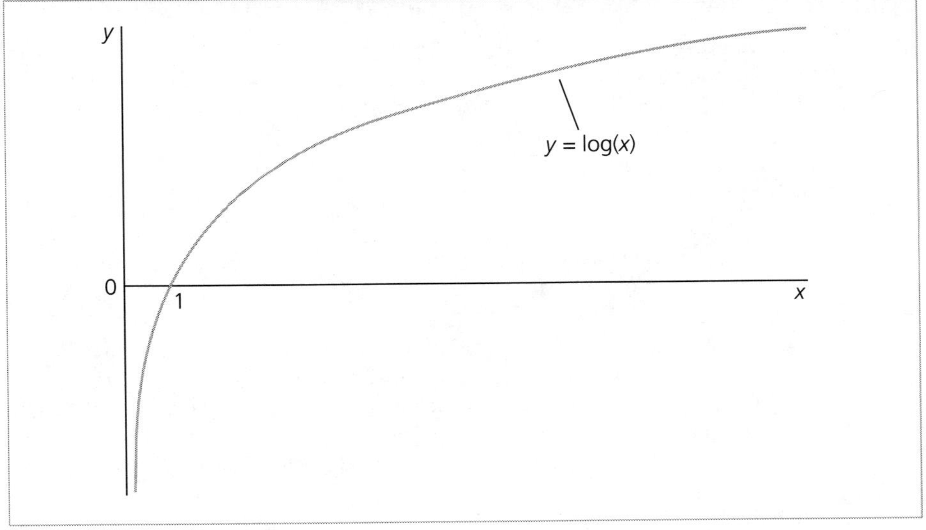

The logarithm can be used for various approximations that arise in econometric applications. First, $\log(1 + x) \approx x$ for $x \approx 0$. You can try this with $x = .02$, .1, and .5 to see how the quality of the approximation deteriorates as x gets larger. Even more useful is the fact that the difference in logs can be used to approximate proportionate changes. Let x_0 and x_1 be positive values. Then, it can be shown (using calculus) that

$$\log(x_1) - \log(x_0) \approx (x_1 - x_0)/x_0 = \Delta x/x_0 \quad \text{[A.22]}$$

for small changes in x. If we multiply equation (A.22) by 100 and write $\Delta\log(x) = \log(x_1) - \log(x_0)$, then

$$100 \cdot \Delta\log(x) \approx \%\Delta x \quad \text{[A.23]}$$

for small changes in x. The meaning of "small" depends on the context, and we will encounter several examples throughout this text.

Why should we approximate the percentage change using (A.23) when the exact percentage change is so easy to compute? Momentarily, we will see why the approximation in (A.23) is useful in econometrics. First, let us see how good the approximation is in two examples.

First, suppose $x_0 = 40$ and $x_1 = 41$. Then, the percentage change in x in moving from x_0 to x_1 is 2.5%, using $100(x_1 - x_0)/x_0$. Now, $\log(41) - \log(40) = .0247$ to four decimal places, which when multiplied by 100 is very close to 2.5. The approximation works pretty well. Now, consider a much bigger change: $x_0 = 40$ and $x_1 = 60$. The exact percentage change is 50%. However, $\log(60) - \log(40) \approx .4055$, so the approximation gives 40.55%, which is much farther off.

Why is the approximation in (A.23) useful if it is only satisfactory for small changes? To build up to the answer, we first define the **elasticity** of y with respect to x as

$$\frac{\Delta y}{\Delta x} \cdot \frac{x}{y} = \frac{\%\Delta y}{\%\Delta x}. \quad \text{[A.24]}$$

In other words, the elasticity of y with respect to x is the percentage change in y when x increases by 1%. This notion should be familiar from introductory economics.

If y is a linear function of x, $y = \beta_0 + \beta_1 x$, then the elasticity is

$$\frac{\Delta y}{\Delta x} \cdot \frac{x}{y} = \beta_1 \cdot \frac{x}{y} = \beta_1 \cdot \frac{x}{\beta_0 + \beta_1 x}, \quad \text{[A.25]}$$

which clearly depends on the value of x. (This is a generalization of the well-known result from basic demand theory: the elasticity is not constant along a straight-line demand curve.)

Elasticities are of critical importance in many areas of applied economics, not just in demand theory. It is convenient in many situations to have *constant* elasticity models, and the log function allows us to specify such models. If we use the approximation in (A.23) for both x and y, then the elasticity is approximately equal to $\Delta\log(y)/\Delta\log(x)$. Thus, a constant elasticity model is approximated by the equation

$$\log(y) = \beta_0 + \beta_1 \log(x), \quad \text{[A.26]}$$

and β_1 is the elasticity of y with respect to x (assuming that $x, y > 0$).

EXAMPLE A.5 CONSTANT ELASTICITY DEMAND FUNCTION

If q is quantity demanded and p is price and these variables are related by

$$\log(q) = 4.7 - 1.25 \log(p),$$

then the price elasticity of demand is -1.25. Roughly, a 1% increase in price leads to a 1.25% fall in the quantity demanded.

For our purposes, the fact that β_1 in (A.26) is only close to the elasticity is not important. In fact, when the elasticity is defined using calculus—as in Section A.5—the definition is exact. For the purposes of econometric analysis, (A.26) defines a **constant elasticity model**. Such models play a large role in empirical economics.

Other possibilities for using the log function often arise in empirical work. Suppose that $y > 0$ and

$$\log(y) = \beta_0 + \beta_1 x. \quad \text{[A.27]}$$

Then, $\Delta\log(y) = \beta_1 \Delta x$, so $100 \cdot \Delta\log(y) = (100 \cdot \beta_1)\Delta x$. It follows that, when y and x are related by equation (A.27),

$$\%\Delta y \approx (100 \cdot \beta_1)\Delta x. \quad \text{[A.28]}$$

EXAMPLE A.6 LOGARITHMIC WAGE EQUATION

Suppose that hourly wage and years of education are related by

$$\log(wage) = 2.78 + .094\ educ.$$

Then, using equation (A.28),

$$\%\Delta wage \approx 100(.094)\ \Delta educ = 9.4\ \Delta educ.$$

It follows that one more year of education increases hourly wage by about 9.4%.

Generally, the quantity $\%\Delta y/\Delta x$ is called the **semi-elasticity** of y with respect to x. The semi-elasticity is the percentage change in y when x increases by one *unit*. What we have just shown is that, in model (A.27), the semi-elasticity is constant and equal to $100 \cdot \beta_1$. In Example A.6, we can conveniently summarize the relationship between wages and education by saying that one more year of education—starting from any amount of education—increases the wage by about 9.4%. This is why such models play an important role in economics.

Another relationship of some interest in applied economics is

$$y = \beta_0 + \beta_1 \log(x), \qquad [A.29]$$

where $x > 0$. How can we interpret this equation? If we take the change in y, we get $\Delta y = \beta_1 \Delta \log(x)$, which can be rewritten as $\Delta y = (\beta_1/100)[100 \cdot \Delta \log(x)]$. Thus, using the approximation in (A.23), we have

$$\Delta y \approx (\beta_1/100)(\%\Delta x). \qquad [A.30]$$

In other words, $\beta_1/100$ is the unit change in y when x increases by 1%.

EXAMPLE A.7 LABOR SUPPLY FUNCTION

Assume that the labor supply of a worker can be described by

$$hours = 33 + 45.1\ \log(wage),$$

where *wage* is hourly wage and *hours* is hours worked per week. Then, from (A.30),

$$\Delta hours \approx (45.1/100)(\%\Delta wage) = .451\ \%\Delta wage.$$

In other words, a 1% increase in *wage* increases the weekly hours worked by about .45, or slightly less than one-half hour. If the wage increases by 10%, then $\Delta hours = .451(10) = 4.51$, or about four and one-half hours. We would not want to use this approximation for much larger percentage changes in wages.

The Exponential Function

Before leaving this section, we need to discuss a special function that is related to the log. As motivation, consider equation (A.27). There, $\log(y)$ is a linear function of x. But how do we find y itself as a function of x? The answer is given by the **exponential function**.

We will write the exponential function as $y = \exp(x)$, which is graphed in Figure A.5. From Figure A.5, we see that $\exp(x)$ is defined for any value of x and is always greater than zero. Sometimes, the exponential function is written as $y = e^x$, but we will not use this notation. Two important values of the exponential function are $\exp(0) = 1$ and $\exp(1) = 2.7183$ (to four decimal places).

The exponential function is the inverse of the log function in the following sense: $\log[\exp(x)] = x$ for all x, and $\exp[\log(x)] = x$ for $x > 0$. In other words, the log "undoes" the exponential, and vice versa. (This is why the exponential function is sometimes called the *anti-log* function.) In particular, note that $\log(y) = \beta_0 + \beta_1 x$ is equivalent to

$$y = \exp(\beta_0 + \beta_1 x).$$

If $\beta_1 > 0$, the relationship between x and y has the same shape as in Figure A.5. Thus, if $\log(y) = \beta_0 + \beta_1 x$ with $\beta_1 > 0$, then x has an *increasing* marginal effect on y. In Example A.6, this means that another year of education leads to a larger change in wage than the previous year of education.

Two useful facts about the exponential function are $\exp(x_1 + x_2) = \exp(x_1)\exp(x_2)$ and $\exp[c \cdot \log(x)] = x^c$.

FIGURE A.5 Graph of $y = \exp(x)$.

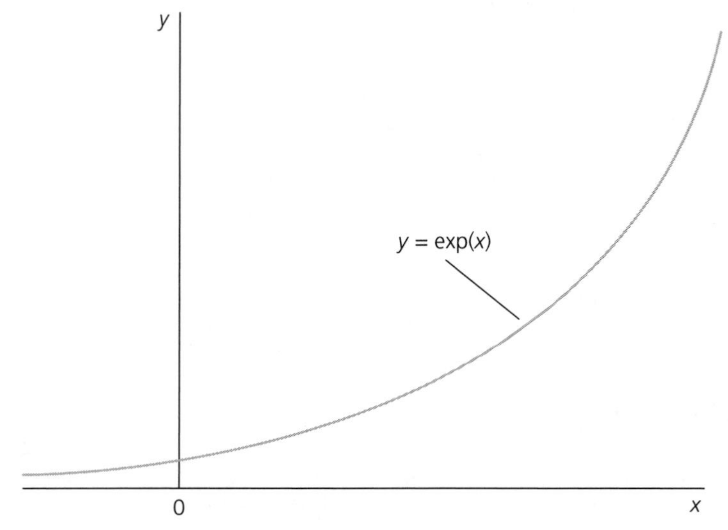

A.5 Differential Calculus

In the previous section, we asserted several approximations that have foundations in calculus. Let $y = f(x)$ for some function f. Then, for small changes in x,

$$\Delta y \approx \frac{df}{dx} \cdot \Delta x, \qquad [A.31]$$

where df/dx is the derivative of the function f, evaluated at the initial point x_0. We also write the derivative as dy/dx.

For example, if $y = \log(x)$, then $dy/dx = 1/x$. Using (A.31), with dy/dx evaluated at x_0, we have $\Delta y \approx (1/x_0)\Delta x$, or $\Delta \log(x) \approx \Delta x/x_0$, which is the approximation given in (A.22).

In applying econometrics, it helps to recall the derivatives of a handful of functions because we use the derivative to define the slope of a function at a given point. We can then use (A.31) to find the approximate change in y for small changes in x. In the linear case, the derivative is simply the slope of the line, as we would hope: if $y = \beta_0 + \beta_1 x$, then $dy/dx = \beta_1$.

If $y = x^c$, then $dy/dx = cx^{c-1}$. The derivative of a sum of two functions is the sum of the derivatives: $d[f(x) + g(x)]/dx = df(x)/dx + dg(x)/dx$. The derivative of a constant times any function is that same constant times the derivative of the function: $d[cf(x)]/dx = c[df(x)/dx]$. These simple rules allow us to find derivatives of more complicated functions. Other rules, such as the product, quotient, and chain rules, will be familiar to those who have taken calculus, but we will not review those here.

Some functions that are often used in economics, along with their derivatives, are

$$y = \beta_0 + \beta_1 x + \beta_2 x^2;\ dy/dx = \beta_1 + 2\beta_2 x$$
$$y = \beta_0 + \beta_1/x;\ dy/dx = -\beta_1/(x^2)$$
$$y = \beta_0 + \beta_1\sqrt{x};\ dy/dx = (\beta_1/2)x^{-1/2}$$
$$y = \beta_0 + \beta_1\log(x);\ dy/dx = \beta_1/x$$
$$y = \exp(\beta_0 + \beta_1 x);\ dy/dx = \beta_1\exp(\beta_0 + \beta_1 x).$$

If $\beta_0 = 0$ and $\beta_1 = 1$ in this last expression, we get $dy/dx = \exp(x)$, when $y = \exp(x)$.

In Section A.4, we noted that equation (A.26) defines a constant elasticity model when calculus is used. The calculus definition of elasticity is $(dy/dx)\cdot(x/y)$. It can be shown using properties of logs and exponentials that, when (A.26) holds, $(dy/dx)\cdot(x/y) = \beta_1$.

When y is a function of multiple variables, the notion of a **partial derivative** becomes important. Suppose that

$$y = f(x_1, x_2). \qquad [A.32]$$

Then, there are two partial derivatives, one with respect to x_1 and one with respect to x_2. The partial derivative of y with respect to x_1, denoted here by $\partial y/\partial x_1$, is just the usual derivative of (A.32) with respect to x_1, where x_2 is treated as a *constant*. Similarly, $\partial y/\partial x_2$ is just the derivative of (A.32) with respect to x_2, holding x_1 fixed.

Partial derivatives are useful for much the same reason as ordinary derivatives. We can approximate the change in y as

$$\Delta y \approx \frac{\partial y}{\partial x_1} \cdot \Delta x_1, \text{ holding } x_2 \text{ fixed.} \qquad [A.33]$$

Thus, calculus allows us to define partial effects in nonlinear models just as we could in linear models. In fact, if

$$y = \beta_0 + \beta_1 x_1 + \beta_2 x_2,$$

then

$$\frac{\partial y}{\partial x_1} = \beta_1, \ \frac{\partial y}{\partial x_2} = \beta_2.$$

These can be recognized as the partial effects defined in Section A.2.

A more complicated example is

$$y = 5 + 4x_1 + x_1^2 - 3x_2 + 7x_1 \cdot x_2. \quad \text{[A.34]}$$

Now, the derivative of (A.34), with respect to x_1 (treating x_2 as a constant), is simply

$$\frac{\partial y}{\partial x_1} = 4 + 2x_1 + 7x_2;$$

note how this depends on x_1 and x_2. The derivative of (A.34), with respect to x_2, is $\partial y/\partial x_2 = -3 + 7x_1$, so this depends only on x_1.

EXAMPLE A.8 WAGE FUNCTION WITH INTERACTION

A function relating wages to years of education and experience is

$$\begin{aligned} wage = {} & 3.10 + .41\ educ + .19\ exper - .004\ exper^2 \\ & + .007\ educ \cdot exper. \end{aligned} \quad \text{[A.35]}$$

The partial effect of *exper* on *wage* is the partial derivative of (A.35):

$$\frac{\partial wage}{\partial exper} = .19 - .008\ exper + .007\ educ.$$

This is the approximate change in wage due to increasing experience by one year. Notice that this partial effect depends on the initial level of *exper* and *educ*. For example, for a worker who is starting with $educ = 12$ and $exper = 5$, the next year of experience increases wage by about $.19 - .008(5) + .007(12) = .234$, or 23.4 cents per hour. The exact change can be calculated by computing (A.35) at $exper = 5$, $educ = 12$ and at $exper = 6$, $educ = 12$, and then taking the difference. This turns out to be .23, which is very close to the approximation.

Differential calculus plays an important role in minimizing and maximizing functions of one or more variables. If $f(x_1, x_2, \ldots, x_k)$ is a differentiable function of k variables, then a necessary condition for $x_1^*, x_2^*, \ldots, x_k^*$ to either minimize or maximize f over all possible values of x_j is

$$\frac{\partial f}{\partial x_j}(x_1^*, x_2^*, \ldots, x_k^*) = 0, j = 1, 2, \ldots, k. \quad \text{[A.36]}$$

In other words, all of the partial derivatives of f must be zero when they are evaluated at the x_h^*. These are called the *first order conditions* for minimizing or maximizing a function. Practically, we hope to solve equation (A.36) for the x_h^*. Then, we can use other criteria to determine whether we have minimized or maximized the function. We will not need those here. [See Sydsaeter and Hammond (1995) for a discussion of multivariable calculus and its use in optimizing functions.]

Summary

The math tools reviewed here are crucial for understanding regression analysis and the probability and statistics that are covered in Appendices B and C. The material on nonlinear functions—especially quadratic, logarithmic, and exponential functions—is critical for understanding modern applied economic research. The level of comprehension required of these functions does not include a deep knowledge of calculus, although calculus is needed for certain derivations.

Key Terms

Average
Ceteris Paribus
Constant Elasticity Model
Derivative
Descriptive Statistic
Diminishing Marginal Effect
Elasticity
Exponential Function
Intercept
Linear Function
Log Function
Marginal Effect
Median
Natural Logarithm
Nonlinear Function
Partial Derivative
Partial Effect
Percentage Change
Percentage Point Change
Proportionate Change
Relative Change
Semi-Elasticity
Slope
Summation Operator

Problems

1 The following table contains monthly housing expenditures for 10 families.

Family	Monthly Housing Expenditures (Dollars)
1	300
2	440
3	350
4	1,100
5	640
6	480
7	450
8	700
9	670
10	530

(i) Find the average monthly housing expenditure.
(ii) Find the median monthly housing expenditure.
(iii) If monthly housing expenditures were measured in hundreds of dollars, rather than in dollars, what would be the average and median expenditures?
(iv) Suppose that family number 8 increases its monthly housing expenditure to \$900, but the expenditures of all other families remain the same. Compute the average and median housing expenditures.

2 Suppose the following equation describes the relationship between the average number of classes missed during a semester (*missed*) and the distance from school (*distance*, measured in miles):

$$missed = 3 + 0.2\ distance.$$

(i) Sketch this line, being sure to label the axes. How do you interpret the intercept in this equation?
(ii) What is the average number of classes missed for someone who lives five miles away?
(iii) What is the difference in the average number of classes missed for someone who lives 10 miles away and someone who lives 20 miles away?

3 In Example A.2, quantity of compact discs was related to price and income by $quantity = 120 - 9.8\ price + .03\ income$. What is the demand for CDs if $price = 15$ and $income = 200$? What does this suggest about using linear functions to describe demand curves?

4 Suppose the unemployment rate in the United States goes from 6.4% in one year to 5.6% in the next.
(i) What is the percentage point decrease in the unemployment rate?
(ii) By what percentage has the unemployment rate fallen?

5 Suppose that the return from holding a particular firm's stock goes from 15% in one year to 18% in the following year. The majority shareholder claims that "the stock return only increased by 3%," while the chief executive officer claims that "the return on the firm's stock increased by 20%." Reconcile their disagreement.

6 Suppose that Person A earns \$35,000 per year and Person B earns \$42,000.
(i) Find the exact percentage by which Person B's salary exceeds Person A's.
(ii) Now, use the difference in natural logs to find the approximate percentage difference.

7 Suppose the following model describes the relationship between annual salary (*salary*) and the number of previous years of labor market experience (*exper*):

$$\log(salary) = 10.6 + .027\ exper.$$

(i) What is *salary* when $exper = 0$? When $exper = 5$? (*Hint:* You will need to exponentiate.)
(ii) Use equation (A.28) to approximate the percentage increase in *salary* when *exper* increases by five years.
(iii) Use the results of part (i) to compute the exact percentage difference in salary when $exper = 5$ and $exper = 0$. Comment on how this compares with the approximation in part (ii).

8 Let *grthemp* denote the proportionate growth in employment, at the county level, from 1990 to 1995, and let *salestax* denote the county sales tax rate, stated as a proportion. Interpret the intercept and slope in the equation

$$grthemp = .043 - .78\ salestax.$$

9 Suppose the yield of a certain crop (in bushels per acre) is related to fertilizer amount (in pounds per acre) as

$$yield = 120 + .19\sqrt{fertilizer}.$$

(i) Graph this relationship by plugging in several values for *fertilizer*.
(ii) Describe how the shape of this relationship compares with a linear relationship between *yield* and *fertilizer*.

10 Suppose that in a particular state a standardized test is given to all graduating seniors. Let *score* denote a student's score on the test. Someone discovers that performance on the test is related to the size of the student's graduating high school class. The relationship is quadratic:

$$score = 45.6 + .082\ class - .000147\ class^2,$$

where *class* is the number of students in the graduating class.

(i) How do you literally interpret the value 45.6 in the equation? By itself, is it of much interest? Explain.
(ii) From the equation, what is the optimal size of the graduating class (the size that maximizes the test score)? (Round your answer to the nearest integer.) What is the highest achievable test score?
(iii) Sketch a graph that illustrates your solution in part (ii).
(iv) Does it seem likely that *score* and *class* would have a deterministic relationship? That is, is it realistic to think that once you know the size of a student's graduating class you know, with certainty, his or her test score? Explain.

APPENDIX

B

Fundamentals of Probability

This appendix covers key concepts from basic probability. Appendices B and C are primarily for review; they are not intended to replace a course in probability and statistics. However, all of the probability and statistics concepts that we use in the text are covered in these appendices.

Probability is of interest in its own right for students in business, economics, and other social sciences. For example, consider the problem of an airline trying to decide how many reservations to accept for a flight that has 100 available seats. If fewer than 100 people want reservations, then these should all be accepted. But what if more than 100 people request reservations? A safe solution is to accept at most 100 reservations. However, because some people book reservations and then do not show up for the flight, there is some chance that the plane will not be full even if 100 reservations are booked. This results in lost revenue to the airline. A different strategy is to book more than 100 reservations and to hope that some people do not show up, so the final number of passengers is as close to 100 as possible. This policy runs the risk of the airline having to compensate people who are necessarily bumped from an overbooked flight.

A natural question in this context is: Can we decide on the optimal (or best) number of reservations the airline should make? This is a nontrivial problem. Nevertheless, given certain information (on airline costs and how frequently people show up for reservations), we can use basic probability to arrive at a solution.

B.1 Random Variables and Their Probability Distributions

Suppose that we flip a coin 10 times and count the number of times the coin turns up heads. This is an example of an **experiment**. Generally, an experiment is any procedure that can, at least in theory, be infinitely repeated and has a well-defined set of outcomes. We could, in principle, carry out the coin-flipping procedure again and again. Before we flip the coin, we know that the number of heads appearing is an integer from 0 to 10, so the outcomes of the experiment are well defined.

A **random variable** is one that takes on numerical values and has an outcome that is determined by an experiment. In the coin-flipping example, the number of heads appearing in 10 flips of a coin is an example of a random variable. Before we flip the coin 10 times, we do not know how many times the coin will come up heads. Once we flip the coin 10 times and count the number of heads, we obtain the outcome of the random variable for this particular trial of the experiment. Another trial can produce a different outcome.

In the airline reservation example mentioned earlier, the number of people showing up for their flight is a random variable: before any particular flight, we do not know how many people will show up.

To analyze data collected in business and the social sciences, it is important to have a basic understanding of random variables and their properties. Following the usual conventions in probability and statistics throughout Appendices B and C, we denote random variables by uppercase letters, usually W, X, Y, and Z; particular outcomes of random variables are denoted by the corresponding lowercase letters, w, x, y, and z. For example, in the coin-flipping experiment, let X denote the number of heads appearing in 10 flips of a coin. Then, X is not associated with any particular value, but we know X will take on a value in the set $\{0, 1, 2, \ldots, 10\}$. A particular outcome is, say, $x = 6$.

We indicate large collections of random variables by using subscripts. For example, if we record last year's income of 20 randomly chosen households in the United States, we might denote these random variables by $X_1, X_2, \ldots, X_{20}$; the particular outcomes would be denoted $x_1, x_2, \ldots, x_{20}$.

As stated in the definition, random variables are always defined to take on numerical values, even when they describe qualitative events. For example, consider tossing a single coin, where the two outcomes are heads and tails. We can define a random variable as follows: $X = 1$ if the coin turns up heads, and $X = 0$ if the coin turns up tails.

A random variable that can only take on the values zero and one is called a **Bernoulli** (or **binary**) **random variable**. In basic probability, it is traditional to call the event $X = 1$ a "success" and the event $X = 0$ a "failure." For a particular application, the success-failure nomenclature might not correspond to our notion of a success or failure, but it is a useful terminology that we will adopt.

Discrete Random Variables

A **discrete random variable** is one that takes on only a finite or countably infinite number of values. The notion of "countably infinite" means that even though an infinite number of values can be taken on by a random variable, those values can be put in a one-to-one correspondence with the positive integers. Because the distinction between "countably infinite" and "uncountably infinite" is somewhat subtle, we will concentrate on discrete random variables that take on only a finite number of values. Larsen and Marx (1986, Chapter 3) provide a detailed treatment.

A Bernoulli random variable is the simplest example of a discrete random variable. The only thing we need to completely describe the behavior of a Bernoulli random variable is the probability that it takes on the value one. In the coin-flipping example, if the coin is "fair," then $P(X = 1) = 1/2$ (read as "the probability that X equals one is one-half"). Because probabilities must sum to one, $P(X = 0) = 1/2$, also.

Social scientists are interested in more than flipping coins, so we must allow for more general situations. Again, consider the example where the airline must decide how many people to book for a flight with 100 available seats. This problem can be analyzed in the context of several Bernoulli random variables as follows: for a randomly selected customer, define a Bernoulli random variable as $X = 1$ if the person shows up for the reservation, and $X = 0$ if not.

There is no reason to think that the probability of any particular customer showing up is 1/2; in principle, the probability can be any number between zero and one. Call this number θ, so that

$$P(X = 1) = \theta \quad [B.1]$$
$$P(X = 0) = 1 - \theta. \quad [B.2]$$

For example, if $\theta = .75$, then there is a 75% chance that a customer shows up after making a reservation and a 25% chance that the customer does not show up. Intuitively, the value of θ is crucial in determining the airline's strategy for booking reservations. Methods for *estimating* θ, given historical data on airline reservations, are a subject of mathematical statistics, something we turn to in Appendix C.

More generally, any discrete random variable is completely described by listing its possible values and the associated probability that it takes on each value. If X takes on the k possible values $\{x_1, \ldots, x_k\}$, then the probabilities $p_1, p_2, \ldots, p_k$ are defined by

$$p_j = P(X = x_j), j = 1, 2, \ldots, k, \quad [B.3]$$

where each p_j is between 0 and 1 and

$$p_1 + p_2 + \ldots + p_k = 1. \quad [B.4]$$

Equation (B.3) is read as: "The probability that X takes on the value x_j is equal to p_j."

Equations (B.1) and (B.2) show that the probabilities of success and failure for a Bernoulli random variable are determined entirely by the value of θ. Because Bernoulli random variables are so prevalent, we have a special notation for them: $X \sim \text{Bernoulli}(\theta)$ is read as "X has a Bernoulli distribution with probability of success equal to θ."

The **probability density function** (**pdf**) of X summarizes the information concerning the possible outcomes of X and the corresponding probabilities:

$$f(x_j) = p_j, j = 1, 2, \ldots, k, \quad [B.5]$$

with $f(x) = 0$ for any x not equal to x_j for some j. In other words, for any real number x, $f(x)$ is the probability that the random variable X takes on the particular value x. When dealing with more than one random variable, it is sometimes useful to subscript the pdf in question: f_X is the pdf of X, f_Y is the pdf of Y, and so on.

Given the pdf of any discrete random variable, it is simple to compute the probability of any event involving that random variable. For example, suppose that X is the number of free throws made by a basketball player out of two attempts, so that X can take on the three values $\{0,1,2\}$. Assume that the pdf of X is given by

$$f(0) = .20, f(1) = .44, \text{ and } f(2) = .36.$$

FIGURE B.1 The pdf of the number of free throws made out of two attempts.

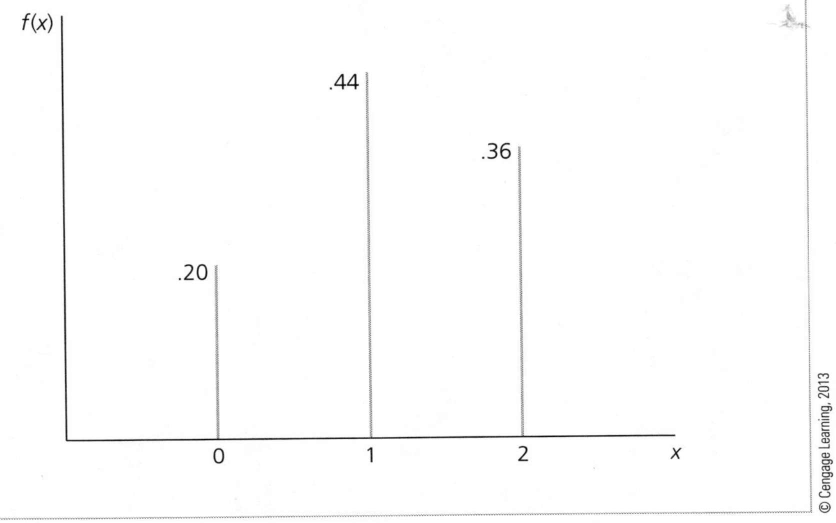

The three probabilities sum to one, as they must. Using this pdf, we can calculate the probability that the player makes *at least* one free throw: $P(X \geq 1) = P(X = 1) + P(X = 2) = .44 + .36 = .80$. The pdf of X is shown in Figure B.1.

Continuous Random Variables

A variable X is a **continuous random variable** if it takes on any real value with *zero* probability. This definition is somewhat counterintuitive because in any application we eventually observe some outcome for a random variable. The idea is that a continuous random variable X can take on so many possible values that we cannot count them or match them up with the positive integers, so logical consistency dictates that X can take on each value with probability zero. While measurements are always discrete in practice, random variables that take on numerous values are best treated as continuous. For example, the most refined measure of the price of a good is in terms of cents. We can imagine listing all possible values of price in order (even though the list may continue indefinitely), which technically makes price a discrete random variable. However, there are so many possible values of price that using the mechanics of discrete random variables is not feasible.

We can define a probability density function for continuous random variables, and, as with discrete random variables, the pdf provides information on the likely outcomes of the random variable. However, because it makes no sense to discuss the probability that a continuous random variable takes on a particular value, we use the pdf of a continuous random variable only to compute events involving a range of values. For example, if a and b are constants where $a < b$, the probability that X lies between the numbers a and b, $P(a \leq X \leq b)$, is the *area* under the pdf between points a and b, as shown in Figure B.2. If you are familiar with calculus, you recognize this as the *integral* of the function f between the points a and b. The entire area under the pdf must always equal one.

FIGURE B.2 The probability that X lies between the points a and b.

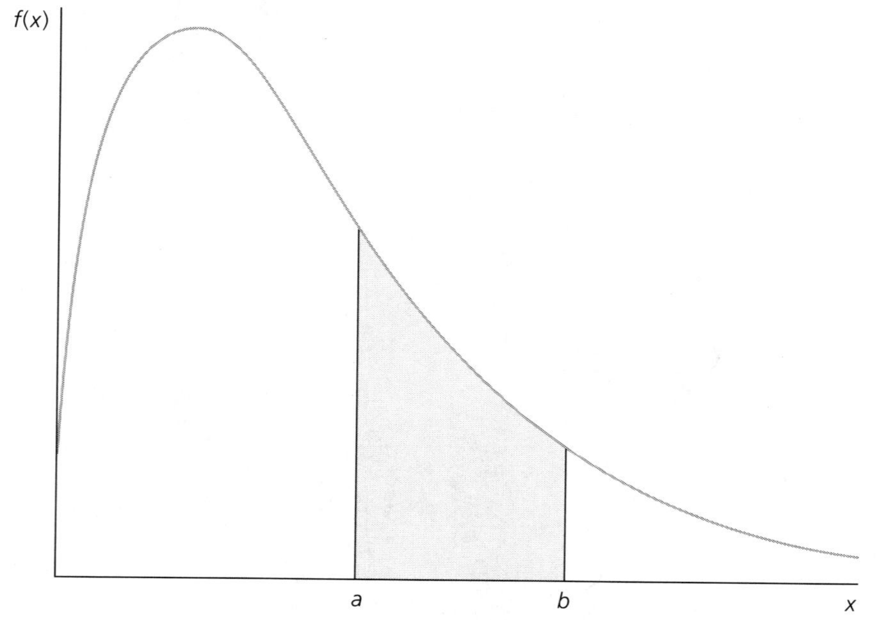

When computing probabilities for continuous random variables, it is easiest to work with the **cumulative distribution function (cdf)**. If X is any random variable, then its cdf is defined for any real number x by

$$F(x) \equiv \mathrm{P}(X \leq x). \quad [B.6]$$

For discrete random variables, (B.6) is obtained by summing the pdf over all values x_j such that $x_j \leq x$. For a continuous random variable, $F(x)$ is the area under the pdf, f, to the left of the point x. Because $F(x)$ is simply a probability, it is always between 0 and 1. Further, if $x_1 < x_2$, then $\mathrm{P}(X \leq x_1) \leq \mathrm{P}(X \leq x_2)$, that is, $F(x_1) \leq F(x_2)$. This means that a cdf is an increasing (or at least a nondecreasing) function of x.

Two important properties of cdfs that are useful for computing probabilities are the following:

$$\text{For any number } c, \ \mathrm{P}(X > c) = 1 - F(c). \quad [B.7]$$

$$\text{For any numbers } a < b, \ \mathrm{P}(a < X \leq b) = F(b) - F(a). \quad [B.8]$$

In our study of econometrics, we will use cdfs to compute probabilities only for continuous random variables, in which case it does not matter whether inequalities in probability statements are strict or not. That is, for a continuous random variable X,

$$P(X \geq c) = P(X > c), \qquad [B.9]$$

and

$$P(a < X < b) = P(a \leq X \leq b) = P(a \leq X < b) = P(a < X \leq b). \qquad [B.10]$$

Combined with (B.7) and (B.8), equations (B.9) and (B.10) greatly expand the probability calculations that can be done using continuous cdfs.

Cumulative distribution functions have been tabulated for all of the important continuous distributions in probability and statistics. The most well known of these is the normal distribution, which we cover along with some related distributions in Section B.5.

B.2 Joint Distributions, Conditional Distributions, and Independence

In economics, we are usually interested in the occurrence of events involving more than one random variable. For example, in the airline reservation example referred to earlier, the airline might be interested in the probability that a person who makes a reservation shows up *and* is a business traveler; this is an example of a *joint probability*. Or, the airline might be interested in the following *conditional probability*: conditional on the person being a business traveler, what is the probability of his or her showing up? In the next two subsections, we formalize the notions of joint and conditional distributions and the important notion of *independence* of random variables.

Joint Distributions and Independence

Let X and Y be discrete random variables. Then, (X,Y) have a **joint distribution**, which is fully described by the *joint probability density function* of (X,Y):

$$f_{X,Y}(x,y) = P(X = x, Y = y), \qquad [B.11]$$

where the right-hand side is the probability that $X = x$ and $Y = y$. When X and Y are continuous, a joint pdf can also be defined, but we will not cover such details because joint pdfs for continuous random variables are not used explicitly in this text.

In one case, it is easy to obtain the joint pdf if we are given the pdfs of X and Y. In particular, random variables X and Y are said to be independent if, and only if,

$$f_{X,Y}(x,y) = f_X(x)f_Y(y) \qquad [B.12]$$

for all x and y, where f_X is the pdf of X and f_Y is the pdf of Y. In the context of more than one random variable, the pdfs f_X and f_Y are often called *marginal probability density functions* to distinguish them from the joint pdf $f_{X,Y}$. This definition of independence is valid for discrete and continuous random variables.

To understand the meaning of (B.12), it is easiest to deal with the discrete case. If X and Y are discrete, then (B.12) is the same as

$$P(X = x, Y = y) = P(X = x)P(Y = y); \qquad [B.13]$$

in other words, the probability that $X = x$ and $Y = y$ is the product of the two probabilities $P(X = x)$ and $P(Y = y)$. One implication of (B.13) is that joint probabilities are fairly easy to compute, since they only require knowledge of $P(X = x)$ and $P(Y = y)$.

If random variables are not independent, then they are said to be *dependent*.

EXAMPLE B.1 FREE THROW SHOOTING

Consider a basketball player shooting two free throws. Let X be the Bernoulli random variable equal to one if she or he makes the first free throw, and zero otherwise. Let Y be a Bernoulli random variable equal to one if he or she makes the second free throw. Suppose that she or he is an 80% free throw shooter, so that $P(X = 1) = P(Y = 1) = .8$. What is the probability of the player making both free throws?

If X and Y are independent, we can easily answer this question: $P(X = 1, Y = 1) = P(X = 1)P(Y = 1) = (.8)(.8) = .64$. Thus, there is a 64% chance of making both free throws. If the chance of making the second free throw depends on whether the first was made—that is, X and Y are not independent—then this simple calculation is not valid.

Independence of random variables is a very important concept. In the next subsection, we will show that if X and Y are independent, then knowing the outcome of X does not change the probabilities of the possible outcomes of Y, and vice versa. One useful fact about independence is that if X and Y are independent and we define new random variables $g(X)$ and $h(Y)$ for any functions g and h, then these new random variables are also independent.

There is no need to stop at two random variables. If $X_1, X_2, \ldots, X_n$ are discrete random variables, then their joint pdf is $f(x_1, x_2, \ldots, x_n) = P(X_1 = x_1, X_2 = x_2, \ldots, X_n = x_n)$. The random variables $X_1, X_2, \ldots, X_n$ are **independent random variables** if, and only if, their joint pdf is the product of the individual pdfs for any $(x_1, x_2, \ldots, x_n)$. This definition of independence also holds for continuous random variables.

The notion of independence plays an important role in obtaining some of the classic distributions in probability and statistics. Earlier, we defined a Bernoulli random variable as a zero-one random variable indicating whether or not some event occurs. Often, we are interested in the number of successes in a sequence of *independent* Bernoulli trials. A standard example of independent Bernoulli trials is flipping a coin again and again. Because the outcome on any particular flip has nothing to do with the outcomes on other flips, independence is an appropriate assumption.

Independence is often a reasonable approximation in more complicated situations. In the airline reservation example, suppose that the airline accepts n reservations for a particular flight. For each $i = 1, 2, \ldots, n$, let Y_i denote the Bernoulli random variable indicating whether customer i shows up: $Y_i = 1$ if customer i appears, and $Y_i = 0$ otherwise. Letting θ again denote the probability of success (using reservation), each Y_i has a Bernoulli(θ) distribution. As an approximation, we might assume that the Y_i are independent of one another, although this is not exactly true in reality: some people travel in groups, which means that whether or not a person shows up is not truly independent of whether all others show up. Modeling this kind of dependence is complex, however, so we might be willing to use independence as an approximation.

The variable of primary interest is the total number of customers showing up out of the n reservations; call this variable X. Since each Y_i is unity when a person shows up, we can write $X = Y_1 + Y_2 + \ldots + Y_n$. Now, assuming that each Y_i has probability of success θ and that the Y_i are independent, X can be shown to have a **binomial distribution**. That is, the probability density function of X is

$$f(x) = \binom{n}{x}\theta^x(1-\theta)^{n-x},\ x = 0, 1, 2, \ldots, n, \qquad \text{[B.14]}$$

where $\binom{n}{x} = \frac{n!}{x!(n-x)!}$, and for any integer n, $n!$ (read "n factorial") is defined as $n! = n\cdot(n-1)\cdot(n-2)\cdots 1$. By convention, $0! = 1$. When a random variable X has the pdf given in (B.14), we write $X \sim \text{Binomial}(n,\theta)$. Equation (B.14) can be used to compute $P(X = x)$ for any value of x from 0 to n.

If the flight has 100 available seats, the airline is interested in $P(X > 100)$. Suppose, initially, that $n = 120$, so that the airline accepts 120 reservations, and the probability that each person shows up is $\theta = .85$. Then, $P(X > 100) = P(X = 101) + P(X = 102) + \ldots + P(X = 120)$, and each of the probabilities in the sum can be found from equation (B.14) with $n = 120$, $\theta = .85$, and the appropriate value of x (101 to 120). This is a difficult hand calculation, but many statistical packages have commands for computing this kind of probability. In this case, the probability that more than 100 people will show up is about .659, which is probably more risk of overbooking than the airline wants to tolerate. If, instead, the number of reservations is 110, the probability of more than 100 passengers showing up is only about .024.

Conditional Distributions

In econometrics, we are usually interested in how one random variable, call it Y, is related to one or more other variables. For now, suppose that there is only one variable whose effects we are interested in, call it X. The most we can know about how X affects Y is contained in the **conditional distribution** of Y given X. This information is summarized by the *conditional probability density function*, defined by

$$f_{Y|X}(y|x) = f_{X,Y}(x,y)/f_X(x) \qquad \text{[B.15]}$$

for all values of x such that $f_X(x) > 0$. The interpretation of (B.15) is most easily seen when X and Y are discrete. Then,

$$f_{Y|X}(y|x) = P(Y = y|X = x), \qquad \text{[B.16]}$$

where the right-hand side is read as "the probability that $Y = y$ given that $X = x$." When Y is continuous, $f_{Y|X}(y|x)$ is not interpretable directly as a probability, for the reasons discussed earlier, but conditional probabilities are found by computing areas under the conditional pdf.

An important feature of conditional distributions is that, if X and Y are independent random variables, knowledge of the value taken on by X tells us nothing about the probability that Y takes on various values (and vice versa). That is, $f_{Y|X}(y|x) = f_Y(y)$, and $f_{X|Y}(x|y) = f_X(x)$.

EXAMPLE B.2 FREE THROW SHOOTING

Consider again the basketball-shooting example, where two free throws are to be attempted. Assume that the conditional density is

$$f_{Y|X}(1|1) = .85, f_{Y|X}(0|1) = .15$$
$$f_{Y|X}(1|0) = .70, f_{Y|X}(0|0) = .30.$$

This means that the probability of the player making the second free throw depends on whether the first free throw was made: if the first free throw is made, the chance of making the second is .85; if the first free throw is missed, the chance of making the second is .70. This implies that X and Y are *not* independent; they are dependent.

We can still compute $\text{P}(X = 1, Y = 1)$ provided we know $\text{P}(X = 1)$. Assume that the probability of making the first free throw is .8, that is, $\text{P}(X = 1) = .8$. Then, from (B.15), we have

$$\text{P}(X = 1, Y = 1) = \text{P}(Y = 1|X = 1) \cdot \text{P}(X = 1) = (.85)(.8) = .68.$$

B.3 Features of Probability Distributions

For many purposes, we will be interested in only a few aspects of the distributions of random variables. The features of interest can be put into three categories: measures of central tendency, measures of variability or spread, and measures of association between two random variables. We cover the last of these in Section B.4.

A Measure of Central Tendency: The Expected Value

The expected value is one of the most important probabilistic concepts that we will encounter in our study of econometrics. If X is a random variable, the **expected value** (or expectation) of X, denoted $\text{E}(X)$ and sometimes μX or simply μ, is a weighted average of all possible values of X. The weights are determined by the probability density function. Sometimes, the expected value is called the *population mean*, especially when we want to emphasize that X represents some variable in a population.

The precise definition of expected value is simplest in the case that X is a discrete random variable taking on a finite number of values, say, $\{x_1, \ldots, x_k\}$. Let $f(x)$ denote the probability density function of X. The expected value of X is the weighted average

$$\text{E}(X) = x_1 f(x_1) + x_2 f(x_2) + \ldots + x_k f(x_k) \equiv \sum_{j=1}^{k} x_j f(x_j). \qquad [B.17]$$

This is easily computed given the values of the pdf at each possible outcome of X.

EXAMPLE B.3 COMPUTING AN EXPECTED VALUE

Suppose that X takes on the values -1, 0, and 2 with probabilities 1/8, 1/2, and 3/8, respectively. Then,

$$\text{E}(X) = (-1)\cdot(1/8) + 0\cdot(1/2) + 2\cdot(3/8) = 5/8.$$

This example illustrates something curious about expected values: the expected value of X can be a number that is not even a possible outcome of X. We know that X takes on the values -1, 0, or 2, yet its expected value is 5/8. This makes the expected value deficient for summarizing the central tendency of certain discrete random variables, but calculations such as those just mentioned can be useful, as we will see later.

If X is a continuous random variable, then $\mathrm{E}(X)$ is defined as an integral:

$$\mathrm{E}(X) = \int_{-\infty}^{\infty} xf(x)dx, \qquad [\text{B.18}]$$

which we assume is well defined. This can still be interpreted as a weighted average. For the most common continuous distributions, $\mathrm{E}(X)$ is a number that is a possible outcome of X. In this text, we will not need to compute expected values using integration, although we will draw on some well-known results from probability for expected values of special random variables.

Given a random variable X and a function $g(\cdot)$, we can create a new random variable $g(X)$. For example, if X is a random variable, then so is X^2 and $\log(X)$ (if $X > 0$). The expected value of $g(X)$ is, again, simply a weighted average:

$$\mathrm{E}[g(X)] = \sum_{j=1}^{k} g(x_j)f_X(x_j) \qquad [\text{B.19}]$$

or, for a continuous random variable,

$$\mathrm{E}[g(X)] = \int_{-\infty}^{\infty} g(x)f_X(x)dx. \qquad [\text{B.20}]$$

EXAMPLE B.4 EXPECTED VALUE OF X^2

For the random variable in Example B.3, let $g(X) = X^2$. Then,

$$\mathrm{E}(X^2) = (-1)^2(1/8) + (0)^2(1/2) + (2)^2(3/8) = 13/8.$$

In Example B.3, we computed $\mathrm{E}(X) = 5/8$, so that $[\mathrm{E}(X)]^2 = 25/64$. This shows that $\mathrm{E}(X^2)$ is *not* the same as $[\mathrm{E}(X)]^2$. In fact, for a nonlinear function $g(X)$, $\mathrm{E}[g(X)] \neq g[\mathrm{E}(X)]$ (except in very special cases).

If X and Y are random variables, then $g(X,Y)$ is a random variable for any function g, and so we can define its expectation. When X and Y are both discrete, taking on values $\{x_1, x_2, \ldots, x_k\}$ and $\{y_1, y_2, \ldots, y_m\}$, respectively, the expected value is

$$\mathrm{E}[g(X,Y)] = \sum_{h=1}^{k}\sum_{j=1}^{m} g(x_h,y_j)f_{X,Y}(x_h,y_j),$$

where $f_{X,Y}$ is the joint pdf of (X,Y). The definition is more complicated for continuous random variables since it involves integration; we do not need it here. The extension to more than two random variables is straightforward.

Properties of Expected Values

In econometrics, we are not so concerned with computing expected values from various distributions; the major calculations have been done many times, and we will largely take these on faith. We will need to manipulate some expected values using a few simple rules. These are so important that we give them labels:

Property E.1: For any constant c, $E(c) = c$.

Property E.2: For any constants a and b, $E(aX + b) = aE(X) + b$.

One useful implication of E.2 is that, if $\mu = E(X)$, and we define a new random variable as $Y = X - \mu$, then $E(Y) = 0$; in E.2, take $a = 1$ and $b = -\mu$.

As an example of Property E.2, let X be the temperature measured in Celsius at noon on a particular day at a given location; suppose the expected temperature is $E(X) = 25$. If Y is the temperature measured in Fahrenheit, then $Y = 32 + (9/5)X$. From Property E.2, the expected temperature in Fahrenheit is $E(Y) = 32 + (9/5)\cdot E(X) = 32 + (9/5)\cdot 25 = 77$.

Generally, it is easy to compute the expected value of a linear function of many random variables.

Property E.3: If $\{a_1, a_2, \ldots, a_n\}$ are constants and $\{X_1, X_2, \ldots, X_n\}$ are random variables, then

$$E(a_1X_1 + a_2X_2 + \ldots + a_nX_n) = a_1E(X_1) + a_2E(X_2) + \ldots + a_nE(X_n).$$

Or, using summation notation,

$$E\left(\sum_{i=1}^{n} a_iX_i\right) = \sum_{i=1}^{n} a_iE(X_i). \quad [B.21]$$

As a special case of this, we have (with each $a_i = 1$)

$$E\left(\sum_{i=1}^{n} X_i\right) = \sum_{i=1}^{n} E(X_i). \quad [B.22]$$

so that the expected value of the sum is the sum of expected values. This property is used often for derivations in mathematical statistics.

EXAMPLE B.5 FINDING EXPECTED REVENUE

Let X_1, X_2, and X_3 be the numbers of small, medium, and large pizzas, respectively, sold during the day at a pizza parlor. These are random variables with expected values $E(X_1) = 25$, $E(X_2) = 57$, and $E(X_3) = 40$. The prices of small, medium, and large pizzas are \$5.50, \$7.60, and \$9.15. Therefore, the expected revenue from pizza sales on a given day is

$$\begin{aligned} E(5.50\,X_1 + 7.60\,X_2 + 9.15\,X_3) &= 5.50\,E(X_1) + 7.60\,E(X_2) + 9.15\,E(X_3) \\ &= 5.50(25) + 7.60(57) + 9.15(40) = 936.70, \end{aligned}$$

that is, \$936.70. The actual revenue on any particular day will generally differ from this value, but this is the *expected* revenue.

We can also use Property E.3 to show that if $X \sim \text{Binomial}(n,\theta)$, then $E(X) = n\theta$. That is, the expected number of successes in n Bernoulli trials is simply the number of trials times the probability of success on any particular trial. This is easily seen by writing X as $X = Y_1 + Y_2 + \ldots + Y_n$, where each $Y_i \sim \text{Bernoulli}(\theta)$. Then,

$$E(X) = \sum_{i=1}^{n} E(Y_i) = \sum_{i=1}^{n} \theta = n\theta.$$

We can apply this to the airline reservation example, where the airline makes $n = 120$ reservations, and the probability of showing up is $\theta = .85$. The *expected* number of people showing up is $120(.85) = 102$. Therefore, if there are 100 seats available, the expected number of people showing up is too large; this has some bearing on whether it is a good idea for the airline to make 120 reservations.

Actually, what the airline should do is define a profit function that accounts for the net revenue earned per seat sold and the cost per passenger bumped from the flight. This profit function is random because the actual number of people showing up is random. Let r be the net revenue from each passenger. (You can think of this as the price of the ticket for simplicity.) Let c be the compensation owed to any passenger bumped from the flight. Neither r nor c is random; these are assumed to be known to the airline. Let Y denote profits for the flight. Then, with 100 seats available,

$$\begin{aligned} Y &= rX \quad \text{if } X \leq 100 \\ &= 100r - c(X - 100) \text{ if } X > 100. \end{aligned}$$

The first equation gives profit if no more than 100 people show up for the flight; the second equation is profit if more than 100 people show up. (In the latter case, the net revenue from ticket sales is $100r$, since all 100 seats are sold, and then $c(X - 100)$ is the cost of making more than 100 reservations.) Using the fact that X has a Binomial(n,.85) distribution, where n is the number of reservations made, expected profits, $E(Y)$, can be found as a function of n (and r and c). Computing $E(Y)$ directly would be quite difficult, but it can be found quickly using a computer. Once values for r and c are given, the value of n that maximizes expected profits can be found by searching over different values of n.

Another Measure of Central Tendency: The Median

The expected value is only one possibility for defining the central tendency of a random variable. Another measure of central tendency is the **median**. A general definition of *median* is too complicated for our purposes. If X is continuous, then the median of X, say, m, is the value such that one-half of the area under the pdf is to the left of m, and one-half of the area is to the right of m.

When X is discrete and takes on a finite number of odd values, the median is obtained by ordering the possible values of X and then selecting the value in the middle. For example, if X can take on the values $\{-4,0,2,8,10,13,17\}$, then the median value of X is 8. If X takes on an even number of values, there are really two median values; sometimes, these are averaged to get a unique median value. Thus, if X takes on the values $\{-5,3,9,17\}$, then the median values are 3 and 9; if we average these, we get a median equal to 6.

In general, the median, sometimes denoted Med(X), and the expected value, $E(X)$, are different. Neither is "better" than the other as a measure of central tendency; they are both valid ways to measure the center of the distribution of X. In one special case, the median

FIGURE B.3 A symmetric probability distribution.

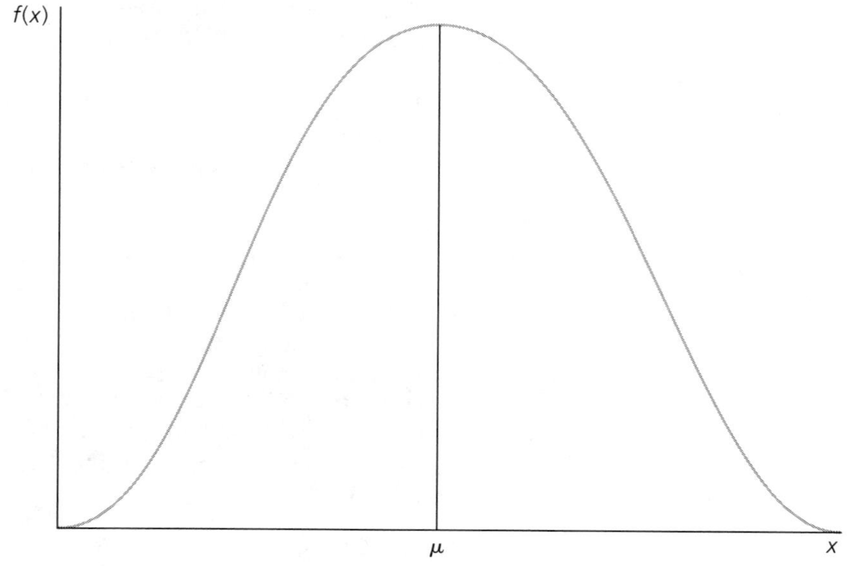

and expected value (or mean) are the same. If X has a **symmetric distribution** about the value μ, then μ is both the expected value and the median. Mathematically, the condition is $f(\mu + x) = f(\mu - x)$ for all x. This case is illustrated in Figure B.3.

Measures of Variability: Variance and Standard Deviation

Although the central tendency of a random variable is valuable, it does not tell us everything we want to know about the distribution of a random variable. Figure B.4 shows the pdfs of two random variables with the same mean. Clearly, the distribution of X is more tightly centered about its mean than is the distribution of Y. We would like to have a simple way of summarizing differences in the spreads of distributions.

Variance

For a random variable X, let $\mu = \mathrm{E}(X)$. There are various ways to measure how far X is from its expected value, but the simplest one to work with algebraically is the squared difference, $(X - \mu)^2$. (The squaring eliminates the sign from the distance measure; the resulting positive value corresponds to our intuitive notion of distance, and treats values above and below μ symmetrically.) This distance is itself a random variable since it can change with every outcome of X. Just as we needed a number to summarize the central tendency of X, we need a number that tells us how far X is from μ, *on average*. One such number is the **variance**, which tells us the expected distance from X to its mean:

$$\mathrm{Var}(X) \equiv \mathrm{E}[(X - \mu)^2]. \quad [B.23]$$

FIGURE B.4 Random variables with the same mean but different distributions.

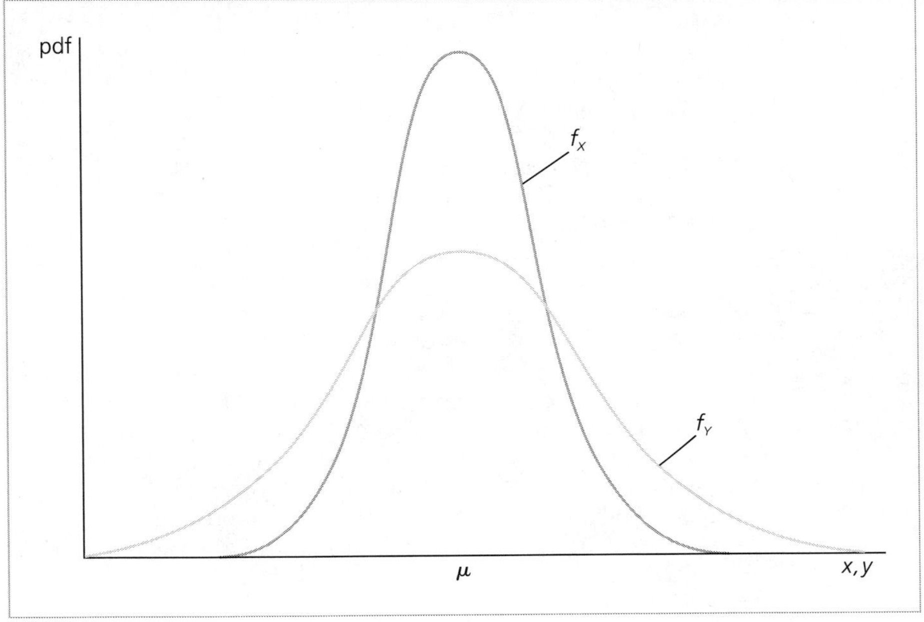

Variance is sometimes denoted σ_X^2, or simply σ^2, when the context is clear. From (B.23), it follows that the variance is always nonnegative.

As a computational device, it is useful to observe that

$$\sigma^2 = \mathrm{E}(X^2 - 2X\mu + \mu^2) = \mathrm{E}(X^2) - 2\mu^2 + \mu^2 = \mathrm{E}(X^2) - \mu^2. \quad \text{[B.24]}$$

In using either (B.23) or (B.24), we need not distinguish between discrete and continuous random variables: the definition of variance is the same in either case. Most often, we first compute E(X), then E(X^2), and then we use the formula in (B.24). For example, if $X \sim$ Bernoulli(θ), then E(X) = θ, and, since $X^2 = X$, E(X^2) = θ. It follows from equation (B.24) that Var(X) = E(X^2) − $\mu^2 = \theta - \theta^2 = \theta(1 - \theta)$.

Two important properties of the variance follow.

Property VAR.1: Var(X) = 0 if, and only if, there is a constant c such that $P(X = c) = 1$, in which case E(X) = c.

This first property says that the variance of any constant is zero and if a random variable has zero variance, then it is essentially constant.

Property VAR.2: For any constants a and b, Var($aX + b$) = a^2Var(X).

This means that adding a constant to a random variable does not change the variance, but multiplying a random variable by a constant increases the variance by a factor equal to the *square* of that constant. For example, if X denotes temperature in Celsius and $Y = 32 + (9/5)X$ is temperature in Fahrenheit, then Var(Y) = $(9/5)^2$Var(X) = (81/25)Var(X).

Standard Deviation

The **standard deviation** of a random variable, denoted sd(X), is simply the positive square root of the variance: $\text{sd}(X) \equiv +\sqrt{\text{Var}(X)}$. The standard deviation is sometimes denoted σ_X, or simply σ, when the random variable is understood. Two standard deviation properties immediately follow from Properties VAR.1 and VAR.2.

Property SD.1: For any constant c, $\text{sd}(c) = 0$.

Property SD.2: For any constants a and b,

$$\text{sd}(aX + b) = |a|\text{sd}(X).$$

In particular, if $a > 0$, then $\text{sd}(aX) = a \cdot \text{sd}(X)$.

This last property makes the standard deviation more natural to work with than the variance. For example, suppose that X is a random variable measured in thousands of dollars, say, income. If we define $Y = 1{,}000X$, then Y is income measured in dollars. Suppose that $\text{E}(X) = 20$, and $\text{sd}(X) = 6$. Then, $\text{E}(Y) = 1{,}000\text{E}(X) = 20{,}000$, and $\text{sd}(Y) = 1{,}000 \cdot \text{sd}(X) = 6{,}000$, so that the expected value and standard deviation both increase by the same factor, 1,000. If we worked with variance, we would have $\text{Var}(Y) = (1{,}000)^2\text{Var}(X)$, so that the variance of Y is one million times larger than the variance of X.

Standardizing a Random Variable

As an application of the properties of variance and standard deviation—and a topic of practical interest in its own right—suppose that given a random variable X, we define a new random variable by subtracting off its mean m and dividing by its standard deviation σ:

$$Z \equiv \frac{X - \mu}{\sigma}, \quad \text{[B.25]}$$

which we can write as $Z = aX + b$, where $a \equiv (1/\sigma)$, and $b \equiv -(\mu/\sigma)$. Then, from Property E.2,

$$\text{E}(Z) = a\text{E}(X) + b = (\mu/\sigma) - (\mu/\sigma) = 0.$$

From Property VAR.2,

$$\text{Var}(Z) = a^2\text{Var}(X) = (\sigma^2/\sigma^2) = 1.$$

Thus, the random variable Z has a mean of zero and a variance (and therefore a standard deviation) equal to one. This procedure is sometimes known as *standardizing* the random variable X, and Z is called a **standardized random variable**. (In introductory statistics courses, it is sometimes called the *z-transform* of X.) It is important to remember that the standard deviation, not the variance, appears in the denominator of (B.25). As we will see, this transformation is frequently used in statistical inference.

As a specific example, suppose that $\text{E}(X) = 2$, and $\text{Var}(X) = 9$. Then, $Z = (X - 2)/3$ has expected value zero and variance one.

Skewness and Kurtosis

We can use the standardized version of a random variable to define other features of the distribution of a random variable. These features are described by using what are called *higher order moments*. For example, the third moment of the random variable Z in (B.25) is used to determine whether a distribution is symmetric about its mean. We can write

$$E(Z^3) = E[(X - \mu)^3]/\sigma^3$$

If X has a symmetric distribution about μ, then Z has a symmetric distribution about zero. (The division by σ^3 does not change whether the distribution is symmetric.) That means the density of Z at any two points z and $-z$ is the same, which means that, in computing $E(Z^3)$, positive values z^3 when $z > 0$ are exactly offset with the negative value $(-z)^3 = -z^3$. It follows that, if X is symmetric about zero, then $E(Z) = 0$. Generally, $E[(X - \mu)^3]/\sigma^3$ is viewed as a measure of **skewness** in the distribution of X. In a statistical setting, we might use data to estimate $E(Z^3)$ to determine whether an underlying population distribution appears to be symmetric. (Computer Exercise C5.4 in Chapter 5 provides an illustration.)

It also can be informative to compute the fourth moment of Z,

$$E(Z^4) = E[(X - \mu)^4]/\sigma^4.$$

Because $Z^4 \geq 0$, $E(Z^4) \geq 0$ (and, in any interesting case, strictly greater than zero). Without having a reference value, it is difficult to interpret values of $E(Z^4)$, but larger values mean that the tails in the distribution of X are thicker. The fourth moment $E(Z^4)$ is called a measure of **kurtosis** in the distribution of X. In Section B.5 we will obtain $E(Z^4)$ for the normal distribution.

B.4 Features of Joint and Conditional Distributions

Measures of Association: Covariance and Correlation

While the joint pdf of two random variables completely describes the relationship between them, it is useful to have summary measures of how, on average, two random variables vary with one another. As with the expected value and variance, this is similar to using a single number to summarize something about an entire distribution, which in this case is a joint distribution of two random variables.

Covariance

Let $\mu_X = E(X)$ and $\mu_Y = E(Y)$ and consider the random variable $(X - \mu_X)(Y - \mu_Y)$. Now, if X is above its mean and Y is above its mean, then $(X - \mu_X)(Y - \mu_Y) > 0$. This is also true if $X < \mu_X$ and $Y < \mu_Y$. On the other hand, if $X > \mu_X$ and $Y < \mu_Y$, or vice versa, then $(X - \mu_X)(Y - \mu_Y) < 0$. How, then, can this product tell us anything about the relationship between X and Y?

The **covariance** between two random variables X and Y, sometimes called the *population covariance* to emphasize that it concerns the relationship between two variables describing a population, is defined as the expected value of the product $(X - \mu_X)(Y - \mu_Y)$:

$$\text{Cov}(X,Y) \equiv \text{E}[(X - \mu_X)(Y - \mu_Y)], \tag{B.26}$$

which is sometimes denoted σ_{XY}. If $\sigma_{XY} > 0$, then, on average, when X is above its mean, Y is also above its mean. If $\sigma_{XY} < 0$, then, on average, when X is above its mean, Y is below its mean.

Several expressions useful for computing $\text{Cov}(X,Y)$ are as follows:

$$\begin{aligned}\text{Cov}(X,Y) &= \text{E}[(X - \mu_X)(Y - \mu_Y)] = \text{E}[(X - \mu_X)Y] \\ &= \text{E}[X(Y - \mu_Y)] = \text{E}(XY) - \mu_X\mu_Y.\end{aligned} \tag{B.27}$$

It follows from (B.27), that if $\text{E}(X) = 0$ or $\text{E}(Y) = 0$, then $\text{Cov}(X,Y) = \text{E}(XY)$.

Covariance measures the amount of *linear* dependence between two random variables. A positive covariance indicates that two random variables move in the same direction, while a negative covariance indicates they move in opposite directions. Interpreting the *magnitude* of a covariance can be a little tricky, as we will see shortly.

Because covariance is a measure of how two random variables are related, it is natural to ask how covariance is related to the notion of independence. This is given by the following property.

Property COV.1: If X and Y are independent, then $\text{Cov}(X,Y) = 0$.

This property follows from equation (B.27) and the fact that $\text{E}(XY) = \text{E}(X)\text{E}(Y)$ when X and Y are independent. It is important to remember that the converse of COV.1 is *not* true: zero covariance between X and Y does not imply that X and Y are independent. In fact, there are random variables X such that, if $Y = X^2$, $\text{Cov}(X,Y) = 0$. [Any random variable with $\text{E}(X) = 0$ and $\text{E}(X^3) = 0$ has this property.] If $Y = X^2$, then X and Y are clearly not independent: once we know X, we know Y. It seems rather strange that X and X^2 could have zero covariance, and this reveals a weakness of covariance as a general measure of association between random variables. The covariance is useful in contexts when relationships are at least approximately linear.

The second major property of covariance involves covariances between linear functions.

Property COV.2: For any constants a_1, b_1, a_2, and b_2,

$$\text{Cov}(a_1X + b_1, a_2Y + b_2) = a_1a_2\text{Cov}(X,Y). \tag{B.28}$$

An important implication of COV.2 is that the covariance between two random variables can be altered simply by multiplying one or both of the random variables by a constant. This is important in economics because monetary variables, inflation rates, and so on can be defined with different units of measurement without changing their meaning.

Finally, it is useful to know that the absolute value of the covariance between any two random variables is bounded by the product of their standard deviations; this is known as the *Cauchy-Schwartz inequality.*

Property COV.3: $|\text{Cov}(X,Y)| \leq \text{sd}(X)\text{sd}(Y)$.

Correlation Coefficient

Suppose we want to know the relationship between amount of education and annual earnings in the working population. We could let X denote education and Y denote earnings and then compute their covariance. But the answer we get will depend on how we choose to measure education and earnings. Property COV.2 implies that the covariance between education and earnings depends on whether earnings are measured in dollars or thousands of dollars, or whether education is measured in months or years. It is pretty clear that how we measure these variables has no bearing on how strongly they are related. But the covariance between them does depend on the units of measurement.

The fact that the covariance depends on units of measurement is a deficiency that is overcome by the **correlation coefficient** between X and Y:

$$\text{Corr}(X,Y) \equiv \frac{\text{Cov}(X,Y)}{\text{sd}(X)\cdot\text{sd}(Y)} = \frac{\sigma_{XY}}{\sigma_X\sigma_Y}; \qquad \text{[B.29]}$$

the correlation coefficient between X and Y is sometimes denoted ρ_{XY} (and is sometimes called the *population correlation*).

Because σ_X and σ_Y are positive, Cov(X,Y) and Corr(X,Y) always have the same sign, and Corr(X,Y) = 0 if, and only if, Cov(X,Y) = 0. Some of the properties of covariance carry over to correlation. If X and Y are independent, then Corr(X,Y) = 0, but zero correlation does not imply independence. (Like the covariance, the correlation coefficient is also a measure of linear dependence.) However, the magnitude of the correlation coefficient is easier to interpret than the size of the covariance due to the following property.

Property CORR.1: $-1 \leq \text{Corr}(X,Y) \leq 1$.

If Corr(X,Y) = 0, or equivalently Cov(X,Y) = 0, then there is no linear relationship between X and Y, and X and Y are said to be **uncorrelated random variables**; otherwise, X and Y are *correlated.* Corr(X,Y) = 1 implies a perfect positive linear relationship, which means that we can write $Y = a + bX$ for some constant a and some constant $b > 0$. Corr(X,Y) = -1 implies a perfect negative linear relationship, so that $Y = a + bX$ for some $b < 0$. The extreme cases of positive or negative 1 rarely occur. Values of ρ_{XY} closer to 1 or -1 indicate stronger linear relationships.

As mentioned earlier, the correlation between X and Y is invariant to the units of measurement of either X or Y. This is stated more generally as follows.

Property CORR.2: For constants a_1, b_1, a_2, and b_2, with $a_1a_2 > 0$,

$$\text{Corr}(a_1X + b_1, a_2Y + b_2) = \text{Corr}(X,Y).$$

If $a_1a_2 < 0$, then

$$\text{Corr}(a_1X + b_1, a_2Y + b_2) = -\text{Corr}(X,Y).$$

As an example, suppose that the correlation between earnings and education in the working population is .15. This measure does not depend on whether earnings are measured in dollars, thousands of dollars, or any other unit; it also does not depend on whether education is measured in years, quarters, months, and so on.

Variance of Sums of Random Variables

Now that we have defined covariance and correlation, we can complete our list of major properties of the variance.

Property VAR.3: For constants a and b,

$$\text{Var}(aX + bY) = a^2\text{Var}(X) + b^2\text{Var}(Y) + 2ab\text{Cov}(X,Y).$$

It follows immediately that, if X and Y are uncorrelated—so that $\text{Cov}(X,Y) = 0$—then

$$\text{Var}(X + Y) = \text{Var}(X) + \text{Var}(Y) \qquad \text{[B.30]}$$

and

$$\text{Var}(X - Y) = \text{Var}(X) + \text{Var}(Y). \qquad \text{[B.31]}$$

In the latter case, note how the variance of the difference is the *sum of the variances*, not the difference in the variances.

As an example of (B.30), let X denote profits earned by a restaurant during a Friday night and let Y be profits earned on the following Saturday night. Then, $Z = X + Y$ is profits for the two nights. Suppose X and Y each have an expected value of \$300 and a standard deviation of \$15 (so that the variance is 225). Expected profits for the two nights is $\text{E}(Z) = \text{E}(X) + \text{E}(Y) = 2\cdot(300) = 600$ dollars. If X and Y are independent, and therefore uncorrelated, then the variance of total profits is the sum of the variances: $\text{Var}(Z) = \text{Var}(X) + \text{Var}(Y) = 2\cdot(225) = 450$. It follows that the standard deviation of total profits is $\sqrt{450}$ or about \$21.21.

Expressions (B.30) and (B.31) extend to more than two random variables. To state this extension, we need a definition. The random variables $\{X_1, \ldots, X_n\}$ are **pairwise uncorrelated random variables** if each variable in the set is uncorrelated with every other variable in the set. That is, $\text{Cov}(X_i,X_j) = 0$, for all $i \neq j$.

Property VAR.4: If $\{X_1, \ldots, X_n\}$ are pairwise uncorrelated random variables and $\{a_i: i = 1, \ldots, n\}$ are constants, then

$$\text{Var}(a_1X_1 + \ldots + a_nX_n) = a_1^2\text{Var}(X_1) + \ldots + a_n^2\text{Var}(X_n).$$

In summation notation, we can write

$$\text{Var}\left(\sum_{i=1}^{n} a_iX_i\right) = \sum_{i=1}^{n} a_i^2\text{Var}(X_i). \qquad \text{[B.32]}$$

A special case of Property VAR.4 occurs when we take $a_i = 1$ for all i. Then, for pairwise uncorrelated random variables, the variance of the sum is the sum of the variances:

$$\text{Var}\left(\sum_{i=1}^{n} X_i\right) = \sum_{i=1}^{n} \text{Var}(X_i). \qquad \text{[B.33]}$$

Because independent random variables are uncorrelated (see Property COV.1), the variance of a sum of independent random variables is the sum of the variances.

If the X_i are not pairwise uncorrelated, then the expression for $\text{Var}\left(\sum_{i=1}^{n} a_iX_i\right)$ is much more complicated; we must add to the right-hand side of (B.32) the terms $2a_ia_j\text{Cov}(x_i,x_j)$ for all $i > j$.

We can use (B.33) to derive the variance for a binomial random variable. Let $X \sim \text{Binomial}(n,\theta)$ and write $X = Y_1 + \dots + Y_n$, where the Y_i are independent Bernoulli(θ) random variables. Then, by (B.33), $\text{Var}(X) = \text{Var}(Y_1) + \dots + \text{Var}(Y_n) = n\theta(1 - \theta)$.

In the airline reservation example with $n = 120$ and $\theta = .85$, the variance of the number of passengers arriving for their reservations is $120(.85)(.15) = 15.3$, so the standard deviation is about 3.9.

Conditional Expectation

Covariance and correlation measure the linear relationship between two random variables and treat them symmetrically. More often in the social sciences, we would like to explain one variable, called Y, in terms of another variable, say, X. Further, if Y is related to X in a nonlinear fashion, we would like to know this. Call Y the explained variable and X the explanatory variable. For example, Y might be hourly wage, and X might be years of formal education.

We have already introduced the notion of the conditional probability density function of Y given X. Thus, we might want to see how the distribution of wages changes with education level. However, we usually want to have a simple way of summarizing this distribution. A single number will no longer suffice, since the distribution of Y given $X = x$ generally depends on the value of x. Nevertheless, we can summarize the relationship between Y and X by looking at the **conditional expectation** of Y given X, sometimes called the *conditional mean.* The idea is this. Suppose we know that X has taken on a particular value, say, x. Then, we can compute the expected value of Y, given that we know this outcome of X. We denote this expected value by $\text{E}(Y|X = x)$, or sometimes $\text{E}(Y|x)$ for shorthand. Generally, as x changes, so does $\text{E}(Y|x)$.

When Y is a discrete random variable taking on values $\{y_1, \dots, y_m\}$, then

$$\text{E}(Y|x) = \sum_{j=1}^{m} y_j f_{Y|X}(y_j|x).$$

When Y is continuous, $\text{E}(Y|x)$ is defined by integrating $yf_{Y|X}(y|x)$ over all possible values of y. As with unconditional expectations, the conditional expectation is a weighted average of possible values of Y, but now the weights reflect the fact that X has taken on a specific value. Thus, $\text{E}(Y|x)$ is just some function of x, which tells us how the expected value of Y varies with x.

As an example, let (X,Y) represent the population of all working individuals, where X is years of education and Y is hourly wage. Then, $\text{E}(Y|X = 12)$ is the average hourly wage for all people in the population with 12 years of education (roughly a high school education). $\text{E}(Y|X = 16)$ is the average hourly wage for all people with 16 years of education. Tracing out the expected value for various levels of education provides important information on how wages and education are related. See Figure B.5 for an illustration.

In principle, the expected value of hourly wage can be found at each level of education, and these expectations can be summarized in a table. Because education can vary

FIGURE B.5 The expected value of hourly wage given various levels of education.

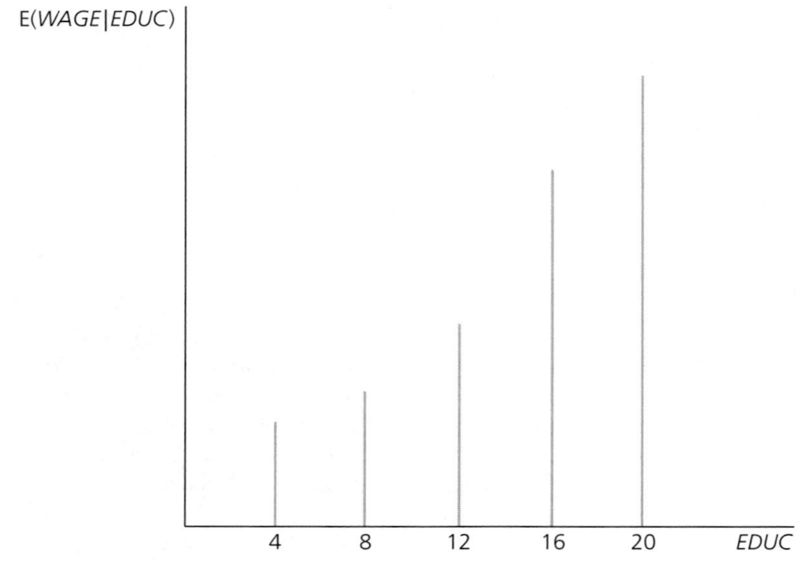

widely—and can even be measured in fractions of a year—this is a cumbersome way to show the relationship between average wage and amount of education. In econometrics, we typically specify simple functions that capture this relationship. As an example, suppose that the expected value of *WAGE* given *EDUC* is the linear function

$$\mathrm{E}(WAGE|EDUC) = 1.05 + .45\ EDUC.$$

If this relationship holds in the population of working people, the average wage for people with 8 years of education is $1.05 + .45(8) = 4.65$, or \$4.65. The average wage for people with 16 years of education is 8.25, or \$8.25. The coefficient on *EDUC* implies that each year of education increases the expected hourly wage by .45, or 45¢.

Conditional expectations can also be nonlinear functions. For example, suppose that $\mathrm{E}(Y|x) = 10/x$, where X is a random variable that is always greater than zero. This function is graphed in Figure B.6. This could represent a demand function, where Y is quantity demanded and X is price. If Y and X are related in this way, an analysis of linear association, such as correlation analysis, would be incomplete.

Properties of Conditional Expectation

Several basic properties of conditional expectations are useful for derivations in econometric analysis.

Property CE.1: $\mathrm{E}[c(X)|X] = c(X)$, for any function $c(X)$.

FIGURE B.6 Graph of $E(Y|x) = 10/x$.

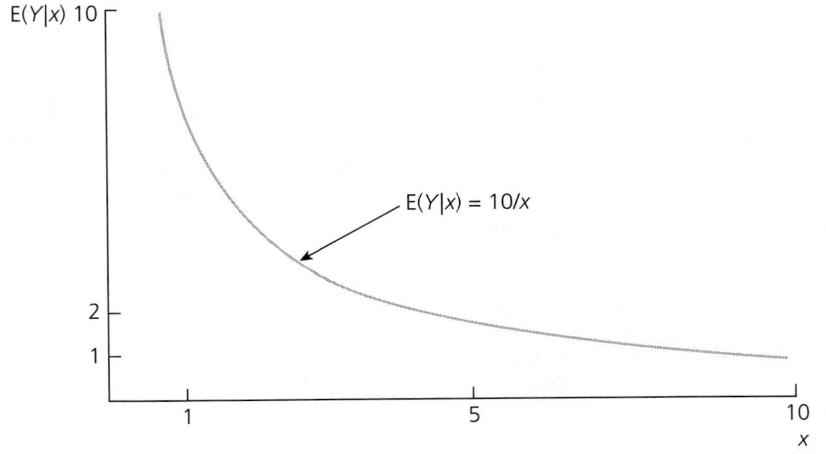

This first property means that functions of X behave as constants when we compute expectations conditional on X. For example, $E(X^2|X) = X^2$. Intuitively, this simply means that if we know X, then we also know X^2.

Property CE.2: For functions $a(X)$ and $b(X)$,

$$E[a(X)Y + b(X)|X] = a(X)E(Y|X) + b(X).$$

For example, we can easily compute the conditional expectation of a function such as $XY + 2X^2$: $E(XY + 2X^2|X) = XE(Y|X) + 2X^2$.

The next property ties together the notions of independence and conditional expectations.

Property CE.3: If X and Y are independent, then $E(Y|X) = E(Y)$.

This property means that, if X and Y are independent, then the expected value of Y given X does not depend on X, in which case, $E(Y|X)$ always equals the (unconditional) expected-value of Y. In the wage and education example, if wages were independent of education, then the average wages of high school and college graduates would be the same. Since this is almost certainly false, we cannot assume that wage and education are independent.

A special case of Property CE.3 is the following: if U and X are independent and $E(U) = 0$, then $E(U|X) = 0$.

There are also properties of the conditional expectation that have to do with the fact that $E(Y|X)$ is a function of X, say, $E(Y|X) = \mu(X)$. Because X is a random variable, $\mu(X)$ is also a random variable. Furthermore, $\mu(X)$ has a probability distribution and therefore an expected value. Generally, the expected value of $\mu(X)$ could be very difficult to compute directly. The **law of iterated expectations** says that the expected value of $\mu(X)$ is simply equal to the expected value of Y. We write this as follows.

Property CE.4: $E[E(Y|X)] = E(Y)$.

This property is a little hard to grasp at first. It means that, if we first obtain $E(Y|X)$ as a function of X and take the expected value of this (with respect to the distribution of X, of course), then we end up with $E(Y)$. This is hardly obvious, but it can be derived using the definition of expected values.

As an example of how to use Property CE.4, let $Y = WAGE$ and $X = EDUC$, where *WAGE* is measured in hours and *EDUC* is measured in years. Suppose the expected value of *WAGE* given *EDUC* is $E(WAGE|EDUC) = 4 + .60\, EDUC$. Further, $E(EDUC) = 11.5$. Then, the law of iterated expectations implies that $E(WAGE) = E(4 + .60\, EDUC) = 4 + .60\, E(EDUC) = 4 + .60(11.5) = 10.90$, or \$10.90 an hour.

The next property states a more general version of the law of iterated expectations.

Property CE.4': $E(Y|X) = E[E(Y|X,Z)|X]$.

In other words, we can find $E(Y|X)$ in two steps. First, find $E(Y|X,Z)$ for any other random variable Z. Then, find the expected value of $E(Y|X,Z)$, conditional on X.

Property CE.5: If $E(Y|X) = E(Y)$, then $Cov(X,Y) = 0$ [and so $Corr(X,Y) = 0$]. In fact, *every* function of X is uncorrelated with Y.

This property means that, if knowledge of X does not change the expected value of Y, then X and Y *must* be uncorrelated, which implies that if X and Y are correlated, then $E(Y|X)$ must depend on X. The converse of Property CE.5 is not true: if X and Y are uncorrelated, $E(Y|X)$ *could* still depend on X. For example, suppose $Y = X^2$. Then, $E(Y|X) = X^2$, which is clearly a function of X. However, as we mentioned in our discussion of covariance and correlation, it is possible that X and X^2 are uncorrelated. The conditional expectation captures the nonlinear relationship between X and Y that correlation analysis would miss entirely.

Properties CE.4 and CE.5 have two important implications: if U and X are random variables such that $E(U|X) = 0$, then $E(U) = 0$, and U and X are uncorrelated.

Property CE.6: If $E(Y^2) < \infty$ and $E[g(X)^2] < \infty$ for some function g, then $E\{[Y - \mu(X)]^2|X\} \leq E\{[Y - g(X)]^2|X\}$ and $E\{[Y - \mu(X)]^2\} \leq E\{[Y - g(X)]^2\}$.

Property CE.6 is very useful in predicting or forecasting contexts. The first inequality says that, if we measure prediction inaccuracy as the *expected* squared prediction error, conditional on X, then the conditional mean is better than any other function of X for predicting Y. The conditional mean also minimizes the unconditional expected squared prediction error.

Conditional Variance

Given random variables X and Y, the variance of Y, conditional on $X = x$, is simply the variance associated with the conditional distribution of Y, given $X = x$: $E\{[Y - E(Y|x)]^2|x\}$. The formula

$$Var(Y|X = x) = E(Y^2|x) - [E(Y|x)]^2$$

is often useful for calculations. Only occasionally will we have to compute a conditional variance. But we will have to make assumptions about and manipulate conditional variances for certain topics in regression analysis.

As an example, let $Y = SAVING$ and $X = INCOME$ (both of these measured annually for the population of all families). Suppose that $\text{Var}(SAVING|INCOME) = 400 + .25\ INCOME$. This says that, as income increases, the variance in saving levels also increases. It is important to see that the relationship between the variance of *SAVING* and *INCOME* is totally separate from that between the *expected value* of *SAVING* and *INCOME*.

We state one useful property about the conditional variance.

Property CV.1: If X and Y are independent, then $\text{Var}(Y|X) = \text{Var}(Y)$.

This property is pretty clear, since the distribution of Y given X does not depend on X, and $\text{Var}(Y|X)$ is just one feature of this distribution.

B.5 The Normal and Related Distributions

The Normal Distribution

The normal distribution and those derived from it are the most widely used distributions in statistics and econometrics. Assuming that random variables defined over populations are normally distributed simplifies probability calculations. In addition, we will rely heavily on the normal and related distributions to conduct inference in statistics and econometrics—even when the underlying population is not necessarily normal. We must postpone the details, but be assured that these distributions will arise many times throughout this text.

A normal random variable is a continuous random variable that can take on any value. Its probability density function has the familiar bell shape graphed in Figure B.7.

FIGURE B.7 The general shape of the normal probability density function.

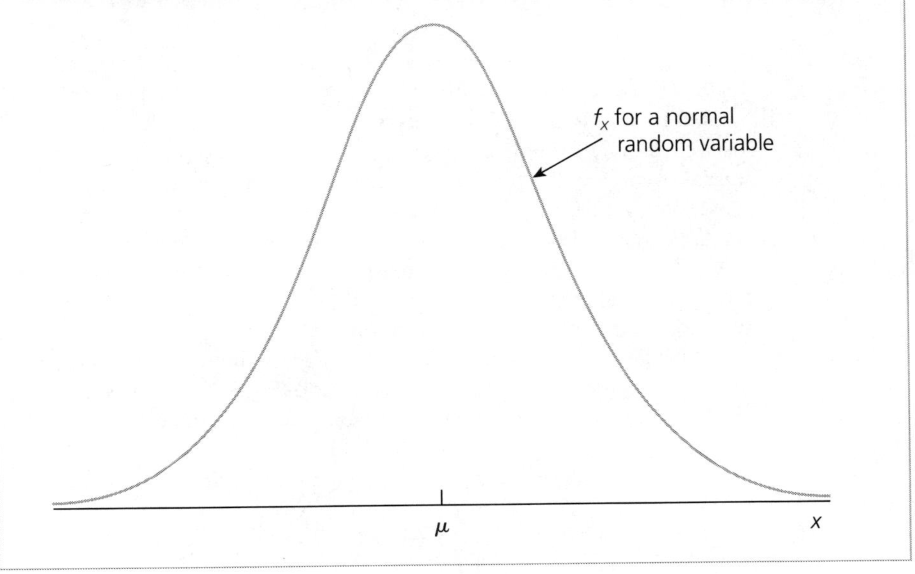

Mathematically, the pdf of X can be written as

$$f(x) = \frac{1}{\sigma\sqrt{2\pi}} \exp[-(x - \mu)^2/2\sigma^2], \quad -\infty < x < \infty, \tag{B.34}$$

where $\mu = \mathrm{E}(X)$ and $\sigma^2 = \mathrm{Var}(X)$. We say that X has a **normal distribution** with expected value μ and variance σ^2, written as $X \sim \mathrm{Normal}(\mu,\sigma^2)$. Because the normal distribution is symmetric about μ, μ is also the median of X. The normal distribution is sometimes called the *Gaussian distribution* after the famous mathematician C. F. Gauss.

Certain random variables appear to roughly follow a normal distribution. Human heights and weights, test scores, and county unemployment rates have pdfs roughly the shape in Figure B.7. Other distributions, such as income distributions, do not appear to follow the normal probability function. In most countries, income is not symmetrically distributed about any value; the distribution is skewed toward the upper tail. In some cases, a variable can be transformed to achieve normality. A popular transformation is the natural log, which makes sense for positive random variables. If X is a positive random variable, such as income, and $Y = \log(X)$ has a normal distribution, then we say that X has a *lognormal distribution*. It turns out that the lognormal distribution fits income distribution pretty well in many countries. Other variables, such as prices of goods, appear to be well described as lognormally distributed.

The Standard Normal Distribution

One special case of the normal distribution occurs when the mean is zero and the variance (and, therefore, the standard deviation) is unity. If a random variable Z has a Normal(0,1) distribution, then we say it has a **standard normal distribution**. The pdf of a standard normal random variable is denoted $\phi(z)$; from (B.34), with $\mu = 0$ and $\sigma^2 = 1$, it is given by

$$\phi(z) = \frac{1}{\sqrt{2\pi}} \exp(-z^2/2), \quad -\infty < z < \infty. \tag{B.35}$$

The standard normal cumulative distribution function is denoted $\Phi(z)$ and is obtained as the area under ϕ, to the left of z; see Figure B.8. Recall that $\Phi(z) = \mathrm{P}(Z \leq z)$; because Z is continuous, $\Phi(z) = \mathrm{P}(Z < z)$ as well.

No simple formula can be used to obtain the values of $\Phi(z)$ [because $\Phi(z)$ is the integral of the function in (B.35), and this intregral has no closed form]. Nevertheless, the values for $\Phi(z)$ are easily tabulated; they are given for z between -3.1 and 3.1 in Table G.1 in Appendix G. For $z \leq -3.1$, $\Phi(z)$ is less than .001, and for $z \geq 3.1$, $\Phi(z)$ is greater than .999. Most statistics and econometrics software packages include simple commands for computing values of the standard normal cdf, so we can often avoid printed tables entirely and obtain the probabilities for any value of z.

Using basic facts from probability—and, in particular, properties (B.7) and (B.8) concerning cdfs—we can use the standard normal cdf for computing the probability of any event involving a standard normal random variable. The most important formulas are

$$\mathrm{P}(Z > z) = 1 - \Phi(z), \tag{B.36}$$

$$\mathrm{P}(Z < -z) = \mathrm{P}(Z > z), \tag{B.37}$$

FIGURE B.8 The standard normal cumulative distribution function.

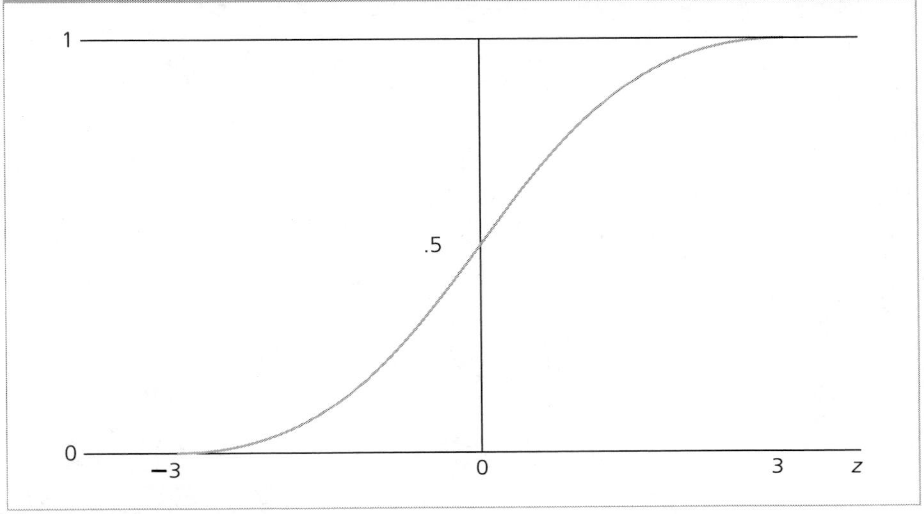

and

$$P(a \leq Z \leq b) = \Phi(b) - \Phi(a). \quad \text{[B.38]}$$

Because Z is a continuous random variable, all three formulas hold whether or not the inequalities are strict. Some examples include $P(Z > .44) = 1 - .67 = .33$, $P(Z < -.92) = P(Z > .92) = 1 - .821 = .179$, and $P(-1 < Z \leq .5) = .692 - .159 = .533$.

Another useful expression is that, for any $c > 0$,

$$\begin{aligned} P(|Z| > c) &= P(Z > c) + P(Z < -c) \\ &= 2 \cdot P(Z > c) = 2[1 - \Phi(c)]. \end{aligned} \quad \text{[B.39]}$$

Thus, the probability that the absolute value of Z is bigger than some positive constant c is simply twice the probability $P(Z > c)$; this reflects the symmetry of the standard normal distribution.

In most applications, we start with a normally distributed random variable, $X \sim \text{Normal}(\mu,\sigma^2)$, where μ is different from zero and $\sigma^2 \neq 1$. Any normal random variable can be turned into a standard normal using the following property.

Property Normal.1: If $X \sim \text{Normal}(\mu,\sigma^2)$, then $(X - \mu)/\sigma \sim \text{Normal}(0,1)$.

Property Normal.1 shows how to turn any normal random variable into a standard normal. Thus, suppose $X \sim \text{Normal}(3,4)$, and we would like to compute $P(X \leq 1)$. The steps always involve the normalization of X to a standard normal:

$$\begin{aligned} P(X \leq 1) &= P(X - 3 \leq 1 - 3) = P\left(\frac{X - 3}{2} \leq -1\right) \\ &= P(Z \leq -1) = \Phi(-1) = .159. \end{aligned}$$

EXAMPLE B.6 PROBABILITIES FOR A NORMAL RANDOM VARIABLE

First, let us compute $P(2 < X \leq 6)$ when $X \sim \text{Normal}(4,9)$ (whether we use $<$ or $\leq$ is irrelevant because X is a continuous random variable). Now,

$$P(2 < X \leq 6) = P\left(\frac{2-4}{3} < \frac{X-4}{3} \leq \frac{6-4}{3}\right) = P(-2/3 < Z \leq 2/3)$$
$$= \Phi(.67) - \Phi(-.67) = .749 - .251 = .498.$$

Now, let us compute $P(|X| > 2)$:

$$\begin{aligned} P(|X| > 2) &= P(X > 2) + P(X < -2) \\ &= P[(X-4)/3 > (2-4)/3] + P[(X-4)/3 < (-2-4)/3] \\ &= 1 - \Phi(-2/3) + \Phi(-2) \\ &= 1 - .251 + .023 = .772. \end{aligned}$$

Additional Properties of the Normal Distribution

We end this subsection by collecting several other facts about normal distributions that we will later use.

Property Normal.2: If $X \sim \text{Normal}(\mu,\sigma^2)$, then $aX + b \sim \text{Normal}(a\mu + b, a^2\sigma^2)$.

Thus, if $X \sim \text{Normal}(1,9)$, then $Y = 2X + 3$ is distributed as normal with mean $2E(X) + 3 = 5$ and variance $2^2 \cdot 9 = 36$; $sd(Y) = 2sd(X) = 2 \cdot 3 = 6$.

Earlier, we discussed how, in general, zero correlation and independence are not the same. In the case of normally distributed random variables, it turns out that zero correlation suffices for independence.

Property Normal.3: If X and Y are jointly normally distributed, then they are independent if, and only if, $\text{Cov}(X,Y) = 0$.

Property Normal.4: Any linear combination of independent, identically distributed normal random variables has a normal distribution.

For example, let X_i, for $i = 1$, 2, and 3, be independent random variables distributed as $\text{Normal}(\mu,\sigma^2)$. Define $W = X_1 + 2X_2 - 3X_3$. Then, W is normally distributed; we must simply find its mean and variance. Now,

$$E(W) = E(X_1) + 2E(X_2) - 3E(X_3) = \mu + 2\mu - 3\mu = 0.$$

Also,

$$\text{Var}(W) = \text{Var}(X_1) + 4\text{Var}(X_2) + 9\text{Var}(X_3) = 14\sigma^2.$$

Property Normal.4 also implies that the average of independent, normally distributed random variables has a normal distribution. If $Y_1, Y_2, \ldots, Y_n$ are independent random variables and each is distributed as $\text{Normal}(\mu, \sigma^2)$, then

$$\bar{Y} \sim \text{Normal}(\mu, \sigma^2/n). \quad \text{[B.40]}$$

This result is critical for statistical inference about the mean in a normal population.

Other features of the normal distribution are worth knowing, although they do not play a central role in the text. Because a normal random variable is symmetric about its mean, it has zero skewness, that is, $\text{E}[(X - \mu)^3] = 0$. Further, it can be shown that

$$\text{E}[(X - \mu)^4]/\sigma^4 = 3,$$

or $\text{E}(Z^4) = 3$, where Z has a standard normal distribution. Because the normal distribution is so prevalent in probability and statistics, the measure of kurtosis for any given random variable X (whose fourth moment exists) is often defined to be $\text{E}[(X - \mu)^4]/\sigma^4 - 3$, that is, relative to the value for the standard normal distribution. If $\text{E}[(X - \mu)^4]/\sigma^4 > 3$, then the distribution of X has fatter tails than the normal distribution (a somewhat common occurrence, such as with the t distribution to be introduced shortly); if $\text{E}[(X - \mu)^4]/\sigma^4 < 3$, then the distribution has thinner tails than the normal (a rarer situation).

The Chi-Square Distribution

The chi-square distribution is obtained directly from independent, standard normal random variables. Let Z_i, $i = 1, 2, \ldots, n$, be independent random variables, each distributed as standard normal. Define a new random variable as the sum of the squares of the Z_i:

$$X = \sum_{i=1}^{n} Z_i^2. \quad \text{[B.41]}$$

Then, X has what is known as a **chi-square distribution** with n **degrees of freedom** (or *df* for short). We write this as $X \sim \chi_n^2$. The *df* in a chi-square distribution corresponds to the number of terms in the sum in (B.41). The concept of degrees of freedom will play an important role in our statistical and econometric analyses.

The pdf for chi-square distributions with varying degrees of freedom is given in Figure B.9; we will not need the formula for this pdf, and so we do not reproduce it here. From equation (B.41), it is clear that a chi-square random variable is always nonnegative, and that, unlike the normal distribution, the chi-square distribution is not symmetric about any point. It can be shown that if $X \sim \chi_n^2$, then the expected value of X is n [the number of terms in (B.41)], and the variance of X is $2n$.

The *t* Distribution

The t distribution is the workhorse in classical statistics and multiple regression analysis. We obtain a t distribution from a standard normal and a chi-square random variable.

Let Z have a standard normal distribution and let X have a chi-square distribution with n degrees of freedom. Further, assume that Z and X are independent. Then, the random variable

$$T = \frac{Z}{\sqrt{X/n}} \quad \text{[B.42]}$$

FIGURE B.9 The chi-square distribution with various degrees of freedom.

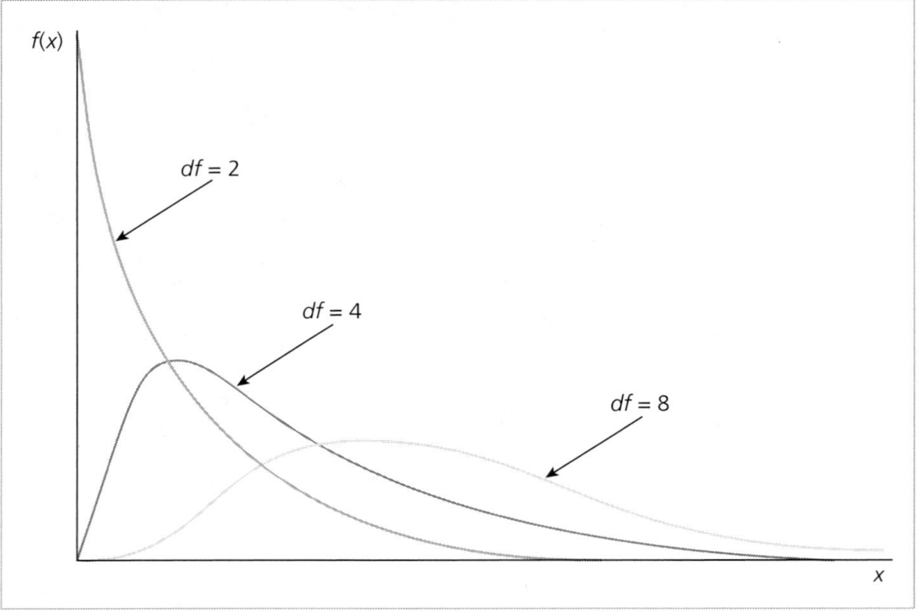

has a ***t* distribution** with n degrees of freedom. We will denote this by $T \sim t_n$. The t distribution gets its degrees of freedom from the chi-square random variable in the denominator of (B.42).

The pdf of the t distribution has a shape similar to that of the standard normal distribution, except that it is more spread out and therefore has more area in the tails. The expected value of a t distributed random variable is zero (strictly speaking, the expected value exists only for $n > 1$), and the variance is $n/(n - 2)$ for $n > 2$. (The variance does not exist for $n \leq 2$ because the distribution is so spread out.) The pdf of the t distribution is plotted in Figure B.10 for various degrees of freedom. As the degrees of freedom gets large, the t distribution approaches the standard normal distribution.

The *F* Distribution

Another important distribution for statistics and econometrics is the F distribution. In particular, the F distribution will be used for testing hypotheses in the context of multiple regression analysis.

To define an F random variable, let $X_1 \sim \chi^2_{k_1}$ and $X_2 \sim \chi^2_{k_2}$ and assume that X_1 and X_2 are independent. Then, the random variable

$$F = \frac{(X_1/k_1)}{(X_2/k_2)} \qquad \text{[B.43]}$$

has an ***F* distribution** with (k_1,k_2) degrees of freedom. We denote this as $F \sim F_{k_1,k_2}$. The pdf of the F distribution with different degrees of freedom is given in Figure B.11.

FIGURE B.10 The t distribution with various degrees of freedom.

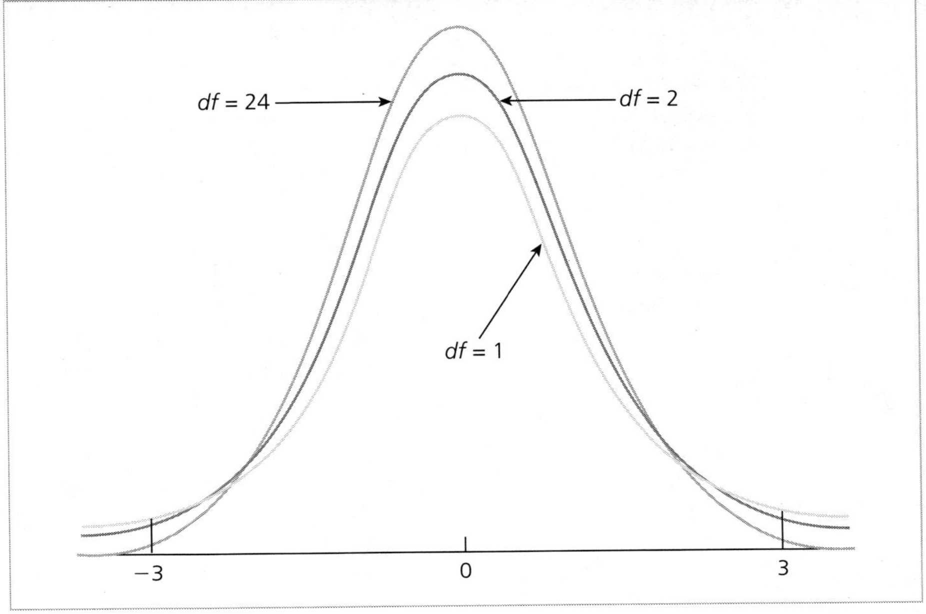

FIGURE B.11 The F_{k_1,k_2} distribution for various degrees of freedom, k_1 and k_2.

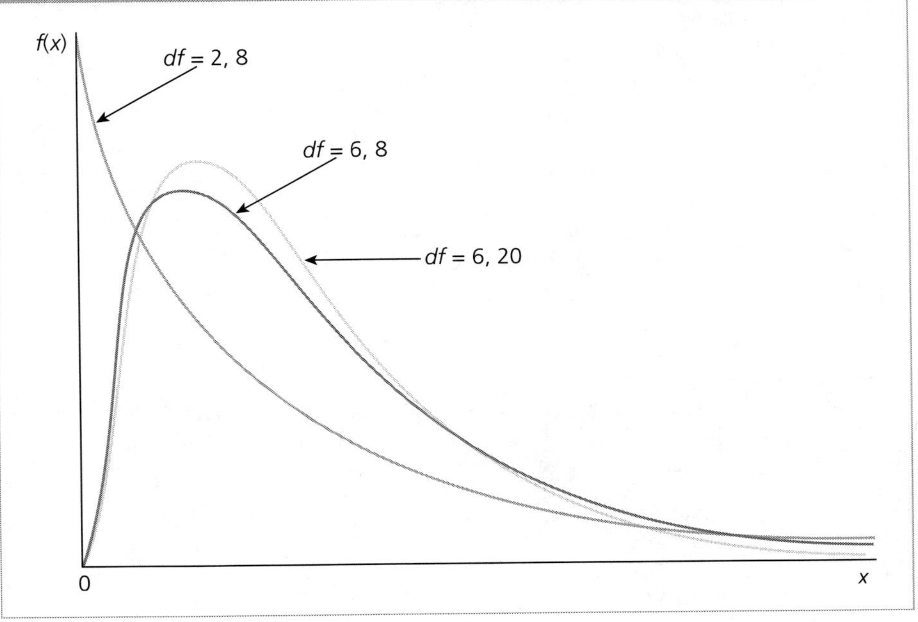

The order of the degrees of freedom in F_{k_1,k_2} is critical. The integer k_1 is called the *numerator degrees of freedom* because it is associated with the chi-square variable in the numerator. Likewise, the integer k_2 is called the *denominator degrees of freedom* because it is associated with the chi-square variable in the denominator. This can be a little tricky because (B.43) can also be written as $(X_1k_2)/(X_2k_1)$, so that k_1 appears in the denominator. Just remember that the numerator *df* is the integer associated with the chi-square variable in the numerator of (B.43), and similarly for the denominator *df*.

Summary

In this appendix, we have reviewed the probability concepts that are needed in econometrics. Most of the concepts should be familiar from your introductory course in probability and statistics. Some of the more advanced topics, such as features of conditional expectations, do not need to be mastered now—there is time for that when these concepts arise in the context of regression analysis in Part 1.

In an introductory statistics course, the focus is on calculating means, variances, covariances, and so on for particular distributions. In Part 1, we will not need such calculations: we mostly rely on the *properties* of expectations, variances, and so on that have been stated in this appendix.

Key Terms

Bernoulli (or Binary) Random Variable
Binomial Distribution
Chi-Square Distribution
Conditional Distribution
Conditional Expectation
Continuous Random Variable
Correlation Coefficient
Covariance
Cumulative Distribution Function (cdf)
Degrees of Freedom
Discrete Random Variable
Expected Value
Experiment
F Distribution
Independent Random Variables
Joint Distribution
Kurtosis
Law of Iterated Expectations
Median
Normal Distribution
Pairwise Uncorrelated Random Variables
Probability Density Function (pdf)
Random Variable
Skewness
Standard Deviation
Standard Normal Distribution
Standardized Random Variable
Symmetric Distribution
t Distribution
Uncorrelated Random Variables
Variance

Problems

1 Suppose that a high school student is preparing to take the SAT exam. Explain why his or her eventual SAT score is properly viewed as a random variable.

2 Let X be a random variable distributed as Normal(5,4). Find the probabilities of the following events:
(i) $P(X \leq 6)$.
(ii) $P(X > 4)$.
(iii) $P(|X - 5| > 1)$.

3 Much is made of the fact that certain mutual funds outperform the market year after year (that is, the return from holding shares in the mutual fund is higher than the return from holding a portfolio such as the S&P 500). For concreteness, consider a 10-year period and let the population be the 4,170 mutual funds reported in *The Wall Street Journal* on January 1, 1995. By saying that performance relative to the market is random, we mean that each fund has a 50–50 chance of outperforming the market in any year and that performance is independent from year to year.

(i) If performance relative to the market is truly random, what is the probability that any particular fund outperforms the market in all 10 years?

(ii) Find the probability that *at least* one fund out of 4,170 funds outperforms the market in all 10 years. What do you make of your answer?

(iii) If you have a statistical package that computes binomial probabilities, find the probability that at least five funds outperform the market in all 10 years.

4 For a randomly selected county in the United States, let X represent the proportion of adults over age 65 who are employed, or the elderly employment rate. Then, X is restricted to a value between zero and one. Suppose that the cumulative distribution function for X is given by $F(x) = 3x^2 - 2x^3$ for $0 \leq x \leq 1$. Find the probability that the elderly employment rate is at least .6 (60%).

5 Just prior to jury selection for O. J. Simpson's murder trial in 1995, a poll found that about 20% of the adult population believed Simpson was innocent (after much of the physical evidence in the case had been revealed to the public). Ignore the fact that this 20% is an estimate based on a subsample from the population; for illustration, take it as the true percentage of people who thought Simpson was innocent prior to jury selection. Assume that the 12 jurors were selected randomly and independently from the population (although this turned out not to be true).

(i) Find the probability that the jury had at least one member who believed in Simpson's innocence prior to jury selection. [*Hint:* Define the Binomial(12,.20) random variable X to be the number of jurors believing in Simpson's innocence.]

(ii) Find the probability that the jury had at least two members who believed in Simpson's innocence. [*Hint:* $P(X \geq 2) = 1 - P(X \leq 1)$, and $P(X \leq 1) = P(X = 0) + P(X = 1)$.]

6 (Requires calculus) Let X denote the prison sentence, in years, for people convicted of auto theft in a particular state in the United States. Suppose that the pdf of X is given by

$$f(x) = (1/9)x^2, \; 0 < x < 3.$$

Use integration to find the expected prison sentence.

7 If a basketball player is a 74% free throw shooter, then, on average, how many free throws will he or she make in a game with eight free throw attempts?

8 Suppose that a college student is taking three courses: a two-credit course, a three-credit course, and a four-credit course. The expected grade in the two-credit course is 3.5, while the expected grade in the three- and four-credit courses is 3.0. What is the expected overall grade point average for the semester? (Remember that each course grade is weighted by its share of the total number of units.)

9 Let X denote the annual salary of university professors in the United States, measured in thousands of dollars. Suppose that the average salary is 52.3, with a standard deviation of 14.6. Find the mean and standard deviation when salary is measured in dollars.

10 Suppose that at a large university, college grade point average, *GPA*, and SAT score, *SAT*, are related by the conditional expectation $E(GPA|SAT) = .70 + .002\ SAT$.

(i) Find the expected *GPA* when $SAT = 800$. Find $E(GPA|SAT = 1{,}400)$. Comment on the difference.

(ii) If the average *SAT* in the university is 1,100, what is the average *GPA*? (*Hint:* Use Property CE.4.)

(iii) If a student's SAT score is 1,100, does this mean he or she will have the GPA found in part (ii)? Explain.

APPENDIX C

Fundamentals of Mathematical Statistics

C.1 Populations, Parameters, and Random Sampling

Statistical inference involves learning something about a population given the availability of a sample from that population. By **population**, we mean any well-defined group of subjects, which could be individuals, firms, cities, or many other possibilities. By "learning," we can mean several things, which are broadly divided into the categories of *estimation* and *hypothesis testing*.

A couple of examples may help you understand these terms. In the population of all working adults in the United States, labor economists are interested in learning about the return to education, as measured by the average percentage increase in earnings given another year of education. It would be impractical and costly to obtain information on earnings and education for the entire working population in the United States, but we can obtain data on a subset of the population. Using the data collected, a labor economist may report that his or her best estimate of the return to another year of education is 7.5%. This is an example of a *point estimate*. Or, she or he may report a range, such as "the return to education is between 5.6% and 9.4%." This is an example of an *interval estimate*.

An urban economist might want to know whether neighborhood crime watch programs are associated with lower crime rates. After comparing crime rates of neighborhoods with and without such programs in a sample from the population, he or she can draw one of two conclusions: neighborhood watch programs do affect crime, or they do not. This example falls under the rubric of hypothesis testing.

The first step in statistical inference is to identify the population of interest. This may seem obvious, but it is important to be very specific. Once we have identified the population, we can specify a model for the population relationship of interest. Such models involve probability distributions or features of probability distributions, and these depend on unknown parameters. Parameters are simply constants that determine the directions and strengths of relationships among variables. In the labor economics example just presented, the parameter of interest is the return to education in the population.

Sampling

For reviewing statistical inference, we focus on the simplest possible setting. Let Y be a random variable representing a population with a probability density function $f(y;\theta)$, which depends on the single parameter θ. The probability density function (pdf) of Y is assumed to be known except for the value of θ; different values of θ imply different population distributions, and therefore we are interested in the value of θ. If we can obtain certain kinds of samples from the population, then we can learn something about θ. The easiest sampling scheme to deal with is random sampling.

Random Sampling. If $Y_1, Y_2, \ldots, Y_n$ are independent random variables with a common probability density function $f(y;\theta)$, then $\{Y_1, \ldots, Y_n\}$ is said to be a **random sample** from $f(y;\theta)$ [or a random sample from the population represented by $f(y;\theta)$].

When $\{Y_1, \ldots, Y_n\}$ is a random sample from the density $f(y;\theta)$, we also say that the Y_i are *independent, identically distributed* (or *i.i.d.*) random variables from $f(y;\theta)$. In some cases, we will not need to entirely specify what the common distribution is.

The random nature of $Y_1, Y_2, \ldots, Y_n$ in the definition of random sampling reflects the fact that many different outcomes are possible before the sampling is actually carried out. For example, if family income is obtained for a sample of $n = 100$ families in the United States, the incomes we observe will usually differ for each different sample of 100 families. Once a sample is obtained, we have a set of numbers, say, $\{y_1, y_2, \ldots, y_n\}$, which constitute the data that we work with. Whether or not it is appropriate to assume the sample came from a random sampling scheme requires knowledge about the actual sampling process.

Random samples from a Bernoulli distribution are often used to illustrate statistical concepts, and they also arise in empirical applications. If $Y_1, Y_2, \ldots, Y_n$ are independent random variables and each is distributed as Bernoulli(θ), so that $P(Y_i = 1) = \theta$ and $P(Y_i = 0) = 1 - \theta$, then $\{Y_1, Y_2, \ldots, Y_n\}$ constitutes a random sample from the Bernoulli(θ) distribution. As an illustration, consider the airline reservation example carried along in Appendix B. Each Y_i denotes whether customer i shows up for his or her reservation; $Y_i = 1$ if passenger i shows up, and $Y_i = 0$ otherwise. Here, θ is the probability that a randomly drawn person from the population of all people who make airline reservations shows up for his or her reservation.

For many other applications, random samples can be assumed to be drawn from a normal distribution. If $\{Y_1, \ldots, Y_n\}$ is a random sample from the Normal(μ,σ^2) population, then the population is characterized by two parameters, the mean μ and the variance σ^2. Primary interest usually lies in μ, but σ^2 is of interest in its own right because making inferences about μ often requires learning about σ^2.

C.2 Finite Sample Properties of Estimators

In this section, we study what are called finite sample properties of estimators. The term "finite sample" comes from the fact that the properties hold for a sample of any size, no matter how large or small. Sometimes, these are called small sample properties. In Section C.3, we cover "asymptotic properties," which have to do with the behavior of estimators as the sample size grows without bound.

Estimators and Estimates

To study properties of estimators, we must define what we mean by an estimator. Given a random sample $\{Y_1, Y_2, \ldots, Y_n\}$ drawn from a population distribution that depends on an unknown parameter θ, an **estimator** of θ is a rule that assigns each possible outcome of the sample a value of θ. The rule is specified before any sampling is carried out; in particular, the rule is the same regardless of the data actually obtained.

As an example of an estimator, let $\{Y_1, \ldots, Y_n\}$ be a random sample from a population with mean μ. A natural estimator of μ is the average of the random sample:

$$\bar{Y} = n^{-1}\sum_{i=1}^{n} Y_i. \qquad \text{[C.1]}$$

$\bar{Y}$ is called the **sample average** but, unlike in Appendix A where we defined the sample average of a set of numbers as a descriptive statistic, $\bar{Y}$ is now viewed as an estimator. Given any outcome of the random variables $Y_1, \ldots, Y_n$, we use the same rule to estimate μ: we simply average them. For actual data outcomes $\{y_1, \ldots, y_n\}$, the **estimate** is just the average in the sample: $\bar{y} = (y_1 + y_2 + \ldots + y_n)/n$.

EXAMPLE C.1 CITY UNEMPLOYMENT RATES

Suppose we obtain the following sample of unemployment rates for 10 cities in the United States:

City	Unemployment Rate
1	5.1
2	6.4
3	9.2
4	4.1
5	7.5
6	8.3
7	2.6
8	3.5
9	5.8
10	7.5

Our estimate of the average city unemployment rate in the United States is $\bar{y} = 6.0$. Each sample generally results in a different estimate. But the *rule* for obtaining the estimate is the same, regardless of which cities appear in the sample, or how many.

More generally, an estimator W of a parameter θ can be expressed as an abstract mathematical formula:

$$W = h(Y_1, Y_2, \ldots, Y_n), \qquad [C.2]$$

for some known function h of the random variables $Y_1, Y_2, \ldots, Y_n$. As with the special case of the sample average, W is a random variable because it depends on the random sample: as we obtain different random samples from the population, the value of W can change. When a particular set of numbers, say, $\{y_1, y_2, \ldots, y_n\}$, is plugged into the function h, we obtain an *estimate* of θ, denoted $w = h(y_1, \ldots, y_n)$. Sometimes, W is called a point estimator and w a point estimate to distinguish these from *interval* estimators and estimates, which we will come to in Section C.5.

For evaluating estimation procedures, we study various properties of the probability distribution of the random variable W. The distribution of an estimator is often called its **sampling distribution**, because this distribution describes the likelihood of various outcomes of W across different random samples. Because there are unlimited rules for combining data to estimate parameters, we need some sensible criteria for choosing among estimators, or at least for eliminating some estimators from consideration. Therefore, we must leave the realm of descriptive statistics, where we compute things such as the sample average to simply summarize a body of data. In mathematical statistics, we study the sampling distributions of estimators.

Unbiasedness

In principle, the entire sampling distribution of W can be obtained given the probability distribution of Y_i and the function h. It is usually easier to focus on a few features of the distribution of W in evaluating it as an estimator of θ. The first important property of an estimator involves its expected value.

Unbiased Estimator. An estimator, W of θ, is an **unbiased estimator** if

$$\mathrm{E}(W) = \theta, \qquad [C.3]$$

for all possible values of θ.

If an estimator is unbiased, then its probability distribution has an expected value equal to the parameter it is supposed to be estimating. Unbiasedness does *not* mean that the estimate we get with any particular sample is equal to θ, or even very close to θ. Rather, if we could *indefinitely* draw random samples on Y from the population, compute an estimate each time, and then average these estimates over all random samples, we would obtain θ. This thought experiment is abstract because, in most applications, we just have one random sample to work with.

For an estimator that is not unbiased, we define its **bias** as follows.

Bias of an Estimator. If W is a **biased estimator** of θ, its bias is defined as

$$\mathrm{Bias}(W) \equiv \mathrm{E}(W) - \theta. \qquad [C.4]$$

Figure C.1 shows two estimators; the first one is unbiased, and the second one has a positive bias.

FIGURE C.1 An unbiased estimator, W_1, and an estimator with positive bias, W_2.

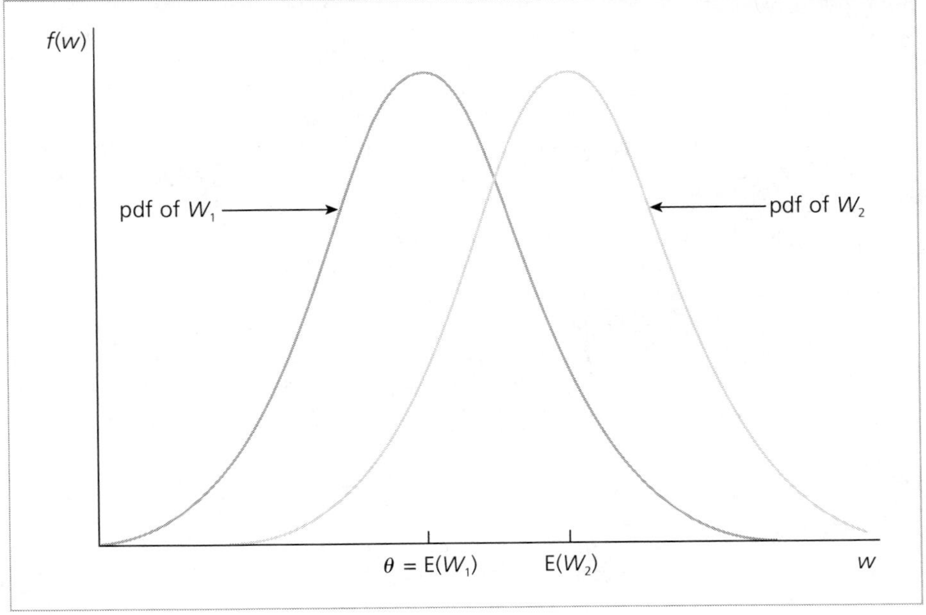

The unbiasedness of an estimator and the size of any possible bias depend on the distribution of Y and on the function h. The distribution of Y is usually beyond our control (although we often choose a *model* for this distribution): it may be determined by nature or social forces. But the choice of the rule h is ours, and if we want an unbiased estimator, then we must choose h accordingly.

Some estimators can be shown to be unbiased quite generally. We now show that the sample average $\bar{Y}$ is an unbiased estimator of the population mean μ, regardless of the underlying population distribution. We use the properties of expected values (E.1 and E.2) that we covered in Section B.3:

$$\begin{aligned} E(\bar{Y}) &= E\left((1/n)\sum_{i=1}^{n} Y_i\right) = (1/n)E\left(\sum_{i=1}^{n} Y_i\right) = (1/n)\left(\sum_{i=1}^{n} E(Y_i)\right) \\ &= (1/n)\left(\sum_{i=1}^{n} \mu\right) = (1/n)(n\mu) = \mu. \end{aligned}$$

For hypothesis testing, we will need to estimate the variance σ^2 from a population with mean μ. Letting $\{Y_1, \ldots, Y_n\}$ denote the random sample from the population with $E(Y) = \mu$ and $\text{Var}(Y) = \sigma^2$, define the estimator as

$$S^2 = \frac{1}{n-1}\sum_{i=1}^{n}(Y_i - \bar{Y})^2, \qquad \text{[C.5]}$$

which is usually called the **sample variance**. It can be shown that S^2 is unbiased for σ^2: $\mathrm{E}(S^2) = \sigma^2$. The division by $n - 1$, rather than n, accounts for the fact that the mean μ is estimated rather than known. If μ were known, an unbiased estimator of σ^2 would be $n^{-1}\sum_{i=1}^{n}(Y_i - \mu)^2$, but μ is rarely known in practice.

Although unbiasedness has a certain appeal as a property for an estimator—indeed, its antonym, "biased," has decidedly negative connotations—it is not without its problems. One weakness of unbiasedness is that some reasonable, and even some very good, estimators are not unbiased. We will see an example shortly.

Another important weakness of unbiasedness is that unbiased estimators exist that are actually quite poor estimators. Consider estimating the mean μ from a population. Rather than using the sample average $\bar{Y}$ to estimate μ, suppose that, after collecting a sample of size n, we discard all of the observations except the first. That is, our estimator of μ is simply $W \equiv Y_1$. This estimator is unbiased because $\mathrm{E}(Y_1) = \mu$. Hopefully, you sense that ignoring all but the first observation is not a prudent approach to estimation: it throws out most of the information in the sample. For example, with $n = 100$, we obtain 100 outcomes of the random variable Y, but then we use only the first of these to estimate $\mathrm{E}(Y)$.

The Sampling Variance of Estimators

The example at the end of the previous subsection shows that we need additional criteria to evaluate estimators. Unbiasedness only ensures that the sampling distribution of an estimator has a mean value equal to the parameter it is supposed to be estimating. This is fine, but we also need to know how spread out the distribution of an estimator is. An estimator can be equal to θ, on average, but it can also be very far away with large probability. In Figure C.2, W_1 and W_2 are both unbiased estimators of θ. But the distribution of W_1 is more tightly centered about θ: the probability that W_1 is greater than any given distance from θ is less than the probability that W_2 is greater than that same distance from θ. Using W_1 as our estimator means that it is less likely that we will obtain a random sample that yields an estimate very far from θ.

To summarize the situation shown in Figure C.2, we rely on the variance (or standard deviation) of an estimator. Recall that this gives a single measure of the dispersion in the distribution. The variance of an estimator is often called its **sampling variance** because it is the variance associated with a sampling distribution. Remember, the sampling variance is not a random variable; it is a constant, but it might be unknown.

We now obtain the variance of the sample average for estimating the mean μ from a population:

$$\begin{aligned}\mathrm{Var}(\bar{Y}) &= \mathrm{Var}\left((1/n)\sum_{i=1}^{n} Y_i\right) = (1/n^2)\mathrm{Var}\left(\sum_{i=1}^{n} Y_i\right) = (1/n^2)\left(\sum_{i=1}^{n}\mathrm{Var}(Y_i)\right) \\ &= (1/n^2)\left(\sum_{i=1}^{n}\sigma^2\right) = (1/n^2)(n\sigma^2) = \sigma^2/n. \qquad \text{[C.6]}\end{aligned}$$

Notice how we used the properties of variance from Sections B.3 and B.4 (VAR.2 and VAR.4), as well as the independence of the Y_i. To summarize: If $\{Y_i: i = 1, 2, \ldots, n\}$ is a random sample from a population with mean μ and variance σ^2, then $\bar{Y}$ has the same mean as the population, but its sampling variance equals the population variance, σ^2, divided by the sample size.

FIGURE C.2 The sampling distributions of two unbiased estimators of θ.

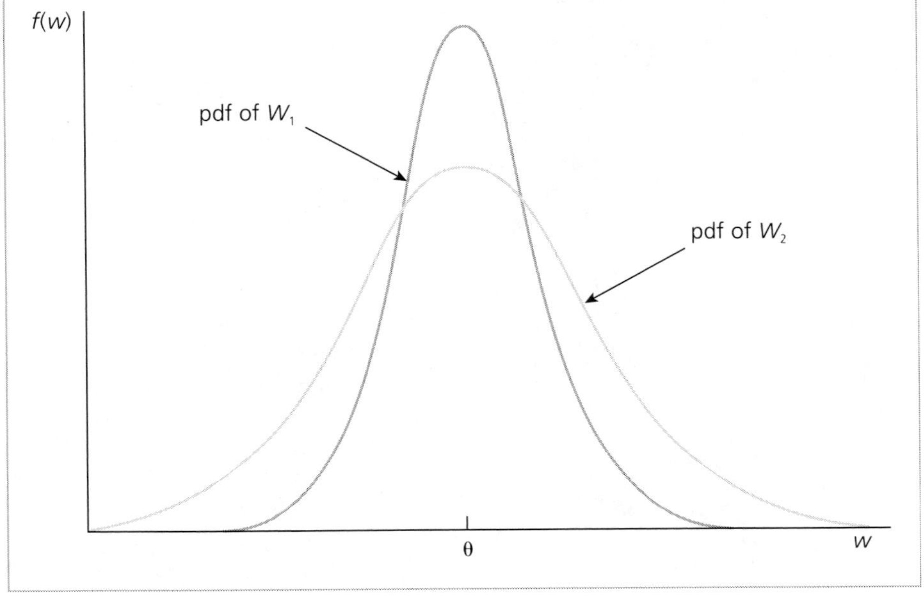

An important implication of $\text{Var}(\bar{Y}) = \sigma^2/n$ is that it can be made very close to zero by increasing the sample size n. This is a key feature of a reasonable estimator, and we return to it in Section C.3.

As suggested by Figure C.2, among unbiased estimators, we prefer the estimator with the smallest variance. This allows us to eliminate certain estimators from consideration. For a random sample from a population with mean μ and variance σ^2, we know that $\bar{Y}$ is unbiased, and $\text{Var}(\bar{Y}) = \sigma^2/n$. What about the estimator Y_1, which is just the first observation drawn? Because Y_1 is a random draw from the population, $\text{Var}(Y_1) = \sigma^2$. Thus, the difference between $\text{Var}(Y_1)$ and $\text{Var}(\bar{Y})$ can be large even for small sample sizes. If $n = 10$, then $\text{Var}(Y_1)$ is 10 times as large as $\text{Var}(\bar{Y}) = \sigma^2/10$. This gives us a formal way of excluding Y_1 as an estimator of μ.

To emphasize this point, Table C.1 contains the outcome of a small simulation study. Using the statistical package Stata®, 20 random samples of size 10 were generated from a normal distribution, with $\mu = 2$ and $\sigma^2 = 1$; we are interested in estimating μ here. For each of the 20 random samples, we compute two estimates, y_1 and $\bar{y}$; these values are listed in Table C.1. As can be seen from the table, the values for y_1 are much more spread out than those for $\bar{y}$: y_1 ranges from -0.64 to 4.27, while $\bar{y}$ ranges only from 1.16 to 2.58. Further, in 16 out of 20 cases, $\bar{y}$ is closer than y_1 to $\mu = 2$. The average of y_1 across the simulations is about 1.89, while that for $\bar{y}$ is 1.96. The fact that these averages are close to 2 illustrates the unbiasedness of both estimators (and we could get these averages closer to 2 by doing more than 20 replications). But comparing just the average outcomes across random draws masks the fact that the sample average $\bar{Y}$ is far superior to Y_1 as an estimator of μ.

TABLE C.1 Simulation of Estimators for a Normal(μ,1) Distribution with $\mu = 2$

Replication	y_1	$\bar{y}$
1	−0.64	1.98
2	1.06	1.43
3	4.27	1.65
4	1.03	1.88
5	3.16	2.34
6	2.77	2.58
7	1.68	1.58
8	2.98	2.23
9	2.25	1.96
10	2.04	2.11
11	0.95	2.15
12	1.36	1.93
13	2.62	2.02
14	2.97	2.10
15	1.93	2.18
16	1.14	2.10
17	2.08	1.94
18	1.52	2.21
19	1.33	1.16
20	1.21	1.75

Efficiency

Comparing the variances of $\bar{Y}$ and Y_1 in the previous subsection is an example of a general approach to comparing different unbiased estimators.

Relative Efficiency. If W_1 and W_2 are two unbiased estimators of θ, W_1 is efficient relative to W_2 when $\text{Var}(W_1) \leq \text{Var}(W_2)$ for all θ, with strict inequality for at least one value of θ.

Earlier, we showed that, for estimating the population mean μ, $\text{Var}(\bar{Y}) < \text{Var}(Y_1)$ for any value of σ^2 whenever $n > 1$. Thus, $\bar{Y}$ is efficient relative to Y_1 for estimating μ. We cannot always choose between unbiased estimators based on the smallest variance criterion: given two unbiased estimators of θ, one can have smaller variance from some values of θ, while the other can have smaller variance for other values of θ.

If we restrict our attention to a certain class of estimators, we can show that the sample average has the smallest variance. Problem C.2 asks you to show that $\bar{Y}$ has the smallest variance among all unbiased estimators that are also linear functions of $Y_1, Y_2, \ldots, Y_n$. The assumptions are that the Y_i have common mean and variance, and that they are pairwise uncorrelated.

If we do not restrict our attention to unbiased estimators, then comparing variances is meaningless. For example, when estimating the population mean μ, we can use a trivial estimator that is equal to zero, regardless of the sample that we draw. Naturally, the variance of this estimator is zero (since it is the same value for every random sample). But the bias of this estimator is $-\mu$, so it is a very poor estimator when $|\mu|$ is large.

One way to compare estimators that are not necessarily unbiased is to compute the **mean squared error** (**MSE**) of the estimators. If W is an estimator of θ, then the MSE of W is defined as $\text{MSE}(W) = \text{E}[(W - \theta)^2]$. The MSE measures how far, on average, the estimator is away from θ. It can be shown that $\text{MSE}(W) = \text{Var}(W) + [\text{Bias}(W)]^2$, so that $\text{MSE}(W)$ depends on the variance and bias (if any is present). This allows us to compare two estimators when one or both are biased.

C.3 Asymptotic or Large Sample Properties of Estimators

In Section C.2, we encountered the estimator Y_1 for the population mean μ, and we saw that, even though it is unbiased, it is a poor estimator because its variance can be much larger than that of the sample mean. One notable feature of Y_1 is that it has the same variance for any sample size. It seems reasonable to require any estimation procedure to improve as the sample size increases. For estimating a population mean μ, $\bar{Y}$ improves in the sense that its variance gets smaller as n gets larger; Y_1 does not improve in this sense.

We can rule out certain silly estimators by studying the *asymptotic* or *large sample* properties of estimators. In addition, we can say something positive about estimators that are not unbiased and whose variances are not easily found.

Asymptotic analysis involves approximating the features of the sampling distribution of an estimator. These approximations depend on the size of the sample. Unfortunately, we are necessarily limited in what we can say about how "large" a sample size is needed for asymptotic analysis to be appropriate; this depends on the underlying population distribution. But large sample approximations have been known to work well for sample sizes as small as $n = 20$.

Consistency

The first asymptotic property of estimators concerns how far the estimator is likely to be from the parameter it is supposed to be estimating as we let the sample size increase indefinitely.

Consistency. Let W_n be an estimator of θ based on a sample $Y_1, Y_2, \ldots, Y_n$ of size n. Then, W_n is a **consistent estimator** of θ if for every $\varepsilon > 0$,

$$P(|W_n - \theta| > \varepsilon) \rightarrow 0 \text{ as } n \rightarrow \infty. \quad [C.7]$$

If W_n is not consistent for θ, then we say it is **inconsistent**.

When W_n is consistent, we also say that θ is the **probability limit** of W_n, written as $\text{plim}(W_n) = \theta$.

Unlike unbiasedness—which is a feature of an estimator for a given sample size—consistency involves the behavior of the sampling distribution of the estimator as the sample size n gets large. To emphasize this, we have indexed the estimator by the sample size in stating this definition, and we will continue with this convention throughout this section.

Equation (C.7) looks technical, and it can be rather difficult to establish based on fundamental probability principles. By contrast, interpreting (C.7) is straightforward. It means that the distribution of W_n becomes more and more concentrated about θ, which roughly means that for larger sample sizes, W_n is less and less likely to be very far from θ. This tendency is illustrated in Figure C.3.

If an estimator is not consistent, then it does not help us to learn about θ, even with an unlimited amount of data. For this reason, consistency is a minimal requirement of an estimator used in statistics or econometrics. We will encounter estimators that are consistent under certain assumptions and inconsistent when those assumptions fail. When estimators are inconsistent, we can usually find their probability limits, and it will be important to know how far these probability limits are from θ.

As we noted earlier, unbiased estimators are not necessarily consistent, but those whose variances shrink to zero as the sample size grows *are* consistent. This can be stated

FIGURE C.3 The sampling distributions of a consistent estimator for three sample sizes.

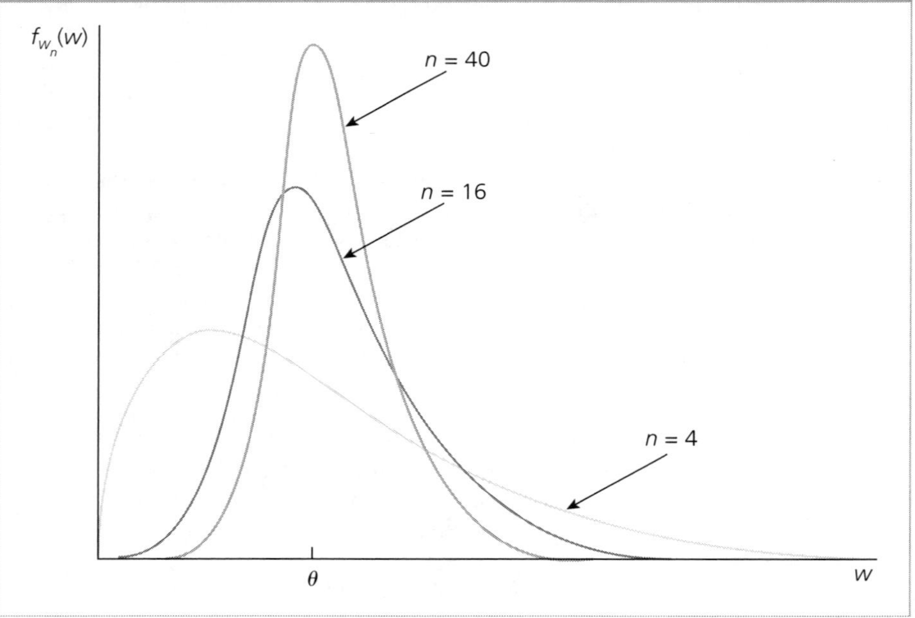

formally: If W_n is an unbiased estimator of θ and $\text{Var}(W_n) \rightarrow 0$ as $n \rightarrow \infty$, then $\text{plim}(W_n) = \theta$. Unbiased estimators that use the entire data sample will usually have a variance that shrinks to zero as the sample size grows, thereby being consistent.

A good example of a consistent estimator is the average of a random sample drawn from a population with mean μ and variance σ^2. We have already shown that the sample average is unbiased for μ. In equation (C.6), we derived $\text{Var}(\bar{Y}_n) = \sigma^2/n$ for any sample size n. Therefore, $\text{Var}(\bar{Y}_n) \rightarrow 0$ as $n \rightarrow \infty$, so $\bar{Y}_n$ is a consistent estimator of μ (in addition to being unbiased).

The conclusion that $\bar{Y}_n$ is consistent for μ holds even if $\text{Var}(\bar{Y}_n)$ does not exist. This classic result is known as the **law of large numbers (LLN)**.

Law of Large Numbers. Let $Y_1, Y_2, \ldots, Y_n$ be independent, identically distributed random variables with mean μ. Then,

$$\text{plim}(\bar{Y}_n) = \mu. \quad \text{[C.8]}$$

The law of large numbers means that, if we are interested in estimating the population average μ, we can get arbitrarily close to μ by choosing a sufficiently large sample. This fundamental result can be combined with basic properties of plims to show that fairly complicated estimators are consistent.

Property PLIM.1: Let θ be a parameter and define a new parameter, $\gamma = g(\theta)$, for some *continuous function* $g(\theta)$. Suppose that $\text{plim}(W_n) = \theta$. Define an estimator of γ by $G_n = g(W_n)$. Then,

$$\text{plim}(G_n) = \gamma. \quad \text{[C.9]}$$

This is often stated as

$$\text{plim } g(W_n) = g(\text{plim } W_n) \quad \text{[C.10]}$$

for a continuous function $g(\theta)$.

The assumption that $g(\theta)$ is continuous is a technical requirement that has often been described nontechnically as "a function that can be graphed without lifting your pencil from the paper." Because all the functions we encounter in this text are continuous, we do not provide a formal definition of a continuous function. Examples of continuous functions are $g(\theta) = a + b\theta$ for constants a and b, $g(\theta) = \theta^2$, $g(\theta) = 1/\theta$, $g(\theta) = \sqrt{\theta}$, $g(\theta) = \exp(\theta)$, and many variants on these. We will not need to mention the continuity assumption again.

As an important example of a consistent but biased estimator, consider estimating the standard deviation, σ, from a population with mean μ and variance σ^2. We already claimed that the sample variance $S_n^2 = (n - 1)^{-1}\sum_{i=1}^{n}(Y_i - \bar{Y}_n)^2$ is unbiased for σ^2. Using the law of large numbers and some algebra, S_n^2 can also be shown to be consistent for σ^2. The natural estimator of $\sigma = \sqrt{\sigma^2}$ is $S_n = \sqrt{S_n^2}$ (where the square root is always the positive square root). S_n, which is called the **sample standard deviation**, is *not* an unbiased estimator because the expected value of the square root is *not* the square root of the expected value (see Section B.3). Nevertheless, by PLIM.1, plim $S_n = \sqrt{\text{plim } S_n^2} = \sqrt{\sigma^2} = \sigma$, so S_n is a consistent estimator of σ.

Here are some other useful properties of the probability limit:

Property PLIM.2: If $\text{plim}(T_n) = \alpha$ and $\text{plim}(U_n) = \beta$, then

(i) $\text{plim}(T_n + U_n) = \alpha + \beta$;
(ii) $\text{plim}(T_n U_n) = \alpha\beta$;
(iii) $\text{plim}(T_n/U_n) = \alpha/\beta$, provided $\beta \neq 0$.

These three facts about probability limits allow us to combine consistent estimators in a variety of ways to get other consistent estimators. For example, let $\{Y_1, \ldots, Y_n\}$ be a random sample of size n on annual earnings from the population of workers with a high school education and denote the population mean by μ_Y. Let $\{Z_1, \ldots, Z_n\}$ be a random sample on annual earnings from the population of workers with a college education and denote the population mean by μ_Z. We wish to estimate the percentage difference in annual earnings between the two groups, which is $\gamma = 100\cdot(\mu_Z - \mu_Y)/\mu_Y$. (This is the percentage by which average earnings for college graduates differs from average earnings for high school graduates.) Because $\bar{Y}_n$ is consistent for μ_Y and $\bar{Z}_n$ is consistent for μ_Z, it follows from PLIM.1 and part (iii) of PLIM.2 that

$$G_n \equiv 100\cdot(\bar{Z}_n - \bar{Y}_n)/\bar{Y}_n$$

is a consistent estimator of γ. G_n is just the percentage difference between $\bar{Z}_n$ and $\bar{Y}_n$ in the sample, so it is a natural estimator. G_n is not an unbiased estimator of γ, but it is still a good estimator except possibly when n is small.

Asymptotic Normality

Consistency is a property of point estimators. Although it does tell us that the distribution of the estimator is collapsing around the parameter as the sample size gets large, it tells us essentially nothing about the *shape* of that distribution for a given sample size. For constructing interval estimators and testing hypotheses, we need a way to approximate the distribution of our estimators. Most econometric estimators have distributions that are well approximated by a normal distribution for large samples, which motivates the following definition.

Asymptotic Normality. Let $\{Z_n: n = 1, 2, \ldots\}$ be a sequence of random variables, such that for all numbers z,

$$P(Z_n \leq z) \rightarrow \Phi(z) \text{ as } n \rightarrow \infty, \quad \text{[C.11]}$$

where $\Phi(z)$ is the standard normal cumulative distribution function. Then, Z_n is said to have an *asymptotic standard normal distribution*. In this case, we often write $Z_n \overset{a}{\sim} \text{Normal}(0,1)$. (The "$a$" above the tilde stands for "asymptotically" or "approximately.")

Property (C.11) means that the cumulative distribution function for Z_n gets closer and closer to the cdf of the standard normal distribution as the sample size n gets large. When **asymptotic normality** holds, for large n we have the approximation

$P(Z_n \le z) \approx \Phi(z)$. Thus, probabilities concerning Z_n can be approximated by standard normal probabilities.

The **central limit theorem** (**CLT**) is one of the most powerful results in probability and statistics. It states that the average from a random sample for *any* population (with finite variance), when standardized, has an asymptotic standard normal distribution.

Central Limit Theorem. Let $\{Y_1, Y_2, \ldots, Y_n\}$ be a random sample with mean μ and variance σ^2. Then,

$$Z_n = \frac{\bar{Y}_n - \mu}{\sigma/\sqrt{n}} \qquad \text{[C.12]}$$

has an asymptotic standard normal distribution.

The variable Z_n in (C.12) is the standardized version of $\bar{Y}_n$: we have subtracted off $E(\bar{Y}_n) = \mu$ and divided by $sd(\bar{Y}_n) = \sigma/\sqrt{n}$. Thus, regardless of the population distribution of Y, Z_n has mean zero and variance one, which coincides with the mean and variance of the standard normal distribution. Remarkably, the entire distribution of Z_n gets arbitrarily close to the standard normal distribution as n gets large.

We can write the standardized variable in equation (C.12) as $\sqrt{n}(\bar{Y}_n - \mu)/\sigma$, which shows that we must multiply the difference between the sample mean and the population mean by the square root of the sample size in order to obtain a useful limiting distribution. Without the multiplication by $\sqrt{n}$, we would just have $(\bar{Y}_n - \mu)/\sigma$, which converges in probability to zero. In other words, the distribution of $(\bar{Y}_n - \mu)/\sigma$ simply collapses to a single point as $n \rightarrow \infty$, which we know cannot be a good approximation to the distribution of $(\bar{Y}_n - \mu)/\sigma$ for reasonable sample sizes. Multiplying by $\sqrt{n}$ ensures that the variance of Z_n remains constant. Practically, we often treat $\bar{Y}_n$ as being approximately normally distributed with mean μ and variance σ^2/n, and this gives us the correct statistical procedures because it leads to the standardized variable in equation (C.12).

Most estimators encountered in statistics and econometrics can be written as functions of sample averages, in which case we can apply the law of large numbers and the central limit theorem. When two consistent estimators have asymptotic normal distributions, we choose the estimator with the smallest asymptotic variance.

In addition to the standardized sample average in (C.12), many other statistics that depend on sample averages turn out to be asymptotically normal. An important one is obtained by replacing σ with its consistent estimator S_n in equation (C.12):

$$\frac{\bar{Y}_n - \mu}{S_n/\sqrt{n}} \qquad \text{[C.13]}$$

also has an approximate standard normal distribution for large n. The exact (finite sample) distributions of (C.12) and (C.13) are definitely not the same, but the difference is often small enough to be ignored for large n.

Throughout this section, each estimator has been subscripted by n to emphasize the nature of asymptotic or large sample analysis. Continuing this convention clutters the notation without providing additional insight, once the fundamentals of asymptotic analysis are understood. Henceforth, we drop the n subscript and rely on you to remember that estimators depend on the sample size, and properties such as consistency and asymptotic normality refer to the growth of the sample size without bound.

C.4 General Approaches to Parameter Estimation

Until this point, we have used the sample average to illustrate the finite and large sample properties of estimators. It is natural to ask: Are there general approaches to estimation that produce estimators with good properties, such as unbiasedness, consistency, and efficiency?

The answer is yes. A detailed treatment of various approaches to estimation is beyond the scope of this text; here, we provide only an informal discussion. A thorough discussion is given in Larsen and Marx (1986, Chapter 5).

Method of Moments

Given a parameter θ appearing in a population distribution, there are usually many ways to obtain unbiased and consistent estimators of θ. Trying all different possibilities and comparing them on the basis of the criteria in Sections C.2 and C.3 is not practical. Fortunately, some methods have been shown to have good general properties, and, for the most part, the logic behind them is intuitively appealing.

In the previous sections, we have studied the sample average as an unbiased estimator of the population average and the sample variance as an unbiased estimator of the population variance. These estimators are examples of **method of moments** estimators. Generally, method of moments estimation proceeds as follows. The parameter θ is shown to be related to some expected value in the distribution of Y, usually $\mathrm{E}(Y)$ or $\mathrm{E}(Y^2)$ (although more exotic choices are sometimes used). Suppose, for example, that the parameter of interest, θ, is related to the population mean as $\theta = g(\mu)$ for some function g. Because the sample average $\bar{Y}$ is an unbiased and consistent estimator of μ, it is natural to replace μ with $\bar{Y}$, which gives us the estimator $g(\bar{Y})$ of θ. The estimator $g(\bar{Y})$ is consistent for θ, and if $g(\mu)$ is a linear function of μ, then $g(\bar{Y})$ is unbiased as well. What we have done is replace the population moment, μ, with its sample counterpart, $\bar{Y}$. This is where the name "method of moments" comes from.

We cover two additional method of moments estimators that will be useful for our discussion of regression analysis. Recall that the covariance between two random variables X and Y is defined as $\sigma_{XY} = \mathrm{E}[(X - \mu_X)(Y - \mu_Y)]$. The method of moments suggests estimating σ_{XY} by $n^{-1}\sum_{i=1}^{n}(X_i - \bar{X})(Y_i - \bar{Y})$. This is a consistent estimator of σ_{XY}, but it turns out to be biased for essentially the same reason that the sample variance is biased if n, rather than $n - 1$, is used as the divisor. The **sample covariance** is defined as

$$S_{XY} = \frac{1}{n-1}\sum_{i=1}^{n}(X_i - \bar{X})(Y_i - \bar{Y}). \qquad \text{[C.14]}$$

It can be shown that this is an unbiased estimator of σ_{XY}. (Replacing n with $n - 1$ makes no difference as the sample size grows indefinitely, so this estimator is still consistent.)

As we discussed in Section B.4, the covariance between two variables is often difficult to interpret. Usually, we are more interested in correlation. Because the population correlation is $\rho_{XY} = \sigma_{XY}/(\sigma_X\sigma_Y)$, the method of moments suggests estimating ρ_{XY} as

$$R_{XY} = \frac{S_{XY}}{S_X S_Y} = \frac{\sum_{i=1}^{n}(X_i - \bar{X})(Y_i - \bar{Y})}{\left(\sum_{i=1}^{n}(X_i - \bar{X})^2\right)^{1/2}\left(\sum_{i=1}^{n}(Y_i - \bar{Y})^2\right)^{1/2}}, \qquad \text{[C.15]}$$

which is called the **sample correlation coefficient** (or *sample correlation* for short). Notice that we have canceled the division by $n - 1$ in the sample covariance and the sample standard deviations. In fact, we could divide each of these by n, and we would arrive at the same final formula.

It can be shown that the sample correlation coefficient is always in the interval $[-1,1]$, as it should be. Because S_{XY}, S_X, and S_Y are consistent for the corresponding population parameter, R_{XY} is a consistent estimator of the population correlation, ρ_{XY}. However, R_{XY} is a biased estimator for two reasons. First, S_X and S_Y are biased estimators of σ_X and σ_Y, respectively. Second, R_{XY} is a ratio of estimators, so it would not be unbiased, even if S_X and S_Y were. For our purposes, this is not important, although the fact that no unbiased estimator of ρ_{XY} exists is a classical result in mathematical statistics.

Maximum Likelihood

Another general approach to estimation is the method of *maximum likelihood*, a topic covered in many introductory statistics courses. A brief summary in the simplest case will suffice here. Let $\{Y_1, Y_2, \ldots, Y_n\}$ be a random sample from the population distribution $f(y;\theta)$. Because of the random sampling assumption, the joint distribution of $\{Y_1, Y_2, \ldots, Y_n\}$ is simply the product of the densities: $f(y_1;\theta)f(y_2;\theta) \cdots f(y_n;\theta)$. In the discrete case, this is $P(Y_1 = y_1, Y_2 = y_2, \ldots, Y_n = y_n)$. Now, define the *likelihood function* as

$$L(\theta;Y_1, \ldots, Y_n) = f(Y_1;\theta)f(Y_2;\theta) \cdots f(Y_n;\theta),$$

which is a random variable because it depends on the outcome of the random sample $\{Y_1, Y_2, \ldots, Y_n\}$. The **maximum likelihood estimator** of θ, call it W, is the value of θ that maximizes the likelihood function. (This is why we write L as a function of θ, followed by the random sample.) Clearly, this value depends on the random sample. The maximum likelihood principle says that, out of all the possible values for θ, the value that makes the likelihood of the observed data largest should be chosen. Intuitively, this is a reasonable approach to estimating θ.

Usually, it is more convenient to work with the *log-likelihood function*, which is obtained by taking the natural log of the likelihood function:

$$\log [L(\theta; Y_1, \ldots, Y_n)] = \sum_{i=1}^{n} \log [f(Y_i; \theta)], \qquad \text{[C.16]}$$

where we use the fact that the log of the product is the sum of the logs. Because (C.16) is the sum of independent, identically distributed random variables, analyzing estimators that come from (C.16) is relatively easy.

Maximum likelihood estimation (MLE) is usually consistent and sometimes unbiased. But so are many other estimators. The widespread appeal of MLE is that it is generally the most asymptotically efficient estimator when the population model $f(y;\theta)$ is correctly specified. In addition, the MLE is sometimes the **minimum variance unbiased estimator**; that is, it has the smallest variance among all unbiased estimators of θ. [See Larsen and Marx (1986, Chapter 5) for verification of these claims.]

In Chapter 17, we will need maximum likelihood to estimate the parameters of more advanced econometric models. In econometrics, we are almost always interested in the distribution of Y conditional on a set of explanatory variables, say, $X_1, X_2, \ldots, X_k$. Then, we replace the density in (C.16) with $f(Y_i|X_{i1}, \ldots, X_{ik}; \theta_1, \ldots, \theta_p)$, where this density is allowed to depend on p parameters, $\theta_1, \ldots, \theta_p$. Fortunately, for successful application of maximum likelihood methods, we do not need to delve much into the computational issues or the large-sample statistical theory. Wooldridge (2010, Chapter 13) covers the theory of maximum likelihood estimation.

Least Squares

A third kind of estimator, and one that plays a major role throughout the text, is called a **least squares estimator**. We have already seen an example of least squares: the sample mean, $\bar{Y}$, is a least squares estimator of the population mean, μ. We already know $\bar{Y}$ is a method of moments estimator. What makes it a least squares estimator? It can be shown that the value of m that makes the sum of squared deviations

$$\sum_{i=1}^{n} (Y_i - m)^2$$

as small as possible is $m = \bar{Y}$. Showing this is not difficult, but we omit the algebra.

For some important distributions, including the normal and the Bernoulli, the sample average $\bar{Y}$ is also the maximum likelihood estimator of the population mean μ. Thus, the principles of least squares, method of moments, and maximum likelihood often result in the *same* estimator. In other cases, the estimators are similar but not identical.

C.5 Interval Estimation and Confidence Intervals

The Nature of Interval Estimation

A point estimate obtained from a particular sample does not, by itself, provide enough information for testing economic theories or for informing policy discussions. A point estimate may be the researcher's best guess at the population value, but, by its nature, it provides no information about how close the estimate is "likely" to be to the population parameter. As an example, suppose a researcher reports, on the basis of a random sample of workers, that job training grants increase hourly wage by 6.4%. How are we to know whether or not this is close to the effect in the population of workers who could have been trained? Because we do not know the population value, we cannot know how close an estimate is for a particular sample. However, we can make statements involving probabilities, and this is where interval estimation comes in.

We already know one way of assessing the uncertainty in an estimator: find its sampling standard deviation. Reporting the standard deviation of the estimator, along with the point estimate, provides some information on the accuracy of our estimate. However, even if the problem of the standard deviation's dependence on unknown population parameters is ignored, reporting the standard deviation along with the point estimate makes no direct statement about where the population value is likely to lie in relation to the estimate. This limitation is overcome by constructing a **confidence interval**.

We illustrate the concept of a confidence interval with an example. Suppose the population has a Normal(μ,1) distribution and let $\{Y_1, \ldots, Y_n\}$ be a random sample from this population. (We assume that the variance of the population is known and equal to unity for the sake of illustration; we then show what to do in the more realistic case that the variance is unknown.) The sample average, $\bar{Y}$, has a normal distribution with mean μ and variance $1/n$: $\bar{Y} \sim \text{Normal}(\mu,1/n)$. From this, we can standardize $\bar{Y}$, and, because the standardized version of $\bar{Y}$ has a standard normal distribution, we have

$$\text{P}\left(-1.96 < \frac{\bar{Y} - \mu}{1/\sqrt{n}} < 1.96\right) = .95.$$

The event in parentheses is identical to the event $\bar{Y} - 1.96/\sqrt{n} < \mu < \bar{Y} + 1.96/\sqrt{n}$, so

$$\text{P}(\bar{Y} - 1.96/\sqrt{n} < \mu < \bar{Y} + 1.96/\sqrt{n}) = .95. \tag{C.17}$$

Equation (C.17) is interesting because it tells us that the probability that the random interval $[\bar{Y} - 1.96/\sqrt{n},\bar{Y} + 1.96/\sqrt{n}]$ contains the population mean μ is .95, or 95%. This information allows us to construct an *interval estimate* of μ, which is obtained by plugging in the sample outcome of the average, $\bar{y}$. Thus,

$$[\bar{y} - 1.96/\sqrt{n},\bar{y} + 1.96/\sqrt{n}] \tag{C.18}$$

is an example of an interval estimate of μ. It is also called a 95% confidence interval. A shorthand notation for this interval is $\bar{y} \pm 1.96/\sqrt{n}$.

The confidence interval in equation (C.18) is easy to compute, once the sample data $\{y_1,y_2, \ldots, y_n\}$ are observed; $\bar{y}$ is the only factor that depends on the data. For example, suppose that $n = 16$ and the average of the 16 data points is 7.3. Then, the 95% confidence interval for μ is $7.3 \pm 1.96/\sqrt{16} = 7.3 \pm .49$, which we can write in interval form as [6.81,7.79]. By construction, $\bar{y} = 7.3$ is in the center of this interval.

Unlike its computation, the meaning of a confidence interval is more difficult to understand. When we say that equation (C.18) is a 95% confidence interval for μ, we mean that the *random* interval

$$[\bar{Y} - 1.96/\sqrt{n},\bar{Y} + 1.96/\sqrt{n}] \tag{C.19}$$

contains μ with probability .95. In other words, *before* the random sample is drawn, there is a 95% chance that (C.19) contains μ. Equation (C.19) is an example of an **interval estimator**. It is a random interval, since the endpoints change with different samples.

A confidence interval is often interpreted as follows: "The probability that μ is in the interval (C.18) is .95." This is incorrect. Once the sample has been observed and $\bar{y}$ has been computed, the limits of the confidence interval are simply numbers (6.81 and 7.79 in the example just given). The population parameter, μ, though unknown, is also just some number. Therefore, μ either is or is not in the interval (C.18) (and we will never know with certainty which is the case). Probability plays no role once the confidence interval is computed for the particular data at hand. The probabilistic interpretation comes from the fact that for 95% of all random samples, the constructed confidence interval will contain μ.

To emphasize the meaning of a confidence interval, Table C.2 contains calculations for 20 random samples (or replications) from the Normal(2,1) distribution with sample size $n = 10$. For each of the 20 samples, $\bar{y}$ is obtained, and (C.18) is computed as $\bar{y} \pm 1.96/\sqrt{10} = \bar{y} \pm .62$ (each rounded to two decimals). As you can see, the interval changes with each random sample. Nineteen of the 20 intervals contain the population value of μ. Only for replication number 19 is μ not in the confidence interval. In other words, 95% of the samples result in a confidence interval that contains μ. This did not have to be the case with only 20 replications, but it worked out that way for this particular simulation.

TABLE C.2 Simulated Confidence Intervals from a Normal(μ,1) Distribution with $\mu = 2$

Replication	$\bar{y}$	95% Interval	Contains μ?
1	1.98	(1.36,2.60)	Yes
2	1.43	(0.81,2.05)	Yes
3	1.65	(1.03,2.27)	Yes
4	1.88	(1.26,2.50)	Yes
5	2.34	(1.72,2.96)	Yes
6	2.58	(1.96,3.20)	Yes
7	1.58	(.96,2.20)	Yes
8	2.23	(1.61,2.85)	Yes
9	1.96	(1.34,2.58)	Yes
10	2.11	(1.49,2.73)	Yes
11	2.15	(1.53,2.77)	Yes
12	1.93	(1.31,2.55)	Yes
13	2.02	(1.40,2.64)	Yes
14	2.10	(1.48,2.72)	Yes
15	2.18	(1.56,2.80)	Yes
16	2.10	(1.48,2.72)	Yes
17	1.94	(1.32,2.56)	Yes
18	2.21	(1.59,2.83)	Yes
19	1.16	(.54,1.78)	No
20	1.75	(1.13,2.37)	Yes

Confidence Intervals for the Mean from a Normally Distributed Population

The confidence interval derived in equation (C.18) helps illustrate how to construct and interpret confidence intervals. In practice, equation (C.18) is not very useful for the mean of a normal population because it assumes that the variance is known to be unity. It is easy to extend (C.18) to the case where the standard deviation σ is known to be any value: the 95% confidence interval is

$$[\bar{y} - 1.96\sigma/\sqrt{n}, \bar{y} + 1.96\sigma/\sqrt{n}]. \qquad \text{[C.20]}$$

Therefore, provided σ is known, a confidence interval for μ is readily constructed. To allow for unknown σ, we must use an estimate. Let

$$s = \left(\frac{1}{n-1}\sum_{i=1}^{n}(y_i - \bar{y})^2\right)^{1/2} \qquad \text{[C.21]}$$

denote the sample standard deviation. Then, we obtain a confidence interval that depends entirely on the observed data by replacing σ in equation (C.20) with its estimate, s. Unfortunately, this does not preserve the 95% level of confidence because s depends on the particular sample. In other words, the random interval $[\bar{Y} \pm 1.96(S/\sqrt{n})]$ no longer contains μ with probability .95 because the constant σ has been replaced with the random variable S.

How should we proceed? Rather than using the standard normal distribution, we must rely on the t distribution. The t distribution arises from the fact that

$$\frac{\bar{Y} - \mu}{S/\sqrt{n}} \sim t_{n-1}, \qquad \text{[C.22]}$$

where $\bar{Y}$ is the sample average and S is the sample standard deviation of the random sample $\{Y_1, \ldots, Y_n\}$. We will not prove (C.22); a careful proof can be found in a variety of places [for example, Larsen and Marx (1986, Chapter 7)].

To construct a 95% confidence interval, let c denote the 97.5th percentile in the t_{n-1} distribution. In other words, c is the value such that 95% of the area in the t_{n-1} is between $-c$ and c: $\text{P}(-c < t_{n-1} < c) = .95$. (The value of c depends on the degrees of freedom $n - 1$, but we do not make this explicit.) The choice of c is illustrated in Figure C.4. Once c has been properly chosen, the random interval $[\bar{Y} - c\cdot S/\sqrt{n}, \bar{Y} + c\cdot S/\sqrt{n}]$ contains μ with probability .95. For a particular sample, the 95% confidence interval is calculated as

$$[\bar{y} - c\cdot s/\sqrt{n}, \bar{y} + c\cdot s/\sqrt{n}]. \qquad \text{[C.23]}$$

FIGURE C.4 The 97.5th percentile, c, in a t distribution.

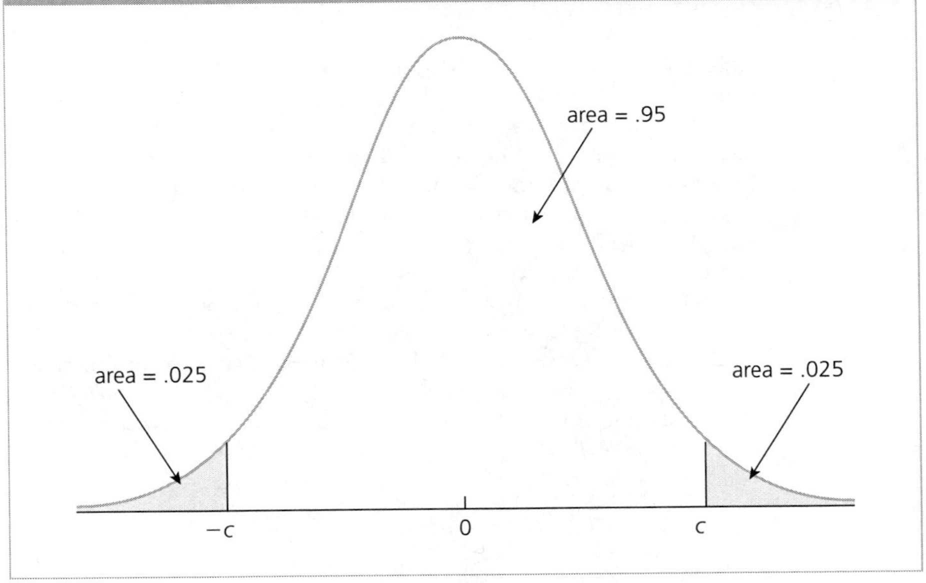

The values of c for various degrees of freedom can be obtained from Table G.2 in Appendix G. For example, if $n = 20$, so that the *df* is $n - 1 = 19$, then $c = 2.093$. Thus, the 95% confidence interval is $[\bar{y} \pm 2.093(s/\sqrt{20})]$, where $\bar{y}$ and s are the values obtained from the sample. Even if $s = \sigma$ (which is very unlikely), the confidence interval in (C.23) is wider than that in (C.20) because $c > 1.96$. For small degrees of freedom, (C.23) is much wider.

More generally, let c_α denote the $100(1 - \alpha)$ percentile in the t_{n-1} distribution. Then, a $100(1 - \alpha)\%$ confidence interval is obtained as

$$[\bar{y} - c_{\alpha/2}s/\sqrt{n}, \bar{y} + c_{\alpha/2}s/\sqrt{n}]. \quad \text{[C.24]}$$

Obtaining $c_{\alpha/2}$ requires choosing α and knowing the degrees of freedom $n - 1$; then, Table G.2 can be used. For the most part, we will concentrate on 95% confidence intervals.

There is a simple way to remember how to construct a confidence interval for the mean of a normal distribution. Recall that $\text{sd}(\bar{Y}) = \sigma/\sqrt{n}$. Thus, $s/\sqrt{n}$ is the point estimate of $\text{sd}(\bar{Y})$. The associated random variable, $S/\sqrt{n}$, is sometimes called the **standard error** of $\bar{Y}$. Because what shows up in formulas is the point estimate $s/\sqrt{n}$, we define the standard error of $\bar{y}$ as $\text{se}(\bar{y}) = s/\sqrt{n}$. Then, (C.24) can be written in shorthand as

$$[\bar{y} \pm c_{\alpha/2} \cdot \text{se}(\bar{y})]. \quad \text{[C.25]}$$

This equation shows why the notion of the standard error of an estimate plays an important role in econometrics.

EXAMPLE C.2 EFFECT OF JOB TRAINING GRANTS ON WORKER PRODUCTIVITY

Holzer, Block, Cheatham, and Knott (1993) studied the effects of job training grants on worker productivity by collecting information on "scrap rates" for a sample of Michigan manufacturing firms receiving job training grants in 1988. Table C.3 lists the scrap rates—measured as number of items per 100 produced that are not usable and therefore need to be scrapped—for 20 firms. Each of these firms received a job training grant in 1988; there were no grants awarded in 1987. We are interested in constructing a confidence interval for the change in the scrap rate from 1987 to 1988 for the population of all manufacturing firms that could have received grants.

We assume that the change in scrap rates has a normal distribution. Since $n = 20$, a 95% confidence interval for the mean change in scrap rates μ is $[\bar{y} \pm 2.093 \cdot \text{se}(\bar{y})]$, where $\text{se}(\bar{y}) = s/\sqrt{n}$. The value 2.093 is the 97.5^{th} percentile in a t_{19} distribution. For the particular sample values, $\bar{y} = -1.15$ and $\text{se}(\bar{y}) = .54$ (each rounded to two decimals), so the 95% confidence interval is $[-2.28, -.02]$. The value zero is excluded from this interval, so we conclude that, with 95% confidence, the average change in scrap rates in the population is not zero.

TABLE C.3 Scrap Rates for 20 Michigan Manufacturing Firms

Firm	1987	1988	Change
1	10	3	–7
2	1	1	0
3	6	5	–1
4	.45	.5	.05
5	1.25	1.54	.29
6	1.3	1.5	.2
7	1.06	.8	–.26
8	3	2	–1
9	8.18	.67	–7.51
10	1.67	1.17	–.5
11	.98	.51	–.47
12	1	.5	–.5
13	.45	.61	.16
14	5.03	6.7	1.67
15	8	4	–4
16	9	7	–2
17	18	19	1
18	.28	.2	–.08
19	7	5	–2
20	3.97	3.83	–.14
Average	4.38	3.23	–1.15

At this point, Example C.2 is mostly illustrative because it has some potentially serious flaws as an econometric analysis. Most importantly, it assumes that any systematic reduction in scrap rates is due to the job training grants. But many things can happen over the course of the year to change worker productivity. From this analysis, we have no way of knowing whether the fall in average scrap rates is attributable to the job training grants or if, at least partly, some external force is responsible.

A Simple Rule of Thumb for a 95% Confidence Interval

The confidence interval in (C.25) can be computed for any sample size and any confidence level. As we saw in Section B.5, the t distribution approaches the standard normal distribution as the degrees of freedom gets large. In particular, for $\alpha = .05$, $c_{\alpha/2} \rightarrow 1.96$ as $n \rightarrow \infty$, although $c_{\alpha/2}$ is always greater than 1.96 for each n. A *rule of thumb* for an approximate 95% confidence interval is

$$[\bar{y} \pm 2 \cdot \text{se}(\bar{y})]. \quad \text{[C.26]}$$

In other words, we obtain $\bar{y}$ and its standard error and then compute $\bar{y}$ plus and minus twice its standard error to obtain the confidence interval. This is slightly too wide for very large n, and it is too narrow for small n. As we can see from Example C.2, even for n as small as 20, (C.26) is in the ballpark for a 95% confidence interval for the mean from a normal distribution. This means we can get pretty close to a 95% confidence interval without having to refer to t tables.

Asymptotic Confidence Intervals for Nonnormal Populations

In some applications, the population is clearly nonnormal. A leading case is the Bernoulli distribution, where the random variable takes on only the values zero and one. In other cases, the nonnormal population has no standard distribution. This does not matter, provided the sample size is sufficiently large for the central limit theorem to give a good approximation for the distribution of the sample average $\bar{Y}$. For large n, an *approximate* 95% confidence interval is

$$[\bar{y} \pm 1.96 \cdot \text{se}(\bar{y})], \tag{C.27}$$

where the value 1.96 is the 97.5th percentile in the standard normal distribution. Mechanically, computing an approximate confidence interval does not differ from the normal case. A slight difference is that the number multiplying the standard error comes from the standard normal distribution, rather than the t distribution, because we are using asymptotics. Because the t distribution approaches the standard normal as the *df* increases, equation (C.25) is also perfectly legitimate as an approximate 95% interval; some prefer this to (C.27) because the former is exact for normal populations.

EXAMPLE C.3 RACE DISCRIMINATION IN HIRING

The Urban Institute conducted a study in 1988 in Washington, D.C., to examine the extent of race discrimination in hiring. Five pairs of people interviewed for several jobs. In each pair, one person was black and the other person was white. They were given résumés indicating that they were virtually the same in terms of experience, education, and other factors that determine job qualification. The idea was to make individuals as similar as possible with the exception of race. Each person in a pair interviewed for the same job, and the researchers recorded which applicant received a job offer. This is an example of a *matched pairs analysis,* where each trial consists of data on two people (or two firms, two cities, and so on) that are thought to be similar in many respects but different in one important characteristic.

Let θ_B denote the probability that the black person is offered a job and let θ_W be the probability that the white person is offered a job. We are primarily interested in the difference, $\theta_B - \theta_W$. Let B_i denote a Bernoulli variable equal to one if the black person gets a job offer from employer i, and zero otherwise. Similarly, $W_i = 1$ if the white person gets a job offer from employer i, and zero otherwise. Pooling across the five pairs of people, there were a total of $n = 241$ trials (pairs of interviews with employers). Unbiased estimators of θ_B and θ_W are $\bar{B}$ and $\bar{W}$, the fractions of interviews for which blacks and whites were offered jobs, respectively.

To put this into the framework of computing a confidence interval for a population mean, define a new variable $Y_i = B_i - W_i$. Now, Y_i can take on three values: -1 if the black person did not get the job but the white person did, 0 if both people either did or did not get the job, and 1 if the black person got the job and the white person did not. Then, $\mu \equiv E(Y_i) = E(B_i) - E(W_i) = \theta_B - \theta_W$.

The distribution of Y_i is certainly not normal—it is discrete and takes on only three values. Nevertheless, an approximate confidence interval for $\theta_B - \theta_W$ can be obtained by using large sample methods.

The data from the Urban Institute audit study are in the file AUDIT.RAW. Using the 241 observed data points, $\bar{b} = .224$ and $\bar{w} = .357$, so $\bar{y} = .224 - .357 = -.133$. Thus, 22.4% of black applicants were offered jobs, while 35.7% of white applicants were offered jobs. This is *prima facie* evidence of discrimination against blacks, but we can learn much more by computing a confidence interval for μ. To compute an approximate 95% confidence interval, we need the sample standard deviation. This turns out to be $s = .482$ [using equation (C.21)]. Using (C.27), we obtain a 95% CI for $\mu = \theta_B - \theta_W$ as $-.133 \pm 1.96(.482/\sqrt{241}) = -.133 \pm .031 = [-.164, -.102]$. The approximate 99% CI is $-.133 \pm 2.58(.482/\sqrt{241}) = [-.213, -.053]$. Naturally, this contains a wider range of values than the 95% CI. But even the 99% CI does not contain the value zero. Thus, we are very confident that the population difference $\theta_B - \theta_W$ is not zero.

Before we turn to hypothesis testing, it is useful to review the various population and sample quantities that measure the spreads in the population distributions and the sampling distributions of the estimators. These quantities appear often in statistical analysis, and extensions of them are important for the regression analysis in the main text. The quantity σ is the (unknown) population standard deviation; it is a measure of the spread in the distribution of Y. When we divide σ by $\sqrt{n}$, we obtain the **sampling standard deviation** of $\bar{Y}$ (the sample average). While σ is a fixed feature of the population, $\text{sd}(\bar{Y}) = \sigma/\sqrt{n}$ shrinks to zero as $n \rightarrow \infty$: our estimator of μ gets more and more precise as the sample size grows.

The estimate of σ for a particular sample, s, is called the sample standard deviation because it is obtained from the sample. (We also call the underlying random variable, S, which changes across different samples, the sample standard deviation.) Like $\bar{y}$ as an estimate of μ, s is our "best guess" at σ given the sample at hand. The quantity $s/\sqrt{n}$ is what we call the standard error of $\bar{y}$, and it is our best estimate of $\sigma/\sqrt{n}$. Confidence intervals for the population parameter μ depend directly on $\text{se}(\bar{y}) = s/\sqrt{n}$. Because this standard error shrinks to zero as the sample size grows, a larger sample size generally means a smaller confidence interval. Thus, we see clearly that one benefit of more data is that they result in narrower confidence intervals. The notion of the standard error of an estimate, which in the vast majority of cases shrinks to zero at the rate $1/\sqrt{n}$, plays a fundamental role in hypothesis testing (as we will see in the next section) and for confidence intervals and testing in the context of multiple regression (as discussed in Chapter 4).

C.6 Hypothesis Testing

So far, we have reviewed how to evaluate point estimators, and we have seen—in the case of a population mean—how to construct and interpret confidence intervals. But sometimes the question we are interested in has a definite yes or no answer. Here are some examples: (1) Does a job training program effectively increase average worker productivity? (see Example C.2); (2) Are blacks discriminated against in hiring? (see Example C.3); (3) Do stiffer state drunk driving laws reduce the number of drunk driving arrests? Devising methods for answering such questions, using a sample of data, is known as hypothesis testing.

Fundamentals of Hypothesis Testing

To illustrate the issues involved with hypothesis testing, consider an election example. Suppose there are two candidates in an election, Candidates A and B. Candidate A is reported to have received 42% of the popular vote, while Candidate B received 58%. These are supposed to represent the true percentages in the voting population, and we treat them as such.

Candidate A is convinced that more people must have voted for him, so he would like to investigate whether the election was rigged. Knowing something about statistics, Candidate A hires a consulting agency to randomly sample 100 voters to record whether or not each person voted for him. Suppose that, for the sample collected, 53 people voted for Candidate A. This sample estimate of 53% clearly exceeds the reported population value of 42%. Should Candidate A conclude that the election was indeed a fraud?

While it appears that the votes for Candidate A were undercounted, we cannot be certain. Even if only 42% of the population voted for Candidate A, it is possible that, in a sample of 100, we observe 53 people who did vote for Candidate A. The question is: How *strong* is the sample evidence against the officially reported percentage of 42%?

One way to proceed is to set up a **hypothesis test**. Let θ denote the true proportion of the population voting for Candidate A. The hypothesis that the reported results are accurate can be stated as

$$H_0: \theta = .42. \qquad [C.28]$$

This is an example of a **null hypothesis**. We always denote the null hypothesis by H_0. In hypothesis testing, the null hypothesis plays a role similar to that of a defendant on trial in many judicial systems: just as a defendant is presumed to be innocent until proven guilty, the null hypothesis is presumed to be true until the data strongly suggest otherwise. In the current example, Candidate A must present fairly strong evidence against (C.28) in order to win a recount.

The **alternative hypothesis** in the election example is that the true proportion voting for Candidate A in the election is greater than .42:

$$H_1: \theta > .42. \qquad [C.29]$$

In order to conclude that H_0 is false and that H_1 is true, we must have evidence "beyond reasonable doubt" against H_0. How many votes out of 100 would be needed before we feel the evidence is strongly against H_0? Most would agree that observing 43 votes out of a sample of 100 is not enough to overturn the original election results; such an outcome is well within the expected sampling variation. On the other hand, we do not need to observe 100 votes for Candidate A to cast doubt on H_0. Whether 53 out of 100 is enough to reject H_0 is much less clear. The answer depends on how we quantify "beyond reasonable doubt."

Before we turn to the issue of quantifying uncertainty in hypothesis testing, we should head off some possible confusion. You may have noticed that the hypotheses in equations (C.28) and (C.29) do not exhaust all possibilities: it could be that θ is less than .42. For the application at hand, we are not particularly interested in that possibility; it has nothing to do with overturning the results of the election. Therefore, we can just state at the outset that we are ignoring alternatives θ with $\theta < .42$. Nevertheless, some authors prefer to state null and alternative hypotheses so that they are exhaustive, in which case our null hypothesis should be H_0: $\theta \leq .42$. Stated in this way, the null hypothesis is a *composite* null hypothesis because it allows for more than one value under H_0. [By contrast, equation (C.28) is an example of a *simple* null hypothesis.] For these kinds of examples, it does not matter whether we state the null as in (C.28) or as a composite null: the most difficult value to reject if $\theta \leq .42$ is $\theta = .42$. (That is, if we reject the value $\theta = .42$, against $\theta > .42$, then logically we must reject any value less than .42.) Therefore, our testing procedure based on (C.28) leads to the same test as if H_0: $\theta \leq .42$. In this text, we always state a null hypothesis as a simple null hypothesis.

In hypothesis testing, we can make two kinds of mistakes. First, we can reject the null hypothesis when it is in fact true. This is called a **Type I error**. In the election example, a Type I error occurs if we reject H_0 when the true proportion of people voting for Candidate A is in fact .42. The second kind of error is failing to reject H_0 when it is actually false. This is called a **Type II error**. In the election example, a Type II error occurs if $\theta > .42$ but we fail to reject H_0.

After we have made the decision of whether or not to reject the null hypothesis, we have either decided correctly or we have committed an error. We will never know with certainty whether an error was committed. However, we can compute the *probability* of making either a Type I or a Type II error. Hypothesis testing rules are constructed to make the probability of committing a Type I error fairly small. Generally, we define the **significance level** (or simply the *level*) of a test as the probability of a Type I error; it is typically denoted by α. Symbolically, we have

$$\alpha = P(\text{Reject } H_0 | H_0). \quad [C.30]$$

The right-hand side is read as: "The probability of rejecting H_0 given that H_0 is true."

Classical hypothesis testing requires that we initially specify a significance level for a test. When we specify a value for α, we are essentially quantifying our tolerance for a Type I error. Common values for α are .10, .05, and .01. If $\alpha = .05$, then the researcher is willing to falsely reject H_0 5% of the time, in order to detect deviations from H_0.

Once we have chosen the significance level, we would then like to minimize the probability of a Type II error. Alternatively, we would like to maximize the **power of a test** against all relevant alternatives. The power of a test is just one minus the probability of a Type II error. Mathematically,

$$\pi(\theta) = P(\text{Reject } H_0 | \theta) = 1 - P(\text{Type II} | \theta),$$

where θ denotes the actual value of the parameter. Naturally, we would like the power to equal unity whenever the null hypothesis is false. But this is impossible to achieve while keeping the significance level small. Instead, we choose our tests to maximize the power for a given significance level.

Testing Hypotheses about the Mean in a Normal Population

In order to test a null hypothesis against an alternative, we need to choose a test statistic (or statistic, for short) and a critical value. The choices for the statistic and critical value are based on convenience and on the desire to maximize power given a significance level for the test. In this subsection, we review how to test hypotheses for the mean of a normal population.

A **test statistic**, denoted T, is some function of the random sample. When we compute the statistic for a particular outcome, we obtain an outcome of the test statistic, which we will denote t.

Given a test statistic, we can define a rejection rule that determines when H_0 is rejected in favor of H_1. In this text, all rejection rules are based on comparing the value of a test statistic, t, to a **critical value**, c. The values of t that result in rejection of the null hypothesis are collectively known as the **rejection region**. To determine the critical value, we must first decide on a significance level of the test. Then, given α, the critical value associated with α is determined by the distribution of T, *assuming* that H_0 is true. We will write this critical value as c, suppressing the fact that it depends on α.

Testing hypotheses about the mean μ from a Normal(μ,σ^2) population is straightforward. The null hypothesis is stated as

$$H_0\colon \mu = \mu_0, \tag{C.31}$$

where μ_0 is a value that we specify. In the majority of applications, $\mu_0 = 0$, but the general case is no more difficult.

The rejection rule we choose depends on the nature of the alternative hypothesis. The three alternatives of interest are

$$H_1\colon \mu > \mu_0, \tag{C.32}$$

$$H_1\colon \mu < \mu_0, \tag{C.33}$$

and

$$H_1\colon \mu \neq \mu_0. \tag{C.34}$$

Equation (C.32) gives a **one-sided alternative**, as does (C.33). When the alternative hypothesis is (C.32), the null is effectively $H_0\colon \mu \leq \mu_0$, since we reject H_0 only when $\mu > \mu_0$. This is appropriate when we are interested in the value of μ only when μ is at least as large as μ_0. Equation (C.34) is a **two-sided alternative**. This is appropriate when we are interested in any departure from the null hypothesis.

Consider first the alternative in (C.32). Intuitively, we should reject H_0 in favor of H_1 when the value of the sample average, $\bar{y}$, is "sufficiently" greater than μ_0. But how should we determine when $\bar{y}$ is large enough for H_0 to be rejected at the chosen significance level? This requires knowing the probability of rejecting the null hypothesis when it is true. Rather than working directly with $\bar{y}$, we use its standardized version, where σ is replaced with the sample standard deviation, s:

$$t = \sqrt{n}(\bar{y} - \mu_0)/s = (\bar{y} - \mu_0)/\text{se}(\bar{y}), \qquad \text{[C.35]}$$

where $\text{se}(\bar{y}) = s/\sqrt{n}$ is the standard error of $\bar{y}$. Given the sample of data, it is easy to obtain t. We work with t because, under the null hypothesis, the random variable

$$T = \sqrt{n}(\bar{Y} - \mu_0)/S$$

has a t_{n-1} distribution. Now, suppose we have settled on a 5% significance level. Then, the critical value c is chosen so that $\text{P}(T > c|\text{H}_0) = .05$; that is, the probability of a Type I error is 5%. Once we have found c, the rejection rule is

$$t > c, \qquad \text{[C.36]}$$

where c is the $100(1 - \alpha)$ percentile in a t_{n-1} distribution; as a percent, the significance level is $100 \cdot \alpha\%$. This is an example of a **one-tailed test** because the rejection region is in one tail of the t distribution. For a 5% significance level, c is the 95th percentile in the t_{n-1} distribution; this is illustrated in Figure C.5. A different significance level leads to a different critical value.

The statistic in equation (C.35) is often called the ***t* statistic** for testing $\text{H}_0: \mu = \mu_0$. The t statistic measures the distance from $\bar{y}$ to μ_0 *relative* to the standard error of $\bar{y}$, $\text{se}(\bar{y})$.

FIGURE C.5 Rejection region for a 5% significance level test against the one-sided alternative $\mu > \mu_0$.

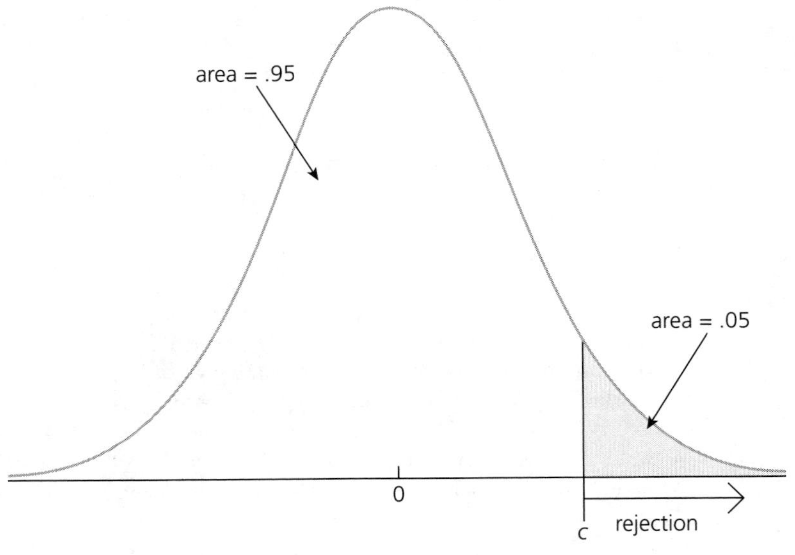

EXAMPLE C.4 EFFECT OF ENTERPRISE ZONES ON BUSINESS INVESTMENTS

In the population of cities granted enterprise zones in a particular state [see Papke (1994) for Indiana], let Y denote the percentage change in investment from the year before to the year after a city became an enterprise zone. Assume that Y has a Normal(μ,σ^2) distribution. The null hypothesis that enterprise zones have no effect on business investment is H_0: $\mu = 0$; the alternative that they have a positive effect is H_1: $\mu > 0$. (We assume that they do not have a negative effect.) Suppose that we wish to test H_0 at the 5% level. The test statistic in this case is

$$t = \frac{\bar{y}}{s/\sqrt{n}} = \frac{\bar{y}}{\text{se}(\bar{y})}. \quad \text{[C.37]}$$

Suppose that we have a sample of 36 cities that are granted enterprise zones. Then, the critical value is $c = 1.69$ (see Table G.2), and we reject H_0 in favor of H_1 if $t > 1.69$. Suppose that the sample yields $\bar{y} = 8.2$ and $s = 23.9$. Then, $t \approx 2.06$, and H_0 is therefore rejected at the 5% level. Thus, we conclude that, at the 5% significance level, enterprise zones have an effect on average investment. The 1% critical value is 2.44, so H_0 is not rejected at the 1% level. The same caveat holds here as in Example C.2: we have not controlled for other factors that might affect investment in cities over time, so we cannot claim that the effect is causal.

The rejection rule is similar for the one-sided alternative (C.33). A test with a significance level of $100 \cdot \alpha\%$ rejects H_0 against (C.33) whenever

$$t < -c; \quad \text{[C.38]}$$

in other words, we are looking for negative values of the t statistic—which implies $\bar{y} < \mu_0$—that are sufficiently far from zero to reject H_0.

For two-sided alternatives, we must be careful to choose the critical value so that the significance level of the test is still α. If H_1 is given by H_1: $\mu \neq \mu_0$, then we reject H_0 if $\bar{y}$ is far from μ_0 in *absolute value*: a $\bar{y}$ much larger or much smaller than μ_0 provides evidence against H_0 in favor of H_1. A $100 \cdot \alpha\%$ level test is obtained from the rejection rule

$$|t| > c, \quad \text{[C.39]}$$

where $|t|$ is the absolute value of the t statistic in (C.35). This gives a **two-tailed test**. We must now be careful in choosing the critical value: c is the $100(1 - \alpha/2)$ percentile in the t_{n-1} distribution. For example, if $\alpha = .05$, then the critical value is the 97.5th percentile in the t_{n-1} distribution. This ensures that H_0 is rejected only 5% of the time when it is true (see Figure C.6). For example, if $n = 22$, then the critical value is $c = 2.08$, the 97.5th percentile in a t_{21} distribution (see Table G.2). The absolute value of the t statistic must exceed 2.08 in order to reject H_0 against H_1 at the 5% level.

It is important to know the proper language of hypothesis testing. Sometimes, the appropriate phrase "we fail to reject H_0 in favor of H_1 at the 5% significance level" is replaced with "we accept H_0 at the 5% significance level." The latter wording is incorrect. With the same set of data, there are usually many hypotheses that cannot be rejected. In the earlier election example, it would be logically inconsistent to say that H_0: $\theta = .42$ and H_0: $\theta = .43$ are both "accepted," since only one of these can be true. But it is entirely possible that neither of these hypotheses is rejected. For this reason, we always say "fail to reject H_0" rather than "accept H_0."

FIGURE C.6 Rejection region for a 5% significance level test against the two-sided alternative $H_1: \mu \neq \mu_0$.

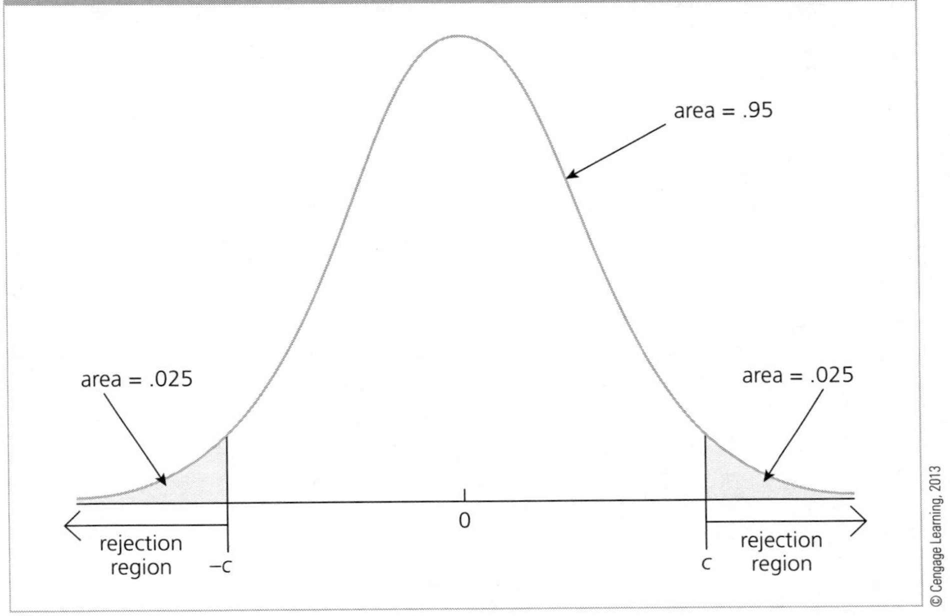

Asymptotic Tests for Nonnormal Populations

If the sample size is large enough to invoke the central limit theorem (see Section C.3), the mechanics of hypothesis testing for population means are the *same* whether or not the population distribution is normal. The theoretical justification comes from the fact that, under the null hypothesis,

$$T = \sqrt{n}(\bar{Y} - \mu_0)/S \overset{a}{\sim} \text{Normal}(0,1).$$

Therefore, with large n, we can compare the t statistic in (C.35) with the critical values from a standard normal distribution. Because the t_{n-1} distribution converges to the standard normal distribution as n gets large, the t and standard normal critical values will be very close for extremely large n. Because asymptotic theory is based on n increasing without bound, it cannot tell us whether the standard normal or t critical values are better. For moderate values of n, say, between 30 and 60, it is traditional to use the t distribution because we know this is correct for normal populations. For $n > 120$, the choice between the t and standard normal distributions is largely irrelevant because the critical values are practically the same.

Because the critical values chosen using either the standard normal or t distribution are only approximately valid for nonnormal populations, our chosen significance levels are also only approximate; thus, for nonnormal populations, our significance levels are really *asymptotic* significance levels. Thus, if we choose a 5% significance level, but our population is nonnormal, then the actual significance level will be larger or smaller than

5% (and we cannot know which is the case). When the sample size is large, the actual significance level will be very close to 5%. Practically speaking, the distinction is not important, so we will now drop the qualifier "asymptotic."

EXAMPLE C.5 RACE DISCRIMINATION IN HIRING

In the Urban Institute study of discrimination in hiring (see Example C.3), we are primarily interested in testing H_0: $\mu = 0$ against H_1: $\mu < 0$, where $\mu = \theta_B - \theta_W$ is the difference in probabilities that blacks and whites receive job offers. Recall that μ is the population mean of in the variable $Y = B - W$, where B and W are binary indicators. Using the $n = 241$ paired comparisons in the data file AUDIT.RAW, we obtained $\bar{y} = -.133$ and $\text{se}(\bar{y}) = .482/\sqrt{241} \approx .031$. The t statistic for testing H_0: $\mu = 0$ is $t = -.133/.031 \approx -4.29$. You will remember from Appendix B that the standard normal distribution is, for practical purposes, indistinguishable from the t distribution with 240 degrees of freedom. The value -4.29 is so far out in the left tail of the distribution that we reject H_0 at any reasonable significance level. In fact, the .005 (one-half of a percent) critical value (for the one-sided test) is about -2.58. A t value of -4.29 is *very* strong evidence against H_0 in favor of H_1. Hence, we conclude that there is discrimination in hiring.

Computing and Using *p*-Values

The traditional requirement of choosing a significance level ahead of time means that different researchers, using the same data and same procedure to test the same hypothesis, could wind up with different conclusions. Reporting the significance level at which we are carrying out the test solves this problem to some degree, but it does not completely remove the problem.

To provide more information, we can ask the following question: What is the *largest* significance level at which we could carry out the test and still fail to reject the null hypothesis? This value is known as the ***p*-value** of a test (sometimes called the *prob-value*). Compared with choosing a significance level ahead of time and obtaining a critical value, computing a *p*-value is somewhat more difficult. But with the advent of quick and inexpensive computing, *p*-values are now fairly easy to obtain.

As an illustration, consider the problem of testing H_0: $\mu = 0$ in a Normal(μ,σ^2) population. Our test statistic in this case is $T = \sqrt{n}\cdot\bar{Y}/S$, and we assume that n is large enough to treat T as having a standard normal distribution under H_0. Suppose that the observed value of T for our sample is $t = 1.52$. (Note how we have skipped the step of choosing a significance level.) Now that we have seen the value t, we can find the largest significance level at which we would fail to reject H_0. This is the significance level associated with using t as our critical value. Because our test statistic T has a standard normal distribution under H_0, we have

$$p\text{-value} = P(T > 1.52|H_0) = 1 - \Phi(1.52) = .065, \quad \text{[C.40]}$$

where $\Phi(\cdot)$ denotes the standard normal cdf. In other words, the *p*-value in this example is simply the area to the right of 1.52, the observed value of the test statistic, in a standard normal distribution. See Figure C.7 for illustration.

FIGURE C.7 The p-value when $t = 1.52$ for the one-sided alternative $\mu . \mu_0$.

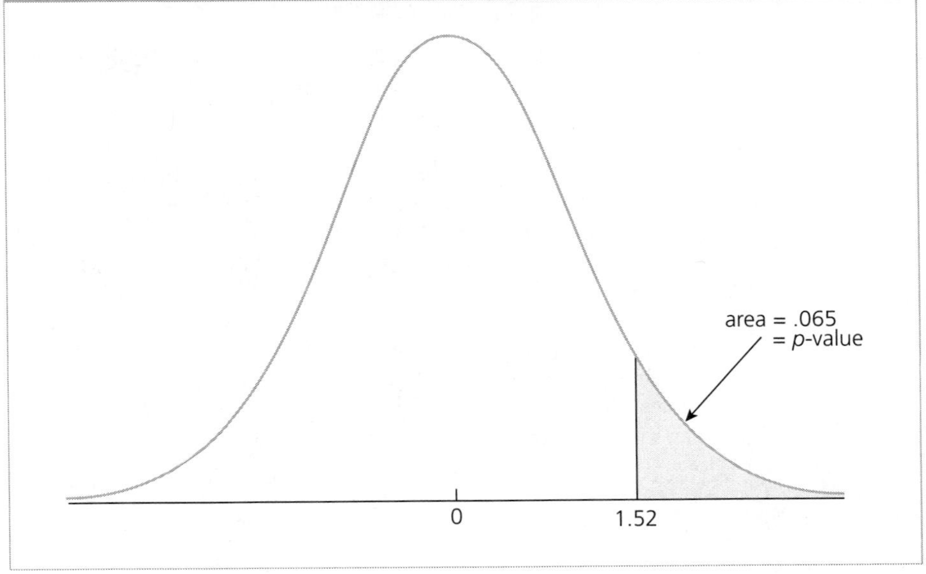

Because the p-value $= .065$, the largest significance level at which we can carry out this test and fail to reject is 6.5%. If we carry out the test at a level below 6.5% (such as at 5%), we fail to reject H_0. If we carry out the test at a level larger than 6.5% (such as 10%), we reject H_0. With the p-value at hand, we can carry out the test at any level.

The p-value in this example has another useful interpretation: it is the probability that we observe a value of T as large as 1.52 when the null hypothesis is true. If the null hypothesis is actually true, we would observe a value of T as large as 1.52 due to chance only 6.5% of the time. Whether this is small enough to reject H_0 depends on our tolerance for a Type I error. The p-value has a similar interpretation in all other cases, as we will see.

Generally, small p-values are evidence *against* H_0, since they indicate that the outcome of the data occurs with small probability if H_0 is true. In the previous example, if t had been a larger value, say, $t = 2.85$, then the p-value would be $1 - \Phi(2.85) \approx .002$. This means that, if the null hypothesis were true, we would observe a value of T as large as 2.85 with probability .002. How do we interpret this? Either we obtained a very unusual sample or the null hypothesis is false. Unless we have a *very* small tolerance for Type I error, we would reject the null hypothesis. On the other hand, a large p-value is weak evidence against H_0. If we had gotten $t = .47$ in the previous example, then the p-value $= 1 - \Phi(.47) = .32$. Observing a value of T larger than .47 happens with probability .32, even when H_0 is true; this is large enough so that there is insufficient doubt about H_0, unless we have a very high tolerance for Type I error.

For hypothesis testing about a population mean using the t distribution, we need detailed tables in order to compute p-values. Table G.2 only allows us to put bounds on p-values. Fortunately, many statistics and econometrics packages now compute p-values routinely, and they also provide calculation of cdfs for the t and other distributions used for computing p-values.

EXAMPLE C.6 EFFECT OF JOB TRAINING GRANTS ON WORKER PRODUCTIVITY

Consider again the Holzer et al. (1993) data in Example C.2. From a policy perspective, there are two questions of interest. First, what is our best estimate of the mean change in scrap rates, μ? We have already obtained this for the sample of 20 firms listed in Table C.3: the sample average of the change in scrap rates is -1.15. Relative to the initial average scrap rate in 1987, this represents a fall in the scrap rate of about 26.3% ($-1.15/4.38 \approx -.263$), which is a nontrivial effect.

We would also like to know whether the sample provides strong evidence for an effect in the population of manufacturing firms that could have received grants. The null hypothesis is H_0: $\mu = 0$, and we test this against H_1: $\mu < 0$, where μ is the average change in scrap rates. Under the null, the job training grants have no effect on average scrap rates. The alternative states that there is an effect. We do not care about the alternative $\mu > 0$, so the null hypothesis is effectively H_0: $\mu \geq 0$.

Since $\bar{y} = -1.15$ and $\text{se}(\bar{y}) = .54$, $t = -1.15/.54 = -2.13$. This is below the 5% critical value of -1.73 (from a t_{19} distribution) but above the 1% critical value, -2.54. The p-value in this case is computed as

$$p\text{-value} = P(T_{19} < -2.13), \qquad [C.41]$$

where T_{19} represents a t distributed random variable with 19 degrees of freedom. The inequality is reversed from (C.40) because the alternative has the form in (C.33). The probability in (C.41) is the area to the left of -2.13 in a t_{19} distribution (see Figure C.8).

FIGURE C.8 The p-value when $t = -2.13$ with 19 degrees of freedom for the one-sided alternative $\mu < 0$.

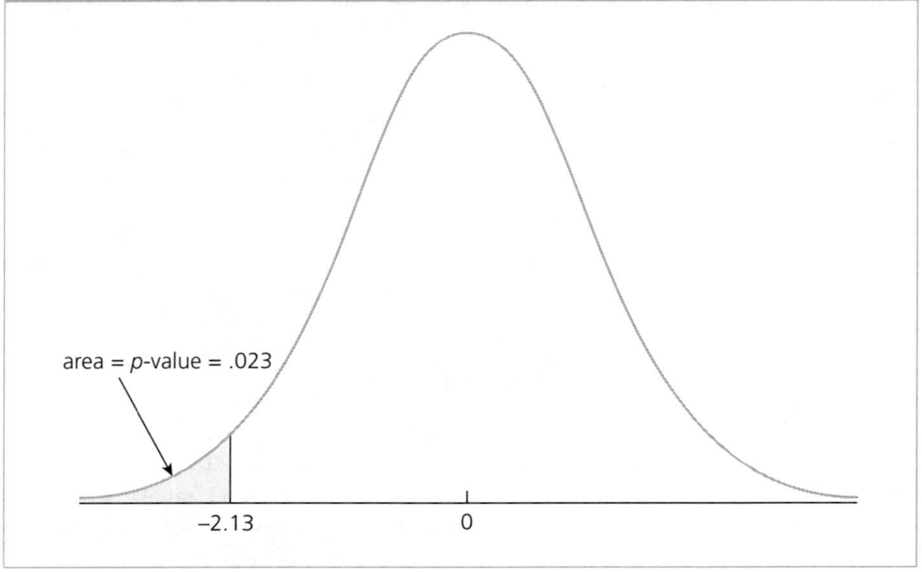

Using Table G.2, the most we can say is that the p-value is between .025 and .01, but it is closer to .025 (since the 97.5th percentile is about 2.09). Using a statistical package, such as Stata, we can compute the exact p-value. It turns out to be about .023, which is reasonable evidence against H_0. This is certainly enough evidence to reject the null hypothesis that the training grants had no effect at the 2.5% significance level (and therefore at the 5% level).

Computing a p-value for a two-sided test is similar, but we must account for the two-sided nature of the rejection rule. For t testing about population means, the p-value is computed as

$$P(|T_{n-1}| > |t|) = 2P(T_{n-1} > |t|), \quad [C.42]$$

where t is the value of the test statistic and T_{n-1} is a t random variable. (For large n, replace T_{n-1} with a standard normal random variable.) Thus, compute the absolute value of the t statistic, find the area to the right of this value in a t_{n-1} distribution, and multiply the area by two.

For nonnormal populations, the exact p-value can be difficult to obtain. Nevertheless, we can find *asymptotic* p-values by using the same calculations. These p-values are valid for large sample sizes. For n larger than, say, 120, we might as well use the standard normal distribution. Table G.1 is detailed enough to get accurate p-values, but we can also use a statistics or econometrics program.

EXAMPLE C.7 RACE DISCRIMINATION IN HIRING

Using the matched pair data from the Urban Institute ($n = 241$), we obtained $t = -4.29$. If Z is a standard normal random variable, $P(Z < -4.29)$ is, for practical purposes, zero. In other words, the (asymptotic) p-value for this example is essentially zero. This is very strong evidence against H_0.

Summary of How to Use p-Values:

(i) Choose a test statistic T and decide on the nature of the alternative. This determines whether the rejection rule is $t > c$, $t < -c$, or $|t| > c$.

(ii) Use the observed value of the t statistic as the critical value and compute the corresponding significance level of the test. This is the p-value. If the rejection rule is of the form $t > c$, then p-value $= P(T > t)$. If the rejection rule is $t < -c$, then p-value $= P(T < t)$; if the rejection rule is $|t| > c$, then p-value $= P(|T| > |t|)$.

(iii) If a significance level α has been chosen, then we reject H_0 at the $100 \cdot \alpha\%$ level if p-value $< \alpha$. If p-value $\geq \alpha$, then we fail to reject H_0 at the $100 \cdot \alpha\%$ level. Therefore, it is a small p-value that leads to rejection.

The Relationship between Confidence Intervals and Hypothesis Testing

Because contructing confidence intervals and hypothesis tests both involve probability statements, it is natural to think that they are somehow linked. It turns out that they are. After a confidence interval has been constructed, we can carry out a variety of hypothesis tests.

The confidence intervals we have discussed are all two-sided by nature. (In this text, we will have no need to construct one-sided confidence intervals.) Thus, confidence intervals can be used to test against *two-sided* alternatives. In the case of a population mean, the null is given by (C.31), and the alternative is (C.34). Suppose we have constructed a 95% confidence interval for μ. Then, if the hypothesized value of μ under H_0, μ_0, is not in the confidence interval, then H_0: $\mu = \mu_0$ is rejected against H_1: $\mu \neq \mu_0$ at the 5% level. If μ_0 lies in this interval, then we fail to reject H_0 at the 5% level. Notice how any value for μ_0 can be tested once a confidence interval is constructed, and since a confidence interval contains more than one value, there are many null hypotheses that will not be rejected.

EXAMPLE C.8 TRAINING GRANTS AND WORKER PRODUCTIVITY

In the Holzer et al. example, we constructed a 95% confidence interval for the mean change in scrap rate μ as $[-2.28, -.02]$. Since zero is excluded from this interval, we reject H_0: $\mu = 0$ against H_1: $\mu \neq 0$ at the 5% level. This 95% confidence interval also means that we fail to reject H_0: $\mu = -2$ at the 5% level. In fact, there is a continuum of null hypotheses that are not rejected given this confidence interval.

Practical versus Statistical Significance

In the examples covered so far, we have produced three kinds of evidence concerning population parameters: point estimates, confidence intervals, and hypothesis tests. These tools for learning about population parameters are equally important. There is an understandable tendency for students to focus on confidence intervals and hypothesis tests because these are things to which we can attach confidence or significance levels. But in any study, we must also interpret the *magnitudes* of point estimates.

The sign and magnitude of $\bar{y}$ determine its **practical significance** and allow us to discuss the direction of an intervention or policy effect, and whether the estimated effect is "large" or "small." On the other hand, **statistical significance** of $\bar{y}$ depends on the magnitude of its t statistic. For testing H_0: $\mu = 0$, the t statistic is simply $t = \bar{y}/\text{se}(\bar{y})$. In other words, statistical significance depends on the ratio of $\bar{y}$ to its standard error. Consequently, a t statistic can be large because $\bar{y}$ is large or $\text{se}(\bar{y})$ is small. In applications, it is important to discuss both practical and statistical significance, being aware that an estimate can be statistically significant without being especially large in a practical sense. Whether an estimate is practically important depends on the context as well as on one's judgment, so there are no set rules for determining practical significance.

EXAMPLE C.9 EFFECT OF FREEWAY WIDTH ON COMMUTE TIME

Let Y denote the change in commute time, measured in minutes, for commuters in a metropolitan area from before a freeway was widened to after the freeway was widened. Assume that $Y \sim \text{Normal}(\mu,\sigma^2)$. The null hypothesis that the widening did not reduce average commute time is H_0: $\mu = 0$; the alternative that it reduced average commute time is H_1: $\mu < 0$. Suppose a random sample of commuters of size $n = 900$ is obtained to determine the effectiveness of the freeway project. The average change in commute time is computed to be $\bar{y} = -3.6$, and the sample standard deviation is $s = 32.7$; thus, $\text{se}(\bar{y}) = 32.7/\sqrt{900} = 1.09$.

The t statistic is $t = -3.6/1.09 \approx -3.30$, which is very statistically significant; the p-value is about .0005. Thus, we conclude that the freeway widening had a statistically significant effect on average commute time.

If the outcome of the hypothesis test is all that were reported from the study, it would be misleading. Reporting only statistical significance masks the fact that the estimated reduction in average commute time, 3.6 minutes, is pretty meager. To be up front, we should report the point estimate of -3.6, along with the significance test.

Finding point estimates that are statistically significant without being practically significant can occur when we are working with large samples. To discuss why this happens, it is useful to have the following definition.

Test Consistency. A **consistent test** rejects H_0 with probability approaching one as the sample size grows whenever H_1 is true.

Another way to say that a test is consistent is that, as the sample size tends to infinity, the power of the test gets closer and closer to unity whenever H_1 is true. All of the tests we cover in this text have this property. In the case of testing hypotheses about a population mean, test consistency follows because the variance of $\bar{Y}$ converges to zero as the sample size gets large. The t statistic for testing H_0: $\mu = 0$ is $T = \bar{Y}/(S/\sqrt{n})$. Since $\text{plim}(\bar{Y}) = \mu$ and $\text{plim}(S) = \sigma$, it follows that if, say, $\mu > 0$, then T gets larger and larger (with high probability) as $n \rightarrow \infty$. In other words, no matter how close μ is to zero, we can be almost certain to reject H_0: $\mu = 0$ given a large enough sample size. This says nothing about whether μ is large in a practical sense.

C.7 Remarks on Notation

In our review of probability and statistics here and in Appendix B, we have been careful to use standard conventions to denote random variables, estimators, and test statistics. For example, we have used W to indicate an estimator (random variable) and w to denote a particular estimate (outcome of the random variable W). Distinguishing between an estimator and an estimate is important for understanding various concepts in estimation and hypothesis testing. However, making this distinction quickly becomes a burden in econometric analysis because the models are more complicated: many random variables and parameters will be involved, and being true to the usual conventions from probability and statistics requires many extra symbols.

In the main text, we use a simpler convention that is widely used in econometrics. If θ is a population parameter, the notation $\hat{\theta}$ ("theta hat") will be used to denote both an estimator and an estimate of θ. This notation is useful in that it provides a simple way of attaching an estimator to the population parameter it is supposed to be estimating. Thus, if the population parameter is β, then $\hat{\beta}$ denotes an estimator or estimate of β; if the parameter is σ^2, $\hat{\sigma}^2$ is an estimator or estimate of σ^2; and so on. Sometimes, we will discuss two estimators of the same parameter, in which case we will need a different notation, such as $\tilde{\theta}$ ("theta tilde").

Although dropping the conventions from probability and statistics to indicate estimators, random variables, and test statistics puts additional responsibility on you, it is not a big deal once the difference between an estimator and an estimate is understood. If we are discussing *statistical* properties of $\hat{\theta}$—such as deriving whether or not it is unbiased or consistent—then we are necessarily viewing $\hat{\theta}$ as an estimator. On the other hand, if we write something like $\hat{\theta} = 1.73$, then we are clearly denoting a point estimate from a given sample of data. The confusion that can arise by using $\hat{\theta}$ to denote both should be minimal once you have a good understanding of probability and statistics.

Summary

We have discussed topics from mathematical statistics that are heavily relied upon in econometric analysis. The notion of an estimator, which is simply a rule for combining data to estimate a population parameter, is fundamental. We have covered various properties of estimators. The most important small sample properties are unbiasedness and efficiency, the latter of which depends on comparing variances when estimators are unbiased. Large sample properties concern the sequence of estimators obtained as the sample size grows, and they are also depended upon in econometrics. Any useful estimator is consistent. The central limit theorem implies that, in large samples, the sampling distribution of most estimators is approximately normal.

The sampling distribution of an estimator can be used to construct confidence intervals. We saw this for estimating the mean from a normal distribution and for computing approximate confidence intervals in nonnormal cases. Classical hypothesis testing, which requires specifying a null hypothesis, an alternative hypothesis, and a significance level, is carried out by comparing a test statistic to a critical value. Alternatively, a p-value can be computed that allows us to carry out a test at any significance level.

Key Terms

Alternative Hypothesis
Asymptotic Normality
Bias
Biased Estimator
Central Limit Theorem (CLT)
Confidence Interval
Consistent Estimator
Consistent Test
Critical Value
Estimate
Estimator
Hypothesis Test
Inconsistent
Interval Estimator
Law of Large Numbers (LLN)
Least Squares Estimator
Maximum Likelihood Estimator
Mean Squared Error (MSE)
Method of Moments
Minimum Variance Unbiased Estimator
Null Hypothesis
One-Sided Alternative
One-Tailed Test
Population
Power of a Test
Practical Significance
Probability Limit
p-Value
Random Sample
Rejection Region
Sample Average
Sample Correlation Coefficient
Sample Covariance
Sample Standard Deviation
Sample Variance
Sampling Distribution
Sampling Standard Deviation
Sampling Variance
Significance Level
Standard Error
Statistical Significance
t Statistic
Test Statistic
Two-Sided Alternative
Two-Tailed Test
Type I Error
Type II Error
Unbiased Estimator

Problems

1 Let Y_1, Y_2, Y_3, and Y_4 be independent, identically distributed random variables from a population with mean μ and variance σ^2. Let $\bar{Y} = \frac{1}{4}(Y_1 + Y_2 + Y_3 + Y_4)$ denote the average of these four random variables.

(i) What are the expected value and variance of $\bar{Y}$ in terms of μ and σ^2?

(ii) Now, consider a different estimator of μ:

$$W = \frac{1}{8}Y_1 + \frac{1}{8}Y_2 + \frac{1}{4}Y_3 + \frac{1}{2}Y_4.$$

This is an example of a *weighted* average of the Y_i. Show that W is also an unbiased estimator of μ. Find the variance of W.

(iii) Based on your answers to parts (i) and (ii), which estimator of μ do you prefer, $\bar{Y}$ or W?

2 This is a more general version of Problem C.1. Let $Y_1, Y_2, \ldots, Y_n$ be n pairwise uncorrelated random variables with common mean μ and common variance σ^2. Let $\bar{Y}$ denote the sample average.

(i) Define the class of *linear estimators* of μ by

$$W_a = a_1Y_1 + a_2Y_2 + \ldots + a_nY_n,$$

where the a_i are constants. What restriction on the a_i is needed for W_a to be an unbiased estimator of μ?

(ii) Find $\text{Var}(W_a)$.

(iii) For any numbers $a_1, a_2, \ldots, a_n$, the following inequality holds: $(a_1 + a_2 + \ldots + a_n)^2/n \leq a_1^2 + a_2^2 + \ldots + a_n^2$. Use this, along with parts (i) and (ii), to show that $\text{Var}(W_a) \geq \text{Var}(\bar{Y})$ whenever W_a is unbiased, so that $\bar{Y}$ is the *best linear unbiased estimator*. [*Hint:* What does the inequality become when the a_i satisfy the restriction from part (i)?]

3 Let $\bar{Y}$ denote the sample average from a random sample with mean μ and variance σ^2. Consider two alternative estimators of μ: $W_1 = [(n - 1)/n]\bar{Y}$ and $W_2 = \bar{Y}/2$.

(i) Show that W_1 and W_2 are both biased estimators of μ and find the biases. What happens to the biases as $n \rightarrow \infty$? Comment on any important differences in bias for the two estimators as the sample size gets large.

(ii) Find the probability limits of W_1 and W_2. {*Hint:* Use Properties PLIM.1 and PLIM.2; for W_1, note that $\text{plim}\,[(n - 1)/n] = 1$.} Which estimator is consistent?

(iii) Find $\text{Var}(W_1)$ and $\text{Var}(W_2)$.

(iv) Argue that W_1 is a better estimator than $\bar{Y}$ if μ is "close" to zero. (Consider both bias and variance.)

4 For positive random variables X and Y, suppose the expected value of Y given X is $\text{E}(Y|X) = \theta X$. The unknown parameter θ shows how the expected value of Y changes with X.

(i) Define the random variable $Z = Y/X$. Show that $\text{E}(Z) = \theta$. [*Hint:* Use Property CE.2 along with the law of iterated expectations, Property CE.4. In particular, first show that $\text{E}(Z|X) = \theta$ and then use CE.4.]

(ii) Use part (i) to prove that the estimator $W_1 = n^{-1}\sum_{i=1}^{n}(Y_i/X_i)$ is unbiased for θ, where $\{(X_i, Y_i): i = 1, 2, \ldots, n\}$ is a random sample.

(iii) Explain why the estimator $W_2 = \bar{Y}/\bar{X}$, where the overbars denote sample averages, is not the same as W_1. Nevertheless, show that W_2 is also unbiased for θ.

(iv) The following table contains data on corn yields for several counties in Iowa. The USDA predicts the number of hectares of corn in each county based on satellite photos. Researchers count the number of "pixels" of corn in the satellite picture (as opposed to, for example, the number of pixels of soybeans or of uncultivated land) and use these to predict the actual number of hectares. To develop a prediction equation to be used for counties in general, the USDA surveyed farmers in selected counties to obtain corn yields in hectares. Let Y_i = corn yield in county i and let X_i = number of corn pixels in the satellite picture for county i. There are $n = 17$ observations for eight counties. Use this sample to compute the estimates of θ devised in parts (ii) and (iii). Are the estimates similar?

Plot	Corn Yield	Corn Pixels
1	165.76	374
2	96.32	209
3	76.08	253
4	185.35	432
5	116.43	367
6	162.08	361
7	152.04	288
8	161.75	369
9	92.88	206
10	149.94	316
11	64.75	145
12	127.07	355
13	133.55	295
14	77.70	223
15	206.39	459
16	108.33	290
17	118.17	307

5 Let Y denote a Bernoulli(θ) random variable with $0 < \theta < 1$. Suppose we are interested in estimating the *odds ratio*, $\gamma = \theta/(1 - \theta)$, which is the probability of success over the probability of failure. Given a random sample $\{Y_1, \ldots, Y_n\}$, we know that an unbiased and consistent estimator of θ is $\bar{Y}$, the proportion of successes in n trials. A natural estimator of γ is $G = \bar{Y}/(1 - \bar{Y})$, the proportion of successes over the proportion of failures in the sample.

(i) Why is G not an unbiased estimator of γ?

(ii) Use PLIM.2(iii) to show that G is a consistent estimator of γ.

6 You are hired by the governor to study whether a tax on liquor has decreased average liquor consumption in your state. You are able to obtain, for a sample of individuals selected at random, the difference in liquor consumption (in ounces) for the years before and after the

tax. For person i who is sampled randomly from the population, Y_i denotes the change in liquor consumption. Treat these as a random sample from a Normal(μ,σ^2) distribution.

(i) The null hypothesis is that there was no change in average liquor consumption. State this formally in terms of μ.

(ii) The alternative is that there was a decline in liquor consumption; state the alternative in terms of μ.

(iii) Now, suppose your sample size is $n = 900$ and you obtain the estimates $\bar{y} = -32.8$ and $s = 466.4$. Calculate the t statistic for testing H_0 against H_1; obtain the p-value for the test. (Because of the large sample size, just use the standard normal distribution tabulated in Table G.1.) Do you reject H_0 at the 5% level? At the 1% level?

(iv) Would you say that the estimated fall in consumption is large in magnitude? Comment on the practical versus statistical significance of this estimate.

(v) What has been implicitly assumed in your analysis about other determinants of liquor consumption over the two-year period in order to infer causality from the tax change to liquor consumption?

7 The new management at a bakery claims that workers are now more productive than they were under old management, which is why wages have "generally increased." Let W_i^b be Worker i's wage under the old management and let W_i^a be Worker i's wage after the change. The difference is $D_i \equiv W_i^a - W_i^b$. Assume that the D_i are a random sample from a Normal(μ,σ^2) distribution.

(i) Using the following data on 15 workers, construct an exact 95% confidence interval for μ.

(ii) Formally state the null hypothesis that there has been no change in average wages. In particular, what is $E(D_i)$ under H_0? If you are hired to examine the validity of the new management's claim, what is the relevant alternative hypothesis in terms of $\mu = E(D_i)$?

(iii) Test the null hypothesis from part (ii) against the stated alternative at the 5% and 1% levels.

(iv) Obtain the p-value for the test in part (iii).

Worker	Wage Before	Wage After
1	8.30	9.25
2	9.40	9.00
3	9.00	9.25
4	10.50	10.00
5	11.40	12.00
6	8.75	9.50
7	10.00	10.25
8	9.50	9.50
9	10.80	11.50
10	12.55	13.10
11	12.00	11.50
12	8.65	9.00
13	7.75	7.75
14	11.25	11.50
15	12.65	13.00

8 The *New York Times* (2/5/90) reported three-point shooting performance for the top 10 three-point shooters in the NBA. The following table summarizes these data:

Player	FGA-FGM
Mark Price	429-188
Trent Tucker	833-345
Dale Ellis	1,149-472
Craig Hodges	1,016-396
Danny Ainge	1,051-406
Byron Scott	676-260
Reggie Miller	416-159
Larry Bird	1,206-455
Jon Sundvold	440-166
Brian Taylor	417-157

Note: *FGA* = field goals attempted and *FGM* = field goals made.

For a given player, the outcome of a particular shot can be modeled as a Bernoulli (zero-one) variable: if Y_i is the outcome of shot i, then $Y_i = 1$ if the shot is made, and $Y_i = 0$ if the shot is missed. Let θ denote the probability of making any particular three-point shot attempt. The natural estimator of θ is $\bar{Y} = FGM/FGA$.

(i) Estimate θ for Mark Price.

(ii) Find the standard deviation of the estimator $\bar{Y}$ in terms of θ and the number of shot attempts, n.

(iii) The asymptotic distribution of $(\bar{Y} - \theta)/\text{se}(\bar{Y})$ is standard normal, where $\text{se}(\bar{Y}) = \sqrt{\bar{y}(1 - \bar{y})/n}$. Use this fact to test H_0: $\theta = .5$ against H_1: $\theta < .5$ for Mark Price. Use a 1% significance level.

9 Suppose that a military dictator in an unnamed country holds a plebiscite (a yes/no vote of confidence) and claims that he was supported by 65% of the voters. A human rights group suspects foul play and hires you to test the validity of the dictator's claim. You have a budget that allows you to randomly sample 200 voters from the country.

(i) Let X be the number of yes votes obtained from a random sample of 200 out of the entire voting population. What is the expected value of X if, in fact, 65% of all voters supported the dictator?

(ii) What is the standard deviation of X, again assuming that the true fraction voting yes in the plebiscite is .65?

(iii) Now, you collect your sample of 200, and you find that 115 people actually voted yes. Use the CLT to approximate the probability that you would find 115 or fewer yes votes from a random sample of 200 if, in fact, 65% of the entire population voted yes.

(iv) How would you explain the relevance of the number in part (iii) to someone who does not have training in statistics?

10 Before a strike prematurely ended the 1994 major league baseball season, Tony Gwynn of the San Diego Padres had 165 hits in 419 at bats, for a .394 batting average. There was discussion about whether Gwynn was a potential .400 hitter that year. This issue can be couched in terms of Gwynn's probability of getting a hit on a particular at bat, call it θ. Let Y_i be the Bernoulli(θ) indicator equal to unity if Gwynn gets a hit during his i^{th} at bat, and zero otherwise. Then, $Y_1, Y_2, \ldots, Y_n$ is a random sample from a Bernoulli(θ) distribution, where θ is the probability of success, and $n = 419$.

Our best point estimate of θ is Gwynn's batting average, which is just the proportion of successes: $\bar{y} = .394$. Using the fact that $\text{se}(\bar{y}) = \sqrt{\bar{y}(1 - \bar{y})/n}$, construct an approximate 95% confidence interval for θ, using the standard normal distribution. Would you say there is strong evidence against Gwynn's being a potential .400 hitter? Explain.

APPENDIX

D

Summary of Matrix Algebra

This appendix summarizes the matrix algebra concepts, including the algebra of probability, needed for the study of multiple linear regression models using matrices in Appendix E. None of this material is used in the main text.

D.1 Basic Definitions

Definition D.1 (Matrix). A **matrix** is a rectangular array of numbers. More precisely, an $m \times n$ matrix has m rows and n columns. The positive integer m is called the *row dimension*, and n is called the *column dimension*.

We use uppercase boldface letters to denote matrices. We can write an $m \times n$ matrix generically as

$$\mathbf{A} = [a_{ij}] = \begin{bmatrix} a_{11} & a_{12} & a_{13} & \ldots & a_{1n} \\ a_{21} & a_{22} & a_{23} & \ldots & a_{2n} \\ \vdots & & & & \\ a_{m1} & a_{m2} & a_{m3} & \ldots & a_{mn} \end{bmatrix},$$

where a_{ij} represents the element in the ith row and the jth column. For example, a_{25} stands for the number in the second row and the fifth column of $\mathbf{A}$. A specific example of a 2×3 matrix is

$$\mathbf{A} = \begin{bmatrix} 2 & -1 & 7 \\ -4 & 5 & 0 \end{bmatrix}, \qquad \text{[D.1]}$$

where $a_{13} = 7$. The shorthand $\mathbf{A} = [a_{ij}]$ is often used to define matrix operations.

Definition D.2 (Square Matrix). A **square matrix** has the same number of rows and columns. The dimension of a square matrix is its number of rows and columns.

Definition D.3 (Vectors)

(i) A $1 \times m$ matrix is called a **row vector** (of dimension m) and can be written as $\mathbf{x} \equiv (x_1, x_2, \ldots, x_m)$.

(ii) An $n \times 1$ matrix is called a **column vector** and can be written as

$$\mathbf{y} \equiv \begin{bmatrix} y_1 \\ y_2 \\ \vdots \\ y_n \end{bmatrix}.$$

Definition D.4 (Diagonal Matrix). A square matrix $\mathbf{A}$ is a **diagonal matrix** when all of its off-diagonal elements are zero, that is, $a_{ij} = 0$ for all $i \neq j$. We can always write a diagonal matrix as

$$\mathbf{A} = \begin{bmatrix} a_{11} & 0 & 0 & \ldots & 0 \\ 0 & a_{22} & 0 & \ldots & 0 \\ \vdots & & & & \\ 0 & 0 & 0 & \ldots & a_{nn} \end{bmatrix}.$$

Definition D.5 (Identity and Zero Matrices)

(i) The $n \times n$ **identity matrix**, denoted $\mathbf{I}$, or sometimes $\mathbf{I}_n$ to emphasize its dimension, is the diagonal matrix with unity (one) in each diagonal position, and zero elsewhere:

$$\mathbf{I} \equiv \mathbf{I}_n \equiv \begin{bmatrix} 1 & 0 & 0 & \ldots & 0 \\ 0 & 1 & 0 & \ldots & 0 \\ \vdots & & & & \\ 0 & 0 & 0 & \ldots & 1 \end{bmatrix}.$$

(ii) The $m \times n$ **zero matrix**, denoted $\mathbf{0}$, is the $m \times n$ matrix with zero for all entries. This need not be a square matrix.

D.2 Matrix Operations

Matrix Addition

Two matrices $\mathbf{A}$ and $\mathbf{B}$, each having dimension $m \times n$, can be added element by element: $\mathbf{A} + \mathbf{B} = [a_{ij} + b_{ij}]$. More precisely,

$$\mathbf{A} + \mathbf{B} = \begin{bmatrix} a_{11} + b_{11} & a_{12} + b_{12} & \ldots & a_{1n} + b_{1n} \\ a_{21} + b_{21} & a_{22} + b_{22} & \ldots & a_{2n} + b_{2n} \\ \vdots & & & \\ a_{m1} + b_{m1} & a_{m2} + b_{m2} & \ldots & a_{mn} + b_{mn} \end{bmatrix}.$$

For example,

$$\begin{bmatrix} 2 & -1 & 7 \\ -4 & 5 & 0 \end{bmatrix} + \begin{bmatrix} 1 & 0 & -4 \\ 4 & 2 & 3 \end{bmatrix} = \begin{bmatrix} 3 & -1 & 3 \\ 0 & 7 & 3 \end{bmatrix}.$$

Matrices of different dimensions cannot be added.

Scalar Multiplication

Given any real number γ (often called a scalar), **scalar multiplication** is defined as $\gamma\mathbf{A} \equiv [\gamma a_{ij}]$, or

$$\gamma\mathbf{A} = \begin{bmatrix} \gamma a_{11} & \gamma a_{12} & \ldots & \gamma a_{1n} \\ \gamma a_{21} & \gamma a_{22} & \ldots & \gamma a_{2n} \\ \vdots & & & \\ \gamma a_{m1} & \gamma a_{m2} & \ldots & \gamma a_{mn} \end{bmatrix}.$$

For example, if $\gamma = 2$ and $\mathbf{A}$ is the matrix in equation (D.1), then

$$\gamma\mathbf{A} = \begin{bmatrix} 4 & -2 & 14 \\ -8 & 10 & 0 \end{bmatrix}.$$

Matrix Multiplication

To multiply matrix **A** by matrix **B** to form the product **AB**, the *column* dimension of **A** must equal the *row* dimension of **B**. Therefore, let **A** be an $m \times n$ matrix and let **B** be an $n \times p$ matrix. Then, **matrix multiplication** is defined as

$$\mathbf{AB} = \left[\sum_{k=1}^{n} a_{ik}b_{kj}\right].$$

In other words, the $(i,j)^{\text{th}}$ element of the new matrix **AB** is obtained by multiplying each element in the ith row of **A** by the corresponding element in the jth column of **B** and adding these n products together. A schematic may help make this process more transparent:

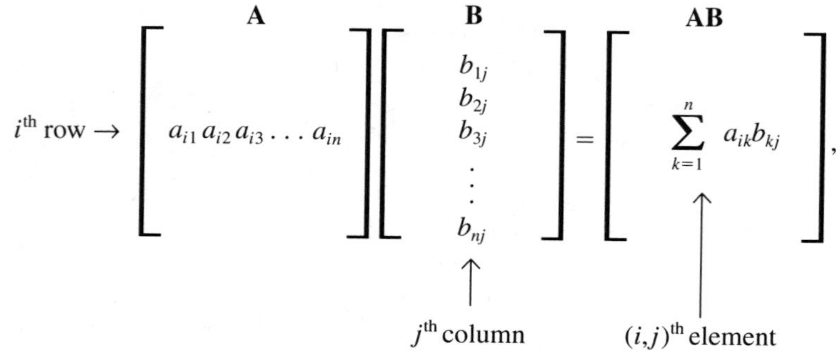

where, by the definition of the summation operator in Appendix A,

$$\sum_{k=1}^{n} a_{ik}b_{kj} = a_{i1}b_{1j} + a_{i2}b_{2j} + \ldots + a_{in}b_{nj}.$$

For example,

$$\begin{bmatrix} 2 & -1 & 0 \\ -4 & 1 & 0 \end{bmatrix} \begin{bmatrix} 0 & 1 & 6 & 0 \\ -1 & 2 & 0 & 1 \\ 3 & 0 & 0 & 0 \end{bmatrix} = \begin{bmatrix} 1 & 0 & 12 & -1 \\ -1 & -2 & -24 & 1 \end{bmatrix}.$$

We can also multiply a matrix and a vector. If $\mathbf{A}$ is an $n \times m$ matrix and $\mathbf{y}$ is an $m \times 1$ vector, then $\mathbf{Ay}$ is an $n \times 1$ vector. If $\mathbf{x}$ is a $1 \times n$ vector, then $\mathbf{xA}$ is a $1 \times m$ vector.

Matrix addition, scalar multiplication, and matrix multiplication can be combined in various ways, and these operations satisfy several rules that are familiar from basic operations on numbers. In the following list of properties, $\mathbf{A}$, $\mathbf{B}$, and $\mathbf{C}$ are matrices with appropriate dimensions for applying each operation, and α and β are real numbers. Most of these properties are easy to illustrate from the definitions.

Properties of Matrix Multiplication. (1) $(\alpha + \beta)\mathbf{A} = \alpha\mathbf{A} + \beta\mathbf{A}$; (2) $\alpha(\mathbf{A} + \mathbf{B}) = \alpha\mathbf{A} + \alpha\mathbf{B}$; (3) $(\alpha\beta)\mathbf{A} = \alpha(\beta\mathbf{A})$; (4) $\alpha(\mathbf{AB}) = (\alpha\mathbf{A})\mathbf{B}$; (5) $\mathbf{A} + \mathbf{B} = \mathbf{B} + \mathbf{A}$; (6) $(\mathbf{A} + \mathbf{B}) + \mathbf{C} = \mathbf{A} + (\mathbf{B} + \mathbf{C})$; (7) $(\mathbf{AB})\mathbf{C} = \mathbf{A}(\mathbf{BC})$; (8) $\mathbf{A}(\mathbf{B} + \mathbf{C}) = \mathbf{AB} + \mathbf{AC}$; (9) $(\mathbf{A} + \mathbf{B})\mathbf{C} = \mathbf{AC} + \mathbf{BC}$; (10) $\mathbf{IA} = \mathbf{AI} = \mathbf{A}$; (11) $\mathbf{A} + \mathbf{0} = \mathbf{0} + \mathbf{A} = \mathbf{A}$; (12) $\mathbf{A} - \mathbf{A} = \mathbf{0}$; (13) $\mathbf{A0} = \mathbf{0A} = \mathbf{0}$; and (14) $\mathbf{AB} \neq \mathbf{BA}$, even when both products are defined.

The last property deserves further comment. If $\mathbf{A}$ is $n \times m$ and $\mathbf{B}$ is $m \times p$, then $\mathbf{AB}$ is defined, but $\mathbf{BA}$ is defined only if $n = p$ (the row dimension of $\mathbf{A}$ equals the column dimension of $\mathbf{B}$). If $\mathbf{A}$ is $m \times n$ and $\mathbf{B}$ is $n \times m$, then $\mathbf{AB}$ and $\mathbf{BA}$ are both defined, but they are not usually the same; in fact, they have different dimensions, unless $\mathbf{A}$ and $\mathbf{B}$ are both square matrices. Even when $\mathbf{A}$ and $\mathbf{B}$ are both square, $\mathbf{AB} \neq \mathbf{BA}$, except under special circumstances.

Transpose

Definition D.6 (Transpose). Let $\mathbf{A} = [a_{ij}]$ be an $m \times n$ matrix. The **transpose** of $\mathbf{A}$, denoted $\mathbf{A}'$ (called $\mathbf{A}$ *prime*), is the $n \times m$ matrix obtained by interchanging the rows and columns of $\mathbf{A}$. We can write this as $\mathbf{A}' \equiv [a_{ji}]$.

For example,

$$\mathbf{A} = \begin{bmatrix} 2 & -1 & 7 \\ -4 & 5 & 0 \end{bmatrix}, \quad \mathbf{A}' = \begin{bmatrix} 2 & -4 \\ -1 & 5 \\ 7 & 0 \end{bmatrix}.$$

Properties of Transpose. (1) $(\mathbf{A}')' = \mathbf{A}$; (2) $(\alpha\mathbf{A})' = \alpha\mathbf{A}'$ for any scalar α; (3) $(\mathbf{A} + \mathbf{B})' = \mathbf{A}' + \mathbf{B}'$; (4) $(\mathbf{AB})' = \mathbf{B}'\mathbf{A}'$, where $\mathbf{A}$ is $m \times n$ and $\mathbf{B}$ is $n \times k$; (5) $\mathbf{x}'\mathbf{x} = \sum_{i=1}^{n} x_i^2$, where $\mathbf{x}$ is an $n \times 1$ vector; and (6) If $\mathbf{A}$ is an $n \times k$ matrix with *rows* given by the $1 \times k$ vectors $\mathbf{a}_1, \mathbf{a}_2, \ldots, \mathbf{a}_n$, so that we can write

$$\mathbf{A} = \begin{bmatrix} \mathbf{a}_1 \\ \mathbf{a}_2 \\ \vdots \\ \mathbf{a}_n \end{bmatrix},$$

then $\mathbf{A}' = (\mathbf{a}_1' \, \mathbf{a}_2' \ldots \mathbf{a}_n')$.

Definition D.7 (Symmetric Matrix). A square matrix $\mathbf{A}$ is a **symmetric matrix** if, and only if, $\mathbf{A}' = \mathbf{A}$.

If $\mathbf{X}$ is any $n \times k$ matrix, then $\mathbf{X}'\mathbf{X}$ is always defined and is a symmetric matrix, as can be seen by applying the first and fourth transpose properties (see Problem 3).

Partitioned Matrix Multiplication

Let $\mathbf{A}$ be an $n \times k$ matrix with rows given by the $1 \times k$ vectors $\mathbf{a}_1, \mathbf{a}_2, \ldots, \mathbf{a}_n$, and let $\mathbf{B}$ be an $n \times m$ matrix with rows given by $1 \times m$ vectors $\mathbf{b}_1, \mathbf{b}_2, \ldots, \mathbf{b}_n$:

$$\mathbf{A} = \begin{bmatrix} \mathbf{a}_1 \\ \mathbf{a}_2 \\ \vdots \\ \mathbf{a}_n \end{bmatrix}, \quad \mathbf{B} = \begin{bmatrix} \mathbf{b}_1 \\ \mathbf{b}_2 \\ \vdots \\ \mathbf{b}_n \end{bmatrix}.$$

Then,

$$\mathbf{A}'\mathbf{B} = \sum_{i=1}^{n} \mathbf{a}_i'\mathbf{b}_i,$$

where for each i, $\mathbf{a}_i'\mathbf{b}_i$ is a $k \times m$ matrix. Therefore, $\mathbf{A}'\mathbf{B}$ can be written as the sum of n matrices, each of which is $k \times m$. As a special case, we have

$$\mathbf{A}'\mathbf{A} = \sum_{i=1}^{n} \mathbf{a}_i'\mathbf{a}_i,$$

where $\mathbf{a}_i'\mathbf{a}_i$ is a $k \times k$ matrix for all i.

Trace

The trace of a matrix is a very simple operation defined only for *square* matrices.

Definition D.8 (Trace). For any $n \times n$ matrix $\mathbf{A}$, the **trace of a matrix A**, denoted $\text{tr}(\mathbf{A})$, is the sum of its diagonal elements. Mathematically,

$$\text{tr}(\mathbf{A}) = \sum_{i=1}^{n} a_{ii}.$$

Properties of Trace. (1) $\text{tr}(\mathbf{I}_n) = n$; (2) $\text{tr}(\mathbf{A}') = \text{tr}(\mathbf{A})$; (3) $\text{tr}(\mathbf{A} + \mathbf{B}) = \text{tr}(\mathbf{A}) + \text{tr}(\mathbf{B})$; (4) $\text{tr}(\alpha\mathbf{A}) = \alpha\text{tr}(\mathbf{A})$, for any scalar α; and (5) $\text{tr}(\mathbf{AB}) = \text{tr}(\mathbf{BA})$, where $\mathbf{A}$ is $m \times n$ and $\mathbf{B}$ is $n \times m$.

Inverse

The notion of a matrix inverse is very important for square matrices.

Definition D.9 (Inverse). An $n \times n$ matrix $\mathbf{A}$ has an **inverse**, denoted $\mathbf{A}^{-1}$, provided that $\mathbf{A}^{-1}\mathbf{A} = \mathbf{I}_n$ and $\mathbf{A}\mathbf{A}^{-1} = \mathbf{I}_n$. In this case, $\mathbf{A}$ is said to be *invertible* or *nonsingular*. Otherwise, it is said to be *noninvertible* or *singular*.

Properties of Inverse. (1) If an inverse exists, it is unique; (2) $(\alpha\mathbf{A})^{-1} = (1/\alpha)\mathbf{A}^{-1}$, if $\alpha \neq 0$ and $\mathbf{A}$ is invertible; (3) $(\mathbf{AB})^{-1} = \mathbf{B}^{-1}\mathbf{A}^{-1}$, if $\mathbf{A}$ and $\mathbf{B}$ are both $n \times n$ and invertible; and (4) $(\mathbf{A}')^{-1} = (\mathbf{A}^{-1})'$.

We will not be concerned with the mechanics of calculating the inverse of a matrix. Any matrix algebra text contains detailed examples of such calculations.

D.3 Linear Independence and Rank of a Matrix

For a set of vectors having the same dimension, it is important to know whether one vector can be expressed as a linear combination of the remaining vectors.

Definition D.10 (Linear Independence). Let $\{\mathbf{x}_1, \mathbf{x}_2, \ldots, \mathbf{x}_r\}$ be a set of $n \times 1$ vectors. These are **linearly independent vectors** if, and only if,

$$\alpha_1\mathbf{x}_1 + \alpha_2\mathbf{x}_2 + \ldots + \alpha_r\mathbf{x}_r = \mathbf{0} \qquad \text{[D.2]}$$

implies that $\alpha_1 = \alpha_2 = \ldots = \alpha_r = 0$. If (D.2) holds for a set of scalars that are not all zero, then $\{\mathbf{x}_1, \mathbf{x}_2, \ldots, \mathbf{x}_r\}$ is *linearly dependent*.

The statement that $\{\mathbf{x}_1, \mathbf{x}_2, \ldots, \mathbf{x}_r\}$ is linearly dependent is equivalent to saying that at least one vector in this set can be written as a linear combination of the others.

Definition D.11 (Rank)

(i) Let $\mathbf{A}$ be an $n \times m$ matrix. The **rank of a matrix A**, denoted rank($\mathbf{A}$), is the maximum number of linearly independent columns of $\mathbf{A}$.

(ii) If $\mathbf{A}$ is $n \times m$ and rank($\mathbf{A}$) $= m$, then $\mathbf{A}$ has *full column rank.*

If $\mathbf{A}$ is $n \times m$, its rank can be at most m. A matrix has full column rank if its columns form a linearly independent set. For example, the 3×2 matrix

$$\begin{bmatrix} 1 & 3 \\ 2 & 6 \\ 0 & 0 \end{bmatrix}$$

can have at most rank two. In fact, its rank is only one because the second column is three times the first column.

Properties of Rank. (1) rank($\mathbf{A}'$) $=$ rank($\mathbf{A}$); (2) If $\mathbf{A}$ is $n \times k$, then rank($\mathbf{A}$) $\leq \min(n,k)$; and (3) If $\mathbf{A}$ is $k \times k$ and rank($\mathbf{A}$) $= k$, then $\mathbf{A}$ is invertible.

D.4 Quadratic Forms and Positive Definite Matrices

Definition D.12 (Quadratic Form). Let $\mathbf{A}$ be an $n \times n$ *symmetric* matrix. The **quadratic form** associated with the matrix $\mathbf{A}$ is the real-valued function defined for all $n \times 1$ vectors $\mathbf{x}$:

$$f(\mathbf{x}) = \mathbf{x}'\mathbf{A}\mathbf{x} = \sum_{i=1}^{n} a_{ii}x_i^2 + 2\sum_{i=1}^{n}\sum_{j>1} a_{ij}x_ix_j.$$

Definition D.13 (Positive Definite and Positive Semi-Definite)

(i) A symmetric matrix $\mathbf{A}$ is said to be **positive definite (p.d.)** if

$$\mathbf{x}'\mathbf{A}\mathbf{x} > 0 \text{ for all } n \times 1 \text{ vectors } \mathbf{x} \text{ except } \mathbf{x} = \mathbf{0}.$$

(ii) A symmetric matrix $\mathbf{A}$ is **positive semi-definite (p.s.d.)** if

$$\mathbf{x}'\mathbf{A}\mathbf{x} \geq 0 \text{ for all } n \times 1 \text{ vectors.}$$

If a matrix is positive definite or positive semi-definite, it is automatically assumed to be symmetric.

Properties of Positive Definite and Positive Semi-Definite Matrices. (1) A positive definite matrix has diagonal elements that are strictly positive, while a p.s.d. matrix has nonnegative diagonal elements; (2) If $\mathbf{A}$ is p.d., then $\mathbf{A}^{-1}$ exists and is p.d.; (3) If $\mathbf{X}$ is $n \times k$, then $\mathbf{X}'\mathbf{X}$ and $\mathbf{X}\mathbf{X}'$ are p.s.d.; and (4) If $\mathbf{X}$ is $n \times k$ and $\text{rank}(\mathbf{X}) = k$, then $\mathbf{X}'\mathbf{X}$ is p.d. (and therefore nonsingular).

D.5 Idempotent Matrices

Definition D.14 (Idempotent Matrix). Let $\mathbf{A}$ be an $n \times n$ symmetric matrix. Then $\mathbf{A}$ is said to be an **idempotent matrix** if, and only if, $\mathbf{A}\mathbf{A} = \mathbf{A}$.

For example,

$$\begin{bmatrix} 1 & 0 & 0 \\ 0 & 0 & 0 \\ 0 & 0 & 1 \end{bmatrix}$$

is an idempotent matrix, as direct multiplication verifies.

Properties of Idempotent Matrices. Let $\mathbf{A}$ be an $n \times n$ idempotent matrix. (1) $\text{rank}(\mathbf{A}) = \text{tr}(\mathbf{A})$, and (2) $\mathbf{A}$ is positive semi-definite.

We can construct idempotent matrices very generally. Let $\mathbf{X}$ be an $n \times k$ matrix with $\text{rank}(\mathbf{X}) = k$. Define

$$\mathbf{P} \equiv \mathbf{X}(\mathbf{X}'\mathbf{X})^{-1}\mathbf{X}'$$

$$\mathbf{M} \equiv \mathbf{I}_n - \mathbf{X}(\mathbf{X}'\mathbf{X})^{-1}\mathbf{X}' = \mathbf{I}_n - \mathbf{P}.$$

Then $\mathbf{P}$ and $\mathbf{M}$ are symmetric, idempotent matrices with $\text{rank}(\mathbf{P}) = k$ and $\text{rank}(\mathbf{M}) = n - k$. The ranks are most easily obtained by using Property 1: $\text{tr}(\mathbf{P}) = \text{tr}[(\mathbf{X}'\mathbf{X})^{-1}\mathbf{X}'\mathbf{X}]$

(from Property 5 for trace) = $\text{tr}(\mathbf{I}_k) = k$ (by Property 1 for trace). It easily follows that $\text{tr}(\mathbf{M}) = \text{tr}(\mathbf{I}_n) - \text{tr}(\mathbf{P}) = n - k$.

D.6 Differentiation of Linear and Quadratic Forms

For a given $n \times 1$ vector $\mathbf{a}$, consider the linear function defined by

$$f(\mathbf{x}) = \mathbf{a}'\mathbf{x},$$

for all $n \times 1$ vectors $\mathbf{x}$. The derivative of f with respect to $\mathbf{x}$ is the $1 \times n$ vector of partial derivatives, which is simply

$$\partial f(\mathbf{x})/\partial \mathbf{x} = \mathbf{a}'.$$

For an $n \times n$ symmetric matrix $\mathbf{A}$, define the quadratic form

$$g(\mathbf{x}) = \mathbf{x}'\mathbf{A}\mathbf{x}.$$

Then,

$$\partial g(\mathbf{x})/\partial \mathbf{x} = 2\mathbf{x}'\mathbf{A},$$

which is a $1 \times n$ vector.

D.7 Moments and Distributions of Random Vectors

In order to derive the expected value and variance of the OLS estimators using matrices, we need to define the expected value and variance of a **random vector**. As its name suggests, a random vector is simply a vector of random variables. We also need to define the multivariate normal distribution. These concepts are simply extensions of those covered in Appendix B.

Expected Value

Definition D.15 (Expected Value)

(i) If $\mathbf{y}$ is an $n \times 1$ random vector, the **expected value** of $\mathbf{y}$, denoted $\text{E}(\mathbf{y})$, is the vector of expected values: $\text{E}(\mathbf{y}) = [\text{E}(y_1), \text{E}(y_2), \ldots, \text{E}(y_n)]'$.

(ii) If $\mathbf{Z}$ is an $n \times m$ random matrix, $\text{E}(\mathbf{Z})$ is the $n \times m$ matrix of expected values: $\text{E}(\mathbf{Z}) = [\text{E}(z_{ij})]$.

Properties of Expected Value. (1) If $\mathbf{A}$ is an $m \times n$ matrix and $\mathbf{b}$ is an $n \times 1$ vector, where both are nonrandom, then $\text{E}(\mathbf{Ay} + \mathbf{b}) = \mathbf{A}\text{E}(\mathbf{y}) + \mathbf{b}$; and (2) If $\mathbf{A}$ is $p \times n$ and $\mathbf{B}$ is $m \times k$, where both are nonrandom, then $\text{E}(\mathbf{AZB}) = \mathbf{A}\text{E}(\mathbf{Z})\mathbf{B}$.

Variance-Covariance Matrix

Definition D.16 (Variance-Covariance Matrix). If $\mathbf{y}$ is an $n \times 1$ random vector, its **variance-covariance matrix**, denoted $\text{Var}(\mathbf{y})$, is defined as

$$\text{Var}(\mathbf{y}) = \begin{bmatrix} \sigma_1^2 & \sigma_{12} & \cdots & \sigma_{1n} \\ \sigma_{21} & \sigma_2^2 & \cdots & \sigma_{2n} \\ \vdots & & & \\ \sigma_{n1} & \sigma_{n2} & \cdots & \sigma_n^2 \end{bmatrix},$$

where $\sigma_j^2 = \text{Var}(y_j)$ and $\sigma_{ij} = \text{Cov}(y_i,y_j)$. In other words, the variance-covariance matrix has the variances of each element of **y** down its diagonal, with covariance terms in the off diagonals. Because $\text{Cov}(y_i,y_j) = \text{Cov}(y_j,y_i)$, it immediately follows that a variance-covariance matrix is symmetric.

Properties of Variance. (1) If **a** is an $n \times 1$ nonrandom vector, then $\text{Var}(\mathbf{a}'\mathbf{y}) = \mathbf{a}'[\text{Var}(\mathbf{y})]\mathbf{a} \geq 0$; (2) If $\text{Var}(\mathbf{a}'\mathbf{y}) > 0$ for all $\mathbf{a} \neq \mathbf{0}$, $\text{Var}(\mathbf{y})$ is positive definite; (3) $\text{Var}(\mathbf{y}) = \text{E}[(\mathbf{y} - \boldsymbol{\mu})(\mathbf{y} - \boldsymbol{\mu})']$, where $\boldsymbol{\mu} = \text{E}(\mathbf{y})$; (4) If the elements of **y** are uncorrelated, $\text{Var}(\mathbf{y})$ is a diagonal matrix. If, in addition, $\text{Var}(y_j) = \sigma^2$ for $j = 1, 2, \ldots, n$, then $\text{Var}(\mathbf{y}) = \sigma^2\mathbf{I}_n$; and (5) If **A** is an $m \times n$ nonrandom matrix and **b** is an $n \times 1$ nonrandom vector, then $\text{Var}(\mathbf{Ay} + \mathbf{b}) = \mathbf{A}[\text{Var}(\mathbf{y})]\mathbf{A}'$.

Multivariate Normal Distribution

The normal distribution for a random variable was discussed at some length in Appendix B. We need to extend the normal distribution to random vectors. We will not provide an expression for the probability distribution function, as we do not need it. It is important to know that a multivariate normal random vector is completely characterized by its mean and its variance-covariance matrix. Therefore, if **y** is an $n \times 1$ multivariate normal random vector with mean $\boldsymbol{\mu}$ and variance-covariance matrix $\boldsymbol{\Sigma}$, we write $\mathbf{y} \sim \text{Normal}(\boldsymbol{\mu},\boldsymbol{\Sigma})$. We now state several useful properties of the **multivariate normal distribution**.

Properties of the Multivariate Normal Distribution. (1) If $\mathbf{y} \sim \text{Normal}(\boldsymbol{\mu},\boldsymbol{\Sigma})$, then each element of **y** is normally distributed; (2) If $\mathbf{y} \sim \text{Normal}(\boldsymbol{\mu},\boldsymbol{\Sigma})$, then y_i and y_j, any two elements of **y**, are independent if, and only if, they are uncorrelated, that is, $\sigma_{ij} = 0$; (3) If $\mathbf{y} \sim \text{Normal}(\boldsymbol{\mu},\boldsymbol{\Sigma})$, then $\mathbf{Ay} + \mathbf{b} \sim \text{Normal}(\mathbf{A}\boldsymbol{\mu} + \mathbf{b},\mathbf{A}\boldsymbol{\Sigma}\mathbf{A}')$, where **A** and **b** are nonrandom; (4) If $\mathbf{y} \sim \text{Normal}(\mathbf{0},\boldsymbol{\Sigma})$, then, for nonrandom matrices **A** and **B**, **Ay** and **By** are independent if, and only if, $\mathbf{A}\boldsymbol{\Sigma}\mathbf{B}' = \mathbf{0}$. In particular, if $\boldsymbol{\Sigma} = \sigma^2\mathbf{I}_n$, then $\mathbf{AB}' = \mathbf{0}$ is necessary and sufficient for independence of **Ay** and **By**; (5) If $\mathbf{y} \sim \text{Normal}(\mathbf{0},\sigma^2\mathbf{I}_n)$, **A** is a $k \times n$ nonrandom matrix, and **B** is an $n \times n$ symmetric, idempotent matrix, then **Ay** and $\mathbf{y}'\mathbf{By}$ are independent if, and only if, $\mathbf{AB} = \mathbf{0}$; and (6) If $\mathbf{y} \sim \text{Normal}(\mathbf{0},\sigma^2\mathbf{I}_n)$ and **A** and **B** are nonrandom symmetric, idempotent matrices, then $\mathbf{y}'\mathbf{Ay}$ and $\mathbf{y}'\mathbf{By}$ are independent if, and only if, $\mathbf{AB} = \mathbf{0}$.

Chi-Square Distribution

In Appendix B, we defined a **chi-square random variable** as the sum of *squared* independent standard normal random variables. In vector notation, if $\mathbf{u} \sim \text{Normal}(\mathbf{0},\mathbf{I}_n)$, then $\mathbf{u}'\mathbf{u} \sim \chi_n^2$.

Properties of the Chi-Square Distribution. (1) If $\mathbf{u} \sim \text{Normal}(\mathbf{0},\mathbf{I}_n)$ and $\mathbf{A}$ is an $n \times n$ symmetric, idempotent matrix with rank($\mathbf{A}$) $= q$, then $\mathbf{u}'\mathbf{A}\mathbf{u} \sim \chi^2_q$; (2) If $\mathbf{u} \sim \text{Normal}(\mathbf{0},\mathbf{I}_n)$ and $\mathbf{A}$ and $\mathbf{B}$ are $n \times n$ symmetric, idempotent matrices such that $\mathbf{AB} = \mathbf{0}$, then $\mathbf{u}'\mathbf{A}\mathbf{u}$ and $\mathbf{u}'\mathbf{B}\mathbf{u}$ are independent, chi-square random variables; and (3) If $\mathbf{z} \sim \text{Normal}(\mathbf{0},\mathbf{C})$ where $\mathbf{C}$ is an $m \times m$ nonsingular matrix, then $\mathbf{z}'\mathbf{C}^{-1}\mathbf{z} \sim \chi^2_m$.

t Distribution

We also defined the ***t* distribution** in Appendix B. Now we add an important property.

Property of the t Distribution. If $\mathbf{u} \sim \text{Normal}(\mathbf{0},\mathbf{I}_n)$, $\mathbf{c}$ is an $n \times 1$ nonrandom vector, $\mathbf{A}$ is a nonrandom $n \times n$ symmetric, idempotent matrix with rank q, and $\mathbf{Ac} = \mathbf{0}$, then $\{\mathbf{c}'\mathbf{u}/(\mathbf{c}'\mathbf{c})^{1/2}\}/(\mathbf{u}'\mathbf{A}\mathbf{u}/q)^{1/2} \sim t_q$.

F Distribution

Recall that an ***F* random variable** is obtained by taking two *independent* chi-square random variables and finding the ratio of each, standardized by degrees of freedom.

Property of the F Distribution. If $\mathbf{u} \sim \text{Normal}(\mathbf{0},\mathbf{I}_n)$ and $\mathbf{A}$ and $\mathbf{B}$ are $n \times n$ nonrandom symmetric, idempotent matrices with rank($\mathbf{A}$) $= k_1$, rank($\mathbf{B}$) $= k_2$, and $\mathbf{AB} = \mathbf{0}$, then $(\mathbf{u}'\mathbf{A}\mathbf{u}/k_1)/(\mathbf{u}'\mathbf{B}\mathbf{u}/k_2) \sim F_{k_1,k_2}$.

Summary

This appendix contains a condensed form of the background information needed to study the classical linear model using matrices. Although the material here is self-contained, it is primarily intended as a review for readers who are familiar with matrix algebra and multivariate statistics, and it will be used extensively in Appendix E.

Key Terms

Chi-Square Random Variable
Column Vector
Diagonal Matrix
Expected Value
F Random Variable
Idempotent Matrix
Identity Matrix
Inverse
Linearly Independent Vectors
Matrix
Matrix Multiplication
Multivariate Normal Distribution
Positive Definite (p.d.)
Positive Semi-Definite (p.s.d.)
Quadratic Form
Random Vector
Rank of a Matrix
Row Vector
Scalar Multiplication
Square Matrix
Symmetric Matrix
t Distribution
Trace of a Matrix
Transpose
Variance-Covariance Matrix
Zero Matrix

Problems

1 (i) Find the product **AB** using

$$\mathbf{A} = \begin{bmatrix} 2 & -1 & 7 \\ -4 & 5 & 0 \end{bmatrix}, \quad \mathbf{B} = \begin{bmatrix} 0 & 1 & 6 \\ 1 & 8 & 0 \\ 3 & 0 & 0 \end{bmatrix}.$$

(ii) Does **BA** exist?

2 If **A** and **B** are $n \times n$ diagonal matrices, show that $\mathbf{AB} = \mathbf{BA}$.

3 Let **X** be any $n \times k$ matrix. Show that $\mathbf{X}'\mathbf{X}$ is a symmetric matrix.

4 (i) Use the properties of trace to argue that $\text{tr}(\mathbf{A}'\mathbf{A}) = \text{tr}(\mathbf{A}\mathbf{A}')$ for any $n \times m$ matrix **A**.

(ii) For $\mathbf{A} = \begin{bmatrix} 2 & 0 & -1 \\ 0 & 3 & 0 \end{bmatrix}$, verify that $\text{tr}(\mathbf{A}'\mathbf{A}) = \text{tr}(\mathbf{A}\mathbf{A}')$.

5 (i) Use the definition of inverse to prove the following: if **A** and **B** are $n \times n$ nonsingular matrices, then $(\mathbf{AB})^{-1} = \mathbf{B}^{-1}\mathbf{A}^{-1}$.

(ii) If **A**, **B**, and **C** are all $n \times n$ nonsingular matrices, find $(\mathbf{ABC})^{-1}$ in terms of $\mathbf{A}^{-1}$, $\mathbf{B}^{-1}$, and $\mathbf{C}^{-1}$.

6 (i) Show that if **A** is an $n \times n$ symmetric, positive definite matrix, then **A** must have strictly positive diagonal elements.

(ii) Write down a 2×2 symmetric matrix with strictly positive diagonal elements that is *not* positive definite.

7 Let **A** be an $n \times n$ symmetric, positive definite matrix. Show that if **P** is any $n \times n$ nonsingular matrix, then $\mathbf{P}'\mathbf{AP}$ is positive definite.

8 Prove Property 5 of variances for vectors, using Property 3.

9 Let **a** be an $n \times 1$ nonrandom vector and let **u** be an $n \times 1$ random vector with $\text{E}(\mathbf{uu}') = \mathbf{I}_n$. Show that $\text{E}[\text{tr}(\mathbf{auu}'\mathbf{a}')] = \sum_{i=1}^{n} a_i^2$.

10 Take as given the properties of the chi-square distribution listed in the text. Show how those properties, along with the definition of an *F* random variable, imply the stated property of the *F* distribution (concerning ratios of quadratic forms).

APPENDIX

E

The Linear Regression Model in Matrix Form

This appendix derives various results for ordinary least squares estimation of the multiple linear regression model using matrix notation and matrix algebra (see Appendix D for a summary). The material presented here is much more advanced than that in the text.

E.1 The Model and Ordinary Least Squares Estimation

Throughout this appendix, we use the t subscript to index observations and an n to denote the sample size. It is useful to write the multiple linear regression model with k parameters as follows:

$$y_t = \beta_0 + \beta_1 x_{t1} + \beta_2 x_{t2} + \ldots + \beta_k x_{tk} + u_t,\ t = 1, 2, \ldots, n, \qquad \text{[E.1]}$$

where y_t is the dependent variable for observation t, and x_{tj}, $j = 1, 2, \ldots, k$, are the independent variables. As usual, β_0 is the intercept and $\beta_1, \ldots, \beta_k$ denote the slope parameters.

For each t, define a $1 \times (k + 1)$ vector, $\mathbf{x}_t = (1, x_{t1}, \ldots, x_{tk})$, and let $\boldsymbol{\beta} = (\beta_0, \beta_1, \ldots, \beta_k)'$ be the $(k + 1) \times 1$ vector of all parameters. Then, we can write (E.1) as

$$y_t = \mathbf{x}_t\boldsymbol{\beta} + u_t,\ t = 1, 2, \ldots, n. \qquad \text{[E.2]}$$

[Some authors prefer to define $\mathbf{x}_t$ as a column vector, in which case $\mathbf{x}_t$ is replaced with $\mathbf{x}_t'$ in (E.2). Mathematically, it makes more sense to define it as a row vector.] We can write (E.2) in full matrix notation by appropriately defining data vectors and matrices. Let $\mathbf{y}$ denote the $n \times 1$ vector of observations on y: the tth element of $\mathbf{y}$ is y_t. Let $\mathbf{X}$ be the $n \times (k + 1)$ vector of observations on the explanatory variables. In other words, the tth row of $\mathbf{X}$ consists of the vector $\mathbf{x}_t$. Written out in detail,

$$\underset{n \times (k+1)}{\mathbf{X}} \equiv \begin{bmatrix} \mathbf{x}_1 \\ \mathbf{x}_2 \\ \vdots \\ \mathbf{x}_n \end{bmatrix} = \begin{bmatrix} 1 & x_{11} & x_{12} & \ldots & x_{1k} \\ 1 & x_{21} & x_{22} & \ldots & x_{2k} \\ \vdots & & & & \\ 1 & x_{n1} & x_{n2} & \ldots & x_{nk} \end{bmatrix}.$$

Finally, let **u** be the $n \times 1$ vector of unobservable errors or disturbances. Then, we can write (E.2) for all n observations in **matrix notation**:

$$\mathbf{y} = \mathbf{X}\boldsymbol{\beta} + \mathbf{u}. \qquad \text{[E.3]}$$

Remember, because $\mathbf{X}$ is $n \times (k + 1)$ and $\boldsymbol{\beta}$ is $(k + 1) \times 1$, $\mathbf{X}\boldsymbol{\beta}$ is $n \times 1$.

Estimation of $\boldsymbol{\beta}$ proceeds by minimizing the sum of squared residuals, as in Section 3.2. Define the sum of squared residuals function for any possible $(k + 1) \times 1$ parameter vector **b** as

$$\text{SSR}(\mathbf{b}) \equiv \sum_{t=1}^{n} (y_t - \mathbf{x}_t\mathbf{b})^2.$$

The $(k + 1) \times 1$ vector of ordinary least squares estimates, $\hat{\boldsymbol{\beta}} = (\hat{\beta}_0, \hat{\beta}_1, \ldots, \hat{\beta}_k)'$, minimizes SSR(**b**) over all possible $(k + 1) \times 1$ vectors **b**. This is a problem in multivariable calculus. For $\hat{\boldsymbol{\beta}}$ to minimize the sum of squared residuals, it must solve the **first order condition**

$$\partial \text{SSR}(\hat{\boldsymbol{\beta}})/\partial \mathbf{b} \equiv 0. \qquad \text{[E.4]}$$

Using the fact that the derivative of $(y_t - \mathbf{x}_t\mathbf{b})^2$ with respect to **b** is the $1 \times (k + 1)$ vector $-2(y_t - \mathbf{x}_t\mathbf{b})\mathbf{x}_t$, (E.4) is equivalent to

$$\sum_{t=1}^{n} \mathbf{x}_t'(y_t - \mathbf{x}_t\hat{\boldsymbol{\beta}}) \equiv \mathbf{0}. \qquad \text{[E.5]}$$

(We have divided by -2 and taken the transpose.) We can write this first order condition as

$$\sum_{t=1}^{n} (y_t - \hat{\beta}_0 - \hat{\beta}_1 x_{t1} - \ldots - \hat{\beta}_k x_{tk}) = 0$$

$$\sum_{t=1}^{n} x_{t1}(y_t - \hat{\beta}_0 - \hat{\beta}_1 x_{t1} - \ldots - \hat{\beta}_k x_{tk}) = 0$$

$$\vdots$$

$$\sum_{t=1}^{n} x_{tk}(y_t - \hat{\beta}_0 - \hat{\beta}_1 x_{t1} - \ldots - \hat{\beta}_k x_{tk}) = 0,$$

which is identical to the first order conditions in equation (3.13). We want to write these in matrix form to make them easier to manipulate. Using the formula for partitioned multiplication in Appendix D, we see that (E.5) is equivalent to

$$\mathbf{X}'(\mathbf{y} - \mathbf{X}\hat{\boldsymbol{\beta}}) = \mathbf{0} \qquad \text{[E.6]}$$

or

$$(\mathbf{X}'\mathbf{X})\hat{\boldsymbol{\beta}} = \mathbf{X}'\mathbf{y}. \qquad \text{[E.7]}$$

It can be shown that (E.7) always has at least one solution. Multiple solutions do not help us, as we are looking for a unique set of OLS estimates given our data set. Assuming that the $(k + 1) \times (k + 1)$ symmetric matrix $\mathbf{X}'\mathbf{X}$ is nonsingular, we can premultiply both sides of (E.7) by $(\mathbf{X}'\mathbf{X})^{-1}$ to solve for the OLS estimator $\hat{\boldsymbol{\beta}}$:

$$\hat{\boldsymbol{\beta}} = (\mathbf{X}'\mathbf{X})^{-1}\mathbf{X}'\mathbf{y}. \qquad \text{[E.8]}$$

This is the critical formula for matrix analysis of the multiple linear regression model. The assumption that $\mathbf{X}'\mathbf{X}$ is invertible is equivalent to the assumption that rank($\mathbf{X}$) = $(k + 1)$, which means that the columns of $\mathbf{X}$ must be linearly independent. This is the matrix version of MLR.3 in Chapter 3.

Before we continue, (E.8) warrants a word of warning. It is tempting to simplify the formula for $\hat{\boldsymbol{\beta}}$ as follows:

$$\hat{\boldsymbol{\beta}} = (\mathbf{X}'\mathbf{X})^{-1}\mathbf{X}'\mathbf{y} = \mathbf{X}^{-1}(\mathbf{X}')^{-1}\mathbf{X}'\mathbf{y} = \mathbf{X}^{-1}\mathbf{y}.$$

The flaw in this reasoning is that $\mathbf{X}$ is usually not a square matrix, so it cannot be inverted. In other words, we cannot write $(\mathbf{X}'\mathbf{X})^{-1} = \mathbf{X}^{-1}(\mathbf{X}')^{-1}$ unless $n = (k + 1)$, a case that virtually never arises in practice.

The $n \times 1$ vectors of OLS fitted values and residuals are given by

$$\hat{\mathbf{y}} = \mathbf{X}\hat{\boldsymbol{\beta}},\ \hat{\mathbf{u}} = \mathbf{y} - \hat{\mathbf{y}} = \mathbf{y} - \mathbf{X}\hat{\boldsymbol{\beta}}, \text{ respectively.}$$

From (E.6) and the definition of $\hat{\mathbf{u}}$, we can see that the first order condition for $\hat{\boldsymbol{\beta}}$ is the same as

$$\mathbf{X}'\hat{\mathbf{u}} = \mathbf{0}. \qquad [E.9]$$

Because the first column of $\mathbf{X}$ consists entirely of ones, (E.9) implies that the OLS residuals always sum to zero when an intercept is included in the equation and that the sample covariance between each independent variable and the OLS residuals is zero. (We discussed both of these properties in Chapter 3.)

The sum of squared residuals can be written as

$$\text{SSR} = \sum_{t=1}^{n} \hat{u}_t^2 = \hat{\mathbf{u}}'\hat{\mathbf{u}} = (\mathbf{y} - \mathbf{X}\hat{\boldsymbol{\beta}})'(\mathbf{y} - \mathbf{X}\hat{\boldsymbol{\beta}}). \qquad [E.10]$$

All of the algebraic properties from Chapter 3 can be derived using matrix algebra. For example, we can show that the total sum of squares is equal to the explained sum of squares plus the sum of squared residuals [see (3.27)]. The use of matrices does not provide a simpler proof than summation notation, so we do not provide another derivation.

The matrix approach to multiple regression can be used as the basis for a geometrical interpretation of regression. This involves mathematical concepts that are even more advanced than those we covered in Appendix D. [See Goldberger (1991) or Greene (1997).]

E.2 Finite Sample Properties of OLS

Deriving the expected value and variance of the OLS estimator $\hat{\boldsymbol{\beta}}$ is facilitated by matrix algebra, but we must show some care in stating the assumptions.

Assumption E.1 Linear in Parameters

The model can be written as in (E.3), where **y** is an observed $n \times 1$ vector, **X** is an $n \times (k + 1)$ observed matrix, and **u** is an $n \times 1$ vector of unobserved errors or disturbances.

Assumption E.2 No Perfect Collinearity

The matrix $\mathbf{X}$ has rank $(k + 1)$.

This is a careful statement of the assumption that rules out linear dependencies among the explanatory variables. Under Assumption E.2, $\mathbf{X}'\mathbf{X}$ is nonsingular, so $\hat{\boldsymbol{\beta}}$ is unique and can be written as in (E.8).

Assumption E.3 Zero Conditional Mean

Conditional on the entire matrix $\mathbf{X}$, each error u_t has zero mean: $\mathrm{E}(u_t|\mathbf{X}) = 0$, $t = 1, 2, \ldots, n$.

In vector form, Assumption E.3 can be written as

$$\mathrm{E}(\mathbf{u}|\mathbf{X}) = \mathbf{0}. \tag{E.11}$$

This assumption is implied by MLR.4 under the random sampling assumption, MLR.2. In time series applications, Assumption E.3 imposes strict exogeneity on the explanatory variables, something discussed at length in Chapter 10. This rules out explanatory variables whose future values are correlated with u_t; in particular, it eliminates lagged dependent variables. Under Assumption E.3, we can condition on the x_{tj} when we compute the expected value of $\hat{\boldsymbol{\beta}}$.

THEOREM E.1 UNBIASEDNESS OF OLS

Under Assumptions E.1, E.2, and E.3, the OLS estimator $\hat{\boldsymbol{\beta}}$ is unbiased for $\boldsymbol{\beta}$.

PROOF: Use Assumptions E.1 and E.2 and simple algebra to write

$$\begin{aligned} \hat{\boldsymbol{\beta}} &= (\mathbf{X}'\mathbf{X})^{-1}\mathbf{X}'\mathbf{y} = (\mathbf{X}'\mathbf{X})^{-1}\mathbf{X}'(\mathbf{X}\boldsymbol{\beta} + \mathbf{u}) \\ &= (\mathbf{X}'\mathbf{X})^{-1}(\mathbf{X}'\mathbf{X})\boldsymbol{\beta} + (\mathbf{X}'\mathbf{X})^{-1}\mathbf{X}'\mathbf{u} = \boldsymbol{\beta} + (\mathbf{X}'\mathbf{X})^{-1}\mathbf{X}'\mathbf{u}, \end{aligned} \tag{E.12}$$

where we use the fact that $(\mathbf{X}'\mathbf{X})^{-1}(\mathbf{X}'\mathbf{X}) = \mathbf{I}_{k+1}$. Taking the expectation conditional on $\mathbf{X}$ gives

$$\begin{aligned} \mathrm{E}(\hat{\boldsymbol{\beta}}|\mathbf{X}) &= \boldsymbol{\beta} + (\mathbf{X}'\mathbf{X})^{-1}\mathbf{X}'\mathrm{E}(\mathbf{u}|\mathbf{X}) \\ &= \boldsymbol{\beta} + (\mathbf{X}'\mathbf{X})^{-1}\mathbf{X}'\mathbf{0} = \boldsymbol{\beta}, \end{aligned}$$

because $\mathrm{E}(\mathbf{u}|\mathbf{X}) = \mathbf{0}$ under Assumption E.3. This argument clearly does not depend on the value of $\boldsymbol{\beta}$, so we have shown that $\hat{\boldsymbol{\beta}}$ is unbiased.

To obtain the simplest form of the variance-covariance matrix of $\hat{\boldsymbol{\beta}}$, we impose the assumptions of homoskedasticity and no serial correlation.

Assumption E.4 Homoskedasticity and No Serial Correlation

(i) $\text{Var}(u_t|\mathbf{X}) = \sigma^2$, $t = 1, 2, \ldots, n$. (ii) $\text{Cov}(u_t, u_s|\mathbf{X}) = 0$, for all $t \neq s$. In matrix form, we can write these two assumptions as

$$\text{Var}(\mathbf{u}|\mathbf{X}) = \sigma^2\mathbf{I}_n, \quad \text{[E.13]}$$

where $\mathbf{I}_n$ is the $n \times n$ identity matrix.

Part (i) of Assumption E.4 is the homoskedasticity assumption: the variance of u_t cannot depend on any element of $\mathbf{X}$, and the variance must be constant across observations, t. Part (ii) is the no serial correlation assumption: the errors cannot be correlated across observations. Under random sampling, and in any other cross-sectional sampling schemes with independent observations, part (ii) of Assumption E.4 automatically holds. For time series applications, part (ii) rules out correlation in the errors over time (both conditional on $\mathbf{X}$ and unconditionally).

Because of (E.13), we often say that $\mathbf{u}$ has a **scalar variance-covariance matrix** when Assumption E.4 holds. We can now derive the **variance-covariance matrix of the OLS estimator**.

THEOREM E.2 VARIANCE-COVARIANCE MATRIX OF THE OLS ESTIMATOR

Under Assumptions E.1 through E.4,

$$\text{Var}(\hat{\boldsymbol{\beta}}|\mathbf{X}) = \sigma^2(\mathbf{X}'\mathbf{X})^{-1}. \quad \text{[E.14]}$$

PROOF: From the last formula in equation (E.12), we have

$$\text{Var}(\hat{\boldsymbol{\beta}}|\mathbf{X}) = \text{Var}[(\mathbf{X}'\mathbf{X})^{-1}\mathbf{X}'\mathbf{u}|\mathbf{X}] = (\mathbf{X}'\mathbf{X})^{-1}\mathbf{X}'[\text{Var}(\mathbf{u}|\mathbf{X})]\mathbf{X}(\mathbf{X}'\mathbf{X})^{-1}.$$

Now, we use Assumption E.4 to get

$$\begin{aligned}\text{Var}(\hat{\boldsymbol{\beta}}|\mathbf{X}) &= (\mathbf{X}'\mathbf{X})^{-1}\mathbf{X}'(\sigma^2\mathbf{I}_n)\mathbf{X}(\mathbf{X}'\mathbf{X})^{-1} \\ &= \sigma^2(\mathbf{X}'\mathbf{X})^{-1}\mathbf{X}'\mathbf{X}(\mathbf{X}'\mathbf{X})^{-1} = \sigma^2(\mathbf{X}'\mathbf{X})^{-1}.\end{aligned}$$

Formula (E.14) means that the variance of $\hat{\beta}_j$ (conditional on $\mathbf{X}$) is obtained by multiplying σ^2 by the jth diagonal element of $(\mathbf{X}'\mathbf{X})^{-1}$. For the slope coefficients, we gave an interpretable formula in equation (3.51). Equation (E.14) also tells us how to obtain the covariance between any two OLS estimates: multiply σ^2 by the appropriate off-diagonal element of $(\mathbf{X}'\mathbf{X})^{-1}$. In Chapter 4, we showed how to avoid explicitly finding covariances for obtaining confidence intervals and hypothesis tests by appropriately rewriting the model.

The Gauss-Markov Theorem, in its full generality, can be proven.

THEOREM E.3

GAUSS-MARKOV THEOREM

Under Assumptions E.1 through E.4, $\hat{\boldsymbol{\beta}}$ is the best linear unbiased estimator.

PROOF: Any other linear estimator of $\boldsymbol{\beta}$ can be written as

$$\tilde{\boldsymbol{\beta}} = \mathbf{A}'\mathbf{y}, \qquad \text{[E.15]}$$

where $\mathbf{A}$ is an $n \times (k + 1)$ matrix. In order for $\tilde{\boldsymbol{\beta}}$ to be unbiased conditional on $\mathbf{X}$, $\mathbf{A}$ can consist of nonrandom numbers and functions of $\mathbf{X}$. (For example, $\mathbf{A}$ cannot be a function of $\mathbf{y}$.) To see what further restrictions on $\mathbf{A}$ are needed, write

$$\tilde{\boldsymbol{\beta}} = \mathbf{A}'(\mathbf{X}\boldsymbol{\beta} + \mathbf{u}) = (\mathbf{A}'\mathbf{X})\boldsymbol{\beta} + \mathbf{A}'\mathbf{u}. \qquad \text{[E.16]}$$

Then,

$$\begin{aligned} \text{E}(\tilde{\boldsymbol{\beta}}|\mathbf{X}) &= \mathbf{A}'\mathbf{X}\boldsymbol{\beta} + \text{E}(\mathbf{A}'\mathbf{u}|\mathbf{X}) \\ &= \mathbf{A}'\mathbf{X}\boldsymbol{\beta} + \mathbf{A}'\text{E}(\mathbf{u}|\mathbf{X}) \text{ because } \mathbf{A} \text{ is a function of } \mathbf{X} \\ &= \mathbf{A}'\mathbf{X}\boldsymbol{\beta} \text{ because } \text{E}(\mathbf{u}|\mathbf{X}) = \mathbf{0}. \end{aligned}$$

For $\tilde{\boldsymbol{\beta}}$ to be an unbiased estimator of $\boldsymbol{\beta}$, it must be true that $\text{E}(\tilde{\boldsymbol{\beta}}|\mathbf{X}) = \boldsymbol{\beta}$ for all $(k + 1) \times 1$ vectors $\boldsymbol{\beta}$, that is,

$$\mathbf{A}'\mathbf{X}\boldsymbol{\beta} = \boldsymbol{\beta} \text{ for all } (k + 1) \times 1 \text{ vectors } \boldsymbol{\beta}. \qquad \text{[E.17]}$$

Because $\mathbf{A}'\mathbf{X}$ is a $(k + 1) \times (k + 1)$ matrix, (E.17) holds if, and only if, $\mathbf{A}'\mathbf{X} = \mathbf{I}_{k+1}$. Equations (E.15) and (E.17) characterize the class of linear, unbiased estimators for $\boldsymbol{\beta}$.

Next, from (E.16), we have

$$\text{Var}(\tilde{\boldsymbol{\beta}}|\mathbf{X}) = \mathbf{A}'[\text{Var}(\mathbf{u}|\mathbf{X})]\mathbf{A} = \sigma^2\mathbf{A}'\mathbf{A},$$

by Assumption E.4. Therefore,

$$\begin{aligned} \text{Var}(\tilde{\boldsymbol{\beta}}|\mathbf{X}) - \text{Var}(\hat{\boldsymbol{\beta}}|\mathbf{X}) &= \sigma^2[\mathbf{A}'\mathbf{A} - (\mathbf{X}'\mathbf{X})^{-1}] \\ &= \sigma^2[\mathbf{A}'\mathbf{A} - \mathbf{A}'\mathbf{X}(\mathbf{X}'\mathbf{X})^{-1}\mathbf{X}'\mathbf{A}] \text{ because } \mathbf{A}'\mathbf{X} = \mathbf{I}_{k+1} \\ &= \sigma^2\mathbf{A}'[\mathbf{I}_n - \mathbf{X}(\mathbf{X}'\mathbf{X})^{-1}\mathbf{X}']\mathbf{A} \\ &\equiv \sigma^2\mathbf{A}'\mathbf{M}\mathbf{A}, \end{aligned}$$

where $\mathbf{M} \equiv \mathbf{I}_n - \mathbf{X}(\mathbf{X}'\mathbf{X})^{-1}\mathbf{X}'$. Because $\mathbf{M}$ is symmetric and idempotent, $\mathbf{A}'\mathbf{M}\mathbf{A}$ is positive semi-definite for any $n \times (k + 1)$ matrix $\mathbf{A}$. This establishes that the OLS estimator $\hat{\boldsymbol{\beta}}$ is BLUE. Why is this important? Let $\mathbf{c}$ be any $(k + 1) \times 1$ vector and consider the linear combination $\mathbf{c}'\boldsymbol{\beta} = c_0\beta_0 + c_1\beta_1 + \ldots + c_k\beta_k$, which is a scalar. The unbiased estimators of $\mathbf{c}'\boldsymbol{\beta}$ are $\mathbf{c}'\hat{\boldsymbol{\beta}}$ and $\mathbf{c}'\tilde{\boldsymbol{\beta}}$. But

$$\text{Var}(\mathbf{c}'\tilde{\boldsymbol{\beta}}|\mathbf{X}) - \text{Var}(\mathbf{c}'\hat{\boldsymbol{\beta}}|\mathbf{X}) = \mathbf{c}'[\text{Var}(\tilde{\boldsymbol{\beta}}|\mathbf{X}) - \text{Var}(\hat{\beta}|\mathbf{X})]\mathbf{c} \geq 0,$$

because $[\text{Var}(\tilde{\boldsymbol{\beta}}|\mathbf{X}) - \text{Var}(\hat{\beta}|\mathbf{X})]$ is p.s.d. Therefore, when it is used for estimating any linear combination of $\boldsymbol{\beta}$, OLS yields the smallest variance. In particular, $\text{Var}(\hat{\beta}_j|\mathbf{X}) \leq \text{Var}(\tilde{\beta}_j|\mathbf{X})$ for any other linear, unbiased estimator of β_j.

The unbiased estimator of the error variance σ^2 can be written as

$$\hat{\sigma}^2 = \hat{\mathbf{u}}'\hat{\mathbf{u}}/(n - k - 1),$$

which is the same as equation (3.56).

THEOREM E.4 UNBIASEDNESS OF $\hat{\sigma}^2$

Under Assumptions E.1 through E.4, $\hat{\sigma}^2$ is unbiased for σ^2: $\mathrm{E}(\hat{\sigma}^2|\mathbf{X}) = \sigma^2$ for all $\sigma^2 > 0$.

PROOF: Write $\hat{\mathbf{u}} = \mathbf{y} - \mathbf{X}\hat{\boldsymbol{\beta}} = \mathbf{y} - \mathbf{X}(\mathbf{X}'\mathbf{X})^{-1}\mathbf{X}'\mathbf{y} = \mathbf{My} = \mathbf{Mu}$, where $\mathbf{M} = \mathbf{I}_n - \mathbf{X}(\mathbf{X}'\mathbf{X})^{-1}\mathbf{X}'$, and the last equality follows because $\mathbf{MX} = \mathbf{0}$. Because $\mathbf{M}$ is symmetric and idempotent,

$$\hat{\mathbf{u}}'\hat{\mathbf{u}} = \mathbf{u}'\mathbf{M}'\mathbf{Mu} = \mathbf{u}'\mathbf{Mu}.$$

Because $\mathbf{u}'\mathbf{Mu}$ is a scalar, it equals its trace. Therefore,

$$\begin{aligned}\mathrm{E}(\mathbf{u}'\mathbf{Mu}|\mathbf{X}) &= \mathrm{E}[\mathrm{tr}(\mathbf{u}'\mathbf{Mu})|\mathbf{X}] = \mathrm{E}[\mathrm{tr}(\mathbf{Muu}')|\mathbf{X}] \\ &= \mathrm{tr}[\mathrm{E}(\mathbf{Muu}'|\mathbf{X})] = \mathrm{tr}[\mathbf{M}\mathrm{E}(\mathbf{uu}'|\mathbf{X})] \\ &= \mathrm{tr}(\mathbf{M}\sigma^2\mathbf{I}_n) = \sigma^2\mathrm{tr}(\mathbf{M}) = \sigma^2(n - k - 1).\end{aligned}$$

The last equality follows from $\mathrm{tr}(\mathbf{M}) = \mathrm{tr}(\mathbf{I}_n) - \mathrm{tr}[\mathbf{X}(\mathbf{X}'\mathbf{X})^{-1}\mathbf{X}'] = n - \mathrm{tr}[(\mathbf{X}'\mathbf{X})^{-1}\mathbf{X}'\mathbf{X}] = n - \mathrm{tr}(\mathbf{I}_{k+1}) = n - (k + 1) = n - k - 1$. Therefore,

$$\mathrm{E}(\hat{\sigma}^2|\mathbf{X}) = \mathrm{E}(\mathbf{u}'\mathbf{Mu}|\mathbf{X})/(n - k - 1) = \sigma^2.$$

E.3 Statistical Inference

When we add the final classical linear model assumption, $\hat{\boldsymbol{\beta}}$ has a multivariate normal distribution, which leads to the t and F distributions for the standard test statistics covered in Chapter 4.

Assumption E.5 Normality of Errors

Conditional on $\mathbf{X}$, the u_t are independent and identically distributed as Normal$(0,\sigma^2)$. Equivalently, $\mathbf{u}$ given $\mathbf{X}$ is distributed as multivariate normal with mean zero and variance-covariance matrix $\sigma^2\mathbf{I}_n$: $\mathbf{u} \sim \mathrm{Normal}(\mathbf{0},\sigma^2\mathbf{I}_n)$.

Under Assumption E.5, each u_t is independent of the explanatory variables for all t. In a time series setting, this is essentially the strict exogeneity assumption.

THEOREM E.5

NORMALITY OF $\hat{\beta}$

Under the classical linear model Assumptions E.1 through E.5, $\hat{\boldsymbol{\beta}}$ conditional on **X** is distributed as multivariate normal with mean $\boldsymbol{\beta}$ and variance-covariance matrix $\sigma^2(\mathbf{X}'\mathbf{X})^{-1}$.

Theorem E.5 is the basis for statistical inference involving $\boldsymbol{\beta}$. In fact, along with the properties of the chi-square, *t*, and *F* distributions that we summarized in Appendix D, we can use Theorem E.5 to establish that *t* statistics have a *t* distribution under Assumptions E.1 through E.5 (under the null hypothesis) and likewise for *F* statistics. We illustrate with a proof for the *t* statistics.

THEOREM E.6

DISTRIBUTION OF t STATISTIC

Under Assumptions E.1 through E.5,

$$(\hat{\beta}_j - \beta_j)/\text{se}(\hat{\beta}_j) \sim t_{n-k-1}, j = 0, 1, \ldots, k.$$

PROOF: The proof requires several steps; the following statements are initially conditional on **X**. First, by Theorem E.5, $(\hat{\beta}_j - \beta_j)/\text{sd}(\hat{\beta}_j) \sim \text{Normal}(0,1)$, where $\text{sd}(\hat{\beta}_j) = \sigma\sqrt{c_{jj}}$, and c_{jj} is the jth diagonal element of $(\mathbf{X}'\mathbf{X})^{-1}$. Next, under Assumptions E.1 through E.5, conditional on **X**,

$$(n - k - 1)\hat{\sigma}^2/\sigma^2 \sim \chi^2_{n-k-1}. \quad \textbf{[E.18]}$$

This follows because $(n - k - 1)\hat{\sigma}^2/\sigma^2 = (\mathbf{u}/\sigma)'\mathbf{M}(\mathbf{u}/\sigma)$, where $\mathbf{M}$ is the $n \times n$ symmetric, idempotent matrix defined in Theorem E.4. But $\mathbf{u}/\sigma \sim \text{Normal}(\mathbf{0},\mathbf{I}_n)$ by Assumption E.5. It follows from Property 1 for the chi-square distribution in Appendix D that $(\mathbf{u}/\sigma)'\mathbf{M}(\mathbf{u}/\sigma) \sim \chi^2_{n-k-1}$ (because **M** has rank $n - k - 1$).

We also need to show that $\hat{\boldsymbol{\beta}}$ and $\hat{\sigma}^2$ are independent. But $\hat{\boldsymbol{\beta}} = \boldsymbol{\beta} + (\mathbf{X}'\mathbf{X})^{-1}\mathbf{X}'\mathbf{u}$, and $\hat{\sigma}^2 = \mathbf{u}'\mathbf{M}\mathbf{u}/(n - k - 1)$. Now, $[(\mathbf{X}'\mathbf{X})^{-1}\mathbf{X}']\mathbf{M} = \mathbf{0}$ because $\mathbf{X}'\mathbf{M} = \mathbf{0}$. It follows, from Property 5 of the multivariate normal distribution in Appendix D, that $\hat{\boldsymbol{\beta}}$ and **Mu** are independent. Because $\hat{\sigma}^2$ is a function of **Mu**, $\hat{\boldsymbol{\beta}}$ and $\hat{\sigma}^2$ are also independent.

$$(\hat{\beta}_j - \beta_j)/\text{se}(\hat{\beta}_j) = [(\hat{\beta}_j - \beta_j)/\text{sd}(\hat{\beta}_j)]/(\hat{\sigma}^2/\sigma^2)^{1/2},$$

which is the ratio of a standard normal random variable and the square root of a $\chi^2_{n-k-1}/(n - k - 1)$ random variable. We just showed that these are independent, so, by definition of a *t* random variable, $(\hat{\beta}_j - \beta_j)/\text{se}(\hat{\beta}_j)$ has the t_{n-k-1} distribution. Because this distribution does not depend on **X**, it is the unconditional distribution of $(\hat{\beta}_j - \beta_j)/\text{se}(\hat{\beta}_j)$ as well.

From this theorem, we can plug in any hypothesized value for β_j and use the *t* statistic for testing hypotheses, as usual.

Under Assumptions E.1 through E.5, we can compute what is known as the *Cramer-Rao* lower bound for the variance-covariance matrix of unbiased estimators of $\boldsymbol{\beta}$ (again conditional on **X**) [see Greene (1997, Chapter 4)]. This can be shown to be $\sigma^2(\mathbf{X}'\mathbf{X})^{-1}$, which is exactly the variance-covariance matrix of the OLS estimator. This implies that $\hat{\boldsymbol{\beta}}$ is the **minimum variance unbiased estimator** of $\boldsymbol{\beta}$ (conditional on $\mathbf{X}$): $\text{Var}(\tilde{\boldsymbol{\beta}}|\mathbf{X}) - \text{Var}(\hat{\boldsymbol{\beta}}|\mathbf{X})$ is positive semi-definite for any other unbiased estimator $\tilde{\boldsymbol{\beta}}$; we no longer have to restrict our attention to estimators linear in $\mathbf{y}$.

It is easy to show that the OLS estimator is in fact the maximum likelihood estimator of $\boldsymbol{\beta}$ under Assumption E.5. For each t, the distribution of y_t given $\mathbf{X}$ is Normal($\mathbf{x}_t\boldsymbol{\beta}, \sigma^2$). Because the y_t are independent conditional on $\mathbf{X}$, the likelihood function for the sample is obtained from the product of the densities:

$$\prod_{t=1}^{n} (2\pi\sigma^2)^{-1/2}\exp[-(y_t - \mathbf{x}_t\boldsymbol{\beta})^2/(2\sigma^2)],$$

where $\prod$ denotes product. Maximizing this function with respect to $\boldsymbol{\beta}$ and σ^2 is the same as maximizing its natural logarithm:

$$\sum_{t=1}^{n} [-(1/2)\log(2\pi\sigma^2) - (y_t - \mathbf{x}_t\boldsymbol{\beta})^2/(2\sigma^2)].$$

For obtaining $\hat{\boldsymbol{\beta}}$, this is the same as minimizing $\sum_{t=1}^{n} (y_t - \mathbf{x}_t\boldsymbol{\beta})^2$—the division by $2\sigma^2$ does not affect the optimization—which is just the problem that OLS solves. The estimator of σ^2 that we have used, SSR/$(n - k)$, turns out not to be the MLE of σ^2; the MLE is SSR/n, which is a biased estimator. Because the unbiased estimator of σ^2 results in t and F statistics with exact t and F distributions under the null, it is always used instead of the MLE.

That the OLS estimator is the MLE under Assumption E.5 implies an interesting robustness property of the MLE based on the normal distribution. The reasoning is simple. We know that the OLS estimator is unbiased under Assumptions E.1 to E.3; normality of the errors is used nowhere in the proof, and neither is Assumption E.4. As the next section shows, the OLS estimator is also consistent without normality, provided the law of large numbers holds (as is widely true). These statistical properties of the OLS estimator imply that the MLE based on the normal log-likelihood function is robust to distributional specification: the distribution can be (almost) anything and yet we still obtain a consistent (and, under E.1 to E.3, unbiased) estimator. As discussed in Section 17.3, a maximum likelihood estimator obtained without assuming the distribution is correct is often called a **quasi-maximum likelihood estimator (QMLE).**

Generally, consistency of the MLE relies on having a correct distribution in order to conclude that it is consistent for the parameters. We have just seen that the normal distribution is a notable exception. There are some other distributions that share this property, including the Poisson distribution—as discussed in Section 17.3. Wooldridge (2010, Chapter 18) discusses some other useful examples.

E.4 Some Asymptotic Analysis

The matrix approach to the multiple regression model can also make derivations of asymptotic properties more concise. In fact, we can give general proofs of the claims in Chapter 11.

We begin by proving the consistency result of Theorem 11.1. Recall that these assumptions contain, as a special case, the assumptions for cross-sectional analysis under random sampling.

Proof of Theorem 11.1. As in Problem E.1 and using Assumption TS.1′, we write the OLS estimator as

$$\hat{\boldsymbol{\beta}} = \left(\sum_{t=1}^{n} \mathbf{x}_t'\mathbf{x}_t\right)^{-1}\left(\sum_{t=1}^{n} \mathbf{x}_t' y_t\right) = \left(\sum_{t=1}^{n} \mathbf{x}_t'\mathbf{x}_t\right)^{-1}\left(\sum_{t=1}^{n} \mathbf{x}_t'(\mathbf{x}_t\boldsymbol{\beta} + u_t)\right)$$

$$= \boldsymbol{\beta} + \left(\sum_{t=1}^{n} \mathbf{x}_t'\mathbf{x}_t\right)^{-1}\left(\sum_{t=1}^{n} \mathbf{x}_t' u_t\right) \quad \text{[E.19]}$$

$$= \boldsymbol{\beta} + \left(n^{-1}\sum_{t=1}^{n} \mathbf{x}_t'\mathbf{x}_t\right)^{-1}\left(n^{-1}\sum_{t=1}^{n} \mathbf{x}_t' u_t\right).$$

Now, by the law of large numbers,

$$n^{-1}\sum_{t=1}^{n} \mathbf{x}_t'\mathbf{x}_t \xrightarrow{p} \mathbf{A} \text{ and } n^{-1}\sum_{t=1}^{n} \mathbf{x}_t' u_t \xrightarrow{p} \mathbf{0}, \quad \text{[E.20]}$$

where $\mathbf{A} = \mathrm{E}(\mathbf{x}_t'\mathbf{x}_t)$ is a $(k + 1) \times (k + 1)$ nonsingular matrix under Assumption TS.2′ and we have used the fact that $\mathrm{E}(\mathbf{x}_t' u_t) = \mathbf{0}$ under Assumption TS.3′. Now, we must use a matrix version of Property PLIM.1 in Appendix C. Namely, because $\mathbf{A}$ is nonsingular,

$$\left(n^{-1}\sum_{t=1}^{n} \mathbf{x}_t'\mathbf{x}_t\right)^{-1} \xrightarrow{p} \mathbf{A}^{-1}. \quad \text{[E.21]}$$

[Wooldridge (2010, Chapter 3) contains a discussion of these kinds of convergence results.] It now follows from (E.19), (E.20), and (E.21) that

$$\mathrm{plim}(\hat{\boldsymbol{\beta}}) = \boldsymbol{\beta} + \mathbf{A}^{-1} \cdot \mathbf{0} = \boldsymbol{\beta}.$$

This completes the proof.

Next, we sketch a proof of the asymptotic normality result in Theorem 11.2.

Proof of Theorem 11.2. From equation (E.19), we can write

$$\sqrt{n}\,(\hat{\boldsymbol{\beta}} - \boldsymbol{\beta}) = \left(n^{-1}\sum_{t=1}^{n} \mathbf{x}_t'\mathbf{x}_t\right)^{-1}\left(n^{-1/2}\sum_{t=1}^{n} \mathbf{x}_t' u_t\right)$$

$$= \mathbf{A}^{-1}\left(n^{-1/2}\sum_{t=1}^{n} \mathbf{x}_t' u_t\right) + o_p(1), \quad \text{[E.22]}$$

where the term "$o_p(1)$" is a remainder term that converges in probability to zero. This term is equal to $\left[\left(n^{-1}\sum_{t=1}^{n} \mathbf{x}_t'\mathbf{x}_t\right)^{-1} - \mathbf{A}^{-1}\right]\left(n^{-1/2}\sum_{t=1}^{n} \mathbf{x}_t' u_t\right)$. The term in brackets converges in probability to zero (by the same argument used in the proof of Theorem 11.1), while $\left(n^{-1/2}\sum_{t=1}^{n} \mathbf{x}_t' u_t\right)$ is bounded in probability because it converges to a multivariate normal distribution by the central limit theorem. A well-known result in asymptotic theory is that the product of such terms converges in probability to zero. Further, $\sqrt{n}\,(\hat{\boldsymbol{\beta}} - \boldsymbol{\beta})$ inherits its asymptotic distribution from $\mathbf{A}^{-1}\left(n^{-1/2}\sum_{t=1}^{n} \mathbf{x}_t' u_t\right)$. See Wooldridge (2010, Chapter 3) for more details on the convergence results used in this proof.

By the central limit theorem, $n^{-1/2}\sum_{t=1}^{n}\mathbf{x}_t'u_t$ has an asymptotic normal distribution with mean zero and, say, $(k+1)\times(k+1)$ variance-covariance matrix $\mathbf{B}$. Then, $\sqrt{n}(\hat{\boldsymbol{\beta}}-\boldsymbol{\beta})$ has an asymptotic multivariate normal distribution with mean zero and variance-covariance matrix $\mathbf{A}^{-1}\mathbf{B}\mathbf{A}^{-1}$. We now show that, under Assumptions TS.4′ and TS.5′, $\mathbf{B}=\sigma^2\mathbf{A}$. (The general expression is useful because it underlies heteroskedasticity-robust and serial-correlation robust standard errors for OLS, of the kind discussed in Chapter 12.) First, under Assumption TS.5′, $\mathbf{x}_t'u_t$ and $\mathbf{x}_s'u_s$ are uncorrelated for $t\neq s$. Why? Suppose $s<t$ for concreteness. Then, by the law of iterated expectations, $\mathrm{E}(\mathbf{x}_t'u_tu_s\mathbf{x}_s)=\mathrm{E}[\mathrm{E}(u_tu_s\mathbf{x}_t'\mathbf{x}_s)|\mathbf{x}_t'\mathbf{x}_s]=\mathrm{E}[\mathrm{E}(u_tu_s|\mathbf{x}_t'\mathbf{x}_s)\mathbf{x}_t'\mathbf{x}_s]=\mathrm{E}[0\cdot\mathbf{x}_t'\mathbf{x}_s]=\mathbf{0}$. The zero covariances imply that the variance of the sum is the sum of the variances. But $\mathrm{Var}(\mathbf{x}_t'u_t)=\mathrm{E}(\mathbf{x}_t'u_tu_t\mathbf{x}_t)=\mathrm{E}(u_t^2\mathbf{x}_t'\mathbf{x}_t)$. By the law of iterated expectations, $\mathrm{E}(u_t^2\mathbf{x}_t'\mathbf{x}_t)=\mathrm{E}[\mathrm{E}(u_t^2\mathbf{x}_t'\mathbf{x}_t|\mathbf{x}_t)]=\mathrm{E}[\mathrm{E}(u_t^2|\mathbf{x}_t)\mathbf{x}_t'\mathbf{x}_t]=\mathrm{E}(\sigma^2\mathbf{x}_t'\mathbf{x}_t)=\sigma^2\mathrm{E}(\mathbf{x}_t'\mathbf{x}_t)=\sigma^2\mathbf{A}$, where we use $\mathrm{E}(u_t^2|\mathbf{x}_t)=\sigma^2$ under Assumptions TS.3′ and TS.4′. This shows that $\mathbf{B}=\sigma^2\mathbf{A}$, and so, under Assumptions TS.1′ to TS.5′, we have

$$\sqrt{n}\,(\hat{\boldsymbol{\beta}}-\boldsymbol{\beta})\overset{a}{\sim}\mathrm{Normal}\,(\mathbf{0},\sigma^2\mathbf{A}^{-1}). \qquad [E.23]$$

This completes the proof.

From equation (E.23), we treat $\hat{\boldsymbol{\beta}}$ as if it is approximately normally distributed with mean $\boldsymbol{\beta}$ and variance-covariance matrix $\sigma^2\mathrm{A}^{-1}/n$. The division by the sample size, n, is expected here: the approximation to the variance-covariance matrix of $\hat{\boldsymbol{\beta}}$ shrinks to zero at the rate $1/n$. When we replace σ^2 with its consistent estimator, $\hat{\sigma}^2=\mathrm{SSR}/(n-k-1)$, and replace A with its consistent estimator, $n^{-1}\sum_{t=1}^{n}\mathbf{x}_t'\mathbf{x}_t=\mathbf{X}'\mathbf{X}/n$, we obtain an estimator for the asymptotic variance of $\hat{\boldsymbol{\beta}}$:

$$\widehat{\mathrm{Avar}(\hat{\boldsymbol{\beta}})}=\hat{\sigma}^2(\mathbf{X}'\mathbf{X})^{-1}. \qquad [E.24]$$

Notice how the two divisions by n cancel, and the right-hand side of (E.24) is just the usual way we estimate the variance matrix of the OLS estimator under the Gauss-Markov assumptions. To summarize, we have shown that, under Assumptions TS.1′ to TS.5′—which contain MLR.1 to MLR.5 as special cases—the usual standard errors and t statistics are asymptotically valid. It is perfectly legitimate to use the usual t distribution to obtain critical values and p-values for testing a single hypothesis. Interestingly, in the general setup of Chapter 11, assuming normality of the errors—say, u_t given $\mathbf{x}_t$, u_{t-1}, $\mathbf{x}_{t-1}$, ..., u_1, $\mathbf{x}_1$ is distributed as Normal$(0,\sigma^2)$—does not necessarily help, as the t statistics would not generally have exact t statistics under this kind of normality assumption. When we do not assume strict exogeneity of the explanatory variables, exact distributional results are difficult, if not impossible, to obtain.

If we modify the argument above, we can derive a heteroskedasticity-robust, variance-covariance matrix. The key is that we must estimate $\mathrm{E}(u_t^2\mathbf{x}_t'\mathbf{x}_t)$ separately because this matrix no longer equals $\sigma^2\mathrm{E}(\mathbf{x}_t'\mathbf{x}_t)$. But, if the $\hat{u}_t$ are the OLS residuals, a consistent estimator is

$$(n-k-1)^{-1}\sum_{t=1}^{n}\hat{u}_t^2\mathbf{x}_t'\mathbf{x}_t, \qquad [E.25]$$

where the division by $n-k-1$ rather than n is a degrees of freedom adjustment that typically helps the finite sample properties of the estimator. When we use the expression in equation (E.25), we obtain

$$\widehat{\text{Avar}(\hat{\boldsymbol{\beta}})} = [n/(n - k - 1)](\mathbf{X}'\mathbf{X})^{-1}\left(\sum_{t=1}^{n} \hat{u}_t^2 \mathbf{x}_t'\mathbf{x}_t\right)(\mathbf{X}'\mathbf{X})^{-1}. \qquad \text{[E.26]}$$

The square roots of the diagonal elements of this matrix are the same heteroskedasticity-robust standard errors we obtained in Section 8.2 for the pure cross-sectional case. A matrix extension of the serial correlation- (and heteroskedasticity-) robust standard errors we obtained in Section 12.5 is also available, but the matrix that must replace (E.25) is complicated because of the serial correlation. See, for example, Hamilton (1994, Section 10.5).

Wald Statistics for Testing Multiple Hypotheses

Similar arguments can be used to obtain the asymptotic distribution of the **Wald statistic** for testing multiple hypotheses. Let **R** be a $q \times (k + 1)$ matrix, with $q \leq (k + 1)$. Assume that the q restrictions on the $(k + 1) \times 1$ vector of parameters, $\boldsymbol{\beta}$, can be expressed as $\text{H}_0\text{:}\, \mathbf{R}\boldsymbol{\beta} = \mathbf{r}$, where $\mathbf{r}$ is a $q \times 1$ vector of known constants. Under Assumptions TS.1′ to TS.5′, it can be shown that, under H_0,

$$[\sqrt{n}(\mathbf{R}\hat{\boldsymbol{\beta}} - \mathbf{r})]'(\sigma^2\mathbf{R}\mathbf{A}^{-1}\mathbf{R}')^{-1}[\sqrt{n}(\mathbf{R}\hat{\boldsymbol{\beta}} - \mathbf{r})] \overset{a}{\sim} \chi_q^2, \qquad \text{[E.27]}$$

where $\mathbf{A} = \text{E}(\mathbf{x}_t'\mathbf{x}_t)$, as in the proofs of Theorems 11.1 and 11.2. The intuition behind equation (E.25) is simple. Because $\sqrt{n}(\hat{\boldsymbol{\beta}} - \boldsymbol{\beta})$ is roughly distributed as Normal$(\mathbf{0},\sigma^2\mathbf{A}^{-1})$, $\mathbf{R}[\sqrt{n}(\hat{\boldsymbol{\beta}} - \boldsymbol{\beta})] = \sqrt{n}\,\mathbf{R}(\hat{\boldsymbol{\beta}} - \boldsymbol{\beta})$ is approximately Normal$(\mathbf{0},\sigma^2\mathbf{R}\mathbf{A}^{-1}\mathbf{R}')$ by Property 3 of the multivariate normal distribution in Appendix D. Under H_0, $\mathbf{R}\boldsymbol{\beta} = \mathbf{r}$, so $\sqrt{n}(\mathbf{R}\hat{\boldsymbol{\beta}} - \mathbf{r}) \sim$ Normal$(\mathbf{0},\sigma^2\mathbf{R}\mathbf{A}^{-1}\mathbf{R}')$ under H_0. By Property 3 of the chi-square distribution, $z'(\sigma^2\mathbf{R}\mathbf{A}^{-1}\mathbf{R}')^{-1}z \sim \chi_q^2$ if $z \sim$ Normal$(\mathbf{0},\sigma^2\mathbf{R}\mathbf{A}^{-1}\mathbf{R}')$. To obtain the final result formally, we need to use an asymptotic version of this property, which can be found in Wooldridge (2010, Chapter 3).

Given the result in (E.25), we obtain a computable statistic by replacing **A** and σ^2 with their consistent estimators; doing so does not change the asymptotic distribution. The result is the so-called Wald statistic, which, after cancelling the sample sizes and doing a little algebra, can be written as

$$W = (\mathbf{R}\hat{\boldsymbol{\beta}} - \mathbf{r})'[\mathbf{R}(\mathbf{X}'\mathbf{X})^{-1}\mathbf{R}']^{-1}(\mathbf{R}\hat{\boldsymbol{\beta}} - \mathbf{r})/\hat{\sigma}^2. \qquad \text{[E.28]}$$

Under $\text{H}_0, W \overset{a}{\sim} \chi_q^2$, where we recall that q is the number of restrictions being tested. If $\hat{\sigma}^2 = \text{SSR}/(n - k - 1)$, it can be shown that W/q is exactly the F statistic we obtained in Chapter 4 for testing multiple linear restrictions. [See, for example, Greene (1997, Chapter 7).] Therefore, under the classical linear model assumptions TS.1 to TS.6 in Chapter 10, W/q has an exact $F_{q,n-k-1}$ distribution. Under Assumptions TS.1′ to TS.5′, we only have the asymptotic result in (E.26). Nevertheless, it is appropriate, and common, to treat the usual F statistic as having an approximate $F_{q,n-k-1}$ distribution.

A Wald statistic that is robust to heteroskedasticity of unknown form is obtained by using the matrix in (E.26) in place of $\hat{\sigma}^2(\mathbf{X}'\mathbf{X})^{-1}$, and similarly for a test statistic robust to both heteroskedasticity and serial correlation. The robust versions of the test statistics cannot be computed via sums of squared residuals or R-squareds from the restricted and unrestricted regressions.

Summary

This appendix has provided a brief treatment of the linear regression model using matrix notation. This material is included for more advanced classes that use matrix algebra, but it is not needed to read the text. In effect, this appendix proves some of the results that we either stated without proof, proved only in special cases, or proved through a more cumbersome method of proof. Other topics—such as asymptotic properties, instrumental variables estimation, and panel data models—can be given concise treatments using matrices. Advanced texts in econometrics, including Davidson and MacKinnon (1993), Greene (1997), Hayashi (2000), and Wooldridge (2010), can be consulted for details.

Key Terms

First Order Condition
Matrix Notation
Minimum Variance Unbiased Estimator
Scalar Variance-Covariance Matrix
Variance-Covariance Matrix of the OLS Estimator
Wald Statistic
Quasi-Maximum Likelihood Estimator (QMLE)

Problems

1 Let $\mathbf{x}_t$ be the $1 \times (k+1)$ vector of explanatory variables for observation t. Show that the OLS estimator $\hat{\boldsymbol{\beta}}$ can be written as

$$\hat{\boldsymbol{\beta}} = \left(\sum_{t=1}^{n} \mathbf{x}_t'\mathbf{x}_t\right)^{-1}\left(\sum_{t=1}^{n} \mathbf{x}_t'y_t\right).$$

Dividing each summation by n shows that $\hat{\boldsymbol{\beta}}$ is a function of sample averages.

2 Let $\hat{\boldsymbol{\beta}}$ be the $(k+1) \times 1$ vector of OLS estimates.

(i) Show that for any $(k+1) \times 1$ vector $\mathbf{b}$, we can write the sum of squared residuals as

$$\text{SSR}(\mathbf{b}) = \hat{\mathbf{u}}'\hat{\mathbf{u}} + (\hat{\boldsymbol{\beta}} - \mathbf{b})'\mathbf{X}'\mathbf{X}(\hat{\boldsymbol{\beta}} - \mathbf{b}).$$

{*Hint:* Write $(\mathbf{y} - \mathbf{X}\mathbf{b})'(\mathbf{y} - \mathbf{X}\mathbf{b}) = [\hat{\mathbf{u}} + \mathbf{X}(\hat{\boldsymbol{\beta}} - \mathbf{b})]'[\hat{\mathbf{u}} + \mathbf{X}(\hat{\boldsymbol{\beta}} - \mathbf{b})]$ and use the fact that $\mathbf{X}'\hat{\mathbf{u}} = \mathbf{0}$.}

(ii) Explain how the expression for SSR($\mathbf{b}$) in part (i) proves that $\hat{\boldsymbol{\beta}}$ uniquely minimizes SSR($\mathbf{b}$) over all possible values of $\mathbf{b}$, assuming $\mathbf{X}$ has rank $k+1$.

3 Let $\hat{\boldsymbol{\beta}}$ be the OLS estimate from the regression of $\mathbf{y}$ on $\mathbf{X}$. Let $\mathbf{A}$ be a $(k+1) \times (k+1)$ nonsingular matrix and define $\mathbf{z}_t \equiv \mathbf{x}_t\mathbf{A}$, $t = 1, \ldots, n$. Therefore, $\mathbf{z}_t$ is $1 \times (k+1)$ and is a nonsingular linear combination of $\mathbf{x}_t$. Let $\mathbf{Z}$ be the $n \times (k+1)$ matrix with rows $\mathbf{z}_t$. Let $\tilde{\boldsymbol{\beta}}$ denote the OLS estimate from a regression of $\mathbf{y}$ on $\mathbf{Z}$.

(i) Show that $\tilde{\boldsymbol{\beta}} = \mathbf{A}^{-1}\hat{\boldsymbol{\beta}}$.

(ii) Let $\hat{y}_t$ be the fitted values from the original regression and let $\tilde{y}_t$ be the fitted values from regressing $\mathbf{y}$ on $\mathbf{Z}$. Show that $\tilde{y}_t = \hat{y}_t$, for all $t = 1, 2, \ldots, n$. How do the residuals from the two regressions compare?

(iii) Show that the estimated variance matrix for $\tilde{\boldsymbol{\beta}}$ is $\hat{\sigma}^2\mathbf{A}^{-1}(\mathbf{X}'\mathbf{X})^{-1}\mathbf{A}^{-1\prime}$, where $\hat{\sigma}^2$ is the usual variance estimate from regressing $\mathbf{y}$ on $\mathbf{X}$.

(iv) Let the $\hat{\beta}_j$ be the OLS estimates from regressing y_t on $1, x_{t1}, \ldots, x_{tk}$, and let the $\tilde{\beta}_j$ be the OLS estimates from the regression of y_t on $1, a_1x_{t1}, \ldots, a_kx_{tk}$, where $a_j \neq 0$, $j = 1, \ldots, k$. Use the results from part (i) to find the relationship between the $\tilde{\beta}_j$ and the $\hat{\beta}_j$.

(v) Assuming the setup of part (iv), use part (iii) to show that $\text{se}(\tilde{\beta}_j) = \text{se}(\hat{\beta}_j)/|a_j|$.

(vi) Assuming the setup of part (iv), show that the absolute values of the t statistics for $\tilde{\beta}_j$ and $\hat{\beta}_j$ are identical.

4 Assume that the model $\mathbf{y} = \mathbf{X}\boldsymbol{\beta} + \mathbf{u}$ satisfies the Gauss-Markov assumptions, let $\mathbf{G}$ be a $(k + 1) \times (k + 1)$ nonsingular, nonrandom matrix, and define $\boldsymbol{\delta} = \mathbf{G}\boldsymbol{\beta}$, so that $\boldsymbol{\delta}$ is also a $(k + 1) \times 1$ vector. Let $\hat{\boldsymbol{\beta}}$ be the $(k + 1) \times 1$ vector of OLS estimators and define $\hat{\boldsymbol{\delta}} = \mathbf{G}\hat{\boldsymbol{\beta}}$ as the OLS estimator of $\boldsymbol{\delta}$.

(i) Show that $\text{E}(\hat{\boldsymbol{\delta}}|\mathbf{X}) = \boldsymbol{\delta}$.

(ii) Find $\text{Var}(\hat{\boldsymbol{\delta}}|\mathbf{X})$ in terms of σ^2, $\mathbf{X}$, and $\mathbf{G}$.

(iii) Use Problem E.3 to verify that $\hat{\boldsymbol{\delta}}$ and the appropriate estimate of $\text{Var}(\hat{\boldsymbol{\delta}}|\mathbf{X})$ are obtained from the regression of $\mathbf{y}$ on $\mathbf{X}\mathbf{G}^{-1}$.

(iv) Now, let $\mathbf{c}$ be a $(k + 1) \times 1$ vector with at least one nonzero entry. For concreteness, assume that $c_k \neq 0$. Define $\theta = \mathbf{c}'\boldsymbol{\beta}$, so that θ is a scalar. Define $\delta_j = \beta_j, j = 0, 1, \ldots, k - 1$ and $\delta_k = \theta$. Show how to define a $(k + 1) \times (k + 1)$ nonsingular matrix $\mathbf{G}$ so that $\boldsymbol{\delta} = \mathbf{G}\boldsymbol{\beta}$. (*Hint:* Each of the first k rows of $\mathbf{G}$ should contain k zeros and a one. What is the last row?)

(v) Show that for the choice of $\mathbf{G}$ in part (iv),

$$\mathbf{G}^{-1} = \begin{bmatrix} 1 & 0 & 0 & . & . & . & 0 \\ 0 & 1 & 0 & . & . & . & 0 \\ . & & & & & & \\ . & & & & & & \\ . & & & & & & \\ 0 & 0 & . & . & . & 1 & 0 \\ -c_0/c_k & -c_1/c_k & . & . & . & -c_{k-1}/c_k & 1/c_k \end{bmatrix}.$$

Use this expression for $\mathbf{G}^{-1}$ and part (iii) to conclude that $\hat{\theta}$ and its standard error are obtained as the coefficient on x_{tk}/c_k in the regression of

$$y_t \text{ on } [1 - (c_0/c_k)x_{tk}], [x_{t1} - (c_1/c_k)x_{tk}], \ldots, [x_{t,k-1} - (c_{k-1}/c_k)x_{tk}], x_{tk}/c_k, t = 1, \ldots, n.$$

This regression is exactly the one obtained by writing β_k in terms of θ and $\beta_0, \beta_1, \ldots, \beta_{k-1}$, plugging the result into the original model, and rearranging. Therefore, we can formally justify the trick we use throughout the text for obtaining the standard error of a linear combination of parameters.

5 Assume that the model $\mathbf{y} = \mathbf{X}\boldsymbol{\beta} + \mathbf{u}$ satisfies the Gauss-Markov assumptions and let $\hat{\boldsymbol{\beta}}$ be the OLS estimator of $\boldsymbol{\beta}$. Let $\mathbf{Z} = \mathbf{G}(\mathbf{X})$ be an $n \times (k + 1)$ matrix function of $\mathbf{X}$ and assume that $\mathbf{Z}'\mathbf{X}$ [a $(k + 1) \times (k + 1)$ matrix] is nonsingular. Define a new estimator of $\boldsymbol{\beta}$ by $\tilde{\boldsymbol{\beta}} = (\mathbf{Z}'\mathbf{X})^{-1}\mathbf{Z}'\mathbf{y}$.

(i) Show that $\text{E}(\tilde{\boldsymbol{\beta}}|\mathbf{X}) = \boldsymbol{\beta}$, so that $\tilde{\boldsymbol{\beta}}$ is also unbiased conditional on $\mathbf{X}$.

(ii) Find $\text{Var}(\tilde{\boldsymbol{\beta}}|\mathbf{X})$. Make sure this is a symmetric, $(k + 1) \times (k + 1)$ matrix that depends on $\mathbf{Z}$, $\mathbf{X}$, and σ^2.

(iii) Which estimator do you prefer, $\hat{\boldsymbol{\beta}}$ or $\tilde{\boldsymbol{\beta}}$? Explain.

APPENDIX F

Answers to Chapter Questions

Chapter 2

Question 2.1: When student ability, motivation, age, and other factors in u are not related to attendance, (2.6) would hold. This seems unlikely to be the case.

Question 2.2: About \$11.05. To see this, from the average wages measured in 1976 and 2003 dollars, we can get the CPI deflator as 19.06/5.90 ≈ 3.23. When we multiply 3.42 by 3.23, we obtain about 11.05.

Question 2.3: 54.65, as can be seen by plugging $shareA = 60$ into equation (2.28). This is not unreasonable: if Candidate A spends 60% of the total money spent, he or she is predicted to receive almost 55% of the vote.

Question 2.4: The equation will be $\widehat{salaryhun} = 9{,}631.91 + 185.01\, roe$, as is easily seen by multiplying equation (2.39) by 10.

Question 2.5: Equation (2.58) can be written as $\mathrm{Var}(\hat{\beta}_0) = (\sigma^2 n^{-1})\left(\sum_{i=1}^{n} x_i^2\right)/\left(\sum_{i=1}^{n}(x_i - \bar{x})^2\right)$, where the term multiplying $\sigma^2 n^{-1}$ is greater than or equal to one, but it is equal to one if, and only if, $\bar{x} = 0$. In this case, the variance is as small as it can possibly be: $\mathrm{Var}(\hat{\beta}_0) = \sigma^2/n$.

Chapter 3

Question 3.1: Just a few factors include age and gender distribution, size of the police force (or, more generally, resources devoted to crime fighting), population, and general historical factors. These factors certainly might be correlated with *prbconv* and *avgsen*, which means (3.5) would not hold. For example, size of the police force is possibly correlated with both *prbcon* and *avgsen*, as some cities put more effort into crime prevention and law enforcement. We should try to bring as many of these factors into the equation as possible.

Question 3.2: We use the third property of OLS concerning predicted values and residuals: when we plug the average values of all independent variables into the OLS regression line, we obtain the average value of the dependent variable. So $\overline{colGPA} = 1.29 + .453\ \overline{hsGPA} + .0094\ \overline{ACT} = 1.29 + .453(3.4) + .0094(24.2) \approx 3.06$. You can check the average of *colGPA* in GPA1.RAW to verify this to the second decimal place.

Question 3.3: No. The variable *shareA* is not an exact linear function of *expendA* and *expendB*, even though it is an exact *nonlinear* function: $shareA = 100\cdot[expendA/(expendA + expendB)]$. Therefore, it is legitimate to have *expendA*, *expendB*, and *shareA* as explanatory variables.

Question 3.4: As we discussed in Section 3.4, if we are interested in the effect of x_1 on y, correlation among the other explanatory variables (x_2, x_3, and so on) does not affect $\text{Var}(\hat{\beta}_1)$. These variables are included as controls, and we do not have to worry about collinearity among the control variables. Of course, we are controlling for them primarily because we think they are correlated with attendance, but this is necessary to perform a ceteris paribus analysis.

Chapter 4

Question 4.1: Under these assumptions, the Gauss-Markov assumptions are satisfied: u is independent of the explanatory variables, so $\text{E}(u|x_1, \ldots, x_k) = \text{E}(u)$, and $\text{Var}(u|x_1, \ldots, x_k) = \text{Var}(u)$. Further, it is easily seen that $\text{E}(u) = 0$. Therefore, MLR.4 and MLR.5 hold. The classical linear model assumptions are not satisfied because u is not normally distributed (which is a violation of MLR.6).

Question 4.2: $\text{H}_0\text{: } \beta_1 = 0$, $\text{H}_1\text{: } \beta_1 < 0$.

Question 4.3: Because $\hat{\beta}_1 = .56 > 0$ and we are testing against $\text{H}_1\text{: } \beta_1 > 0$, the one-sided p-value is one-half of the two-sided p-value, or .043.

Question 4.4: $\text{H}_0\text{: } \beta_5 = \beta_6 = \beta_7 = \beta_8 = 0$. $k = 8$ and $q = 4$. The restricted version of the model is

$$score = \beta_0 + \beta_1 classize + \beta_2 expend + \beta_3 tchcomp + \beta_4 enroll + u.$$

Question 4.5: The F statistic for testing exclusion of *ACT* is $[(.291 - .183)/(1 - .291)](680 - 3) \approx 103.13$. Therefore, the absolute value of the t statistic is about 10.16. The t statistic on *ACT* is negative, because $\hat{\beta}_{ACT}$ is negative, so $t_{ACT} = -10.16$.

Question 4.6: Not by much. The F test for joint significance of *droprate* and *gradrate* is easily computed from the R-squareds in the table: $F = [(.361 - .353)/(1 - .361)](402/2) \approx 2.52$. The 10% critical value is obtained from Table G.3a as 2.30, while the 5% critical value from Table G.3b is 3. The p-value is about .082. Thus, *droprate* and *gradrate* are jointly significant at the 10% level, but not at the 5% level. In any case, controlling for these variables has a minor effect on the *b/s* coefficient.

Chapter 5

Question 5.1: This requires some assumptions. It seems reasonable to assume that $\beta_2 > 0$ (*score* depends positively on *priGPA*) and $\text{Cov}(skipped,priGPA) < 0$ (*skipped* and *priGPA* are negatively correlated). This means that $\beta_2\delta_1 < 0$, which means that plim $\tilde{\beta}_1 < \beta_1$. Because β_1 is thought to be negative (or at least nonpositive), a simple regression is likely to overestimate the importance of skipping classes.

Question 5.2: $\hat{\beta}_j \pm 1.96\text{se}(\hat{\beta}_j)$ is the asymptotic 95% confidence interval. Or, we can replace 1.96 with 2.

Chapter 6

Question 6.1: Because *fincdol* = 1,000·*faminc*, the coefficient on *fincdol* will be the coefficient on *faminc* divided by 1,000, or .0927/1,000 = .0000927. The standard error also drops by a factor of 1,000, so the t statistic does not change, nor do any of the other OLS statistics. For readability, it is better to measure family income in thousands of dollars.

Question 6.2: We can do this generally. The equation is

$$\log(y) = \beta_0 + \beta_1\log(x_1) + \beta_2 x_2 + \ldots,$$

where x_2 is a proportion rather than a percentage. Then, ceteris paribus, $\Delta\log(y) = \beta_2\Delta x_2$, $100\cdot\Delta\log(y) = \beta_2(100\cdot\Delta x_2)$, or $\%\Delta y \approx \beta_2(100\cdot\Delta x_2)$. Now, because Δx_2 is the change in the proportion, $100\cdot\Delta x_2$ is a percentage point change. In particular, if $\Delta x_2 = .01$, then $100\cdot\Delta x_2 = 1$, which corresponds to a one percentage point change. But then β_2 is the percentage change in y when $100\cdot\Delta x_2 = 1$.

Question 6.3: The new model would be $stndfnl = \beta_0 + \beta_1 atndrte + \beta_2 priGPA + \beta_3 ACT + \beta_4 priGPA^2 + \beta_5 ACT^2 + \beta_6 priGPA\cdot atndrte + \beta_7 ACT\cdot atndrte + u$. Therefore, the partial effect of *atndrte* on *stndfnl* is $\beta_1 + \beta_6 priGPA + \beta_7 ACT$. This is what we multiply by $\Delta atndrte$ to obtain the ceteris paribus change in *stndfnl*.

Question 6.4: From equation (6.21), $\bar{R}^2 = 1 - \hat{\sigma}^2/[\text{SST}/(n - 1)]$. For a given sample and a given dependent variable, $\text{SST}/(n - 1)$ is fixed. When we use different sets of explanatory variables, only $\hat{\sigma}^2$ changes. As $\hat{\sigma}^2$ decreases, $\bar{R}^2$ increases. If we make $\hat{\sigma}$, and therefore $\hat{\sigma}^2$, as small as possible, we are making $\bar{R}^2$ as large as possible.

Question 6.5: One possibility is to collect data on annual earnings for a sample of actors, along with profitability of the movies in which they each appeared. In a simple regression analysis, we could relate earnings to profitability. But we should probably control for other factors that may affect salary, such as age, gender, and the kinds of movies in which the actors performed. Methods for including qualitative factors in regression models are considered in Chapter 7.

Chapter 7

Question 7.1: No, because it would not be clear when *party* is one and when it is zero. A better name would be something like *Dem*, which is one for Democratic candidates and zero for Republicans. Or, *Rep*, which is one for Republicans and zero for Democrats.

Question 7.2: With *outfield* as the base group, we would include the dummy variables *frstbase*, *scndbase*, *thrdbase*, *shrtstop*, and *catcher*.

Question 7.3: The null in this case is H_0: $\delta_1 = \delta_2 = \delta_3 = \delta_4 = 0$, so that there are four restrictions. As usual, we would use an F test (where $q = 4$ and k depends on the number of other explanatory variables).

Question 7.4: Because *tenure* appears as a quadratic, we should allow separate quadratics for men and women. That is, we would add the explanatory variables *female·tenure* and $female \cdot tenure^2$.

Question 7.5: We plug $pcnv = 0$, $avgsen = 0$, $tottime = 0$, $ptime86 = 0$, $qemp86 = 4$, $black = 1$, and $hispan = 0$ into (7.31): $\widehat{arr86} = .380 - .038(4) + .170 = .398$, or almost .4. It is hard to know whether this is "reasonable." For someone with no prior convictions who was employed throughout the year, this estimate might seem high, but remember that the population consists of men who were already arrested at least once prior to 1986.

Chapter 8

Question 8.1: This statement is clearly false. For example, in equation (8.7), the usual standard error for *black* is .147, while the heteroskedasticity-robust standard error is .118.

Question 8.2: The F test would be obtained by regressing $\hat{u}^2$ on *marrmale*, *marrfem*, and *singfem* (*singmale* is the base group). With $n = 526$ and three independent variables in this regression, the *df* are 3 and 522.

Question 8.3: Certainly the outcome of the statistical test suggests some cause for concern. A t statistic of 2.96 is very significant, and it implies that there is heteroskedasticity in the wealth equation. As a practical matter, we know that the WLS standard error, .063, is substantially below the heteroskedasticity-robust standard error for OLS, .104, and so the heteroskedasticity seems to be practically important. (Plus, the nonrobust OLS standard error is .061, which is too optimistic. Therefore, even if we simply adjust the OLS standard error for heteroskedasticity of unknown form, there are nontrivial implications.)

Question 8.4: The 1% critical value in the F distribution with $(2, \infty)$ df is 4.61. An F statistic of 11.15 is well above the 1% critical value, and so we strongly reject the null hypothesis that the transformed errors, $u_i/\sqrt{h_i}$, are homoskedastic. (In fact, the p-value is less than .00002, which is obtained from the $F_{2,804}$ distribution.) This means that our model for $\text{Var}(u|\mathbf{x})$ is inadequate for fully eliminating the heteroskedasticity in u.

Chapter 9

Question 9.1: These are binary variables, and squaring them has no effect: $black^2 = black$, and $hispan^2 = hispan$.

Question 9.2: When $educ \cdot IQ$ is in the equation, the coefficient on *educ*, say, β_1, measures the effect of *educ* on log(*wage*) when $IQ = 0$. (The partial effect of education is $\beta_1 + \beta_9 IQ$.) There is no one in the population of interest with an IQ close to zero. At the average population IQ, which is 100, the estimated return to education from column (3) is $.018 + .00034(100) = .052$, which is almost what we obtain as the coefficient on *educ* in column (2).

Question 9.3: No. If *educ** is an integer—which means someone has no education past the previous grade completed—the measurement error is zero. If *educ** is not an integer, $educ < educ^*$, so the measurement error is negative. At a minimum, e_1 cannot have zero mean, and e_1 and *educ** are probably correlated.

Question 9.4: An incumbent's decision not to run may be systematically related to how he or she expects to do in the election. Therefore, we may only have a sample of incumbents who are stronger, on average, than all possible incumbents who could run. This results in a sample selection problem if the population of interest includes all incumbents. If we are only interested in the effects of campaign expenditures on election outcomes for incumbents who seek reelection, there is no sample selection problem.

Chapter 10

Question 10.1: The impact propensity is .48, while the long-run propensity is $.48 - .15 + .32 = .65$.

Question 10.2: The explanatory variables are $x_{t1} = z_t$ and $x_{t2} = z_{t-1}$. The absence of perfect collinearity means that these cannot be constant, and there cannot be an exact linear relationship between them in the sample. This rules out the possibility that all the $z_1, \ldots, z_n$ take on the same value or that the $z_0, z_1, \ldots, z_{n-1}$ take on the same value. But it eliminates other patterns as well. For example, if $z_t = a + bt$ for constants a and b, then $z_{t-1} = a + b(t - 1) = (a + bt) - b = z_t - b$, which is a perfect linear function of z_t.

Question 10.3: If $\{z_t\}$ is slowly moving over time—as is the case for the levels or logs of many economic time series—then z_t and z_{t-1} can be highly correlated. For example, the correlation between $unem_t$ and $unem_{t-1}$ in PHILLIPS.RAW is .75.

Question 10.4: No, because a linear time trend with $\alpha_1 < 0$ becomes more and more negative as t gets large. Since *gfr* cannot be negative, a linear time trend with a negative trend coefficient cannot represent *gfr* in all future time periods.

Question 10.5: The intercept for March is $\beta_0 + \delta_2$. Seasonal dummy variables are strictly exogenous because they follow a deterministic pattern. For example, the months do not change based upon whether either the explanatory variables or the dependent variable change.

Chapter 11

Question 11.1: (i) No, because $E(y_t) = \delta_0 + \delta_1 t$ depends on t. (ii) Yes, because $y_t - E(y_t) = e_t$ is an i.i.d. sequence.

Question 11.2: We plug $inf_t^e = (1/2)inf_{t-1} + (1/2)inf_{t-2}$ into $inf_t - inf_t^e = \beta_1(unem_t - \mu_0) + e_t$ and rearrange: $inf_t - (1/2)(inf_{t-1} + inf_{t-2}) = \beta_0 + \beta_1 unem_t + e_t$, where $\beta_0 = -\beta_1\mu_0$, as before. Therefore, we would regress y_t on $unem_t$, where $y_t = inf_t - (1/2)(inf_{t-1} + inf_{t-2})$. Note that we lose the first two observations in constructing y_t.

Question 11.3: No, because u_t and u_{t-1} are correlated. In particular, $Cov(u_t,u_{t-1}) = E[(e_t + \alpha_1 e_{t-1})(e_{t-1} + \alpha_1 e_{t-2})] = \alpha_1 E(e_{t-1}^2) = \alpha_1\sigma_e^2 \neq 0$ if $\alpha_1 \neq 0$. If the errors are serially correlated, the model cannot be dynamically complete.

Chapter 12

Question 12.1: We use equation (12.4). Now, only adjacent terms are correlated. In particular, the covariance between $x_t u_t$ and $x_{t+1}u_{t+1}$ is $x_t x_{t+1}\text{Cov}(u_t, u_{t+1}) = x_t x_{t+1}\alpha\sigma_e^2$. Therefore, the formula is

$$\begin{aligned}\text{Var}(\hat{\beta}_1) &= \text{SST}_x^{-2}\left(\sum_{t=1}^{n} x_t^2\text{Var}(u_t) + 2\sum_{t=1}^{n-1} x_t x_{t+1}\text{E}(u_t u_{t+1})\right) \\ &= \sigma^2/\text{SST}_x + (2/\text{SST}_x^2)\sum_{t=1}^{n-1} \alpha\sigma_e^2 x_t x_{t+1} \\ &= \sigma^2/\text{SST}_x + \alpha\sigma_e^2(2/\text{SST}_x^2)\sum_{t=1}^{n-1} x_t x_{t+1},\end{aligned}$$

where $\sigma^2 = \text{Var}(u_t) = \sigma_e^2 + \alpha_1^2\sigma_e^2 = \sigma_e^2(1 + \alpha_1^2)$. Unless x_t and x_{t+1} are uncorrelated in the sample, the second term is nonzero whenever $\alpha \neq 0$. Notice that if x_t and x_{t+1} are positively correlated and $\alpha < 0$, the true variance is actually *smaller* than the usual variance. When the equation is in levels (as opposed to being differenced), the typical case is $\alpha > 0$, with positive correlation between x_t and x_{t+1}.

Question 12.2: $\hat{\rho} \pm 1.96\text{se}(\hat{\rho})$, where $\text{se}(\hat{\rho})$ is the standard error reported in the regression. Or, we could use the heteroskedasticity-robust standard error. Showing that this is asymptotically valid is complicated because the OLS residuals depend on $\hat{\beta}_j$, but it can be done.

Question 12.3: The model we have in mind is $u_t = \rho_1 u_{t-1} + \rho_4 u_{t-4} + e_t$, and we want to test H_0: $\rho_1 = 0$, $\rho_4 = 0$ against the alternative that H_0 is false. We would run the regression of $\hat{u}_t$ on $\hat{u}_{t-1}$ and $\hat{u}_{t-4}$ to obtain the usual F statistic for joint significance of the two lags. (We are testing two restrictions.)

Question 12.4: We would probably estimate the equation using first differences, as $\hat{\rho} = .92$ is close enough to 1 to raise questions about the levels regression. See Chapter 18 for more discussion.

Question 12.5: Because there is only one explanatory variable, the White test is easy to compute. Simply regress $\hat{u}_t^2$ on $return_{t-1}$ and $return_{t-1}^2$ (with an intercept, as always) and compute the F test for joint significance of $return_{t-1}$ and $return_{t-1}^2$. If these are jointly significant at a small enough significance level, we reject the null of homoskedasticity.

Chapter 13

Question 13.1: Yes, assuming that we have controlled for all relevant factors. The coefficient on *black* is 1.076, and, with a standard error of .174, it is not statistically different from 1. The 95% confidence interval is from about .735 to 1.417.

Question 13.2: The coefficient on *highearn* shows that, in the absence of any change in the earnings cap, high earners spend much more time—on the order of 29.2% on average [because $\exp(.256) - 1 \approx .292$]—on workers' compensation.

Question 13.3: First, $\text{E}(v_{i1}) = \text{E}(a_i + u_{i1}) = \text{E}(a_i) + \text{E}(v_{i1}) = 0$. Similarly, $\text{E}(v_{i2}) = 0$. Therefore, the covariance between v_{i1} and v_{i2} is simply $\text{E}(v_{i1}v_{i2}) = \text{E}[(a_i + u_{i1})(a_i + u_{i2})] = \text{E}(a_i^2) + \text{E}(a_i u_{i1}) + \text{E}(a_i u_{i2}) + \text{E}(u_{i1}u_{i2}) = \text{E}(a_i^2)$, because all of the covariance terms are zero by assumption. But $E(a_i^2) = Var(a_i)$, because $E(a_i) = 0$. This causes positive serial correlation across time in the errors within each i, which biases the usual OLS standard errors in a pooled OLS regression.

Question 13.4: Because $\Delta admn = admn_{90} - admn_{85}$ is the difference in binary indicators, it can be -1 if, and only if, $admn_{90} = 0$ and $admn_{85} = 1$. In other words, Washington state had an administrative per se law in 1985 but it was repealed by 1990.

Question 13.5: No, just as it does not cause bias and inconsistency in a time series regression with strictly exogenous explanatory variables. There are two reasons it is a concern. First, serial correlation in the errors in any equation generally biases the usual OLS standard errors and test statistics. Second, it means that pooled OLS is not as efficient as estimators that account for the serial correlation (as in Chapter 12).

Chapter 14

Question 14.1: Whether we use first differencing or the within transformation, we will have trouble estimating the coefficient on $kids_{it}$. For example, using the within transformation, if $kids_{it}$ does not vary for family i, then $\ddot{kids}_{it} = kids_{it} - \overline{kids}_i = 0$ for $t = 1,2,3$. As long as some families have variation in $kids_{it}$, then we can compute the fixed effects estimator, but the $kids$ coefficient could be very imprecisely estimated. This is a form of multicollinearity in fixed effects estimation (or first-differencing estimation).

Question 14.2: If a firm did not receive a grant in the first year, it may or may not receive a grant in the second year. But if a firm did receive a grant in the first year, it could not get a grant in the second year. That is, if $grant_{-1} = 1$, then $grant = 0$. This induces a negative correlation between $grant$ and $grant_{-1}$. We can verify this by computing a regression of $grant$ on $grant_{-1}$, using the data in JTRAIN.RAW for 1989. Using all firms in the sample, we get

$$\widehat{grant} = .248 - .248\, grant_{-1}$$
$$(.035) \quad (.072)$$
$$n = 157, R^2 = .070.$$

The coefficient on $grant_{-1}$ must be the negative of the intercept because $\widehat{grant} = 0$ when $grant_{-1} = 1$.

Question 14.3: It suggests that the unobserved effect a_i is positively correlated with $union_{it}$. Remember, pooled OLS leaves a_i in the error term, while fixed effects removes a_i. By definition, a_i has a positive effect on log($wage$). By the standard omitted variables analysis (see Chapter 3), OLS has an upward bias when the explanatory variable ($union$) is positively correlated with the omitted variable (a_i). Thus, belonging to a union appears to be positively related to time-constant, unobserved factors that affect wage.

Question 14.4: Not if all sisters within a family have the same mother and father. Then, because the parents' race variables would not change by sister, they would be differenced away in (14.13).

Chapter 15

Question 15.1: Probably not. In the simple equation (15.18), years of education is part of the error term. If some men who were assigned low draft lottery numbers obtained additional schooling, then lottery number and education are negatively correlated, which violates the first requirement for an instrumental variable in equation (15.4).

Question 15.2: (i) For (15.27), we require that high school peer group effects carry over to college. Namely, for a given SAT score, a student who went to a high school where smoking marijuana was more popular would smoke more marijuana in college. Even if the identification condition (15.27) holds, the link might be weak.

(ii) We have to assume that percentage of students using marijuana at a student's high school is not correlated with unobserved factors that affect college grade point average. Although we are somewhat controlling for high school quality by including *SAT* in the equation, this might not be enough. Perhaps high schools that did a better job of preparing students for college also had fewer students smoking marijuana. Or marijuana usage could be correlated with average income levels. These are, of course, empirical questions that we may or may not be able to answer.

Question 15.3: Although prevalence of the NRA and subscribers to gun magazines are probably correlated with the presence of gun control legislation, it is not obvious that they are uncorrelated with unobserved factors that affect the violent crime rate. In fact, we might argue that a population interested in guns is a reflection of high crime rates, and controlling for economic and demographic variables is not sufficient to capture this. It would be hard to argue persuasively that these are truly exogenous in the violent crime equation.

Question 15.4: As usual, there are two requirements. First, it should be the case that growth in government spending is systematically related to the party of the president, after netting out the investment rate and growth in the labor force. In other words, the instrument must be partially correlated with the endogenous explanatory variable. While we might think that government spending grows more slowly under Republican presidents, this certainly has not always been true in the United States and would have to be tested using the t statistic on REP_{t-1} in the reduced form $gGOV_t = \pi_0 + \pi_1 REP_{t-1} + \pi_2 INVRAT_t + \pi_3 gLAB_t + v_t$. We must assume that the party of the president has no separate effect on *gGDP*. This would be violated if, for example, monetary policy differs systematically by presidential party and has a separate effect on GDP growth.

Chapter 16

Question 16.1: Probably not. It is because firms choose price and advertising expenditures jointly that we are not interested in the experiment where, say, advertising changes exogenously and we want to know the effect on price. Instead, we would model price and advertising each as a function of demand and cost variables. This is what falls out of the economic theory.

Question 16.2: We must assume two things. First, money supply growth should appear in equation (16.22), so that it is partially correlated with *inf*. Second, we must assume that money supply growth does not appear in equation (16.23). If we think we must include money supply growth in equation (16.23), then we are still short an instrument for *inf*. Of course, the assumption that money supply growth is exogenous can also be questioned.

Question 16.3: Use the Hausman test from Chapter 15. In particular, let $\hat{v}_2$ be the OLS residuals from the reduced form regression of *open* on log(*pcinc*) and log(*land*). Then, use an OLS regression of *inf* on *open*, log(*pcinc*), and $\hat{v}_2$ and compute the *t* statistic for significance of $\hat{v}_2$. If $\hat{v}_2$ is significant, the 2SLS and OLS estimates are statistically different.

Question 16.4: The demand equation looks like

$$\log(fish_t) = \beta_0 + \beta_1 \log(prcfish_t) + \beta_2 \log(inc_t) + \beta_3 \log(prcchick_t) + \beta_4 \log(prcbeef_t) + u_{t1},$$

where logarithms are used so that all elasticities are constant. By assumption, the demand function contains no seasonality, so the equation does not contain monthly dummy variables (say, feb_t, mar_t, …, dec_t, with January as the base month). Also, by assumption, the supply of fish is seasonal, which means that the supply function does depend on at least some of the monthly dummy variables. Even without solving the reduced form for log(*prcfish*), we conclude that it depends on the monthly dummy variables. Since these are exogenous, they can be used as instruments for log(*prcfish*) in the demand equation. Therefore, we can estimate the demand-for-fish equation using monthly dummies as the IVs for log(*prcfish*). Identification requires that at least one monthly dummy variable appears with a nonzero coefficient in the reduced form for log(*prcfish*).

Chapter 17

Question 17.1: H_0: $\beta_4 = \beta_5 = \beta_6 = 0$, so that there are three restrictions and therefore three *df* in the *LR* or Wald test.

Question 17.2: We need the partial derivative of $\Phi(\hat{\beta}_0 + \hat{\beta}_1 nwifeinc + \hat{\beta}_2 educ + \hat{\beta}_3 exper + \hat{\beta}_4 exper^2 + \ldots)$ with respect to *exper*, which is $\phi(\cdot)(\hat{\beta}_3 + 2\hat{\beta}_4 exper)$, where $\phi(\cdot)$ is evaluated at the given values and the initial level of experience. Therefore, we need to evaluate the standard normal probability density at $.270 - .012(20.13) + .131(12.3) + .123(10) - .0019(10^2) - .053(42.5) - .868(0) + .036(1) \approx .463$, where we plug in the initial level of experience (10). But $\phi(.463) = (2\pi)^{-1/2}\exp[-(.463^2)/2] \approx .358$. Next, we multiply this by $\hat{\beta}_3 + 2\hat{\beta}_4 exper$, which is evaluated at $exper = 10$. The partial effect using the calculus approximation is $.358[.123 - 2(.0019)(10)] \approx .030$. In other words, at the given values of the explanatory variables and starting at $exper = 10$, the next year of experience increases the probability of labor force participation by about .03.

Question 17.3: No. The number of extramarital affairs is a nonnegative integer, which presumably takes on zero or small numbers for a substantial fraction of the population. It is not realistic to use a Tobit model, which, while allowing a pileup at zero, treats *y* as being continuously distributed over positive values. Formally, assuming that $y = \max(0, y^*)$, where y^* is normally distributed, is at odds with the discreteness of the number of extramarital affairs when $y > 0$.

Question 17.4: The adjusted standard errors are the usual Poisson MLE standard errors multiplied by $\hat{\sigma} = \sqrt{2} \approx 1.41$, so the adjusted standard errors will be about 41% higher.

The quasi-LR statistic is the usual LR statistic divided by $\hat{\sigma}^2$, so it will be one-half of the usual LR statistic.

Question 17.5: By assumption, $mvp_i = \beta_0 + \mathbf{x}_i\boldsymbol{\beta} + u_i$, where, as usual, $\mathbf{x}_i\boldsymbol{\beta}$ denotes a linear function of the exogenous variables. Now, observed wage is the largest of the minimum wage and the marginal value product, so $wage_i = \max(minwage_i, mvp_i)$, which is very similar to equation (17.34), except that the max operator has replaced the min operator.

Chapter 18

Question 18.1: We can plug these values directly into equation (18.1) and take expectations. First, because $z_s = 0$, for all $s < 0$, $y_{-1} = \alpha + u_{-1}$. Then, $z_0 = 1$, so $y_0 = \alpha + \delta_0 + u_0$. For $h \geq 1$, $y_h = \alpha + \delta_{h-1} + \delta_h + u_h$. Because the errors have zero expected values, $\mathrm{E}(y_{-1}) = \alpha$, $\mathrm{E}(y_0) = \alpha + \delta_0$, and $\mathrm{E}(y_h) = \alpha + \delta_{h-1} + \delta$, for all $h \geq 1$. As $h \to \infty$, $\delta_h \to 0$. It follows that $\mathrm{E}(y_h) \to \alpha$ as $h \to \infty$, that is, the expected value of y_h returns to the expected value before the increase in z, at time zero. This makes sense: although the increase in z lasted for two periods, it is still a temporary increase.

Question 18.2: Under the described setup, Δy_t and Δx_t are i.i.d. sequences that are independent of one another. In particular, Δy_t and Δx_t are uncorrelated. If $\hat{\gamma}_1$ is the slope coefficient from regressing Δy_t on Δx_t, $t = 1, 2, \ldots, n$, then plim $\hat{\gamma}_1 = 0$. This is as it should be, as we are regressing one I(0) process on another I(0) process, and they are uncorrelated. We write the equation $\Delta y_t = \gamma_0 + \gamma_1\Delta x_t + e_t$, where $\gamma_0 = \gamma_1 = 0$. Because $\{e_t\}$ is independent of $\{\Delta x_t\}$, the strict exogeneity assumption holds. Moreover, $\{e_t\}$ is serially uncorrelated and homoskedastic. By Theorem 11.2 in Chapter 11, the t statistic for $\hat{\gamma}_1$ has an approximate standard normal distribution. If e_t is normally distributed, the classical linear model assumptions hold, and the t statistic has an exact t distribution.

Question 18.3: Write $x_t = x_{t-1} + a_t$, where $\{a_t\}$ is I(0). By assumption, there is a linear combination, say, $s_t = y_t - \beta x_t$, which is I(0). Now, $y_t - \beta x_{t-1} = y_t - \beta(x_t - a_t) = s_t + \beta a_t$. Because s_t and a_t are I(0) by assumption, so is $s_t + \beta a_t$.

Question 18.4: Just use the sum of squared residuals form of the F test and assume homoskedasticity. The restricted SSR is obtained by regressing $\Delta hy6_t - \Delta hy3_{t-1} + (hy6_{t-1} - hy3_{t-2})$ on a constant. Notice that α_0 is the only parameter to estimate in $\Delta hy6_t = \alpha_0 + \gamma_0\Delta hy3_{t-1} + \delta(hy6_{t-1} - hy3_{t-2})$ when the restrictions are imposed. The unrestricted sum of squared residuals is obtained from equation (18.39).

Question 18.5: We are fitting two equations: $\hat{y}_t = \hat{\alpha} + \hat{\beta}t$ and $\hat{y}_t = \hat{\gamma} + \hat{\delta}year_t$. We can obtain the relationship between the parameters by noting that $year_t = t + 49$. Plugging this into the second equation gives $\hat{y}_t = \hat{\gamma} + \hat{\delta}(t + 49) = (\hat{\gamma} + 49\hat{\delta}) + \hat{\delta}t$. Matching the slope and intercept with the first equation gives $\hat{\delta} = \hat{\beta}$—so that the slopes on t and $year_t$ are identical—and $\hat{\alpha} = \hat{\gamma} + 49\hat{\delta}$. Generally, when we use $year$ rather than t, the intercept will change, but the slope will not. (You can verify this by using one of the time series data sets, such as HSEINV.RAW or INVEN.RAW.) Whether we use t or some measure of $year$ does not change fitted values, and, naturally, it does not change forecasts of future values. The intercept simply adjusts appropriately to different ways of including a trend in the regression.

APPENDIX

G

Statistical Tables

TABLE G.1 Cumulative Areas under the Standard Normal Distribution

z	0	1	2	3	4	5	6	7	8	9
−3.0	0.0013	0.0013	0.0013	0.0012	0.0012	0.0011	0.0011	0.0011	0.0010	0.0010
−2.9	0.0019	0.0018	0.0018	0.0017	0.0016	0.0016	0.0015	0.0015	0.0014	0.0014
−2.8	0.0026	0.0025	0.0024	0.0023	0.0023	0.0022	0.0021	0.0021	0.0020	0.0019
−2.7	0.0035	0.0034	0.0033	0.0032	0.0031	0.0030	0.0029	0.0028	0.0027	0.0026
−2.6	0.0047	0.0045	0.0044	0.0043	0.0041	0.0040	0.0039	0.0038	0.0037	0.0036
−2.5	0.0062	0.0060	0.0059	0.0057	0.0055	0.0054	0.0052	0.0051	0.0049	0.0048
−2.4	0.0082	0.0080	0.0078	0.0075	0.0073	0.0071	0.0069	0.0068	0.0066	0.0064
−2.3	0.0107	0.0104	0.0102	0.0099	0.0096	0.0094	0.0091	0.0089	0.0087	0.0084
−2.2	0.0139	0.0136	0.0132	0.0129	0.0125	0.0122	0.0119	0.0116	0.0113	0.0110
−2.1	0.0179	0.0174	0.0170	0.0166	0.0162	0.0158	0.0154	0.0150	0.0146	0.0143
−2.0	0.0228	0.0222	0.0217	0.0212	0.0207	0.0202	0.0197	0.0192	0.0188	0.0183
−1.9	0.0287	0.0281	0.0274	0.0268	0.0262	0.0256	0.0250	0.0244	0.0239	0.0233
−1.8	0.0359	0.0351	0.0344	0.0336	0.0329	0.0322	0.0314	0.0307	0.0301	0.0294
−1.7	0.0446	0.0436	0.0427	0.0418	0.0409	0.0401	0.0392	0.0384	0.0375	0.0367
−1.6	0.0548	0.0537	0.0526	0.0516	0.0505	0.0495	0.0485	0.0475	0.0465	0.0455
−1.5	0.0668	0.0655	0.0643	0.0630	0.0618	0.0606	0.0594	0.0582	0.0571	0.0559
−1.4	0.0808	0.0793	0.0778	0.0764	0.0749	0.0735	0.0721	0.0708	0.0694	0.0681
−1.3	0.0968	0.0951	0.0934	0.0918	0.0901	0.0885	0.0869	0.0853	0.0838	0.0823
−1.2	0.1151	0.1131	0.1112	0.1093	0.1075	0.1056	0.1038	0.1020	0.1003	0.0985
−1.1	0.1357	0.1335	0.1314	0.1292	0.1271	0.1251	0.1230	0.1210	0.1190	0.1170
−1.0	0.1587	0.1562	0.1539	0.1515	0.1492	0.1469	0.1446	0.1423	0.1401	0.1379
−0.9	0.1841	0.1814	0.1788	0.1762	0.1736	0.1711	0.1685	0.1660	0.1635	0.1611
−0.8	0.2119	0.2090	0.2061	0.2033	0.2005	0.1977	0.1949	0.1922	0.1894	0.1867
−0.7	0.2420	0.2389	0.2358	0.2327	0.2296	0.2266	0.2236	0.2206	0.2177	0.2148
−0.6	0.2743	0.2709	0.2676	0.2643	0.2611	0.2578	0.2546	0.2514	0.2483	0.2451
−0.5	0.3085	0.3050	0.3015	0.2981	0.2946	0.2912	0.2877	0.2843	0.2810	0.2776

(continued)

TABLE G.1 (Continued)

z	0	1	2	3	4	5	6	7	8	9
−0.4	0.3446	0.3409	0.3372	0.3336	0.3300	0.3264	0.3228	0.3192	0.3156	0.3121
−0.3	0.3821	0.3783	0.3745	0.3707	0.3669	0.3632	0.3594	0.3557	0.3520	0.3483
−0.2	0.4207	0.4168	0.4129	0.4090	0.4052	0.4013	0.3974	0.3936	0.3897	0.3859
−0.1	0.4602	0.4562	0.4522	0.4483	0.4443	0.4404	0.4364	0.4325	0.4286	0.4247
−0.0	0.5000	0.4960	0.4920	0.4880	0.4840	0.4801	0.4761	0.4721	0.4681	0.4641
0.0	0.5000	0.5040	0.5080	0.5120	0.5160	0.5199	0.5239	0.5279	0.5319	0.5359
0.1	0.5398	0.5438	0.5478	0.5517	0.5557	0.5596	0.5636	0.5675	0.5714	0.5753
0.2	0.5793	0.5832	0.5871	0.5910	0.5948	0.5987	0.6026	0.6064	0.6103	0.6141
0.3	0.6179	0.6217	0.6255	0.6293	0.6331	0.6368	0.6406	0.6443	0.6480	0.6517
0.4	0.6554	0.6591	0.6628	0.6664	0.6700	0.6736	0.6772	0.6808	0.6844	0.6879
0.5	0.6915	0.6950	0.6985	0.7019	0.7054	0.7088	0.7123	0.7157	0.7190	0.7224
0.6	0.7257	0.7291	0.7324	0.7357	0.7389	0.7422	0.7454	0.7486	0.7517	0.7549
0.7	0.7580	0.7611	0.7642	0.7673	0.7704	0.7734	0.7764	0.7794	0.7823	0.7852
0.8	0.7881	0.7910	0.7939	0.7967	0.7995	0.8023	0.8051	0.8078	0.8106	0.8133
0.9	0.8159	0.8186	0.8212	0.8238	0.8264	0.8289	0.8315	0.8340	0.8365	0.8389
1.0	0.8413	0.8438	0.8461	0.8485	0.8508	0.8531	0.8554	0.8577	0.8599	0.8621
1.1	0.8643	0.8665	0.8686	0.8708	0.8729	0.8749	0.8770	0.8790	0.8810	0.8830
1.2	0.8849	0.8869	0.8888	0.8907	0.8925	0.8944	0.8962	0.8980	0.8997	0.9015
1.3	0.9032	0.9049	0.9066	0.9082	0.9099	0.9115	0.9131	0.9147	0.9162	0.9177
1.4	0.9192	0.9207	0.9222	0.9236	0.9251	0.9265	0.9279	0.9292	0.9306	0.9319
1.5	0.9332	0.9345	0.9357	0.9370	0.9382	0.9394	0.9406	0.9418	0.9429	0.9441
1.6	0.9452	0.9463	0.9474	0.9484	0.9495	0.9505	0.9515	0.9525	0.9535	0.9545
1.7	0.9554	0.9564	0.9573	0.9582	0.9591	0.9599	0.9608	0.9616	0.9625	0.9633
1.8	0.9641	0.9649	0.9656	0.9664	0.9671	0.9678	0.9686	0.9693	0.9699	0.9706
1.9	0.9713	0.9719	0.9726	0.9732	0.9738	0.9744	0.9750	0.9756	0.9761	0.9767
2.0	0.9772	0.9778	0.9783	0.9788	0.9793	0.9798	0.9803	0.9808	0.9812	0.9817
2.1	0.9821	0.9826	0.9830	0.9834	0.9838	0.9842	0.9846	0.9850	0.9854	0.9857
2.2	0.9861	0.9864	0.9868	0.9871	0.9875	0.9878	0.9881	0.9884	0.9887	0.9890
2.3	0.9893	0.9896	0.9898	0.9901	0.9904	0.9906	0.9909	0.9911	0.9913	0.9916
2.4	0.9918	0.9920	0.9922	0.9925	0.9927	0.9929	0.9931	0.9932	0.9934	0.9936
2.5	0.9938	0.9940	0.9941	0.9943	0.9945	0.9946	0.9948	0.9949	0.9951	0.9952
2.6	0.9953	0.9955	0.9956	0.9957	0.9959	0.9960	0.9961	0.9962	0.9963	0.9964
2.7	0.9965	0.9966	0.9967	0.9968	0.9969	0.9970	0.9971	0.9972	0.9973	0.9974
2.8	0.9974	0.9975	0.9976	0.9977	0.9977	0.9978	0.9979	0.9979	0.9980	0.9981
2.9	0.9981	0.9982	0.9982	0.9983	0.9984	0.9984	0.9985	0.9985	0.9986	0.9986
3.0	0.9987	0.9987	0.9987	0.9988	0.9988	0.9989	0.9989	0.9989	0.9990	0.9990

Examples: If Z ~ Normal(0,1), then $P(Z \leq -1.32) = .0934$ and $P(Z \leq 1.84) = .9671$.

Source: This table was generated using the Stata® function normprob.

TABLE G.2 Critical Values of the *t* Distribution

		Significance Level			
1-Tailed:	**.10**	**.05**	**.025**	**.01**	**.005**
2-Tailed:	**.20**	**.10**	**.05**	**.02**	**.01**
1	3.078	6.314	12.706	31.821	63.657
2	1.886	2.920	4.303	6.965	9.925
3	1.638	2.353	3.182	4.541	5.841
4	1.533	2.132	2.776	3.747	4.604
5	1.476	2.015	2.571	3.365	4.032
6	1.440	1.943	2.447	3.143	3.707
7	1.415	1.895	2.365	2.998	3.499
8	1.397	1.860	2.306	2.896	3.355
9	1.383	1.833	2.262	2.821	3.250
10	1.372	1.812	2.228	2.764	3.169
11	1.363	1.796	2.201	2.718	3.106
12	1.356	1.782	2.179	2.681	3.055
13	1.350	1.771	2.160	2.650	3.012
14	1.345	1.761	2.145	2.624	2.977
15	1.341	1.753	2.131	2.602	2.947
16	1.337	1.746	2.120	2.583	2.921
17	1.333	1.740	2.110	2.567	2.898
18	1.330	1.734	2.101	2.552	2.878
19	1.328	1.729	2.093	2.539	2.861
20	1.325	1.725	2.086	2.528	2.845
21	1.323	1.721	2.080	2.518	2.831
22	1.321	1.717	2.074	2.508	2.819
23	1.319	1.714	2.069	2.500	2.807
24	1.318	1.711	2.064	2.492	2.797
25	1.316	1.708	2.060	2.485	2.787
26	1.315	1.706	2.056	2.479	2.779
27	1.314	1.703	2.052	2.473	2.771
28	1.313	1.701	2.048	2.467	2.763
29	1.311	1.699	2.045	2.462	2.756
30	1.310	1.697	2.042	2.457	2.750
40	1.303	1.684	2.021	2.423	2.704
60	1.296	1.671	2.000	2.390	2.660
90	1.291	1.662	1.987	2.368	2.632
120	1.289	1.658	1.980	2.358	2.617
∞	1.282	1.645	1.960	2.326	2.576

(Row labels: **Degrees of Freedom**)

Examples: The 1% critical value for a one-tailed test with 25 *df* is 2.485. The 5% critical value for a two-tailed test with large (> 120) *df* is 1.96.

Source: This table was generated using the Stata® function invttail.

TABLE G.3a 10% Critical Values of the *F* Distribution

Denominator Degrees of Freedom	Numerator Degrees of Freedom: 1	2	3	4	5	6	7	8	9	10
10	3.29	2.92	2.73	2.61	2.52	2.46	2.41	2.38	2.35	2.32
11	3.23	2.86	2.66	2.54	2.45	2.39	2.34	2.30	2.27	2.25
12	3.18	2.81	2.61	2.48	2.39	2.33	2.28	2.24	2.21	2.19
13	3.14	2.76	2.56	2.43	2.35	2.28	2.23	2.20	2.16	2.14
14	3.10	2.73	2.52	2.39	2.31	2.24	2.19	2.15	2.12	2.10
15	3.07	2.70	2.49	2.36	2.27	2.21	2.16	2.12	2.09	2.06
16	3.05	2.67	2.46	2.33	2.24	2.18	2.13	2.09	2.06	2.03
17	3.03	2.64	2.44	2.31	2.22	2.15	2.10	2.06	2.03	2.00
18	3.01	2.62	2.42	2.29	2.20	2.13	2.08	2.04	2.00	1.98
19	2.99	2.61	2.40	2.27	2.18	2.11	2.06	2.02	1.98	1.96
20	2.97	2.59	2.38	2.25	2.16	2.09	2.04	2.00	1.96	1.94
21	2.96	2.57	2.36	2.23	2.14	2.08	2.02	1.98	1.95	1.92
22	2.95	2.56	2.35	2.22	2.13	2.06	2.01	1.97	1.93	1.90
23	2.94	2.55	2.34	2.21	2.11	2.05	1.99	1.95	1.92	1.89
24	2.93	2.54	2.33	2.19	2.10	2.04	1.98	1.94	1.91	1.88
25	2.92	2.53	2.32	2.18	2.09	2.02	1.97	1.93	1.89	1.87
26	2.91	2.52	2.31	2.17	2.08	2.01	1.96	1.92	1.88	1.86
27	2.90	2.51	2.30	2.17	2.07	2.00	1.95	1.91	1.87	1.85
28	2.89	2.50	2.29	2.16	2.06	2.00	1.94	1.90	1.87	1.84
29	2.89	2.50	2.28	2.15	2.06	1.99	1.93	1.89	1.86	1.83
30	2.88	2.49	2.28	2.14	2.05	1.98	1.93	1.88	1.85	1.82
40	2.84	2.44	2.23	2.09	2.00	1.93	1.87	1.83	1.79	1.76
60	2.79	2.39	2.18	2.04	1.95	1.87	1.82	1.77	1.74	1.71
90	2.76	2.36	2.15	2.01	1.91	1.84	1.78	1.74	1.70	1.67
120	2.75	2.35	2.13	1.99	1.90	1.82	1.77	1.72	1.68	1.65
∞	2.71	2.30	2.08	1.94	1.85	1.77	1.72	1.67	1.63	1.60

Example: The 10% critical value for numerator $df = 2$ and denominator $df = 40$ is 2.44.

Source: This table was generated using the Stata® function invFtail.

TABLE G.3b 5% Critical Values of the *F* Distribution

Denominator Degrees of Freedom	Numerator Degrees of Freedom									
	1	**2**	**3**	**4**	**5**	**6**	**7**	**8**	**9**	**10**
10	4.96	4.10	3.71	3.48	3.33	3.22	3.14	3.07	3.02	2.98
11	4.84	3.98	3.59	3.36	3.20	3.09	3.01	2.95	2.90	2.85
12	4.75	3.89	3.49	3.26	3.11	3.00	2.91	2.85	2.80	2.75
13	4.67	3.81	3.41	3.18	3.03	2.92	2.83	2.77	2.71	2.67
14	4.60	3.74	3.34	3.11	2.96	2.85	2.76	2.70	2.65	2.60
15	4.54	3.68	3.29	3.06	2.90	2.79	2.71	2.64	2.59	2.54
16	4.49	3.63	3.24	3.01	2.85	2.74	2.66	2.59	2.54	2.49
17	4.45	3.59	3.20	2.96	2.81	2.70	2.61	2.55	2.49	2.45
18	4.41	3.55	3.16	2.93	2.77	2.66	2.58	2.51	2.46	2.41
19	4.38	3.52	3.13	2.90	2.74	2.63	2.54	2.48	2.42	2.38
20	4.35	3.49	3.10	2.87	2.71	2.60	2.51	2.45	2.39	2.35
21	4.32	3.47	3.07	2.84	2.68	2.57	2.49	2.42	2.37	2.32
22	4.30	3.44	3.05	2.82	2.66	2.55	2.46	2.40	2.34	2.30
23	4.28	3.42	3.03	2.80	2.64	2.53	2.44	2.37	2.32	2.27
24	4.26	3.40	3.01	2.78	2.62	2.51	2.42	2.36	2.30	2.25
25	4.24	3.39	2.99	2.76	2.60	2.49	2.40	2.34	2.28	2.24
26	4.23	3.37	2.98	2.74	2.59	2.47	2.39	2.32	2.27	2.22
27	4.21	3.35	2.96	2.73	2.57	2.46	2.37	2.31	2.25	2.20
28	4.20	3.34	2.95	2.71	2.56	2.45	2.36	2.29	2.24	2.19
29	4.18	3.33	2.93	2.70	2.55	2.43	2.35	2.28	2.22	2.18
30	4.17	3.32	2.92	2.69	2.53	2.42	2.33	2.27	2.21	2.16
40	4.08	3.23	2.84	2.61	2.45	2.34	2.25	2.18	2.12	2.08
60	4.00	3.15	2.76	2.53	2.37	2.25	2.17	2.10	2.04	1.99
90	3.95	3.10	2.71	2.47	2.32	2.20	2.11	2.04	1.99	1.94
120	3.92	3.07	2.68	2.45	2.29	2.17	2.09	2.02	1.96	1.91
∞	3.84	3.00	2.60	2.37	2.21	2.10	2.01	1.94	1.88	1.83

Example: The 5% critical value for numerator $df = 4$ and large denominator $df\,(\infty)$ is 2.37.

Source: This table was generated using the Stata® function invFtail.

TABLE G.3c 1% Critical Values of the *F* Distribution

	Numerator Degrees of Freedom									
Denominator Degrees of Freedom	1	2	3	4	5	6	7	8	9	10
10	10.04	7.56	6.55	5.99	5.64	5.39	5.20	5.06	4.94	4.85
11	9.65	7.21	6.22	5.67	5.32	5.07	4.89	4.74	4.63	4.54
12	9.33	6.93	5.95	5.41	5.06	4.82	4.64	4.50	4.39	4.30
13	9.07	6.70	5.74	5.21	4.86	4.62	4.44	4.30	4.19	4.10
14	8.86	6.51	5.56	5.04	4.69	4.46	4.28	4.14	4.03	3.94
15	8.68	6.36	5.42	4.89	4.56	4.32	4.14	4.00	3.89	3.80
16	8.53	6.23	5.29	4.77	4.44	4.20	4.03	3.89	3.78	3.69
17	8.40	6.11	5.18	4.67	4.34	4.10	3.93	3.79	3.68	3.59
18	8.29	6.01	5.09	4.58	4.25	4.01	3.84	3.71	3.60	3.51
19	8.18	5.93	5.01	4.50	4.17	3.94	3.77	3.63	3.52	3.43
20	8.10	5.85	4.94	4.43	4.10	3.87	3.70	3.56	3.46	3.37
21	8.02	5.78	4.87	4.37	4.04	3.81	3.64	3.51	3.40	3.31
22	7.95	5.72	4.82	4.31	3.99	3.76	3.59	3.45	3.35	3.26
23	7.88	5.66	4.76	4.26	3.94	3.71	3.54	3.41	3.30	3.21
24	7.82	5.61	4.72	4.22	3.90	3.67	3.50	3.36	3.26	3.17
25	7.77	5.57	4.68	4.18	3.85	3.63	3.46	3.32	3.22	3.13
26	7.72	5.53	4.64	4.14	3.82	3.59	3.42	3.29	3.18	3.09
27	7.68	5.49	4.60	4.11	3.78	3.56	3.39	3.26	3.15	3.06
28	7.64	5.45	4.57	4.07	3.75	3.53	3.36	3.23	3.12	3.03
29	7.60	5.42	4.54	4.04	3.73	3.50	3.33	3.20	3.09	3.00
30	7.56	5.39	4.51	4.02	3.70	3.47	3.30	3.17	3.07	2.98
40	7.31	5.18	4.31	3.83	3.51	3.29	3.12	2.99	2.89	2.80
60	7.08	4.98	4.13	3.65	3.34	3.12	2.95	2.82	2.72	2.63
90	6.93	4.85	4.01	3.54	3.23	3.01	2.84	2.72	2.61	2.52
120	6.85	4.79	3.95	3.48	3.17	2.96	2.79	2.66	2.56	2.47
∞	6.63	4.61	3.78	3.32	3.02	2.80	2.64	2.51	2.41	2.32

Example: The 1% critical value for numerator $df = 3$ and denominator $df = 60$ is 4.13.

Source: This table was generated using the Stata® function invFtail.

TABLE G.4 Critical Values of the Chi-Square Distribution

	Significance Level		
Degrees of Freedom	.10	.05	.01
1	2.71	3.84	6.63
2	4.61	5.99	9.21
3	6.25	7.81	11.34
4	7.78	9.49	13.28
5	9.24	11.07	15.09
6	10.64	12.59	16.81
7	12.02	14.07	18.48
8	13.36	15.51	20.09
9	14.68	16.92	21.67
10	15.99	18.31	23.21
11	17.28	19.68	24.72
12	18.55	21.03	26.22
13	19.81	22.36	27.69
14	21.06	23.68	29.14
15	22.31	25.00	30.58
16	23.54	26.30	32.00
17	24.77	27.59	33.41
18	25.99	28.87	34.81
19	27.20	30.14	36.19
20	28.41	31.41	37.57
21	29.62	32.67	38.93
22	30.81	33.92	40.29
23	32.01	35.17	41.64
24	33.20	36.42	42.98
25	34.38	37.65	44.31
26	35.56	38.89	45.64
27	36.74	40.11	46.96
28	37.92	41.34	48.28
29	39.09	42.56	49.59
30	40.26	43.77	50.89

Example: The 5% critical value with $df = 8$ is 15.51.
Source: This table was generated using the Stata® function invchi2tail.

REFERENCES

Angrist, J. D. (1990), "Lifetime Earnings and the Vietnam Era Draft Lottery: Evidence from Social Security Administrative Records," *American Economic Review* 80, 313–336.

Angrist, J. D., and A. B. Krueger (1991), "Does Compulsory School Attendance Affect Schooling and Earnings?" *Quarterly Journal of Economics* 106, 979–1014.

Ashenfelter, O., and A. B. Krueger (1994), "Estimates of the Economic Return to Schooling from a New Sample of Twins," *American Economic Review* 84, 1157–1173.

Averett, S., and S. Korenman (1996), "The Economic Reality of the Beauty Myth," *Journal of Human Resources* 31, 304–330.

Ayres, I., and S. D. Levitt (1998), "Measuring Positive Externalities from Unobservable Victim Precaution: An Empirical Analysis of Lojack," *Quarterly Journal of Economics* 108, 43–77.

Banerjee, A., J. Dolado, J. W. Galbraith, and D. F. Hendry (1993), *Co-Integration, Error-Correction, and the Econometric Analysis of Non-Stationary Data*. Oxford: Oxford University Press.

Bartik, T. J. (1991), "The Effects of Property Taxes and Other Local Public Policies on the Intrametropolitan Pattern of Business Location," in *Industry Location and Public Policy*, ed. H. W. Herzog and A. M. Schlottmann, 57–80. Knoxville: University of Tennessee Press.

Becker, G. S. (1968), "Crime and Punishment: An Economic Approach," *Journal of Political Economy* 76, 169–217.

Belsley, D., E. Kuh, and R. Welsch (1980), *Regression Diagnostics: Identifying Influential Data and Sources of Collinearity*. New York: Wiley.

Berk, R. A. (1990), "A Primer on Robust Regression," in *Modern Methods of Data Analysis*, ed. J. Fox and J. S. Long, 292–324. Newbury Park, CA: Sage Publications.

Betts, J. R. (1995), "Does School Quality Matter? Evidence from the National Longitudinal Survey of Youth," *Review of Economics and Statistics* 77, 231–250.

Biddle, J. E., and D. S. Hamermesh (1990), "Sleep and the Allocation of Time," *Journal of Political Economy* 98, 922–943.

Biddle, J. E., and D. S. Hamermesh (1998), "Beauty, Productivity, and Discrimination: Lawyers' Looks and Lucre," *Journal of Labor Economics* 16, 172–201.

Blackburn, M., and D. Neumark (1992), "Unobserved Ability, Efficiency Wages, and Interindustry Wage Differentials," *Quarterly Journal of Economics* 107, 1421–1436.

Blomström, M., R. E. Lipsey, and M. Zejan (1996), "Is Fixed Investment the Key to Economic Growth?" *Quarterly Journal of Economics* 111, 269–276.

Blundell, R., A. Duncan, and K. Pendakur (1998), "Semiparametric Estimation and Consumer Demand," *Journal of Applied Econometrics* 13, 435–461.

Bollerslev, T., R. Y. Chou, and K. F. Kroner (1992), "ARCH Modeling in Finance: A Review of the Theory and Empirical Evidence," *Journal of Econometrics* 52, 5–59.

Bollerslev, T., R. F. Engle, and D. B. Nelson (1994), "ARCH Models," in *Handbook of Econometrics*, volume 4, chapter 49, ed. R. F. Engle and D. L. McFadden, 2959–3038. Amsterdam: North-Holland.

Bound, J., D. A. Jaeger, and R. M. Baker (1995), "Problems with Instrumental Variables Estimation when the Correlation between the Instruments and Endogenous Explanatory Variables Is Weak," *Journal of the American Statistical Association* 90, 443–450.

Breusch, T. S., and A. R. Pagan (1979), "A Simple Test for Heteroskedasticity and Random Coefficient Variation," *Econometrica* 47, 987–1007.

Cameron, A. C., and P. K. Trivedi (1998), *Regression Analysis of Count Data*. Cambridge: Cambridge University Press.

Campbell, J. Y., and N. G. Mankiw (1990), "Permanent Income, Current Income, and Consumption," *Journal of Business and Economic Statistics* 8, 265–279.

Card, D. (1995), "Using Geographic Variation in College Proximity to Estimate the Return to Schooling," in *Aspects of Labour Market Behavior: Essays in Honour of John Vanderkamp*, ed. L. N. Christophides, E. K. Grant, and R. Swidinsky, 201–222. Toronto: University of Toronto Press.

Card, D., and A. Krueger (1992), "Does School Quality Matter? Returns to Education and the Characteristics of Public Schools in the United States," *Journal of Political Economy* 100, 1–40.

Castillo-Freeman, A. J., and R. B. Freeman (1992), "When the Minimum Wage Really Bites: The Effect of the U.S.-Level Minimum on Puerto Rico," in *Immigration and the Work Force*, ed. G. J. Borjas and R. B. Freeman, 177–211. Chicago: University of Chicago Press.

Clark, K. B. (1984), "Unionization and Firm Performance: The Impact on Profits, Growth, and Productivity," *American Economic Review* 74, 893–919.

Cloninger, D. O. (1991), "Lethal Police Response as a Crime Deterrent: 57-City Study Suggests a Decrease in Certain Crimes," *American Journal of Economics and Sociology* 50, 59–69.

Cloninger, D. O., and L. C. Sartorius (1979), "Crime Rates, Clearance Rates and Enforcement Effort: The Case of Houston, Texas," *American Journal of Economics and Sociology* 38, 389–402.

Cochrane, J. H. (1997), "Where Is the Market Going? Uncertain Facts and Novel Theories," *Economic Perspectives* 21, Federal Reserve Bank of Chicago, 3–37.

Cornwell, C., and W. N. Trumbull (1994), "Estimating the Economic Model of Crime Using Panel Data," *Review of Economics and Statistics* 76, 360–366.

Craig, B. R., W. E. Jackson III, and J. B. Thomson (2007), "Small Firm Finance, Credit Rationing, and the Impact of SBA-Guaranteed Lending on Local Economic Growth," *Journal of Small Business Management* 45, 116–132.

Currie, J. (1995), *Welfare and the Well-Being of Children*. Chur, Switzerland: Harwood Academic Publishers.

Currie, J., and N. Cole (1993), "Welfare and Child Health: The Link between AFDC Participation and Birth Weight," *American Economic Review* 83, 971–983.

Currie, J., and D. Thomas (1995), "Does Head Start Make a Difference?" *American Economic Review* 85, 341–364.

Davidson, R., and J. G. MacKinnon (1981), "Several Tests of Model Specification in the Presence of Alternative Hypotheses," *Econometrica* 49, 781–793.

Davidson, R., and J. G. MacKinnon (1993), *Estimation and Inference in Econometrics*. New York: Oxford University Press.

De Long, J. B., and L. H. Summers (1991), "Equipment Investment and Economic Growth," *Quarterly Journal of Economics* 106, 445–502.

Dickey, D. A., and W. A. Fuller (1979), "Distributions of the Estimators for Autoregressive Time Series with a Unit Root," *Journal of the American Statistical Association* 74, 427–431.

Diebold, F. X. (2001), *Elements of Forecasting*. 2nd ed. Cincinnati: South-Western.

Downes, T. A., and S. M. Greenstein (1996), "Understanding the Supply Decisions of Nonprofits: Modeling the Location of Private Schools," *Rand Journal of Economics* 27, 365–390.

Draper, N., and H. Smith (1981), *Applied Regression Analysis*. 2nd ed. New York: Wiley.

Duan, N. (1983), "Smearing Estimate: A Nonparametric Retransformation Method," *Journal of the American Statistical Association* 78, 605–610.

Durbin, J. (1970), "Testing for Serial Correlation in Least Squares Regressions when Some of the Regressors Are Lagged Dependent Variables," *Econometrica* 38, 410–421.

Durbin, J., and G. S. Watson (1950), "Testing for Serial Correlation in Least Squares Regressions I," *Biometrika* 37, 409–428.

Eicker, F. (1967), "Limit Theorems for Regressions with Unequal and Dependent Errors," *Proceedings of the Fifth Berkeley Symposium on Mathematical Statistics and Probability* 1, 59–82. Berkeley: University of California Press.

Eide, E. (1994), *Economics of Crime: Deterrence and the Rational Offender*. Amsterdam: North-Holland.

Engle, R. F. (1982), "Autoregressive Conditional Heteroskedasticity with Estimates of the Variance of United Kingdom Inflation," *Econometrica* 50, 987–1007.

Engle, R. F., and C. W. J. Granger (1987), "Cointegration and Error Correction: Representation, Estimation, and Testing," *Econometrica* 55, 251–276.

Evans, W. N., and R. M. Schwab (1995), "Finishing High School and Starting College: Do Catholic Schools Make a Difference?" *Quarterly Journal of Economics* 110, 941–974.

Fair, R. C. (1996), "Econometrics and Presidential Elections," *Journal of Economic Perspectives* 10, 89–102.

Franses, P. H., and R. Paap (2001), *Quantitative Models in Marketing Research*. Cambridge: Cambridge University Press.

Freeman, D. G. (2007), "Drunk Driving Legislation and Traffic Fatalities: New Evidence on BAC 08 Laws," *Contemporary Economic Policy* 25, 293–308.

Friedman, B. M., and K. N. Kuttner (1992), "Money, Income, Prices, and Interest Rates," *American Economic Review* 82, 472–492.

Geronimus, A. T., and S. Korenman (1992), "The Socioeconomic Consequences of Teen Childbearing Reconsidered," *Quarterly Journal of Economics* 107, 1187–1214.

Goldberger, A. S. (1991), *A Course in Econometrics*. Cambridge, MA: Harvard University Press.

Graddy, K. (1995), "Testing for Imperfect Competition at the Fulton Fish Market," *Rand Journal of Economics* 26, 75–92.

Graddy, K. (1997), "Do Fast-Food Chains Price Discriminate on the Race and Income Characteristics of an Area?" *Journal of Business and Economic Statistics* 15, 391–401.

Granger, C. W. J., and P. Newbold (1974), "Spurious Regressions in Econometrics," *Journal of Econometrics* 2, 111–120.

Greene, W. (1997), *Econometric Analysis*. 3rd ed. New York: MacMillan.

Griliches, Z. (1957), "Specification Bias in Estimates of Production Functions," *Journal of Farm Economics* 39, 8–20.

Grogger, J. (1990), "The Deterrent Effect of Capital Punishment: An Analysis of Daily Homicide Counts," *Journal of the American Statistical Association* 410, 295–303.

Grogger, J. (1991), "Certainty vs. Severity of Punishment," *Economic Inquiry* 29, 297–309.

Hall, R. E. (1988), "The Relation between Price and Marginal Cost in U.S. Industry," *Journal of Political Economy* 96, 921–948.

Hamermesh, D. S., and J. E. Biddle (1994), "Beauty and the Labor Market," *American Economic Review* 84, 1174–1194.

Hamermesh, D. H., and A. Parker (2005), "Beauty in the Classroom: Instructors' Pulchritude and Putative Pedagogical Productivity," *Economics of Education Review* 24, 369–376.

Hamilton, J. D. (1994), *Time Series Analysis*. Princeton, NJ: Princeton University Press.

Hanushek, E. (1986), "The Economics of Schooling: Production and Efficiency in Public Schools," *Journal of Economic Literature* 24, 1141–1177.

Harvey, A. (1990), *The Econometric Analysis of Economic Time Series*. 2nd ed. Cambridge, MA: MIT Press.

Hausman, J. A. (1978), "Specification Tests in Econometrics," *Econometrica* 46, 1251–1271.

Hausman, J. A., and D. A. Wise (1977), "Social Experimentation, Truncated Distributions, and Efficient Estimation," *Econometrica* 45, 319–339.

Hayasyi, F. (2000), *Econometrics*. Princeton, NJ: Princeton University Press.

Heckman, J. J. (1976), "The Common Structure of Statistical Models of Truncation, Sample Selection, and Limited Dependent Variables and a Simple Estimator for Such Models," *Annals of Economic and Social Measurement* 5, 475–492.

Herrnstein, R. J., and C. Murray (1994), *The Bell Curve: Intelligence and Class Structure in American Life*. New York: Free Press.

Hersch, J., and L. S. Stratton (1997), "Housework, Fixed Effects, and Wages of Married Workers," *Journal of Human Resources* 32, 285–307.

Hines, J. R. (1996), "Altered States: Taxes and the Location of Foreign Direct Investment in America," *American Economic Review* 86, 1076–1094.

Holzer, H. (1991), "The Spatial Mismatch Hypothesis: What Has the Evidence Shown?" *Urban Studies* 28, 105–122.

Holzer, H., R. Block, M. Cheatham, and J. Knott (1993), "Are Training Subsidies Effective? The Michigan Experience," *Industrial and Labor Relations Review* 46, 625–636.

Horowitz, J. (2001), "The Bootstrap," in *Handbook of Econometrics*, volume 5, chapter 52, ed. E. Leamer and J. L. Heckman, 3159–3228. Amsterdam: North Holland.

Hoxby, C. M. (1994), "Do Private Schools Provide Competition for Public Schools?" National Bureau of Economic Research Working Paper Number 4978.

Huber, P. J. (1967), "The Behavior of Maximum Likelihood Estimates under Nonstandard Conditions," *Proceedings of the Fifth Berkeley Symposium on Mathematical Statistics and Probability* 1, 221–233. Berkeley: University of California Press.

Hunter, W. C., and M. B. Walker (1996), "The Cultural Affinity Hypothesis and Mortgage Lending Decisions," *Journal of Real Estate Finance and Economics* 13, 57–70.

Hylleberg, S. (1992), *Modelling Seasonality*. Oxford: Oxford University Press.

Imbens, G. W., and J. M. Wooldridge (2007), "What's New in Econometrics?" Lecture Notes, National Bureau of Economic Research Summer Institute, 2007.

Kane, T. J., and C. E. Rouse (1995), "Labor-Market Returns to Two- and Four-Year Colleges," *American Economic Review* 85, 600–614.

Kiefer, N. M., and T. J. Vogelsang (2005), "A New Asymptotic Theory for Heteroskedasticity-Autocorrelation Robust Tests," *Econometric Theory* 21, 1130–1164.

Kiel, K. A., and K. T. McClain (1995), "House Prices during Siting Decision Stages: The Case of an Incinerator from Rumor through Operation," *Journal of Environmental Economics and Management* 28, 241–255.

Kleck, G., and E. B. Patterson (1993), "The Impact of Gun Control and Gun Ownership Levels on Violence Rates," *Journal of Quantitative Criminology* 9, 249–287.

Koenker, R. (1981), "A Note on Studentizing a Test for Heteroskedasticity," *Journal of Econometrics* 17, 107–112.

Koenker, R. (2005), *Quantile Regression*. Cambridge: Cambridge University Press.

Korenman, S., and D. Neumark (1991), "Does Marriage Really Make Men More Productive?" *Journal of Human Resources* 26, 282–307.

Korenman, S., and D. Neumark (1992), "Marriage, Motherhood, and Wages," *Journal of Human Resources* 27, 233–255.

Krueger, A. B. (1993), "How Computers Have Changed the Wage Structure: Evidence from Microdata, 1984–1989," *Quarterly Journal of Economics* 108, 33–60.

Krupp, C. M., and P. S. Pollard (1996), "Market Responses to Antidumping Laws: Some Evidence from the U.S. Chemical Industry," *Canadian Journal of Economics* 29, 199–227.

Kwiatkowski, D., P. C. B. Phillips, P. Schmidt, and Y. Shin (1992), "Testing the Null Hypothesis of Stationarity against the Alternative of a Unit Root: How Sure Are We That Economic Time Series Have a Unit Root?" *Journal of Econometrics* 54, 159–178.

Lalonde, R. J. (1986), "Evaluating the Econometric Evaluations of Training Programs with Experimental Data," *American Economic Review* 76, 604–620.

Larsen, R. J., and M. L. Marx (1986), *An Introduction to Mathematical Statistics and Its Applications*. 2nd ed. Englewood Cliffs, NJ: Prentice-Hall.

Leamer, E. E. (1983), "Let's Take the Con Out of Econometrics," *American Economic Review* 73, 31–43.

Levine, P. B., A. B. Trainor, and D. J. Zimmerman (1996), "The Effect of Medicaid Abortion Funding Restrictions on Abortions, Pregnancies, and Births," *Journal of Health Economics* 15, 555–578.

Levine, P. B., and D. J. Zimmerman (1995), "The Benefit of Additional High-School Math and Science Classes for Young Men and Women," *Journal of Business and Economics Statistics* 13, 137–149.

Levitt, S. D. (1994), "Using Repeat Challengers to Estimate the Effect of Campaign Spending on Election Outcomes in the U.S. House," *Journal of Political Economy* 102, 777–798.

Levitt, S. D. (1996), "The Effect of Prison Population Size on Crime Rates: Evidence from Prison Overcrowding Legislation," *Quarterly Journal of Economics* 111, 319–351.

Low, S. A., and L. R. McPheters (1983), "Wage Differentials and the Risk of Death: An Empirical Analysis," *Economic Inquiry* 21, 271–280.

Lynch, L. M. (1992), "Private Sector Training and the Earnings of Young Workers," *American Economic Review* 82, 299–312.

MacKinnon, J. G., and H. White (1985), "Some Heteroskedasticity Consistent Covariance Matrix Estimators with Improved Finite Sample Properties," *Journal of Econometrics* 29, 305–325.

Maloney, M. T., and R. E. McCormick (1993), "An Examination of the Role that Intercollegiate Athletic Participation Plays in Academic Achievement: Athletes' Feats in the Classroom," *Journal of Human Resources* 28, 555–570.

Mankiw, N. G. (1994), *Macroeconomics*. 2nd ed. New York: Worth.

Mark, S. T., T. J. McGuire, and L. E. Papke (2000), "The Influence of Taxes on Employment and Population Growth: Evidence from the Washington, D.C. Metropolitan Area," *National Tax Journal* 53, 105–123.

McCarthy, P. S. (1994), "Relaxed Speed Limits and Highway Safety: New Evidence from California," *Economics Letters* 46, 173–179.

McClain, K. T., and J. M. Wooldridge (1995), "A Simple Test for the Consistency of Dynamic Linear Regression in Rational Distributed Lag Models," *Economics Letters* 48, 235–240.

McCormick, R. E., and M. Tinsley (1987), "Athletics versus Academics: Evidence from SAT Scores," *Journal of Political Economy* 95, 1103–1116.

McFadden, D. L. (1974), "Conditional Logit Analysis of Qualitative Choice Behavior," in *Frontiers in Econometrics*, ed. P. Zarembka, 105–142. New York: Academic Press.

Meyer, B. D. (1995), "Natural and Quasi-Experiments in Economics," *Journal of Business and Economic Statistics* 13, 151–161.

Meyer, B. D., W. K. Viscusi, and D. L. Durbin (1995), "Workers' Compensation and Injury Duration: Evidence from a Natural Experiment," *American Economic Review* 85, 322–340.

Mizon, G. E., and J. F. Richard (1986), "The Encompassing Principle and Its Application to Testing Nonnested Hypotheses," *Econometrica* 54, 657–678.

Mroz, T. A. (1987), "The Sensitivity of an Empirical Model of Married Women's Hours of Work to Economic and Statistical Assumptions," *Econometrica* 55, 765–799.

Mullahy, J., and P. R. Portney (1990), "Air Pollution, Cigarette Smoking, and the Production of Respiratory Health," *Journal of Health Economics* 9, 193–205.

Mullahy, J., and J. L. Sindelar (1994), "Do Drinkers Know When to Say When? An Empirical Analysis of Drunk Driving," *Economic Inquiry* 32, 383–394.

Netzer, D. (1992), "Differences in Reliance on User Charges by American State and Local Governments," *Public Finance Quarterly* 20, 499–511.

Neumark, D. (1996), "Sex Discrimination in Restaurant Hiring: An Audit Study," *Quarterly Journal of Economics* 111, 915–941.

Neumark, D., and W. Wascher (1995), "Minimum Wage Effects on Employment and School Enrollment," *Journal of Business and Economic Statistics* 13, 199–206.

Newey, W. K., and K. D. West (1987), "A Simple, Positive Semi-Definite Heteroskedasticity and Autocorrelation Consistent Covariance Matrix," *Econometrica* 55, 703–708.

Papke, L. E. (1987), "Subnational Taxation and Capital Mobility: Estimates of Tax-Price Elasticities," *National Tax Journal* 40, 191–203.

Papke, L. E. (1994), "Tax Policy and Urban Development: Evidence from the Indiana Enterprise Zone Program," *Journal of Public Economics* 54, 37–49.

Papke, L. E. (1995), "Participation in and Contributions to 401(k) Pension Plans: Evidence from Plan Data," *Journal of Human Resources* 30, 311–325.

Papke, L. E. (1999), "Are 401(k) Plans Replacing Other Employer-Provided Pensions? Evidence from Panel Data," *Journal of Human Resources*, 34, 346–368.

Papke, L. E. (2005), "The Effects of Spending on Test Pass Rates: Evidence from Michigan," *Journal of Public Economics* 89, 821–839.

Park, R. (1966), "Estimation with Heteroskedastic Error Terms," *Econometrica* 34, 888.

Peek, J. (1982), "Interest Rates, Income Taxes, and Anticipated Inflation," *American Economic Review* 72, 980–991.

Pindyck, R. S., and D. L. Rubinfeld (1992), *Microeconomics*. 2nd ed. New York: Macmillan.

Ram, R. (1986), "Government Size and Economic Growth: A New Framework and Some Evidence from Cross-Section and Time-Series Data," *American Economic Review* 76, 191–203.

Ramanathan, R. (1995), *Introductory Econometrics with Applications*. 3rd ed. Fort Worth: Dryden Press.

Ramey, V. (1991), "Nonconvex Costs and the Behavior of Inventories," *Journal of Political Economy* 99, 306–334.

Ramsey, J. B. (1969), "Tests for Specification Errors in Classical Linear Least-Squares Analysis," *Journal of the Royal Statistical Association*, Series B, 71, 350–371.

Romer, D. (1993), "Openness and Inflation: Theory and Evidence," *Quarterly Journal of Economics* 108, 869–903.

Rose, N. L. (1985), "The Incidence of Regulatory Rents in the Motor Carrier Industry," *Rand Journal of Economics* 16, 299–318.

Rose, N. L., and A. Shepard (1997), "Firm Diversification and CEO Compensation: Managerial Ability or Executive Entrenchment?" *Rand Journal of Economics* 28, 489–514.

Rouse, C. E. (1998), "Private School Vouchers and Student Achievement: An Evaluation of the Milwaukee Parental Choice Program," *Quarterly Journal of Economics* 113, 553–602.

Sander, W. (1992), "The Effect of Women's Schooling on Fertility," *Economic Letters* 40, 229–233.

Savin, N. E., and K. J. White (1977), "The Durbin-Watson Test for Serial Correlation with Extreme Sample Sizes or Many Regressors," *Econometrica* 45, 1989–1996.

Shea, J. (1993), "The Input-Output Approach to Instrument Selection," *Journal of Business and Economic Statistics* 11, 145–155.

Shughart, W. F., and R. D. Tollison (1984), "The Random Character of Merger Activity," *Rand Journal of Economics* 15, 500–509.

Solon, G. (1985), "The Minimum Wage and Teenage Employment: A Re-analysis with Attention to Serial Correlation and Seasonality," *Journal of Human Resources* 20, 292–297.

Staiger, D., and J. H. Stock (1997), "Instrumental Variables Regression with Weak Instruments," *Econometrica* 65, 557–586.

Stigler, S. M. (1986), *The History of Statistics.* Cambridge, MA: Harvard University Press.

Stock, J. H., and M. W. Watson (1989), "Interpreting the Evidence on Money-Income Causality," *Journal of Econometrics* 40, 161–181.

Stock, J. H., and M. W. Watson (1993), "A Simple Estimator of Cointegrating Vectors in Higher Order Integrated Systems," *Econometrica* 61, 783–820.

Sydsaeter, K., and P. J. Hammond (1995), *Mathematics for Economic Analysis.* Englewood Cliffs, NJ: Prentice Hall.

Terza, J. V. (2002), "Alcohol Abuse and Employment: A Second Look," *Journal of Applied Econometrics* 17, 393–404.

Tucker, I. B. (2004), "A Reexamination of the Effect of Big-time Football and Basketball Success on Graduation Rates and Alumni Giving Rates," *Economics of Education Review* 23, 655–661.

Vella, F., and M. Verbeek (1998), "Whose Wages Do Unions Raise? A Dynamic Model of Unionism and Wage Rate Determination for Young Men," *Journal of Applied Econometrics* 13, 163–183.

Wald, A. (1940), "The Fitting of Straight Lines if Both Variables Are Subject to Error," *Annals of Mathematical Statistics* 11, 284–300.

Wallis, K. F. (1972), "Testing for Fourth-Order Autocorrelation in Quarterly Regression Equations," *Econometrica* 40, 617–636.

White, H. (1980), "A Heteroskedasticity-Consistent Covariance Matrix Estimator and a Direct Test for Heteroskedasticity," *Econometrica* 48, 817–838.

White, H. (1984), *Asymptotic Theory for Econometricians*. Orlando: Academic Press.

White, M. J. (1986), "Property Taxes and Firm Location: Evidence from Proposition 13," in *Studies in State and Local Public Finance*, ed. H. S. Rosen, 83–112. Chicago: University of Chicago Press.

Whittington, L. A., J. Alm, and H. E. Peters (1990), "Fertility and the Personal Exemption: Implicit Pronatalist Policy in the United States," *American Economic Review* 80, 545–556.

Wooldridge, J. M. (1989), "A Computationally Simple Heteroskedasticity and Serial Correlation-Robust Standard Error for the Linear Regression Model," *Economics Letters* 31, 239–243.

Wooldridge, J. M. (1991a), "A Note on Computing *R*-Squared and Adjusted *R*-Squared for Trending and Seasonal Data," *Economics Letters* 36, 49–54.

Wooldridge, J. M. (1991b), "On the Application of Robust, Regression-Based Diagnostics to Models of Conditional Means and Conditional Variances," *Journal of Econometrics* 47, 5–46.

Wooldridge, J. M. (1994a), "A Simple Specification Test for the Predictive Ability of Transformation Models," *Review of Economics and Statistics* 76, 59–65.

Wooldridge, J. M. (1994b), "Estimation and Inference for Dependent Processes," in *Handbook of Econometrics*, volume 4, chapter 45, ed. R. F. Engle and D. L. McFadden, 2639–2738. Amsterdam: North-Holland.

Wooldridge, J. M. (1995), "Score Diagnostics for Linear Models Estimated by Two Stage Least Squares," in *Advances in Econometrics and Quantitative Economics*, ed. G. S. Maddala, P. C. B. Phillips, and T. N. Srinivasan, 66–87. Oxford: Blackwell.

Wooldridge, J. M. (2010), *Econometric Analysis of Cross Section and Panel Data*. 2nd ed. Cambridge, MA: MIT Press.

GLOSSARY

A

Adjusted *R*-Squared: A goodness-of-fit measure in multiple regression analysis that penalizes additional explanatory variables by using a degrees of freedom adjustment in estimating the error variance.

Alternative Hypothesis: The hypothesis against which the null hypothesis is tested.

AR(1) Serial Correlation: The errors in a time series regression model follow an AR(1) model.

Asymptotic Bias: *See* inconsistency.

Asymptotic Confidence Interval: A confidence interval that is approximately valid in large sample sizes.

Asymptotic Normality: The sampling distribution of a properly normalized estimator converges to the standard normal distribution.

Asymptotic Properties: Properties of estimators and test statistics that apply when the sample size grows without bound.

Asymptotic Standard Error: A standard error that is valid in large samples.

Asymptotic *t* Statistic: A *t* statistic that has an approximate standard normal distribution in large samples.

Asymptotic Variance: The square of the value by which we must divide an estimator in order to obtain an asymptotic standard normal distribution.

Asymptotically Efficient: For consistent estimators with asymptotically normal distributions, the estimator with the smallest asymptotic variance.

Asymptotically Uncorrelated: A time series process in which the correlation between random variables at two points in time tends to zero as the time interval between them increases. (*See also* weakly dependent.)

Attenuation Bias: Bias in an estimator that is always toward zero; thus, the expected value of an estimator with attenuation bias is less in magnitude than the absolute value of the parameter.

Augmented Dickey-Fuller Test: A test for a unit root that includes lagged changes of the variable as regressors.

Autocorrelation: *See* serial correlation.

Autoregressive Conditional Heteroskedasticity (ARCH): A model of dynamic heteroskedasticity where the variance of the error term, given past information, depends linearly on the past squared errors.

Autoregressive Process of Order One [AR(1)]: A time series model whose current value depends linearly on its most recent value plus an unpredictable disturbance.

Auxiliary Regression: A regression used to compute a test statistic—such as the test statistics for heteroskedasticity and serial correlation—or any other regression that does not estimate the model of primary interest.

Average: The sum of n numbers divided by n.

Average Marginal Effect: *See* average partial effect.

Average Partial Effect: For nonconstant partial effects, the partial effect averaged across the specified population.

Average Treatment Effect: A treatment, or policy, effect averaged across the population.

B

Balanced Panel: A panel data set where all years (or periods) of data are available for all cross-sectional units.

Base Group: The group represented by the overall intercept in a multiple regression model that includes dummy explanatory variables.

Base Period: For index numbers, such as price or production indices, the period against which all other time periods are measured.

Base Value: The value assigned to the base period for constructing an index number; usually the base value is 1 or 100.

Benchmark Group: *See* base group.

Bernoulli (or Binary) Random Variable: A random variable that takes on the values zero or one.

Best Linear Unbiased Estimator (BLUE): Among all linear unbiased estimators, the one with the smallest variance. OLS is BLUE, conditional on the sample values of the explanatory variables, under the Gauss-Markov assumptions.

Beta Coefficients: *See* standardized coefficients.

Bias: The difference between the expected value of an estimator and the population value that the estimator is supposed to be estimating.

Biased Estimator: An estimator whose expectation, or sampling mean, is different from the population value it is supposed to be estimating.

Biased Towards Zero: A description of an estimator whose expectation in absolute value is less than the absolute value of the population parameter.

Binary Response Model: A model for a binary (dummy) dependent variable.

Binary Variable: *See* dummy variable.

Binomial Distribution: The probability distribution of the number of successes out of n independent Bernoulli trials, where each trial has the same probability of success.

Bivariate Regression Model: *See* simple linear regression model.

BLUE: *See* best linear unbiased estimator.

Bootstrap: A resampling method that draws random samples, with replacement, from the original data set.

Bootstrap Standard Error: A standard error obtained as the sample standard deviation of an estimate across all bootstrap samples.

Breusch-Godfrey Test: An asymptotically justified test for AR(p) serial correlation, with AR(1) being the most popular; the test allows for lagged dependent variables as well as other regressors that are not strictly exogenous.

Breusch-Pagan Test: A test for heteroskedasticity where the squared OLS residuals are regressed on the explanatory variables in the model.

C

Causal Effect: A ceteris paribus change in one variable that has an effect on another variable.

Censored Normal Regression Model: The special case of the censored regression model where the underlying population model satisfies the classical linear model assumptions.

Censored Regression Model: A multiple regression model where the dependent variable has been censored above or below some known threshold.

Central Limit Theorem (CLT): A key result from probability theory which implies that the sum of independent random variables, or even weakly dependent random variables, when standardized by its standard deviation, has a distribution that tends to standard normal as the sample size grows.

Ceteris Paribus: All other relevant factors are held fixed.

Chi-Square Distribution: A probability distribution obtained by adding the squares of independent standard normal random variables. The number of terms in the sum equals the degrees of freedom in the distribution.

Chi-Square Random Variable: A random variable with a chi-square distribution.

Chow Statistic: An F statistic for testing the equality of regression parameters across different groups (say, men and women) or time periods (say, before and after a policy change).

Classical Errors-in-Variables (CEV): A measurement error model where the observed measure equals the actual variable plus an independent, or at least an uncorrelated, measurement error.

Classical Linear Model: The multiple linear regression model under the full set of classical linear model assumptions.

Classical Linear Model (CLM) Assumptions: The ideal set of assumptions for multiple regression analysis: for cross-sectional analysis, Assumptions MLR.1 through MLR.6, and for time series analysis, Assumptions TS.1 through TS.6. The assumptions include linearity in the parameters, no perfect collinearity, the zero conditional mean assumption, homoskedasticity, no serial correlation, and normality of the errors.

Cluster Effect: An unobserved effect that is common to all units, usually people, in the cluster.

Cluster Sample: A sample of natural clusters or groups that usually consist of people.

Clustering: In the context of panel data, computing standard errors and test statistics that are robust to any form of serial correlation (and heteroskedasticity).

Cochrane-Orcutt (CO) Estimation: A method of estimating a multiple linear regression model with AR(1) errors and strictly exogenous explanatory variables; unlike Prais-Winsten, Cochrane-Orcutt does not use the equation for the first time period.

Coefficient of Determination: *See* R-squared.

Cointegration: The notion that a linear combination of two series, each of which is integrated of order one, is integrated of order zero.

Column Vector: A vector of numbers arranged as a column.

Composite Error Term: In a panel data model, the sum of the time-constant unobserved effect and the idiosyncratic error.

Conditional Distribution: The probability distribution of one random variable, given the values of one or more other random variables.

Conditional Expectation: The expected or average value of one random variable, called the dependent or explained variable, that depends on the values of one or more other variables, called the independent or explanatory variables.

Conditional Forecast: A forecast that assumes the future values of some explanatory variables are known with certainty.

Conditional Median: The median of a response variable conditional on some explanatory variables.

Conditional Variance: The variance of one random variable, given one or more other random variables.

Confidence Interval (CI): A rule used to construct a random interval so that a certain percentage of all data sets, determined by the confidence level, yields an interval that contains the population value.

Confidence Level: The percentage of samples in which we want our confidence interval to contain the population value; 95% is the most common confidence level, but 90% and 99% are also used.

Consistency: An estimator converges in probability to the correct population value as the sample size grows.

Consistent Estimator: An estimator that converges in probability to the population parameter as the sample size grows without bound.

Consistent Test: A test where, under the alternative hypothesis, the probability of rejecting the null hypothesis converges to one as the sample size grows without bound.

Constant Elasticity Model: A model where the elasticity of the dependent variable, with respect to an explanatory variable, is constant; in multiple regression, both variables appear in logarithmic form.

Contemporaneously Homoskedastic: Describes a time series or panel data applications in which the variance of the error term, conditional on the regressors in the same time period, is constant.

Contemporaneously Exogenous: Describes a time series or panel data application in which a regressor is contemporaneously exogenous if it is uncorrelated with the error term in the same time period, although it may be correlated with the errors in other time periods.

Continuous Random Variable: A random variable that takes on any particular value with probability zero.

Control Group: In program evaluation, the group that does not participate in the program.

Control Variable: *See* explanatory variable.

Corner Solution Response: A nonnegative dependent variable that is roughly continuous over strictly positive values but takes on the value zero with some regularity.

Correlated Random Effects: An approach to panel data analysis where the correlation between the unobserved effect and the explanatory variables is modeled, usually as a linear relationship.

Correlation Coefficient: A measure of linear dependence between two random variables that does not depend on units of measurement and is bounded between –1 and 1.

Count Variable: A variable that takes on nonnegative integer values.

Covariance: A measure of linear dependence between two random variables.

Covariance Stationary: A time series process with constant mean and variance where the covariance between any two random variables in the sequence depends only on the distance between them.

Covariate: *See* explanatory variable.

Critical Value: In hypothesis testing, the value against which a test statistic is compared to determine whether or not the null hypothesis is rejected.

Cross-Sectional Data Set: A data set collected by sampling a population at a given point in time.

Cumulative Distribution Function (cdf): A function that gives the probability of a random variable being less than or equal to any specified real number.

Cumulative Effect: At any point in time, the change in a response variable after a permanent increase in an explanatory variable—usually in the context of distributed lag models.

D

Data Censoring: A situation that arises when we do not always observe the outcome on the dependent variable because at an upper (or lower) threshold we only know that the outcome was above (or below) the threshold. (*See also* censored regression model.)

Data Frequency: The interval at which time series data are collected. Yearly, quarterly, and monthly are the most common data frequencies.

Data Mining: The practice of using the same data set to estimate numerous models in a search to find the "best" model.

Davidson-MacKinnon Test: A test that is used for testing a model against a nonnested alternative; it can be implemented as a t test on the fitted values from the competing model.

Degrees of Freedom (*df*): In multiple regression analysis, the number of observations minus the number of estimated parameters.

Denominator Degrees of Freedom: In an F test, the degrees of freedom in the unrestricted model.

Dependent Variable: The variable to be explained in a multiple regression model (and a variety of other models).

Derivative: The slope of a smooth function, as defined using calculus.

Descriptive Statistic: A statistic used to summarize a set of numbers; the sample average, sample median, and sample standard deviation are the most common.

Deseasonalizing: The removing of the seasonal components from a monthly or quarterly time series.

Detrending: The practice of removing the trend from a time series.

Diagonal Matrix: A matrix with zeros for all off-diagonal entries.

Dickey-Fuller Distribution: The limiting distribution of the t statistic in testing the null hypothesis of a unit root.

Dickey-Fuller (DF) Test: A t test of the unit root null hypothesis in an AR(1) model. (*See also* augmented Dickey-Fuller test.)

Difference in Slopes: A description of a model where some slope parameters may differ by group or time period.

Difference-in-Differences Estimator: An estimator that arises in policy analysis with data for two time periods. One version of the estimator applies to independently pooled cross sections and another to panel data sets.

Difference-Stationary Process: A time series sequence that is I(0) in its first differences.

Diminishing Marginal Effect: The marginal effect of an explanatory variable becomes smaller as the value of the explanatory variable increases.

Discrete Random Variable: A random variable that takes on at most a finite or countably infinite number of values.

Distributed Lag Model: A time series model that relates the dependent variable to current and past values of an explanatory variable.

Disturbance: *See* error term.

Downward Bias: The expected value of an estimator is below the population value of the parameter.

Dummy Dependent Variable: *See* binary response model.

Dummy Variable: A variable that takes on the value zero or one.

Dummy Variable Regression: In a panel data setting, the regression that includes a dummy variable for each cross-sectional unit, along with the remaining explanatory variables. It produces the fixed effects estimator.

Dummy Variable Trap: The mistake of including too many dummy variables among the independent variables; it occurs when an overall intercept is in the model and a dummy variable is included for each group.

Duration Analysis: An application of the censored regression model where the dependent variable is time elapsed until a certain event occurs, such as the time before an unemployed person becomes reemployed.

Durbin-Watson (DW) Statistic: A statistic used to test for first order serial correlation in the errors of a time series regression model under the classical linear model assumptions.

Dynamically Complete Model: A time series model where no further lags of either the dependent variable or the explanatory variables help to explain the mean of the dependent variable.

E

Econometric Model: An equation relating the dependent variable to a set of explanatory variables and unobserved disturbances, where unknown population parameters determine the ceteris paribus effect of each explanatory variable.

Economic Model: A relationship derived from economic theory or less formal economic reasoning.

Economic Significance: *See* practical significance.

Elasticity: The percentage change in one variable given a 1% ceteris paribus increase in another variable.

Empirical Analysis: A study that uses data in a formal econometric analysis to test a theory, estimate a relationship, or determine the effectiveness of a policy.

Endogeneity: A term used to describe the presence of an endogenous explanatory variable.

Endogenous Explanatory Variable: An explanatory variable in a multiple regression model that is correlated with the error term, either because of an omitted variable, measurement error, or simultaneity.

Endogenous Sample Selection: Nonrandom sample selection where the selection is related to the dependent variable, either directly or through the error term in the equation.

Endogenous Variables: In simultaneous equations models, variables that are determined by the equations in the system.

Engle-Granger Test: A test of the null hypothesis that two time series are not cointegrated; the statistic is obtained as the Dickey-Fuller statistic using OLS residuals.

Engle-Granger Two-Step Procedure: A two-step method for estimating error correction models whereby the cointegrating parameter is estimated in the first stage, and the error correction parameters are estimated in the second.

Error Correction Model: A time series model in first differences that also contains an error correction term, which works to bring two I(1) series back into long-run equilibrium.

Error Term: The variable in a simple or multiple regression equation that contains unobserved factors which affect the dependent variable. The error term may also include measurement errors in the observed dependent or independent variables.

Error Variance: The variance of the error term in a multiple regression model.

Errors-in-Variables: A situation where either the dependent variable or some independent variables are measured with error.

Estimate: The numerical value taken on by an estimator for a particular sample of data.

Estimator: A rule for combining data to produce a numerical value for a population parameter; the form of the rule does not depend on the particular sample obtained.

Event Study: An econometric analysis of the effects of an event, such as a change in government regulation or economic policy, on an outcome variable.

Excluding a Relevant Variable: In multiple regression analysis, leaving out a variable that has a nonzero partial effect on the dependent variable.

Exclusion Restrictions: Restrictions which state that certain variables are excluded from the model (or have zero population coefficients).

Exogenous Explanatory Variable: An explanatory variable that is uncorrelated with the error term.

Exogenous Sample Selection: A sample selection that either depends on exogenous explanatory variables or is independent of the error term in the equation of interest.

Exogenous Variable: Any variable that is uncorrelated with the error term in the model of interest.

Expected Value: A measure of central tendency in the distribution of a random variable, including an estimator.

Experiment: In probability, a general term used to denote an event whose outcome is uncertain. In econometric analysis, it denotes a situation where data are collected by randomly assigning individuals to control and treatment groups.

Experimental Data: Data that have been obtained by running a controlled experiment.

Experimental Group: *See* treatment group.

Explained Sum of Squares (SSE): The total sample variation of the fitted values in a multiple regression model.

Explained Variable: *See* dependent variable.

Explanatory Variable: In regression analysis, a variable that is used to explain variation in the dependent variable.

Exponential Function: A mathematical function defined for all values that has an increasing slope but a constant proportionate change.

Exponential Smoothing: A simple method of forecasting a variable that involves a weighting of all previous outcomes on that variable.

Exponential Trend: A trend with a constant growth rate.

F

***F* Distribution:** The probability distribution obtained by forming the ratio of two independent chi-square random variables, where each has been divided by its degrees of freedom.

***F* Random Variable:** A random variable with an *F* distribution.

***F* Statistic:** A statistic used to test multiple hypotheses about the parameters in a multiple regression model.

Feasible GLS (FGLS) Estimator: A GLS procedure where variance or correlation parameters are unknown and therefore must first be estimated. (*See also* generalized least squares estimator.)

Finite Distributed Lag (FDL) Model: A dynamic model where one or more explanatory variables are allowed to have lagged effects on the dependent variable.

First Difference: A transformation on a time series constructed by taking the difference of adjacent time periods, where the earlier time period is subtracted from the later time period.

First-Differenced (FD) Equation: In time series or panel data models, an equation where the dependent and independent variables have all been first differenced.

First-Differenced (FD) Estimator: In a panel data setting, the pooled OLS estimator applied to first differences of the data across time.

First Order Autocorrelation: For a time series process ordered chronologically, the correlation coefficient between pairs of adjacent observations.

First Order Conditions: The set of linear equations used to solve for the OLS estimates.

Fitted Values: The estimated values of the dependent variable when the values of the independent variables for each observation are plugged into the OLS regression line.

Fixed Effect: *See* unobserved effect.

Fixed Effects Estimator: For the unobserved effects panel data model, the estimator obtained by applying pooled OLS to a time-demeaned equation.

Fixed Effects Model: An unobserved effects panel data model where the unobserved effects are allowed to be arbitrarily correlated with the explanatory variables in each time period.

Fixed Effects Transformation: For panel data, the time-demeaned data.

Forecast Error: The difference between the actual outcome and the forecast of the outcome.

Forecast Interval: In forecasting, a confidence interval for a yet unrealized future value of a time series variable. (*See also* prediction interval.)

Functional Form Misspecification: A problem that occurs when a model has omitted functions of the explanatory variables (such as quadratics) or uses the wrong functions of either the dependent variable or some explanatory variables.

G

Gauss-Markov Assumptions: The set of assumptions (Assumptions MLR.1 through MLR.5 or TS.1 through TS.5) under which OLS is BLUE.

Gauss-Markov Theorem: The theorem that states that, under the five Gauss-Markov assumptions (for cross-sectional or time series models), the OLS estimator is BLUE (conditional on the sample values of the explanatory variables).

Generalized Least Squares (GLS) Estimator: An estimator that accounts for a known structure of the error variance (heteroskedasticity), serial correlation pattern in the errors, or both, via a transformation of the original model.

Geometric (or Koyck) Distributed Lag: An infinite distributed lag model where the lag coefficients decline at a geometric rate.

Goodness-of-Fit Measure: A statistic that summarizes how well a set of explanatory variables explains a dependent or response variable.

Granger Causality: A limited notion of causality where past values of one series (x_t) are useful for predicting future values of another series (y_t), after past values of y_t have been controlled for.

Growth Rate: The proportionate change in a time series from the previous period. It may be approximated as the difference in logs or reported in percentage form.

H

Heckit Method: An econometric procedure used to correct for sample selection bias due to incidental truncation or some other form of nonrandomly missing data.

Heterogeneity Bias: The bias in OLS due to omitted heterogeneity (or omitted variables).

Heteroskedasticity: The variance of the error term, given the explanatory variables, is not constant.

Heteroskedasticity of Unknown Form: Heteroskedasticity that may depend on the explanatory variables in an unknown, arbitrary fashion.

Heteroskedasticity-Robust *F* Statistic: An *F*-type statistic that is (asymptotically) robust to heteroskedasticity of unknown form.

Heteroskedasticity-Robust *LM* Statistic: An *LM* statistic that is robust to heteroskedasticity of unknown form.

Heteroskedasticity-Robust Standard Error: A standard error that is (asymptotically) robust to heteroskedasticity of unknown form.

Heteroskedasticity-Robust *t* Statistic: A *t* statistic that is (asymptotically) robust to heteroskedasticity of unknown form.

Highly Persistent: A time series process where outcomes in the distant future are highly correlated with current outcomes.

Homoskedasticity: The errors in a regression model have constant variance conditional on the explanatory variables.

Hypothesis Test: A statistical test of the null, or maintained, hypothesis against an alternative hypothesis.

I

Idempotent Matrix: A (square) matrix where multiplication of the matrix by itself equals itself.

Identification: A population parameter, or set of parameters, can be consistently estimated.

Identified Equation: An equation whose parameters can be consistently estimated, especially in models with endogenous explanatory variables.

Identity Matrix: A square matrix where all diagonal elements are one and all off-diagonal elements are zero.

Idiosyncratic Error: In panel data models, the error that changes over time as well as across units (say, individuals, firms, or cities).

Impact Elasticity: In a distributed lag model, the immediate percentage change in the dependent variable given a 1% increase in the independent variable.

Impact Multiplier: *See* impact propensity.

Impact Propensity: In a distributed lag model, the immediate change in the dependent variable given a one-unit increase in the independent variable.

Incidental Truncation: A sample selection problem whereby one variable, usually the dependent variable, is only observed for certain outcomes of another variable.

Inclusion of an Irrelevant Variable: The including of an explanatory variable in a regression model that has a zero population parameter in estimating an equation by OLS.

Inconsistency: The difference between the probability limit of an estimator and the parameter value.

Inconsistent: Describes an estimator that does not converge (in probability) to the correct population parameter as the sample size grows.

Independent Random Variables: Random variables whose joint distribution is the product of the marginal distributions.

Independent Variable: *See* explanatory variable.

Independently Pooled Cross Section: A data set obtained by pooling independent random samples from different points in time.

Index Number: A statistic that aggregates information on economic activity, such as production or prices.

Infinite Distributed Lag (IDL) Model: A distributed lag model where a change in the explanatory variable can have an impact on the dependent variable into the indefinite future.

Influential Observations: *See* outliers.

Information Set: In forecasting, the set of variables that we can observe prior to forming our forecast.

In-Sample Criteria: Criteria for choosing forecasting models that are based on goodness-of-fit within the sample used to obtain the parameter estimates.

Instrument Exogeneity: In instrumental variables estimation, the requirement that an instrumental variable is uncorrelated with the error term.

Instrument Relevance: In instrumental variables estimation, the requirement that an instrumental variable helps to partially explain variation in the endogenous explanatory variable.

Instrumental Variable (IV): In an equation with an endogenous explanatory variable, an IV is a variable that does not appear in the equation, is uncorrelated with the error in the equation, and is (partially) correlated with the endogenous explanatory variable.

Instrumental Variables (IV) Estimator: An estimator in a linear model used when instrumental variables are available for one or more endogenous explanatory variables.

Integrated of Order One [I(1)]: A time series process that needs to be first-differenced in order to produce an I(0) process.

Integrated of Order Zero [I(0)]: A stationary, weakly dependent time series process that, when used in regression analysis, satisfies the law of large numbers and the central limit theorem.

Interaction Effect: In multiple regression, the partial effect of one explanatory variable depends on the value of a different explanatory variable.

Interaction Term: An independent variable in a regression model that is the product of two explanatory variables.

Intercept: In the equation of a line, the value of the y variable when the x variable is zero.

Intercept Parameter: The parameter in a multiple linear regression model that gives the expected value of the dependent variable when all the independent variables equal zero.

Intercept Shift: The intercept in a regression model differs by group or time period.

Internet: A global computer network that can be used to access information and download databases.

Interval Estimator: A rule that uses data to obtain lower and upper bounds for a population parameter. (*See also* confidence interval.)

Inverse: For an $n \times n$ matrix, its inverse (if it exists) is the $n \times n$ matrix for which pre- and post-multiplication by the original matrix yields the identity matrix.

Inverse Mills Ratio: A term that can be added to a multiple regression model to remove sample selection bias.

J

Joint Distribution: The probability distribution determining the probabilities of outcomes involving two or more random variables.

Joint Hypotheses Test: A test involving more than one restriction on the parameters in a model.

Jointly Insignificant: Failure to reject, using an F test at a specified significance level, that all coefficients for a group of explanatory variables are zero.

Jointly Statistically Significant: The null hypothesis that two or more explanatory variables have zero population coefficients is rejected at the chosen significance level.

Just Identified Equation: For models with endogenous explanatory variables, an equation that is identified but would not be identified with one fewer instrumental variable.

K

Kurtosis: A measure of the thickness of the tails of a distribution based on the fourth moment of the standardized random variable; the measure is usually compared to the value for the standard normal distribution, which is three.

L

Lag Distribution: In a finite or infinite distributed lag model, the lag coefficients graphed as a function of the lag length.

Lagged Dependent Variable: An explanatory variable that is equal to the dependent variable from an earlier time period.

Lagged Endogenous Variable: In a simultaneous equations model, a lagged value of one of the endogenous variables.

Lagrange Multiplier (LM) Statistic: A test statistic with large-sample justification that can be used to test for omitted variables, heteroskedasticity, and serial correlation, among other model specification problems.

Large Sample Properties: *See* asymptotic properties.

Latent Variable Model: A model where the observed dependent variable is assumed to be a function of an underlying latent, or unobserved, variable.

Law of Iterated Expectations: A result from probability that relates unconditional and conditional expectations.

Law of Large Numbers (LLN): A theorem that says that the average from a random sample converges in probability to the population average; the LLN also holds for stationary and weakly dependent time series.

Leads and Lags Estimator: An estimator of a cointegrating parameter in a regression with I(1) variables, where the current, some past, and some future first differences in the explanatory variable are included as regressors.

Least Absolute Deviations (LAD): A method for estimating the parameters of a multiple regression model based on minimizing the sum of the absolute values of the residuals.

Least Squares Estimator: An estimator that minimizes a sum of squared residuals.

Level-Level Model: A regression model where the dependent variable and the independent variables are in level (or original) form.

Level-Log Model: A regression model where the dependent variable is in level form and (at least some of) the independent variables are in logarithmic form.

Likelihood Ratio Statistic: A statistic that can be used to test single or multiple hypotheses when the constrained and unconstrained models have been estimated by maximum likelihood. The statistic is twice the difference in the unconstrained and constrained log-likelihoods.

Limited Dependent Variable (LDV): A dependent or response variable whose range is restricted in some important way.

Linear Function: A function where the change in the dependent variable, given a one-unit change in an independent variable, is constant.

Linear Probability Model (LPM): A binary response model where the response probability is linear in its parameters.

Linear Time Trend: A trend that is a linear function of time.

Linear Unbiased Estimator: In multiple regression analysis, an unbiased estimator that is a linear function of the outcomes on the dependent variable.

Linearly Independent Vectors: A set of vectors such that no vector can be written as a linear combination of the others in the set.

Log Function: A mathematical function, defined only for strictly positive arguments, with a positive but decreasing slope.

Logarithmic Function: A mathematical function defined for positive arguments that has a positive, but diminishing, slope.

Logit Model: A model for binary response where the response probability is the logit function evaluated at a linear function of the explanatory variables.

Log-Level Model: A regression model where the dependent variable is in logarithmic form and the independent variables are in level (or original) form.

Log-Likelihood Function: The sum of the log-likelihoods, where the log-likelihood for each observation is the log of the density of the dependent variable given the explanatory variables; the log-likelihood function is viewed as a function of the parameters to be estimated.

Log-Log Model: A regression model where the dependent variable and (at least some of) the explanatory variables are in logarithmic form.

Longitudinal Data: *See* panel data.

Long-Run Elasticity: The long-run propensity in a distributed lag model with the dependent and independent variables in logarithmic form; thus, the long-run elasticity is the eventual percentage increase in the explained variable, given a permanent 1% increase in the explanatory variable.

Long-Run Multiplier: *See* long-run propensity.

Long-Run Propensity (LRP): In a distributed lag model, the eventual change in the dependent variable given a permanent, one-unit increase in the independent variable.

Loss Function: A function that measures the loss when a forecast differs from the actual outcome; the most common examples are absolute value loss and squared loss.

M

Marginal Effect: The effect on the dependent variable that results from changing an independent variable by a small amount.

Martingale: A time series process whose expected value, given all past outcomes on the series, simply equals the most recent value.

Martingale Difference Sequence: The first difference of a martingale. It is unpredictable (or has a zero mean), given past values of the sequence.

Matched Pair Sample: A sample where each observation is matched with another, as in a sample consisting of a husband and wife or a set of two siblings.

Matrix: An array of numbers.

Matrix Multiplication: An algorithm for multiplying together two conformable matrices.

Matrix Notation: A convenient mathematical notation, grounded in matrix algebra, for expressing and manipulating the multiple regression model.

Maximum Likelihood Estimation (MLE): A broadly applicable estimation method where the parameter estimates are chosen to maximize the log-likelihood function.

Maximum Likelihood Estimator: An estimator that maximizes the (log of the) likelihood function.

Mean: *See* expected value.

Mean Absolute Error (MAE): A performance measure in forecasting, computed as the average of the absolute values of the forecast errors.

Mean Independent: The key requirement in multiple regression analysis, which says the unobserved error has a mean that does not change across subsets of the population defined by different values of the explanatory variables.

Mean Squared Error (MSE): The expected squared distance that an estimator is from the population value; it equals the variance plus the square of any bias.

Measurement Error: The difference between an observed variable and the variable that belongs in a multiple regression equation.

Median: In a probability distribution, it is the value where there is a 50% chance of being below the value and a 50% chance of being above it. In a sample of numbers, it is the middle value after the numbers have been ordered.

Method of Moments Estimator: An estimator obtained by using the sample analog of population moments; ordinary least squares and two stage least squares are both method of moments estimators.

Micronumerosity: A term introduced by Arthur Goldberger to describe properties of econometric estimators with small sample sizes.

Minimum Variance Unbiased Estimator: An estimator with the smallest variance in the class of all unbiased estimators.

Missing Data: A data problem that occurs when we do not observe values on some variables for certain observations (individuals, cities, time periods, and so on) in the sample.

Misspecification Analysis: The process of determining likely biases that can arise from omitted variables, measurement error, simultaneity, and other kinds of model misspecification.

Moving Average Process of Order One [MA(1)]: A time series process generated as a linear function of the current value and one lagged value of a zero-mean, constant variance, uncorrelated stochastic process.

Multicollinearity: A term that refers to correlation among the independent variables in a multiple regression model; it is usually invoked when some correlations are "large," but an actual magnitude is not well defined.

Multiple Hypotheses Test: A test of a null hypothesis involving more than one restriction on the parameters.

Multiple Linear Regression (MLR) Model: A model linear in its parameters, where the dependent variable is a function of independent variables plus an error term.

Multiple Regression Analysis: A type of analysis that is used to describe estimation of and inference in the multiple linear regression model.

Multiple Restrictions: More than one restriction on the parameters in an econometric model.

Multiple-Step-Ahead Forecast: A time series forecast of more than one period into the future.

Multiplicative Measurement Error: Measurement error where the observed variable is the product of the true unobserved variable and a positive measurement error.

Multivariate Normal Distribution: A distribution for multiple random variables where each linear combination of the random variables has a univariate (one-dimensional) normal distribution.

N

***n-R*-Squared Statistic:** *See* Lagrange multiplier statistic.

Natural Experiment: A situation where the economic environment—sometimes summarized by an explanatory variable—exogenously changes, perhaps inadvertently, due to a policy or institutional change.

Natural Logarithm: *See* logarithmic function.

Nominal Variable: A variable measured in nominal or current dollars.

Nonexperimental Data: Data that have not been obtained through a controlled experiment.

Nonlinear Function: A function whose slope is not constant.

Nonnested Models: Two (or more) models where no model can be written as a special case of the other by imposing restrictions on the parameters.

Nonrandom Sample: A sample obtained other than by sampling randomly from the population of interest.

Nonstationary Process: A time series process whose joint distributions are not constant across different epochs.

Normal Distribution: A probability distribution commonly used in statistics and econometrics for modeling a population. Its probability distribution function has a bell shape.

Normality Assumption: The classical linear model assumption which states that the error (or dependent variable) has a normal distribution, conditional on the explanatory variables.

Null Hypothesis: In classical hypothesis testing, we take this hypothesis as true and require the data to provide substantial evidence against it.

Numerator Degrees of Freedom: In an F test, the number of restrictions being tested.

O

Observational Data: *See* nonexperimental data.

OLS: *See* ordinary least squares.

OLS Intercept Estimate: The intercept in an OLS regression line.

OLS Regression Line: The equation relating the predicted value of the dependent variable to the independent variables, where the parameter estimates have been obtained by OLS.

OLS Slope Estimate: A slope in an OLS regression line.

Omitted Variable Bias: The bias that arises in the OLS estimators when a relevant variable is omitted from the regression.

Omitted Variables: One or more variables, which we would like to control for, have been omitted in estimating a regression model.

One-Sided Alternative: An alternative hypothesis that states that the parameter is greater than (or less than) the value hypothesized under the null.

One-Step-Ahead Forecast: A time series forecast one period into the future.

One-Tailed Test: A hypothesis test against a one-sided alternative.

Online Databases: Databases that can be accessed via a computer network.

Online Search Services: Computer software that allows the Internet or databases on the Internet to be searched by topic, name, title, or keywords.

Order Condition: A necessary condition for identifying the parameters in a model with one or more endogenous explanatory variables: the total number of exogenous variables must be at least as great as the total number of explanatory variables.

Ordinal Variable: A variable where the ordering of the values conveys information but the magnitude of the values does not.

Ordinary Least Squares (OLS): A method for estimating the parameters of a multiple linear regression model. The ordinary least squares estimates are obtained by minimizing the sum of squared residuals.

Outliers: Observations in a data set that are substantially different from the bulk of the data, perhaps because of errors or because some data are generated by a different model than most of the other data.

Out-of-Sample Criteria: Criteria used for choosing forecasting models which are based on a part of the sample that was not used in obtaining parameter estimates.

Over Controlling: In a multiple regression model, including explanatory variables that should not be held fixed when studying the ceteris paribus effect of one or more other explanatory variables; this can occur when variables that are themselves outcomes of an intervention or a policy are included among the regressors.

Overall Significance of a Regression: A test of the joint significance of all explanatory variables appearing in a multiple regression equation.

Overdispersion: In modeling a count variable, the variance is larger than the mean.

Overidentified Equation: In models with endogenous explanatory variables, an equation where the number of instrumental variables is strictly greater than the number of endogenous explanatory variables.

Overidentifying Restrictions: The extra moment conditions that come from having more instrumental variables than endogenous explanatory variables in a linear model.

Overspecifying a Model: *See* inclusion of an irrelevant variable.

P

***p*-Value:** The smallest significance level at which the null hypothesis can be rejected. Equivalently, the largest significance level at which the null hypothesis cannot be rejected.

Pairwise Uncorrelated Random Variables: A set of two or more random variables where each pair is uncorrelated.

Panel Data: A data set constructed from repeated cross sections over time. With a *balanced* panel, the same units appear in each time period. With an *unbalanced* panel, some units do not appear in each time period, often due to attrition.

Parameter: An unknown value that describes a population relationship.

Parsimonious Model: A model with as few parameters as possible for capturing any desired features.

Partial Derivative: For a smooth function of more than one variable, the slope of the function in one direction.

Partial Effect: The effect of an explanatory variable on the dependent variable, holding other factors in the regression model fixed.

Partial Effect at the Average (PEA): In models with nonconstant partial effects, the partial effect evaluated at the average values of the explanatory variables.

Percent Correctly Predicted: In a binary response model, the percentage of times the prediction of zero or one coincides with the actual outcome.

Percentage Change: The proportionate change in a variable, multiplied by 100.

Percentage Point Change: The change in a variable that is measured as a percentage.

Perfect Collinearity: In multiple regression, one independent variable is an exact linear function of one or more other independent variables.

Plug-In Solution to the Omitted Variables Problem: A proxy variable is substituted for an unobserved omitted variable in an OLS regression.

Point Forecast: The forecasted value of a future outcome.

Poisson Distribution: A probability distribution for count variables.

Poisson Regression Model: A model for a count dependent variable where the dependent variable, conditional on the explanatory variables, is nominally assumed to have a Poisson distribution.

Policy Analysis: An empirical analysis that uses econometric methods to evaluate the effects of a certain policy.

Pooled Cross Section: A data configuration where independent cross sections, usually collected at different points in time, are combined to produce a single data set.

Pooled OLS Estimation: OLS estimation with independently pooled cross sections, panel data, or cluster samples, where the observations are pooled across time (or group) as well as across the cross-sectional units.

Population: A well-defined group (of people, firms, cities, and so on) that is the focus of a statistical or econometric analysis.

Population Model: A model, especially a multiple linear regression model, that describes a population.

Population *R*-Squared: In the population, the fraction of the variation in the dependent variable that is explained by the explanatory variables.

Population Regression Function: *See* conditional expectation.

Positive Definite: A symmetric matrix such that all quadratic forms, except the trivial one that must be zero, are strictly positive.

Positive Semi-Definite: A symmetric matrix such that all quadratic forms are nonnegative.

Power of a Test: The probability of rejecting the null hypothesis when it is false; the power depends on the values of the population parameters under the alternative.

Practical Significance: The practical or economic importance of an estimate, which is measured by its sign and magnitude, as opposed to its statistical significance.

Prais-Winsten (PW) Estimation: A method of estimating a multiple linear regression model with AR(1) errors and strictly exogenous explanatory variables; unlike Cochrane-Orcutt, Prais-Winsten uses the equation for the first time period in estimation.

Predetermined Variable: In a simultaneous equations model, either a lagged endogenous variable or a lagged exogenous variable.

Predicted Variable: *See* dependent variable.

Prediction: The estimate of an outcome obtained by plugging specific values of the explanatory variables into an estimated model, usually a multiple regression model.

Prediction Error: The difference between the actual outcome and a prediction of that outcome.

Prediction Interval: A confidence interval for an unknown outcome on a dependent variable in a multiple regression model.

Predictor Variable: *See* explanatory variable.

Probability Density Function (pdf): A function that, for discrete random variables, gives the probability that the random variable takes on each value; for continuous random variables, the area under the pdf gives the probability of various events.

Probability Limit: The value to which an estimator converges as the sample size grows without bound.

Probit Model: A model for binary responses where the response probability is the standard normal cdf evaluated at a linear function of the explanatory variables.

Program Evaluation: An analysis of a particular private or public program using econometric methods to obtain the causal effect of the program.

Proportionate Change: The change in a variable relative to its initial value; mathematically, the change divided by the initial value.

Proxy Variable: An observed variable that is related but not identical to an unobserved explanatory variable in multiple regression analysis.

Pseudo *R*-Squared: Any number of goodness-of-fit measures for limited dependent variable models.

Q

Quadratic Form: A mathematical function where the vector argument both pre- and post-multiplies a square, symmetric matrix.

Quadratic Functions: Functions that contain squares of one or more explanatory variables; they capture diminishing or increasing effects on the dependent variable.

Qualitative Variable: A variable describing a nonquantitative feature of an individual, a firm, a city, and so on.

Quasi-Demeaned Data: In random effects estimation for panel data, it is the original data in each time period minus a fraction of the time average; these calculations are done for each cross-sectional observation.

Quasi-Differenced Data: In estimating a regression model with AR(1) serial correlation, it is the difference between the current time period and a multiple of the previous time period, where the multiple is the parameter in the AR(1) model.

Quasi-Experiment: *See* natural experiment.

Quasi-Likelihood Ratio Statistic: A modification of the likelihood ratio statistic that accounts for possible distributional misspecification, as in a Poisson regression model.

Quasi-Maximum Likelihood Estimation (QMLE): Maximum likelihood estimation where the log-likelihood function may not correspond to the actual conditional distribution of the dependent variable.

R

***R*-Bar Squared:** *See* adjusted *R*-squared.

***R*-Squared:** In a multiple regression model, the proportion of the total sample variation in the dependent variable that is explained by the independent variable.

***R*-Squared Form of the *F* Statistic:** The *F* statistic for testing exclusion restrictions expressed in terms of the *R*-squareds from the restricted and unrestricted models.

Random Coefficient (Slope) Model: A multiple regression model where the slope parameters are allowed to depend on unobserved unit-specific variables.

Random Effects Estimator: A feasible GLS estimator in the unobserved effects model where the unobserved effect is assumed to be uncorrelated with the explanatory variables in each time period.

Random Effects Model: The unobserved effects panel data model where the unobserved effect is assumed to be uncorrelated with the explanatory variables in each time period.

Random Sample: A sample obtained by sampling randomly from the specified population.

Random Sampling: A sampling scheme whereby each observation is drawn at random from the population. In particular, no unit is more likely to be selected than any other unit, and each draw is independent of all other draws.

Random Variable: A variable whose outcome is uncertain.

Random Vector: A vector consisting of random variables.

Random Walk: A time series process where next period's value is obtained as this period's value, plus an independent (or at least an uncorrelated) error term.

Random Walk with Drift: A random walk that has a constant (or drift) added in each period.

Rank Condition: A sufficient condition for identification of a model with one or more endogenous explanatory variables.

Rank of a Matrix: The number of linearly independent columns in a matrix.

Rational Distributed Lag (RDL) Model: A type of infinite distributed lag model where the lag distribution depends on relatively few parameters.

Real Variable: A monetary value measured in terms of a base period.

Reduced Form Equation: A linear equation where an endogenous variable is a function of exogenous variables and unobserved errors.

Reduced Form Error: The error term appearing in a reduced form equation.

Reduced Form Parameters: The parameters appearing in a reduced form equation.

Regressand: *See* dependent variable.

Regression Specification Error Test (RESET): A general test for functional form in a multiple regression model; it is an *F* test of joint significance of the squares, cubes, and perhaps higher powers of the fitted values from the initial OLS estimation.

Regression through the Origin: Regression analysis where the intercept is set to zero; the slopes are obtained by minimizing the sum of squared residuals, as usual.

Regressor: *See* explanatory variable.

Rejection Region: The set of values of a test statistic that leads to rejecting the null hypothesis.

Rejection Rule: In hypothesis testing, the rule that determines when the null hypothesis is rejected in favor of the alternative hypothesis.

Relative Change: *See* proportionate change.

Resampling Method: A technique for approximating standard errors (and distributions of test statistics) whereby a series of samples are obtained from the original data set and estimates are computed for each subsample.

Residual: The difference between the actual value and the fitted (or predicted) value; there is a residual for each observation in the sample used to obtain an OLS regression line.

Residual Analysis: A type of analysis that studies the sign and size of residuals for particular observations after a multiple regression model has been estimated.

Residual Sum of Squares: *See* sum of squared residuals.

Response Probability: In a binary response model, the probability that the dependent variable takes on the value one, conditional on explanatory variables.

Response Variable: *See* dependent variable.

Restricted Model: In hypothesis testing, the model obtained after imposing all of the restrictions required under the null.

Retrospective Data: Data collected based on past, rather than current, information.

Root Mean Squared Error (RMSE): Another name for the standard error of the regression in multiple regression analysis.

Row Vector: A vector of numbers arranged as a row.

S

Sample Average: The sum of n numbers divided by n; a measure of central tendency.

Sample Correlation: For outcomes on two random variables, the sample covariance divided by the product of the sample standard deviations.

Sample Correlation Coefficient: An estimate of the (population) correlation coefficient from a sample of data.

Sample Covariance: An unbiased estimator of the population covariance between two random variables.

Sample Regression Function (SRF): *See* OLS regression line.

Sample Selection Bias: Bias in the OLS estimator which is induced by using data that arise from endogenous sample selection.

Sample Standard Deviation: A consistent estimator of the population standard deviation.

Sample Variance: An unbiased, consistent estimator of the population variance.

Sampling Distribution: The probability distribution of an estimator over all possible sample outcomes.

Sampling Standard Deviation: The standard deviation of an estimator, that is, the standard deviation of a sampling distribution.

Sampling Variance: The variance in the sampling distribution of an estimator; it measures the spread in the sampling distribution.

Scalar Multiplication: The algorithm for multiplying a scalar (number) by a vector or matrix.

Scalar Variance-Covariance Matrix: A variance-covariance matrix where all off-diagonal terms are zero and the diagonal terms are the same positive constant.

Score Statistic: *See* Lagrange multiplier statistic.

Seasonal Dummy Variables: A set of dummy variables used to denote the quarters or months of the year.

Seasonality: A feature of monthly or quarterly time series where the average value differs systematically by season of the year.

Seasonally Adjusted: Monthly or quarterly time series data where some statistical procedure—possibly regression on seasonal dummy variables—has been used to remove the seasonal component.

Selected Sample: A sample of data obtained not by random sampling but by selecting on the basis of some observed or unobserved characteristic.

Self-Selection: Deciding on an action based on the likely benefits, or costs, of taking that action.

Semi-Elasticity: The percentage change in the dependent variable given a one-unit increase in an independent variable.

Sensitivity Analysis: The process of checking whether the estimated effects and statistical significance of key explanatory variables are sensitive to inclusion of other explanatory variables, functional form, dropping of potentially outlying observations, or different methods of estimation.

Sequentially Exogenous: A feature of an explanatory variable in time series (or panel data) models where the error term in the current time period has a zero mean conditional on all current and past explanatory variables; a weaker version is stated in terms of zero correlations.

Serial Correlation: In a time series or panel data model, correlation between the errors in different time periods.

Serial Correlation-Robust Standard Error: A standard error for an estimator that is (asymptotically) valid whether or not the errors in the model are serially correlated.

Serially Uncorrelated: The errors in a time series or panel data model are pairwise uncorrelated across time.

Short-Run Elasticity: The impact propensity in a distributed lag model when the dependent and independent variables are in logarithmic form.

Significance Level: The probability of a Type I error in hypothesis testing.

Simple Linear Regression Model: A model where the dependent variable is a linear function of a single independent variable, plus an error term.

Simultaneity: A term that means at least one explanatory variable in a multiple linear regression model is determined jointly with the dependent variable.

Simultaneity Bias: The bias that arises from using OLS to estimate an equation in a simultaneous equations model.

Simultaneous Equations Model (SEM): A model that jointly determines two or more endogenous variables, where each endogenous variable can be a function of other endogenous variables as well as of exogenous variables and an error term.

Skewness: A measure of how far a distribution is from being symmetric, based on the third moment of the standardized random variable.

Slope: In the equation of a line, the change in the *y* variable when the *x* variable increases by one.

Slope Parameter: The coefficient on an independent variable in a multiple regression model.

Smearing Estimate: A retransformation method particularly useful for predicting the level of a response variable when a linear model has been estimated for the natural log of the response variable.

Spreadsheet: Computer software used for entering and manipulating data.

Spurious Correlation: A correlation between two variables that is not due to causality, but perhaps to the dependence of the two variables on another unobserved factor.

Spurious Regression Problem: A problem that arises when regression analysis indicates a relationship between two or more unrelated time series processes simply because each has a trend, is an integrated time series (such as a random walk), or both.

Square Matrix: A matrix with the same number of rows as columns.

Stable AR(1) Process: An AR(1) process where the parameter on the lag is less than one in absolute value. The correlation between two random variables in the sequence declines to zero at a geometric rate as the distance between the random variables increases, and so a stable AR(1) process is weakly dependent.

Standard Deviation: A common measure of spread in the distribution of a random variable.

Standard Deviation of $\hat{\beta}_j$: A common measure of spread in the sampling distribution of $\hat{\beta}_j$.

Standard Error: Generically, an estimate of the standard deviation of an estimator.

Standard Error of $\hat{\beta}_j$: An estimate of the standard deviation in the sampling distribution of $\hat{\beta}_j$.

Standard Error of the Estimate: *See* standard error of the regression.

Standard Error of the Regression (SER): In multiple regression analysis, the estimate of the standard deviation of the population error, obtained as the square root of the sum of squared residuals over the degrees of freedom.

Standard Normal Distribution: The normal distribution with mean zero and variance one.

Standardized Coefficients: Regression coefficients that measure the standard deviation change in the dependent variable given a one standard deviation increase in an independent variable.

Standardized Random Variable: A random variable transformed by subtracting off its expected value and dividing the result by its standard deviation; the new random variable has mean zero and standard deviation one.

Static Model: A time series model where only contemporaneous explanatory variables affect the dependent variable.

Stationary Process: A time series process where the marginal and all joint distributions are invariant across time.

Statistical Inference: The act of testing hypotheses about population parameters.

Statistical Significance: The importance of an estimate as measured by the size of a test statistic, usually a *t* statistic.

Statistically Different from Zero: *See* statistically significant.

Statistically Insignificant: Failure to reject the null hypothesis that a population parameter is equal to zero, at the chosen significance level.

Statistically Significant: Rejecting the null hypothesis that a parameter is equal to zero against the specified alternative, at the chosen significance level.

Stochastic Process: A sequence of random variables indexed by time.

Stratified Sampling: A nonrandom sampling scheme whereby the population is first divided into several nonoverlapping, exhaustive strata, and then random samples are taken from within each stratum.

Strict Exogeneity: An assumption that holds in a time series or panel data model when the explanatory variables are strictly exogenous.

Strictly Exogenous: A feature of explanatory variables in a time series or panel data model where the error term at any time period has zero expectation, conditional on the explanatory variables in all time periods; a less restrictive version is stated in terms of zero correlations.

Strongly Dependent: *See* highly persistent.

Structural Equation: An equation derived from economic theory or from less formal economic reasoning.

Structural Error: The error term in a structural equation, which could be one equation in a simultaneous equations model.

Structural Parameters: The parameters appearing in a structural equation.

Studentized Residuals: The residuals computed by excluding each observation, in turn, from the estimation, divided by the estimated standard deviation of the error.

Sum of Squared Residuals (SSR): In multiple regression analysis, the sum of the squared OLS residuals across all observations.

Summation Operator: A notation, denoted by Σ, used to define the summing of a set of numbers.

Symmetric Distribution: A probability distribution characterized by a probability density function that is symmetric around its median value, which must also be the mean value (whenever the mean exists).

Symmetric Matrix: A (square) matrix that equals its transpose.

T

***t* Distribution:** The distribution of the ratio of a standard normal random variable and the square root of an independent chi-square random variable, where the chi-square random variable is first divided by its *df*.

***t* Ratio:** *See t* statistic.

***t* Statistic:** The statistic used to test a single hypothesis about the parameters in an econometric model.

Test Statistic: A rule used for testing hypotheses where each sample outcome produces a numerical value.

Text Editor: Computer software that can be used to edit text files.

Text (ASCII) File: A universal file format that can be transported across numerous computer platforms.

Time-Demeaned Data: Panel data where, for each cross-sectional unit, the average over time is subtracted from the data in each time period.

Time Series Data: Data collected over time on one or more variables.

Time Series Process: *See* stochastic process.

Time Trend: A function of time that is the expected value of a trending time series process.

Tobit Model: A model for a dependent variable that takes on the value zero with positive probability but is roughly continuously distributed over strictly positive values. (*See also* corner solution response.)

Top Coding: A form of data censoring where the value of a variable is not reported when it is above a given threshold; we only know that it is at least as large as the threshold.

Total Sum of Squares (SST): The total sample variation in a dependent variable about its sample average.

Trace of a Matrix: For a square matrix, the sum of its diagonal elements.

Transpose: For any matrix, the new matrix obtained by interchanging its rows and columns.

Treatment Group: In program evaluation, the group that participates in the program.

Trending Process: A time series process whose expected value is an increasing or a decreasing function of time.

Trend-Stationary Process: A process that is stationary once a time trend has been removed; it is usually implicit that the detrended series is weakly dependent.

True Model: The actual population model relating the dependent variable to the relevant independent variables, plus a disturbance, where the zero conditional mean assumption holds.

Truncated Normal Regression Model: The special case of the truncated regression model where the underlying population model satisfies the classical linear model assumptions.

Truncated Regression Model: A linear regression model for cross-sectional data in which the sampling scheme entirely excludes, on the basis of outcomes on the dependent variable, part of the population.

Two-Sided Alternative: An alternative where the population parameter can be either less than or greater than the value stated under the null hypothesis.

Two Stage Least Squares (2SLS) Estimator: An instrumental variables estimator where the IV for an endogenous explanatory variable is obtained as the fitted value from regressing the endogenous explanatory variable on all exogenous variables.

Two-Tailed Test: A test against a two-sided alternative.

Type I Error: A rejection of the null hypothesis when it is true.

Type II Error: The failure to reject the null hypothesis when it is false.

U

Unbalanced Panel: A panel data set where certain years (or periods) of data are missing for some cross-sectional units.

Unbiased Estimator: An estimator whose expected value (or mean of its sampling distribution) equals the population value (regardless of the population value).

Uncentered *R*-squared: The *R*-squared computed without subtracting the sample average of the dependent variable when obtaining the total sum of squares (SST).

Unconditional Forecast: A forecast that does not rely on knowing, or assuming values for, future explanatory variables.

Uncorrelated Random Variables: Random variables that are not linearly related.

Underspecifying a Model: *See* excluding a relevant variable.

Unidentified Equation: An equation with one or more endogenous explanatory variables where sufficient instrumental variables do not exist to identify the parameters.

Unit Root Process: A highly persistent time series process where the current value equals last period's value, plus a weakly dependent disturbance.

Unobserved Effect: In a panel data model, an unobserved variable in the error term that does not change over time. For cluster samples, an unobserved variable that is common to all units in the cluster.

Unobserved Effects Model: A model for panel data or cluster samples where the error term contains an unobserved effect.

Unobserved Heterogeneity: *See* unobserved effect.

Unrestricted Model: In hypothesis testing, the model that has no restrictions placed on its parameters.

Upward Bias: The expected value of an estimator is greater than the population parameter value.

V

Variance: A measure of spread in the distribution of a random variable.

Variance-Covariance Matrix: For a random vector, the positive semi-definite matrix defined by putting the variances down the diagonal and the covariances in the appropriate off-diagonal entries.

Variance-Covariance Matrix of the OLS Estimator: The matrix of sampling variances and covariances for the vector of OLS coefficients.

Variance Inflation Factor: In multiple regression analysis under the Gauss-Markov assumptions, the term in the sampling variance affected by correlation among the explanatory variables.

Variance of the Prediction Error: The variance in the error that arises when predicting a future value of the dependent variable based on an estimated multiple regression equation.

Vector Autoregressive (VAR) Model: A model for two or more time series where each variable is modeled as a linear function of past values of all variables, plus disturbances that have zero means given all past values of the observed variables.

W

Wald Statistic: A general test statistic for testing hypotheses in a variety of econometric settings; typically, the Wald statistic has an asymptotic chi-square distribution.

Weak Instruments: Instrumental variables that are only slightly correlated with the relevant endogenous explanatory variable or variables.

Weakly Dependent: A term that describes a time series process where some measure of dependence between random variables at two points in time—such as correlation—diminishes as the interval between the two points in time increases.

Weighted Least Squares (WLS) Estimator: An estimator used to adjust for a known form of heteroskedasticity, where each squared residual is weighted by the inverse of the (estimated) variance of the error.

White Test: A test for heteroskedasticity that involves regressing the squared OLS residuals on the OLS fitted values and on the squares of the fitted values; in its most general form, the squared OLS residuals are regressed on the explanatory variables, the squares of the explanatory variables, and all the nonredundant interactions of the explanatory variables.

Within Estimator: *See* fixed effects estimator.

Within Transformation: *See* fixed effects transformation.

Y

Year Dummy Variables: For data sets with a time series component, dummy (binary) variables equal to one in the relevant year and zero in all other years.

Z

Zero Conditional Mean Assumption: A key assumption used in multiple regression analysis that states that, given any values of the explanatory variables, the expected value of the error equals zero. (*See* Assumptions MLR.4, TS.3, and TS.3' in the text.)

Zero Matrix: A matrix where all entries are zero.

Zero-One Variable: *See* dummy variable.

INDEX

Numbers

A

B

C

D

E

F

G

H

I

M

N

O

P

Q

R

T

U

Y

Z